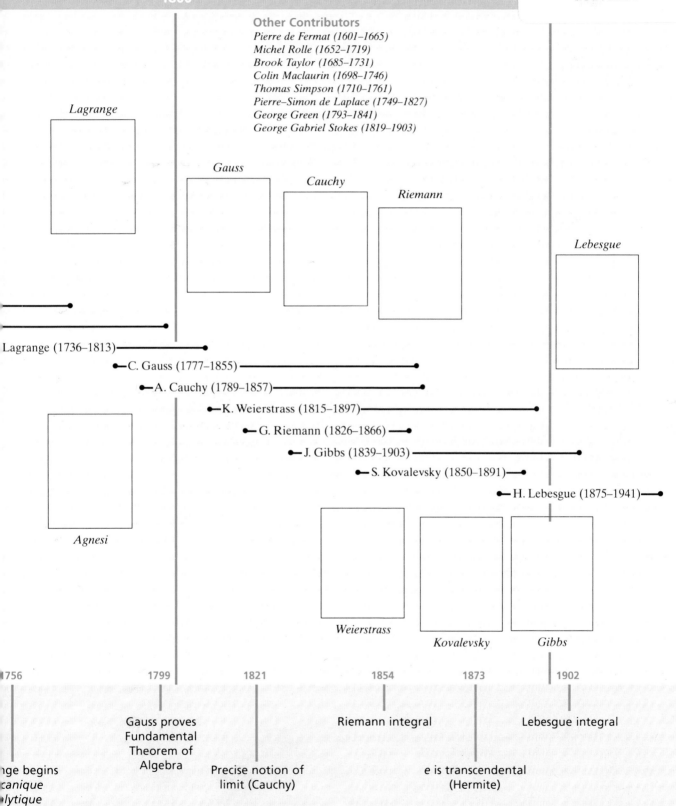

1800

Other Contributors
Pierre de Fermat (1601–1665)
Michel Rolle (1652–1719)
Brook Taylor (1685–1731)
Colin Maclaurin (1698–1746)
Thomas Simpson (1710–1761)
Pierre–Simon de Laplace (1749–1827)
George Green (1793–1841)
George Gabriel Stokes (1819–1903)

Lagrange

Gauss

Cauchy

Riemann

Lebesgue

Lagrange (1736–1813)

●—C. Gauss (1777–1855)————————————

●—A. Cauchy (1789–1857)——————————

●—K. Weierstrass (1815–1897)——————————————

●—G. Riemann (1826–1866)—●

●—J. Gibbs (1839–1903)————————————————●

●—S. Kovalevsky (1850–1891)—●

●—H. Lebesgue (1875–1941)—●

Agnesi

Weierstrass

Kovalevsky

Gibbs

1756	1799	1821	1854	1873	1902

Gauss proves
Fundamental
Theorem of
Algebra

Riemann integral

Lebesgue integral

nge begins
canique
lytique

Precise notion of
limit (Cauchy)

e is transcendental
(Hermite)

Calculus

for Biology and Medicine
with Student's Solutions Manual

A Custom Edition for
**Calculus with Applications
Math 11A & 11B**
University of California
Santa Cruz

Taken from:

Calculus for Biology and Medicine, Third Edition
by Claudia Neuhauser

Student's Solutions Manual
by Max Sterelyukhin to accompany
Calculus for Biology and Medicine, Third Edition
by Claudia Neuhauser

Learning Solutions

New York Boston San Francisco
London Toronto Sydney Tokyo Singapore Madrid
Mexico City Munich Paris Cape Town Hong Kong Montreal

Cover Art: Courtesy of Sandra Yates

Taken from:

Calculus for Biology and Medicine, Third Edition
by Claudia Neuhauser
Copyright © 2011, 2004, 2000 by Pearson Education, Inc.
Published by Prentice Hall
Upper Saddle River, New Jersey 07458

Student's Solutions Manual
by Max Sterelyukhin
to accompany *Calculus for Biology and Medicine*, Third Edition
by Claudia Neuhauser
Copyright © 2011, 2004, 2000 by Pearson Education, Inc.
Published by Prentice Hall
Upper Saddle River, New Jersey 07458

Pearson Learning Solutions, 501 Boylston Street, Suite 900, Boston, MA 02116
A Pearson Education Company
www.pearsoned.com

Printed in the United States of America

5 6 7 8 9 10 XXXX 15 14 13 12

000200010270573644

RH

ISBN 10: 0-558-82346-7
ISBN 13: 978-0-558-82346-7

About the Author

Claudia Neuhauser is Vice Chancellor for Academic Affairs and Director of the Center for Learning Innovation at the University of Minnesota Rochester (UMR). She is a Distinguished McKnight University Professor, Howard Hughes Medical Institute Professor, and Morse-Alumni Distinguished Teaching Professor. She received her Diploma in Mathematics from the Universität Heidelberg (Germany), and a Ph.D. in Mathematics from Cornell University. Before joining UMR in July 2008, she was Professor and Head in the Department of Ecology, Evolution and Behavior at the University of Minnesota Twin Cities, and a faculty member in mathematics departments at the University of Southern California, UW-Madison, University of Minnesota, and UC Davis.

Dr. Neuhauser's research is at the interface of ecology and evolution. She investigates effects of spatial structure on community dynamics, in particular, the effect of competition on the spatial structure of competitors and the effect of symbionts on the spatial distribution of their hosts. In addition, her research in population genetics has resulted in the development of statistical tools for random samples of genes.

In her role as Director of the Center for Learning Innovation at the University of Minnesota Rochester, Dr. Neuhauser is responsible for the development of the Bachelor of Science in Health Sciences. The Center promotes a learner-centered, concept-based learning environment in which ongoing assessment guides and monitors student learning and is the basis for data-driven research on learning. Dr. Neuhauser's interest in furthering the quantitative training of biology undergraduate students has resulted in a textbook titled *Calculus for Biology and Medicine* and a web page called Numb3r5 Count! (http://bioquest.org/numberscount/). In her spare time, she enjoys riding her bike, working out in the gym, and reading history and philosophy.

Contents

Taken from: *Calculus for Biology and Medicine*, Third Edition, by Claudia Neuhauser

Taken from:

Student's Solutions Manual
by Max Sterelyukhin, to accompany
Calculus for Biology and Medicine, Third Edition
by Claudia Neuhauser

Preface

Though it has been several years since the first edition was published, my goal of the first edition of *Calculus for Biology and Medicine* remains true in this edition:

> ***To show students right from the beginning how calculus is used to analyze phenomena in nature without compromising the rigor of the presentation of calculus.***

The result of this goal is a calculus text that has plentiful life and health sciences applications and that provides students with the knowledge and skills necessary to analyze and interpret mathematical models of a diverse array of phenomena in the living world. Since this text is written for college freshmen, the examples were chosen so that no formal training in biology is needed.

The rigor of the text prepares students well for more advanced courses in mathematics and statistics. My hope is that students will find calculus concepts easier to understand and more interesting if they are related to their major and career aspirations.

While the table of contents resembles that of a traditional calculus text, the content does not: abstract calculus concepts are introduced in a biological context and students learn how to transfer and apply these concepts to biological situations. The book does not teach modeling, but students are exposed to and asked to apply numerous models while they begin to see how simple models can capture the essence of natural phenomena.

New to this Edition

- Approximately 20% of the problems have been updated and new problems have been added.
- The application problems are now labeled to make it easier to identify the area of application.
- Learning objectives have been added to each chapter to help students structure their learning and help teachers organize their syllabus and class notes.
- Some sections have been rewritten or reorganized in response to users.
- Additional explanations and examples have been added to aid student understanding.
- Where necessary, figures have been added to aid students in visualizing the mathematics.
- The basic organization of the text has remained the same; however, some changes to the organization have been made: Practicing integration and partial fraction decomposition are now in separate sections. The final chapter on probability and statistics has been expanded to include more statistics and more on stochastic processes, and it can now be used for a semester-based course.

Features of the Text

Examples and Explanations Each topic is inspired by biological examples. This motivating introduction is followed by a thorough discussion *outside* of the life science context to enable students to become familiar with both the meaning and the mechanics of the mathematical topic. Finally, biological examples are presented to teach students how to apply the material in a life science context. Examples in the text are completely worked out, and the steps in the calculations are frequently explained in words.

Exercises   Calculus cannot be learned by watching someone do it. Because of this, *Calculus for Biology and Medicine*, Third Edition, provides students with skill-based exercises as well as word problems. Word problems are an integral part of teaching calculus in a life science context. The word problems contained in the text are up-to-date and are adapted from either standard biology texts or original research. The exercises and word problems are at the end of each section and are organized by subsection to help students reference specific subsections of content while completing homework. This also aids instructors in assigning homework problems.

Technology   *Calculus for Biology and Medicine* takes advantage of graphing calculators. This allows students to develop a much better visual understanding of the concepts in calculus. Beyond this, no special software is required.

Reflections and Outlook

The process of revising this book gave me good reason to look back and reflect upon how this book came about and to make decisions as to where it should go in the future. The motivation for writing this book more than ten years ago came from my teaching the second quarter of calculus to a large group of students at the University of Minnesota Twin Cities. The course covered standard calculus material, primarily focused on integration techniques, and the students came from diverse majors outside of the physical and engineering sciences. In fact, many of the students were life science majors.

Through interactions with colleagues in the life sciences, I increasingly became aware that much of what was taught in a standard first-year calculus course was of little use to the students in their pursuit of careers in the life and health sciences. Since life science majors rarely take more than a year of calculus, they are left with some rudimentary knowledge of an enormously useful area, but with few skills in applying this knowledge. I was fortunate to be in an environment where I was able to experiment with a different kind of calculus course with the support of my department (School of Mathematics) and departments within the College of Biological Sciences. I developed the course in 1997–98 and taught it for the first time in 1998–99.

Much has happened since then. The life and health sciences have undergone an information revolution. The human genome project was completed in 2003. Many more complete genomes have become available since then. High-throughput technologies, sensor systems, imaging devices, and other new technologies generate data at a breath-taking pace. The data will ultimately enable us to find solutions to challenges in areas as diverse as health, energy, environment, and national security. These revolutionary changes necessitate changes in how we educate future scientists.

National reports on quantitative education of students in the life and health sciences have addressed the needed changes. Foremost, Bio2010, a 2003 report[1] by the National Research Council, examined the undergraduate education of life and health science majors and identified fundamental science and mathematics skills needed to prepare them for a career in biomedical research. More recently, I was a member of a committee that was convened by the Association of the American Medical Colleges (AAMC) and the Howard Hughes Medical Institute (HHMI) and that prepared a report[2] on scientific competencies for medical school graduates and undergraduate students interested in going to medical school. Both reports emphasize the need for undergraduate students to develop *quantitative reasoning skills* to analyze, model, and predict phenomena in the natural world. Increasingly, students must be able to extract information from large data sets. Many of the mathematics concepts listed in Bio2010 are covered in this book, including dynamical systems and probability and statistics.

---

(1) Bio2010: Transforming Undergraduate Education for Future Research Biologists. Committee on Undergraduate Biology Education to Prepare Research Scientists for the 21st Century, Board of Life Sciences, Division on Earth and Life Studies, the National Research Council of the National Academies. 2003. **(2)** Scientific Foundations for Future Physicians. Report of the AAMC-HHMI Committee. 2009.

I continue to question the way we teach mathematics, statistics, and computation to students in the life and health sciences. We need to prepare our students for this data-rich environment. The traditional way of completing paper-and-pencil exercises and working with moderately-sized data sets (with a focus on developing the skills to master differentiation and integration techniques) is no longer sufficient.

I have been fortunate to receive funding from HHMI as a HHMI Professor to develop quantitative curricula for the life and health sciences. This growing set of resources is available on my web site NUMB3R5 COUNT! (http://bioquest.org/numberscount/). The goal is to take a data-driven approach to algebra, calculus, probability, and statistics. Worksheets and spreadsheets with authentic data sets have been written to supplement this book and enrich this course. It is my goal that students will begin to explore calculus concepts with real data.

■ Chapter Summary

Chapter 1 Basic tools from algebra and trigonometry are summarized in Section 1.1. Section 1.2 contains the basic functions used in this text, including exponential and logarithmic functions. Their graphical properties and their biological relevance are emphasized. Section 1.3 covers log-log and semi-log plots; these are graphical tools that are frequently used in the life sciences. In addition, a section on translating verbal descriptions of biological phenomena into graphs will provide students with skills that they will need when they read biological literature.

Chapter 2 This chapter covers difference equations (or discrete time models) and sequences, which provides a more natural way to explain the need for limits. The chapter ends with classical models of population growth, giving students a first glimpse at how models can aid in understanding biological phenomena.

Chapter 3 Limits and continuity are key concepts for understanding the conceptual parts of calculus. Visual intuition is emphasized before the theory is discussed. The formal definition of limits is at the end of the chapter and can be omitted.

Chapter 4 The geometric definition of a derivative as the slope of a tangent line is given before the formal treatment. After the formal definition of the derivative, differential equations are introduced as models for biological phenomena. Differentiation rules are discussed. These sections give students time to acquaint themselves with the basic rules of differentiation before applications are discussed. Related rates and error propagation, in addition to differential equations, are the main applications.

Chapter 5 This chapter presents biological and more traditional applications of differentiation. Many of the applications are consequences of the mean value theorem. The word problems originate from either biology textbooks or research articles. This use of sources puts the traditional applications (such as extrema, monotonicity, and concavity) in a biological context. Analysis of difference equations is available in an optional section.

Chapter 6 Integration is motivated geometrically. The fundamental theorem of calculus and its consequences are discussed in depth. Both biological and traditional applications of integration are provided before integration techniques are covered.

Chapter 7 This chapter contains integration techniques. However, only the most important techniques are covered. A section on Taylor polynomials is also included in this chapter. The section on using tables of integrals was moved to the end of the chapter and is optional. While computer software is not required in this book, it is likely that students will have access via the web to easy-to-use, free software to calculate integrals. For instance, WolframAlpha (http://www.wolframalpha.com/) allows integration of functions on the web and shows the steps.

Chapter 8 This chapter provides an introduction to differential equations. The treatment is not complete, but it will equip students with both analytical and graphical skills to analyze differential equations. Eigenvalues are introduced early to facilitate the analytical treatment of systems of differential equations in Chapter 11. Many of the differential equations discussed in the text are important models in biology. Though this text is not a modeling text, students will see how differential equations can model biological phenomena and will be able to interpret differential equations. Chapter 8 contains a large number of up-to-date applications of differential equations in biology.

Chapter 9 Matrix algebra is an indispensible tool for every life scientist. The material in this chapter covers the most basic concepts and is tailored to Chapters 10 and 11, where matrix algebra is frequently used. Special emphasis is given to the treatment of eigenvalues and eigenvectors because of their importance in analyzing systems of differential equations.

Chapter 10 This is an introduction to multidimensional calculus. The treatment is brief and tailored to Chapter 11, where systems of differential equations are discussed. The main topics are partial derivatives and linearization of vector-valued functions. The discussions of gradient and diffusion and the section on extrema and Lagrange multipliers are not needed for Chapter 11. If difference equations were covered early in the course, the final section in this chapter provides an introduction to systems of difference equations with many biological examples.

Chapter 11 This material is most relevant for students in the life sciences. Both graphical and analytical tools are developed to enable students to analyze systems of differential equations. The material is divided into linear and nonlinear systems. Understanding the stability of linear systems in terms of vector fields, eigenvectors, and eigenvalues helps students to master the more difficult analysis of nonlinear systems. Theory is explained before applications are given. This sequencing allows students to become familiar with the mechanics before delving into applications. An extensive problem set allows students to experience the power of this modeling tool in a biological context.

Chapter 12 This chapter contains some basic probabilistic and statistical tools. The statistics section has been expanded and more on stochastic processes has been added. The chapter can now be used for a full-semester course in probability and statistics, in particular if supplemented by real data sets, which are available on my web site: NUMB3R5 COUNT! (http://bioquest.org/numberscount/).

▮ How to Use This Book

This book contains more material than can be covered in one year. The intent is to allow for more flexibility in the choice of material covered. Sections whose heading says "Optional" can easily be omitted; the material in those sections is not needed in subsequent sections.

The book's content can be arranged so that the course can be taught as a one-semester, two-quarter, two-semester, four-quarter, or three-semester course. Chapters 1–4 must be covered in that order before any of the other sections are covered. In addition to Chapters 1–4, the following sections can be chosen:

One semester—integration emphasis 5.1–5.6, 5.8, 6.1–6.3 (without 6.3.4 and 6.3.5)

One semester—differential equation emphasis 5.1–5.6, 5.8, 6.1, 6.2, 8.2 (without solving any of the differential equations)

Two quarters 5.1–5.6, 5.8, 6.1–6.3 (without 6.3.4 and 6.3.5), Chapter 7, Chapter 8

Two semesters 5.1–5.6, 5.8, 6.1–6.3, Chapters 7, 8, and 9, 10.1–10.4, 10.7, 11.1–11.4 (select two of the subsections in Section 11.4)

Four quarters or three semesters All sections that are not labeled optional; optional sections should be chosen as time permits

One semester—probability emphasis Chapter 1, only Section 2.2.1 and 2.2.2 in Chapter 2, Chapter 3 (except 3.6), Chapter 4, 5.1–5.4, 5.8, 6.1, 6.2, 7.1, 7.2.1, 12.1–12.5 (without 12.5.5), 12.6 (if time permits)

■ Supplements

Online Instructor's Solutions Manual Provides fully worked-out solutions to every textbook exercise, including the Chapter Review problems. Available to download online at the Instructor Resource Center at www.pearsonhighered.com/irc

Student's Solutions Manual Provides fully worked-out solutions to the odd-numbered exercises in the section and Chapter Review problems. ISBN-13: 978-0-321-64492-3, ISBN-10: 0-321-64492-1

■ Acknowledgments

This book would not have been possible without the help of numerous people. The book greatly benefited from critical reviews of an earlier draft.

> Youn-Sha Chan, *University of Houston—Downtown*
> Jeong-Mi Yoon, *University of Houston—Downtown*
> Guillermo Goldsztein, *Georgia Institute of Technology*
> Peter Howard, *Texas A&M University*
> Petr Lisonek, *Simon Fraser University*
> Lawrence Marx, *University of California—Davis*

Thanks to all my students who took this course over the years at the University of Minnesota and the University of California–Davis for their constructive criticism and enthusiasm. I owe a special thanks to George Lobell, my former mathematics editor at Prentice Hall, who made this book possible in the first place; to Eric Frank, my math editor for the second edition; and to the staff at Pearson Education who helped develop this third edition: Deirdre Lynch, Editor-in-Chief; Jennifer Crum, Executive Editor; Joanne Dill, Senior Project Editor; Jeff Weidenaar, Executive Marketing Manager; Heather Scott, Art Director; Bayani DeLeon, Assistant Managing Editor; Rob Merenoff, Project Manager; Tracy Patruno, Senior Production Supervisor; Joanne Wendelken, Editorial Assistant; and Kendra Bassi, Marketing Coordinator.

Finally, I wish to thank my husband, Maury Bramson, who again patiently put up with my long hours of working on the third edition of the book.

Claudia Neuhauser
neuha001@umn.edu
University of Minnesota Rochester

Calculus

for Biology and Medicine

Preview and Review

1

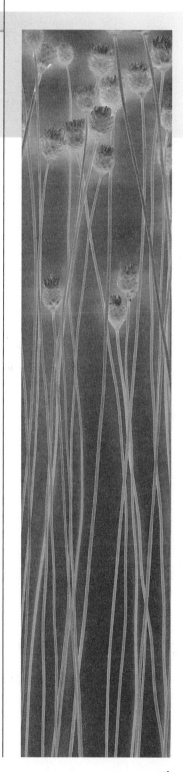

LEARNING OBJECTIVES

The first two sections of this chapter serve as a review of algebra, trigonometry, and precalculus, material needed to master the topics covered in this book. Section 1.3 reviews graphing functions and introduces the important concept of transforming functions into linear functions. The section includes a subsection on visualizing verbal descriptions of biological phenomena.

A Brief Overview of Calculus

Isaac Newton (1642–1727) and Gottfried Wilhelm Leibniz (1646–1716) are typically credited with the invention of calculus and were the first to develop the subject systematically.

Calculus has two parts: differential and integral calculus. Historically, differential calculus was concerned with finding lines tangent to curves and with calculating extrema (i.e., maxima and minima) of curves. Integral calculus has its roots in attempting to determine the areas of regions bounded by curves or in finding the volumes of solids. The two parts of calculus are closely related: The basic operation of one can be considered the inverse of the other. This result is known as the *fundamental theorem of calculus* and goes back to Newton and Leibniz, who were the first to understand its meaning and to put it to use in solving difficult problems.

Finding tangents, locating extrema, and calculating areas are basic geometric problems, and it may be somewhat surprising that their solution led to the development of methods that are useful in a wide range of scientific fields. The main reason for this historical development is that the slope of a tangent line at a given point is related to how quickly the function changes at that point. Knowing how quickly a function changes at a point opens up the possibility of a dynamic description of biology, such as a description of population growth, the speed at which a chemical reaction proceeds, the firing rate of neurons, and the speed at which an invasive species invades a new habitat. For this reason, calculus has been one of the most powerful tools in the mathematical formulation of scientific concepts. Applications of calculus are not restricted to biology, however; in fact, physics was the driving force in the original development of calculus. In this text we will be concerned primarily with how calculus is used in biology.

In addition to developing the theory of differential and integral calculus, we will consider many examples in which calculus is used to describe or model situations in the biological sciences. The use of quantitative reasoning is becoming increasingly more important in biology—for instance, in modeling interactions among species in a community, describing the activities of neurons, explaining genetic diversity in populations, and predicting the impact of global warming on vegetation. Today, calculus (Chapters 2–11) and probability and statistics (Chapter 12) are among the most important quantitative tools of a biologist.

■ 1.1 Preliminaries

This section reviews some of the concepts and techniques from algebra and trigonometry that are frequently used in calculus. The problems at the end of the section will help you reacquaint yourself with this material.

■ 1.1.1 The Real Numbers

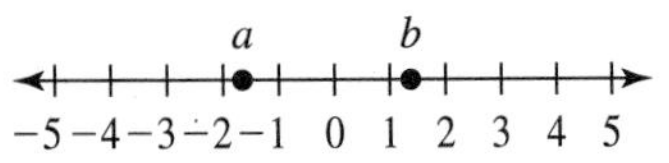

The **real numbers** can most easily be visualized on the **real-number line** (see Figure 1.1), on which numbers are ordered so that if $a < b$, then a is to the left of b. Sets (collections) of real numbers are typically denoted by the capital letters A, B, C, etc. To describe the set A, we write

$$A = \{x : \text{condition}\}$$

where "condition" tells us which numbers are in the set A. The most important sets in calculus are **intervals**. We use the following notations: If $a < b$, then

the **open** interval $(a, b) = \{x : a < x < b\}$

and

the **closed** interval $[a, b] = \{x : a \leq x \leq b\}$

We also use **half-open** intervals:

$$[a, b) = \{x : a \leq x < b\} \qquad \text{and} \qquad (a, b] = \{x : a < x \leq b\}$$

Unbounded intervals are sets of the form $\{x : x > a\}$. Here are the possible cases:

$$[a, \infty) = \{x : x \geq a\}$$
$$(-\infty, a] = \{x : x \leq a\}$$
$$(a, \infty) = \{x : x > a\}$$
$$(-\infty, a) = \{x : x < a\}$$

The symbols "∞" and "$-\infty$" mean "plus infinity" and "minus infinity," respectively. These symbols are *not* real numbers, but are used merely for notational convenience. The real-number line, denoted by **R**, does not have endpoints, and we can write **R** in the following equivalent forms:

$$\mathbf{R} = \{x : -\infty < x < \infty\} = (-\infty, \infty)$$

The location of the number 0 on the real-number line is called the **origin**, and we can measure the distance of the number x to the origin. For instance, -5 is 5 units to the left of the origin. A convenient notation for measuring distances from the origin on the real-number line is the absolute value of a real number.

Definition The **absolute value** of a real number a, denoted by $|a|$, is

$$|a| = \begin{cases} a & \text{if } a \geq 0 \\ -a & \text{if } a < 0 \end{cases}$$

For example, $|-7| = -(-7) = 7$. We can use absolute values to find the distance between any two numbers x_1 and x_2 as follows:

$$\text{distance between } x_1 \text{ and } x_2 = |x_1 - x_2|$$

Note that $|x_1 - x_2| = |x_2 - x_1|$. To find the distance between -2 and 4, we compute $|-2 - 4| = |-6| = 6$, or $|4 - (-2)| = |4 + 2| = 6$.

Figure 1.1 The real-number line.

We will frequently need to solve equations containing absolute values, for which the following property is useful:

Let $b \geq 0$. Then

1. For $a \geq 0$, $|a| = b$ is equivalent to $a = b$.
2. For $a < 0$, $|a| = b$ is equivalent to $-a = b$.

EXAMPLE 1

Solve $|x - 4| = 2$.

Solution

If $x - 4 \geq 0$, then $x - 4 = 2$ and thus $x = 6$. If $x - 4 < 0$, then $-(x - 4) = 2$ and thus $x = 2$. The solutions, illustrated graphically in Figure 1.2, are therefore $x = 6$ and $x = 2$. The points of intersection of $y = |x - 4|$ and $y = 2$ are at $x = 6$ and $x = 2$. Solving $|x - 4| = 2$ can also be interpreted as finding the two numbers that have distance 2 from 4. ∎

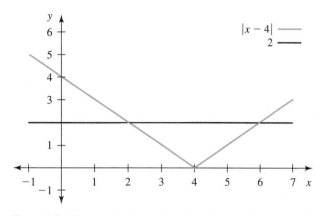

Figure 1.2 The graph of $y = |x - 4|$ and $y = 2$. The points of intersection are at $x = 6$ and $x = 2$.

We write the solution of an equation of the form $|a| = |b|$ as either $a = b$ or $a = -b$, illustrated in the next example.

EXAMPLE 2

Solve $|\frac{3}{2}x - 1| = |\frac{1}{2}x + 1|$.

Solution

Either

$$\frac{3}{2}x - 1 = \frac{1}{2}x + 1 \qquad \text{or} \qquad \frac{3}{2}x - 1 = -\left(\frac{1}{2}x + 1\right)$$

$$x = 2 \qquad\qquad \frac{3}{2}x - 1 = -\frac{1}{2}x - 1$$

$$2x = 0$$

$$x = 0$$

A graphical solution of this example is shown in Figure 1.3. ∎

Returning to Example 1, where we found the two points whose distance from 4 was equal to 2, we can also try to find those points whose distance from 4 is less than (or greater than) 2. This amounts to solving inequalities with absolute values. Looking back at Figure 1.2, we see that the set of x-values whose distance from 4 is less than 2 (i.e., $|x - 4| < 2$) is the interval $(2, 6)$. Similarly, the set of x-values whose distance from 4 is greater than 2 (i.e., $|x - 4| > 2$) is the union of the two intervals $(-\infty, 2)$ and $(6, \infty)$, or $(-\infty, 2) \cup (6, \infty)$.

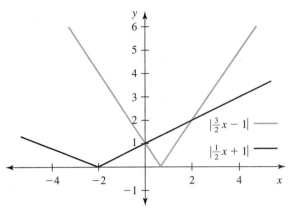

Figure 1.3 The graphs of $y = |\frac{3}{2}x - 1|$ and $y = |\frac{1}{2}x + 1|$. The points of intersection are at $x = 0$ and $x = 2$.

In general, to solve absolute-value inequalities, the following two properties are useful:

Let $b > 0$. Then

    1. $|a| < b$ is equivalent to $-b < a < b$.
    2. $|a| > b$ is equivalent to $a > b$ or $a < -b$.

EXAMPLE 3

(a) Solve $|2x - 5| < 3$.   **(b)** Solve $|4 - 3x| \geq 2$.

Solution

(a) We rewrite $|2x - 5| < 3$ as

$$-3 < 2x - 5 < 3$$

Adding 5 to all three parts, we obtain

$$2 < 2x < 8$$

Dividing the result by 2, we find that

$$1 < x < 4$$

The solution is therefore the set $\{x : 1 < x < 4\}$. In interval notation, the solution can be written as the open interval $(1, 4)$.

(b) To solve $|4 - 3x| \geq 2$, we go through the following steps:

$$
\begin{array}{ccc}
4 - 3x \geq 2 & & 4 - 3x \leq -2 \\
-3x \geq -2 & \text{or} & -3x \leq -6 \\
x \leq \dfrac{2}{3} & & x \geq 2
\end{array}
$$

The solution is the set $\{x : x \geq 2 \text{ or } x \leq \frac{2}{3}\}$, or, in interval notation, $(-\infty, \frac{2}{3}] \cup [2, \infty)$.

■

■ 1.1.2 Lines in the Plane

We will frequently encounter situations in which the relationship between quantities can be described by a **linear equation**. For example, when a weight is attached to a helical spring made of some elastic material (and the weight is not too heavy), the relationship between the length y of the spring and the weight x is

$$y = y_0 + kx \tag{1.1}$$

where y_0 denotes the length of the spring when no weight is attached to it and k is a positive constant. Equation (1.1) is an example of a linear equation, and we say that x and y satisfy a linear equation.

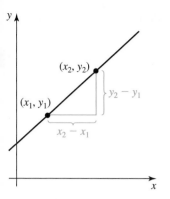

Figure 1.4 The slope of a straight line.

The **standard** form of a linear equation is given by

$$Ax + By + C = 0$$

where A, B, and C are constants, A and B are not both equal to 0, and x and y are the two variables. In algebra, you learned that the graph of a linear equation is a straight line.

If the two points (x_1, y_1) and (x_2, y_2) lie on a straight line, then the **slope** of the line is

$$m = \frac{y_2 - y_1}{x_2 - x_1}$$

(See Figure 1.4.) Two points (or one point and the slope) are sufficient to determine the equation of a straight line.

If you are given one point and the slope, you can use the **point–slope** form of a straight line to write its equation, given by

$$y - y_0 = m(x - x_0)$$

where m is the slope and (x_0, y_0) is a point on the line. If you are given two points, first compute the slope and then use one of the points and the slope to find the equation of the straight line in point–slope form.

Lastly, the most frequently used form of a linear equation is the **slope–intercept** form

$$y = mx + b$$

where m is the slope and b is the y-intercept, which is the point of intersection of the line with the y-axis; the y-intercept has coordinates $(0, b)$.

We summarize these three forms of linear equations in the following box:

$Ax + By + C = 0$	(Standard Form)
$y - y_0 = m(x - x_0)$	(Point–Slope Form)
$y = mx + b$	(Slope–Intercept Form)

EXAMPLE 4　Determine, in slope–intercept form, the equation of the line passing through $(-2, 1)$ and $(3, -\frac{1}{2})$.

Solution　The slope of the line is

$$m = \frac{y_2 - y_1}{x_2 - x_1} = \frac{-\frac{1}{2} - 1}{3 - (-2)} = \frac{-\frac{3}{2}}{5} = -\frac{3}{10}$$

Using the point–slope form with $(-2, 1)$, we find that

$$y - 1 = -\frac{3}{10}(x - (-2))$$

or, in slope–intercept form,

$$y = -\frac{3}{10}x + \frac{2}{5}$$

We could have used the other point, $(3, -\frac{1}{2})$, and obtained the same result. ■

We now recall two special cases that we illustrate in Figure 1.5:

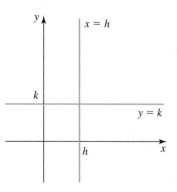

Figure 1.5 The horizontal line $y = k$ and the vertical line $x = h$.

$y = k$	horizontal line (slope 0)
$x = h$	vertical line (slope undefined)

In the next example, we show how to determine the slope and the y-intercept of a given straight line.

EXAMPLE 5

Determine the slope and the y-intercept of the line $3y - 2x + 9 = 0$.

Solution

We solve for y in $3y = 2x - 9$. We obtain $y = \frac{2}{3}x - 3$. We can now read off the slope $m = \frac{2}{3}$ and the y-intercept $b = -3$. ■

When two quantities x and y are linearly related so that

$$y = mx$$

we say that y is **proportional** to x, with m denoting the **constant of proportionality**, and we write

$$y \propto x$$

The symbol $\propto$ is read "is proportional to." If we write Equation (1.1) in the form

$$y - y_0 = kx$$

then the change in length $y - y_0$ is proportional to the attached weight with constant of proportionality k, and we can write

$$y - y_0 \propto x$$

There are two more properties of straight lines we wish to mention. When two lines l_1 and l_2 in the plane have no points in common or are identical, they are called **parallel**, denoted by $l_1 \parallel l_2$. The following criterion is useful in deciding whether two lines are parallel: Two noncoincident lines l_1 and l_2 are parallel ($l_1 \parallel l_2$) if and only if their slopes are identical. For two noncoincident, nonvertical lines l_1 and l_2 with slopes m_1 and m_2, respectively, the criterion becomes

$$l_1 \parallel l_2 \qquad \text{if and only if} \qquad m_1 = m_2$$

Two lines l_1 and l_2 are called **perpendicular** ($l_1 \perp l_2$) if their intersection forms an angle of 90°. The following criterion is useful for deciding whether two lines are perpendicular: Two nonvertical lines are perpendicular if and only if their slopes are negative reciprocals. That is, if l_1 and l_2 are nonvertical lines with slopes m_1 and m_2, then

$$l_1 \perp l_2 \qquad \text{if and only if} \qquad m_1 m_2 = -1$$

We will prove this result in Problem 54 at the end of this section.

■ 1.1.3 Equation of the Circle

A **circle** is the set of all points at a given distance, called the **radius**, from a given point, called the **center**. If r is the distance from (x_0, y_0) to (x, y) (see Figure 1.6), then, using the Pythagorean theorem, we find that

$$r^2 = (x - x_0)^2 + (y - y_0)^2$$

If $r = 1$ and $(x_0, y_0) = (0, 0)$, the circle is called the **unit circle**.

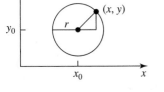

Figure 1.6 Circle with radius r centered at (x_0, y_0).

EXAMPLE 6

Find the equation of the circle with center $(2, 3)$ and passing through $(5, 7)$.

Solution

Using the Pythagorean theorem, we can compute the distance in the plane between $(2, 3)$ and $(5, 7)$:

$$\sqrt{(5 - 2)^2 + (7 - 3)^2} = \sqrt{9 + 16} = 5$$

Thus, this circle has radius 5 and center $(2, 3)$, and its equation is

$$25 = (x - 2)^2 + (y - 3)^2$$

■

■ 1.1.4 Trigonometry

We will need a few results from trigonometry. Recall that angles are measured in either degrees or radians and that a complete revolution on a unit circle (Figure 1.7) corresponds to $360°$, or 2π. For reasons that will become clear, the radian measure is preferred in calculus. To convert between degree and radian measure, we use the formula

$$\frac{\theta \text{ measured in degrees}}{360°} = \frac{\theta \text{ measured in radians}}{2\pi}$$

For instance, to convert $23°$ into radian measure, we compute

$$\theta = 23° \frac{2\pi}{360°} = 0.401$$

To convert $\frac{\pi}{6}$ into degrees, we compute

$$\theta = \frac{\pi}{6} \frac{360°}{2\pi} = 30°$$

There are four trigonometric functions that you should be familiar with: sine, cosine, tangent, and secant; the other two, cotangent and cosecant, are rarely used. The six are defined on a unit circle (see Figure 1.7) and are abbreviated as sin, cos, tan, sec, cot, and csc, respectively. Recall that a positive angle is measured counterclockwise from the positive x-axis, whereas a negative angle is measured clockwise. The six trigonometric functions are defined as follows:

$$\sin\theta = \frac{y}{1} = y \qquad \csc\theta = \frac{1}{\sin\theta} = \frac{1}{y}$$

$$\cos\theta = \frac{x}{1} = x \qquad \sec\theta = \frac{1}{\cos\theta} = \frac{1}{x}$$

$$\tan\theta = \frac{y}{x} \qquad \cot\theta = \frac{1}{\tan\theta} = \frac{x}{y}$$

There are a number of frequently used trigonometric identities. First, since $\tan\theta = y/x$ with $y = \sin\theta$ and $x = \cos\theta$, it follows that

$$\tan\theta = \frac{\sin\theta}{\cos\theta}$$

Now, applying the Pythagorean theorem to the triangle in Figure 1.7 and using the notation $\sin^2\theta = (\sin\theta)^2$, we find that

$$\sin^2\theta + \cos^2\theta = 1$$

Next, if we divide the preceding identity by $\cos^2\theta$, we obtain

$$\frac{\sin^2\theta}{\cos^2\theta} + 1 = \frac{1}{\cos^2\theta}$$

Using $\tan\theta = \sin\theta/\cos\theta$ and $\sec\theta = 1/\cos\theta$, we can write this as

$$\tan^2\theta + 1 = \sec^2\theta$$

In the next example, we solve a trigonometric equation.

EXAMPLE 7 Solve

$$2\sin\theta\cos\theta = \cos\theta \quad \text{on } [0, 2\pi)$$

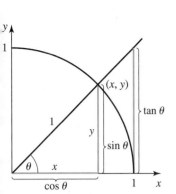

Figure 1.7 The trigonometric functions on a unit circle.

Solution

We should not be tempted to cancel $\cos\theta$ on each side; this would cause us to lose solutions. Instead, we bring $\cos\theta$ to the left side and factor $\cos\theta$ to obtain

$$\cos\theta(2\sin\theta - 1) = 0$$

That is,

$$\cos\theta = 0 \quad \text{or} \quad 2\sin\theta - 1 = 0$$

Solving $\cos\theta = 0$, we find that

$$\theta = \frac{\pi}{2} \quad \text{or} \quad \theta = \frac{3\pi}{2}$$

Solving $2\sin\theta - 1 = 0$, we get

$$\sin\theta = \frac{1}{2}$$

which yields

$$\theta = \frac{\pi}{6} \quad \text{or} \quad \theta = \frac{5\pi}{6}$$

The solution set is therefore $\{\frac{\pi}{6}, \frac{\pi}{2}, \frac{5\pi}{6}, \frac{3\pi}{2}\}$.   ■

Figure 1.8 yields the following two identities when we compare the two angles θ and $-\theta$ (a positive angle is measured counterclockwise from the positive x-axis, whereas a negative angle is measured clockwise):

$$\sin(-\theta) = -\sin\theta \quad \text{and} \quad \cos(-\theta) = \cos\theta$$

Some exact trigonometric values are collected in Table 1-1. Of course, $\frac{1}{2}\sqrt{0} = 0$, $\frac{1}{2}\sqrt{1} = \frac{1}{2}$, and $\frac{1}{2}\sqrt{4} = 1$, and you should memorize these simplified values. Rewriting Table 1-1 will make it easier to re-create the table in case you forget the exact values. Using $\tan\theta = \sin\theta/\cos\theta$, you immediately get the values for $\tan\theta$.

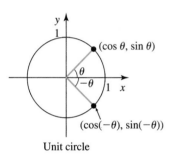

Unit circle

Figure 1.8 Using the unit circle to define trigonometric identities.

TABLE 1-1   Some Exact Trigonometric Values

Angle θ	0	$\dfrac{\pi}{6}$	$\dfrac{\pi}{4}$	$\dfrac{\pi}{3}$	$\dfrac{\pi}{2}$
	(0°)	(30°)	(45°)	(60°)	(90°)
$\sin\theta$	$\dfrac{1}{2}\sqrt{0}$	$\dfrac{1}{2}\sqrt{1}$	$\dfrac{1}{2}\sqrt{2}$	$\dfrac{1}{2}\sqrt{3}$	$\dfrac{1}{2}\sqrt{4}$
$\cos\theta$	$\dfrac{1}{2}\sqrt{4}$	$\dfrac{1}{2}\sqrt{3}$	$\dfrac{1}{2}\sqrt{2}$	$\dfrac{1}{2}\sqrt{1}$	$\dfrac{1}{2}\sqrt{0}$

■ **1.1.5 Exponentials and Logarithms**

Exponentials and logarithms are particularly important in biological contexts.

An exponential is an expression of the form

$$a^r$$

where a is called the **base** and r the **exponent**. Unless r is an integer or unless r is a rational number of the form p/q where p is an integer and q is an odd integer, we will assume that a is positive. We summarize some of the properties of an exponential as follows:

$$a^r a^s = a^{r+s} \qquad (ab)^r = a^r b^r$$

$$\frac{a^r}{a^s} = a^{r-s} \qquad \left(\frac{a}{b}\right)^r = \frac{a^r}{b^r}$$

$$a^{-r} = \frac{1}{a^r} \qquad \left(a^r\right)^s = a^{rs}$$

EXAMPLE 8

Evaluate the following exponential expressions:

(a) $3^2 3^{5/2} = 3^{2+5/2} = 3^{9/2}$

(b) $\dfrac{2^{-4} 2^3}{2^2} = \dfrac{2^{-1}}{2^2} = 2^{-1-2} = 2^{-3} = \dfrac{1}{2^3} = \dfrac{1}{8}$

(c) $\dfrac{a^k a^{3k}}{a^{5k}} = a^{k+3k-5k} = a^{-k} = \dfrac{1}{a^k}$ ■

Logarithms allow us to solve equations of the form

$$2^x = 8$$

The solution of this equation is $x = 3$, which we can write as

$$x = \log_2 8 = 3$$

In other words, a logarithm is an exponent. The expression

$$\log_a y$$

is the exponent on the base a that yields the number y. Logarithms are defined only for $y > 0$ (where the base is assumed to be positive and different from 1). We have the following correspondence between logarithms and exponentials:

$$x = \log_a y \qquad \text{is equivalent to} \qquad y = a^x$$

EXAMPLE 9

Which real number x satisfies

(a) $\log_3 x = -2$?   **(b)** $\log_{1/2} 8 = x$?

Solution

(a) We write this in the equivalent form

$$x = 3^{-2}$$

Hence,

$$x = \frac{1}{3^2} = \frac{1}{9}$$

(b) We write this in the equivalent form

$$\left(\frac{1}{2}\right)^x = 8$$
$$2^{-x} = 2^3$$
$$2^x = 2^{-3}$$

Setting the exponents equal to each other, we find that $x = -3$. Note that, in order to compare exponents, the bases must be the same.   ■

Some important properties of logarithms are as follows:

$$\log_a(xy) = \log_a x + \log_a y$$
$$\log_a\left(\frac{x}{y}\right) = \log_a x - \log_a y$$
$$\log_a x^r = r \log_a x$$

The most important logarithm is the **natural logarithm**, which has the number e as its base. The number e is an irrational number whose value is approximately 2.7182818. The natural logarithm is written $\ln x$; that is, $\log_e x = \ln x$.

EXAMPLE 10 Assume that x and y are positive, and simplify the following expressions:

(a) $\log_3(9x^2) = \log_3 9 + \log_3 x^2 = 2 + 2\log_3 x$

(b) $\log_5 \frac{x^2+3}{5x} = \log_5(x^2 + 3) - \log_5 5 - \log_5 x = \log_5(x^2 + 3) - 1 - \log_5 x$

[Note that $\log_5(x^2 + 3)$ cannot be simplified any further.]

(c) $-\ln\frac{1}{2} = \ln(\frac{1}{2})^{-1} = \ln 2$

(d) $\ln\frac{3x^2}{\sqrt{y}} = \ln 3 + \ln x^2 - \ln\sqrt{y} = \ln 3 + 2\ln x - \frac{1}{2}\ln y$

(In the last step, we used the fact that $\sqrt{y} = y^{1/2}$.) ■

In algebra, you learned how to solve equations of the form $e^{2x} = 3$ or $\ln(x+1) = 5$. We will need to do this frequently. The key to solving such equations are the two identities

$$\log_a a^x = x \qquad \text{and} \qquad a^{\log_a x} = x$$

The next example illustrates how to use these identities.

EXAMPLE 11 Solve for x.

(a) $e^{2x} = 3$ **(b)** $\ln(x+1) = 5$ **(c)** $5^{2x-1} = 2^x$

Solution **(a)** To solve $e^{2x} = 3$ for x, we take logarithms to base e on both sides:

$$\ln e^{2x} = \ln 3$$

But $\ln e^{2x} = 2x$; hence,

$$2x = \ln 3, \qquad \text{or} \qquad x = \frac{1}{2}\ln 3$$

(b) To solve $\ln(x+1) = 5$, we write the equation in exponential form:

$$e^{\ln(x+1)} = e^5$$

This simplifies to

$$x + 1 = e^5, \qquad \text{or} \qquad x = e^5 - 1$$

(c) To solve $5^{2x-1} = 2^x$ for x, we observe that the two bases are different. We therefore cannot compare the exponents directly. Instead, we take logarithms on both sides. Any positive base (different from 1) for the logarithm would work, and we choose base e, since it is the most commonly used base in calculus. Doing so yields

$$\ln 5^{2x-1} = \ln 2^x$$

or, after simplifying,

$$(2x - 1)\ln 5 = x\ln 2$$

Solving for x, we find that

$$2x\ln 5 - x\ln 2 = \ln 5$$
$$x(2\ln 5 - \ln 2) = \ln 5$$

Hence,

$$x = \frac{\ln 5}{2\ln 5 - \ln 2}$$

■

■ **1.1.6** Complex Numbers and Quadratic Equations

The square of a real number is always nonnegative. However, there are situations in which we need to take a square root of a negative number. Since the resulting square root cannot be a real number, we introduce a new symbol, which we denote by i, that will allow us to deal with this case. We set

$$i^2 = -1$$

The symbol i is called the **imaginary unit**. Thus, instead of writing $\sqrt{-17}$, for instance, we can now write $i\sqrt{17}$.

The symbol i allows us to introduce a new number system, the set of **complex numbers**:

> A **complex number** is a number of the form
>
> $$z = a + bi$$
>
> where a and b are real numbers. The real number a is the **real part** of $a + bi$, and the real number b is the **imaginary part**.

For instance, $-3 + 7i$ has real part -3 and imaginary part 7, and $2 - 5i$ has real part 2 and imaginary part -5. Since $a + 0i = a$, it follows that the set of real numbers is a subset of the set of complex numbers. Complex numbers of the form bi are called **purely imaginary numbers**.

Two complex numbers are equal if their respective real and imaginary parts are equal; that is,

$$a + bi = c + di \quad \text{if and only if} \quad a = c \quad \text{and} \quad b = d$$

To add two complex numbers, we use the following rule:

$$(a + bi) + (c + di) = (a + c) + (b + d)i$$

This rule says that real and imaginary parts are added separately. To calculate the product of two complex numbers, we proceed as follows:

$$
\begin{aligned}
(a + bi)(c + di) &= ac + adi + bci + bdi^2 \\
&= ac + (ad + bc)i - bd \\
&= (ac - bd) + (ad + bc)i
\end{aligned}
$$

Note that we used $i^2 = -1$ in the penultimate step. There is no need to memorize the product of two complex numbers, since we can always compute it by the distributive law.

EXAMPLE 12   Find

(a) $(2 + 3i) - (5 - 6i)$,   (b) $(5 - 3i)(1 + 2i)$.

Solution
(a) $(2 + 3i) - (5 - 6i) = 2 + 3i - 5 + 6i = -3 + 9i$,
(b) $(5 - 3i)(1 + 2i) = 5 + 10i - 3i - 6i^2 = 5 + 7i - (6)(-1) = 11 + 7i$.   ■

> If $z = a + bi$ is a complex number, its **conjugate**, denoted by $\bar{z}$, is defined as
>
> $$\bar{z} = a - bi$$

For complex numbers z and w, it can be shown (see Problems 113–115) that

$$\overline{(\overline{z})} = z$$
$$\overline{z + w} = \overline{z} + \overline{w}$$
$$\overline{zw} = \overline{z}\,\overline{w}$$

Furthermore, if we multiply a complex number by its conjugate, we find that

$$z\overline{z} = (a + bi)(a - bi) = a^2 - abi + abi - b^2 i^2$$
$$= a^2 + b^2$$

That is,

If $z = a + bi$, then
$$z\overline{z} = a^2 + b^2$$

EXAMPLE 13   Let $z = 3 + 2i$.
   (a) Find $\overline{z}$.   (b) Compute $z\overline{z}$.

Solution   (a) $\overline{z} = 3 - 2i$.
   (b) $z\overline{z} = (3 + 2i)(3 - 2i) = 9 - 4i^2 = 9 + 4 = 13$. ■

We encounter complex numbers primarily when we solve quadratic equations. Recall that, to solve
$$ax^2 + bx + c = 0$$

for $a \neq 0$, we use the quadratic formula

$$x_{1,2} = \frac{-b \pm \sqrt{b^2 - 4ac}}{2a}$$

where $x_{1,2}$ refers to the two solutions x_1 (with the "+" sign) and x_2 (with the "−" sign).

EXAMPLE 14   Solve
$$x^2 + 4x + 5 = 0$$

Solution   Using the quadratic formula, we obtain

$$x_{1,2} = \frac{-4 \pm \sqrt{4^2 - (4)(1)(5)}}{(2)(1)}$$

$$= \frac{-4 \pm \sqrt{16 - 20}}{2} = \frac{-4 \pm \sqrt{-4}}{2}$$

If we allowed solutions only in the real-number system, we would conclude that $x^2 + 4x + 5 = 0$ has no solutions. But if we allow solutions in the complex number system, we find that

$$x_{1,2} = \frac{-4 \pm \sqrt{4i^2}}{2} = \frac{-4 \pm 2i}{2} = \frac{2(-2 \pm i)}{2} = -2 \pm i$$

That is, $x_1 = -2 + i$ and $x_2 = -2 - i$. ■

The term $b^2 - 4ac$ under the square root sign in the quadratic formula is called the **discriminant**. If the discriminant is nonnegative, the two solutions of the corresponding quadratic equation are real. (When the discriminant is equal to 0, the two solutions are identical.) If the discriminant is negative, the two solutions are complex conjugates of each other.

EXAMPLE 15   Without solving

$$2x^2 - 3x + 7 = 0$$

what can you say about the solution?

Solution   We compute the discriminant

$$b^2 - 4ac = (-3)^2 - (4)(2)(7) = 9 - 56 = -47 < 0$$

Since the discriminant is negative, the equation $2x^2 - 3x + 7 = 0$ has two complex solutions, which are conjugates of each other.   ■

Section 1.1 Problems

■ **1.1.1**

1. Find the two numbers that have distance 3 from −1 by **(a)** measuring the distances on the real-number line and **(b)** solving an appropriate equation involving an absolute value.

2. Find all pairwise distances between the numbers −5, 2, and 7 by **(a)** measuring the distances on the real-number line and **(b)** computing the distances by using absolute values.

3. Solve the following equations:
(a) $|2x - 4| = 6$ **(b)** $|x - 3| = 2$
(c) $|2x + 3| = 5$ **(d)** $|7 - 3x| = -2$

4. Solve the following equations:
(a) $|2x + 4| = |5x - 2|$ **(b)** $|5 - 3u| = |3 + 2u|$
(c) $|4 + \frac{t}{2}| = |\frac{3}{2}t - 2|$ **(d)** $|2s - 3| = |7 - s|$

5. Solve the following inequalities:
(a) $|5x - 2| \le 4$ **(b)** $|1 - 3x| > 8$
(c) $|7x + 4| \ge 3$ **(d)** $|6 - 5x| < 7$

6. Solve the following inequalities:
(a) $|2x + 3| < 6$ **(b)** $|3 - 4x| \ge 2$
(c) $|x + 5| \le 1$ **(d)** $|7 - 2x| < 0$

■ **1.1.2**

In Problems 7–42, determine the equation of the line that satisfies the stated requirements. Put the equation in standard form.

7. The line passing through (2, 4) with slope $-\frac{1}{3}$

8. The line passing through (1, −2) with slope 2

9. The line passing through (0, −2) with slope −3

10. The line passing through (−3, 5) with slope 1/2

11. The line passing through (−2, −3) and (1, 4)

12. The line passing through (−1, 4) and (2, −$\frac{1}{2}$)

13. The line passing through (0, 4) and (3, 0)

14. The line passing through (1, −1) and (4, 5)

15. The horizontal line through (3, $\frac{3}{2}$)

16. The horizontal line through (0, −1)

17. The vertical line through (−1, $\frac{7}{2}$)

18. The vertical line through (2, −3)

19. The line with slope 3 and y-intercept (0, 2)

20. The line with slope −1 and y-intercept (0, −3)

21. The line with slope 1/2 and y-intercept (0, 2)

22. The line with slope −1/3 and y-intercept (0, −1)

23. The line with slope −2 and x-intercept (1, 0)

24. The line with slope 1 and x-intercept (−2, 0)

25. The line with slope −1/4 and x-intercept (3, 0)

26. The line with slope 1/5 and x-intercept (−1/2, 0)

27. The line passing through (2, −3) and parallel to

$$x + 2y - 4 = 0$$

28. The line passing through (1, 2) and parallel to

$$x - 3y - 6 = 0$$

29. The line passing through (−1, −1) and parallel to the line passing through (0, 1) and (3, 0)

30. The line passing through (2, −3) and parallel to the line passing through (0, −1) and (2, 1)

31. The line passing through (1, 4) and perpendicular to

$$2y - 5x + 7 = 0$$

32. The line passing through (−1, −1) and perpendicular to

$$x - y + 3 = 0$$

33. The line passing through (5, −1) and perpendicular to the line passing through (−2, 1) and (1, −2)

34. The line passing through (4, −1) and perpendicular to the line passing through (−2, 0) and (1, 1)

35. The line passing through (4, 2) and parallel to the horizontal line passing through (1, −2)

36. The line passing through (−1, 5) and parallel to the horizontal line passing through (2, −1)

37. The line passing through (−1, 1) and parallel to the vertical line passing through (2, −1)

38. The line passing through (3, 1) and parallel to the vertical line passing through (−1, −2)

39. The line passing through (1, −3) and perpendicular to the horizontal line passing through (−1, −1)

40. The line passing through $(4, 2)$ and perpendicular to the horizontal line passing through $(3, 1)$

41. The line passing through $(7, 3)$ and perpendicular to the vertical line passing through $(-2, 4)$

42. The line passing through $(-2, 5)$ and perpendicular to the vertical line passing through $(1, 4)$

43. To convert a length measured in feet to a length measured in centimeters, we use the facts that a length measured in feet is proportional to a length measured in centimeters and that 1 ft corresponds to 30.5 cm. If x denotes the length measured in ft and y denotes the length measured in cm, then

$$y = 30.5x$$

(a) Explain how to use this relationship.

(b) Use the relationship to convert the following measurements into centimeters:

(i) 6 ft   **(ii)** 3 ft, 2 in   **(iii)** 1 ft, 7 in

(c) Use the relationship to convert the following measurements into ft:

(i) 173 cm   **(ii)** 75 cm   **(iii)** 48 cm

44. (a) To convert the weight of an object from kilograms (kg) to pounds (lb), you use the facts that a weight measured in kilograms is proportional to a weight measured in pounds and that 1 kg corresponds to 2.20 lb. Find an equation that relates weight measured in kilograms to weight measured in pounds.

(b) Use your answer in (a) to convert the following measurements:

(i) 63 lb   **(ii)** 150 lb   **(iii)** 2.5 kg   **(iv)** 140 kg

45. Assume that the distance a car travels is proportional to the time it takes to cover the distance. Find an equation that relates distance and time if it takes the car 15 min to travel 10 mi. What is the constant of proportionality if distance is measured in miles and time is measured in hours?

46. Assume that the number of seeds a plant produces is proportional to its aboveground biomass. Find an equation that relates number of seeds and aboveground biomass if a plant that weighs 217 g has 17 seeds.

47. Experimental study plots are often squares of length 1 m. If 1 ft corresponds to 0.305 m, compute the area of a square plot of length 1 m in ft^2.

48. Large areas are often measured in hectares (ha) or in acres. If 1 ha = 10,000 m^2 and 1 acre = 4046.86 m^2, how many acres is 1 hectare?

49. To convert the volume of a liquid measured in ounces to a volume measured in liters, we use the fact that 1 liter equals 33.81 ounces. Denote by x the volume measured in ounces and by y the volume measured in liters. Assume a linear relationship between these two units of measurements.

(a) Find the equation relating x and y.

(b) A typical soda can contains 12 ounces of liquid. How many liters is this?

50. To convert a distance measured in miles to a distance measured in kilometers, we use the fact that 1 mile equals 1.609 kilometers. Denote by x the distance measured in miles and by y the distance measured in kilometers. Assume a linear relationship between these two units of measurements.

(a) Find an equation relating x and y.

(b) The distance between Minneapolis and Madison is 261 miles. How many kilometers is this?

51. Car speed in many countries is measured in kilometers per hour. In the United States, car speed is measured in miles per hour. To convert between these units, use the fact that 1 mile equals 1.609 kilometers.

(a) The speed limit on many U.S. highways is 55 miles per hour. Convert this number into kilometers per hour.

(b) The recommended speed limit on German highways is 130 kilometers per hour. Convert this number into miles per hour.

To measure temperature, three scales are commonly used: Fahrenheit, Celsius, and Kelvin. These scales are linearly related. We discuss these scales in Problems 52 and 53.

52. (a) The Celsius scale is devised so that 0°C is the freezing point of water (at 1 atmosphere of pressure) and 100°C is the boiling point of water (at 1 atmosphere of pressure). If you are more familiar with the Fahrenheit scale, then you know that water freezes at 32°F and boils at 212°F. Find a linear equation that relates temperature measured in degrees Celsius and temperature measured in degrees Fahrenheit.

(b) The normal body temperature in humans ranges from 97.6°F to 99.6°F. Convert this temperature range into degrees Celsius.

53. (a) The Kelvin (K) scale is an **absolute** scale of temperature. The zero point of the scale (0 K) denotes **absolute zero**, the coldest possible temperature; that is, no body can have a temperature below 0 K. It has been determined experimentally that 0 K corresponds to -273.15°C. If 1 K denotes the same temperature difference as 1°C, find an equation that relates the Kelvin and Celsius scales.

(b) Pure nitrogen and pure oxygen can be produced cheaply by first liquefying purified air and then allowing the temperature of the liquid air to rise slowly. Since nitrogen and oxygen have different boiling points, they are distilled at different temperatures. The boiling point of nitrogen is 77.4 K and of oxygen is 90.2 K. Convert each of these boiling-point temperatures into Celsius. If you solved Problem 52(a), convert the boiling-point temperatures into Fahrenheit as well. Consider the two techniques described for distilling nitrogen and oxygen. Which element gets distilled first?

54. Use the following steps to show that if two nonvertical lines l_1 and l_2 with slopes m_1 and m_2, respectively, are perpendicular, then $m_1 m_2 = -1$: Assume that $m_1 < 0$ and $m_2 > 0$.

(a) Use a graph to show that if θ_1 and θ_2 are the respective angles of inclination of the lines l_1 and l_2, then $\theta_1 = \theta_2 + \frac{\pi}{2}$. (The angle of inclination of a line is the angle $\theta \in [0, \pi)$ between the line and the positively directed x-axis.)

(b) Use the fact that $\tan(\pi - x) = -\tan x$ to show that $m_1 = \tan \theta_1$ and $m_2 = \tan \theta_2$.

(c) Use the fact that $\tan(\frac{\pi}{2} - x) = \cot x$ and $\cot(-x) = -\cot x$ to show that $m_1 = -\cot \theta_2$.

(d) From the latter equation, deduce the truth of the claim set forth at the beginning of this problem.

■ **1.1.3**

55. Find the equation of a circle with center $(-1, 4)$ and radius 3.

56. Find the equation of a circle with center $(2, 3)$ and radius 4.

57. (a) Find the equation of a circle with center $(2, 5)$ and radius 3.

(b) Where does the circle intersect the y-axis?

(c) Does the circle intersect the x-axis? Explain.

58. (a) Find all possible radii of a circle centered at $(3, 6)$ so that the circle intersects only one axis.

b) Find all possible radii of a circle centered at (3, 6) so that the circle intersects both axes.

9. Find the center and the radius of the circle given by the equation

$$(x - 2)^2 + y^2 = 16$$

0. Find the center and the radius of the circle given by the equation

$$(x + 1)^2 + (y - 3)^2 = 9$$

1. Find the center and the radius of the circle given by the equation

$$0 = x^2 + y^2 - 4x + 2y - 11$$

To do this, you must complete the squares.)

2. Find the center and the radius of the circle given by the equation

$$x^2 + y^2 + 2x - 4y + 1 = 0$$

To do this, you must complete the squares.)

■ 1.1.4

3. (a) Convert $75°$ to radian measure.

b) Convert $\frac{17}{12}\pi$ to degree measure.

4. (a) Convert $-15°$ to radian measure.

b) Convert $\frac{3}{4}\pi$ to degree measure.

5. Evaluate the following expressions without using a calculator:
a) $\sin(-\frac{5\pi}{4})$ **(b)** $\cos(\frac{5\pi}{6})$ **(c)** $\tan(\frac{\pi}{3})$

6. Evaluate the following expressions without using a calculator:
a) $\sin(\frac{3\pi}{4})$ **(b)** $\cos(-\frac{13\pi}{6})$ **(c)** $\tan(\frac{4\pi}{3})$

7. (a) Find the values of $\alpha \in [0, 2\pi)$ that satisfy

$$\sin \alpha = -\frac{1}{2}\sqrt{3}$$

b) Find the values of $\alpha \in [0, 2\pi)$ that satisfy

$$\tan \alpha = \sqrt{3}$$

8. (a) Find the values of $\alpha \in [0, 2\pi)$ that satisfy

$$\cos \alpha = -\frac{1}{2}\sqrt{2}$$

b) Find the values of $\alpha \in [0, 2\pi)$ that satisfy

$$\sec \alpha = 2$$

9. Show that the identity

$$1 + \tan^2 \theta = \sec^2 \theta$$

follows from

$$\sin^2 \theta + \cos^2 \theta = 1$$

0. Show that the identity

$$1 + \cot^2 \theta = \csc^2 \theta$$

follows from

$$\sin^2 \theta + \cos^2 \theta = 1$$

1. Solve $2 \cos \theta \sin \theta = \sin \theta$ on $[0, 2\pi)$.
2. Solve $\sec^2 x = \sqrt{3} \tan x + 1$ on $[0, \pi)$.

■ 1.1.5

3. Evaluate the following exponential expressions:

(a) $4^3 4^{-2/3}$ **(b)** $\frac{3^2 3^{1/2}}{3^{-1/2}}$ **(c)** $\frac{5^k 5^{2k-1}}{5^{1-k}}$

74. Evaluate the following exponential expressions:

(a) $(2^4 2^{-3/2})^2$ **(b)** $\left(\frac{6^{5/2} 6^{2/3}}{6^{1/3}}\right)^3$ **(c)** $\left(\frac{3^{-2k+3}}{3^{4+k}}\right)^3$

75. Which real number x satisfies
(a) $\log_4 x = -2$?   **(b)** $\log_{1/3} x = -3$?   **(c)** $\log_{10} x = -2$?

76. Which real number x satisfies
(a) $\log_{1/2} x = -4$?   **(b)** $\log_{1/4} x = 2$?   **(c)** $\log_5 x = 3$?

77. Which real number x satisfies
(a) $\log_{1/2} 32 = x$?   **(b)** $\log_{1/3} 81 = x$?   **(c)** $\log_{10} 0.001 = x$?

78. Which real number x satisfies
(a) $\log_4 64 = x$?   **(b)** $\log_{1/5} 625 = x$?   **(c)** $\log_{10} 10,000 = x$?

79. Simplify the following expressions:
(a) $-\ln \frac{1}{3}$ **(b)** $\log_4(x^2 - 4)$ **(c)** $\log_2 4^{3x-1}$

80. Simplify the following expressions:
(a) $-\ln \frac{1}{5}$ **(b)** $\ln \frac{x^2-y^2}{\sqrt{x}}$ **(c)** $\log_3 3^{2x+1}$

81. Solve for x.
(a) $e^{3x-1} = 2$ **(b)** $e^{-2x} = 10$ **(c)** $e^{x^2-1} = 10$

82. Solve for x.
(a) $3^x = 81$ **(b)** $9^{2x+1} = 27$ **(c)** $10^{5x} = 1000$

83. Solve for x.
(a) $\ln(x - 3) = 5$ **(b)** $\ln(x + 2) + \ln(x - 2) = 1$
(c) $\log_3 x^2 - \log_3 2x = 2$

84. Solve for x.
(a) $\ln(2x - 3) = 0$ **(b)** $\log_2(1 - x) = 3$
(c) $\ln x^3 - 2 \ln x = 1$

■ 1.1.6

In Problems 85–92, simplify each expression and write it in the standard form $a + bi$.

85. $(3 - 2i) - (-2 + 5i)$ **86.** $(7 + i) - 4$
87. $(4 - 2i) + (9 + 4i)$ **88.** $(6 - 4i) + (2 + 5i)$
89. $3(5 + 3i)$ **90.** $(2 - 3i)(5 + 2i)$
91. $(6 - i)(6 + i)$ **92.** $(-4 - 3i)(4 + 2i)$

In Problems 93–98, let $z = 3 - 2i$, $u = -4 + 3i$, $v = 3 + 5i$, and $w = 1 - i$. Compute the following expressions:

93. $\bar{z}$ **94.** $z + u$ **95.** $\overline{z + v}$
96. $\overline{v - w}$ **97.** $\overline{vw}$ **98.** $\overline{uz}$
99. If $z = a + bi$, find $z + \bar{z}$ and $z - \bar{z}$.
100. If $z = a + bi$, find $\bar{z}$. Use your answer to compute $\overline{(\bar{z})}$, and compare your answer with z.

In Problems 101–106, solve each quadratic equation in the complex number system.

101. $2x^2 - 3x + 2 = 0$ **102.** $3x^2 - 2x + 1 = 0$
103. $-x^2 + x + 2 = 0$ **104.** $-2x^2 + x + 3 = 0$
105. $4x^2 - 3x + 1 = 0$ **106.** $-2x^2 + 4x - 3 = 0$

In Problems 107–112, first determine whether the solutions of each quadratic equation are real or complex without solving the equation. Then solve the equation.

107. $3x^2 - 4x - 7 = 0$ **108.** $3x^2 - 4x + 7 = 0$
109. $-x^2 + 2x - 1 = 0$ **110.** $4x^2 - x + 1 = 0$
111. $3x^2 - 5x + 6 = 0$ **112.** $-x^2 + 7x - 2 = 0$
113. Show $\overline{(\bar{z})} = z$.
114. Show $\overline{z + w} = \bar{z} + \bar{w}$.
115. Show $\overline{zw} = \bar{z}\,\bar{w}$.

■ 1.2 Elementary Functions

■ 1.2.1 What Is a Function?

Scientific investigations often study relationships between quantities, such as how enzyme activity depends on temperature or how the length of a fish is related to its age. To describe such relationships mathematically, the concept of a function is useful.

The word *function* (or, more precisely, its Latin equivalent *functio*, which means "execution") was introduced by Leibniz in 1694 in order to describe curves. Later, Euler (1707–1783) used it to describe any equation involving variables and constants. The modern definition is much broader and emphasizes the basic idea of expressing relationships between any two sets.

> **Definition** A **function** f is a rule that assigns each element x in the set A exactly one element y in the set B. The element y is called the **image** (or **value**) of x under f and is denoted by $f(x)$ (read "f of x"). The set A is called the **domain** of f, the set B is called the **codomain** of f, and the set $f(A) = \{y : y = f(x)$ for some $x \in A\}$ is called the **range** of f.

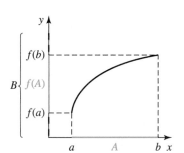

Figure 1.9 A function $f(x)$ with domain A, codomain B, and range $f(A)$.

To define a function, we use the notation

$$f : A \to B$$
$$x \to f(x)$$

where A and B are subsets of the set of real numbers. Frequently, we simply write $y = f(x)$ and call x the **independent** variable and y the **dependent** variable. We can illustrate functions graphically in the x–y plane. In Figure 1.9, we see the graph of $y = f(x)$, with domain A, codomain B, and range $f(A)$.

The function $f(x)$ must be specified; for example, $f(x)$ could be given by a graph as in Figure 1.9, or it could be expressed algebraically, such as $f(x) = x^2$. Note that $f(A) \subset B$, but not every element in the codomain B must be in $f(A)$. For instance, let

$$f : \mathbf{R} \to \mathbf{R}$$
$$x \to x^2$$

The domain of f is $\mathbf{R}$, but the range of f is only $[0, \infty)$ because the square of a real number is nonnegative; that is, $f(\mathbf{R}) = [0, \infty) \neq \mathbf{R}$. Also, the domain of a function need not be the largest possible set on which we can define the function, as $\mathbf{R}$ is in the preceding example. For instance, we could have defined f on a smaller set, such as $[0, 1]$, calling the new function g, given by

$$g : [0, 1] \to \mathbf{R}$$
$$x \to x^2$$

Although the same rule is used for f and g, the two functions are not the same, because their respective domains are different.

> Two functions f and g are **equal** if and only if
>
> **1.** f and g are defined on the same domain, and
> **2.** $f(x) = g(x)$ for all x in the domain.

EXAMPLE 1   Let

$$f_1 : [0, 1] \to \mathbf{R}$$
$$x \to x^2$$
$$f_2 : [0, 1] \to \mathbf{R}$$
$$x \to \sqrt{x^4}$$

and

$$f_3 : \mathbf{R} \to \mathbf{R}$$
$$x \to x^2$$

Determine which of these functions are equal.

Solution   Because f_1 and f_2 are defined on the same domain and $f_1(x) = f_2(x) = x^2$ for all $x \in [0, 1]$, it follows that f_1 and f_2 are equal.

Neither f_1 nor f_2 is equal to f_3, because the domain of f_3 is different from the domains of f_1 and f_2.   ■

The choices of domains for the functions that we have thus far considered may look somewhat arbitrary (and they are arbitrary in the examples we have seen so far). In applications, however, there is often a natural choice of domain. For instance, if we look at a certain plant response (such as total biomass or the ratio of above to below biomass) as a function of nitrogen concentration in the soil, then, given that nitrogen concentration cannot be negative, the domain for this function could be the set of nonnegative real numbers. As another example, suppose we define a function that depends on the fraction of a population infected with a certain virus; then a natural choice for the domain of this function would be the interval [0, 1] because a fraction of a population must be a number between 0 and 1.

In our definition of a function, we stated that a function is a rule that assigns, to each element $x \in A$, *exactly* one element $y \in B$. When we graph $y = f(x)$ in the x–y plane, there is a simple test to decide whether or not $f(x)$ is a function: If each vertical line intersects the graph of $y = f(x)$ at most once, then $f(x)$ is a function. Figure 1.10 shows the graph of a function: Each vertical line intersects the graph of $y = f(x)$ at most once. The graph of $y = f(x)$ in Figure 1.11 is not a function, since there are x-values that are assigned to more than one y-value, as illustrated by the vertical line that intersects the graph more than once.

Sometimes functions show certain symmetries. For example, in Figure 1.12, $f(x) = x$ is symmetric about the origin; that is, $f(x) = -f(-x)$. In Figure 1.13, $g(x) = x^2$ is symmetric about the y-axis; that is, $g(x) = g(-x)$. In the first case, we say that f is odd; in the second case, that g is even. To check whether a function is even or odd, we use the following definition:

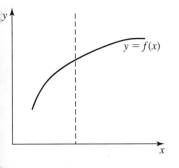

Figure 1.10 The vertical line test shows that the graph of $y = f(x)$ is a function.

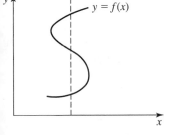

Figure 1.11 The vertical line test shows that the graph of $y = f(x)$ is not a function.

A function $f : A \to B$ is called

1. **even** if $f(x) = f(-x)$ for all $x \in A$, and
2. **odd** if $f(x) = -f(-x)$ for all $x \in A$.

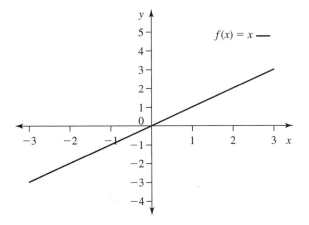

Figure 1.12 The graph of $y = x$ is symmetric about the origin.

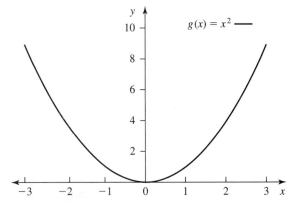

Figure 1.13 The graph of $y = x^2$ is symmetric about the y-axis.

Using this criterion, we can show that $f(x) = x$, $x \in \mathbf{R}$, is an odd function:

$$-f(-x) = -(-x) = x = f(x) \qquad \text{for all } x \in \mathbf{R}$$

Likewise, to show that $g(x) = x^2$, $x \in \mathbf{R}$, is an even function, we compute

$$g(-x) = (-x)^2 = x^2 = g(x) \qquad \text{for all } x \in \mathbf{R}$$

We will now look at the case where one quantity is given as a function of another quantity that, in turn, can be written as a function of yet another quantity. To illustrate this situation, suppose we are interested in the abundance of a predator, which depends on the abundance of a herbivore, which, in turn, depends on the abundance of plant biomass. If we denote the plant biomass by x and the herbivore biomass by u, then x and u are related via a function g, namely, $u = g(x)$. Likewise, if we denote the predator biomass by y, then u and y are related via a function f, namely, $y = f(u)$. We can express the predator biomass as a function of the plant biomass by substituting $g(x)$ for u. That is, we find $y = f[g(x)]$. Functions that are defined in such a way are called composite functions.

Definition The **composite function** $f \circ g$ (also called the **composition** of f and g) is defined as

$$(f \circ g)(x) = f[g(x)]$$

for each x in the domain of g for which $g(x)$ is in the domain of f.

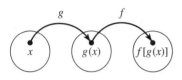

Figure 1.14 The composition of functions.

The composition of functions is illustrated in Figure 1.14. We call g the inner function and f the outer function. The phrase "for each x in the domain of g for which $g(x)$ is in the domain of f" is best explained with the use of Figure 1.14. In order to compute $f(u)$, u needs to be in the domain of f. But since $u = g(x)$, we really require that $g(x)$ be in the domain of f for the values of x we use to compute $g(x)$.

EXAMPLE 2   If $f(x) = \sqrt{x}$, $x \geq 0$, and $g(x) = x^2 + 1$, $x \in \mathbf{R}$, find

(a) $(f \circ g)(x)$ and   (b) $(g \circ f)(x)$.

Solution   (a) To find $(f \circ g)(x)$, we set $f(u) = \sqrt{u}$ and $g(x) = x^2 + 1$. Then

$$y = f(u) = f[g(x)] = f(x^2 + 1) = \sqrt{x^2 + 1}$$

To determine the domain of $f \circ g$, we observe that the domain of the inner function g is $\mathbf{R}$ and its range is $[1, \infty)$. Since the range of g is contained in the domain of the outer function f ($[1, \infty) \subset [0, \infty)$), the domain of $f \circ g$ is $\mathbf{R}$.

(b) To find $(g \circ f)(x)$, we set $g(u) = u^2 + 1$ and $f(x) = \sqrt{x}$. Then

$$y = g(u) = g[f(x)] = g(\sqrt{x}) = (\sqrt{x})^2 + 1 = x + 1$$

To determine the domain of $g \circ f$, we observe that the domain of the inner function f is $[0, \infty)$ and its range is $[0, \infty)$. The range of f is contained in the domain of the outer function g ($[0, \infty) \subset \mathbf{R}$), so the domain of $g \circ f$ is $[0, \infty)$. ■

In the last example, you should observe that $f \circ g$ is different from $g \circ f$, which implies that the order in which you compose functions is important. The notation $f \circ g$ means that you apply g first and then f. In addition, you should pay attention to the domains of composite functions. In the next example, the domain is harder to find.

EXAMPLE 3   If $f(x) = 2x^2$, $x \geq 2$, and $g(x) = \sqrt{x}$, $x \geq 0$, find $(f \circ g)(x)$ together with its domain.

Solution   We compute

$$(f \circ g)(x) = f[g(x)] = f(\sqrt{x}) = 2(\sqrt{x})^2 = 2x$$

This part was not difficult. However, finding the domain of $f \circ g$ is more complicated. The domain of the inner function g is the interval $[0, \infty)$; hence, the range of g is the interval $[0, \infty)$. The domain of f is only $[2, \infty)$, which means that the range of g is *not* contained in the domain of f. We therefore need to restrict the domain of g to ensure that its range is contained in the domain of f. We can choose only values of x such that $g(x) \in [2, \infty)$. Since $g(x) = \sqrt{x}$, we need to restrict x to $[4, \infty)$. Thus, for every $x \in [4, \infty)$, $g(x) \in [2, \infty)$, which is the domain of f. Therefore,

$$(f \circ g)(x) = 2x, \quad x \geq 4$$

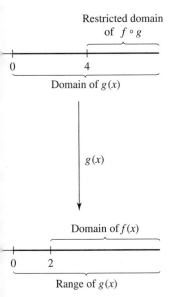

Restricted domain of $f \circ g$

0   4

Domain of $g(x)$

$g(x)$

Domain of $f(x)$

0   2

Range of $g(x)$

Figure 1.15 Finding the domain of a compositie function: The domain of $g(x)$ must be restricted in Example 3.

See Figure 1.15.   ■

In the subsections that follow, we introduce the basic functions that are used throughout the remainder of this book.

■ 1.2.2 Polynomial Functions

Polynomial functions are the simplest elementary functions.

> **Definition** A **polynomial** function is a function of the form
>
> $$f(x) = a_0 + a_1 x + a_2 x^2 + \cdots + a_n x^n$$
>
> where n is a nonnegative integer and $a_0, a_1, \ldots, a_n$ are (real-valued) constants with $a_n \neq 0$. The coefficient a_n is called the **leading coefficient**, and n is called the **degree** of the polynomial function. The largest possible domain of f is **R**.

We have already encountered polynomials, namely, the constant function $f(x) = c$, the linear function $f(x) = mx + b$, and the quadratic function $f(x) = ax^2$. The constant, nonzero function has degree 0, the linear function has degree 1, and the quadratic function has degree 2. Other examples are $f(x) = 4x^3 - 3x + 1$, $x \in \mathbf{R}$, which is a polynomial of degree 3, and $f(x) = 2 - x^7$, $x \in \mathbf{R}$, which is a polynomial of degree 7. In Figure 1.16, we display $y = x^n$ for $n = 2$ and 3. Looking at the figure, we see that $y = x^n$ is an even function (i.e., symmetric about the y-axis) when $n = 2$ and an odd function (i.e., symmetric about the origin) when $n = 3$. This property holds in general: $y = x^n$ is an even function when n is even and an odd function when n is odd. We can show this algebraically by using the criterion in Section 1.2.1. (See Problem 28 at the end of this section.)

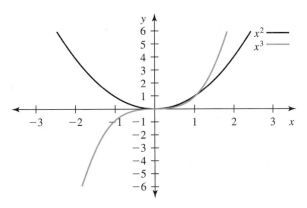

Figure 1.16 The graphs of $y = x^n$ for $n = 2$ and $n = 3$.

Polynomials arise naturally in many situations. We present two examples.

EXAMPLE 4

Suppose that at time 0 an apple begins to drop from a tree that is 64 ft tall. Ignoring air resistance, we can show that at time t (measured in seconds) the apple is at height $h(t)$ (measured in feet) given by

$$h(t) = 64 - 16t^2$$

We assume that the height of the ground level is equal to 0. Show that $h(t)$ is a polynomial and determine its degree. How long will it take the apple to hit the ground? Find an appropriate domain for $h(t)$.

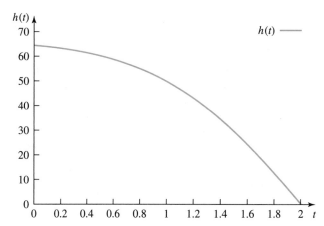

Figure 1.17 The graph of $h(t) = 64 - 16t^2$ for $0 \le t \le 2$ of Example 4.

Solution

The function $h(t)$ is a polynomial of degree 2, with $a_0 = 64$, $a_1 = 0$, and $a_2 = -16$. The graph of $h(t)$ is shown in Figure 1.17. The apple will hit the ground when $h(t) = 0$. That is, we must solve the quadratic equation $0 = 64 - 16t^2$ as follows:

$$0 = 64 - 16t^2$$

$$t^2 = \frac{64}{16} = 4$$

$$t = 2 \quad (\text{or } t = -2)$$

Since the apple begins to drop at time $t = 0$, we can ignore the solution $t = -2 < 0$. We find that it takes the apple 2 seconds to hit the ground (ignoring air resistance). Note that because $h(t) \ge 0$ [where $h(t)$ is the height above the ground and the height of the ground level is equal to 0], the range is [0, 64]. Because $t \ge 0$, the domain of $h(t)$ is the interval [0, 2]. ■

EXAMPLE 5

A Chemical Reaction Consider the reaction rate of the chemical reaction

$$A + B \longrightarrow AB$$

in which the molecular reactants A and B form the molecular product AB. The rate at which this reaction proceeds depends on how often A and B molecules collide. The **law of mass action** states that the rate at which this reaction proceeds is proportional to the product of the respective concentrations of the reactants. Here, *concentration* means the number of molecules per fixed volume. If we denote the reaction rate by R and the concentration of A and B by [A] and [B], respectively, then the law of mass action says that

$$R \propto [A] \cdot [B]$$

Introducing the proportionality factor k, we obtain

$$R = k[A] \cdot [B]$$

Note that $k > 0$, because [A], [B], and R are positive. We assume now that the reaction occurs in a closed vessel; that is, we add specific amounts of A and B to the vessel at the beginning of the reaction and then let the reaction proceed without further additions.

We can express the concentrations of the reactants A and B during the reaction in terms of their initial concentrations a and b and the concentration of the molecular product [AB]. If $x = $ [AB], then

$$[A] = a - x \quad \text{for } 0 \leq x \leq a \qquad \text{and} \qquad [B] = b - x \quad \text{for } 0 \leq x \leq b$$

The concentration of AB cannot exceed either of the concentrations of A and B. (For example, suppose five A molecules and seven B molecules are allowed to react; then a maximum of five AB molecules can result, at which point all of the A molecules are used up and the reaction ceases. The two B molecules left over have no A molecules to react with.) Therefore, we get

$$R(x) = k(a - x)(b - x) \quad \text{for } 0 \leq x \leq a \text{ and } 0 \leq x \leq b$$

The condition $0 \leq x \leq a$ and $0 \leq x \leq b$ can be written as $0 \leq x \leq \min(a, b)$, where $\min(a, b)$ denotes the minimum of a and b. To see that $R(x)$ is indeed a polynomial function, we expand the expression for $R(x)$ as

$$R(x) = k(ab - ax - bx + x^2)$$
$$= kx^2 - k(a + b)x + kab$$

for $0 \leq x \leq \min(a, b)$. We now see that $R(x)$ is a polynomial of degree 2.

A graph of $R(x), 0 \leq x \leq a$, is shown in Figure 1.18 for the case $a \leq b$. (We chose $k = 2$, $a = 2$, and $b = 5$ in the figure.) Notice that when $x = 0$ (i.e., when no AB molecules have yet formed), the rate at which the reaction proceeds is at a maximum. As more and more AB molecules form and, consequently, the concentrations of the reactants decline, the reaction rate decreases. This should also be intuitively clear: As fewer and fewer A and B molecules are in the vessel, it becomes less and less likely that they will collide to form the molecular product AB. When $x = a = \min(a, b)$, the reaction rate $R(a) = 0$. This is the point at which all A molecules are exhausted and the reaction necessarily ceases. ■

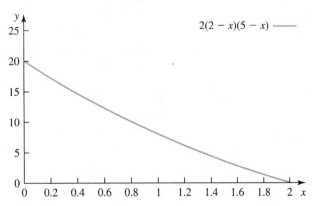

Figure 1.18 The graph of $R(x) = 2(2 - x)(5 - x)$ for $0 \leq x \leq 2$.

■ 1.2.3 Rational Functions

Rational functions are built from polynomial functions.

> **Definition** A **rational** function is the quotient of two polynomial functions $p(x)$ and $q(x)$:
>
> $$f(x) = \frac{p(x)}{q(x)} \quad \text{for } q(x) \neq 0$$

Since division by 0 is not allowed, we must exclude those values of x for which $q(x) = 0$. Here are a couple of examples of rational functions, together with their largest possible domains:

$$y = \frac{1}{x}, \quad x \neq 0$$

$$y = \frac{x^2 + 2x - 1}{x - 3}, \quad x \neq 3$$

An important example of a rational function is the hyperbola, together with its largest possible domain:

$$y = \frac{1}{x}, \quad x \neq 0$$

The graph of y is shown in Figure 1.19.

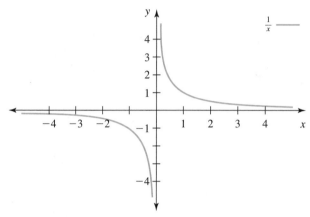

Figure 1.19 The graph of $y = \frac{1}{x}$ for $x \neq 0$.

Throughout this text, we will encounter populations whose sizes change with time. The change in population size is described by the **growth rate**. Roughly speaking, the growth rate tells you how much a population changes during a small time interval. (The growth rate is analogous to the velocity of a car: Velocity is also a rate; it tells you how much the position changes in a small time interval. We will give a precise definition of rates in Section 4.1.) The **per capita** growth rate is the growth rate divided by the population size. The per capita growth rate is also called the **specific** growth rate. The next example introduces a function that is frequently used to describe growth rates.

EXAMPLE 6

Monod Growth Function There is a function that is frequently used to describe the per capita growth rate of organisms when the rate depends on the concentration of some nutrient and becomes saturated for large enough nutrient concentrations. If we denote the concentration of the nutrient by N, then the per capita growth rate $r(N)$ is given by the *Monod growth function*

$$r(N) = \frac{aN}{k + N}, \quad N \geq 0$$

where a and k are positive constants. The graph of $r(N)$ is shown in Figure 1.20; it is a piece of a hyperbola. The graph shows a decelerating rise approaching the saturation level a, which is the maximal specific growth rate. When $N = k$, $r(N) = a/2$; for this reason, k is called the *half-saturation constant*. The growth rate increases with nutrient concentration N; however, doubling the nutrient concentration has a much bigger effect on the growth rate for small values of N than when N is already large. When this type of function is used in biochemistry to describe enzymatic reactions, it is called the Michaelis–Menten function. ■

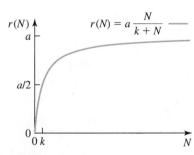

Figure 1.20 The graph of the Monod function $r(N) = a\frac{N}{k+N}$ for $N \geq 0$.

■ **1.2.4** Power Functions

> Definition A **power** function is of the form
>
> $$f(x) = x^r$$
>
> where r is a real number.

Examples of power functions, with their largest possible domains, are

$$y = x^{1/3}, \qquad x \in \mathbf{R}$$
$$y = x^{5/2}, \qquad x \geq 0$$
$$y = x^{1/2}, \qquad x \geq 0$$
$$y = x^{-1/2}, \qquad x > 0$$

Polynomials of the form $y = x^n$, $n = 1, 2, \ldots$, are a special case of power functions. Since power functions may involve even roots, as in $y = x^{3/2} = (\sqrt{x})^3$, we frequently need to restrict their domain.

Figure 1.21 compares the power functions $y = x^{5/2}$, $y = x^{1/2}$, and $y = x^{-1/2}$ for $x > 0$. Pay close attention to how the exponent determines the ranking according to size for x between 0 and 1 and for $x > 1$. We find that $x^{5/2} < x^{1/2} < x^{-1/2}$ for $0 < x < 1$, but $x^{5/2} > x^{1/2} > x^{-1/2}$ for $x > 1$.

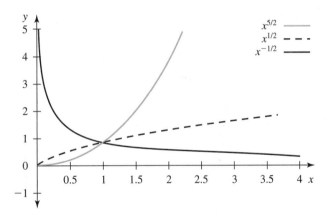

Figure 1.21 Some power functions with rational exponents.

EXAMPLE 7

Power functions are frequently found in "scaling relations" between biological variables (e.g., organ sizes). These are relations of the form

$$y \propto x^r$$

where r is a nonzero real number. That is, y is proportional to some power of x. Recall that we can write this relationship as an equation if we introduce the proportionality factor k:

$$y = kx^r$$

Finding such relationships is the objective of **allometry**. For example, in a study of 45 species of unicellular algae, a relationship between cell volume and cell biomass was sought. It was found [see, for instance, Niklas (1994)] that

$$\text{cell biomass} \propto (\text{cell volume})^{0.794}$$

Most scaling relations are to be interpreted in a statistical sense; they are obtained by fitting a curve to data points. The data points are typically scattered about the fitted curve given by the scaling relation. (See Figure 1.22.) ■

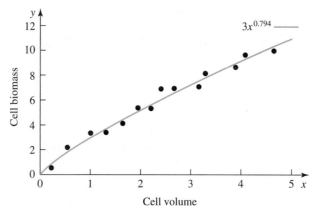

Figure 1.22 Some data points and the fitted curve of Example 7. (*Note*: The "data points" aren't real.)

The next example relates the volume and the surface area of a cube. This relationship is not to be understood in a statistical sense, because it is an exact relationship resulting from geometric considerations.

EXAMPLE 8

Suppose that we wish to know the scaling relation between the surface area S and the volume V of a cube. The scaling relations of each of these quantities with the length L of the cube are as follows:

$$S \propto L^2 \quad \text{or} \quad S = k_1 L^2$$
$$V \propto L^3 \quad \text{or} \quad V = k_2 L^3$$

Here, k_1 and k_2 denote the constants of proportionality. (We label them with different subscripts to indicate that they might be different.) To express S in terms of V, we must first solve L in terms of V and then substitute L in the equation for S. Because $L = (V/k_2)^{1/3}$, it follows that

$$S = k_1 \left[\left(\frac{V}{k_2} \right)^{1/3} \right]^2 = \frac{k_1}{k_2^{2/3}} V^{2/3}$$

Introducing the constant of proportionality $k = k_1/k_2^{2/3}$, we find that

$$S = kV^{2/3}, \quad \text{or simply} \quad S \propto V^{2/3}$$

In words, the surface area of a cube scales with the volume in proportion to $V^{2/3}$. We can now ask, for instance, by what factor the surface area increases when we double the volume. When we double the volume, we find that the resulting surface area, denoted by S', is

$$S' = k(2V)^{2/3} = 2^{2/3} \underbrace{kV^{2/3}}_{S}$$

That is, the surface area increases by a factor of $2^{2/3} \approx 1.587$ if we double the volume of the cube. This scaling has implications on heat retention in animals: A larger body has a relatively smaller surface area and will retain more heat. ■

■ 1.2.5 Exponential Functions

In our study of exponential functions, let's first look at an example that illustrates where they occur.

EXAMPLE 9

Exponential Growth Bacteria reproduce asexually by cellular fission, in which the parent cell splits into two daughter cells after duplication of the genetic material. This division may happen as often as every 20 minutes; under ideal conditions, a bacterial colony can double in size in that time.

Let us measure time such that one unit of time corresponds to the doubling time of the colony. If we denote the size of the population at time t by $N(t)$, then the function

$$N(t) = 2^t, \quad t \geq 0$$

has the property of doubling its value every unit of time

$$N(t + 1) = 2^{t+1} = 2 \cdot 2^t = 2N(t) \tag{1.2}$$

The function $N(t) = 2^t, t \geq 0$, is an exponential function because the variable t is in the exponent. We call the number 2 the base of the exponential function $N(t) = 2^t$.

We find that when $t = 0$, $N(0) = 1$; that is, there is just one individual in the population at time $t = 0$. If, at time $t = 0$, 40 individuals were present in the population, we would write $N(0) = 40$ and

$$N(t) = 40 \cdot 2^t, \quad t \geq 0 \tag{1.3}$$

You can verify that $N(t)$ in (1.3) also satisfies $N(t + 1) = 2N(t)$.

It is often desirable not to specify the initial number of individuals in the equation describing $N(t)$. This approach has the advantage that the equation for $N(t)$ then describes a more general situation, in the sense that we can use the same equation for different initial population sizes. We often denote the population size at time 0 by N_0 (read "N sub 0") instead of $N(0)$. The equation for $N(t)$ is then

$$N(t) = N_0 2^t, \quad t \geq 0$$

We can verify that $N(0) = N_0 2^0 = N_0$ and that $N(t + 1) = N_0 2^{t+1} = 2(N_0 2^t) = 2N(t)$. ■

The function $f(t) = 2^t$ can be defined for all $t \in \mathbf{R}$; its graph is shown in Figure 1.23.

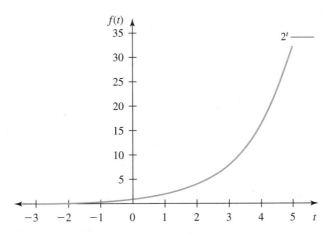

Figure 1.23 The function $f(t) = 2^t, t \in \mathbf{R}$.

Here is the definition of an exponential function:

Definition The function f is an **exponential** function with base a if

$$f(x) = a^x$$

where a is a positive constant other than 1. The largest possible domain of f is $\mathbf{R}$.

When $a = 1$, $f(x) = 1$ for all values of x. This is a case that will occur in biological examples, but is excluded from the definition since it is simply the constant function.

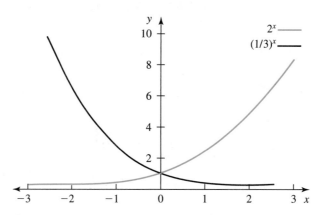

Figure 1.24 Exponential growth and exponential decay.

The basic shape of the exponential function $f(x) = a^x$ depends on the base a; two examples are shown in Figure 1.24. As x increases, the graph of $f(x) = 2^x$ shows a rapid increase, whereas the graph of $f(x) = (1/3)^x$ shows a rapid decrease toward 0. We find the rapid increase whenever $a > 1$ and the rapid decrease whenever $0 < a < 1$. Therefore, we say that we have exponential *growth* when $a > 1$ and exponential *decay* when $0 < a < 1$.

Recall that $a^0 = 1$ and $a^{1/k} = \sqrt[k]{a}$, where k is a positive integer. In Subsection 1.1.5, we summarized the properties of exponentials. Since they are very important, we list them again here:

$$a^r a^s = a^{r+s}$$

$$\frac{a^r}{a^s} = a^{r-s}$$

$$a^{-r} = \frac{1}{a^r}$$

$$\left(a^r\right)^s = a^{rs}$$

In many applications, the exponential function is expressed in terms of the base $e = 2.718\ldots$, which we encountered in Subsection 1.1.5. The number e is called the **natural exponential base**. The exponential function with base e is alternatively written as $\exp(x)$. That is,

$$\exp(x) = e^x$$

The advantage of this alternative form can be seen when we try to write something like $e^{x^2/\sqrt{x^3+1}}$: $\exp(x^2/\sqrt{x^3+1})$ is easier to read. More generally, if $g(x)$ is a function in x, then we can write, equivalently,

$$\exp[g(x)] \qquad \text{or} \qquad e^{g(x)}$$

Bases 2 and 10 are also frequently used; in calculus, however, e will turn out to be the most common base.

The next two examples provide an important application of exponential functions.

EXAMPLE 10

Radioactive Decay Radioactive isotopes such as carbon 14 are used to determine the absolute age of fossils or minerals, establishing an absolute chronology of the geological time scale. This technique was discovered in the early years of the 20th century and is based on the property of certain atoms to transform spontaneously by giving off protons, neutrons, or electrons. The phenomenon, called *radioactive* *decay*, occurs at a constant rate that is independent of environmental conditions. The method was used, for instance, to trace the successive emergence of the Hawaiian islands, from the oldest, Kauai, to the youngest, Hawaii (which is about 100,000 years old).

Carbon 14 is formed high in the atmosphere. It is radioactive and decays into nitrogen (N^{14}). There is an equilibrium between atmospheric carbon 12 (C^{12}) and carbon 14 (C^{14})—a ratio that has been relatively constant over a fairly long period. When plants capture carbon dioxide (CO_2) molecules from the atmosphere and build them into a product (such as cellulose), the initial ratio of C^{14} to C^{12} is the same as that in the atmosphere. Once the plants die, however, their uptake of CO_2 ceases, and the radioactive decay of C^{14} causes the ratio of C^{14} to C^{12} to decline. Because the law of radioactive decay is known, the change in ratio provides an accurate measure of the time since the plants' death.

According to the radioactive decay law, if the amount of C^{14} at time t is denoted by $W(t)$, with $W(0) = W_0$, then

$$W(t) = W_0 e^{-\lambda t}, \quad t \geq 0$$

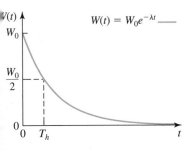

$$W(t) = W_0 e^{-\lambda t}$$

Figure 1.25 The function $W(t) = W_0 e^{-\lambda t}$.

where $\lambda > 0$ (λ is the lowercase Greek letter lambda) denotes the **decay rate**. The function $W(t) = W_0 e^{-\lambda t}$ is another example of an exponential function. Its graph is shown in Figure 1.25.

Frequently, the decay rate is expressed in terms of the **half-life** of the material, which is the length of time that it takes for half of the material to decay. If we denote this time by T_h, then (see Figure 1.25)

$$W(T_h) = \frac{1}{2} W_0 = W_0 e^{-\lambda T_h}$$

from which we obtain

$$\frac{1}{2} = e^{-\lambda T_h}$$

$$2 = e^{\lambda T_h}$$

Recall from algebra (or Subsection 1.1.5) that, to solve for the exponent λT_h, we must take logarithms on both sides. Since the exponent has base e, we use natural logarithms and find that

$$\ln 2 = \lambda T_h$$

Solving for T_h or λ yields

$$T_h = \frac{\ln 2}{\lambda} \quad \text{or} \quad \lambda = \frac{\ln 2}{T_h}$$

It is known that the half-life of C^{14} is 5730 years. Hence,

$$\lambda = \frac{\ln 2}{5730 \text{ years}}$$

Note that the unit "years" appears in the denominator. It is important to carry the units along. When we compute λt in the exponent of $e^{-\lambda t}$, we need to measure t in units of years in order for the units to cancel properly. For example, suppose $t = 2000$ years; then

$$\lambda t = \frac{\ln 2}{5730 \text{ years}} 2000 \text{ years} = \frac{(\ln 2)(2000)}{5730} \approx 0.2419$$

and we see that "years" appears in both the numerator and the denominator and thus can be canceled.

An application of the C^{14} dating method is given in the next example.

EXAMPLE 11 Suppose that, on the basis of their C^{12} content, samples of wood found in an archeological excavation site contain about 23% as much C^{14} as does living plant material. Determine when the wood was cut.

Solution The ratio of the current amount of C^{14} to the amount of living plant material is expressed as

$$0.23 = \frac{W(t)}{W(0)} = e^{-\lambda t}$$

Taking logarithms (base e) on both sides, we obtain

$$\ln(0.23) = -\lambda t$$

or

$$\lambda t = -\ln(0.23) = \ln \frac{1}{0.23}$$

With $\lambda = \ln 2/(5730 \text{ years})$ from Example 10,

$$t = \frac{5730 \text{ years}}{\ln 2} \ln \frac{1}{0.23}$$

Using a calculator to compute this result, we find that the wood was cut about 12,150 years ago. ■

■ 1.2.6 Inverse Functions

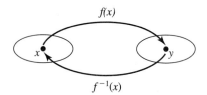

$f(x)$

$f^{-1}(x)$

Figure 1.26 The function $y = f(x)$ and its inverse.

Before we can introduce logarithmic functions, we must understand the concept of inverse functions. Roughly speaking, the inverse of a function f reverses the effect of f. That is, if f maps x into $y = f(x)$, then the inverse function, denoted by f^{-1} (read "f inverse"), takes y and maps it back into x. (See Figure 1.26.) Not every function has an inverse: Because an inverse function is a function itself, we require that every value y in the range of f be mapped into exactly one value x. In other words, for a function to have an inverse, it must be that whenever $x_1 \neq x_2$, it follows that $f(x_1) \neq f(x_2)$ or, equivalently, that $f(x_1) = f(x_2)$ implies $x_1 = x_2$. (Recall the definition of a function, in which we required that each element in the domain be assigned to *exactly one* element in the range.)

Functions that have the property "$x_1 \neq x_2$ implies $f(x_1) \neq f(x_2)$" [or, equivalently, "$f(x_1) = f(x_2)$ implies $x_1 = x_2$"] are called **one to one**. If you know what the graph of a particular function looks like over its domain, then it is easy to determine whether or not the function is one to one: If no horizontal line intersects the graph of the function f more than once, then f is one to one. This criterion is called the horizontal line test. We illustrate it in Figures 1.27 and 1.28.

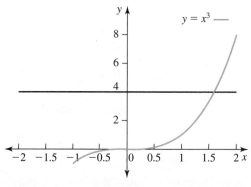

Figure 1.27 Horizontal line test successful.

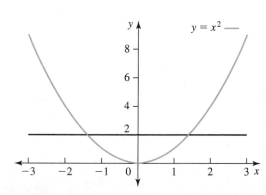

Figure 1.28 Horizontal line test unsuccessful.

Now consider $y = x^3$ and $y = x^2$, for $x \in \mathbf{R}$. The function $y = x^3$, $x \in \mathbf{R}$, has an inverse function, because $x_1^3 \neq x_2^3$ whenever $x_1 \neq x_2$. (See Figure 1.27.) The function $y = x^2$, $x \in \mathbf{R}$, does *not* have an inverse function, because $x_1 \neq x_2$ does not imply $x_1^2 \neq x_2^2$ (or, equivalently, $x_1^2 = x_2^2$ does not imply $x_1 = x_2$; see Figure 1.28). The equation $x_1^2 = x_2^2$ implies only that $|x_1| = |x_2|$. Since x_1 and x_2 can be positive or negative, we cannot simply drop the absolute-value signs. For instance, both -2 and 2 are mapped into 4, and we find that $f(-2) = f(2)$ but $-2 \neq 2$. (Note that $|-2| = |2|$.) To invert this function, we would have to map 4 into -2 and 2, but then it would no longer be a function by our definition. By restricting the domain of $y = x^2$ to, say, $x \geq 0$, we can define an inverse function of $y = x^2$, $x \geq 0$.

Here is the formal definition of an inverse function:

Definition Let $f : A \to B$ be a one-to-one function with range $f(A)$. The **inverse** function f^{-1} has domain $f(A)$ and range A and is defined by

$$f^{-1}(y) = x \quad \text{if and only if} \quad y = f(x)$$

for all $y \in f(A)$.

EXAMPLE 12

Find the inverse function of $f(x) = x^3 + 1$, $x \geq 0$.

Solution

First, note that $f(x)$ is one to one. To see this quickly, graph the function and apply the horizontal line test. (See Figure 1.29.) Be aware, though, that unless you know what the graph looks like over its entire domain, the graphical approach can be misleading. To demonstrate it algebraically, start with $f(x_1) = f(x_2)$ and show that this implies $x_1 = x_2$:

$$f(x_1) = f(x_2)$$
$$x_1^3 + 1 = x_2^3 + 1$$
$$x_1^3 = x_2^3$$

Taking the third root on both sides gives $x_1 = x_2$, which tells us that $f(x)$ has an inverse. Now we will find f^{-1}.

To find an inverse function, we follow three steps:

1. Write $y = f(x)$:

$$y = x^3 + 1$$

2. Solve for x:

$$x^3 = y - 1$$
$$x = \sqrt[3]{y - 1}$$

The range of f is $[1, \infty)$, and this range becomes the domain of f^{-1}, so we obtain

$$f^{-1}(y) = \sqrt[3]{y - 1}, \quad y \geq 1$$

Typically, we write functions in terms of x. To do this, we need to interchange x and y in $x = f^{-1}(y)$. This is the third step:

3. Interchange x and y:

$$y = f^{-1}(x) = \sqrt[3]{x - 1}, \ x \geq 1$$

Note that switching x and y in step 3 corresponds to reflecting the graph of $y = f(x)$ about the line $y = x$. The graphs of f and f^{-1} are shown in Figure 1.30. Look at the graphs carefully, and observe how they are related to each other: Each can be obtained from the other by reflection about the line $y = x$.

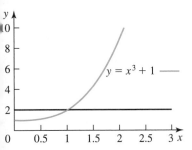

Figure 1.29 The graph of $f(x) = x^3 + 1$ in Example 12. The horizontal line test is successful.

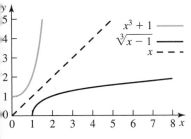

Figure 1.30 Inverse functions.

As mentioned in the beginning of this subsection, the inverse of a function f reverses the effect of f. If we first apply f to x and then f^{-1} to $f(x)$, we obtain the original value x. Likewise, if we first apply f^{-1} to x and then f to $f^{-1}(x)$, we obtain the original value x. That is, if $f : A \to B$ has an inverse f^{-1}, then

$$f^{-1}[f(x)] = x \qquad \text{for all } x \in A$$
$$f[f^{-1}(x)] = x \qquad \text{for all } x \in f(A)$$

[A note of warning: The superscript in f^{-1} does *not* indicate the reciprocal of f (i.e., $1/f$). This difference is further explained in Problem 74 at the end of this section.]

■ 1.2.7 Logarithmic Functions

Recall from algebra (or Subsection 1.1.5) that, to solve the equation

$$e^x = 3$$

for x, you must take logarithms on both sides:

$$x = \ln 3$$

In other words, applying the natural logarithm undoes the operation of raising e to the x power. Thus, the natural logarithm is the inverse of the exponential function, and conversely, the exponential function is the inverse of the logarithmic function.

We will now define the inverse of the exponential function $f(x) = a^x$, $x \in \mathbf{R}$. The base a can be any positive number, except 1.

> **Definition** The inverse of $f(x) = a^x$ is called the **logarithm to base a** and is written $f^{-1}(x) = \log_a x$.

The maximum domain of $f(x) = a^x$ is the set of all real numbers, and its range is the set of all positive numbers. Since the range of f is the domain of f^{-1}, we find that the maximum domain of $f^{-1}(x) = \log_a x$ is the set of positive numbers.

Because $y = \log_a x$ is the inverse function of $y = a^x$, we can find the graph of $y = \log_a x$ by reflecting the graph of $y = a^x$ about the line $y = x$. Recall that the graph of $y = a^x$ had two basic shapes, depending on whether $0 < a < 1$ or $a > 1$. (See Figure 1.24.) Figure 1.31 illustrates the graphs of $y = a^x$ and $y = \log_a x$ when $a > 1$.

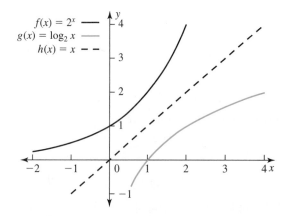

$f(x) = 2^x$ ——
$g(x) = \log_2 x$ ——
$h(x) = x$ – –

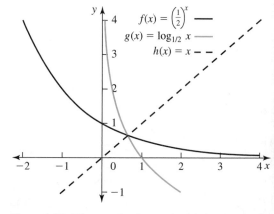

$f(x) = \left(\frac{1}{2}\right)^x$ ——
$g(x) = \log_{1/2} x$ ——
$h(x) = x$ – –

Figure 1.31 The graph of $y = a^x$ and the graph of $y = \log_a x$ for $a = 2$.

Figure 1.32 The graph of $y = a^x$ and the graph of $y = \log_a x$ for $a = \frac{1}{2}$.

Figure 1.32 shows the graphs of $y = a^x$ and $y = \log_a x$ when $0 < a < 1$.

We can now summarize the relationship between the exponential and the logarithmic functions:

> **1.** $a^{\log_a x} = x$ for $x > 0$
>
> **2.** $\log_a a^x = x$ for $x \in \mathbf{R}$

It is important to remember that the logarithm is defined only for positive numbers; that is, $y = \log_a x$ is defined only for $x > 0$. The logarithm satisfies the following properties:

$$\log_a(st) = \log_a s + \log_a t$$

$$\log_a\left(\frac{s}{t}\right) = \log_a s - \log_a t$$

$$\log_a s^r = r \log_a s$$

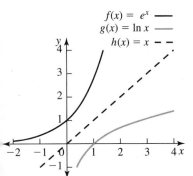

$f(x) = e^x$ ——
$g(x) = \ln x$ ——
$h(x) = x$ – – –

Figure 1.33 The graphs of $y = e^x$ and $y = \ln x$.

The inverse of the exponential function with the natural base e is denoted by $\ln x$ and is called the natural logarithm of x. The graphs of $y = e^x$ and $y = \ln x$ are shown in Figure 1.33. Note that both e^x and $\ln x$ are increasing functions. However, whereas e^x climbs very quickly for large values of x, $\ln x$ increases very slowly for large values of x. Looking at both graphs, we can see that each can be obtained as the reflection of the other about the line $y = x$.

The logarithm to base 10 is frequently written as $\log x$ (i.e., the base of 10 in $\log_{10} x$ is omitted).

EXAMPLE 13

Simplify the following expressions:

(a) $\log_2[8(x-2)]$ **(b)** $\log_3 9^x$ **(c)** $\ln e^{3x^2+1}$

Solution

(a) We simplify as follows:

$$\log_2[8(x-2)] = \log_2 8 + \log_2(x-2) = 3 + \log_2(x-2)$$

No further simplification is possible.

(b) Simplifying yields

$$\log_3 9^x = x \log_3 9 = x \log_3 3^2 = 2x$$

The fact that $\log_3 9 = 2$ can be seen in two ways: We can write $9 = 3^2$ and say that applying $\log_3$ undoes raising 3 to the second power (as we did previously), or we can say that $\log_3 9$ denotes the exponent to which we must raise 3 in order to get 9.

(c) We use the fact that $\ln x$ and e^x are inverse functions and find that

$$\ln e^{3x^2+1} = 3x^2 + 1$$

∎

Any exponential function with base a can be written as an exponential function with base e. Likewise, any logarithm to base a can be written in terms of the natural logarithm. The following two identities show how:

> $$a^x = \exp[x \ln a]$$
>
> $$\log_a x = \frac{\ln x}{\ln a}$$

The first identity follows from the fact that exp and ln are inversely related (which implies that $a^x = \exp[\ln a^x]$) and the fact that $\ln a^x = x \ln a$. To understand the second identity, note that

$$y = \log_a x \qquad \text{means} \qquad a^y = x$$

Taking logarithms to base e on both sides of $a^y = x$, we get

$$\ln a^y = \ln x$$

or

$$y \ln a = \ln x$$

Hence,

$$y = \frac{\ln x}{\ln a}$$

EXAMPLE 14   Write the following expressions in terms of base e:

    (a) 2^x **(b)** 10^{x^2+1} **(c)** $\log_3 x$ **(d)** $\log_2(3x - 1)$

Solution   **(a)** $2^x = \exp(\ln 2^x) = \exp(x \ln 2) = e^{x \ln 2}$

    (b) $10^{x^2+1} = \exp(\ln 10^{x^2+1}) = \exp\left[(x^2 + 1) \ln 10\right] = e^{(x^2+1) \ln 10}$

    (c) $\log_3 x = \dfrac{\ln x}{\ln 3}$

    (d) $\log_2(3x - 1) = \dfrac{\ln(3x - 1)}{\ln 2}$

EXAMPLE 15   DNA sequences evolve over time by various processes. One such process is the substitution of one nucleotide for another. The simplest substitution scheme is that of Jukes and Cantor (1969), which assumes that substitutions are equally likely among the four types of nucleotide. In comparing two DNA sequences that have a common origin, it is possible to estimate the number of substitutions per site. Since more than one substitution can occur per site, the number of observed substitutions may be smaller than the number of actual substitutions, particularly when the time of divergence is large. Mathematical models are used to correct for this difference. The proportion p of observed nucleotide differences between two sequences that share a common ancestor can be used to find an estimate of the actual number K of substitutions per site since the time of divergence. According to the substitution scheme of Jukes and Cantor, K and p are related by

$$K = -\frac{3}{4} \ln \left(1 - \frac{4}{3}p\right)$$

provided that p is not too large. Assume that two sequences of length 150 nucleotides differ from each other by 23 nucleotides. Find K.

Solution   The variable p denotes the proportion of observed nucleotide differences, which is $23/150 \approx 0.1533$ in this example. We thus obtain

$$K = -\frac{3}{4} \ln \left(1 - \frac{4}{3}\frac{23}{150}\right) \approx 0.1715$$

■ **1.2.8 Trigonometric Functions**

The trigonometric functions are examples of periodic functions.

> **Definition** A function $f(x)$ is **periodic** if there is a positive constant a such that
>
> $$f(x + a) = f(x)$$
>
> for all x in the domain of f. If a is the smallest number with this property, we call it the **period** of $f(x)$.

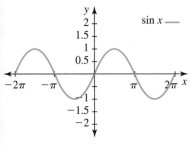

Figure 1.34 The graph of $y = \sin x$.

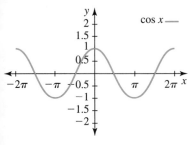

Figure 1.35 The graph of $y = \cos x$.

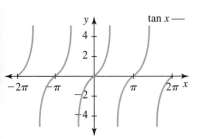

Figure 1.36 The graph of $y = \tan x$.

We begin with the sine and cosine functions. In Subsection 1.1.4, we recalled the definition of sine and cosine on a unit circle. There, $\sin \theta$ and $\cos \theta$ represented trigonometric functions of angles, and θ was measured in degrees or radians. Now we define the trigonometric functions as functions of *real numbers*. For instance, we define $f(x) = \sin x$ for $x \in \mathbf{R}$. The value of $\sin x$ is then, *by definition*, the sine of an angle of x radians (and similarly for all the other trigonometric functions).

The graphs of the sine and cosine functions are shown in Figures 1.34 and 1.35, respectively.

The sine function, $y = \sin x$, is defined for all $x \in \mathbf{R}$. Its range is $-1 \le y \le 1$. Likewise, the cosine function, $y = \cos x$, is defined for all $x \in \mathbf{R}$ with range $-1 \le y \le 1$. Both functions are periodic with period 2π. That is, $\sin(x + 2\pi) = \sin x$ and $\cos(x + 2\pi) = \cos x$. [We also have $\sin(x + 4\pi) = \sin x$, $\sin(x + 6\pi) = \sin x, \ldots$, and $\cos(x + 4\pi) = \cos x$, $\cos(x + 6\pi) = \cos x, \ldots$, but, by convention, we use the smallest possible value to specify the period.] We see from Figures 1.34 and 1.35 that the graph of the cosine function can be obtained by shifting the graph of the sine function a distance of $\pi/2$ units to the left. (We will discuss horizontal shifts of graphs in more detail in the next section.)

To define the tangent function, $y = \tan x$, recall that

$$\tan x = \frac{\sin x}{\cos x}$$

Because $\cos x = 0$ for values of x that are odd integer multiples of $\pi/2$, the domain of $\tan x$ consists of all real numbers with the exception of odd integer multiples of $\pi/2$. The range of $y = \tan x$ is $-\infty < y < \infty$. The graph of $y = \tan x$ is shown in Figure 1.36, from which we see that $\tan x$ is periodic with period π.

The graphs of the remaining three trigonometric functions are shown in Figures 1.37–1.39. Recall that $\sec x = \frac{1}{\cos x}$, $\csc x = \frac{1}{\sin x}$, and $\cot x = \frac{1}{\tan x}$. It follows that the domain of the secant function $y = \sec x$ consists of all real numbers with the exception of odd integer multiples of $\pi/2$; the range is $|y| \ge 1$. The domain of the cosecant function $y = \csc x$ consists of all real numbers with the exception of integer multiples of π; the range is $|y| \ge 1$. The domain of the cotangent function $y = \cot x$ consists of all real numbers with the exception of integer multiples of π; the range is $-\infty < y < \infty$.

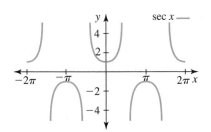

Figure 1.37 The graph of $y = \sec x$.

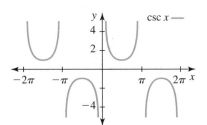

Figure 1.38 The graph of $y = \csc x$.

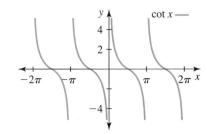

Figure 1.39 The graph of $y = \cot x$.

Since the sine and cosine functions are of particular importance, we now describe them in more detail. Consider the function

$$f(x) = a \sin(kx) \qquad \text{for } x \in \mathbf{R}$$

where a is a real number and $k \ne 0$. Now, $f(x)$ takes on values between $-a$ and a. We call $|a|$ the **amplitude**. The function $f(x)$ is periodic. To find the period p of $f(x)$, we set

$$|k|p = 2\pi \qquad \text{or} \qquad p = \frac{2\pi}{|k|}$$

Because the cosine function can be obtained from the sine function by a horizontal shift, we can define the amplitude and period analogously for the cosine function. That is, $f(x) = a \cos(kx)$ has amplitude $|a|$ and period $p = 2\pi/|k|$.

EXAMPLE 16   Compare

$$f(x) = 3 \sin\left(\frac{\pi}{4}x\right) \quad \text{and} \quad g(x) = \sin x$$

Solution   The amplitude of $f(x)$ is 3, whereas the amplitude of $g(x)$ is 1. The period p of $f(x)$ satisfies $\frac{\pi}{4}p = 2\pi$ or $p = 8$, whereas the period of $g(x)$ is 2π. Graphs of $f(x)$ and $g(x)$ are shown in Figure 1.40. ■

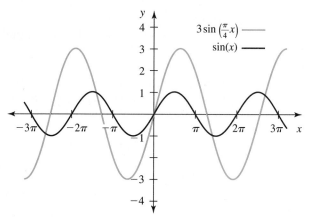

Figure 1.40 The graphs of $y = 3\sin(\frac{\pi}{4}x)$ and $g(x) = \sin x$ in Example 16.

Remark.   A number is called **algebraic** if it is the solution of a polynomial equation with rational coefficients. For instance, $\sqrt{2}$ is algebraic, as it satisfies the equation $x^2 - 2 = 0$. Numbers that are not algebraic are called **transcendental**. For instance, π and e are transcendental.

A similar distinction is made for functions. We call a function $y = f(x)$ algebraic if it is the solution of an equation of the form

$$P_n(x)y^n + \cdots + P_1(x)y + P_0(x) = 0$$

in which the coefficients are polynomial functions in x with rational coefficients. For instance, the function $y = 1/(1 + x)$ is algebraic, as it satisfies the equation $(x + 1)y - 1 = 0$. Here, $P_1(x) = x + 1$ and $P_0(x) = -1$. Other examples of algebraic functions are polynomial functions with rational coefficients and rational functions with rational coefficients.

Functions that are not algebraic are called transcendental. All the trigonometric, exponential, and logarithmic functions that we introduced in this section are transcendental functions.

Section 1.2 Problems

■ **1.2.1**

In Problems 1–4, state the range for the given functions. Graph each function.

1. $f(x) = x^2, x \in \mathbf{R}$

2. $f(x) = x^2, x \in [0, 1]$

3. $f(x) = x^2, -1 < x \le 0$

4. $f(x) = x^2, -\frac{1}{2} < x < \frac{1}{2}$

5. (a) Show that, for $x \ne 1$,

$$\frac{x^2 - 1}{x - 1} = x + 1$$

(b) Are the functions

$$f(x) = \frac{x^2 - 1}{x - 1}, \quad x \ne 1$$

and

$$g(x) = x + 1, \quad x \in \mathbf{R}$$

equal?

6. (a) Show that

$$2|x - 1| = \begin{cases} 2(x - 1) & \text{for } x \ge 1 \\ 2(1 - x) & \text{for } x \le 1 \end{cases}$$

(b) Are the functions

$$f(x) = \begin{cases} 2 - 2x & \text{for } 0 \le x \le 1 \\ 2x - 2 & \text{for } 1 \le x \le 2 \end{cases}$$

and

$$g(x) = 2|x - 1|, \quad x \in [0, 2]$$

equal?

In Problems 7–12, sketch the graph of each function and decide in each case whether the function is (i) even, (ii) odd, or (iii) does not show any obvious symmetry. Then use the criteria in Subsection 1.2.1 to check your answers.

7. $f(x) = 2x$ **8.** $f(x) = 3x^2$

9. $f(x) = |3x|$ **10.** $f(x) = 2x + 1$

11. $f(x) = -|x|$ **12.** $f(x) = 3x^3$

13. Suppose that

$$f(x) = x^2, \quad x \in \mathbf{R}$$

and

$$g(x) = 3 + x, \quad x \in \mathbf{R}$$

(a) Show that

$$(f \circ g)(x) = (3 + x)^2, \quad x \in \mathbf{R}$$

(b) Show that

$$(g \circ f)(x) = 3 + x^2, \quad x \in \mathbf{R}$$

14. Suppose that

$$f(x) = x^3, \quad x \in \mathbf{R}$$

and

$$g(x) = 1 - x, \quad x \in \mathbf{R}$$

(a) Show that

$$(f \circ g)(x) = (1 - x)^3, \quad x \in \mathbf{R}$$

(b) Show that

$$(g \circ f)(x) = 1 - x^3, \quad x \in \mathbf{R}$$

15. Suppose that

$$f(x) = 1 - x^2, \quad x \in \mathbf{R}$$

and

$$g(x) = 2x, \quad x \ge 0$$

(a) Find

$$(f \circ g)(x)$$

together with its domain.

(b) Find

$$(g \circ f)(x)$$

together with its domain.

16. Suppose that

$$f(x) = \frac{1}{x + 1}, \quad x \ne -1$$

and

$$g(x) = 2x^2, \quad x \in \mathbf{R}$$

(a) Find $(f \circ g)(x)$.   **(b)** Find $(g \circ f)(x)$.
In both (a) and (b), find the domain.

17. Suppose that

$$f(x) = 3x^2, \quad x \ge 3$$

and

$$g(x) = \sqrt{x}, \quad x \ge 0$$

Find $(f \circ g)(x)$ together with its domain.

18. Suppose that

$$f(x) = x^4, \quad x \ge 3$$

and

$$g(x) = \sqrt{x + 1}, \quad x \ge 3$$

Find $(f \circ g)(x)$ together with its domain.

19. Suppose that $f(x) = x^2, x \ge 0$, and $g(x) = \sqrt{x}, x \ge 0$. Typically, $f \circ g \ne g \circ f$, but this is an example in which the order of composition does not matter. Show that $f \circ g = g \circ f$.

20. Suppose that $f(x) = x^4, x \ge 0$. Find $g(x)$ so that $f \circ g = g \circ f$.

■ **1.2.2**

21. Use a graphing calculator to graph $f(x) = x^2, x \ge 0$, and $g(x) = x^4, x \ge 0$, together. For which values of x is $f(x) > g(x)$, and for which is $f(x) < g(x)$?

22. Use a graphing calculator to graph $f(x) = x^3, x \ge 0$, and $g(x) = x^5, x \ge 0$, together. When is $f(x) > g(x)$, and when is $f(x) < g(x)$?

23. Graph $y = x^n, x \ge 0$, for $n = 1, 2, 3$, and 4 in one coordinate system. Where do the curves intersect?

24. **(a)** Graph $f(x) = x, x \ge 0$, and $g(x) = x^2, x \ge 0$, together, in one coordinate system.

(b) For which values of x is $f(x) \ge g(x)$, and for which values of x is $f(x) \le g(x)$?

25. **(a)** Graph $f(x) = x^2$ and $g(x) = x^3$ for $x \ge 0$, together, in one coordinate system.

(b) Show algebraically that

$$x^2 \ge x^3$$

for $0 \le x \le 1$.

(c) Show algebraically that

$$x^2 \le x^3$$

for $x \ge 1$.

26. Show algebraically that if $n \ge m$,

$$x^n \le x^m \quad \text{for } 0 \le x \le 1$$

and

$$x^n \ge x^m \quad \text{for } x \ge 1$$

27. **(a)** Show that $y = x^2, x \in \mathbf{R}$, is an even function.

(b) Show that $y = x^3, x \in \mathbf{R}$, is an odd function.

28. Show that

(a) $y = x^n, x \in \mathbf{R}$, is an even function when n is an even integer.

(b) $y = x^n, x \in \mathbf{R}$, is an odd function when n is an odd integer.

29. In Example 5 of this section, we considered the chemical reaction

$$A + B \to AB$$

Assume that initially only A and B are in the reaction vessel and that the initial concentrations are $a = [A] = 3$ and $b = [B] = 4$.

(a) We found that the reaction rate $R(x)$, where x is the concentration of AB, is given by

$$R(x) = k(a - x)(b - x)$$

where a is the initial concentration of A, b is the initial concentration of B, and k is the constant of proportionality. Suppose that the reaction rate $R(x)$ is equal to 9 when the concentration of AB is $x = 1$. Use this relationship to find the reaction rate $R(x)$.

(b) Determine the appropriate domain of $R(x)$, and use a graphing calculator to sketch the graph of $R(x)$.

30. An autocatalytic reaction uses its resulting product for the formation of a new product, as in the reaction

$$A + X \rightarrow X$$

If we assume that this reaction occurs in a closed vessel, then the reaction rate is given by

$$R(x) = kx(a - x)$$

for $0 \leq x \leq a$, where a is the initial concentration of A and x is the concentration of X.

(a) Show that $R(x)$ is a polynomial and determine its degree.

(b) Graph $R(x)$ for $k = 2$ and $a = 6$. Find the value of x at which the reaction rate is maximal.

31. Suppose that a beetle walks up a tree along a straight line at a constant speed of 1 meter per hour. What distance will the beetle have covered after 1 hour, 2 hours, and 3 hours? Write an equation that expresses the distance (in meters) as a function of the time (in hours), and show that this function is a polynomial of degree 1.

32. Suppose that a fungal disease originates in the middle of an orchard, initially affecting only one tree. The disease spreads out radially at a constant speed of 10 feet per day. What area will be affected after 2 days, 4 days, and 8 days? Write an equation that expresses the affected area as a function of time, measured in days, and show that this function is a polynomial of degree 2.

■ **1.2.3**

In Problems 33–36, for each function, find the largest possible domain and determine the range.

33. $f(x) = \dfrac{1}{1 - x}$ **34.** $f(x) = \dfrac{2x}{(x - 2)(x + 3)}$

35. $f(x) = \dfrac{x - 2}{x^2 - 9}$ **36.** $f(x) = \dfrac{1}{x^2 + 1}$

37. Compare $y = \frac{1}{x}$ and $y = \frac{1}{x^2}$ for $x > 0$ by graphing the two functions. Where do the curves intersect? Which function is greater for small values of x? for large values of x?

38. Let n and m be two positive integers with $m \leq n$. Answer the following questions about $y = x^{-n}$ and $y = x^{-m}$ for $x > 0$: Where do the curves intersect? Which function is greater for small values of x? for large values of x?

39. Let

$$f(x) = \frac{1}{x + 1}, \quad x > -1$$

(a) Use a graphing calculator to graph $f(x)$.

(b) On the basis of the graph in (a), determine the range of $f(x)$.

(c) For which values of x is $f(x) = 2$?

(d) On the basis of the graph in (a), determine how many solutions $f(x) = a$ has, where a is in the range of $f(x)$.

40. Let

$$f(x) = \frac{2x}{3 + x}, \quad x \geq 0$$

(a) Use a graphing calculator to graph $f(x)$.

(b) Find the range of $f(x)$.

(c) For which values of x is $f(x) = 1$?

(d) Based on the graph in (a), explain in words why, for any value a in the range of $f(x)$, you can find exactly one value $x \geq 0$ such that $f(x) = a$. Determine x by solving $f(x) = a$.

41. Let

$$f(x) = \frac{3x}{1 + x}, \quad x \geq 0$$

(a) Use a graphing calculator to graph $f(x)$.

(b) Find the range of $f(x)$.

(c) For which values of x is $f(x) = 2$?

(d) On the basis of the graph in (a), explain in words why, for any value a in the range of $f(x)$, you can find exactly one value $x \geq 0$ such that $f(x) = a$. Determine x by solving $f(x) = a$.

In Problems 42–44, we discuss the Monod growth function, which was introduced in Example 6 of this section.

42. Use a graphing calculator to investigate the Monod growth function

$$r(N) = \frac{aN}{k + N}, \quad N \geq 0$$

where a and k are positive constants.

(a) Graph $r(N)$ for (i) $a = 5$ and $k = 1$, (ii) $a = 5$ and $k = 3$, and (iii) $a = 8$ and $k = 1$. Place all three graphs in one coordinate system.

(b) On the basis of the graphs in (a), describe in words what happens when you change a.

(c) On the basis of the graphs in (a), describe in words what happens when you change k.

43. The Monod growth function $r(N)$ describes growth as a function of nutrient concentration N. Assume that

$$r(N) = 5\frac{N}{1 + N}, \quad N \geq 0$$

Find the percentage increase when the nutrient concentration is doubled from $N = 0.1$ to $N = 0.2$. Compare this result with what you find when you double the nutrient concentration from $N = 10$ to $N = 20$. This is an example of *diminishing return*.

44. The Monod growth function $r(N)$ describes growth as a function of nutrient concentration N. Assume that

$$r(N) = a\frac{N}{k + N}, \quad N \geq 0$$

where a and k are positive constants.

(a) What happens to $r(N)$ as N increases? Use this relationship to explain why a is called the saturation level.

(b) Show that k is the half-saturation constant; that is, show that if $N = k$, then $r(N) = a/2$.

45. Let

$$f(x) = \frac{x^2}{4 + x^2}, \quad x \geq 0$$

(a) Use a graphing calculator to graph $f(x)$.

(b) On the basis of your graph in (a), find the range of $f(x)$.

(c) What happens to $f(x)$ as x gets larger?

46. The function

$$f(x) = \frac{x^n}{b^n + x^n}, \quad x \geq 0$$

where n is a positive integer and b is a positive real number, is used in biochemistry to model reaction rates as a function of the concentration of some reactants.

(a) Use a graphing calculator to graph $f(x)$ for $n = 1, 2$, and 3 in one coordinate system when $b = 2$.

(b) Where do the three graphs in (a) intersect?

(c) What happens to $f(x)$ as x gets larger?

(d) For an arbitrary positive value of b, show that $f(b) = 1/2$. On the basis of this demonstration and your answer in (c), explain why b is called the half-saturation constant.

■ **1.2.4**

In Problems 47–50, use a graphing calculator to sketch the graphs of the functions.

47. $y = x^{3/2}, x \geq 0$ **48.** $y = x^{1/3}, x \geq 0$

49. $y = x^{-1/4}, x > 0$ **50.** $y = 2x^{-7/8}, x > 0$

51. (a) Graph $y = x^{-1/2}, x > 0$, and $y = x^{1/2}, x \geq 0$, together, in one coordinate system.

(b) Show algebraically that

$$x^{-1/2} \geq x^{1/2}$$

for $0 < x \leq 1$.

(c) Show algebraically that

$$x^{-1/2} \leq x^{1/2}$$

for $x \geq 1$.

52. (a) Graph $y = x^{5/2}, x \geq 0$, and $y = x^{1/2}, x \geq 0$, together, in one coordinate system.

(b) Show algebraically that

$$x^{5/2} \leq x^{1/2}$$

for $0 \leq x \leq 1$. (*Hint:* Show that $x^{1/2}/x^{-1/2} = x \leq 1$ for $0 < x \leq 1$.)

(c) Show algebraically that

$$x^{5/2} \geq x^{1/2}$$

for $x \geq 1$.

In Problems 53–56, sketch each scaling relation (Niklas, 1994).

53. In a sample based on 46 species, leaf area was found to be proportional to (stem diameter)$^{1.84}$. On the basis of your graph, as stem diameter increases, does leaf area increase or decrease?

54. In a sample based on 28 species, the volume fraction of spongy mesophyll was found to be proportional to (leaf thickness)$^{-0.49}$. (The spongy mesophyll is part of the internal tissue of a leaf blade.) On the basis of your graph, as leaf thickness increases, does the volume fraction of spongy mesophyll increase or decrease?

55. In a sample of 60 species of trees, wood density was found to be proportional to (breaking strength)$^{0.82}$. On the basis of your graph, does breaking strength increase as wood density increases? or as wood density decreases?

56. Suppose that a cube of length L and volume V has mass M and that $M = 0.35V$. How does the length of the cube depend on its mass?

■ **1.2.5**

57. Assume that a population size at time t is $N(t)$ and that

$$N(t) = 2^t, \quad t \geq 0$$

(a) Find the population size for $t = 0, 1, 2, 3$, and 4.

(b) Graph $N(t)$ for $t \geq 0$.

58. Assume that a population size at time t is $N(t)$ and that

$$N(t) = 40 \cdot 2^t, \quad t \geq 0$$

(a) Find the population size at time $t = 0$.

(b) Show that

$$N(t) = 40e^{t \ln 2}, \quad t \geq 0$$

(c) How long will it take until the population size reaches 1000? [*Hint:* Find t so that $N(t) = 1000$.]

59. The half-life of C^{14} is 5730 years. If a sample of C^{14} has a mass of 20 micrograms at time $t = 0$, how much is left after 2000 years?

60. The half-life of C^{14} is 5730 years. If a sample of C^{14} has a mass of 20 micrograms at time 0, how long will it take until **(a)** 10 grams and **(b)** 5 grams are left?

61. After 7 days, a particular radioactive substance decays to half of its original amount. Find the decay rate of this substance.

62. After 5 days, a particular radioactive substance decays to 37% of its original amount. Find the half-life of this substance.

63. Polonium 210 (Po^{210}) has a half-life of 140 days.

(a) If a sample of Po^{210} has a mass of 300 micrograms, find a formula for the mass after t days.

(b) How long would it take this sample to decay to 20% of its original amount?

(c) Sketch the graph of the amount of mass left after t days.

64. The half-life of C^{14} is 5730 years. Suppose that wood found at an archeological excavation site contains about 35% as much C^{14} (in relation to C^{12}) as does living plant material. Determine when the wood was cut.

65. The half-life of C^{14} is 5730 years. Suppose that wood found at an archeological excavation site is 15,000 years old. How much C^{14} (based on C^{12} content) does the wood contain relative to living plant material?

66. The age of rocks of volcanic origin can be estimated with isotopes of argon 40 (Ar^{40}) and potassium 40 (K^{40}). K^{40} decays into Ar^{40} over time. If a mineral that contains potassium is buried under the right circumstances, argon forms and is trapped. Since argon is driven off when the mineral is heated to very high temperatures, rocks of volcanic origin do not contain argon when they are formed. The amount of argon found in such rocks can therefore be used to determine the age of the rock. Assume that a sample of volcanic rock contains 0.00047% K^{40}. The sample also contains 0.000079% Ar^{40}. How old is the rock? (The decay rate of K^{40} to Ar^{40} is 5.335×10^{-10}/yr.)

67. (*Adapted from Moss, 1980*) Hall (1964) investigated the change in population size of the zooplankton species *Daphnia galeata mendota* in Base Line Lake, Michigan. The population size $N(t)$ at time t was modeled by the equation

$$N(t) = N_0 e^{rt}$$

where N_0 denotes the population size at time 0. The constant r is called the **intrinsic rate of growth**.

(a) Plot $N(t)$ as a function of t if $N_0 = 100$ and $r = 2$. Compare your graph against the graph of $N(t)$ when $N_0 = 100$ and $r = 3$. Which population grows faster?

(b) The constant r is an important quantity because it describes how quickly the population changes. Suppose that you determine the size of the population at the beginning and at the end of a period of length 1, and you find that at the beginning there were 200 individuals and after one unit of time there were 250 individuals. Determine r. [*Hint:* Consider the ratio $N(t+1)/N(t)$.]

68. Fish are indeterminate growers; that is, they grow throughout their lifetime. The growth of fish can be described by the von Bertalanffy function

$$L(x) = L_\infty(1 - e^{-kx})$$

for $x \geq 0$, where $L(x)$ is the length of the fish at age x and k and L_∞ are positive constants.
(a) Use a graphing calculator to graph $L(x)$ for $L_\infty = 20$, for **(i)** $k = 1$ and **(ii)** $k = 0.1$.
(b) For $k = 1$, find x so that the length is 90% of L_∞. Repeat for 99% of L_∞. Can the fish ever attain length L_∞? Interpret the meaning of L_∞.
(c) Compare the graphs obtained in (a). Which growth curve reaches 90% of L_∞ faster? Can you explain what happens to the curve of $L(x)$ when you vary k (for fixed L_∞)?

■ **1.2.6**

69. Which of the following functions is one to one (use the horizontal line test)?
(a) $f(x) = x^2, x \geq 0$ **(b)** $f(x) = x^2, x \in \mathbf{R}$
(c) $f(x) = \frac{1}{x}, x > 0$ **(d)** $f(x) = e^x, x \in \mathbf{R}$
(e) $f(x) = \frac{1}{x^2}, x \neq 0$ **(f)** $f(x) = \frac{1}{x^2}, x > 0$

70. (a) Show that $f(x) = x^3 - 1, x \in \mathbf{R}$, is one to one, and find its inverse together with its domain.
(b) Graph $f(x)$ and $f^{-1}(x)$ in one coordinate system, together with the line $y = x$, and convince yourself that the graph of $f^{-1}(x)$ can be obtained by reflecting the graph of $f(x)$ about the line $y = x$.

71. (a) Show that $f(x) = x^2 + 1, x \geq 0$, is one to one, and find its inverse together with its domain.
(b) Graph $f(x)$ and $f^{-1}(x)$ in one coordinate system, together with the line $y = x$, and convince yourself that the graph of $f^{-1}(x)$ can be obtained by reflecting the graph of $f(x)$ about the line $y = x$.

72. (a) Show that $f(x) = \sqrt{x}, x \geq 0$, is one to one, and find its inverse together with its domain.
(b) Graph $f(x)$ and $f^{-1}(x)$ in one coordinate system, together with the line $y = x$, and convince yourself that the graph of $f^{-1}(x)$ can be obtained by reflecting the graph of $f(x)$ about the line $y = x$.

73. (a) Show that $f(x) = 1/x^3, x > 0$, is one to one, and find its inverse together with its domain.
(b) Graph $f(x)$ and $f^{-1}(x)$ in one coordinate system, together with the line $y = x$, and convince yourself that the graph of $f^{-1}(x)$ can be obtained by reflecting the graph of $f(x)$ about the line $y = x$.

74. The reciprocal of a function $f(x)$ can be written as either $1/f(x)$ or $[f(x)]^{-1}$. The point of this problem is to make clear that a reciprocal of a function has nothing to do with the inverse of a function. As an example, let $f(x) = 2x + 1, x \in \mathbf{R}$. Find both $[f(x)]^{-1}$ and $f^{-1}(x)$, and compare the two functions. Graph all three functions together.

■ **1.2.7**

75. Find the inverse of $f(x) = 3^x, x \in \mathbf{R}$, together with its domain, and graph both functions in the same coordinate system.
76. Find the inverse of $f(x) = 5^x, x \in \mathbf{R}$, together with its domain, and graph both functions in the same coordinate system.
77. Find the inverse of $f(x) = (\frac{1}{4})^x, x \in \mathbf{R}$, together with its domain, and graph both functions in the same coordinate system.
78. Find the inverse of $f(x) = (\frac{1}{3})^x, x \in \mathbf{R}$, together with its domain, and graph both functions in the same coordinate system.
79. Find the inverse of $f(x) = 2^x, x \geq 0$, together with its domain, and graph both functions in the same coordinate system.
80. Find the inverse of $f(x) = (\frac{1}{2})^x, x \geq 0$, together with its domain, and graph both functions in the same coordinate system.
81. Simplify the following expressions:
(a) $2^{5\log_2 x}$ **(b)** $3^{4\log_3 x}$
(c) $5^{5\log_{1/5} x}$ **(d)** $4^{-2\log_2 x}$
(e) $2^{3\log_{1/2} x}$ **(f)** $4^{-\log_{1/2} x}$
82. Simplify the following expressions:
(a) $\log_4 16^x$ **(b)** $\log_2 16^x$
(c) $\log_3 27^x$ **(d)** $\log_{1/2} 4^x$
(e) $\log_{1/2} 8^{-x}$ **(f)** $\log_3 9^{-x}$
83. Simplify the following expressions:
(a) $\ln x^2 + \ln x^3$ **(b)** $\ln x^4 - \ln x^{-2}$
(c) $\ln(x^2 - 1) - \ln(x + 1)$ **(d)** $\ln x^{-1} + \ln x^{-3}$
84. Simplify the following expressions:
(a) $e^{3\ln x}$ **(b)** $e^{-\ln(x^2+1)}$
(c) $e^{-2\ln(1/x)}$ **(d)** $e^{-2\ln x}$
85. Write the following expressions in terms of base e, and simplify:
(a) 3^x **(b)** 4^{x^2-1} **(c)** 2^{-x-1} **(d)** 3^{-4x+1}
86. Write the following expressions in terms of base e:
(a) $\log_2(x^2 - 1)$ **(b)** $\log_3(5x + 1)$
(c) $\log(x + 2)$ **(d)** $\log_2(2x^2 - 1)$
87. Show that the function $y = (1/2)^x$ can be written in the form $y = e^{-\mu x}$, where μ is a positive constant. Determine μ.
88. Show that if $0 < a < 1$, then the function $y = a^x$ can be written in the form $y = e^{-\mu x}$, where μ is a positive constant. Write μ in terms of a.
89. Assume that two DNA sequences of common origin, each of length 300 nucleotides, differ from each other by 47 nucleotides. Use the Jukes and Cantor correction of Example 15 to find an estimate for the number K of substitutions per site.
90. A community measure that takes both species abundance and species richness into account is the Shannon diversity index H. To calculate H, the proportion p_i of species i in the community is used. Assume that the community consists of S species. Then

$$H = -(p_1 \ln p_1 + p_2 \ln p_2 + \cdots + p_S \ln p_S)$$

(a) Assume that $S = 5$ and that all species are equally abundant; that is, $p_1 = p_2 = \cdots = p_5$. Compute H.
(b) Assume that $S = 10$ and that all species are equally abundant; that is, $p_1 = p_2 = \cdots = p_{10}$. Compute H.
(c) A measure of equitability (or evenness) of the species distribution can be measured by dividing the diversity index H by $\ln S$. Compute $H/\ln S$ for $S = 5$ and $S = 10$.
(d) Show that, in general, if there are N species and all species are equally abundant, then

$$\frac{H}{\ln S} = 1$$

In Problems 91–96, for each given pair of functions, use a graphing calculator to compare the functions. Describe what you see.

91. $y = \sin x$ and $y = 2\sin x$

92. $y = \sin x$ and $y = \sin(2x)$

93. $y = \cos x$ and $y = 2\cos x$

94. $y = \cos x$ and $y = \cos(2x)$

95. $y = \tan x$ and $y = 2\tan x$

96. $y = \tan x$ and $y = \tan(2x)$

97. Let
$$f(x) = 3\sin(4x), \quad x \in \mathbf{R}$$
Find the amplitude and the period of $f(x)$.

98. Let
$$f(x) = -2\sin\left(\frac{x}{2}\right), \quad x \in \mathbf{R}$$
Find the amplitude and the period of $f(x)$.

99. Let
$$f(x) = 4\sin(2\pi x), \quad x \in \mathbf{R}$$
Find the amplitude and the period of $f(x)$.

100. Let
$$f(x) = -\frac{3}{2}\sin\left(\frac{\pi}{3}x\right), \quad x \in \mathbf{R}$$

Find the amplitude and the period of $f(x)$.

101. Let
$$f(x) = 4\cos\left(\frac{x}{4}\right), \quad x \in \mathbf{R}$$
Find the amplitude and the period of $f(x)$.

102. Let
$$f(x) = 7\cos(2x), \quad x \in \mathbf{R}$$
Find the amplitude and the period of $f(x)$.

103. Let
$$f(x) = -3\cos\left(\frac{\pi x}{5}\right), \quad x \in \mathbf{R}$$
Find the amplitude and the period of $f(x)$.

104. Let
$$f(x) = -\frac{2}{3}\cos\left(\frac{3x}{\pi}\right), \quad x \in \mathbf{R}$$
Find the amplitude and the period of $f(x)$.

105. Use the fact that $\sec x = \frac{1}{\cos x}$ to explain why the maximum domain of $y = \sec x$ consists of all real numbers except odd integer multiples of $\pi/2$.

106. Use the fact that $\csc x = \frac{1}{\sin x}$ to explain why the maximum domain of $y = \csc x$ consists of all real numbers except integer multiples of π.

■ 1.3 Graphing

In the preceding section, we introduced the functions most important to our study. You must be able to graph the following functions without a calculator: $y = c, x, x^2$, $x^3, 1/x, e^x, \ln x, \sin x, \cos x, \sec x,$ and $\tan x$. This will help you to sketch functions quickly and to come up with an analytical description of a function based on a graph. In this section, you will learn how to obtain new functions from these basic functions and how to graph them. In addition, we will introduce important transformations that are often used to display data graphically.

■ 1.3.1 Graphing and Basic Transformations of Functions

In this subsection, we will recall some basic transformations: vertical and horizontal translations, reflections about $x = 0$ and $y = 0$, and stretching and compressing.

> **Definition** The graph of
> $$y = f(x) + a$$
> is a **vertical translation** of the graph of $y = f(x)$. If $a > 0$, the graph of $y = f(x)$ is shifted up a units; if $a < 0$, the graph of $y = f(x)$ is shifted down $|a|$ units.

This definition is illustrated in Figure 1.41, where we display $y = x^2, y = x^2 + 2$, and $y = x^2 - 2$.

> **Definition** The graph of
> $$y = f(x - c)$$
> is a **horizontal translation** of the graph of $y = f(x)$. If $c > 0$, the graph of $y = f(x)$ is shifted c units to the right; if $c < 0$, the graph of $y = f(x)$ is shifted $|c|$ units to the left.

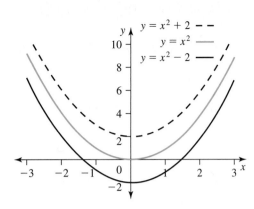

Figure 1.41 The graphs of $y = x^2$, $y = x^2 + 2$ and $y = x^2 - 2$.

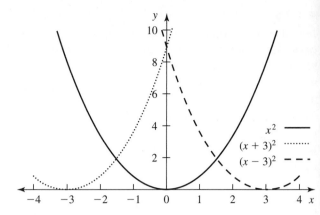

Figure 1.42 The graphs of $y = x^2$, $y = (x - 3)^2$, and $y = (x + 3)^2$.

This definition is illustrated in Figure 1.42, where we display $y = x^2$, $y = (x - 3)^2$, and $y = (x + 3)^2$. Note that $y = (x + 3)^2$ is shifted to the left, since $y = (x - (-3))^2$ and therefore $c = -3 < 0$.

Reflections about the x-axis ($y = 0$) and the y-axis ($x = 0$) are illustrated in Figure 1.43. We graph $y = \sqrt{x}$; its reflection about the x-axis, $y = -\sqrt{x}$; and its reflection about the y-axis, $y = \sqrt{-x}$.

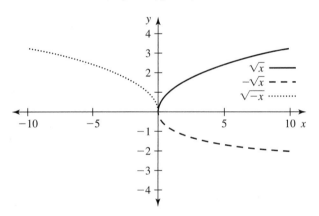

Figure 1.43 Reflections about the x-axis and the y-axis.

Multiplying a function by a factor between 0 and 1 compresses the graph of the function; multiplying a function by a factor greater than 1 stretches the graph of the function. These operations are illustrated in Figure 1.44, where we graph $y = x^2$ and $y = \frac{1}{2}x^2$, and in Figure 1.45, where we graph $y = x^2$ and $y = 2x^2$.

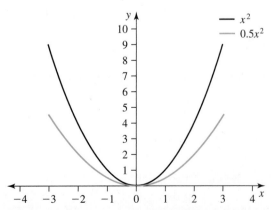

Figure 1.44 The graphs of $y = x^2$ and $y = \frac{1}{2}x^2$.

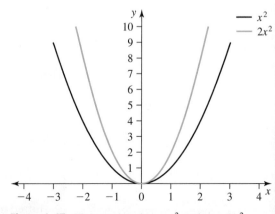

Figure 1.45 The graphs of $y = x^2$ and $y = 2x^2$.

We illustrate the preceding transformations in the next two examples.

EXAMPLE 1   Explain how the graph of

$$y = 2 \sin \left(x - \frac{\pi}{4} \right) \quad \text{for } x \in \mathbf{R}$$

can be obtained from the graph of $y = \sin x,\ x \in \mathbf{R}$.

Solution   We transform $y = \sin x$ in two steps, illustrated in Figure 1.46. First we shift $y = \sin x$ to the right $\frac{\pi}{4}$ units. This yields $y = \sin(x - \frac{\pi}{4})$. Then we multiply $y = \sin(x - \frac{\pi}{4})$ by 2. This corresponds to stretching $y = \sin(x - \frac{\pi}{4})$ by the factor 2.   ■

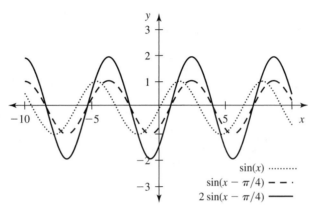

Figure 1.46 The graphs of $y = \sin x$, $y = \sin(x - \frac{\pi}{4})$, and $y = 2 \sin(x - \frac{\pi}{4})$.

EXAMPLE 2   Explain how the graph of

$$y = -\sqrt{x - 3} - 1, \quad x \geq 3$$

can be obtained from the graph of $y = \sqrt{x},\ x \geq 0$.

Solution   We transform $y = \sqrt{x}$ in three steps, illustrated in Figure 1.47. First we shift $y = \sqrt{x}$ three units to the right and obtain $y = \sqrt{x - 3}$. Then we reflect $y = \sqrt{x - 3}$ about the x-axis, which yields $y = -\sqrt{x - 3}$. Finally, we shift $y = -\sqrt{x - 3}$ down one unit. This is the graph of $y = -\sqrt{x - 3} - 1$.   ■

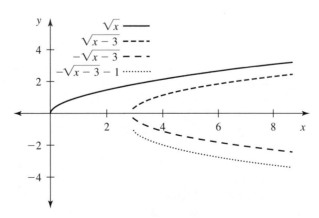

Figure 1.47 The graphs for Example 2.

■ 1.3.2 The Logarithmic Scale

We often encounter sizes that vary over a wide range. For instance, lengths in the metric system are measured in meters (m). (A meter is a bit longer than a yard: 1 meter is equal to 1.0936 yards.) A longer metric unit that is commonly used is a kilometer (km), which is 1000 m. Shorter commonly used metric units are a millimeter (mm), which is 1/1000 of a meter; a micrometer (μm), which is 1/1,000,000 (one-millionth) of a meter; and a nanometer (nm), which is 1/1,000,000,000 (one-billionth) of a meter. Here are some examples of lengths of organisms: A ribosome is about 20 nm ($= 2 \times 10^{-8}$ m), a poxvirus is about 400 nm (4×10^{-7} m), a bacterium is about 1 μm ($= 10^{-6}$ m), a tardigrade (or "water bear") is about 1.2 mm ($= 1.2 \times 10^{-3}$ m), an adult human is about 1.8 m, a blue whale is between 25 and 35 m, the diameter of the earth is 12,755 km ($\approx 1.3 \times 10^{7}$ m), and the average distance from the sun to the earth is about 150 million km ($= 1.5 \times 10^{11}$ m). These sizes are conveniently illustrated with the use of a **logarithmic scale**—a scale according to which multiples of 10 are equally distant (Figure 1.48).

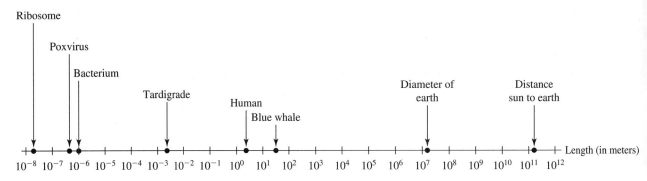

Figure 1.48

When we take logarithms to base 10 of the quantities displayed in Figure 1.48, we find that the transformed scale looks like the arithmetic scale we are familiar with (Figure 1.49). The numbers on the logarithmic scale in Figure 1.49 correspond to exponents.

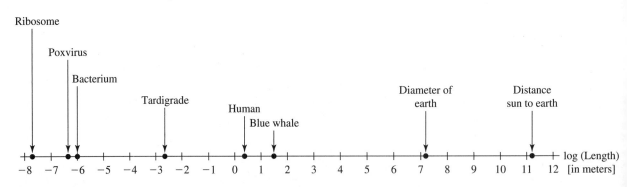

Figure 1.49

Let's look at the two number lines in more detail. The origin of the number line in Figure 1.49 corresponds to the number 1 in Figure 1.48, since $\log 1 = 0$. If we go to the left of 1 on the line in Figure 1.48, we get smaller and smaller numbers, but they are *all* positive. (Because $\log x$ is defined only for $x > 0$, we cannot logarithmically transform negative numbers.) Going to the left of 1 in Figure 1.48 corresponds to going to the left of 0 in Figure 1.49. The negative numbers on the number line in Figure 1.49 correspond to negative exponents; for instance, the -8 in Figure 1.49 means $\log x = -8$, or $x = 10^{-8}$. A similar interpretation holds when we go to the right of 1 in Figure 1.48 (or to the right of 0 in Figure 1.49). A logarithmic scale is typically based on logarithms to base 10, since this base makes conversion between the two representations in Figures 1.48 and 1.49 easier.

The lengths in the preceding examples differed by many factors of 10. Instead of saying that quantities differ by many factors of 10, we will say that they differ by many **orders of magnitude**: If two quantities differ by a factor of 10, they differ by one order of magnitude. (If they differ by a factor of 100, they differ by two orders of magnitude, and so on.) Orders of magnitude are approximate comparisons: A 1.8-m-tall human and a 25-m-long blue whale differ by about one order of magnitude.

EXAMPLE 3

Display the numbers 0.003, 0.1, 0.5, 6, 200, and 4000 on a logarithmic scale.

Solution

To display the numbers, we need to take logarithms first:

x	0.003	0.1	0.5	6	200	4000
log x	−2.5229	−1	−0.3010	0.7782	2.3010	3.6021

Since $\log 0.003 = -2.5229$, we find this number 2.5229 units to the left of 0 on the logarithmic scale. Similarly, since $\log 0.1 = -1$, this number is one unit to the left of 0, and $\log 200 = 2.3010$ is 2.3010 units to the right of 0 (Figure 1.50).

Figure 1.50 Example 3.

Figure 1.51 Example 3.

In the biological literature, x rather than $\log x$ is used to label logarithmic number lines. The locations of the numbers are the same; only the labeling changes. That is, 0.003 would be −2.5229 units to the left of the origin of the line (which is now at 1). The line in Figure 1.50 would then look like the line in Figure 1.51. ■

■ 1.3.3 Transformations into Linear Functions

When you look through a biology textbook, you very likely find graphs like the ones in Figures 1.52 and 1.53. In either graph, you see a straight line (with data points scattered about it). In Figure 1.52, the vertical axis is logarithmically transformed and the horizontal axis is on a linear scale; in Figure 1.53, both axes are logarithmically transformed. Why do we display data like this, and what do these graphs mean?

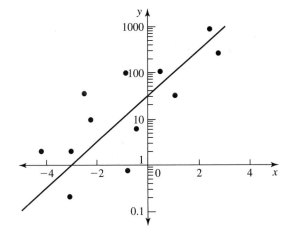

Figure 1.52 A straight line when the vertical axis is logarithmically transformed.

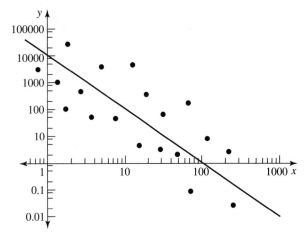

Figure 1.53 A straight line when both axes are logarithmically transformed.

The first question is quick to answer: Straight lines (or linear relationships) are easy to recognize visually. If transforming data results in data points lying along a straight line, we should do the transformation, because, as we will see, this will allow us to obtain a functional relationship between quantities. Now on to the second question: What do these graphs mean?

Exponential Functions   Let's look at Figure 1.52 and redraw just the straight line, using $\log y$ (instead of y) on the vertical axis and x on the horizontal axis (Figure 1.54). Set $Y = \log y$ and forget for a moment where the graph came from. We see a linear relationship between Y and x — a relationship of the form

$$Y = c + mx$$

where c is the Y-intercept and m is the slope. We can read these two quantities off of the graph in Figure 1.54:

$$c = 1.5 \qquad m = 0.5$$

That is, we have

$$Y = 1.5 + 0.5x$$

Now, $Y = \log y$, and thus

$$\log y = 1.5 + 0.5x$$

Exponentiating both sides, we find that

$$y = 10^{1.5+0.5x} = 10^{1.5}(10^{0.5})^x$$

Since $10^{1.5} \approx 31.62$ and $10^{0.5} \approx 3.162$, we can write the preceding equation as

$$y = (31.62)(3.162^x) \tag{1.4}$$

Looking at (1.4), we see that it is an exponential function.

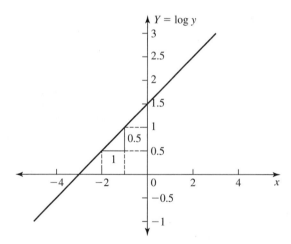

Figure 1.54   Figure 1.52 redrawn. Now the vertical axis is labeled $\log y$.

A graph in which the vertical axis is on a logarithmic scale and the horizontal axis is on a linear scale is called a **log-linear plot** or a **semilog plot**. If we display an exponential function of the form $y = ba^x$ on a semilog plot, a straight line results. To see this, we take logarithms to base 10 on both sides of $y = ba^x$:

$$\log y = \log(ba^x) \tag{1.5}$$

Using the properties of logarithms, we simplify the right-hand side to

$$\log(ba^x) = \log b + \log a^x = \log b + x \log a$$

If we set $Y = \log y$, then (1.5) becomes

$$Y = \log b + (\log a)x \tag{1.6}$$

Comparing this equation with the general form of a linear function $Y = c + mx$, we see that the Y-intercept is $\log b$ and the slope is $\log a$. You do not need to memorize this statement, since you can always do the calculation that resulted in (1.6), but you should memorize the fact that an exponential function results in a straight line on a semilog plot. If $a > 1$, the slope of the line is positive; if $0 < a < 1$, the slope of the line is negative.

EXAMPLE 4

Graph

$$y = 2.5 \cdot 3^x, \quad x \in \mathbf{R}$$

on a semilog plot.

Solution

We take logarithms first:

$$\log y = \log(2.5 \cdot 3^x)$$
$$= \underbrace{\log 2.5}_{\approx 0.3979} + x \underbrace{\log 3}_{\approx 0.4771}$$

The graph is shown in Figure 1.55. Note that the origin of the coordinate system is where $x = 0$ and $y = 1$ (or $\log y = 0$). The labeling on the vertical axis is for y, and we see that the labels are multiples of 10. To find 2.5 on the vertical axis, we use the fact that $\log 2.5 = 0.3979$ and that 2.5 is therefore 0.3979 units above the x-axis, as illustrated in Figure 1.55. (One unit on the vertical axis corresponds to a factor of 10.) ■

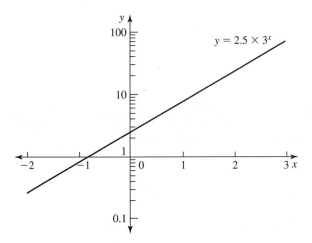

Figure 1.55 The graph of $y = 2.5 \times 3^x$ on a semilog plot.

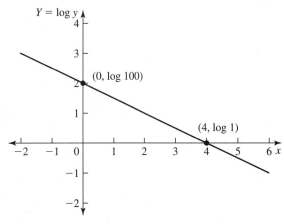

Figure 1.56 The graph for Example 5. The line goes through the points $(0, 2)$ and $(4, 0)$.

EXAMPLE 5

Find the functional relationship between x and y based on the graph in Figure 1.56.

Solution

Figure 1.56 shows a semilog plot. We set $Y = \log y$. Then, in an x–Y graph, the Y-intercept is $\log 100 = 2$, and, using the two points $(0, \log 100)$ and $(4, \log 1)$, we find that the slope of the line is $(\log 1 - \log 100)/(4 - 0) = (0 - 2)/(4 - 0) = -0.5$. Hence,

$$Y = c + mx = 2 - 0.5x$$

Since $Y = \log y$, after exponentiating the linear equation, we obtain

$$y = 10^{2 - 0.5x} = 10^2 (10^{-0.5})^x = (100)(0.3162)^x$$ ■

Power Functions Let's look back at Figure 1.53. There, both axes are logarithmically transformed. We redraw just the straight line, using $Y = \log y$ on the vertical axis and $X = \log x$ on the horizontal axis (Figure 1.57).

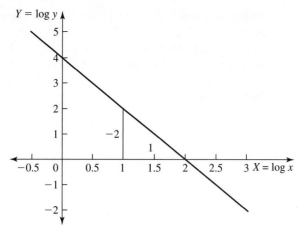

Figure 1.57 Figure 1.53 redrawn. Now the vertical axis is labeled $\log y$ and the horizontal axis is labeled $\log x$.

Using the linear equation $Y = c + mX$, where c is the Y-intercept and m is the slope, we find, from Figure 1.57, that

$$c = 4 \quad \text{and} \quad m = -2$$

With $Y = \log y$ and $X = \log x$, the linear equation becomes

$$\log y = 4 - 2 \log x$$

Exponentiating both sides, we get

$$y = 10^{4-2\log x} = 10^4 (10^{\log x^{-2}}) = 10^4 x^{-2}$$

The function $y = 10^4 x^{-2}$ is a power function.

A graph in which both the vertical and the horizontal axis are logarithmically scaled is called a **log-log plot** or **double-log plot**. If we display a power function $y = bx^r$ in a double-log plot, a straight line results. To see this, we take logarithms to base 10 on both sides of $y = bx^r$:

$$\log y = \log(bx^r) \tag{1.7}$$

Using the properties of logarithms on the right-hand side of (1.7), we get

$$\log(bx^r) = \log b + \log x^r = \log b + r \log x$$

If we set $Y = \log y$ and $X = \log x$, then (1.7) becomes

$$Y = \log b + rX$$

Comparing this equation with the general form of a linear function, $Y = c + mX$, we see that the Y-intercept is $\log b$ and the slope is r. If $r > 0$, the slope is positive. If $r < 0$, the slope is negative.

EXAMPLE 6   Graph

$$y = 100x^{-2/3}, \quad x > 0$$

on a double-log plot.

Solution   We take logarithms first:

$$\log y = \log(100x^{-2/3}) = \log 100 - \frac{2}{3} \log x$$

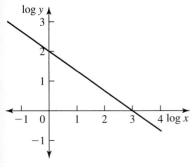

Figure 1.58 The graph $y = 100x^{-2/3}$ on a double-log plot where the axes are labeled $X = \log x$ and $Y = \log y$.

We set $Y = \log y$ and $X = \log x$. Then, with $\log 100 = 2$, we find that

$$Y = 2 - \frac{2}{3}X$$

This is the equation of a straight line with X-intercept 3 and Y-intercept 2 (and thus slope $-2/3$). We graph this function in Figure 1.58, where we have X and Y on the two axes. If we use x and y on the two axes (Figure 1.59), the labels change: The y-intercept is now 100 (corresponding to $\log 100 = 2$) and the x-intercept is 1000 (corresponding to $\log 1000 = 3$). Note that the origin in Figure 1.58 is $X = 0$ and $Y = 0$; the origin in Figure 1.59 is $x = 1$ and $y = 1$. ■

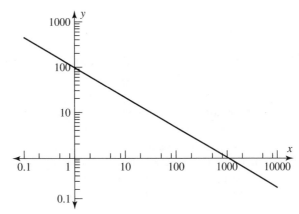

Figure 1.59 The graph $y = 100x^{-2/3}$ on a double-log plot where the axes are labeled x and y.

EXAMPLE 7 Find the functional relationship between x and y on the basis of the graph in Figure 1.60.

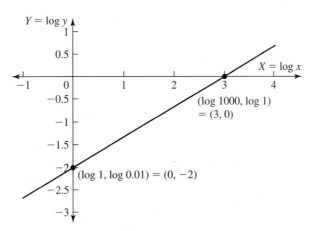

Figure 1.60 The graph of the function for Example 7: The two points on the double-log plot used for finding the relationship are $(\log 1, \log 0.01)$ and $(\log 1000, \log 1)$.

Solution If $Y = \log y$ and $X = \log x$, then, in an X–Y graph, the Y-intercept is $\log 0.01 = -2$ and, using the two points $(\log 1, \log 0.01)$ and $(\log 1000, \log 1)$, we calculate the slope as

$$\frac{\log 1 - \log 0.01}{\log 1000 - \log 1} = \frac{0 - (-2)}{3 - 0} = \frac{2}{3}$$

Hence, the equation is

$$Y = -2 + \frac{2}{3}X$$

With $Y = \log y$ and $X = \log x$, we find that

$$\log y = -2 + \frac{2}{3} \log x$$

and, after exponentiating both sides of this equation, we get

$$y = 10^{-2+\frac{2}{3} \log x} = 10^{-2} 10^{\log x^{2/3}} = (0.01)x^{2/3}$$

Thus, the functional relationship between x and y is a power function of the form

$$y = (0.01)x^{2/3}$$

■

Applications

EXAMPLE 8

When growing plants at sufficiently high initial densities, we often observe that the number of plants decreases as the size of the plants grows. This property is called *self-thinning*. When the per-plant dry weight of the aboveground biomass is plotted on a log-log plot as a function of the density of survivors, we frequently find that the data lie along a straight line with slope $-3/2$. Assume that, for a particular plant, such a relationship holds for plant densities between 10^2 and 10^4 plants per square meter and that, at a density of 100 plants per square meter, the dry weight per plant is about 10 grams. Find the functional relationship between dry weight and plant density, and graph this function on a log-log plot.

Solution

Since the relationship between density (x) and dry weight (y) follows a straight line with slope $-3/2$ on a log-log plot, we set

$$\log y = C - \frac{3}{2} \log x \quad \text{for } 10^2 \leq x \leq 10^4$$

where C is a constant. To find C, we use the fact that when $x = 100$, $y = 10$. Therefore,

$$\log 10 = C - \frac{3}{2} \log 100$$

or

$$1 = C - \frac{3}{2} \cdot 2, \qquad \text{which implies that} \qquad C = 4$$

Hence,

$$\log y = 4 - \frac{3}{2} \log x$$

Exponentiating both sides (and remembering that "log" denotes the logarithm to base 10), we find that

$$y = 10^4 x^{-3/2} \quad \text{for } 10^2 \leq x \leq 10^4$$

The graph of this function on a log-log scale is shown in Figure 1.61.

■

EXAMPLE 9

Polonium 210 (Po^{210}) is a radioactive material. To determine the half-life of Po^{210} experimentally, we measure the amount of radioactive material left after time t for various values of t. When we plot the data on a semilog plot, we find that we can fit a straight line to the curve. The slope of the straight line is -0.0022/day. Find the half-life of Po^{210}.

Solution

Radioactive decay follows the equation

$$W(t) = W(0)e^{-\lambda t} \quad \text{for } t \geq 0$$

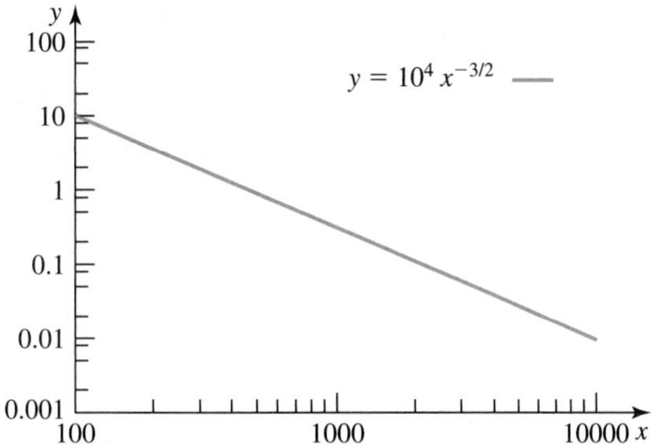

Figure 1.61 The graph of the function for Example 8: The line has slope $-3/2$ and goes through the point $(\log 100, \log 10)$ on a double-log plot.

where $W(t)$ is the amount of radioactive material left after time t. If we log transform this equation, we obtain

$$\log W(t) = \log W(0) - \lambda t \log e$$

Note that we use logarithms to base 10. If we plot $W(t)$ as a function of t on a semilog plot, we obtain a straight line with slope $-\lambda \log e$. Matching this slope with the number given in the example, we obtain

$$\lambda \log e = 0.0022/\text{day}$$

Solving for λ yields

$$\lambda = \frac{1}{\log e} 0.0022/\text{day}$$

To find the half-life T_h, we use the formula (see Subsection 1.2.5)

$$T_h = \frac{\ln 2}{\lambda} = \frac{\ln 2}{0.0022}(\log e)\,\text{days}$$

$$\approx 136.8\,\text{days}$$ ■

Note that in the preceding example we used logarithms to base 10 to do the log transformation. The radioactive law was given in terms of the natural exponent e. The slope therefore contained the factor $\log e \approx 0.4343$.

EXAMPLE 10

Light intensity in lakes decreases with depth. Denote by $I(z)$ the light intensity at depth z, with $z = 0$ representing the surface. Then the percentage surface radiation at depth z, denoted by $\text{PSR}(z)$, is computed as

$$\text{PSR}(z) = 100\frac{I(z)}{I(0)}$$

When we graph the percentage surface radiation as a function of depth on a semilog plot, a straight line results. An example of such a curve is given in Figure 1.62, where the coordinate system is rotated clockwise by $90°$ so that the depth axis points downward. Derive an equation for $I(z)$ on the basis of the graph.

Solution

We see that the dependent variable, $100I(z)/I(0)$, is logarithmically transformed, whereas the independent variable, z, is on a linear scale. The graph is a straight line. We thus find that

$$\log 100\frac{I(z)}{I(0)} = c + mz$$

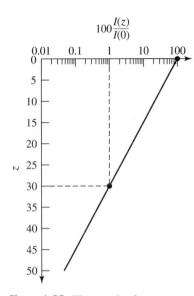

Figure 1.62 The graph of percentage surface radiation as a function of depth.

where c is the intercept on the percentage surface radiation axis and m is the slope. We see that

$$c = \log 100$$

and, using the points (0, 100) and (30, 1), we get

$$m = \frac{\log 100 - \log 1}{0 - 30} = -\frac{2}{30} = -\frac{1}{15}$$

Hence,

$$\log 100 \frac{I(z)}{I(0)} = \log 100 - \frac{1}{15}z$$

The left-hand side simplifies to $\log 100 + \log \frac{I(z)}{I(0)}$. After canceling $\log 100$ on both sides and exponentiating both sides, we find that

$$\frac{I(z)}{I(0)} = 10^{-(1/15)z} = \exp[\ln 10^{-(1/15)z}]$$

Thus

$$I(z) = I(0)e^{-(\frac{1}{15}\ln 10)z}$$

The number $\frac{1}{15} \ln 10$ is called the *vertical attenuation coefficient*. The magnitude of this number tells us how quickly light is absorbed in a lake. ■

■ 1.3.4 From a Verbal Description to a Graph (Optional)

Being able to sketch a graph on the basis of a verbal explanation of some phenomenon is an extremely useful skill since a graph can summarize a complex situation that can be more easily communicated and remembered. Let's look at an example.

EXAMPLE 11   The following quote in Rosenzweig and Abramsky (1993) relates primary productivity (i.e., the rate at which autotrophs convert light or inorganic chemical energy into chemical energy of organic compounds) to species diversity (i.e., number of species):

> The relationship of primary productivity and species diversity on a regional scale ($10^6 \, \text{km}^2$) is not simple. But within such regions, and perhaps even larger ones, a pattern is emerging: as productivity rises, first diversity increases, then it declines.

If we wanted to translate this verbal description into a graph, we would first determine the independent and the dependent variable. Here, we consider species diversity as a function of primary productivity; hence, primary productivity is the independent variable and species diversity is the dependent variable. We will therefore use a coordinate system whose horizontal axis denotes primary productivity and whose vertical axis denotes species diversity. Since both primary productivity and species diversity are nonnegative, we need to draw only the first quadrant (Figure 1.63).

Going back to the quote, we see that as productivity increases, diversity first increases, then decreases. The graph in Figure 1.64 illustrates this behavior.

The exact shape of the curve cannot be inferred from the quote and will depend on the system studied. For instance, the graph in Figure 1.65 resembles the curve from a study in the Costa Rican forests; as productivity increases, the curve shows an initial increase followed by a decrease in species diversity. The shape of the curve in Figure 1.65 is quantitatively different from the graph in Figure 1.64, but both have the same qualitative features of an initial increase followed by a decrease.

As another example, we will look at the *functional response* of a predator to its prey density. ■

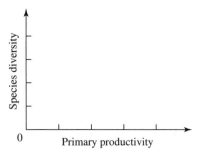

Figure 1.63 The coordinate system for species diversity as a function of primary productivity can be restricted to the first quadrant.

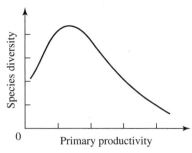

Figure 1.64 The graph of species diversity as a function of primary productivity is hump shaped.

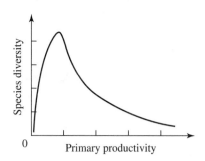

Figure 1.65 The graph of species diversity as a function of primary productivity in Costa Rican forests (redrawn after Holdrige et al. 1971).

EXAMPLE 12 The functional response of a predator to its prey density relates the number of prey consumed per predator (the dependent variable) to the prey density (the independent variable). Holling (1959) introduced three basic types of response. Type 1 describes a response in which the number of prey eaten per predator as a function of prey density rises linearly to a plateau. The type 2 functional response increases at a decelerating rate and eventually levels off. The type 3 functional response is S shaped, or sigmoidal, and also eventually levels off. Now let's translate these three ways into graphs. All graphs will be plotted in coordinate systems, with prey density on the horizontal axis and the number of prey eaten per predator on the vertical axis. Since both prey density and number of prey eaten per predator are nonnegative variables, we need to draw only the first quadrant.

Even though this was not mentioned, we will assume that when the prey density is equal to zero, the number of prey eaten per predator will also be zero, and once the prey density is positive, the number of prey eaten per predator will be positive. This means that the three functional response curves all go through the origin.

The type 1 functional response first increases linearly (i.e., results in a straight line) and then reaches a plateau (stays constant) (See Figure 1.66.)

The type 2 functional response is described as a function that increases at a decelerating rate. This means that the function will increase less quickly as prey density increases (Figure 1.67). In contrast to the type 1 functional response, the type 2 response will continue to increase and approach, but not actually reach, the plateau at a finite value of prey density.

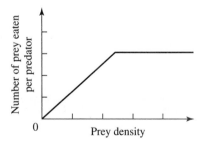

Figure 1.66 The type 1 functional response.

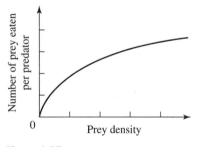

Figure 1.67 The type 2 functional response.

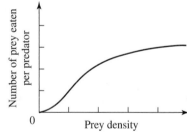

Figure 1.68 The type 3 functional response.

The type 3 functional response is described as sigmoidal. Sigmoidal curves are characterized by an initial accelerating increase followed by an increase at a decelerating rate (Figure 1.68). Similar to the type 2 functional response, the type 3 functional response approaches a plateau as prey density increases, but will not reach the plateau at a finite value of prey density. ■

For each example discussed so far, the functional relationship depended on just one variable, such as the number of prey eaten per predator as a function of prey density. Often, however, a response depends on more than one independent variable.

The next example presents a response that depends on two independent variables, and shows how to draw a graph of this more complex relationship.

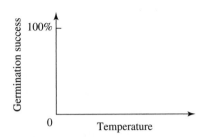

Figure 1.69 The coordinate system for germination success as a function of temperature can be restricted to the first quadrant. Germination success will be between 0 and 100%.

EXAMPLE 13

The successful germination of seeds depends on both temperature and humidity. When the humidity is too low, seeds tend not to germinate at all, regardless of the temperature. Germination success is highest for intermediate values of temperature. Finally, seeds tend to germinate better when humidity levels are higher.

One way to translate this information into a graph is to graph germination success as a function of temperature for different levels of humidity. If we measure temperature in Fahrenheit or Celsius, we can restrict the graphs to the first quadrant (Figure 1.69), since the temperature needs to be well above freezing for germination to occur (the temperature at which freezing starts is $0°C$, or $32°F$). Germination success will be between 0 and 100%. To sketch the graphs, it is better not to label the axes beyond what we provided in Figure 1.69, because we do not know the exact numerical response.

There is enough information to provide three graphs: one for low humidity, one for intermediate humidity, and one for high humidity. We will graph them all in one coordinate system, so that it is easier to compare the different responses. The graph for low humidity is a horizontal line where germination success is 0%. For intermediate and high humidity, the graphs are hump shaped, since germination success is highest for intermediate values of temperature. The graph for high humidity is above the graph for intermediate humidity, because seeds tend to germinate better when humidity levels are higher (Figure 1.70).   ■

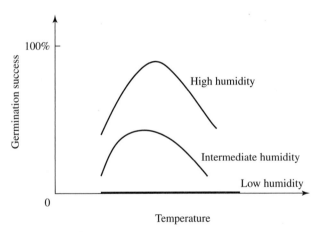

Figure 1.70 Germination success as a function of temperature for three humidity levels (low, intermediate, high).

Section 1.3 Problems

■ **1.3.1**

In Problems 1–22, sketch the graph of each function. Do not use a graphing calculator. (Assume the largest possible domain.)

1. $y = x^2 + 1$

2. $y = -(x - 2)^2 + 1$

3. $y = x^3 - 2$

4. $y = -x^4 + 1$

5. $y = -2x^2 - 3$

6. $y = -(3 - x)^2$

7. $y = 3 + 1/x$

8. $y = 1 - 1/x$

9. $y = 1/(x - 1)$

10. $y = 1 + 1/(x + 2)^2$

11. $y = \exp(x - 2)$

12. $y = \exp(-x)$

13. $y = e^{-(x+3)}$

14. $y = 3e^{2x+1}$

15. $y = \ln(x + 1)$

16. $y = \ln(x - 3)$

17. $y = -\ln(x - 1) + 1$

18. $y = -\ln(1 - x)$

19. $y = 2\sin(x + \pi/4)$

20. $y = 0.2\cos(-x)$

21. $y = -\sin(\pi x/2)$

22. $y = -2\cos(\pi x/4)$

23. Explain how the following functions can be obtained from $y = x^2$ by basic transformations:

(a) $y = x^2 - 2$ **(b)** $y = (x - 1)^2 + 1$ **(c)** $y = -2(x + 2)^2$

24. Explain how the following functions can be obtained from $y = x^3$ by basic transformations:

(a) $y = x^3 + 1$ **(b)** $y = (x + 1)^3 - 1$ **(c)** $y = -3(x - 2)^3$

25. Explain how the following functions can be obtained from $y = 1/x$ by basic transformations:

(a) $y = 1 - \dfrac{1}{x}$ **(b)** $y = -\dfrac{1}{x - 1}$ **(c)** $y = \dfrac{x}{x + 1}$

26. Explain how the following functions can be obtained from $y = 1/x^2$ by basic transformations:

(a) $y = \dfrac{1}{x^2} + 1$ **(b)** $y = -\dfrac{1}{(x+1)^2}$ **(c)** $y = -\dfrac{1}{x^2} - 2$

27. Explain how the following functions can be obtained from $y = e^x$ by basic transformations:

(a) $y = 2e^x - 1$ **(b)** $y = -e^{-x}$ **(c)** $y = e^{x-2} + 1$

28. Explain how the following functions can be obtained from $y = e^x$ by basic transformations:

(a) $y = e^{-x} - 1$ **(b)** $y = -e^x + 1$ **(c)** $y = -e^{x-3} - 2$

29. Explain how the following functions can be obtained from $y = \ln x$ by basic transformations:

(a) $y = \ln(x-1)$ **(b)** $y = -\ln x + 1$ **(c)** $y = \ln(x+3) - 1$

30. Explain how the following functions can be obtained from $y = \ln x$ by basic transformations:

(a) $y = \ln(1-x)$ **(b)** $y = \ln(2+x) - 1$
(c) $y = -\ln(2-x) + 1$

31. Explain how the following functions can be obtained from $y = \sin x$ by basic transformations:

(a) $y = 1 - \sin x$ **(b)** $y = \sin\left(x - \dfrac{\pi}{4}\right)$

(c) $y = -\sin\left(x + \dfrac{\pi}{3}\right)$

32. Explain how the following functions can be obtained from $y = \cos x$ by basic transformations:

(a) $y = 1 + 2\cos x$ **(b)** $y = -\cos\left(x + \dfrac{\pi}{4}\right)$

(c) $y = -\cos\left(\dfrac{\pi}{2} - x\right)$

■ **1.3.2**

33. Find the following numbers on a number line that is on a logarithmic scale (base 10): 0.0002, 0.02, 1, 5, 50, 100, 1000, 8000, and 20000.

34. Find the following numbers on a number line that is on a logarithmic scale (base 10): 0.03, 0.7, 1, 2, 5, 10, 17, 100, 150, and 2000.

35. (a) Find the following numbers on a number line that is on a logarithmic scale (base 10): 10^2, 10^{-3}, 10^{-4}, 10^{-7}, and 10^{-10}.

(b) Can you find 0 on a number line that is on a logarithmic scale?

(c) Can you find negative numbers on a number line that is on a logarithmic scale?

36. (a) Find the following numbers on a number line that is on a logarithmic scale (base 10):
(i) $10^{-3}, 2 \times 10^{-3}, 5 \times 10^{-3}$ **(ii)** $10^{-1}, 2 \times 10^{-1}, 5 \times 10^{-1}$
(iii) $10^2, 2 \times 10^2, 5 \times 10^2$

(b) From your answers to (a), how many units (on a logarithmic scale) is **(i)** 2×10^{-3} from 10^{-3} **(ii)** 2×10^{-1} from 10^{-1} and **(iii)** 2×10^2 from 10^2?

(c) From your answers to (a), how many units (on a logarithmic scale) is **(i)** 5×10^{-3} from 10^{-3} **(ii)** 5×10^{-1} from 10^{-1} and **(iii)** 5×10^2 from 10^2?

In Problems 37–42, insert an appropriate number in the blank space.

37. The longest known species of worms is the earthworm *Microchaetus rappi* of South Africa; in 1937, a 6.7-m-long specimen was collected from the Transvaal. The shortest worm is *Chaetogaster annandalei*, which measures less than 0.51 mm in length. *M. rappi* is _____ order(s) of magnitude longer than *C. annandalei*.

38. Both the La Plata river dolphin (*Pontoporia blainvillei*) and the sperm whale (*Physeter macrocephalus*) belong to the suborder Odontoceti (individuals that have teeth). A La Plata river dolphin weighs between 30 and 50 kg, whereas a sperm whale weighs between 35,000 and 40,000 kg. A sperm whale is _____ order(s) of magnitude heavier than a La Plata river dolphin.

39. Compare a ball of radius 1 cm against a ball of radius 10 cm. The radius of the larger ball is _____ order(s) of magnitude bigger than the radius of the smaller ball. The volume of the larger ball is _____ order(s) of magnitude bigger than the volume of the smaller ball.

40. Compare a square with side length 1 m against a square with side length 100 m. The area of the larger square is _____ order(s) of magnitude larger than the area of the smaller square.

41. The diameter of a typical bacterium is about 0.5 to 1 μm. An exception is the bacterium *Epulopiscium fishelsoni*, which is about 600 μm long and 80 μm wide. The volume of *E. fishelsoni* is about _____ order(s) of magnitude larger than that of a typical bacterium. (*Hint*: Approximate the shape of a typical bacterium by a sphere and the shape of *E. fishelsoni* by a cylinder.)

42. The length of a typical bacterial cell is about one-tenth that of a small eukaryotic cell. Consequently, the cell volume of a bacterium is about _____ order(s) of magnitude smaller than that of a small eukaryotic cell. (*Hint*: Approximate the shapes of both types of cells by spheres.)

■ **1.3.3**

In Problems 43–46, when log y is graphed as a function of x, a straight line results. Graph straight lines, each given by two points, on a log-linear plot, and determine the functional relationship. (The original x–y coordinates are given.)

43. $(x_1, y_1) = (0, 5), (x_2, y_2) = (3, 1)$

44. $(x_1, y_1) = (-1, 4), (x_2, y_2) = (2, 8)$

45. $(x_1, y_1) = (-2, 3), (x_2, y_2) = (1, 1)$

46. $(x_1, y_1) = (1, 4), (x_2, y_2) = (6, 1)$

In Problems 47–54, use a logarithmic transformation to find a linear relationship between the given quantities and graph the resulting linear relationship on a log-linear plot.

47. $y = 3 \times 10^{-2x}$ **48.** $y = 4 \times 10^{5x}$

49. $y = 2e^{-1.2x}$ **50.** $y = 7e^{3x}$

51. $y = 5 \times 2^{4x}$ **52.** $y = 6 \times 2^{-0.9x}$

53. $y = 4 \times 3^{2x}$ **54.** $y = 5^{-6x}$

In Problems 55–58, when log y is graphed as a function of log x, a straight line results. Graph straight lines, each given by two points, on a log-log plot, and determine the functional relationship. (The original x–y coordinates are given.)

55. $(x_1, y_1) = (1, 2), (x_2, y_2) = (5, 1)$

56. $(x_1, y_1) = (3, 5), (x_2, y_2) = (1, 5)$

57. $(x_1, y_1) = (4, 2), (x_2, y_2) = (8, 8)$

58. $(x_1, y_1) = (2, 5), (x_2, y_2) = (5, 2)$

In Problems 59–66, use a logarithmic transformation to find a linear relationship between the given quantities and graph the resulting linear relationship on a log-log plot.

59. $y = 2x^5$ **60.** $y = 3x^2$

61. $y = x^6$ **62.** $y = 5x^3$

63. $y = x^{-2}$ **64.** $y = 6x^{-1}$

65. $y = 4x^{-3}$ **66.** $y = 7x^{-5}$

In Problems 67–72, use a logarithmic transformation to find a linear relationship between the given quantities and determine whether a log-log or log-linear plot should be used to graph the resulting linear relationship.

67. $f(x) = 3x^{1.7}$ **68.** $g(s) = 1.8e^{-0.2s}$

69. $N(t) = 130 \times 2^{1.2t}$ **70.** $I(u) = 4.8u^{-0.89}$

71. $R(t) = 3.6t^{1.2}$ **72.** $L(c) = 1.7 \times 10^{2.3c}$

73. The following table is based on a functional relationship between x and y that is either an exponential or a power function:

x	y
1	1.8
2	2.07
4	2.38
10	2.85
20	3.28

Use an appropriate logarithmic transformation and a graph to decide whether the table comes from a power function or an exponential function, and find the functional relationship between x and y.

74. The following table is based on a functional relationship between x and y that is either an exponential or a power function:

x	y
0.5	7.81
1	3.4
1.5	2.09
2	1.48
2.5	1.13

Use an appropriate logarithmic transformation and a graph to decide whether the table comes from a power function or an exponential function, and find the functional relationship between x and y.

75. The following table is based on a functional relationship between x and y that is either an exponential or a power function:

x	y
−1	0.398
−0.5	1.26
0	4
0.5	12.68
1	40.18

Use an appropriate logarithmic transformation and a graph to decide whether the table comes from a power function or an exponential function, and find the functional relationship between x and y.

76. The following table is based on a functional relationship between x and y that is either an exponential or a power function:

x	y
0	3
0.5	2.20
1	1.61
1.5	1.18
2	0.862

Use an appropriate logarithmic transformation and a graph to decide whether the table comes from a power function or an exponential function, and find the functional relationship between x and y.

77. The following table is based on a functional relationship between x and y that is either an exponential or a power function:

x	y
0.1	0.045
0.5	1.33
1	5.7
1.5	13.36
2	24.44

Use an appropriate logarithmic transformation and a graph to decide whether the table comes from a power function or an exponential function, and find the functional relationship between x and y.

78. The following table is based on a functional relationship between x and y that is either an exponential or a power function:

x	y
0.1	1.72
0.5	1.41
1	1.11
1.5	0.872
2	0.685

Use an appropriate logarithmic transformation and a graph to decide whether the table comes from a power function or an exponential function, and find the functional relationship between x and y.

So far, we have always used base 10 for a logarithmic transformation. The reason for this is that our number system is based on base 10 and it is therefore easy to logarithmically transform numbers of the form $\dots, 0.01, 0.1, 1, 10, 100, 1000, \dots$ when we use base 10. In Problems 79–82, use the indicated base to logarithmically transform each exponential relationship so that a linear relationship results. Then use the indicated base to graph each relationship in a coordinate system whose axes are accordingly transformed so that a straight line results.

79. $y = 2^x$; base 2   **80.** $y = 3^x$; base 3

81. $y = 2^{-x}$; base 2   **82.** $y = 3^{-x}$; base 3

83. Suppose that $N(t)$ denotes a population size at time t and satisfies the equation

$$N(t) = 2e^{3t} \quad \text{for } t \geq 0$$

(a) If you graph $N(t)$ as a function of t on a semilog plot, a straight line results. Explain why.

(b) Graph $N(t)$ as a function of t on a semilog plot, and determine the slope of the resulting straight line.

84. Suppose that you follow a population over time. When you plot your data on a semilog plot, a straight line with slope 0.03 results. Furthermore, assume that the population size at time 0 was 20. If $N(t)$ denotes the population size at time t, what function best describes the population size at time t?

85. Species–Area Curves Many studies have shown that the number of species on an island increases with the area of the island. Frequently, the functional relationship between the number of species (S) and the area (A) is approximated by $S = CA^z$, where z is a constant that depends on the particular species and habitat in the study. (Actual values of z range from about 0.2 to 0.35.) Suppose that the best fit to your data points on a log-log scale is a straight line. Is your model $S = CA^z$ an appropriate description of your data? If yes, how would you find z?

86. Michaelis–Menten Equation Enzymes serve as catalysts in many chemical reactions in living systems. The simplest such reactions transform a single substrate into a product with the help of an enzyme. The Michaelis–Menten equation describes the initial velocity of such enzymatically controlled reactions. The equation, which gives the relationship between the initial velocity of the reaction (v_0) and the concentration of the substrate (s_0), is

$$v_0 = \frac{v_{max}s_0}{s_0 + K_m}$$

where v_{max} is the maximum velocity at which the product may be formed and K_m is the Michaelis–Menten constant. Note that this equation has the same form as the Monod growth function.

(a) Show that the Michaelis–Menten equation can be written in the form

$$\frac{1}{v_0} = \frac{K_m}{v_{max}}\frac{1}{s_0} + \frac{1}{v_{max}}$$

This formula is known as the Lineweaver–Burk equation and shows that there is a linear relationship between $1/v_0$ and $1/s_0$.

(b) Sketch the graph of the Lineweaver–Burk equation. Use a coordinate system in which $1/s_0$ is on the horizontal axis and $1/v_0$ is on the vertical axis. Show that the resulting graph is a line that intersects the horizontal axis at $-1/K_m$ and the vertical axis at $1/v_{max}$.

(c) To determine K_m and v_{max}, we measure the initial velocity of the reaction, denoted by v_0, as a function of the concentration of the substrate, denoted by s_0, and fit a straight line through the points in a coordinate system in which the horizontal axis is $1/s_0$ and the vertical axis is $1/v_0$. Explain how to determine K_m and v_{max} from the graph.

(Note that this is an example in which a nonlogarithmic transformation is used to obtain a linear relationship. Since the reciprocals of both quantities of interest are used, the resulting plot is called a double-reciprocal plot.)

87. (*Continuation of Problem 86*) Estimating v_{max} and K_m from the Lineweaver–Burk graph as described in Problem 86 is not always satisfactory. A different transformation typically yields better estimates (Dowd and Riggs, 1965). Show that the Michaelis–Menten equation can be written as

$$\frac{v_0}{s_0} = \frac{v_{max}}{K_m} - \frac{1}{K_m}v_0$$

and explain why this transformation results in a straight line when you graph v_0 on the horizontal axis and $\frac{v_0}{s_0}$ on the vertical axis. Explain how you can estimate v_{max} and K_m from the graph.

88. (*Adapted from Reiss, 1989*) In a case study in which the maximal rates of oxygen consumption (in ml/s) of nine species of wild African mammals (Taylor et al., 1980) were plotted against body mass (in kg) on a log-log plot, it was found that the data points fell on a straight line with slope approximately equal to 0.8 and vertical-axis intercept approximately equal to 0.105. Find an equation that relates maximal oxygen consumption and body mass.

89. (*Adapted from Benton and Harper, 1997*) In vertebrates, embryos and juveniles have large heads relative to their overall body size. As the animal grows older, proportions change; for instance, the ratio of skull length to body length diminishes. That

this is the case not only for living vertebrates, but also for fossil vertebrates, is shown by the following example:

Ichthyosaurs are a group of marine reptiles that appeared in the early Triassic and died out well before the end of the Cretaceous.[1] They were fish shaped and comparable in size to dolphins. In a study of 20 fossil skeletons, the following allometric relationship between skull length S (measured in cm) and backbone length B (measured in cm) was found:

$$S = 1.162B^{0.93}$$

(a) Choose suitable transformations of S and B so that the resulting relationship is linear. Plot the transformed relationship, and find the slope and the y-intercept.

(b) Explain why the allometric equation confirms that juveniles had relatively large heads. (*Hint*: Compute the ratio of S to B for a number of different values of B—say, 10 cm, 100 cm, 500 cm—and compare.)

90. Light intensity in lakes decreases exponentially with depth. If $I(z)$ denotes the light intensity at depth z, with $z = 0$ representing the surface, then

$$I(z) = I(0)e^{-\alpha z}, \quad z \geq 0$$

where α is a positive constant called the *vertical attenuation coefficient*. Figure 1.71 shows the percentage surface radiation, defined as $100I(z)/I(0)$, as a function of depth in different lakes.

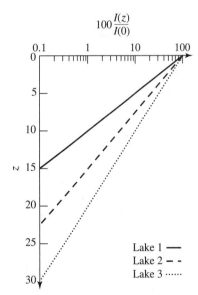

Figure 1.71 Light intensity as a function of depth for Problem 90.

(a) On the basis of the graph, estimate α for each lake.

(b) Reproduce a graph like the one in Figure 1.71 for Lake Constance (Germany) in May ($\alpha = 0.768\,\text{m}^{-1}$) and December ($\alpha = 0.219\,\text{m}^{-1}$) (data from Tilzer et al., 1982).

(c) Explain why the graphs are straight lines.

---

(1) The Triassic is a geological period that began about 248 million years ago and ended about 213 million years ago; the Cretaceous began about 144 million years ago and ended 65 million years ago.

91. The absorption of light in a uniform water column follows an exponential law; that is, the intensity $I(z)$ at depth z is

$$I(z) = I(0)e^{-\alpha z}$$

where $I(0)$ is the intensity at the surface (i.e., when $z = 0$) and α is the *vertical attenuation coefficient*. (We assume here that α is constant. In reality, α depends on the wavelength of the light penetrating the surface.)

(a) Suppose that 10% of the light is absorbed in the uppermost meter. Find α. What are the units of α?

(b) What percentage of the remaining intensity at 1 m is absorbed in the second meter? What percentage of the remaining intensity at 2 m is absorbed in the third meter?

(c) What percentage of the initial intensity remains at 1 m, at 2 m, and at 3 m?

(d) Plot the light intensity as a percentage of the surface intensity on both a linear plot and a log-linear plot.

(e) Relate the slope of the curve on the log-linear plot to the attenuation coefficient α.

(f) The level at which 1% of the surface intensity remains is of biological significance. Approximately, it is the level where algal growth ceases. The zone above this level is called the *euphotic zone*. Express the depth of the euphotic zone as a function of α.

(g) Compare a very clear lake with a milky glacier stream. Is the attenuation coefficient α for the clear lake greater or smaller than the attenuation coefficient α for the milky stream?

92. When plants are grown at high densities, we often observe that the number of plants decreases as plant weights increase (due to plant growth). If we plot the logarithm of the total aboveground dry-weight biomass per plant, $\log w$, against the logarithm of the density of survivors, $\log d$ (base 10), a straight line with slope $-3/2$ results. Find the equation that relates w and d, assuming that $w = 1$ g when $d = 10^3$ m^{-2}.

In Problems 93–98, find each functional relationship on the basis of the given graph.

93. Figure 1.72   **94.** Figure 1.73

95. Figure 1.74   **96.** Figure 1.75

97. Figure 1.76 (*Hint:* This relationship is different from the ones considered so far. The x-axis is logarithmically transformed, but the y-axis is linear.)

98. Figure 1.77 (*Hint:* This relationship is different from the ones considered so far. The x-axis is logarithmically transformed, but the y-axis is linear.)

99. The free energy ΔG expended in transporting an uncharged solute across a membrane from concentration c_1 to one of concentration c_2 follows the equation

$$\Delta G = 2.303 RT \, \log \frac{c_2}{c_1}$$

where $R = 1.99$ kcal K^{-1} kmol^{-1} is the universal gas constant and T is temperature measured in kelvins (K). Plot ΔG as a function of the concentration ratio c_2/c_1 when $T = 298$ K (25°C). Use a

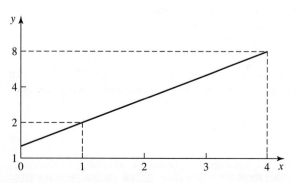

Figure 1.72 Graph for Problem 93.

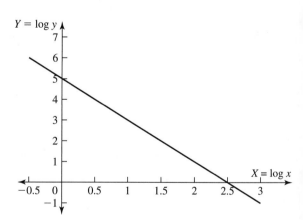

Figure 1.73 Graph for Problem 94.

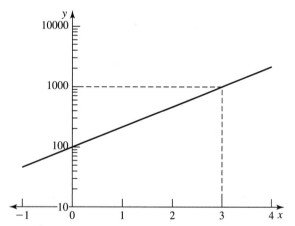

Figure 1.74 Graph for Problem 95.

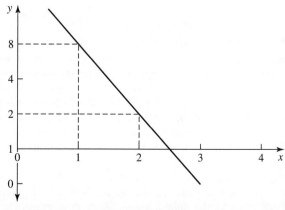

Figure 1.75 Graph for Problem 96.

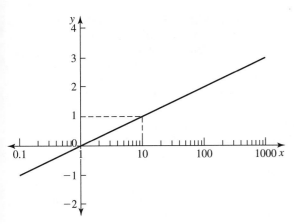

Figure 1.76 Graph for Problem 97.

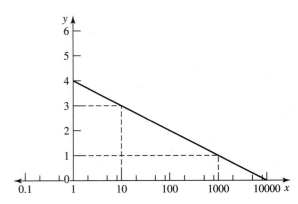

Figure 1.77 Graph for Problem 98.

coordinate system in which the vertical axis is on a linear scale and the horizontal axis is on a logarithmic scale.

100. Logistic Transformation Suppose that

$$f(x) = \frac{1}{1 + e^{-(b+mx)}} \qquad (1.8)$$

A function of the form (1.8) is called a **logistic** function. The logistic function was introduced by the Dutch mathematical biologist Verhulst around 1840 to describe the growth of populations with limited food resources. Show that

$$\ln \frac{f(x)}{1 - f(x)} = b + mx \qquad (1.9)$$

This transformation is called the *logistic transformation*. It is a standard transformation for linearizing functions of the form (1.8).

■ **1.3.4**

101. Not every study of species richness as a function of productivity produces a hump-shaped curve. Owen (1988) studied rodent assemblages in Texas and found that the number of species was a decreasing function of productivity. Sketch a graph that would describe this situation.

102. Species diversity in a community may be controlled by disturbance frequency. The intermediate disturbance hypothesis states that species diversity is greatest at intermediate disturbance levels. Sketch a graph of species diversity as a function of disturbance level that illustrates this hypothesis.

103. Preston (1962) investigated the dependence of number of bird species on island area in the West Indian islands. He found that the number of bird species increased at a decelerating rate as island area increased. Sketch this relationship.

104. Phytoplankton converts carbon dioxide to organic compounds during photosynthesis. This process requires sunlight. It has been observed that the rate of photosynthesis is a function of light intensity: The rate of photosynthesis increases approximately linearly with light intensity at low intensities, saturates at intermediate levels, and decreases slightly at high intensities. Sketch a graph of the rate of photosynthesis as a function of light intensity.

105. Brown lemming densities in the tundra areas of North America and Eurasia show cyclic behavior: Every three to four years, lemming densities build up very rapidly, and they typically crash the next year. Sketch a graph that describes this situation.

106. Nitrogen productivity can be defined as the amount of dry matter produced per unit of nitrogen per unit of time. Experimental studies suggest that nitrogen productivity increases as a function of light intensity at a decelerating rate. Sketch a graph of nitrogen productivity as a function of light intensity.

107. A study of Borchert's (1994) investigated the relationship between stem water storage and wood density in a number of tree species in Costa Rica. The study showed that water storage is inversely related to wood density; that is, higher wood density corresponds to lower water content. Sketch a graph of water content as a function of wood density that illustrates this situation.

108. Species richness can be a hump-shaped function of productivity. In the same coordinate system, sketch two hump-shaped graphs of species richness as a function of productivity, one in which the maximum occurs at low productivity and one in which the maximum occurs at high productivity.

109. The size distribution of zooplankton in a lake is typically a hump-shaped curve; that is, if the frequency (in percent) of zooplankton is plotted against the body length of zooplankton, a curve that first increases and then decreases results. Brooks and Dodson (1965) studied the effects of introducing a planktivorous fish in a lake. They found that the composition of zooplankton after the fish was introduced shifted to smaller individuals. In the same coordinate system, sketch the size distribution of zooplankton before and after the introduction of the planktivorous fish.

110. *Daphnia* is a genus of zooplankton that comprises a number of species. The body growth rate of *Daphnia* depends on food concentration. A minimum food concentration is required for growth: Below this level, the growth rate is negative; above, it is positive. In a study by Gliwicz (1990), it was found that growth rate is an increasing function of food concentration and that the minimum food concentration required for growth decreases with increasing size of the animal. Sketch two graphs in the same coordinate system, one for a large and one for a small *Daphnia* species, that illustrates this situation.

111. Grant (1982) investigated egg weight as a function of adult body weight among 10 species of Darwin's finches. He found that the relationship between the logarithm of the average egg size and the logarithm of the average body size is linear and that smaller species lay smaller eggs and larger species lay larger eggs. Graph this relationship.

112. Grant et al. (1985) investigated the relationship between mean wing length and mean weight among males of populations of six ground finch species. They found a positive and nearly linear relationship between these two quantities. Graph this relationship.

113. Bohlen et al. (2001) investigated stream nitrate concentration along an elevation gradient at the Hubbard Brook Experimental Forest in New Hampshire. They found that the nitrate concentration in stream water declined with decreasing elevation. Sketch stream nitrate concentration as a function of elevation.

114. In Example 13, we discussed germination success as a function of temperature for varying levels of humidity. We can also consider germination success as a function of humidity for various levels of temperature. Sketch the following graphs of germination success as a function of humidity: one for low temperature, one for intermediate temperature, and one for high temperature.

115. Boulinier et al. (2001) studied the dynamics of forest bird communities. They found that the mean local extinction rate of area-sensitive species declined with mean forest patch size, whereas the mean extinction rate of non-area-sensitive species did not depend on mean forest size. In the same coordinate system, graph the mean extinction rate as a function of mean forest patch size for **(a)** an area-sensitive species and **(b)** a non-area-sensitive species.

116. Dalling et al. (2001) compared net photosynthetic rates of two pioneer trees—*Alseis blackiana* and *Miconia argenta*—as a function of gap size in Barro Colorado Island. They found that net photosynthetic rates (measured on a per-unit basis) increased with gap size for both trees and that the photosynthetic rate for *Miconia argenta* was higher than that for *Alseis blackiana*. In the same coordinate system, graph the net photosynthetic rates as functions of gap size for both tree species.

Chapter 1 Key Terms

Discuss the following definitions and concepts:

1. Real numbers

2. Intervals: open, closed, half-open

3. Absolute value

4. Proportional

5. Lines: standard form, point–slope form, slope–intercept form

6. Parallel and perpendicular lines

7. Circle: radius, center, equation of circle, unit circle

8. Angle: radians, degrees

9. Trigonometric identities

10. Complex numbers: real part, imaginary part

11. Function: domain, codomain, range, image

12. Symmetry of functions: even, odd

13. Composition of functions

14. Polynomial

15. Degree of a polynomial

16. Chemical reaction: law of mass action

17. Rational function

18. Growth rate

19. Specific growth rate and per capita growth rate

20. Monod growth function

21. Power function

22. Allometry and scaling relations

23. Exponential function

24. Exponential growth

25. Natural exponential base

26. Radioactive decay

27. Half-life

28. Inverse function, one to one

29. Logarithmic function

30. Relationship between exponential and logarithmic functions

31. Periodic function

32. Trigonometric function

33. Amplitude, period

34. Translation: horizontal, vertical

35. Logarithmic scale

36. Order of magnitude

37. Logarithmic transformation

38. Log-log plot

39. Semilog plot

Chapter 1 Review Problems

1. Population Growth Suppose that the number of bacteria in a petri dish is given by

$$B(t) = 10,000e^{0.1t}$$

where t is measured in hours.

(a) How many bacteria are present at $t = 0, 1, 2, 3$, and 4?

(b) Find the time t when the number of bacteria reaches 100,000.

2. Population Decline Suppose that a pathogen is introduced into a population of bacteria at time 0. The number of bacteria then declines as

$$B(t) = 25,000e^{-2t}$$

where t is measured in hours.

(a) How many bacteria are left after 3 hours?

(b) How long will it be until only 1% of the initial number of bacteria are left?

3. Chemical Reaction Consider the chemical reaction

$$A + 2B \rightarrow AB_2$$

Assume that the reaction occurs in a closed vessel and that the initial concentrations of A and B are $a = [A]$ and $b = [B]$, respectively.

(a) Explain why the reaction rate $R(x)$ is given by

$$R(x) = k(a - x)(b - 2x)^2$$

where $x = [AB_2]$.

(b) Show that $R(x)$ is a polynomial and determine its degree.

(c) Graph $R(x)$ for the relevant values of x when $a = 5, b = 6$, and $k = 0.3$.

4. History of Mathematics Euclid, a Greek mathematician who lived around 300 B.C., wrote the *Elements*, by far the most important mathematical text of that period. The book, arranged in 13 volumes, is a systematic exposition of most of the mathematical knowledge of that time. In Book III, Euclid discusses the construction of a tangent to a circle at a point P on the circle. To phrase the construction in modern terminology, we draw a straight line through the point P that is perpendicular to the line through the center of the circle and the point P on the circle.

(a) Use this geometric construction to find the equation of the line that is tangent to the unit circle at the point $(\frac{1}{2}\sqrt{3}, \frac{1}{2})$.

(b) Determine the angle θ between the positive x-axis and the tangent line found in (a). What is the relationship between the angle θ and the slope of the tangent line found in (a)?

5. Hypothetical Plants To compare logarithmic and exponential growth, we consider two hypothetical plants that are of the same genus, but that exhibit rather different growth rates. Both plants produce a single leaf whose length continues to increase as long as the plant is alive. One plant is called *Growthus logarithmiensis*; the other one is called *Growthus exponentialis*. The length L (measured in feet) of the leaf of *G. logarithmiensis* at age t (measured in years) is given by

$$L(t) = \ln(t + 1), \quad t \geq 0$$

The length E (measured in feet) of the leaf of *G. exponentialis* at age t (measured in years), is given by

$$E(t) = e^t - 1, \quad t \geq 0$$

(a) Find the length of each leaf after 1, 10, 100, and 1000 years.

(b) How long would it take for the leaf of *G. exponentialis* to reach a length of 233,810 mi, the average distance from the earth to the moon? (Note that 1 mi = 5280 ft.) How long would the leaf of *G. logarithmiensis* then be?

(c) How many years would it take the leaf of *G. logarithmiensis* to reach a length of 233,810 mi? Compare this with the length of time since life appeared on earth, about 3500 million years. If *G. logarithmiensis* had appeared 3,500 million years ago, and if there was a plant of this species that had actually survived throughout the entire period, how long would its leaf be today?

(d) Plants started to conquer land only in the late Ordovician period, around 450 million years ago.[2] If both *G. exponentialis* and *G. logarithmiensis* had appeared then, and there was a plant of each species that had actually survived throughout the entire period, how long would their respective leaves be today?

6. Population Growth In Chapter 3 of *The Origin of Species* (Darwin, 1859), Charles Darwin asserts that a "struggle for existence inevitably follows from the high rate at which all organic beings tend to increase. ... Although some species may be now increasing, more or less rapidly, in numbers, all cannot do so, for the world would not hold them." To illustrate this point, he continues as follows:

> There is no exception to the rule that every organic being naturally increases at so high a rate, that, if not destroyed, the earth would soon be covered by the progeny of a single pair. Even slow-breeding man has doubled in twenty-five years, and at this rate, in a few thousand years, there would literally not be standing room for his progeny.

Starting with a single pair, compute the world's population after 1000 years and after 2000 years under Darwin's assumption that the world's population doubles every 25 years, and find the resulting population densities (number of people per square foot). To answer the last part, you need to know that the earth's diameter is about 7900 mi, the surface of a sphere is $4\pi r^2$, where r is the radius of a sphere, and the continents make up about 29% of the earth's surface. (Note that 1 mi = 5280 ft.)

7. Population Growth Assume that a population grows q% each year. How many years will it take the population to double in size? Give the functional relationship between the doubling time T and the annual percentage increase q. Produce a table that shows the doubling time T as a function of q for $q = 1, 2, \ldots, 10$, and graph T as a function of q. What happens to T as q gets closer to 0?

8. Beverton–Holt Recruitment Curve Many organisms show density-dependent mortality. The following is a simple mathematical model that incorporates this effect: Denote the density of parents by N_b and the density of *surviving* offspring by N_a.

(a) Suppose that without density-dependent mortality, the number of surviving offspring per parent is equal to R. Show that if we plot N_b/N_a versus N_b, the result is a horizontal line with y-intercept $1/R$. That is,

$$\frac{N_b}{N_a} = \frac{1}{R}$$

or

$$N_a = R \cdot N_b$$

The constant R is called the **net reproductive rate**.

(b) To include density-dependent mortality, we assume that N_b/N_a is an increasing function of N_b. The simplest way to do this is to assume that the graph of N_b/N_a versus N_b is a straight line with y-intercept $1/R$ and that goes through the point $(K, 1)$. Show that this implies that

$$N_a = \frac{RN_b}{1 + \frac{(R-1)N_b}{K}}$$

This relationship is called the Beverton–Holt recruitment curve.

(c) Explain in words why, for small initial densities N_b, the model described by the Beverton–Holt recruitment curve behaves like the model for density-independent mortality described in (a).

(d) Show that if $N_b = K$, then $N_a = K$. Furthermore, show that $N_b < K$ implies $N_b < N_a < K$ and that $N_b > K$ implies $K < N_a < N_b$. Explain in words what this means. (Note that K is called the *carrying capacity*.)

(e) Plot N_a as a function of N_b for $R = 2$ and $K = 20$. What happens for large values of N_b? Explain in words what this means.

9. Fish Yield (*Adapted from Moss, 1980*) Oglesby (1977) investigated the relationship between annual fish yield (Y) and summer phytoplankton chlorophyll concentration (C). Fish yield was measured in grams dry weight per square meter per year, and the chlorophyll concentration was measured in micrograms per liter. Data from 19 lakes, mostly in the Northern Hemisphere, yielded the following relationship:

$$\log_{10} Y = 1.17 \log_{10} C - 1.92 \qquad (1.10)$$

(a) Plot $\log_{10} Y$ as a function of $\log_{10} C$.

(b) Find the relationship between Y and C; that is, write Y as a function of C. Explain the advantage of the log–log transformation resulting in (1.10) versus writing Y as a function of C. [*Hint:* Try to plot Y as a function of C, and compare with your answer in (a).]

(c) Find the predicted yield (Y_p) as a function of the current yield (Y_c) if the current summer phytoplankton chlorophyll concentration were to double.

(d) By what percentage would the summer phytoplankton chlorophyll concentration need to increase to obtain a 10% increase in fish yield?

10. Radioactive Decay (*Adapted from Moss, 1980*) To trace the history of a lake, a sample of mud from a core is taken and dated. One dating method uses radioactive isotopes. The C^{14} method is effective for sediments that are younger than 60,000 years. The $C^{14} : C^{12}$ ratio has been essentially constant in the atmosphere over a long time, and living organisms take up carbon in that ratio.

---

(2) The Ordovician lasted from about 505 million years ago to about 438 million years ago.

Upon death, the uptake of carbon ceases and C^{14} decays, which changes the $C^{14}:C^{12}$ ratio according to

$$\left(\frac{C^{14}}{C^{12}}\right)_t = \left(\frac{C^{14}}{C^{12}}\right)_{initial} e^{-\lambda t}$$

where t is the time since death.

(a) If the $C^{14}:C^{12}$ ratio in the atmosphere is 10^{-12} and the half-life of C^{14} is 5730 years, find an expression for t, the age of the material being dated, as a function of the $C^{14}:C^{12}$ ratio in the material being dated.

(b) Use your answer in (a) to find the age of a mud sample from a core for which the $C^{14}:C^{12}$ ratio is 1.61×10^{-13}.

11. Fossil Coral Growth (*Adapted from Futuyama, 1995, and Dott and Batten, 1976*) Corals deposit a single layer of lime each day. In addition, seasonal fluctuation in the thickness of the layers allows for grouping them into years. In modern corals, we can count 365 layers per year. J. Wells, a paleontologist, counted such growth layers on fossil corals. To his astonishment, he found that Devonian[3] corals that lived about 380 million years ago had about 400 daily layers per year.

(a) Today, the earth rotates about its axis every 24 hours and revolves around the sun every $365\frac{1}{4}$ days. Astronomers have determined that the earth's rotation has slowed down in recent centuries at the rate of about 2 seconds every 100,000 years. That is, 100,000 years ago, a day was 2 seconds shorter than today. Extrapolate the slowdown back to the Devonian, and determine the length of a day and the length of a year back when Wells's corals lived. (*Hint*: The number of hours per year remains constant. Why?)

(b) Find a linear equation that relates geologic time (in million of years) to the number of hours per day at a given time.

(c) Algal stromatolites also show daily layers. A sample of some fossil stromatolites showed 400 to 420 daily layers per year. Use your answer in (b) to date the stromatolites.

12. Tree Growth The height y in feet of a certain tree as a function of age x in years can be approximated by

$$y = 132e^{-20/x}$$

(a) Use a graphing calculator to plot the graph of this function. Describe in words how the tree grows, paying particular attention to questions such as the following: Does the tree grow equally fast over time? What happens when the tree is young? What happens when the tree is old?

(b) How many years will it take for the tree to reach 100 ft in height?

(c) Can the tree ever reach a height of 200 ft? Is there a final height—that is, a maximum height that the tree will eventually reach?

13. Model for Aging The probability that an individual lives beyond age t is called the *survivorship function* and is denoted by $S(t)$. The Weibull model is a popular model in reliability theory and in studies of biological aging. Its survivorship function is described by two parameters, λ and β, and is given by

$$S(t) = \exp[-(\lambda t)^{\beta}]$$

Mortality data from a *Drosophila melanogaster* population in Dr. Jim Curtsinger's lab at the University of Minnesota were collected and fitted to this model separately for males and females (Pletcher, 1998). The following parameter values were obtained (t was measured in days):

Sex	λ	β
Males	0.019	3.41
Females	0.022	3.24

(a) Use a graphing calculator to sketch the survivorship function for both the female and male populations.

(b) For each population, find the value of t for which the probability of living beyond that age is 1/2.

(c) If you had a male and a female of this species, which would you expect to live longer?

14. Carbon Isotope Carbon has two stable isotopes: C^{12} and C^{13}. Organic material contains both stable isotopes but the ratio $[C^{13}]:[C^{12}]$ in organic material is smaller than that in inorganic material, reflecting the fact that light carbon (C^{12}) is preferentially taken up by plants during photosynthesis. This process is called *isotopic fractionation* and is measured as

$$\delta^{13}C = \left[\frac{([C^{13}]:[C^{12}])_{sample}}{([C^{13}]:[C^{12}])_{standard}} - 1\right]$$

The standard is taken from the isotope ratio in the carbon of belemnite shells found in the Cretaceous Pedee formation of South Carolina. Explain, on the basis of the preceding information, why the following quotation from Krauskopf and Bird (1995) makes sense:

> The low [negative] values of $\delta^{13}C$ in the hydrocarbons of petroleum are one of the important bits of evidence for ascribing the origin of petroleum to the alteration of organic material rather than to condensation of primeval gases from the Earth's interior.

15. Chemical Reaction The speed of an enzymatic reaction is frequently described by the Michaelis–Menten equation

$$v = \frac{ax}{k + x}$$

where v is the velocity of the reaction, x is the concentration of the substrate, a is the maximum reaction velocity, and k is the substrate concentration at which the velocity is half of the maximum velocity. This curve describes how the reaction velocity depends on the substrate concentration.

(a) Show that when $x = k$, the velocity of the reaction is half the maximum velocity.

(b) Show that an 81-fold change in substrate concentration is needed to change the velocity from 10% to 90% of the maximum velocity, regardless of the value of k.

16. Lake Acidification Atmospheric pollutants can cause acidification of lakes (by acid rain). This can be a serious problem for lake organisms; for instance, in fish the ability of hemoglobin to transport oxygen decreases with decreasing pH levels of the water. Experiments with the zooplankton *Daphnia magna* showed a negligible decline in survivorship at pH $= 6$, but a marked decline in survivorship at pH $= 3.5$, resulting in no survivors after just eight hours. Illustrate graphically the percentage survivorship as a function of time for pH $= 6$ and pH $= 3.5$.

---

(3) The Devonian period lasted from about 408 million years ago to about 360 million years ago.

17. Lake Chemistry The pH level of a lake controls the concentrations of harmless ammonium ions (NH_4^+) and toxic ammonia (NH_3) in the lake. For pH levels below 8, concentrations of NH_4^+ ions are little affected by changes in the pH value, but they decline over many orders of magnitude as pH levels increase beyond pH $= 8$. By contrast, NH_3 concentrations are negligible at low pH, increase over many orders of magnitude as the pH level increases, and reach a high plateau at about pH $= 10$ (after which levels of NH_3 are little affected by changes in pH levels). Illustrate the behavior of $[NH_4^+]$ and $[NH_3]$ graphically.

18. Development and Growth Egg development times of the zooplankton *Daphnia longispina* depend on temperature. It takes only about 3 days at 20°C, but almost 20 days at 5°C, for an egg to develop and hatch. When graphed on a log–log plot, egg development time (in days) as a function of temperature (in °C) is a straight line.

(a) Sketch a graph of egg development time as a function of temperature on a log-log plot.

(b) Use the data to find the function that relates egg development time and temperature for *D. longispina*.

(c) Use your answer in (b) to predict egg development time of *D. longispina* at 10°C.

(d) Suppose you measured egg development time in hours and temperature in Fahrenheit. Would you still find a straight line on a log-log plot?

19. Resource Model Organisms consume resources. The rate of resource consumption, denoted by v, depends on resource concentration, denoted by S. The *Blackman* model of resource consumption assumes a linear relationship between resource consumption rate and resource concentration: Below a threshold concentration (S_k), the consumption rate increases linearly with $S = 0$ when $v = 0$; when $S = S_k$, the consumption rate v reaches its maximum value v_{max}; for $S > S_k$, the resource consumption rate stays at the maximum value v_{max}. A function like this, with a sharp transition, cannot be described analytically by just one expression; it needs to be defined piecewise:

$$v = \begin{cases} g(S) & \text{for } 0 \le S < S_k \\ v_{max} & \text{for } S \ge S_k \end{cases}$$

Find $g(S)$, and graph the resource consumption rate v as a function of resource concentration S.

20. Light Intensity Light intensity in lakes decreases exponentially with depth. If $I(z)$ denotes the light intensity at depth z, with $z = 0$ representing the surface, then

$$I(z) = I(0)e^{-\alpha z}, \quad z \ge 0$$

where α is a positive constant called the *vertical attenuation coefficient*. This coefficient depends on the wavelength of the light

and on the amount of dissolved matter and particles in the water. In the following, we assume that the water is pure:

(a) About 65% of red light (720 nm) is absorbed in the first meter. Find α.

(b) About 5% of blue light (475 nm) is absorbed in the first meter. Find α.

(c) Explain in words why a diver would not see red hues a few meters below the surface of a lake.

21. Light Intensity Light intensity in lakes decreases with depth according to the relationship

$$I(z) = I(0)e^{-\alpha z}, \quad z \ge 0$$

where $I(z)$ denotes the light intensity at depth z, $z = 0$ represents the surface, and α is a positive constant denoting the vertical attenuation coefficient. The depth where light intensity is about 1% of the surface light intensity is important for photosynthesis in phytoplankton: Below this level, photosynthesis is insufficient to compensate for respiratory losses. The 1% level is called the *compensation level*. An often used and relatively reliable method for determining the compensation level is the *Secchi disk* method. A Secchi disk is a white disk with radius 10 cm. The disk depth is the depth at which the disk disappears from the viewer. Twice this depth approximately coincides with the compensation level.

(a) Find α for a lake with Secchi disk depth of 9 m.

(b) Find the Secchi disk depth for a lake with $\alpha = 0.473$ m^{-1}.

22. Population Growth Assume that the population size $N(t)$ at time $t \ge 0$ is given by

$$N(t) = N_0 e^{rt}$$

with $N_0 = N(0)$. The parameter r is called the *average annual growth rate*.

(a) Show that

$$r = \ln \frac{N(t+1)}{N(t)} \tag{1.11}$$

Formula (1.11) is used, for instance, by the U.S. Census Bureau to track world population growth.

(b) Suppose a population doubles in size within a single year.
(i) What is the percent increase of the population during that year?
(ii) What is the average annual growth rate in percent during that year, according to (1.11)?

(c) Suppose the average annual growth rate of a population is 1.3%. How many years will it take the population to double in size?

(d) To calculate the doubling time of a growing population with a constant average annual growth rate, we divide the percent average annual growth rate into 70. Apply this "Rule of 70" to (c) and compare your answers. Derive the "Rule of 70."

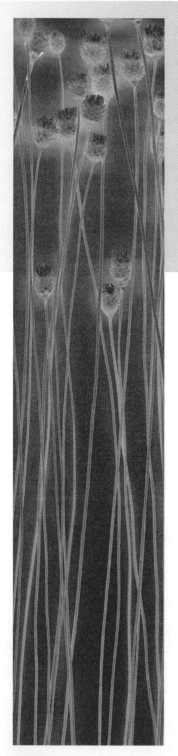

2 Discrete-Time Models, Sequences, and Difference Equations

LEARNING OBJECTIVES

In this chapter, we discuss models for populations that reproduce at discrete times and we develop some of the theory needed to analyze this type of model. The models are given by functions whose domains are subsets of the set of nonnegative integers $\mathbf{N} = \{0,1,2,\ldots\}$. These functions are used extensively in biology to describe, for instance, the population size of a plant that reproduces once a year and then dies (an annual plant). Specifically, we will learn how to

- describe discrete-time models of population growth and decay—with tables and graphs, explicitly as functions of time, and recursively from one time step to the next;
- describe sequences a_n explicitly, with formulas for the nth term and recursively;
- calculate limits and fixed points of sequences;
- describe the relationship between fixed points and limits of a sequence;
- give examples of density-dependent population growth models and describe their long-term behavior on the basis of graphs of the size of the population as a function of time.

■ 2.1 Exponential Growth and Decay

■ 2.1.1 Modeling Population Growth in Discrete Time

Imagine that we observe bacteria that divide every 20 minutes and that, at the start of the experiment, there was one bacterium. How will the number of bacteria change over time? We call the time when we started the observation time 0. At time 0, there is one bacterium. After 20 minutes, the bacterium splits in two, so there are two bacteria at time 20. Twenty minutes later, each of the bacteria splits again, resulting in four bacteria at time 40, and so on (Figure 2.1).

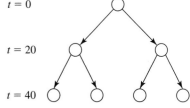

Figure 2.1 Bacteria split every 20 units of time.

We can produce a table that describes the growth of this population:

Time (min)	0	20	40	60	80	100	120
Population size	1	2	4	8	16	32	64

We can simplify the description of the growth of the bacterial population if we measure time in more convenient units. We say that one unit of time equals 20 minutes. Two units of time then corresponds to 40 minutes, three units of time to 60 minutes, and so on. We reproduce the table of population growth with these new units:

Time (20 min)	0	1	2	3	4	5	6
Population size	1	2	4	8	16	32	64

The new time units make it easier to write a general formula for the population size at time t. Denoting by $N(t)$ the population size at time t, where t is now measured in the new units (one unit is equal to 20 minutes), we guess from the second table that

$$N(t) = 2^t, \quad t = 0, 1, 2, \ldots \tag{2.1}$$

We encountered this function in Section 1.2 when we discussed exponential functions. There, the function was defined for all $t \geq 0$, whereas now, the function is defined only for nonnegative integer values. Equation (2.1) allows us to determine the population size at any discrete time t directly, without first calculating the population sizes at all previous time steps. For instance, at time $t = 5$, we find that $N(5) = 2^5 = 32$, as shown in the second table, or, at time $t = 10$, $N(10) = 2^{10} = 1024$. The graph of $N(t) = 2^t$ is shown in Figure 2.2.

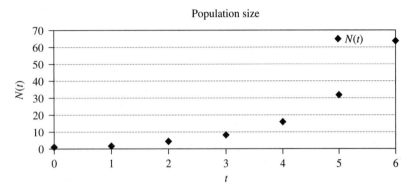

Figure 2.2 The graph of $N(t) = 2^t$ for $t = 0, 1, 2, \ldots, 6$.

The function $N(t) = 2^t$, $t = 0, 1, 2, \ldots$, is an exponential function, and we call the type of population growth that it represents **exponential growth**. The base 2 reflects the fact that the population size doubles every unit of time.

Instead of $N(t)$, we will often write N_t. The subscript notation is used only for functions $N(t)$ where t is a nonnegative integer. So, instead of writing $N(t) = 2^t$, $t = 0, 1, 2, \ldots$, we can write $N_t = 2^t$, $t = 0, 1, 2, \ldots$.

So far, we assumed that $N(0) = N_0 = 1$. Let's see what N_t looks like if $N_0 = 100$. Regardless of N_0, the population size doubles every unit of time. We obtain the following table, where time is again measured in units of 20 minutes:

Time (20 min)	0	1	2	3	4	5	6
Population size	100	200	400	800	1600	3200	6400

We can guess the general form of N_t with $N_0 = 100$ from the table:

$$N_t = 100 \cdot 2^t, \quad t = 0, 1, 2, \ldots$$

We see that the initial population size $N_0 = 100$ appears as a multiplicative factor in front of the term 2^t. If we do not want to specify a numerical value for the population size N_0 at time 0, we can write

$$N_t = N_0 2^t, \quad t = 0, 1, 2, \ldots$$

We already mentioned that the base 2 indicates that the population size doubles every unit of time. Replacing 2 by another number, we can describe other populations. For instance,

$$N_t = 3^t, \quad t = 0, 1, 2, \ldots$$

describes a population with $N_0 = 1$ and that triples in size every unit of time. The corresponding table is

Time	0	1	2	3	4
Population size	1	3	9	27	81

Now that we have some experience with exponential growth in discrete time, we give the general formula:

$$N_t = N_0 R^t, \quad t = 0, 1, 2, \ldots \tag{2.2}$$

The parameter R is a positive constant called the **growth constant**. The constant N_0 is nonnegative and denotes the population size at time 0. The assumptions $R > 0$ and $N_0 \geq 0$ are made for biological reasons: Negative values for R or N_0 would result in negative population sizes, and $R = 0$ would be uninteresting.

EXAMPLE 1

Suppose a population of cells reproduces every 15 minutes and we measure its size every 30 minutes:

Time (min)	0	30	60	90	120	150	180
Population size	1	4	16	64	256	1024	4096

Write a formula for time $n = 0, 1, 2, \ldots$ when (a) one unit of time is 30 minutes, (b) one unit of time is 60 minutes, and (c) one unit of time is 15 minutes.

Solution

(a) We see from the values listed in the table that when one unit of time is 30 minutes, the population quadruples every unit of time, with $N_0 = 1$. Thus,

$$N_t = 4^t, \quad t = 0, 1, 2, \ldots$$

(b) This time, we see from the values in the table that when one unit of time is equal to 60 minutes, the population grows by a factor of 16 each unit of time. Again, $N_0 = 1$. Hence,

$$N_s = 16^s, \quad s = 0, 1, 2, \ldots$$

We could also have arrived at this answer by noting that the time step in (b) is twice that of the time step in (a). In other words, when one unit of time elapses in (b), two units of time elapse in (a):

t	0	1	2	3	4	5	6
s	0		1		2		3

We find that $t = 2s$. If we substitute $2s$ for t in (a), we find that

$$N_t = 4^t \quad \text{yields} \quad N_s = 4^{2s} = 16^s$$

for $s = 0, 1, 2, \ldots$.

(c) When one unit of time is 15 minutes, and we use the variable $u = 0, 1, 2, \ldots$ to denote time, it follows that $t = u/2$ and

$$N_t = 4^t \quad \text{yields} \quad N_u = 4^{u/2} = 2^u$$

for $u = 0, 1, 2, \ldots$. ■

The function $N_t = N_0 R^t, t = 0, 1, 2, \ldots$, is an exponential function. We discussed exponential functions in the previous chapter. There, we looked at $f(x) = a^x$, $x \in \mathbf{R}$. To make the comparison easier, we choose $N_0 = 1$ in (2.2) and restrict the function $f(x) = a^x$ to $x \geq 0$. If we choose the same values for R and a, then the two functions N_t and $f(x)$ use the same rule to compute their values. The difference is in the domain: N_t is defined only for nonnegative integers, whereas $f(x)$ is defined for all nonnegative real numbers. The two functions agree where they are both defined. This can be seen when we graph N_t and $f(x)$ in the same coordinate system for $R = a$ (Figure 2.3).

In Chapter 1, we learned how $f(x) = a^x, x \in \mathbf{R}$, behaves for different values of a. We can use this behavior now to describe that of $N_t = N_0 R^t, t = 0, 1, 2, \ldots$. In Figure 2.4, we show the function $f(x) = a^x, x \geq 0$, for different values of a. Superimposed are the graphs of $N_t = N_0 R^t, t = 0, 1, 2, \ldots$, for $R = a$ and $N_0 = 1$.

We see that when $R > 1$, the population size N_t increases indefinitely; when $R = 1$, the population size N_t stays the same for all $t = 0, 1, 2, \ldots$; and when $0 < R < 1$, the population size N_t declines and approaches 0 as t increases. The behavior is the same for other positive initial population sizes ($N_0 > 0$).

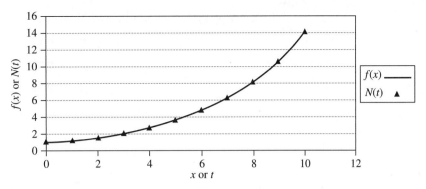

Figure 2.3 The graphs of $f(x) = a^x$, $0 \le x \le 10$, and $N(t) = R^t$, $t = 0, 1, 2, \ldots, 10$, when $a = R = 1.3$.

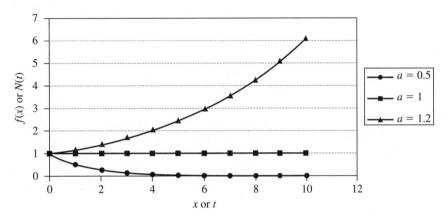

Figure 2.4 The graphs of $f(x) = a^x$, $0 \le x \le 10$, and $N(t) = R^t$, $t = 0, 1, 2, \ldots, 10$, for three different values of $a = R$: $a = R = 0.5$, $a = R = 1$, and $a = R = 1.2$.

■ 2.1.2 Recursions

When we constructed the tables for the bacterial population size with $R = 2$ at consecutive time steps, we doubled the population size from time step to time step. In other words, we computed the population size at time $t + 1$ on the basis of the population size at time t, using the equation

$$N_{t+1} = 2N_t \tag{2.3}$$

Equation (2.3) is a rule that is applied repeatedly to go from one time step to the next and is called a **recursion**. We say that Equation (2.3) defines the population size **recursively**.

If we want to use Equation (2.3) to find the population size, say, at time $t = 4$, we need to know the population size at some earlier time, say, time $t = 0$. Let's assume that $N_0 = 1$. Then, applying the recursion (2.3) repeatedly, we find that

$$N_1 = 2N_0 = 2$$
$$N_2 = 2N_1 = 4$$
$$N_3 = 2N_2 = 8$$
$$N_4 = 2N_3 = 16$$

We thus have two equivalent ways to describe this population: For $t = 0, 1, 2, \ldots$,

$$N_t = 2^t \quad \text{is equivalent to} \quad N_{t+1} = 2N_t \quad \text{with } N_0 = 1$$

The recursion for a general value of R is

$$N_{t+1} = RN_t \quad \text{with } N_0 = \text{population size at time 0} \tag{2.4}$$

Applying (2.4) repeatedly, we obtain

$$N_1 = RN_0$$
$$N_2 = RN_1 = R^2 N_0$$
$$N_3 = RN_2 = R^3 N_0$$
$$N_4 = RN_3 = R^4 N_0$$
$$\vdots$$
$$N_t = RN_{t-1} = R^t N_0$$

The two descriptions for $t = 0, 1, 2, \ldots$, namely,

$$N_t = N_0 R^t \qquad \text{and} \qquad N_{t+1} = RN_t \quad \text{with } N_0 = \text{population size at time 0}$$

are equivalent. We say that $N_t = N_0 R^t$ is a **solution** of the recursion $N_{t+1} = RN_t$ with initial condition N_0 at time 0, since the function $N_t = N_0 R^t$ satisfies the recursion with initial condition $N(0) = N_0$.

We can visualize recursions by plotting N_t on the horizontal axis and N_{t+1} on the vertical axis. The exponential growth recursion

$$N_{t+1} = RN_t \tag{2.5}$$

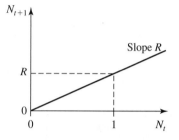

Figure 2.5 The exponential growth recursion $N_{t+1} = RN_t$ when $R > 0$.

is then a straight line through the origin with slope R (Figure 2.5). Since $N_t \geq 0$ for biological reasons, we restrict the graph to the first quadrant.

What does this graph tell us? For any current population size N_t, it allows us to find the population size in the next time step, namely, N_{t+1}. For instance, if $R = 2$ and $N_0 = 1$, then successive population sizes are 1, 2, 4, 8, 16, 32, ... For this choice of N_0, we will never see a population size of, say, 5 or 10. Thus, for a specific choice of N_0, only a selected number of points on the graph $N_{t+1} = RN_t$ will be realized (Figure 2.6). A different choice of initial condition would yield a different set of points.

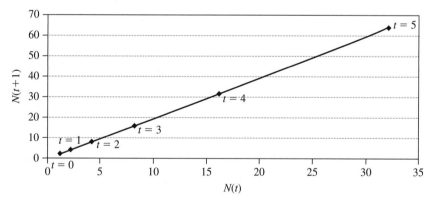

Figure 2.6 Successive population sizes on the graph of the exponential growth recursion when $R = 2$ for $t = 0, 1, 2, \ldots, 5$.

We also see from Figure 2.6 that unless we label the points according to the corresponding t-value, we would not be able to tell at what time a point (N_t, N_{t+1}) was realized. We say that time is *implicit* in this graph. Compare Figure 2.6 with Figure 2.2, in which we graphed N_t as a function of t for the same values of R and N_0; in Figure 2.2, time is *explicit*.

The hallmark of exponential growth is that the ratio of successive population sizes, N_t / N_{t+1}, is constant. When $N_t > 0$ (and hence $N_{t+1} > 0$), it follows from $N_{t+1} = RN_t$ that

$$\frac{N_t}{N_{t+1}} = \frac{1}{R}$$

If the population consists of annual plants, we can interpret the ratio N_t / N_{t+1} as the parent–offspring ratio. If this ratio is constant, parents produce the same number of

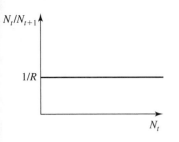

Figure 2.7 The graph of the parent–offspring ratio $\frac{N_t}{N_{t+1}}$ as a function of N_t when $N_t > 0$.

offspring, regardless of the current population density. Such growth is called **density independent**.

When $R > 1$, it follows that $1/R$, the parent–offspring ratio, is less than 1, implying that the number of offspring exceeds the number of parents. Density-independent growth with $R > 1$ results in an ever-increasing population size. This model eventually becomes biologically unrealistic, since any population will sooner or later experience food or habitat limitations that will limit its growth. (We will discuss models that include such limitations in Section 2.3.)

The density independence in exponential growth is reflected in a graph of N_t/N_{t+1} as a function of N_t, which is a horizontal line at level $1/R$ (Figure 2.7).

As before, only a selected number of points are realized on the graph of N_t/N_{t+1} as a function of N_t, and time is implicit in the graph. (See Figure 2.8, with $R = 2$ and $N_0 = 1$.)

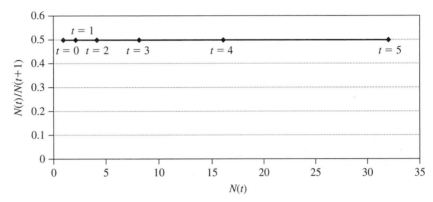

Figure 2.8 The graph of the parent–offspring ratio $\frac{N_t}{N_{t+1}}$ as a function of N_t when $N_t = 1$ and $R = 2$.

Section 2.1 Problems

In Problems 1–4, produce a table for $t = 0, 1, 2, \ldots, 5$ and graph the function N_t.

1. $N_t = 3^t$

2. $N_t = 10 \cdot 2^t$

3. $N_t = \dfrac{25}{4^t}$

4. $N_t = (0.3)(0.9)^t$

In Problems 5–10, give a formula for $N(t)$, $t = 0, 1, 2, \ldots$, on the basis of the information provided.

5. $N_0 = 2$; population doubles every 20 minutes; one unit of time is 20 minutes

6. $N_0 = 4$; population doubles every 40 minutes; one unit of time is 40 minutes

7. $N_0 = 1$; population doubles every 40 minutes; one unit of time is 80 minutes

8. $N_0 = 6$; population doubles every 40 minutes; one unit of time is 60 minutes

9. $N_0 = 2$; population quadruples every 30 minutes; one unit of time is 15 minutes

10. $N_0 = 10$; population quadruples every 20 minutes; one unit of time is 10 minutes

11. Suppose $N_t = 20 \cdot 4^t$, $t = 0, 1, 2, \ldots$, and one unit of time corresponds to 3 hours. Determine the amount of time it takes the population to double in size.

12. Suppose $N_t = 100 \cdot 2^t$, $t = 0, 1, 2, \ldots$, and one unit of time corresponds to 2 hours. Determine the amount of time it takes the population to triple in size.

13. A strain of bacteria reproduces asexually every hour. That is, every hour, each bacterial cell splits into two cells. If, initially, there is one bacterium, find the number of bacterial cells after 1 hour, 2 hours, 3 hours, 4 hours, and 5 hours.

14. A strain of bacteria reproduces asexually every 30 minutes. That is, every 30 minutes, each bacterial cell splits into two cells. If, initially, there is one bacterium, find the number of bacterial cells after 1 hour, 2 hours, 3 hours, 4 hours, and 5 hours.

15. A strain of bacteria reproduces asexually every 23 minutes. That is, every 23 minutes, each bacterial cell splits into two cells. If, initially, there is 1 bacterium, how long will it take until there are 128 bacteria?

16. A strain of bacteria reproduces asexually every 42 minutes. That is, every 42 minutes, each bacterial cell splits into two cells. If, initially, there is 1 bacterium, how long will it take until there are 512 bacteria?

17. A strain of bacteria reproduces asexually every 10 minutes. That is, every 10 minutes, each bacterial cell splits into two cells. If, initially, there are 3 bacteria, how long will it take until there are 96 bacteria?

18. A strain of bacteria reproduces asexually every 50 minutes. That is, every 50 minutes, each bacterial cell splits into two cells. If, initially, there are 10 bacteria, how long will it take until there are 640 bacteria?

19. Find the exponential growth equation for a population that doubles in size every unit of time and that has 40 individuals at time 0.

20. Find the exponential growth equation for a population that doubles in size every unit of time and that has 53 individuals at time 0.

21. Find the exponential growth equation for a population that triples in size every unit of time and that has 20 individuals at time 0.

22. Find the exponential growth equation for a population that triples in size every unit of time and that has 72 individuals at time 0.

23. Find the exponential growth equation for a population that quadruples in size every unit of time and that has five individuals at time 0.

24. Find the exponential growth equation for a population that quadruples in size every unit of time and that has 17 individuals at time 0.

25. Find the recursion for a population that doubles in size every unit of time and that has 20 individuals at time 0.

26. Find the recursion for a population that doubles in size every unit of time and that has 37 individuals at time 0.

27. Find the recursion for a population that triples in size every unit of time and that has 10 individuals at time 0.

28. Find the recursion for a population that triples in size every unit of time and that has 84 individuals at time 0.

29. Find the recursion for a population that quadruples in size every unit of time and that has 30 individuals at time 0.

30. Find the recursion for a population that quadruples in size every unit of time and that has 62 individuals at time 0.

In Problems 31–34, graph the functions $f(x) = a^x$, $x \in [0, \infty)$, and $N_t = R^t$, $t \in \mathbf{N}$, together in one coordinate system for the indicated values of a and R.

31. $a = R = 2$ **32.** $a = R = 3$

33. $a = R = 1/2$ **34.** $a = R = 1/3$

In Problems 35–46, find the population sizes for $t = 0, 1, 2, \ldots, 5$ for each recursion.

35. $N_{t+1} = 2N_t$ with $N_0 = 3$ **36.** $N_{t+1} = 2N_t$ with $N_0 = 5$

37. $N_{t+1} = 3N_t$ with $N_0 = 2$ **38.** $N_{t+1} = 3N_t$ with $N_0 = 7$

39. $N_{t+1} = 5N_t$ with $N_0 = 1$ **40.** $N_{t+1} = 7N_t$ with $N_0 = 4$

41. $N_{t+1} = \frac{1}{2}N_t$ with $N_0 = 1024$

42. $N_{t+1} = \frac{1}{2}N_t$ with $N_0 = 4096$

43. $N_{t+1} = \frac{1}{3}N_t$ with $N_0 = 729$

44. $N_{t+1} = \frac{1}{3}N_t$ with $N_0 = 3645$

45. $N_{t+1} = \frac{1}{5}N_t$ with $N_0 = 31250$

46. $N_{t+1} = \frac{1}{4}N_t$ with $N_0 = 8192$

In Problems 47–58, write N_t as a function of t for each recursion.

47. $N_{t+1} = 2N_t$ with $N_0 = 15$ **48.** $N_{t+1} = 2N_t$ with $N_0 = 7$

49. $N_{t+1} = 3N_t$ with $N_0 = 12$ **50.** $N_{t+1} = 3N_t$ with $N_0 = 3$

51. $N_{t+1} = 4N_t$ with $N_0 = 24$ **52.** $N_{t+1} = 5N_t$ with $N_0 = 17$

53. $N_{t+1} = \frac{1}{2}N_t$ with $N_0 = 5000$

54. $N_{t+1} = \frac{1}{2}N_t$ with $N_0 = 2300$

55. $N_{t+1} = \frac{1}{3}N_t$ with $N_0 = 8000$

56. $N_{t+1} = \frac{1}{3}N_t$ with $N_0 = 3500$

57. $N_{t+1} = \frac{1}{5}N_t$ with $N_0 = 1200$

58. $N_{t+1} = \frac{1}{7}N_t$ with $N_0 = 6400$

In Problems 59–66, graph the line $N_{t+1} = RN_t$ in the N_t–N_{t+1} plane for the indicated value of R and locate the points (N_t, N_{t+1}), $t = 0$, 1, and 2, for the given value of N_0.

59. $R = 2, N_0 = 2$ **60.** $R = 2, N_0 = 3$

61. $R = 3, N_0 = 1$ **62.** $R = 4, N_0 = 2$

63. $R = \frac{1}{2}, N_0 = 16$ **64.** $R = \frac{1}{2}, N_0 = 64$

65. $R = \frac{1}{3}, N_0 = 81$ **66.** $R = \frac{1}{4}, N_0 = 16$

In Problems 67–74, graph the line $\frac{N_t}{N_{t+1}} = \frac{1}{R}$ in the N_t–$\frac{N_t}{N_{t+1}}$ plane for the indicated value of R and locate the points $(N_t, \frac{N_t}{N_{t+1}})$, $t = 0$, 1, 2, for the given value of N_0. Find the parent–offspring ratio.

67. $R = 2, N_0 = 2$ **68.** $R = 2, N_0 = 4$

69. $R = 3, N_0 = 2$ **70.** $R = 4, N_0 = 1$

71. $R = \frac{1}{2}, N_0 = 16$ **72.** $R = \frac{1}{2}, N_0 = 128$

73. $R = \frac{1}{3}, N_0 = 27$ **74.** $R = \frac{1}{4}, N_0 = 64$

75. A bird population lives in a habitat where the number of nesting sites is a limiting factor in population growth. In which of the following cases would you expect that the growth of this bird population over the next few generations could be reasonably well approximated by exponential growth?
(a) All nesting sites are occupied.
(b) The bird population just invaded the habitat, and the population size is still much smaller than the available nesting sites.
(c) In the previous year, a hurricane killed more than 90% of the birds in this habitat.

76. Pollen records show that the number of Scotch pine (*Pinus sylvestris*) grew exponentially for about 500 years after colonization of the Norfolk region of Great Britain about 9500 years ago. Can you find a possible explanation for this growth?

77. Exponential growth generally occurs when population growth is density independent. List conditions under which a population might stop growing exponentially.

■ 2.2 Sequences

■ 2.2.1 What Are Sequences?

Before we explore other discrete-time population models, we need to develop further the theory of functions with domain **N**. The functions are of the form

$$f : \mathbf{N} \to \mathbf{R}$$
$$n \to f(n)$$

When the independent variable denotes time, we will frequently use t instead of n. Tables and graphs are useful tools to illustrate these functions.

EXAMPLE 1

Let

$$f : \mathbf{N} \to \mathbf{R}$$
$$n \to f(n) = \frac{1}{n+1}$$

Produce a table for $n = 0, 1, 2 \ldots, 5$ and graph the function.

Solution

The table is

n	0	1	2	3	4	5
$\frac{1}{n+1}$	1	$\frac{1}{2}$	$\frac{1}{3}$	$\frac{1}{4}$	$\frac{1}{5}$	$\frac{1}{6}$

The graph of this function consists of discrete points (Figure 2.9). On the horizontal axis, we display the variable n; on the vertical axis, the function $f(n)$. Note that we did not connect the points with lines or curves. ■

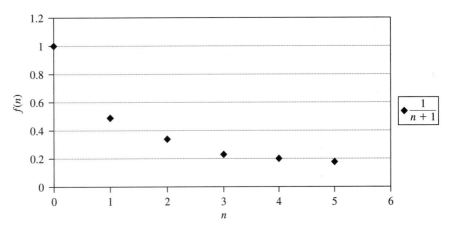

Figure 2.9 The graph of the function $f(n) = \frac{1}{n+1}$ in Example 1.

We can write the function

$$f : \mathbf{N} \to \mathbf{R}$$
$$n \to f(n)$$

as a list of numbers $a_0, a_1, a_2, \ldots$, where $a_n = f(n)$. We refer to this list as a **sequence**. We will write $\{a_n : n \in \mathbf{N}\}$ (or $\{a_n\}$ for short) if we mean the entire sequence. Note that we list the values of the sequence $\{a_n\}$ in order of increasing n:

$$a_0, a_1, a_2, \ldots$$

EXAMPLE 2

The sequence

$$a_n = (-1)^n, \quad n = 0, 1, 2, \ldots$$

takes on values

$$1, -1, 1, -1, 1, \ldots$$ ■

When we see a sequence and recognize a pattern, we can often write an expression for a_n.

EXAMPLE 3   Find a_n for the sequence
$$0, 1, 4, 9, 16, 25, \ldots$$

Solution   Looking at the sequence, we can guess the next terms, namely, 36, 49, 64, and so on. We thus find that
$$a_n = n^2, \quad n = 0, 1, 2, \ldots$$

We do not need to start a sequence at $n = 0$. If we started the sequence at $n = 1$, we would write
$$a_n = (n - 1)^2, \quad n = 1, 2, 3, \ldots$$

In either case, it is important to include the domain of the sequence.   ■

EXAMPLE 4   Find a_n for the sequence
$$1, -\frac{1}{4}, \frac{1}{9}, -\frac{1}{16}, \frac{1}{25}, \ldots$$

Solution   This sequence has alternating signs: The first term is positive, the second negative, the third positive, and so on. This indicates that we need a factor $(-1)^n, n = 0, 1, 2, \ldots$. The numerators are all equal to 1, and the denominators are successive squares of integers, starting with the integer 1. We can thus write

$$a_0 = (-1)^0 \frac{1}{(1)^2} = 1$$

$$a_1 = (-1)^1 \frac{1}{(2)^2} = -\frac{1}{4}$$

$$a_2 = (-1)^2 \frac{1}{(3)^2} = \frac{1}{9}$$

and so on. This set of equations suggests that

$$a_n = (-1)^n \frac{1}{(n+1)^2}, \quad n = 0, 1, 2, \ldots$$

If we wanted to start the sequence at $n = 1$, we could write

$$a_n = (-1)^{n-1} \frac{1}{n^2}, \quad n = 1, 2, 3, \ldots$$

or

$$a_n = (-1)^{n+1} \frac{1}{n^2}, \quad n = 1, 2, 3, \ldots$$

Look carefully at the exponent of (-1). Any of the terms $(-1)^n, (-1)^{n-1}$, and $(-1)^{n+1}$ produces alternating signs. Since the first term in the sequence $\{a_n\}$ is positive, we need to use $(-1)^n$ if we start with $n = 0$, and either $(-1)^{n-1}$ or $(-1)^{n+1}$ if we start with $n = 1$.   ■

The exponential growth model we considered in the previous section is an example of a sequence. We gave two descriptions, one explicit and the other recursive. These two descriptions can be used for sequences in general. An explicit description is of the form
$$a_n = f(n), \quad n = 0, 1, 2, \ldots$$
where $f(n)$ is a function of n.

A recursive description is of the form

$$a_{n+1} = g(a_n), \quad n = 0, 1, 2, \ldots$$

where $g(a_n)$ is a function of a_n. If, as is shown here, the value of a_{n+1} depends only on the value one time step back, namely, a_n, then the recursion is called a **first-order recursion**. Later in the chapter, we will see an example of a second-order recursion, in which the value of a_{n+1} depends on the values a_n and a_{n-1}—that is, on the values one and two time steps back. To determine the values of successive members of a sequence given in recursive form, we need to specify an initial value a_0 if we start the sequence at $n = 0$ (or a_1 if we start the sequence at $n = 1$).

In the notation of this section, the exponential growth of the previous section is given explicitly by

$$a_n = a_0 R^n, \quad n = 0, 1, 2, \ldots$$

and recursively by

$$a_{n+1} = R a_n, \quad n = 0, 1, 2, \ldots$$

Note that, in the recursive definition, the initial value a_0 needs to be specified.

■ 2.2.2 Limits

When studying populations over time, we are often interested in their **long-term behavior**. Specifically, if N_t is the population size at time t, $t = 0, 1, 2, \ldots$, we want to know how N_t behaves as t increases, or, more precisely, as t tends to infinity. Using the notation of this section, we want to know the behavior of a_n as n tends to infinity. When we let n tend to infinity, we say that "we take the limit of the sequence a_n as n goes to infinity" and use the shorthand notation

$$\lim_{n \to \infty} a_n \quad \text{or} \quad \lim_{n \to \infty} a_n$$

read as "the limit of a_n as n tends to infinity," in equations. Let's first discuss limits informally to get an idea of what can happen.

EXAMPLE 5

Let

$$a_n = \frac{1}{n+1}, \quad n = 0, 1, 2, \ldots$$

Find $\lim_{n \to \infty} a_n$.

Solution

Plugging successive values of n into a_n, we find that a_n is the sequence

$$1, \frac{1}{2}, \frac{1}{3}, \frac{1}{4}, \frac{1}{5}, \ldots$$

and we guess that the terms will approach 0 as n tends to infinity. This is indeed the case, and we will learn shortly how to show that

$$\lim_{n \to \infty} \frac{1}{n+1} = 0$$

Since the limiting value is a unique number, we say that the limit exists. ■

Note that plugging in successive values of n into a_n is only a heuristic way of determining how a_n behaves as $n \to \infty$.

EXAMPLE 6

Let

$$a_n = (-1)^n, \quad n = 0, 1, 2, \ldots$$

Find $\lim_{n \to \infty} a_n$.

Solution

The sequence is of the form

$$1, -1, 1, -1, 1, \ldots$$

and we see that its terms alternate between 1 and -1. There is thus no single number we could assign as the limit of a_n as $n \to \infty$. We then say that the limit does not exist.

■

EXAMPLE 7

Let

$$a_n = 2^n, \quad n = 0, 1, 2, \ldots$$

Find $\lim_{n \to \infty} a_n$.

Solution   Successive terms of a_n, namely,

$$1, 2, 4, 8, 16, 32, \ldots$$

indicate that the terms continue to grow. Hence, a_n goes to infinity as $n \to \infty$, and we can write $\lim_{n\to\infty} a_n = \infty$. Since infinity ($\infty$) is not a real number, we say that the limit does not exist.   ■

Let's look at one more example of a limit that exists before we give a formal definition.

EXAMPLE 8   Find

$$\lim_{n\to\infty} \frac{n+1}{n}$$

Solution   Starting with $n = 1$ and computing successive terms, we find that

$$2, \frac{3}{2}, \frac{4}{3}, \frac{5}{4}, \frac{6}{5}, \ldots$$

We see that the terms get closer and closer to 1, and, indeed,

$$\lim_{n\to\infty} \frac{n+1}{n} = 1$$

■

The way we solved the first four examples is unsatisfying: We guessed the limiting values. How do we know that our guesses are correct? There is a formal definition of limits that can be used to compute them. However, except in the simplest cases, the formal definition is quite cumbersome to use. Fortunately, there are mathematical laws that build on simple limits (which can be computed from the formal definition). We will first discuss the formal definition (as an optional topic) and then introduce the limit laws.

Formal Definition of Limits (Optional)   Example 8 will motivate the formal definition of limits. When we guessed the limit in Example 8, we realized that successive terms approached 1. This means that no matter how small an interval about 1 we choose, all points must lie in this interval for all sufficiently large values of n. Graphically, the points of the graph of a_n must lie between the two dashed lines in Figure 2.10 for all large enough values of n, no matter how close those lines are to the horizontal line at height 1.

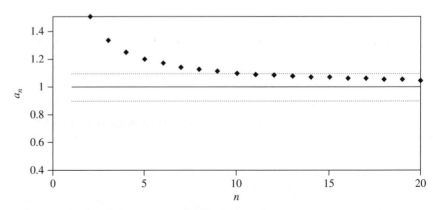

Figure 2.10 Convergence of the sequence $a_n = \frac{n+1}{n}$ to $a = 1$.

Translating this condition into a formal statement for the general case, we arrive at the following definition:

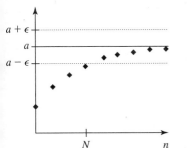

Figure 2.11 An illustration of the formal definition of limits to show convergence of the sequence a_n to a as $n \to \infty$: For all $n > N$, a_n lies in the strip of width 2ϵ and centered at a.

> **Formal Definition of Limits** The sequence $\{a_n\}$ has **limit** a, written as $\lim_{n\to\infty} a_n = a$, if, for every $\epsilon > 0$, there exists an integer N such that
>
> $$|a_n - a| < \epsilon \qquad \text{whenever } n > N$$
>
> If the limit exists, the sequence is called **convergent** and we say that a_n **converges** to a as n tends to infinity. If the sequence has no limit, it is called **divergent**.

The value of N will typically depend on ϵ: The smaller ϵ is, the larger N is. We illustrate the concept of a converging sequence in Figure 2.11. The horizontal dashed lines are at heights $a + \epsilon$ and $a - \epsilon$, respectively. They form a strip of width 2ϵ centered at the horizontal line at height a. Points a_n within this strip satisfy the inequality $|a_n - a| < \epsilon$. For a sequence to be convergent, we require that *all* points a_n lie in this strip for *all* n sufficiently large (namely, larger than some N).

EXAMPLE 9

Show that

$$\lim_{n\to\infty} \frac{1}{n} = 0$$

Solution

Before we show this for any arbitrary ϵ, let's try to find N for a particular choice of ϵ, say, $\epsilon = 0.03$. We need to find an integer N such that

$$\left| \frac{1}{n} - 0 \right| < 0.03 \quad \text{whenever } n > N$$

Solving the inequality $|\frac{1}{n} - 0| < 0.03$ for n positive, we find that

$$\left| \frac{1}{n} \right| < 0.03, \qquad \text{or} \qquad n > \frac{1}{0.03} \approx 33.33$$

The smallest value for N that we can choose is $N = 33$, which is the largest integer less than or equal to $1/0.03$. Successive values for $n > 33$ give us confidence that we are on the right track but don't prove that our choice is correct:

$$a_{34} = \frac{1}{34} \approx 0.0294, \quad a_{35} = \frac{1}{35} \approx 0.0286, \quad \text{and so on}$$

To see that our choice for N works, we need to show that $n > 33$ implies $|1/n| < 0.03$. Now, since n takes on only integer values, $n > 33$ is equivalent to $n \geq 34$, which implies that $1/n \leq 1/34 \approx 0.0294$. Since $n > 0$, we have

$$\left| \frac{1}{n} - 0 \right| < 0.03 \quad \text{whenever } n > 33$$

To show that $a_n = \frac{1}{n}$ converges to 0, we need to do the same calculation for any arbitrary ϵ. That is, we need to show that, for every $\epsilon > 0$, we can find an N such that

$$\left| \frac{1}{n} - 0 \right| < \epsilon \quad \text{whenever } n > N$$

To find a candidate for N, we solve the inequality $|\frac{1}{n}| < \epsilon$. Since $\frac{1}{n} > 0$, we can drop the absolute-value signs and find

$$\frac{1}{n} < \epsilon, \qquad \text{or} \quad n > \frac{1}{\epsilon}$$

Let's choose N so that $1/N \geq \epsilon$ and $1/(N+1) < \epsilon$, or, equivalently, $N \leq 1/\epsilon$ and $N+1 > 1/\epsilon$. This means that we choose N to be the largest integer less than or equal to $1/\epsilon$. If $n > N$, then $n \geq N+1$, which is equivalent to $1/n \leq 1/(N+1)$. Since N is the largest integer less than or equal to $1/\epsilon$, it follows that $1/n \leq 1/(N+1) < \epsilon \leq 1/N$ for $n > N$. This condition, together with $n > 0$, shows that if N is the largest integer less than or equal to $1/\epsilon$, then

$$\left| \frac{1}{n} - 0 \right| < \epsilon \quad \text{whenever } n > N$$

■

Limit Laws The formal definition of limits is cumbersome when we want to compute limits in specific examples. Fortunately, there are mathematical laws that facilitate the computation of limits:

Limit Laws If $\lim_{n \to \infty} a_n$ and $\lim_{n \to \infty} b_n$ exist and c is a constant, then

$$\lim_{n \to \infty} (a_n + b_n) = \lim_{n \to \infty} a_n + \lim_{n \to \infty} b_n$$

$$\lim_{n \to \infty} (c a_n) = c \lim_{n \to \infty} a_n$$

$$\lim_{n \to \infty} (a_n b_n) = \left(\lim_{n \to \infty} a_n \right)\left(\lim_{n \to \infty} b_n \right)$$

$$\lim_{n \to \infty} \frac{a_n}{b_n} = \frac{\lim_{n \to \infty} a_n}{\lim_{n \to \infty} b_n}, \quad \text{provided } \lim_{n \to \infty} b_n \neq 0$$

Although we do not need to know the formal definition of limits in order to use the limit laws, in the next two examples we will need to know that

$$\lim_{n \to \infty} \frac{1}{n} = 0 \tag{2.6}$$

which was proved (using the formal definition of limits) in Example 9.

EXAMPLE 10 Find

$$\lim_{n \to \infty} \frac{n+1}{n}$$

Solution We break $\frac{n+1}{n}$ into a sum of two terms, namely, $1 + \frac{1}{n}$. Since $\lim_{n \to \infty} 1$ and $\lim_{n \to \infty} \frac{1}{n}$ exist [the former is equal to 1 and the latter to 0, according to (2.6)], it follows that

$$\lim_{n \to \infty} \frac{n+1}{n} = \lim_{n \to \infty} \left(1 + \frac{1}{n}\right) = \lim_{n \to \infty} (1) + \lim_{n \to \infty} \frac{1}{n} = 1 + 0 = 1$$

as claimed in Example 8.

■

EXAMPLE 11 Find

$$\lim_{n \to \infty} \frac{4n^2 - 1}{n^2}$$

Solution We rewrite a_n:

$$a_n = \frac{4n^2 - 1}{n^2} = 4 - \frac{1}{n^2} = 4 - \frac{1}{n} \cdot \frac{1}{n}$$

Since $\lim_{n \to \infty} 4$ and $\lim_{n \to \infty} \frac{1}{n}$ exist, we have

$$\lim_{n \to \infty} \frac{4n^2 - 1}{n^2} = \lim_{n \to \infty} \left(4 - \frac{1}{n} \cdot \frac{1}{n}\right) = \lim_{n \to \infty} 4 - \left(\lim_{n \to \infty} \frac{1}{n}\right)\left(\lim_{n \to \infty} \frac{1}{n}\right)$$

$$= 4 - 0 \cdot 0 = 4$$

■

EXAMPLE 12

Without proof, we will state the long-term behavior of exponential growth. For $R > 0$, exponential growth is given by

$$a_n = a_0 R^n, n = 0, 1, 2, \ldots$$

Figure 2.12 indicates that

$$\lim_{n \to \infty} a_n = \begin{cases} 0 & \text{if } 0 < R < 1 \\ a_0 & \text{if } R = 1 \\ \infty & \text{if } R > 1 \end{cases}$$

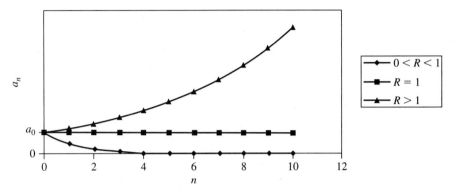

Figure 2.12 Exponential growth in Example 12 for three different values of R.

This conclusion can also be shown rigorously by using the formal definition of limits. ■

■ 2.2.3 Recursions

In the previous subsection, we learned how to find $\lim_{n \to \infty} a_n$ when a_n is given explicitly as a function of n. We will now discuss how to find such a limit when a_n is defined recursively.

When we define a first-order sequence $\{a_n\}$ recursively, we express a_{n+1} in terms of a_n and specify a value for a_0. We can then compute successive values of a_n, which might allow us to guess the limit if it exists. In some cases (as in the next example), we can find a solution of the recursion and then determine the limit (if it exists), as in Subsection 2.2.2.

EXAMPLE 13

Compute a_n for $n = 1, 2, \ldots, 5$ when

$$a_{n+1} = \frac{1}{4}a_n + \frac{3}{4} \quad \text{with } a_0 = 2 \tag{2.7}$$

Find a solution of the recursion, and then take a guess at the limiting behavior of the sequence.

Solution

By repeatedly applying the recursion, we find that

$$a_1 = \frac{1}{4}a_0 + \frac{3}{4} = \frac{1}{4} \cdot 2 + \frac{3}{4} = \frac{5}{4} = 1.25$$

$$a_2 = \frac{1}{4}a_1 + \frac{3}{4} = \frac{1}{4} \cdot \frac{5}{4} + \frac{3}{4} = \frac{17}{16} = 1.0625$$

$$a_3 = \frac{1}{4}a_2 + \frac{3}{4} = \frac{1}{4} \cdot \frac{17}{16} + \frac{3}{4} = \frac{65}{64} \approx 1.0156$$

$$a_4 = \frac{1}{4}a_3 + \frac{3}{4} = \frac{1}{4} \cdot \frac{65}{64} + \frac{3}{4} = \frac{257}{256} \approx 1.0039$$

$$a_5 = \frac{1}{4}a_4 + \frac{3}{4} = \frac{1}{4} \cdot \frac{257}{256} + \frac{3}{4} = \frac{1025}{1024} \approx 1.0010$$

There seems to be a pattern, namely, that the denominators are powers of 4 and the numerators are just 1 larger than the denominators. We therefore set

$$a_n = \frac{4^n + 1}{4^n} \tag{2.8}$$

and check whether this is indeed a solution of the recursion. First, we need to check the initial condition: $a_0 = \frac{4^0 + 1}{4^0} = \frac{2}{1} = 2$. This agrees with the given initial condition. Next, we need to check whether a_n satisfies the recursion. Accordingly, we write

$$a_{n+1} = \frac{4^{n+1} + 1}{4^{n+1}} = 1 + \frac{1}{4 \cdot 4^n} = 1 + \frac{1}{4}\frac{1}{4^n}$$

Now, $a_n = \frac{4^n + 1}{4^n}$ implies that $a_n = 1 + \frac{1}{4^n}$, or $\frac{1}{4^n} = a_n - 1$. Using the latter equation and simplifying then yields

$$a_{n+1} = 1 + \frac{1}{4}\frac{1}{4^n} = 1 + \frac{1}{4}(a_n - 1) = \frac{1}{4}a_n + \frac{3}{4}$$

which is the given recursion and thus proves that (2.8) is a solution of (2.7). We can now use (2.8) to find the limit. We have

$$\lim_{n \to \infty} a_n = \lim_{n \to \infty} \frac{4^n + 1}{4^n} = \lim_{n \to \infty} \left(1 + \frac{1}{4^n}\right) = 1$$

since $\lim_{n \to \infty} \frac{1}{4^n} = \lim_{n \to \infty} \left(\frac{1}{4}\right)^n = 0$, according to Example 12. ■

Finding an explicit expression for a_n as in Example 13 is often not a feasible strategy, because solving recursions can be very difficult or even impossible. How, then, can we say anything about the limiting behavior of a recursively defined sequence?

The following procedure will allow us to identify *candidates* for limits: A **fixed point** is a point such that if a_0 is equal to the fixed point, then all successive values of a_n are also equal to the fixed point. In mathematical terms, if we call the fixed point a, then if $a_0 = a$, we have $a_1 = a$, $a_2 = a$, and so on.

Now, if $a_{n+1} = g(a_n)$, then if $a_0 = a$ and a is a fixed point, it follows that $a_1 = g(a_0) = g(a) = a$, $a_2 = g(a_1) = g(a) = a$, and so on. That is, a fixed point satisfies the equation

$$a = g(a) \tag{2.9}$$

We will use (2.9) to find fixed points.

In Example 13, we had the recursion $a_{n+1} = \frac{1}{4}a_n + \frac{3}{4}$. Fixed points for the recursion thus satisfy

$$a = \frac{1}{4}a + \frac{3}{4}$$

Solving this equation for a, we find that $a = 1$. It turns out that in Example 13 the fixed point is also the limiting point. This will not always be the case: A fixed point is only a *candidate* for a limit; a sequence does not have to converge to a given fixed point (unless a_0 is already equal to the fixed point). The next two examples illustrate convergence and nonconvergence, respectively.

EXAMPLE 14

Assume that $\lim_{n \to \infty} a_n$ exists for

$$a_{n+1} = \sqrt{3a_n} \quad \text{with } a_0 = 2$$

Find $\lim_{n \to \infty} a_n$.

Solution

Since the problem tells us that the limit exists, we don't have to worry about existence. The problem that remains is to identify the limit. To do this, we compute the fixed points. We solve

$$a = \sqrt{3a}$$

which has two solutions, namely, $a = 0$ and $a = 3$. When $a_0 = 2$, we have $a_n > 2$ for all $n = 1, 2, 3, \ldots$, so we can exclude $a = 0$ as the limiting value. This leaves only one possibility, and we conclude that

$$\lim_{n \to \infty} a_n = 3$$

Using a calculator, we can find successive values of a_n, which we collect in the following table (accurate to two decimals):

n	0	1	2	3	4	5	6	7
a_n	2	2.45	2.71	2.85	2.92	2.96	2.98	2.99

The tabulated values suggest that the limit is indeed 3. ■

EXAMPLE 15   Let

$$a_{n+1} = \frac{3}{a_n}$$

Find the fixed points of this recursion, and investigate the limiting behavior of a_n when a_0 is not equal to a fixed point.

Solution   To find the fixed points, we need to solve

$$a = \frac{3}{a}$$

This equation is equivalent to $a^2 = 3$; hence, $a = \sqrt{3}$ or $a = -\sqrt{3}$. These are the two fixed points. If $a_0 = \sqrt{3}$, then $a_1 = \sqrt{3}$, $a_2 = \sqrt{3}$, and so on, and likewise, if $a_0 = -\sqrt{3}$, then $a_1 = -\sqrt{3}$, $a_2 = -\sqrt{3}$, and so on.

Let's start with a value that is not equal to one of the fixed points—say, $a_0 = 2$. Using the recursion, we find that

$$a_1 = \frac{3}{a_0} = \frac{3}{2}$$

$$a_2 = \frac{3}{a_1} = \frac{3}{\frac{3}{2}} = 3 \cdot \frac{2}{3} = 2$$

$$a_3 = \frac{3}{a_2} = \frac{3}{2}$$

$$a_4 = \frac{3}{a_3} = \frac{3}{\frac{3}{2}} = 3 \cdot \frac{2}{3} = 2$$

and so on. That is, successive terms alternate between 2 and 3/2. Let's try another initial value, say, $a_0 = -3$. Then

$$a_1 = \frac{3}{a_0} = \frac{3}{-3} = -1$$

$$a_2 = \frac{3}{a_1} = \frac{3}{-1} = -3$$

$$a_3 = \frac{3}{a_2} = \frac{3}{-3} = -1$$

$$a_4 = \frac{3}{a_3} = \frac{3}{-1} = -3$$

and so on. Successive terms now alternate between -3 and -1. Alternating between two values, one of which is the initial value, happens with any initial value that is not one of the fixed points. Specifically, we have

$$a_1 = \frac{3}{a_0} \quad \text{and} \quad a_2 = \frac{3}{a_1} = \frac{3}{\frac{3}{a_0}} = a_0$$

Thus, a_3 is the same as a_1, a_4 is the same as a_2 and hence a_0, and so on. ■

The last two examples illustrate that fixed points are only *candidates* for limits and that, depending on the initial condition, the sequence $\{a_n\}$ may or may not converge to a given fixed point. If we know, however, that a sequence $\{a_n\}$ does converge, then the limit of the sequence must be one of the fixed points.

There is a graphical method for finding fixed points, which we will mention briefly here: If the recursion is of the form $a_{n+1} = g(a_n)$, then a fixed point satisfies $a = g(a)$. This suggests that if we graph $y = g(x)$ and $y = x$ in the same coordinate system, then fixed points are located where the two graphs intersect, as shown in Figure 2.13.

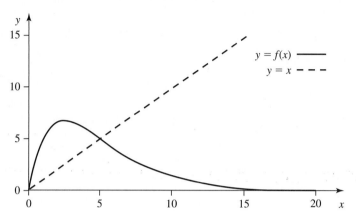

Figure 2.13 A graphical way to find fixed points. (See text for explanation.)

We will return to the relationship between fixed points and limits in Section 5.6, where we will learn methods that allow us to determine whether a sequence converges to a particular fixed point.

Section 2.2 Problems

■ **2.2.1**

In Problems 1–16, determine the values of the sequence $\{a_n\}$ for $n = 0, 1, 2, \ldots, 5$.

1. $a_n = n$

2. $a_n = 3n^2$

3. $a_n = \dfrac{1}{n+2}$

4. $f(n) = \dfrac{1}{1+n^2}$

5. $f(n) = \dfrac{1}{(1+n)^2}$

6. $a_n = \dfrac{1}{\sqrt{n+1}}$

7. $f(n) = (n+1)^2$

8. $f(n) = \sqrt{n+4}$

9. $a_n = (-1)^n n$

10. $a_n = \dfrac{(-1)^n}{(n+1)^2}$

11. $a_n = \dfrac{n^2}{n+1}$

12. $a_n = n^3\sqrt{n+1}$

13. $f(n) = e^{\sqrt{n}}$

14. $f(n) = 3e^{-0.1n}$

15. $f(n) = \left(\dfrac{1}{3}\right)^n$

16. $f(n) = 2^{0.2n}$

In Problems 17–24, find the next four values of the sequence $\{a_n\}$ on the basis of the values of $a_0, a_1, a_2, \ldots, a_5$.

17. $1, 2, 3, 4, 5$

18. $0, 1, \sqrt{2}, \sqrt{3}, \sqrt{4}$

19. $1, \dfrac{1}{4}, \dfrac{1}{9}, \dfrac{1}{16}, \dfrac{1}{25}$

20. $-1, \dfrac{1}{4}, -\dfrac{1}{9}, \dfrac{1}{16}, -\dfrac{1}{25}$

21. $\dfrac{1}{2}, \dfrac{2}{3}, \dfrac{3}{4}, \dfrac{4}{5}, \dfrac{5}{6}$

22. $\dfrac{1}{5}, \dfrac{4}{10}, \dfrac{9}{17}, \dfrac{16}{26}, \dfrac{25}{37},$

23. $\sqrt{1+e}, \sqrt{2+e^2}, \sqrt{3+e^3}, \sqrt{4+e^4}, \sqrt{5+e^5}$

24. $\sin\dfrac{\pi}{2}, -\sin\dfrac{\pi}{4}, \sin\dfrac{\pi}{6}, -\sin\dfrac{\pi}{8}, \sin\dfrac{\pi}{10}$

In Problems 25–36, find an expression for a_n on the basis of the values of $a_0, a_1, a_2, \ldots$.

25. $0, 1, 2, 3, 4, \ldots$

26. $0, 2, 4, 6, 8, \ldots$

27. $1, 2, 4, 8, 16, \ldots$

28. $1, 3, 5, 7, 9, \ldots$

29. $1, \dfrac{1}{3}, \dfrac{1}{9}, \dfrac{1}{27}, \dfrac{1}{81}, \ldots$

30. $\dfrac{1}{3}, \dfrac{2}{5}, \dfrac{3}{7}, \dfrac{4}{9}, \dfrac{5}{11}, \ldots$

31. $-1, 2, -3, 4, -5, \ldots$

32. $2, -4, 6, -8, 10, \ldots$

33. $-\dfrac{1}{2}, \dfrac{1}{3}, -\dfrac{1}{4}, \dfrac{1}{5}, -\dfrac{1}{6}, \ldots$

34. $\dfrac{1}{2}, -\dfrac{1}{8}, \dfrac{1}{18}, -\dfrac{1}{32}, \dfrac{1}{50}, \ldots$

35. $\sin(\pi), \sin(2\pi), \sin(3\pi), \sin(4\pi), \sin(5\pi), \ldots$

36. $-\cos\dfrac{\pi}{2}, \cos\dfrac{\pi}{4}, -\cos\dfrac{\pi}{6}, \cos\dfrac{\pi}{8}, -\cos\dfrac{\pi}{10}, \ldots$

■ **2.2.2**

In Problems 37–44, write the first five terms of the sequence $\{a_n\}$, $n = 0, 1, 2, 3, \ldots$, and find $\lim_{n \to \infty} a_n$.

37. $a_n = \dfrac{1}{n+2}$

38. $a_n = \dfrac{2}{n+1}$

39. $a_n = \dfrac{n}{n+1}$

40. $a_n = \dfrac{2n}{n+2}$

41. $a_n = \dfrac{1}{n^2+1}$

42. $a_n = \dfrac{1}{\sqrt{n+1}}$

43. $a_n = \dfrac{(-1)^n}{n+1}$ **44.** $a_n = \dfrac{(-1)^n}{n^3+3}$

In Problems 45–52, write the first five terms of the sequence $\{a_n\}$, $n = 0, 1, 2, 3, \ldots$, and determine whether $\lim_{n \to \infty} a_n$ exists. If the limit exists, find it.

45. $a_n = \dfrac{n^2}{n+1}$ **46.** $a_n = \dfrac{n^3}{n+1}$

47. $a_n = \sqrt{n}$ **48.** $a_n = n^2$

49. $a_n = 2^n$ **50.** $a_n = \left(\dfrac{1}{2}\right)^n$

51. $a_n = 3^n$ **52.** $a_n = \left(\dfrac{1}{3}\right)^n$

Formal Definition of Limits: In Problems 53–64, $\lim_{n \to \infty} a_n = a$. Find the limit a, and determine N so that $|a_n - a| < \epsilon$ for all $n > N$ for the given value of ϵ.

53. $a_n = \dfrac{1}{n}, \epsilon = 0.01$ **54.** $a_n = \dfrac{1}{n}, \epsilon = 0.02$

55. $a_n = \dfrac{1}{n^2}, \epsilon = 0.01$ **56.** $a_n = \dfrac{1}{n^2}, \epsilon = 0.001$

57. $a_n = \dfrac{1}{\sqrt{n}}, \epsilon = 0.1$ **58.** $a_n = \dfrac{1}{\sqrt{n}}, \epsilon = 0.05$

59. $a_n = \dfrac{(-1)^n}{n}, \epsilon = 0.01$ **60.** $a_n = \dfrac{(-1)^n}{n}, \epsilon = .001$

61. $a_n = \dfrac{n}{n+1}, \epsilon = 0.01$ **62.** $a_n = \dfrac{n+1}{n}, \epsilon = .05$

63. $a_n = \dfrac{n^2}{n^2+1}, \epsilon = 0.01$ **64.** $a_n = \dfrac{n^2}{n^2+1}, \epsilon = .001$

Formal Definition of Limits: In Problems 65–70, use the formal definition of limits to show that $\lim_{n \to \infty} a_n = a$; that is, find N such that for every $\epsilon > 0$, there exists an N such that $|a_n - a| < \epsilon$ whenever $n > N$.

65. $\lim\limits_{n \to \infty} \dfrac{1}{n} = 0$ **66.** $\lim\limits_{n \to \infty} \dfrac{1}{n+1} = 0$

67. $\lim\limits_{n \to \infty} \dfrac{1}{n^2} = 0$ **68.** $\lim\limits_{n \to \infty} \dfrac{1}{n^2+1} = 0$

69. $\lim\limits_{n \to \infty} \dfrac{n+1}{n} = 1$ **70.** $\lim\limits_{n \to \infty} \dfrac{n}{n+1} = 1$

In Problems 71–82, use the limit laws to determine $\lim\limits_{n \to \infty} a_n = a$.

71. $\lim\limits_{n \to \infty} \left(\dfrac{1}{n} + \dfrac{1}{n^2}\right)$ **72.** $\lim\limits_{n \to \infty} \left(\dfrac{2}{n} - \dfrac{1}{n^2+1}\right)$

73. $\lim\limits_{n \to \infty} \left(\dfrac{n+1}{n}\right)$ **74.** $\lim\limits_{n \to \infty} \left(\dfrac{2n-3}{n}\right)$

75. $\lim\limits_{n \to \infty} \left(\dfrac{n^2+1}{n^2}\right)$ **76.** $\lim\limits_{n \to \infty} \left(\dfrac{3n^2-5}{n^2}\right)$

77. $\lim\limits_{n \to \infty} \left(\dfrac{n+1}{n^2-1}\right)$ **78.** $\lim\limits_{n \to \infty} \left(\dfrac{n+2}{n^2-4}\right)$

79. $\lim\limits_{n \to \infty} \left[\left(\dfrac{1}{3}\right)^n + \left(\dfrac{1}{2}\right)^n\right]$ **80.** $\lim\limits_{n \to \infty} \left(3^{-n} - 4^{-n}\right)$

81. $\lim\limits_{n \to \infty} \dfrac{n + 2^{-n}}{n}$ **82.** $\lim\limits_{n \to \infty} \dfrac{n + 3^{-n}}{n}$

■ 2.2.3

In Problems 83–92, the sequence $\{a_n\}$ is recursively defined. Compute a_n for $n = 1, 2, \ldots, 5$.

83. $a_{n+1} = 2a_n, a_0 = 1$ **84.** $a_{n+1} = 2a_n, a_0 = 3$

85. $a_{n+1} = 3a_n - 2, a_0 = 1$ **86.** $a_{n+1} = 3a_n - 2, a_0 = 2$

87. $a_{n+1} = 4 - 2a_n, a_0 = 5$ **88.** $a_{n+1} = 4 - 2a_n, a_0 = \dfrac{4}{3}$

89. $a_{n+1} = \dfrac{a_n}{1+a_n}, a_0 = 1$ **90.** $a_{n+1} = \dfrac{a_n}{a_n+3}, a_0 = 2$

91. $a_{n+1} = a_n + \dfrac{1}{a_n}, a_0 = 1$ **92.** $a_{n+1} = 5a_n - \dfrac{5}{a_n}, a_0 = 2$

In Problems 93–102, the sequence $\{a_n\}$ is recursively defined. Find all fixed points of $\{a_n\}$.

93. $a_{n+1} = \dfrac{1}{2}a_n + 2$ **94.** $a_{n+1} = \dfrac{1}{3}a_n + \dfrac{4}{3}$

95. $a_{n+1} = \dfrac{2}{5}a_n - \dfrac{9}{5}$ **96.** $a_{n+1} = -\dfrac{1}{3}a_n + \dfrac{1}{4}$

97. $a_{n+1} = \dfrac{4}{a_n}$ **98.** $a_{n+1} = \dfrac{7}{a_n}$

99. $a_{n+1} = \dfrac{2}{a_n + 2}$ **100.** $a_{n+1} = \dfrac{3}{a_n - 2}$

101. $a_{n+1} = \sqrt{5a_n}$ **102.** $a_{n+1} = \sqrt{7a_n}$

In Problems 103–110, assume that $\lim_{n \to \infty} a_n$ exists. Find all fixed points of $\{a_n\}$, and use a table or other reasoning to guess which fixed point is the limiting value for the given initial condition.

103. $a_{n+1} = \dfrac{1}{2}(a_n + 5), a_0 = 1$

104. $a_{n+1} = \dfrac{1}{3}\left(a_n + \dfrac{1}{9}\right), a_0 = 1$

105. $a_{n+1} = \sqrt{2a_n}, a_0 = 1$

106. $a_{n+1} = \sqrt{2a_n}, a_0 = 0$

107. $a_{n+1} = 2a_n(1 - a_n), a_0 = 0.1$

108. $a_{n+1} = 2a_n(1 - a_n), a_0 = 0$

109. $a_{n+1} = \dfrac{1}{2}\left(a_n + \dfrac{4}{a_n}\right), a_0 = 1$

110. $a_{n+1} = \dfrac{1}{2}\left(a_n + \dfrac{9}{a_n}\right), a_0 = -1$

■ 2.3 More Population Models

The material presented in this section will be revisited in Section 5.6. Section 2.3 can be postponed until then.

An important biological application of sequences consists of models of seasonally breeding populations with nonoverlapping generations where the population size at one generation depends only on the population size of the previous generation. The exponential growth model of Section 2.1 fits into this category. We denote the population size at time t by $N(t)$ or N_t, $t = 0, 1, 2, \ldots$. To model how the population size at generation $t + 1$ is related to the population size at generation

t, we write

$$N_{t+1} = f(N_t) \tag{2.10}$$

where the function f describes the density dependence of the population dynamics.

As explained in Section 2.2, a recursion of the form (2.10) is called a first-order recursion because, to obtain the population size at time $t+1$, only the population size at the previous time step t needs to be known. A recursion is also called a **difference equation** or an **iterated map**. [The name *difference equation* comes from writing the dynamics in the form $N_{t+1} - N_t = g(N_t)$, which allows us to track population size changes from one time step to the next. The name *iterated map* refers to the recursive definition.]

When we study population models, we are frequently interested in asking questions about the long-term behavior of the population, such as, Will the population size reach a constant value? Will it oscillate predictably? or Will it fluctuate widely without any recognizable patterns? We will explore these questions in the examples that follow, in which we will see that discrete-time population models show very rich and complex behavior.

■ 2.3.1 Restricted Population Growth: The Beverton–Holt Recruitment Curve

In Section 2.1, we discussed exponential growth defined by the recursion

$$N_{t+1} = RN_t \quad \text{with } N_0 = \text{population size at time 0}$$

When $R > 1$, the population size will grow indefinitely, provided that $N_0 > 0$. We can understand why this happens if we look at the parent–offspring ratio for $N_t > 0$, N_t/N_{t+1}, which is equal to the constant $1/R$. This means that, regardless of the current population density, the number of offspring per parent is a constant. Such growth, called density-independent growth, is biologically unrealistic. As the size of the population increases, individuals will start to compete with each other for resources, such as food or nesting sites, thereby reducing population growth. We call population growth that depends on population density *density-dependent growth*.

To find a model that incorporates a reduction in growth when the population size gets large, we start with the ratio of successive population sizes in the exponential growth model and assume that N_0 is positive, so that all successive population sizes are positive:

$$\frac{N_t}{N_{t+1}} = \frac{1}{R} \tag{2.11}$$

The ratio N_t/N_{t+1} is a constant. If we graphed this ratio as a function of the current population size N_t, we would obtain a horizontal line in a coordinate system in which N_t is on the horizontal axis and the ratio N_t/N_{t+1} is on the vertical axis (Figure 2.7). Note that as long as the parent–offspring ratio N_t/N_{t+1} is less than 1, the population size increases, since there are fewer parents than offspring. Once the ratio is equal to 1, the population size stays the same from one time step to the next. When the ratio is greater than 1, the population size decreases.

To model the reduction in growth when the population size gets larger, we drop the assumption that the parent–offspring ratio N_t/N_{t+1} is constant and assume instead that the ratio is an increasing function of the population size N_t. That is, we replace the constant $1/R$ in (2.11) by a function that increases with N_t. The simplest such function is linear. Graphically, this is a straight line with positive slope (Figure 2.14). To compare the model with density dependence with the exponential growth model (2.11), we assume that the two models agree when the population sizes are very small. We can achieve this agreement by assuming that the line corresponding to density-dependent growth goes through the point $(0, 1/R)$. To make sure that the population grows at low densities, we also assume that $R > 1$. The population density where the parent–offspring ratio is equal to 1 is of particular importance, since it corresponds to the population size, which does not change from one generation to the next. We call this population size the **carrying capacity** and denote it by K, where

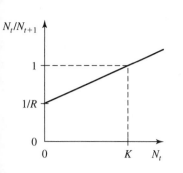

Figure 2.14 Density-dependent growth: The parent–offspring ratio increases as a function of current population size. (Note that this ratio is defined only for $N_t > 0$.)

K is a positive constant. We thus require that the line corresponding to density-dependent growth connect the points $(0, 1/R)$ and $(K, 1)$ in a graph in which N_t is on the horizontal axis and the ratio N_t/N_{t+1} is on the vertical axis (Figure 2.14).

The straight line in Figure 2.14 has slope $(1 - 1/R)/K$ and vertical-axis intercept $1/R$, which yields the equation

$$\frac{N_t}{N_{t+1}} = \frac{1}{R} + \frac{1 - \frac{1}{R}}{K} N_t$$

We solve this equation for N_{t+1} to obtain a recursion. Multiplying both sides by N_{t+1} yields

$$N_t = N_{t+1} \left(\frac{1}{R} + \frac{1 - \frac{1}{R}}{K} N_t \right)$$

which allows us to isolate N_{t+1}:

$$N_{t+1} = \frac{N_t}{\frac{1}{R} + \frac{1 - \frac{1}{R}}{K} N_t}$$

We next simplify the right-hand expression by multiplying numerator and denominator by R:

$$N_{t+1} = \frac{R N_t}{1 + \frac{R-1}{K} N_t} \tag{2.12}$$

This recursion is known as the **Beverton–Holt recruitment curve**.

Using results from Section 2.2, we can compute the fixed points of (2.12). Solving

$$N = \frac{R N}{1 + \frac{R-1}{K} N}$$

for N, we immediately find that $N = 0$. If $N \neq 0$, we divide both sides by N, producing

$$1 = \frac{R}{1 + \frac{R-1}{K} N}$$

Algebraic manipulation then yields

$$1 + \frac{R-1}{K} N = R \qquad \text{or} \qquad \frac{R-1}{K} N = R - 1$$

from which we solve for N to obtain

$$N = \frac{R-1}{\frac{R-1}{K}} = (R-1) \frac{K}{R-1} = K$$

We thus have two fixed points when $R > 1$: the fixed point $N = 0$, which we call **trivial**, since it corresponds to the absence of the population, and the fixed point $N = K$, which we call **nontrivial**, since it corresponds to a positive population size.

In Figure 2.15, we set $K = 20$ and $R = 1.4$ and plot N_t as a function of t for three different initial population sizes. For clarity, we include the lines that connect successive population sizes. We see from the figure that if $N_0 > 0$, then N_t will eventually approach $K = 20$. (If $N_0 = K$, then $N_t = K$ for all $t = 1, 2, 3, \ldots$, since K is a fixed point.) This is the reason for calling K the carrying capacity. On the basis of on Figure 2.15, we conclude that, when $K > 0$, $R > 1$, and $N_0 > 0$, we have

$$\lim_{t \to \infty} N_t = K$$

At this point, we need to rely on graphs and tables to investigate the long-term behavior of the population. This is a serious limitation, since it restricts our investigations to specific parameter values and we cannot then explore all possible parameter

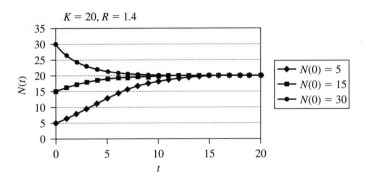

Figure 2.15 The population sizes N_t when $K = 20$ and $R = 1.4$ in the Beverton–Holt recruitment model for different initial population densities.

values. It turns out that this example has the same qualitative behavior for all R and K, provided that $R > 1$ and $K > 0$. In Section 5.6, we will learn analytical methods that will allow us to make general statements (like the one in the previous sentence) about the behavior of discrete-time population models such that that behavior will not depend on tables and graphs. In the next subsection, we will see an example where the behavior depends strongly on the choice of parameters.

■ 2.3.2 The Discrete Logistic Equation

The most popular discrete-time single-species model is the discrete logistic equation, whose recursion is given by

$$N_{t+1} = N_t \left[1 + R \left(1 - \frac{N_t}{K} \right) \right] \tag{2.13}$$

where R and K are positive constants. R is called the **growth parameter** and K is called the **carrying capacity**. The analysis that folllows will explain the terminology. This model of population growth exhibits very complicated dynamics, described in an influential review paper by Robert May (1976).

Before we illustrate its behavior, we will rewrite the model in what is called the *canonical form*. The advantage of this form is that the resulting recursion will be simpler. The algebraic steps presented next are not obvious, but will lead to the canonical form of the discrete logistic equation. We write

$$N_{t+1} = N_t \left[1 + R \left(1 - \frac{N_t}{K} \right) \right]$$

$$= N_t \left[1 + R - \frac{R}{K} N_t \right]$$

$$= N_t (1 + R) \left[1 - \frac{R}{K(1 + R)} N_t \right]$$

Now, dividing by $1 + R$ yields

$$\frac{1}{1 + R} N_{t+1} = N_t \left[1 - \frac{R}{K(1 + R)} N_t \right]$$

Let's multiply both sides by R/K (you'll see why in a moment):

$$\frac{R}{K(1 + R)} N_{t+1} = \frac{R}{K} N_t \left[1 - \frac{R}{K(1 + R)} N_t \right] \tag{2.14}$$

If we define the new variable as

$$x_t = \frac{R}{K(1 + R)} N_t \tag{2.15}$$

then

$$\frac{R}{K(1+R)}N_{t+1} = x_{t+1} \quad \text{and} \quad \frac{R}{K}N_t = (1+R)x_t$$

and (2.14) becomes

$$x_{t+1} = (1+R)x_t(1-x_t)$$

At this point, the new parameter $r = 1 + R$ is customarily introduced. Note that $r > 1$, since $R > 0$. We thus arrive at the canonical form of the logistic recursion:

$$x_{t+1} = rx_t(1-x_t) \tag{2.16}$$

The advantage of this form is threefold: (1) The recursion (2.16) looks simpler than the original recursion (2.13); (2) instead of two parameters (R and K), there is just one (r); and (3) the quantity x_t is *dimensionless*. The last point needs some explanation. The original variable N_t has units (or dimension) of number of individuals; the parameter K has the same units. Dividing N_t by K in (2.15), we see that the units cancel and we say that the quantity x_t is dimensionless. [The parameter R does not have a dimension, so multiplying N_t/K by $R/(1+R)$ does not introduce any additional units.] A dimensionless variable has the advantage that it has the same numerical value regardless of what the units of measurement are in the original variable. (See Problems 31–34.) The process of making a quantity dimensionless is called **nondimensionalization**.

Let's go back to the discrete logistic equation in its canonical form (2.16) and see what its behavior is. The function $f(x) = rx(1-x)$ is an upside-down parabola, since $r > 1$ (Figure 2.16). We see from the figure that if x is outside of the interval $(0, 1)$, $f(x)$ is nonpositive. Since $x_t = \frac{R}{K(1+R)}N_t$ [see (2.15)], and we want N_t to be positive (it is a population size, after all), we require x_t to be positive. This means that we need to ensure that $x_{t+1} = f(x_t)$ stays within the interval $(0, 1)$. The maximum value of $f(x)$ occurs at $x = 1/2$, and $f(1/2) = r/4$, so, in order to make sure that $f(x_t) \in (0, 1)$, we require that $r/4 < 1$, or $r < 4$. We already require that $r > 1$, since $R > 0$. To summarize, if $1 < r < 4$, then x_t stays within the interval $(0, 1)$ for all $t = 1, 2, 3, \ldots$, provided that $x_0 \in (0, 1)$. In what follows, we will therefore assume that $1 < r < 4$ and $x_0 \in (0, 1)$.

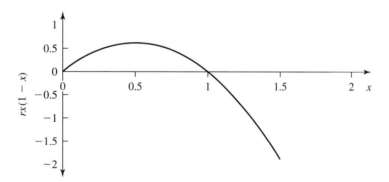

Figure 2.16 A graph of the discrete logistic equation in its canonical form. (Here, $r = 2.5$.)

We first compute fixed points of (2.16). We need to solve

$$x = rx(1-x)$$

Solving immediately yields the solution $x = 0$. If $x \neq 0$, we divide both sides by x and find that

$$1 = r(1-x), \quad \text{or} \quad x = 1 - \frac{1}{r}$$

(See Figure 2.17.) Provided that $r > 1$, both fixed points are in $[0, 1)$.

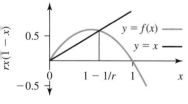

Figure 2.17 A graphical illustration of the fixed points of the discrete logistic equation in its canonical form. The fixed points are where the parabola and the line $y = x$ intersect.

We return to the original variable N_t for a moment to see what $x = 0$ and $x = 1 - 1/r$ mean in terms of N. Since $x = \frac{R}{K(1+R)}N$, the fixed point $x = 0$ corresponds to the fixed point $N = 0$, which is why we call $x = 0$ a trivial equilibrium. When $x = 1 - 1/r$, then, using $r = 1 + R$, we obtain

$$N = \frac{K(1+R)}{R}x = \frac{K(1+R)}{R}\left(1 - \frac{1}{1+R}\right)$$
$$= \frac{K(1+R)}{R}\frac{1+R-1}{1+R} = K$$

so $N = K$ is the other fixed point.

The long-term behavior of the discrete logistic equation is very complicated. We will go through the different cases by simply listing them. Later, in Section 5.6, we will be able, at least to some extent, to understand why this equation has such complicated behavior.

When $1 < r < 3$ and $x_0 \in (0, 1)$, x_t converges to the fixed point $1 - 1/r$ (Figure 2.18). Increasing r to a value between 3 and $3.449\ldots$, we learn that x_t settles into a cycle of period 2 (Figure 2.19). This means that, for large enough times, x_t will oscillate back and forth between a larger and a smaller value. For r between $3.449\ldots$ and $3.544\ldots$, the period doubles: A cycle of period 4 appears for large enough times. The population size now oscillates between the same four values (Figure 2.20). Increasing r continues to double the period: A cycle of period 8 is born when $r = 3.544\ldots$, a cycle of period 16 when $r = 3.564\ldots$, and a cycle of period 32 when $r = 3.567\ldots$. This doubling of the period continues until r reaches a value of about 3.57, when the population pattern becomes **chaotic** (Figure 2.21). The population dynamics seem to be random, although the rules are entirely deterministic! There is no regular pattern we can discern: x_t no longer oscillates between the same values; the dynamics are **aperiodic**. Furthermore, starting from ever so slightly different initial conditions quickly produces very different trajectories (Figure 2.22). This sensitivity to initial conditions is characteristic of chaotic behavior.

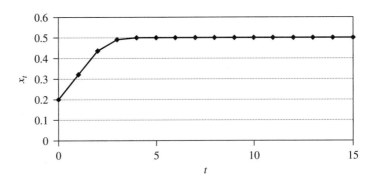

Figure 2.18 A graph of x_t as a function of t when $r = 2$.

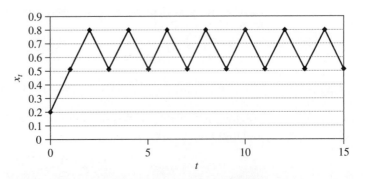

Figure 2.19 A graph of x_t as a function of t when $r = 3.2$.

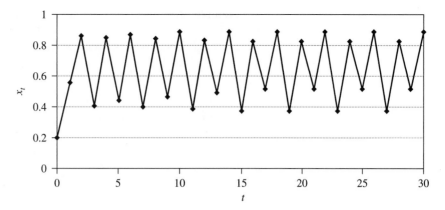

Figure 2.20 A graph of x_t as a function of t when $r = 3.52$.

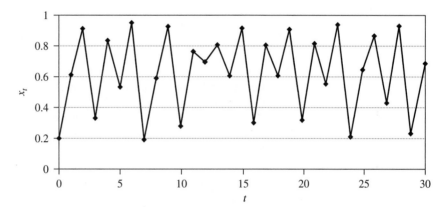

Figure 2.21 A graph of x_t as a function of t when $r = 3.8$.

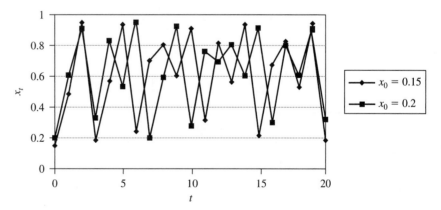

Figure 2.22 Graphs of x_t as a function of t when $r = 3.8$ for two different initial values of x_0.

To obtain biologically sensible results, we needed to restrict both r and x_0. The reason was that if $x_t > 1$, then x_{t+1} is negative. This situation can be easily remedied by changing the dynamics slightly. We discuss such a model in the next subsection.

■ 2.3.3 Ricker's Curve

The discrete logistic map has the biologically unrealistic feature that, unless one restricts the initial population size and the growth parameter, negative population sizes can occur. The reason is that the function $f(x) = rx(1 - x)$ takes on negative values for $x > 1$, so if $x_t > 1$, then $x_{t+1} < 0$. It is not difficult to avoid this problem.

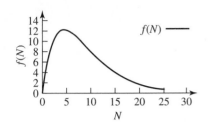

Figure 2.23 Ricker's curve when $R = 2.8$ and $K = 9$.

One example of an iterated map that has the same (desirable) properties as the logistic map but does not admit negative population sizes (provided that the population size at time 0 is positive) is **Ricker's curve**. The recursion, called the **Ricker logistic equation**, is given by

$$N_{t+1} = N_t \exp\left[R \left(1 - \frac{N_t}{K}\right) \right] \tag{2.17}$$

where R and K are positive parameters. As in the discrete logistic model, R is the growth parameter and K is the carrying capacity. The graph of Ricker's curve (Figure 2.23), $f(N_t) = N_t \exp\left[R \left(1 - \frac{N_t}{K}\right) \right]$, is positive for all $N_t > 0$, thus avoiding the problem of negative population sizes we encountered in the discrete logistic equation.

Fixed points of (2.17) satisfy

$$N = N \exp\left[R \left(1 - \frac{N}{K}\right) \right] \tag{2.18}$$

We find the trivial fixed point $N = 0$. If $N \neq 0$, we can divide both sides of (2.18) by N, obtaining

$$1 = \exp\left[R \left(1 - \frac{N}{K}\right) \right]$$

This equation holds if $R(1 - N/K) = 0$, from which it follows that $N = K$. The parameter K has the same meaning as in the discrete logistic equation, namely, that it is the carrying capacity.

The Ricker logistic equation shows the same complex dynamics as the discrete logistic map [convergence to the fixed point for small positive values of R (Figure 2.24), periodic behavior with the period doubling as R increases, and chaotic behavior for larger values of R (Figure 2.25)]. The values of R where the behavior changes are different than in the discrete logistic equation. For instance, the onset of chaos in the discrete logistic equation occurs for $R = 2.570\ldots$, whereas the onset of chaos in the Ricker logistic equation occurs for $R = 2.692\ldots$.

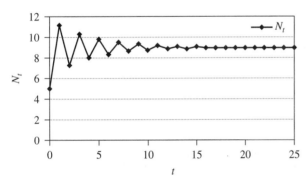

Figure 2.24 The population size N_t as a function of t when $R = 1.8$ and $K = 9$.

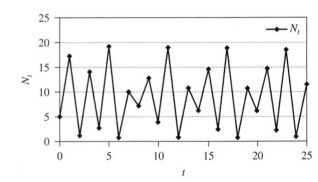

Figure 2.25 The population size N_t as a function of t when $R = 2.8$ and $K = 9$.

■ 2.3.4 Fibonacci Sequences

As a last example in this section, we will look at a **second-order difference equation**—an equation in which N_{t+1} depends on both N_t and N_{t-1}.

A famous example of a second-order difference equation is the **Fibonacci sequence**. The equation comes from the following problem posed in 1202 by Leonardo of Pisa (1175–1250), an Italian mathematician known by the name Fibonacci: How many pairs of rabbits are produced if each pair reproduces one pair of rabbits at age one month and another pair of rabbits at age two months and initially there is one pair of newborn rabbits?

If N_t denotes the number of newborn rabbit pairs at time t (measured in months), then at time 0, there is one pair of rabbits ($N_0 = 1$). At time 1, the pair of rabbits we started with is one month old and produces a pair of newborn rabbits, so $N_1 = 1$.

At time 2, there is one pair of two-month-old rabbits and one pair of one-month-old rabbits. Each pair produces a pair of newborn rabbits, so $N_2 = 2$. At time 3, our original pair of rabbits is now three months old and will stop reproducing; there is then one pair of two-month-old rabbits and two pairs of one-month-old rabbits. Since each pair of one-month-old and two-month-old rabbits produces a pair of newborn rabbits, at time $t = 3$ there will be $2 + 1 = 3$ newborn rabbits. More generally, to find the number of pairs of newborn rabbits, we need to add up the number of pairs of one-month-old rabbits and two-month-old rabbits. The one-month-old rabbits at time $t + 1$ were newborn rabbits at time t; the two-month-old rabbits were newborns at time $t - 1$. So the number of pairs of newborn rabbits at time $t + 1$ is

$$N_{t+1} = N_t + N_{t-1}, \ t = 1, 2, 3, \ldots \quad \text{with } N_0 = 1 \text{ and } N_1 = 1$$

Note that we need to specify N_t for $t = 0$ and $t = 1$ in order to be able to use the recursion. Using the recursion, we find the sequence

$$1, 1, 2, 3, 5, 8, 13, \ldots$$

We see that the number of newborn pairs of rabbits will go to infinity as t tends to infinity, so N_t will not converge to a finite limit. It turns out, however, that the ratio N_{t+1}/N_t converges (although we cannot show this here). We can find a candidate for the limiting value as follows: Start with the recursion

$$N_{t+1} = N_t + N_{t-1}$$

and divide both sides by N_t, yielding

$$\frac{N_{t+1}}{N_t} = 1 + \frac{N_{t-1}}{N_t} \tag{2.19}$$

If we now assume that

$$\lim_{t \to \infty} \frac{N_{t+1}}{N_t} = \lambda$$

(λ is the lowercase Greek letter lambda), which also implies that

$$\lim_{t \to \infty} \frac{N_t}{N_{t-1}} = \lambda$$

then

$$\lim_{t \to \infty} \frac{N_{t-1}}{N_t} = \lim_{t \to \infty} \frac{1}{\frac{N_t}{N_{t-1}}} = \frac{1}{\lim_{t \to \infty} \frac{N_t}{N_{t-1}}} = \frac{1}{\lambda}$$

Taking the limit as $t \to \infty$ in (2.19), we find that

$$\lambda = 1 + \frac{1}{\lambda}$$

which is $\lambda^2 = \lambda + 1$ after multiplying both sides by λ. We thus need to solve

$$\lambda^2 - \lambda - 1 = 0$$

The formula for solving quadratic equations yields

$$\lambda_{1,2} = \frac{1 \pm \sqrt{1 + 4}}{2} = \frac{1 \pm \sqrt{5}}{2}$$

One solution is positive, the other negative. Only the positive solution is relevant when $N_0 = N_1 = 1$, since then $N_{t+1}/N_t > 0$ for all $t = 0, 1, 2, \ldots$. The ratio

$$\frac{1 + \sqrt{5}}{2} \approx 1.61803$$

is the limit of N_{t+1}/N_t as $t \to \infty$ and is called the **golden mean**.

A rectangle whose sides bear the golden ratio is called a **golden rectangle**; it is thought to be the visually most pleasing proportion a rectangle can have. Golden rectangles were known to the ancient Greeks, who used them to scale the dimensions of their buildings (e.g., the Parthenon). Ratios of successive Fibonacci numbers can be found in nature as well. For instance, the florets on plants such as the sunflower run in spirals, and the ratios of the number of spirals running in opposite directions are often successive Fibonacci numbers.

Section 2.3 Problems

■ 2.3.1

In Problems 1–6, assume that the population growth is described by the Beverton–Holt recruitment curve with growth parameter R and carrying capacity K. For the given values of R and K, graph N_t/N_{t+1} as a function of N_t and find the recursion for the Beverton–Holt recruitment curve.

1. $R = 2, K = 15$
2. $R = 2, K = 50$
3. $R = 1.5, K = 40$
4. $R = 3, K = 120$
5. $R = 2.5, K = 90$
6. $R = 2, K = 150$

In Problems 7–12, assume that the population growth is described by the Beverton–Holt recruitment curve with growth parameter R and carrying capacity K. Find R and K.

7. $N_{t+1} = \dfrac{2N_t}{1 + N_t/20}$
8. $N_{t+1} = \dfrac{3N_t}{1 + 2N_t/40}$

9. $N_{t+1} = \dfrac{1.5N_t}{1 + 0.5N_t/30}$
10. $N_{t+1} = \dfrac{2N_t}{1 + N_t/200}$

11. $N_{t+1} = \dfrac{4N_t}{1 + N_t/150}$
12. $N_{t+1} = \dfrac{5N_t}{1 + N_t/20}$

In Problems 13–18, assume that the population growth is described by the Beverton–Holt recruitment curve with growth parameter R and carrying capacity K. Find all fixed points.

13. $N_{t+1} = \dfrac{4N_t}{1 + N_t/30}$
14. $N_{t+1} = \dfrac{3N_t}{1 + N_t/60}$

15. $N_{t+1} = \dfrac{2N_t}{1 + N_t/30}$
16. $N_{t+1} = \dfrac{2N_t}{1 + N_t/100}$

17. $N_{t+1} = \dfrac{3N_t}{1 + N_t/30}$
18. $N_{t+1} = \dfrac{5N_t}{1 + N_t/120}$

In Problems 19–24, assume that the population growth is described by the Beverton–Holt recruitment curve with growth parameter R and carrying capacity K. Find the population sizes for $t = 1, 2, \ldots,$ 5 and find $\lim_{t\to\infty} N_t$ for the given initial value N_0.

19. $R = 2, K = 10, N_0 = 2$
20. $R = 2, K = 20, N_0 = 5$
21. $R = 3, K = 15, N_0 = 1$
22. $R = 3, K = 30, N_0 = 0$
23. $R = 4, K = 40, N_0 = 3$
24. $R = 4, K = 20, N_0 = 10$

■ 2.3.2

In Problems 25–30, assume that the discrete logistic equation is used with parameters R and K. Write the equation in the canonical form $x_{t+1} = rx_t(1 - x_t)$, and determine r and x_t in terms of R, K, and N_t.

25. $R = 1, K = 10$
26. $R = 1, K = 20$
27. $R = 2, K = 15$
28. $R = 2, K = 20$
29. $R = 2.5, K = 30$
30. $R = 2.5, K = 50$

In Problems 31–34, we will investigate the advantage of dimensionless variables.

31. (a) Let N_t denote the population size at time t and let K denote the carrying capacity. Both quantities are measured in units of number of individuals. Show that $x_t = N_t/K$ is dimensionless.

(b) Let M_t denote the population size at time t and let L denote the carrying capacity. Assume that M_t and L are measured in units of 1000 individuals. Show that $y_t = M_t/L$ is dimensionless.

(c) How are N_t and M_t related? How are K and L related?

(d) Use (c) to find M_t and L if there are 20,000 individuals at time t and the carrying capacity is 5000.

(e) Show that, for the population size and the carrying capacity in (d), $x_t = y_t$.

32. To quantify the spatial structure of a plant population, it might be convenient to introduce a characteristic length scale. This length scale might be characterized by the average dispersal distance of the plant under study. Assume that the characteristic length scale is denoted by L. Denote by x the distance of seeds from their source. Define $z = x/L$. Find z if $x = 100$ cm and $L = 50$ cm, and show that z has the same value if x and L are measured in units of meters instead.

33. Suppose a bacterium divides every 20 minutes, which we call the characteristic time scale and denote by T. Let t be the time elapsed since the beginning of an experiment that involves this bacterium. Define $z = t/T$. Find z if $t = 120$ minutes, and show that z has the same value if t and T are measured in units of hours instead.

34. The time to the most recent common ancestor of a pair of individuals from a randomly mating population depends on the population size. Let t denote the time, measured in units of generations, to the most recent common ancestor, and let T be equal to N generations, where N is the population size of the randomly mating population. Define $z = t/T$. Show that z is dimensionless and that the value of z does not change, regardless of whether t and T are measured in units of generations or in units of, say, years. (Assume that one generation is equal to n years.)

In Problems 35–46, we investigate the behavior of the discrete logistic equation

$$x_{t+1} = rx_t(1 - x_t)$$

Compute x_t for $t = 0, 1, 2, \ldots, 20$ for the given values of r and x_0, and graph x_t as a function of t.

35. $r = 2, x_0 = 0.2$
36. $r = 2, x_0 = 0.1$
37. $r = 2, x_0 = 0.9$
38. $r = 2, x_0 = 0$
39. $r = 3.1, x_0 = 0.5$
40. $r = 3.1, x_0 = 0.1$
41. $r = 3.1, x_0 = 0.9$
42. $r = 3.1, x_0 = 0$
43. $r = 3.8, x_0 = 0.5$
44. $r = 3.8, x_0 = 0.1$
45. $r = 3.8, x_0 = 0.9$
46. $r = 3.8, x_0 = 0$

■ **2.3.3**

In Problems 47–50, graph the Ricker's curve

$$N_{t+1} = N_t \exp\left[R\left(1 - \frac{N_t}{K}\right)\right]$$

in the N_t–N_{t+1} plane for the given values of R and K. Find the points of intersection of this graph with the line $N_{t+1} = N_t$.

47. $R = 2, K = 10$ **48.** $R = 3, K = 15$

49. $R = 2.5, K = 12$ **50.** $R = 4, K = 20$

In Problems 51–54, we investigate the behavior of the Ricker's curve

$$N_{t+1} = N_t \exp\left[R\left(1 - \frac{N_t}{K}\right)\right]$$

Compute N_t for $t = 1, 2, \ldots, 20$ for the given values of R, K, and N_0, and graph N_t as a function of t.

51. (a) $R = 1, K = 20, N_0 = 5$

(b) $R = 1, K = 20, N_0 = 10$

(c) $R = 1, K = 20, N_0 = 20$ **(d)** $R = 1, K = 20, N_0 = 0$

52. (a) $R = 1.8, K = 20, N_0 = 5$

(b) $R = 1.8, K = 20, N_0 = 10$

(c) $R = 1.8, K = 20, N_0 = 20$ **(d)** $R = 1.8, K = 20, N_0 = 0$

53. (a) $R = 2.1, K = 20, N_0 = 5$

(b) $R = 2.1, K = 20, N_0 = 10$

(c) $R = 2.1, K = 20, N_0 = 20$ **(d)** $R = 2.1, K = 20, N_0 = 0$

54. (a) $R = 2.8, K = 20, N_0 = 5$

(b) $R = 2.8, K = 20, N_0 = 10$

(c) $R = 2.8, K = 20, N_0 = 20$ **(d)** $R = 2.8, K = 20, N_0 = 0$

■ **2.3.4**

55. Compute N_t and N_t/N_{t-1} for $t = 2, 3, 4, \ldots, 20$ when

$$N_{t+1} = N_t + N_{t-1}$$

with $N_0 = 1$ and $N_1 = 1$.

56. Compute N_t and N_t/N_{t-1} for $t = 2, 3, 4, \ldots, 20$ when

$$N_{t+1} = N_t + 2N_{t-1}$$

with $N_0 = 1$ and $N_1 = 1$.

57. In the text, an interpretation of the Fibonacci recursion

$$N_{t+1} = N_t + N_{t-1}$$

is given. Use a similar example to give an interpretation of the recursion

$$N_{t+1} = N_t + 2N_{t-1}$$

58. In the text, an interpretation of the Fibonacci recursion

$$N_{t+1} = N_t + N_{t-1}$$

is given. Use a similar example to give an interpretation of the recursion

$$N_{t+1} = 2N_t + N_{t-1}$$

Chapter 2 Key Terms

Discuss the following definitions and concepts:

1. Exponential growth
2. Growth constant
3. Fixed point
4. Equilibrium
5. Recursion
6. Solution
7. Density independence
8. Sequence
9. First-order recursion
10. Limit
11. Long-term behavior
12. Convergence, divergence
13. Limit laws
14. Difference equation
15. Beverton–Holt recruitment curve
16. Density dependence
17. Carrying capacity
18. Growth parameter
19. Discrete logistic equation
20. Nondimensionalization
21. Periodic behavior
22. Chaos
23. Ricker's curve
24. Fibonacci sequence
25. Golden mean

Chapter 2 Review Problems

In Problems 1–10, find the limits.

1. $\displaystyle\lim_{n\to\infty} 2^{-n}$

2. $\displaystyle\lim_{n\to\infty} 3^n$

3. $\displaystyle\lim_{n\to\infty} 40(1 - 4^{-n})$

4. $\displaystyle\lim_{n\to\infty} \frac{2}{1 + 2^{-n}}$

5. $\displaystyle\lim_{n\to\infty} a^n$ when $a > 1$

6. $\displaystyle\lim_{n\to\infty} a^n$ when $0 < a < 1$

7. $\displaystyle\lim_{n\to\infty} \frac{n(n+1)}{n^2 - 1}$

8. $\displaystyle\lim_{n\to\infty} \frac{n^2 + n - 6}{n - 2}$

9. $\displaystyle\lim_{n\to\infty} \frac{\sqrt{n}}{n+1}$

10. $\displaystyle\lim_{n\to\infty} \frac{n+1}{\sqrt{n}}$

In Problems 11–14, write a_n explicitly as a function of n on the basis of the first five terms of the sequence a_n, $n = 0, 1, 2, \ldots$.

11. $\dfrac{1}{2}, \dfrac{3}{4}, \dfrac{5}{6}, \dfrac{7}{8}, \dfrac{9}{10}$

12. $\dfrac{2}{2}, \dfrac{6}{4}, \dfrac{12}{8}, \dfrac{20}{16}, \dfrac{30}{32}$

13. $\dfrac{1}{2}, \dfrac{2}{5}, \dfrac{3}{10}, \dfrac{4}{17}, \dfrac{5}{26}$

14. $0, \dfrac{1}{3}, \dfrac{2}{4}, \dfrac{3}{5}, \dfrac{4}{6}$

15. Density-Dependent Growth The Beverton–Holt recruitment curve is given by the recursion

$$N_{t+1} = \frac{RN_t}{1 + \frac{R-1}{K}N_t}$$

where $R > 1$ and $K > 0$. When $N_0 > 0$, $\lim_{t\to\infty} N_t = K$ for all values of $R > 0$. To investigate how R affects the limiting behavior of N_t, find N_t for $t = 1, 2, 3, \ldots, 10$ for $K = 100$ and $N_0 = 20$ when **(a)** $R = 2$, **(b)** $R = 5$, and **(c)** $R = 10$, and plot N_t as a function of t for the three choices of R in one coordinate system.

In Problems 16–18, we discuss population models when the population size at time $t + 1$ depends not only on the population size at time t, but also on the growth conditions at time t, which may vary over time.

16. Temporally Varying Environment The recursion

$$N_{t+1} = R_t N_t$$

describes growth in a temporally varying environment if we interpret R_t as the growth parameter in generation t. A population was followed over 10 years and the population sizes were recorded each year. Use the data provided to find R_t for $t = 0, 1, 2, \ldots, 9$:

t	N_t
0	10
1	15.5
2	15.6
3	10.8
4	15.6
5	32.2
6	95.1
7	103.2
8	165.0
9	418.7
10	15.7

17. Temporally Varying Environment The recursion

$$N_{t+1} = R_t N_t$$

describes growth in a temporally varying environment if we interpret R_t as the growth parameter in generation t. A population was followed over 20 years and the population sizes were recorded every year. The following table provides the population size data and the inferred values of R_t for each of the 20 years:

t	N_t	R_t
0	10.0	2.78
1	27.8	0.29
2	8.10	0.43
3	3.49	0.25
4	0.87	2.90
5	2.52	1.67
6	4.21	1.17
7	4.94	0.69
8	3.39	1.45
9	4.92	1.13
10	5.56	0.08
11	0.45	0.88
12	0.40	2.69
13	1.06	0.36
14	0.38	0.08
15	0.03	2.34
16	0.07	2.13
17	0.15	2.20
18	0.34	2.80
19	0.94	0.29
20	0.28	1.22

The values of N_t indicate that the population heads toward extinction. The long-term behavior of the geometric mean of the growth parameter, denoted by $\hat{R}_t$ (read "R sub t hat"), is defined as

$$\hat{R}_t = \left(R_0 R_1 \cdots R_{t-1}\right)^{1/t}$$

and determines whether the population will go extinct. Specifically, if

$$\lim_{t \to \infty} \hat{R}_t < 1$$

then the population will go extinct. Compute $\hat{R}_t$ for $t = 1, 2, \ldots, 20$.

18. Temporally Varying Environment The recursion

$$N_{t+1} = R_t N_t$$

describes growth in a temporally varying environment if we interpret R_t as the growth parameter in generation t.

(a) Show that

$$N_t = (R_{t-1} R_{t-2} \cdots R_1 R_0) N_0$$

(b) The quantity $\hat{R}_t$ (read "R sub t hat"), defined as

$$\hat{R}_t = (R_{t-1} R_{t-2} \cdots R_1 R_0)^{1/t}$$

is called the **geometric mean**. Show that

$$N_t = (\hat{R}_t)^t N_0$$

(c) The **arithmetic mean** of a sequence of numbers $x_0, x_1, \ldots, x_{n-1}$ is defined as

$$\overline{x}_n = \frac{x_0 + x_1 + \cdots + x_{n-1}}{n}$$

Set $r_t = \ln R_t$ and show that

$$\overline{r}_t = \frac{\ln R_{t-1} + \ln R_{t-2} + \cdots + \ln R_0}{t}$$

(d) Use (c) to show that

$$N_t = N_0 e^{\overline{r}_t t}$$

19. Harvesting Model Let N_t denote the population size at time t, and assume that

$$N_{t+1} = (1 - c)N_t \exp\left[R\left(1 - \frac{(1 - c)N_t}{K}\right)\right]$$

where R and K are positive constants and c is the fraction harvested. Find N_t for $t = 1, 2, \ldots, 20$ when $R = 1$, $K = 100$, and $N_0 = 50$ for (a) $c = 0.1$, (b) $c = 0.5$, and (c) $c = 0.9$.

20. Harvesting Model Let N_t denote the population size at time t, and assume that

$$N_{t+1} = (1 - c)N_t \exp\left[R\left(1 - \frac{(1 - c)N_t}{K}\right)\right]$$

where R and K are positive constants and c is the fraction harvested. Find N_t for $t = 1, 2, \ldots, 20$ when $R = 3$, $K = 100$, and $N_0 = 50$ for (a) $c = 0.1$, (b) $c = 0.5$, and (c) $c = 0.9$.

Limits and Continuity

3

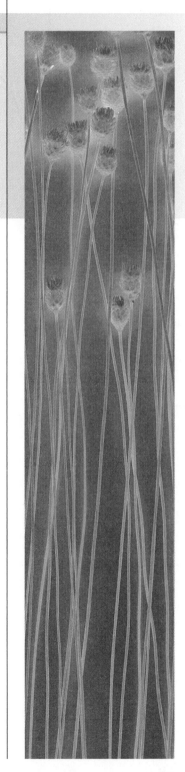

LEARNING OBJECTIVES

The two concepts of limits and continuity are fundamental to differential calculus. Specifically, in this chapter we will learn how to

- determine the value of a function $f(x)$ at $x = c$ as x approaches c, both from graphs and mathematical expressions defining the function;
- determine whether a function is continuous or discontinuous at a point;
- identify where a function is continuous and where it is discontinuous;
- extract information from continuous functions on the basis of generic properties of such functions.

■ 3.1 Limits

In Chapter 2, we discussed limits of the form $\lim_{n \to \infty} a_n$, where n took on integer values. In this chapter, we will consider limits of the form

$$\lim_{x \to c} f(x) \tag{3.1}$$

where x is now a continuously varying real variable that tends to a fixed value c (which may be finite or infinite). Let's look at an example that will motivate the need for limits of the form (3.1).

Population growth in populations with discrete breeding seasons (as in Chapter 2) can be described by the change in population size from generation to generation. By contrast, in populations that breed continuously, there is no natural time scale such as generations. Instead, we will look at how the population size changes over small time intervals. We denote the population size at time t by $N(t)$, where t is now varying continuously over the interval $[0, \infty)$. We will investigate how the population size changes during the interval $[t, t + h]$, where $h > 0$. The absolute change during this interval, denoted by ΔN, is

$$\Delta N = N(t + h) - N(t)$$

(The symbol Δ indicates that we are taking a difference.) To obtain the change relative to the length of the interval $[t, t + h]$, we divide ΔN by the length of the interval, denoted by Δt, which is $(t + h) - t = h$. We find that

$$\frac{\Delta N}{\Delta t} = \frac{N(t + h) - N(t)}{h}$$

This ratio is called the **average growth rate**.

We see from Figure 3.1 that $\Delta N/\Delta t$ is the slope of the secant line connecting the points $(t, N(t))$ and $(t+h, N(t+h))$. The average growth rate $\Delta N/\Delta t$ depends on the length of the interval Δt. This dependency is illustrated in Figure 3.2, where we see that the slopes of the two secant lines (lines 1 and 2) are different. But we also see that, as we choose smaller and smaller intervals, the secant lines converge to the tangent line at the point $(t, N(t))$ of the graph of $N(t)$ (line 3).

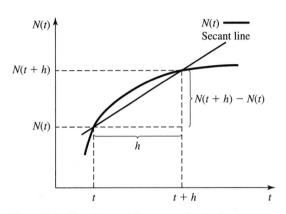

Figure 3.1 The slope of the secant line is the average growth rate.

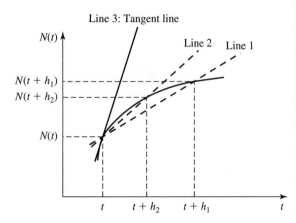

Figure 3.2 The slope of the secant line converges to the slope of the tangent line as the length of the interval $[t, t+h]$ shrinks to 0.

The slope of the tangent line is called the **instantaneous growth rate** and is a convenient way to describe the growth of a continuously breeding population. To obtain this quantity, we need to take a limit; that is, we need to shrink the length of the interval $[t, t+h]$ to 0 by letting h tend to 0. We express this operation as

$$\lim_{h \to 0} \frac{N(t+h) - N(t)}{h} \tag{3.2}$$

In (3.2), we take a limit of a quantity in which a continuously varying variable, namely, h, approaches some fixed value, namely, 0. This is a limit of the form (3.1).

■ 3.1.1 An Informal Discussion of Limits

Definition The "**limit of $f(x)$, as x approaches c, is equal to L**" means that $f(x)$ becomes arbitrarily close to L whenever x is sufficiently close (but not equal) to c. We denote this statement by

$$\lim_{x \to c} f(x) = L$$

or $f(x) \to L$ as $x \to c$.

If $\lim_{x \to c} f(x) = L$ and L is a finite number, we say that the limit **exists** and that $f(x)$ **converges** to L. If the limit does not exist, we say that $f(x)$ **diverges** as x tends to c.

Note that we say that we choose x close, but not equal, to c. That is, when finding the limit of $f(x)$ as x approaches c, we do not simply plug c into $f(x)$. In fact, we will see examples in which $f(x)$ is not even defined at $x = c$. The value of $f(c)$ is irrelevant when we compute the value of $\lim_{x \to c} f(x)$.

Furthermore, when we say "x approaches c," we mean that x approaches c in any fashion. When x approaches c from only one side, we use the notation

$$\lim_{x \to c^+} f(x) \quad \text{when } x \text{ approaches } c \text{ from the right}$$

$$\lim_{x \to c^-} f(x) \quad \text{when } x \text{ approaches } c \text{ from the left}$$

and talk about right-handed and left-handed limits, respectively. The notation "$x \to c^+$" indicates that when x approaches c from the right, values of x are greater than c, and when x approaches c from the left ("$x \to c^-$"), values of x are less than than c.

Let's look at some examples.

Limits That Exist

EXAMPLE 1   Define $f(x) = x^2, x \in \mathbf{R}$. Find

$$\lim_{x \to 2} f(x)$$

Solution   The graph of $f(x) = x^2$ (see Figure 3.3) immediately shows that the limit of x^2 is 4 as x approaches 2 (from either side). We also suspect this from the following table, where we compute values of x^2 for x close, but not equal, to 2:

x	x^2	x	x^2
1.9	3.61	2.1	4.41
1.99	3.9601	2.01	4.0401
1.999	3.996001	2.001	4.004001
1.9999	3.99960001	2.0001	4.00040001

Note that in the left half of the table we approach $x = 2$ from the left ($x \to 2^-$), whereas in the right half of the table we approach x from the right ($x \to 2^+$).

We find that

$$\lim_{x \to 2} x^2 = 4$$

Since this limit is a finite number, we say that the limit exists and that x^2 converges to 4 as x tends to 2. The fact that $f(x) = x^2$ at $x = 2$ is 4 as well is a nice property that will be introduced and named later. Not all functions are like that. ■

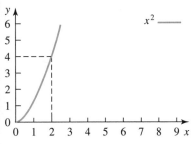

Figure 3.3 As x approaches 2, $f(x) = x^2$ approaches 4.

EXAMPLE 2   **(a)** Define

$$g(x) = \begin{cases} x^2 & \text{if } x \neq 2 \\ 5 & \text{if } x = 2 \end{cases}$$

Find

$$\lim_{x \to 2} g(x)$$

(b) Define $h(x) = x^2, x \neq 2$. Find

$$\lim_{x \to 2} h(x)$$

Solution   **(a)** In computing the value of $\lim_{x \to 2} g(x)$, the value of $g(2)$ is irrelevant. We find, as in Example 1, that

$$\lim_{x \to 2} g(x) = \lim_{x \to 2} x^2 = 4$$

We note that $\lim_{x \to 2} g(x) \neq g(2)$.

(b) To obtain the limit of $h(x)$ as $x \to 2$, the function $h(x)$ need not be defined at $x = 2$. We obtain

$$\lim_{x \to 2} h(x) = \lim_{x \to 2} x^2 = 4$$ ■

EXAMPLE 3 Find

$$\lim_{x \to 3} \frac{x^2 - 9}{x - 3}$$

Solution   In the previous two examples, determining the limits did not require any calculations. This is not the case here, since both numerator and denominator tend to 0 as $x \to 3$. We define $f(x) = \dfrac{x^2 - 9}{x - 3}$, $x \neq 3$. Since the denominator of $f(x)$ is equal to 0 when $x = 3$, we exclude $x = 3$ from the domain. When $x \neq 3$, we can simplify the expression, namely,

$$f(x) = \frac{x^2 - 9}{x - 3} = \frac{(x - 3)(x + 3)}{x - 3} = x + 3 \qquad \text{for } x \neq 3$$

We were able to cancel the term $x - 3$ because $x - 3 \neq 0$ for $x \neq 3$ and we assumed that $x \neq 3$. (If we allowed $x = 3$, then canceling $x - 3$ would mean dividing by 0.) The graph of $f(x)$ is a straight line with one point deleted at $x = 3$. (See Figure 3.4.) Taking the limit, we find that

$$\lim_{x \to 3} \frac{x^2 - 9}{x - 3} = \lim_{x \to 3} (x + 3)$$

Now, using either the graph of $y = x + 3$ for $x \neq 3$ or a table, we suspect that

$$\lim_{x \to 3} (x + 3) = 6$$

We conclude that $\lim_{x \to 3} f(x)$ exists and that $f(x)$ converges to 6 as x tends to 3. Note that $f(x)$ is not defined at $x = 3$. ■

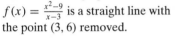

Figure 3.4 The graph of $f(x) = \frac{x^2-9}{x-3}$ is a straight line with the point $(3, 6)$ removed.

One-Sided Limits   To compute one-sided limits, we use the notation

$$\lim_{x \to c^+} f(x) \quad \text{when } x \text{ approaches } c \text{ from the right}$$

$$\lim_{x \to c^-} f(x) \quad \text{when } x \text{ approaches } c \text{ from the left}$$

that was introduced previously.

EXAMPLE 4 Find

$$\lim_{x \to 0} e^{-|x|}$$

Solution   We set

$$f(x) = e^{-|x|} = \begin{cases} e^{-x} & \text{for } x > 0 \\ e^{x} & \text{for } x < 0 \end{cases}$$

Figure 3.5 indicates that $\lim_{x \to 0^+} f(x) = \lim_{x \to 0^+} e^{-x} = 1$ and $\lim_{x \to 0^-} f(x) = \lim_{x \to 0^-} e^{x} = 1$. We therefore conclude that

$$\lim_{x \to 0} e^{-|x|} = 1$$ ■

EXAMPLE 5 Find

$$\lim_{x \to 0^+} \frac{|x|}{x} \quad \text{and} \quad \lim_{x \to 0^-} \frac{|x|}{x}$$

Solution   We set $f(x) = \dfrac{|x|}{x}$, $x \neq 0$. Since $|x| = x$ for $x \geq 0$ and $|x| = -x$ for $x \leq 0$, we find that

$$f(x) = \frac{|x|}{x} = \begin{cases} +1 & \text{for } x > 0 \\ -1 & \text{for } x < 0 \end{cases}$$

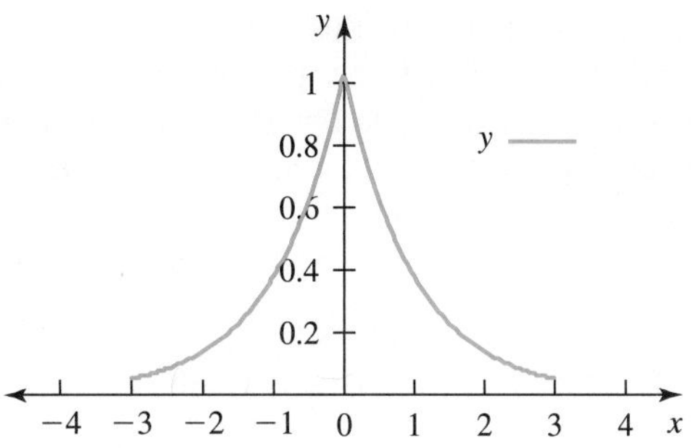

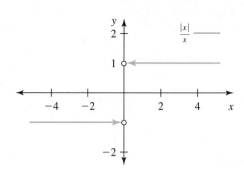

Figure 3.5 The graph of $f(x) = e^{-|x|}$ in Example 4.

Figure 3.6 The graph of $\frac{|x|}{x}$ in Example 5: The function is not defined at $x = 0$.

The graph of $f(x)$ is shown in Figure 3.6. This function can be used to model a switch, where the value of $f(x)$ switches from -1 to $+1$ as x goes through 0. We see that $f(x)$ converges to 1 as x tends to 0 from the right and that $f(x)$ converges to -1 as x tends to 0 from the left. We can write this property as

$$\lim_{x \to 0^+} \frac{|x|}{x} = 1 \quad \text{and} \quad \lim_{x \to 0^-} \frac{|x|}{x} = -1$$

and observe that the one-sided limits exist. ■

In Example 5, we computed one-sided limits. Since the right-hand limit differs from the left-hand limit, we conclude that

$$\lim_{x \to 0} \frac{|x|}{x} \quad \text{does not exist}$$

because the phrase "x approaches 0" (or, in symbols, $\lim_{x \to 0}$) means that x approaches 0 in any fashion.

More Limits That Do Not Exist

EXAMPLE 6   Find

$$\lim_{x \to 0} \frac{1}{x^2}$$

Solution   A graph of $f(x) = 1/x^2, x \neq 0$, reveals that $f(x)$ increases without bound as $x \to 0$. (See Figure 3.7.) We also suspect such an increase when we plug in values close to 0. By choosing values sufficiently close to 0, we can get arbitrarily large values of $f(x)$:

x	-0.1	-0.01	-0.001	0.001	0.01	0.1
$f(x)$	100	10,000	10^6	10^6	10,000	100

This table of values indicates that the limit does not exist. ■

When $\lim_{x \to c} f(x)$ does not exist, we say that $f(x)$ *diverges* as x tends to c. The divergence in Example 6 was such that the function grew without bound. This is an important case, and we define it in the following box:

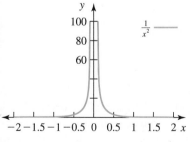

Figure 3.7 The graph of $f(x) = \frac{1}{x^2}$ in Example 6: The function grows without bound as x tends to 0.

$$\lim_{x \to c} f(x) = +\infty \quad \text{if } f(x) \text{ increases without bound as } x \to c$$

$$\lim_{x \to c} f(x) = -\infty \quad \text{if } f(x) \text{ decreases without bound as } x \to c$$

Similar definitions can be given for one-sided limits, which we will need in the next example. Note that when we write $\lim_{x \to c} f(x) = +\infty$ (or $-\infty$), we say that $f(x)$

diverges as $x \to c$. In particular, this means that $\lim_{x \to c} f(x)$ does *not* exist. (The symbols $+\infty$ and $-\infty$ do not refer to real real numbers.) Nevertheless, we write $\lim_{x \to c} f(x) = +\infty$ (or $-\infty$) if $f(x)$ increases (or decreases) without bound as $x \to c$, since it is useful to know when a function does that.

EXAMPLE 7 Find

$$\lim_{x \to 3} \frac{1}{x - 3}$$

Solution The graph of $f(x) = 1/(x - 3)$, $x \neq 3$, in Figure 3.8 reveals that

$$\lim_{x \to 3+} \frac{1}{x - 3} = +\infty \quad \text{and} \quad \lim_{x \to 3-} \frac{1}{x - 3} = -\infty$$

We arrive at the same conclusion when we compute values of $f(x)$ for x close to 3. We see that if x is slightly larger than 3, then $f(x)$ is positive and increases without bound as x approaches 3 from the right. Likewise, if x is slightly smaller than 3, $f(x)$ is negative and decreases without bound as x approaches 3 from the left. We conclude that $f(x)$ diverges as x approaches 3. ■

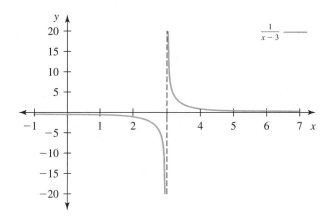

Figure 3.8 The graph of $f(x) = \frac{1}{x-3}$ in Example 7 grows without bound as x approaches 3 from the right and decreases without bound as x approaches 3 from the left.

The next example shows that a function can diverge without having one-sided limits or without going to $+\infty$ or $-\infty$.

EXAMPLE 8 Find

$$\lim_{x \to 0} \sin \frac{\pi}{x}$$

Solution Simply using a calculator and plugging in values to find limits can yield wrong answers if we do not exercise proper caution. If we produced a table of values of $f(x) = \sin \frac{\pi}{x}$ for $x = 0.1, 0.01, 0.001, \ldots$, we would find that $\sin \frac{\pi}{0.1} = 0$, $\sin \frac{\pi}{0.01} = 0$, $\sin \frac{\pi}{0.001} = 0$, and so on. (Note that we measure angles in radians.) These calculations might prompt us to conclude that the limit of the function is 0. But let's look at its graph, which is shown in Figure 3.9. The graph does not support our calculator-based conclusion.

What we find instead is that the values of $f(x)$ oscillate infinitely often between -1 and $+1$ as $x \to 0$. We can see why as follows: As $x \to 0^+$, the argument in the sine function goes to infinity. (Likewise, as $x \to 0^-$, the argument goes to negative infinity.) That is,

$$\lim_{x \to 0+} \frac{\pi}{x} = \infty \quad \text{and} \quad \lim_{x \to 0-} \frac{\pi}{x} = -\infty$$

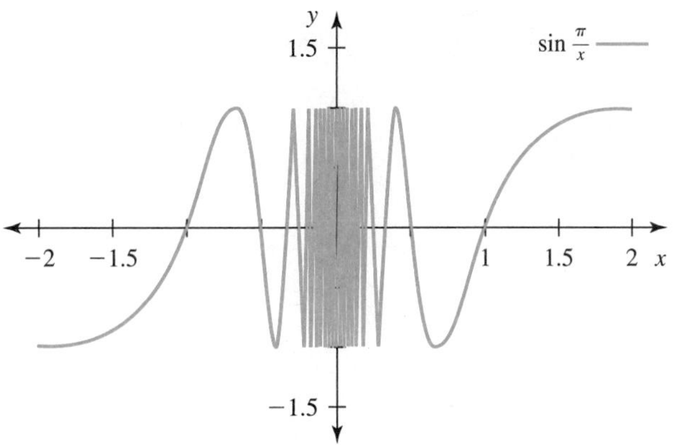

Figure 3.9 The graph of $f(x) = \sin\frac{\pi}{x}$ in Example 8.

As the argument of the sine function goes to $+\infty$ or $-\infty$, the function values oscillate between -1 and $+1$. Therefore, $\sin\frac{\pi}{x}$ continues to oscillate between -1 and $+1$ as $x \to 0$. ■

The behavior exhibited in Example 8 is called **divergence by oscillation**.

Pitfalls The next example is an interesting one that shows other limitations of using a calculator to compute limits.

EXAMPLE 9 Find

$$\lim_{x\to 0} \frac{\sqrt{x^2+16}-4}{x^2}$$

Solution The graph of $f(x) = \frac{\sqrt{x^2+16}-4}{x^2}$, $x \neq 0$, in Figure 3.10 indicates that the limit exists. So, on the basis of the graph, we conjecture that the limit is equal to 0.125. If, instead, we use a calculator to produce a table of values of $f(x)$ close to 0, something strange seems to happen:

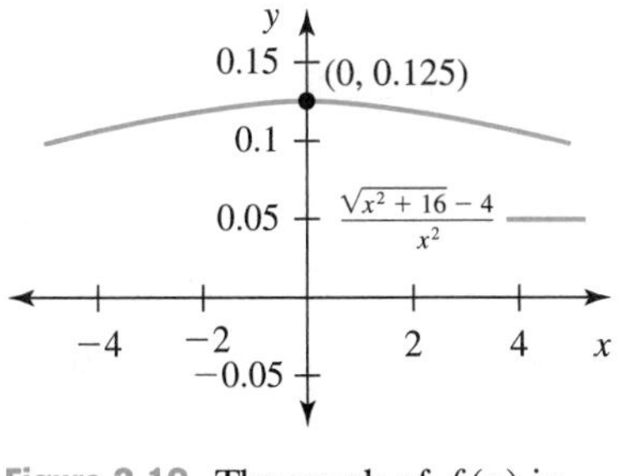

Figure 3.10 The graph of $f(x)$ in Example 9: As x tends to 0, the function approaches 0.125.

x	0.01	0.001	0.0001	0.00001	0.000001	0.0000001
$f(x)$	0.1249998	0.125	0.125	0.125	0.1	0

As we get closer to 0, we first find that $f(x)$ gets closer to 0.125, but when we get very close to 0, $f(x)$ seems to drop to 0. What is going on? First, before you worry too much, note that $\lim_{x\to 0} f(x) = 0.125$. In the next section, we will learn how to compute this limit without resorting to the (somewhat dubious) help of the calculator. The strange behavior of the calculated values happens because, when x is very small, the difference in the numerator is so close to 0 that the calculator can no longer accurately determine its value. The calculator can compute only a certain number of digits accurately, which is good enough for most cases. Here, however, we need greater accuracy. The same strange thing happens when you try to graph this function on a graphing calculator. When the x range of the viewing window is too small, the graph is no longer accurate. (Try, for instance, $-0.00001 \le x \le 0.00001$ and $-0.03 \le y \le 0.15$ as the range for the viewing window.) ■

At the end of this chapter, we will discuss how limits are formally defined. The formal definition is conceptually similar to the one we used to define limits of the form $\lim_{n\to\infty} a_n$, but we will not use it to compute limits. As in Chapter 2, there are mathematical laws that will allow us to compute limits much more easily.

■ 3.1.2 Limit Laws

We encountered limit laws in Chapter 2. Analogous laws hold for limits of the type $\lim_{x\to c} f(x)$.

Limit Laws Suppose that a is a constant and that

$$\lim_{x \to c} f(x) \quad \text{and} \quad \lim_{x \to c} g(x)$$

exist. Then the following rules hold:

1. $\lim\limits_{x \to c} af(x) = a \lim\limits_{x \to c} f(x)$

2. $\lim\limits_{x \to c}[f(x) + g(x)] = \lim\limits_{x \to c} f(x) + \lim\limits_{x \to c} g(x)$

3. $\lim\limits_{x \to c}[f(x) \cdot g(x)] = \lim\limits_{x \to c} f(x) \cdot \lim\limits_{x \to c} g(x)$

4. $\lim\limits_{x \to c} \dfrac{f(x)}{g(x)} = \dfrac{\lim\limits_{x \to c} f(x)}{\lim\limits_{x \to c} g(x)}$ provided that $\lim\limits_{x \to c} g(x) \neq 0$

You are probably easily convinced that

$$\lim_{x \to c} x = c \tag{3.3}$$

In Section 3.6, we will use the formal definition of limits to show that this equation is true. For now, we accept (3.3) as a fact. Starting from that equation, we can use the limit laws to compute limits of polynomials and rational functions.

EXAMPLE 10   Find

$$\lim_{x \to 2}[x^3 + 4x - 1]$$

Solution   Using Rules 1 and 2, we see that this equation becomes

$$\lim_{x \to 2} x^3 + 4 \lim_{x \to 2} x - \lim_{x \to 2} 1$$

provided that the individual limits exist. For the first term, we use Rule 3,

$$\lim_{x \to 2} x^3 = \left(\lim_{x \to 2} x\right)\left(\lim_{x \to 2} x\right)\left(\lim_{x \to 2} x\right)$$

provided that $\lim_{x \to 2} x$ exists. From (3.3), it then follows that $\lim_{x \to 2} x = 2$ and we find that

$$\left(\lim_{x \to 2} x\right)\left(\lim_{x \to 2} x\right)\left(\lim_{x \to 2} x\right) = (2)(2)(2) = 8$$

To compute the second term, we use (3.3) again to obtain $\lim_{x \to 2} x = 2$. For the last term, we find that $\lim_{x \to 2} 1 = 1$. Now that we have shown that the individual limits exist, we can use Rules 1 and 2 to evaluate

$$\lim_{x \to 2}[x^3 + 4x - 1] = \lim_{x \to 2} x^3 + 4 \lim_{x \to 2} x - \lim_{x \to 2} 1 = 8 + (4)(2) - 1 = 15 \qquad ■$$

EXAMPLE 11   Find

$$\lim_{x \to 4} \frac{x^2 + 1}{x - 3}$$

Solution   Using Rule 4, we find that

$$\lim_{x \to 4} \frac{x^2 + 1}{x - 3} = \frac{\lim_{x \to 4}(x^2 + 1)}{\lim_{x \to 4}(x - 3)}$$

provided that the limits in the numerator and denominator exist and the limit in the denominator is not equal to 0. Using Rules 2 and 3 in the numerator, we obtain

$$\lim_{x \to 4}(x^2 + 1) = \left(\lim_{x \to 4} x^2\right) + \left(\lim_{x \to 4} 1\right) = (4)(4) + 1 = 17$$

Breaking up the limit of the sum in the numerator into a sum of limits is justified only after we have shown that the individual limits exist. Using Rules 1 and 2 in the denominator, we get

$$\lim_{x \to 4}(x - 3) = \lim_{x \to 4} x - \lim_{x \to 4} 3 = 4 - 3 = 1$$

Again, using the limit laws is justified only after we have demonstrated that the individual limits exist. Since the limits in both the denominator and the numerator exist and the limit in the denominator is not equal to 0, we obtain

$$\lim_{x \to 4} \frac{x^2 + 1}{x - 3} = \frac{17}{1} = 17 \qquad \blacksquare$$

The computations in Examples 10 and 11 look somewhat awkward, and it appears that what we have done is plug 2 into the expression $x^3 + 4x - 1$ in Example 10 and 4 into the expression $\frac{x^2+1}{x-3}$ in Example 11, even though we emphasized in the informal definition of limits that we are not allowed to simply plug c into $f(x)$ when computing $\lim_{x \to c} f(x)$. But, in essence, we did the calculation

$$\lim_{x \to 2}[x^3 + 4x - 1] = 2^3 + (4)(2) - 1 = 15$$

in Example 10 and the calculation

$$\lim_{x \to 4} \frac{x^2 + 1}{x - 3} = \frac{17}{1} = 17$$

in Example 11.

Even though we made a point that we cannot simply substitute the value c into $f(x)$ when we take the limit $x \to c$ of $f(x)$, the limit laws and (3.3) (which we will prove in Section 3.6) show that we can do just that when we take a limit of a polynomial or a rational function. Let's summarize this property and then look at two more examples that show how to compute limits of polynomials or rational functions by using these results.

If $f(x)$ is a polynomial, then

$$\lim_{x \to c} f(x) = f(c)$$

If $f(x)$ is a rational function

$$f(x) = \frac{p(x)}{q(x)}$$

where $p(x)$ and $q(x)$ are polynomials, and if $q(c) \neq 0$, then

$$\lim_{x \to c} f(x) = \lim_{x \to c} \frac{p(x)}{q(x)} = \frac{p(c)}{q(c)} = f(c)$$

EXAMPLE 12   Find

$$\lim_{x \to 3}[x^2 - 2x + 1]$$

Solution   Since $f(x) = x^2 - 2x + 1$ is a polynomial, it follows that

$$\lim_{x \to 3}[x^2 - 2x + 1] = 9 - 6 + 1 = 4 \qquad ■$$

EXAMPLE 13   Find

$$\lim_{x \to -1} \frac{2x^3 - x + 5}{x^2 + 3x + 1}$$

Solution   Note that

$$f(x) = \frac{2x^3 - x + 5}{x^2 + 3x + 1}$$

is a rational function that is defined for $x = -1$. (The denominator is not equal to 0 when we substitute $x = -1$.) We find that

$$\lim_{x \to -1} \frac{2x^3 - x + 5}{x^2 + 3x + 1} = \frac{2(-1)^3 - (-1) + 5}{(-1)^2 + 3(-1) + 1} = \frac{4}{-1} = -4 \qquad ■$$

When you use the limit laws for finding limits of the form

$$\lim_{x \to c}[f(x) + g(x)] \qquad \text{or} \qquad \lim_{x \to c}[f(x) \cdot g(x)] \qquad \text{or} \qquad \lim_{x \to c} \frac{f(x)}{g(x)}$$

you need to check first that both $\lim_{x \to c} f(x)$ and $\lim_{x \to c} g(x)$ exist and, in the case of $\lim_{x \to c} \frac{f(x)}{g(x)}$, that $\lim_{x \to c} g(x) \neq 0$. The next two examples illustrate the importance of checking the assumptions in the limit laws before applying them.

EXAMPLE 14   Find

$$\lim_{x \to 0} \frac{\frac{1}{x}}{\frac{1}{x} + 1}$$

Solution   We observe that neither

$$\lim_{x \to 0} \frac{1}{x} \qquad \text{nor} \qquad \lim_{x \to 0}\left(\frac{1}{x} + 1\right)$$

exist. So we cannot use Rule 4 right away. Multiplying both numerator and denominator by x, however, will help:

$$\lim_{x \to 0} \frac{\frac{1}{x}}{\frac{1}{x} + 1} = \lim_{x \to 0} \frac{1}{1 + x}$$

Now we have a rational function on the right-hand side, and we can plug in 0 because the denominator, $1 + x$, will be different from 0. We get

$$\lim_{x \to 0} \frac{1}{1 + x} = \frac{1}{1 + 0} = 1 \qquad ■$$

EXAMPLE 15   Find

$$\lim_{x \to 4} \frac{x^2 - 16}{x - 4}$$

Solution The function $f(x) = \frac{x^2 - 16}{x - 4}$ is a rational function, but since $\lim_{x \to 4}(x - 4) = 0$, we cannot use Rule 4. Instead, we need to simplify $f(x)$ first:

$$\lim_{x \to 4} \frac{x^2 - 16}{x - 4} = \lim_{x \to 4} \frac{(x - 4)(x + 4)}{x - 4}$$

Because $x \neq 4$, we can cancel $x - 4$ in the numerator and denominator, which yields

$$\lim_{x \to 4}(x + 4) = 8$$

where we used the fact that $x + 4$ is a polynomial in computing the limit. ■

Section 3.1 Problems

■ 3.1.1

In Problems 1–32, use a table or a graph to investigate each limit.

1. $\lim\limits_{x \to 2}(x^2 - 4x + 1)$

2. $\lim\limits_{x \to 2} \dfrac{x^2 + 3}{x + 2}$

3. $\lim\limits_{x \to -1} \dfrac{2x}{1 + x^2}$

4. $\lim\limits_{s \to 2} s(s^2 - 4)$

5. $\lim\limits_{x \to \pi} 3 \cos \dfrac{x}{4}$

6. $\lim\limits_{t \to \pi/9} \sin(3t)$

7. $\lim\limits_{x \to \pi/2} 2 \sec \dfrac{x}{3}$

8. $\lim\limits_{x \to \pi/2} \tan \dfrac{x - \pi/2}{2}$

9. $\lim\limits_{x \to -2} e^{-x^2/2}$

10. $\lim\limits_{x \to 0} \dfrac{e^x + 1}{2x + 3}$

11. $\lim\limits_{x \to 0} \ln(x + 1)$

12. $\lim\limits_{t \to e} \ln t^3$

13. $\lim\limits_{x \to 3} \dfrac{x^2 - 16}{x - 4}$

14. $\lim\limits_{x \to 2} \dfrac{x^2 - 4}{x + 2}$

15. $\lim\limits_{x \to \pi/2} \sin(2x)$

16. $\lim\limits_{x \to \pi/2} \cos(x - \pi)$

17. $\lim\limits_{x \to 0} \dfrac{1}{1 + x^2}$

18. $\lim\limits_{x \to 0} \dfrac{1}{x^2 - 1}$

19. $\lim\limits_{x \to 0^+}(1 - e^{-x})$

20. $\lim\limits_{x \to 0^-}(1 + e^x)$

21. $\lim\limits_{x \to 4^-} \dfrac{2}{x - 4}$

22. $\lim\limits_{x \to 3^+} \dfrac{1}{x - 3}$

23. $\lim\limits_{x \to 1^-} \dfrac{2}{1 - x}$

24. $\lim\limits_{x \to 2^+} \dfrac{4}{2 - x}$

25. $\lim\limits_{x \to 1^-} \dfrac{1}{1 - x^2}$

26. $\lim\limits_{x \to 2^+} \dfrac{2}{x^2 - 4}$

27. $\lim\limits_{x \to 3} \dfrac{1}{(x - 3)^2}$

28. $\lim\limits_{x \to 0} \dfrac{1 - x^2}{x^2}$

29. $\lim\limits_{x \to 0} \dfrac{\sqrt{x^2 + 9} - 3}{x^2}$

30. $\lim\limits_{x \to 0} \dfrac{\sqrt{x^2 + 4} - 2}{x}$

31. $\lim\limits_{x \to 0} \dfrac{1 - \sqrt{1 - x^2}}{x^2}$

32. $\lim\limits_{x \to 0} \dfrac{\sqrt{2 - x} - \sqrt{2}}{2x}$

33. Use a table and a graph to find out what happens to

$$f(x) = \frac{2}{x^2}$$

as $x \to \infty$. What happens as $x \to -\infty$? What happens as $x \to 0$?

34. Use a table and a graph to find out what happens to

$$f(x) = \frac{2x}{x - 1}$$

as $x \to \infty$. What happens as $x \to -\infty$? What happens as $x \to 1$?

35. Use a graphing calculator to investigate

$$\lim_{x \to 1} \sin \frac{1}{x - 1}$$

36. Use a graphing calculator to investigate

$$\lim_{x \to 0} \cos \frac{1}{x}$$

■ 3.1.2

In Problems 37–54, use the limit laws to evaluate each limit.

37. $\lim\limits_{x \to -1}(x^3 + 7x - 1)$

38. $\lim\limits_{x \to 2}(3x^4 - 2x + 1)$

39. $\lim\limits_{x \to -5}(4 + 2x^2)$

40. $\lim\limits_{x \to 2}(8x^3 - 2x + 4)$

41. $\lim\limits_{x \to 3}\left(2x^2 - \dfrac{1}{x}\right)$

42. $\lim\limits_{x \to -2}\left(\dfrac{x^2}{2} - \dfrac{2}{x^2}\right)$

43. $\lim\limits_{x \to -3} \dfrac{x^3 - 20}{x + 1}$

44. $\lim\limits_{x \to 1} \dfrac{x^3 - 1}{x + 2}$

45. $\lim\limits_{x \to 3} \dfrac{3x^2 + 1}{2x - 3}$

46. $\lim\limits_{x \to -2} \dfrac{1 + x}{1 - x}$

47. $\lim\limits_{x \to 1} \dfrac{1 - x^2}{1 - x}$

48. $\lim\limits_{u \to 3} \dfrac{9 - u^2}{3 - u}$

49. $\lim\limits_{x \to 3} \dfrac{x^2 - 2x - 3}{x - 3}$

50. $\lim\limits_{x \to 1} \dfrac{(x - 1)^2}{x^2 - 1}$

51. $\lim\limits_{x \to 2} \dfrac{2 - x}{x^2 - 4}$

52. $\lim\limits_{x \to -4} \dfrac{x + 4}{16 - x^2}$

53. $\lim\limits_{x \to -2} \dfrac{2x^2 + 3x - 2}{x + 2}$

54. $\lim\limits_{x \to 1/2} \dfrac{1 - x - 2x^2}{1 - 2x}$

■ 3.2 Continuity

■ 3.2.1 What Is Continuity?

Consider the two functions

$$f(x) = \begin{cases} \dfrac{x^2-9}{x-3} & \text{if } x \neq 3 \\ 6 & \text{if } x = 3 \end{cases}$$

and

$$g(x) = \begin{cases} \dfrac{x^2-9}{x-3} & \text{if } x \neq 3 \\ 7 & \text{if } x = 3 \end{cases}$$

We are interested in how these functions behave for x close to 3. Both functions are defined for all $x \in \mathbf{R}$ and are the same for $x \neq 3$. Furthermore, as we saw in Example 3 of Section 3.1,

$$\lim_{x \to 3} f(x) = \lim_{x \to 3} g(x) = \lim_{x \to 3} \frac{x^2-9}{x-3} = 6 \tag{3.4}$$

But the two functions differ at $x = 3$: $f(3) = 6$ and $g(3) = 7$. Comparing these results with (3.4), we see that

$$\lim_{x \to 3} f(x) = f(3) \qquad \text{but} \qquad \lim_{x \to 3} g(x) \neq g(3)$$

This difference can also be seen graphically [Figures 3.11(a) and 3.11(b)]: Although the graph of $f(x)$ can be drawn without lifting the pencil, in graphing $g(x)$ we need to lift the pencil at $x = 3$, since $\lim_{x \to 3} g(x) \neq g(3)$. We say that the function $f(x)$ is **continuous** at $x = 3$, whereas $g(x)$ is **discontinuous** at $x = 3$. Here is the definition of continuity at a point:

> **Definition** A function f is said to be **continuous** at $x = c$ if
> $$\lim_{x \to c} f(x) = f(c)$$

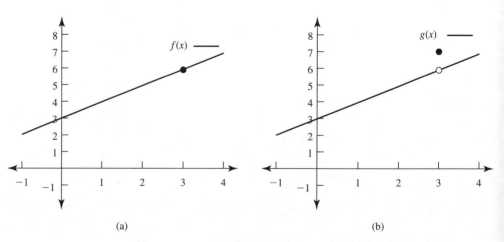

(a)   (b)

Figure 3.11 (a) The graph of $y = f(x)$ is continuous at $x = 3$. (b) The graph of $y = g(x)$ is discontinuous at $x = 3$.

To check whether a function is continuous at $x = c$, we need to check the following three conditions:

1. $f(x)$ is defined at $x = c$.
2. $\lim\limits_{x \to c} f(x)$ exists.
3. $\lim\limits_{x \to c} f(x)$ is equal to $f(c)$.

If any of these three conditions fails, the function is **discontinuous** at $x = c$.

EXAMPLE 1

Show that $f(x) = 2x - 3$, $x \in \mathbf{R}$, is continuous at $x = 1$.

Solution

We must check all three conditions:

1. $f(x)$ is defined at $x = 1$, since $f(1) = 2 \cdot 1 - 3 = -1$.
2. We use the fact that $\lim_{x \to c} x = c$ to conclude that $\lim_{x \to 1} f(x)$ exists.
3. Using the limit laws, we find that $\lim_{x \to 1} f(x) = -1$. This is the same as $f(1)$.

Since all three conditions are satisfied, $f(x) = 2x - 3$ is continuous at $x = 1$. ■

EXAMPLE 2

Let

$$f(x) = \begin{cases} \dfrac{x^2 - x - 6}{x - 3} & \text{if } x \neq 3 \\ a & \text{if } x = 3 \end{cases}$$

and find a so that $f(x)$ is continuous at $x = 3$.

Solution

To compute

$$\lim_{x \to 3} \frac{x^2 - x - 6}{x - 3}$$

we factor the numerator: $x^2 - x - 6 = (x - 3)(x + 2)$. Hence, since $x \neq 3$,

$$\lim_{x \to 3} \frac{x^2 - x - 6}{x - 3} = \lim_{x \to 3} \frac{(x - 3)(x + 2)}{x - 3} = \lim_{x \to 3} (x + 2) = 5$$

To ensure that $f(x)$ is continuous at $x = 3$, we require that

$$\lim_{x \to 3} f(x) = f(3)$$

We therefore need to choose 5 for a. This is the only choice for a that will make $f(x)$ continuous. Any other value of a would result in $f(x)$ being discontinuous. ■

The function $y = \frac{x^2 - x - 6}{x - 3}$, $x \neq 3$, is not defined at $x = 3$ and is therefore automatically discontinuous there. (Condition 1 does not hold.) But we saw in Example 2 that we can *remove the discontinuity* by appropriately defining the function at $x = 3$. Still, it is not always possible to remove discontinuities, as the next three examples will show. In the first two, the discontinuity is a jump; that is, both the left-hand and the right-hand limits exist at the point where the jump occurs, but the limits differ. In the third example, the function grows without bound where it is discontinuous.

EXAMPLE 3

The floor function

$$f(x) = \lfloor x \rfloor = \text{the largest integer less than or equal to } x$$

is graphed in Figure 3.12. The closed circles in the figure correspond to endpoints that are contained in the graph of the function, whereas the open circles correspond to endpoints that are not contained in the graph of the function. To explain this function, we compute a few values: $f(2.1) = 2$, $f(2) = 2$, and $f(1.9999) = 1$. The function jumps whenever x is an integer. Let k be an integer; then $f(k) = k$ and

$$\lim_{x \to k^+} f(x) = k, \qquad \lim_{x \to k^-} f(x) = k - 1$$

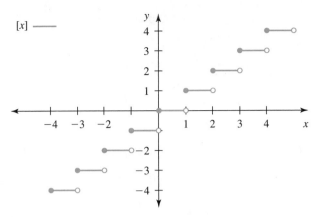

Figure 3.12 The floor function $f(x) = \lfloor x \rfloor$.

That is, only when x approaches an integer from the right is the limit equal to the value of the function. The function is therefore discontinuous at integer values, and the discontinuity cannot be removed. If c is *not* an integer, then $f(x)$ is continuous at $x = c$. ■

Example 3 motivates the definition of one-sided continuity:

> **Definition** A function f is said to be continuous from the right at $x = c$ if
>
> $$\lim_{x \to c^+} f(x) = f(c)$$
>
> and continuous from the left at $x = c$ if
>
> $$\lim_{x \to c^-} f(x) = f(c)$$

The function $f(x) = \lfloor x \rfloor$, $x \in \mathbf{R}$, of Example 3, is therefore continuous from the right but not from the left. In the next example, the discontinuity is again a jump; however, this time we do not even have one-sided continuity.

EXAMPLE 4 Show that

$$f(x) = \begin{cases} \dfrac{|x|}{x} & \text{if } x \neq 0 \\ 0 & \text{if } x = 0 \end{cases}$$

is discontinuous at $x = 0$ and that the discontinuity cannot be removed.

Solution The graph of $f(x)$ is shown in Figure 3.13. We can write

$$f(x) = \begin{cases} 1 & \text{for } x > 0 \\ 0 & \text{for } x = 0 \\ -1 & \text{for } x < 0 \end{cases}$$

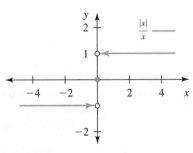

Figure 3.13 The function $f(x) = \frac{|x|}{x}$ is discontinuous at $x = 0$.

since $|x| = x$ for $x > 0$ and $|x| = -x$ for $x < 0$. We therefore get

$$\lim_{x \to 0^+} f(x) = 1 \quad \text{and} \quad \lim_{x \to 0^-} f(x) = -1$$

The one-sided limits exist, but they are not equal [which implies that $\lim_{x \to 0} f(x)$ does not exist]. When we graph the function, a jump occurs at $x = 0$. (See Figure 3.13.) This function does not exhibit even one-sided continuity because $f(x)$ is neither 1 nor -1 at $x = 0$. There is no way that we could assign a value to $f(0)$ such that the function would be continuous at $x = 0$. ■

EXAMPLE 5   At which point is the function

$$f(x) = \frac{1}{(x-4)^2}$$

discontinuous? Can the discontinuity be removed?

Solution   The graph of $f(x)$ is shown in Figure 3.14. The function $f(x)$ cannot be defined for $x = 4$, since $f(x)$ is of the form $\frac{1}{0}$ when $x = 4$. The function is defined for all other values of x. Therefore, we look at $x = 4$. We find that

$$\lim_{x \to 4} \frac{1}{(x-4)^2} = \infty \quad \text{(limit does not exist)}$$

Because ∞ is not a real number, we cannot assign a value to $f(4)$ such that $f(x)$ would be continuous at $x = 4$. We therefore conclude that $f(x)$ is discontinuous at $x = 4$ and the discontinuity cannot be removed.   ■

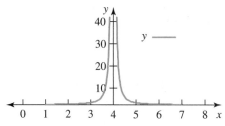

Figure 3.14 The function $f(x) = \frac{1}{(x-4)^2}$ is discontinuous at $x = 4$.

■ 3.2.2 Combinations of Continuous Functions

Using the limit laws, we find that the following statements hold for combinations of continuous functions:

Suppose that a is a constant and the functions f and g are continuous at $x = c$. Then the following functions are continuous at $x = c$:

1. $a \cdot f$
2. $f + g$
3. $f \cdot g$
4. $\dfrac{f}{g}$ provided that $g(c) \neq 0$

Proof We will prove only the second statement. We must show that conditions 1–3 of the previous subsection hold:

1. Note that $[f + g](x) = f(x) + g(x)$. Therefore, $f + g$ is defined at $x = c$ and $[f + g](c) = f(c) + g(c)$.
2. We assumed that f and g are continuous at $x = c$. This means, in particular, that

$$\lim_{x \to c} f(x) \quad \text{and} \quad \lim_{x \to c} g(x)$$

both exist. That is, the hypothesis in the limit laws holds, and we can apply Rule 2 for limits and find that

$$\lim_{x \to c}[f + g](x) = \lim_{x \to c}[f(x) + g(x)] = \lim_{x \to c} f(x) + \lim_{x \to c} g(x) \qquad (3.5)$$

In other words, $\lim_{x \to c}[f + g](x)$ exists and condition 2 holds.

3. Since f and g are continuous at $x = c$, it follows that

$$\lim_{x \to c} f(x) = f(c) \quad \text{and} \quad \lim_{x \to c} g(x) = g(c) \tag{3.6}$$

Therefore, combining (3.5) and (3.6), we obtain

$$\lim_{x \to c}[f+g](x) = \lim_{x \to c} f(x) + \lim_{x \to c} g(x) = f(c) + g(c)$$

which is equal to $[f+g](c)$ and hence condition 3 holds.

Since we showed that all three conditions hold, it follows that $f+g$ is continuous at $x = c$. The other statements are shown in a similar way, using the limit laws. ■

We say that a function f is continuous on an interval I if f is continuous for all $x \in I$. Note that if I is a closed interval, then continuity at the left (and, respectively, right) endpoint of the interval means continuous from the right (and, respectively, left). Many of the elementary functions are indeed continuous wherever they are defined. For polynomials and rational functions, this statement follows immediately from the fact that certain combinations of continuous functions are continuous. We give a list of the most important cases:

The following functions are continuous wherever they are defined:

1. polynomial functions
2. rational functions
3. power functions
4. trigonometric functions
5. exponential functions of the form a^x, $a > 0$ and $a \neq 1$
6. logarithmic functions of the form $\log_a x$, $a > 0$ and $a \neq 1$

The phrase "wherever they are defined" is crucial. It helps us to identify points where a function might be discontinuous. For instance, the power function $1/x^2$ is defined only for $x \neq 0$, and the logarithmic function $\log_a x$ is defined only for $x > 0$. We will illustrate the six cases cited in the preceding box in the next example, paying particular attention to the phrase "wherever they are defined."

EXAMPLE 6   For which values of $x \in \mathbf{R}$ are the following functions continuous?

(a) $f(x) = 2x^3 - 3x + 1$ (b) $f(x) = \dfrac{x^2 + x + 1}{x - 2}$ (c) $f(x) = x^{1/4}$

(d) $f(x) = 3 \sin x$ (e) $f(x) = \tan x$ (f) $f(x) = 3^x$

(g) $2 \ln(x + 1)$

Solution   (a) $f(x)$ is a polynomial and is defined for all $x \in \mathbf{R}$; it is therefore continuous for all $x \in \mathbf{R}$.

(b) $f(x)$ is a rational function defined for all $x \neq 2$; it is therefore continuous for all $x \neq 2$.

(c) $f(x) = x^{1/4} = \sqrt[4]{x}$ is a power function defined for $x \geq 0$; it is therefore continuous for $x \geq 0$.

(d) $f(x)$ is a trigonometric function. Because $\sin x$ is defined for all $x \in \mathbf{R}$, $3 \sin x$ is continuous for all $x \in \mathbf{R}$.

(e) $f(x)$ is a trigonometric function. The tangent function is defined for all $x \neq \frac{\pi}{2} + k\pi$, where k is an integer; it is therefore continuous for all $x \neq \frac{\pi}{2} + k\pi$, where k is an integer.

(f) $f(x)$ is an exponential function. $f(x) = 3^x$ is defined for all $x \in \mathbf{R}$ and is therefore continuous for all $x \in \mathbf{R}$.

(g) $f(x)$ is a logarithmic function. $f(x) = 2\ln(x+1)$ is defined as long as $x+1 > 0$ or $x > -1$; it is therefore continuous for all $x > -1$. ■

The following result is useful in determining whether a composition of functions is continuous:

> **Theorem** If $g(x)$ is continuous at $x = c$ with $g(c) = L$ and $f(x)$ is continuous at $x = L$, then $(f \circ g)(x)$ is continuous at $x = c$. In particular,
>
> $$\lim_{x \to c}(f \circ g)(x) = \lim_{x \to c} f[g(x)] = f[\lim_{x \to c} g(x)] = f[g(c)] = f(L)$$

To explain this theorem, recall what it means to compute $(f \circ g)(c) = f[g(c)]$. When we compute $f[g(c)]$, we take the value c, compute $g(c)$, and then take the result $g(c)$ and plug it into the function f to obtain $f[g(c)]$. If, at each step, the functions are continuous, the resulting function will be continuous.

EXAMPLE 7 Determine where the following functions are continuous:

(a) $h(x) = e^{-x^2}$ **(b)** $h(x) = \sin\dfrac{\pi}{x}$ **(c)** $h(x) = \dfrac{1}{1 + 2x^{1/3}}$

Solution   **(a)** Set $g(x) = -x^2$ and $f(x) = e^x$. Then $h(x) = (f \circ g)(x)$. Since $g(x)$ is a polynomial, it is continuous for all $x \in \mathbf{R}$, and the range of $g(x)$ is $(-\infty, 0]$. $f(x)$ is continuous for all values in the range of $g(x)$. [In fact, $f(x)$ is continuous for all $x \in \mathbf{R}$.] It therefore follows that $h(x)$ is continuous for all $x \in \mathbf{R}$.

(b) Set $g(x) = \frac{\pi}{x}$ and $f(x) = \sin x$. $g(x)$ is continuous for all $x \neq 0$. The range of $g(x)$ is the set of all real numbers, excluding 0. $f(x)$ is continuous for all x in the range of $g(x)$. Hence, $h(x)$ is continuous for all $x \neq 0$. Recall that we showed in Example 8 of Section 3.1 that

$$\lim_{x \to 0} \sin\frac{\pi}{x}$$

does not exist. That is, $h(x)$ is discontinuous at $x = 0$.

(c) Set $g(x) = x^{1/3}$ and $f(x) = \frac{1}{1+2x}$. Then $h(x) = (f \circ g)(x)$. $g(x)$ is continuous for all $x \in \mathbf{R}$, since $g(x) = x^{1/3} = \sqrt[3]{x}$ and 3 is an odd integer. The range of $g(x)$ is $(-\infty, \infty)$. $f(x)$ is continuous for all real x different from $-1/2$. Since $g(-\frac{1}{8}) = -\frac{1}{2}$, $h(x)$ is continuous for all real x different from $-1/8$. Another way to see that we need to exclude $-\frac{1}{8}$ from the domain of $h(x)$ is by looking directly at the denominator of $h(x)$. We have $1 + 2x^{1/3} = 0$ when $x = -\frac{1}{8}$. ■

When we compute $\lim_{x \to c} f(x)$ and we know that $f(x)$ is continuous at $x = c$, it follows that $\lim_{x \to c} f(x) = f(c)$. The next three examples illustrate this property.

EXAMPLE 8 Find

$$\lim_{x \to 3} \sin\left(\pi\frac{x^2 - 1}{4}\right)$$

Solution   The function $f(x) = \sin\left(\pi\frac{x^2-1}{4}\right)$ is continuous at $x = 3$. Hence,

$$\lim_{x \to 3} \sin\left(\pi\frac{x^2 - 1}{4}\right) = \sin\left(\pi\frac{9 - 1}{4}\right) = \sin(2\pi) = 0$$

■

EXAMPLE 9   Find

$$\lim_{x \to 1} \sqrt{2x^3 - 1}$$

Solution   The function $f(x) = \sqrt{2x^3 - 1}$ is continuous at $x = 1$. Thus,

$$\lim_{x \to 1} \sqrt{2x^3 - 1} = \sqrt{(2)(1)^3 - 1} = \sqrt{1} = 1$$ ■

EXAMPLE 10   Find

$$\lim_{x \to 0} e^{x-1}$$

Solution   The function $f(x) = e^{x-1}$ is continuous at $x = 0$. Therefore,

$$\lim_{x \to 0} e^{x-1} = e^{0-1} = e^{-1}$$ ■

We conclude this section by calculating the limit of the expression in Example 9 of Section 3.1.

EXAMPLE 11   Find

$$\lim_{x \to 0} \frac{\sqrt{x^2 + 16} - 4}{x^2}$$

Solution   We cannot apply Rule 4 of Section 3.1, since $f(x) = (\sqrt{x^2 + 16} - 4)/x^2$ is not defined for $x = 0$. (If we plug in 0, we get the expression $0/0$.) We use a trick that will allow us to find the limit: We rationalize the numerator. For $x \neq 0$, we find that

$$\frac{\sqrt{x^2 + 16} - 4}{x^2} = \frac{(\sqrt{x^2 + 16} - 4)}{x^2} \frac{(\sqrt{x^2 + 16} + 4)}{(\sqrt{x^2 + 16} + 4)}$$

$$= \frac{x^2 + 16 - 16}{x^2(\sqrt{x^2 + 16} + 4)} = \frac{x^2}{x^2(\sqrt{x^2 + 16} + 4)}$$

$$= \frac{1}{\sqrt{x^2 + 16} + 4}$$

Note that we are allowed to divide by x^2 in the last step, since we are assuming that $x \neq 0$. We can now apply Rule 4 to $1/(\sqrt{x^2 + 16} + 4)$. When we do, we obtain

$$\lim_{x \to 0} \frac{\sqrt{x^2 + 16} - 4}{x^2} = \lim_{x \to 0} \frac{1}{\sqrt{x^2 + 16} + 4} = \frac{1}{8} = 0.125$$

as we saw in Example 9 of Section 3.1. In Chapter 5, we will learn another method for finding the limit of expressions of the form $0/0$.   ■

Section 3.2 Problems

■ **3.2.1**

In Problems 1–4, show that each function is continuous at the given value.

1. $f(x) = 2x, c = 1/2$

2. $f(x) = -x, c = 1$

3. $f(x) = x^3 - 2x + 1, c = 2$

4. $f(x) = x^2 + 1, c = -1$

5. Show that

$$f(x) = \begin{cases} \dfrac{x^2 - x - 2}{x - 2} & \text{if } x \neq 2 \\ 3 & \text{if } x = 2 \end{cases}$$

is continuous at $x = 2$.

6. Show that

$$f(x) = \begin{cases} \dfrac{2x^2 + x - 6}{x + 2} & \text{if } x \neq -2 \\ -7 & \text{if } x = -2 \end{cases}$$

is continuous at $x = -2$.

7. Let

$$f(x) = \begin{cases} \dfrac{x^2 - 9}{x - 3} & \text{if } x \neq 3 \end{cases}$$

Which value must you assign to a so that $f(x)$ is continuous at $x = 3$?

8. Let

$$f(x) = \begin{cases} \dfrac{x^2 + x - 2}{x - 1} & \text{if } x \neq 1 \\ a & \text{if } x = 1 \end{cases}$$

Which value must you assign to a so that $f(x)$ is continuous at $x = 1$?

In Problems 9–12, determine at which points $f(x)$ is discontinuous.

9. $f(x) = \dfrac{1}{x - 3}$

10. $f(x) = \dfrac{1}{x^2 - 1}$

11. $f(x) = \begin{cases} \dfrac{x^2 - 3x + 2}{x - 2} & \text{if } x \neq 1 \\ 1 & \text{if } x = 1 \end{cases}$

12. $f(x) = \begin{cases} x^2 - 1 & \text{if } x \leq 0 \\ x & \text{if } x > 0 \end{cases}$

13. Show that the floor function $f(x) = \lfloor x \rfloor$ is continuous at $x = 5/2$ but discontinuous at $x = 3$.

14. Show that the floor function $f(x) = \lfloor x \rfloor$ is continuous from the right at $x = 2$.

■ **3.2.2**

In Problems 15–24, find the values of $x \in \mathbf{R}$ for which the given functions are continuous.

15. $f(x) = 3x^4 - x^2 + 4$

16. $f(x) = \sqrt{x^2 - 1}$

17. $f(x) = \dfrac{x^2 + 1}{x - 1}$

18. $f(x) = \cos(2x)$

19. $f(x) = e^{-|x|}$

20. $f(x) = \ln(x - 2)$

21. $f(x) = \ln \dfrac{x}{x + 1}$

22. $f(x) = \exp[-\sqrt{x - 1}]$

23. $f(x) = \tan(2\pi x)$

24. $f(x) = \sin\left(\dfrac{2x}{3 + x}\right)$

25. Let

$$f(x) = \begin{cases} x^2 + 2 & \text{for } x \leq 0 \\ x + c & \text{for } x > 0 \end{cases}$$

(a) Graph $f(x)$ when $c = 1$, and determine whether $f(x)$ is continuous for this choice of c.

(b) How must you choose c so that $f(x)$ is continuous for all $x \in (-\infty, \infty)$?

26. Let

$$f(x) = \begin{cases} \dfrac{1}{x} & \text{for } x \geq 1 \\ 2x + c & \text{for } x < 1 \end{cases}$$

(a) Graph $f(x)$ when $c = 0$, and determine whether $f(x)$ is continuous for this choice of c.

(b) How must you choose c so that $f(x)$ is continuous for all $x \in (-\infty, \infty)$?

27. (a) Show that

$$f(x) = \sqrt{x - 1}, \quad x \geq 1$$

is continuous from the right at $x = 1$.

(b) Graph $f(x)$.

(c) Does it make sense to look at continuity from the left at $x = 1$?

28. (a) Show that

$$f(x) = \sqrt{x^2 - 4}, \quad |x| \geq 2$$

is continuous from the right at $x = 2$ and continuous from the left at $x = -2$.

(b) Graph $f(x)$.

(c) Does it make sense to look at continuity from the left at $x = 2$ and at continuity from the right at $x = -2$?

In Problems 29–48, find the limits.

29. $\lim\limits_{x \to \pi/3} \sin\left(\dfrac{x}{2}\right)$

30. $\lim\limits_{x \to -\pi/2} \cos(2x)$

31. $\lim\limits_{x \to \pi/2} \dfrac{\cos^2 x}{1 - \sin^2 x}$

32. $\lim\limits_{x \to -\pi/2} \dfrac{1 + \tan^2 x}{\sec^2 x}$

33. $\lim\limits_{x \to -1} \sqrt{4 + 5x^4}$

34. $\lim\limits_{x \to -2} \sqrt{6 + x}$

35. $\lim\limits_{x \to -1} \sqrt{x^2 + 2x + 2}$

36. $\lim\limits_{x \to 1} \sqrt{x^3 + 4x - 1}$

37. $\lim\limits_{x \to 0} e^{-x^2/3}$

38. $\lim\limits_{x \to 0} e^{3x+2}$

39. $\lim\limits_{x \to 3} e^{x^2 - 9}$

40. $\lim\limits_{x \to -1} e^{x^2/2 - 1}$

41. $\lim\limits_{x \to 0} \dfrac{e^{2x} - 1}{e^x - 1}$

42. $\lim\limits_{x \to 0} \dfrac{e^{-x} - e^x}{e^{-x} + 1}$

43. $\lim\limits_{x \to -2} \dfrac{1}{\sqrt{5x^2 - 4}}$

44. $\lim\limits_{x \to 1} \dfrac{1}{\sqrt{3 - 2x^2}}$

45. $\lim\limits_{x \to 0} \dfrac{\sqrt{x^2 + 9} - 3}{x^2}$

46. $\lim\limits_{x \to 0} \dfrac{5 - \sqrt{25 + x^2}}{2x^2}$

47. $\lim\limits_{x \to 0} \ln(1 - x)$

48. $\lim\limits_{x \to 1} \ln[e^x \cos(x - 1)]$

■ 3.3 Limits at Infinity

The limit laws discussed in Subsection 3.1.2 also hold as x tends to ∞ (or $-\infty$).

EXAMPLE 1 Find

$$\lim_{x \to \infty} \dfrac{x}{x + 1}$$

Solution   We set $f(x) = x$ and $g(x) = x+1$. Obviously, neither $\lim_{x\to\infty} f(x)$ nor $\lim_{x\to\infty} g(x)$ exists. Thus, we cannot use Rule 4 from Section 3.1. But we can divide both numerator and denominator by x. When we do, we find that

$$\lim_{x\to\infty} \frac{x}{x+1} = \lim_{x\to\infty} \frac{1}{1+\frac{1}{x}}$$

Since $\lim_{x\to\infty} 1 = 1$ and $\lim_{x\to\infty}(1+\frac{1}{x}) = 1$, both limits exist. Furthermore, $\lim_{x\to\infty}(1+\frac{1}{x}) \neq 0$. We can now apply Rule 4 of Section 3.1 after having done the algebraic manipulation:

$$\lim_{x\to\infty} \frac{x}{x+1} = \lim_{x\to\infty} \frac{1}{1+\frac{1}{x}} = \frac{\lim_{x\to\infty} 1}{\lim_{x\to\infty}(1+\frac{1}{x})} = \frac{1}{1} = 1$$ ■

In Example 1, we computed the limit of a rational function as x tended to infinity. Rational functions are ratios of polynomials. To find out how the limit of a rational function behaves as x tends to infinity, we will first compare the relative growth of functions of the form $y = x^n$: If $n > m$, then x^n dominates x^m for large x, in the sense that

$$\lim_{x\to\infty} \frac{x^n}{x^m} = \infty \quad \text{and} \quad \lim_{x\to\infty} \frac{x^m}{x^n} = 0$$

The preceding statement follows immediately if we simplify the fractions

$$\frac{x^n}{x^m} = x^{n-m} \quad \text{with } n-m > 0$$

and

$$\frac{x^m}{x^n} = \frac{1}{x^{n-m}} \quad \text{with } n-m > 0$$

This limiting behavior is important when we compute limits of rational functions as $x \to \infty$. We compare the following three limits:

(a) $\displaystyle\lim_{x\to\infty} \frac{x^2 + 2x - 1}{x^3 - 3x + 1}$

(b) $\displaystyle\lim_{x\to\infty} \frac{2x^3 - 4x + 7}{3x^3 + 7x^2 - 1}$

(c) $\displaystyle\lim_{x\to\infty} \frac{x^4 + 2x - 5}{x^2 - x + 2}$

To determine whether the numerator or the denominator dominates, we look at each of their leading terms. (The leading term is the term with the largest exponent.) The leading term of a polynomial tells us how quickly the polynomial increases as x increases.

(a) The leading term in the numerator is x^2, and the leading term in the denominator is x^3. As $x \to \infty$, the denominator grows much faster than the numerator. We therefore expect the limit to be equal to 0. We can show this by dividing both numerator and denominator by the higher of the two powers, namely, x^3. We get

$$\lim_{x\to\infty} \frac{x^2 + 2x - 1}{x^3 - 3x + 1} = \lim_{x\to\infty} \frac{\frac{1}{x} + \frac{2}{x^2} - \frac{1}{x^3}}{1 - \frac{3}{x^2} + \frac{1}{x^3}}$$

Since $\lim_{x\to\infty}(\frac{1}{x} + \frac{2}{x^2} - \frac{1}{x^3})$ exists (it is equal to 0), and $\lim_{x\to\infty}(1 - \frac{3}{x^2} + \frac{1}{x^3})$ exists and is not equal to 0 (it is equal to 1), we can apply Rule 4 to find that

$$\lim_{x\to\infty} \frac{\frac{1}{x} + \frac{2}{x^2} - \frac{1}{x^3}}{1 - \frac{3}{x^2} + \frac{1}{x^3}} = \frac{\lim_{x\to\infty}(\frac{1}{x} + \frac{2}{x^2} - \frac{1}{x^3})}{\lim_{x\to\infty}\left(1 - \frac{3}{x^2} + \frac{1}{x^3}\right)} = \frac{0}{1} = 0$$

(b) The leading term in both the numerator and the denominator is x^3, so we divide numerator and denominator by x^3 and obtain

$$\lim_{x\to\infty} \frac{2x^3 - 4x + 7}{3x^3 + 7x^2 - 1} = \lim_{x\to\infty} \frac{2 - \frac{4}{x^2} + \frac{7}{x^3}}{3 + \frac{7}{x} - \frac{1}{x^3}} = \frac{2}{3}$$

In the last step, we used the facts that the limits in both the numerator and the denominator exist and that the limit in the denominator is not equal to 0. Applying Rule 4 yields the limiting value. Note that the limiting value is equal to the ratio of the coefficients of the leading terms in the numerator and the denominator.

(c) The leading term in the numerator is x^4 and the leading term in the denominator is x^2. Since the leading term in the numerator grows much more quickly than the leading term in the denominator, we expect the limit to be undefined. This is indeed the case and can be seen if we divide the numerator by the denominator. We find that

$$\lim_{x\to\infty} \frac{x^4 + 2x - 5}{x^2 - x + 2} = \lim_{x\to\infty}\left(x^2 + x - 1 - \frac{x+3}{x^2 - x + 2}\right) \quad \text{does not exist}$$

It is often useful to determine whether the limit tends to $+\infty$ or $-\infty$. Since $x^2 + x - 1$ tends to $+\infty$ as $x \to \infty$ and the ratio $\frac{x+3}{x^2-x+2}$ tends to 0 as $x \to \infty$, the limit of $\frac{x^4+2x-5}{x^2-x+2}$ tends to $+\infty$ as $x \to +\infty$.

Let's summarize our findings: If $f(x)$ is a rational function of the form $f(x) = p(x)/q(x)$, where $p(x)$ is a polynomial of degree $\deg(p)$ and $q(x)$ is a polynomial of degree $\deg(q)$, then

$$\lim_{x\to\infty} f(x) = \lim_{x\to\infty} \frac{p(x)}{q(x)} = \begin{cases} 0 & \text{if } \deg(p) < \deg(q) \\ L \neq 0 & \text{if } \deg(p) = \deg(q) \\ \text{does not exist} & \text{if } \deg(p) > \deg(q) \end{cases}$$

Here, L is a real number that is the ratio of the coefficients of the leading terms in the numerator and denominator. The same behavior holds as $x \to -\infty$.

EXAMPLE 2

Compute

(a) $\displaystyle\lim_{x\to-\infty} \frac{1 - x + 2x^2}{3x - 5x^2}$

(b) $\displaystyle\lim_{x\to\infty} \frac{1 - x^3}{1 + x^5}$

(c) $\displaystyle\lim_{x\to\infty} \frac{2 - x^2}{1 + 2x}$

(d) $\displaystyle\lim_{x\to-\infty} \frac{4 + 3x^2}{1 - 7x}$

Solution

(a) Since the degree of the numerator is equal to the degree of the denominator,

$$\lim_{x\to-\infty} \frac{1 - x + 2x^2}{3x - 5x^2} = \frac{2}{-5} = -\frac{2}{5}$$

(b) Since the degree of the numerator is less than the degree of the denominator,

$$\lim_{x\to\infty} \frac{1 - x^3}{1 + x^5} = 0$$

(c) Since the degree of the numerator is greater than the degree of the denominator, the limit does not exist. When x is very large, the expression $\frac{2-x^2}{1+2x}$ behaves like $\frac{-x^2}{2x} = -\frac{x}{2}$, which tends to $-\infty$ as $x \to \infty$. Hence,

$$\lim_{x\to\infty} \frac{2 - x^2}{1 + 2x} = -\infty \quad \text{(limit does not exist)}$$

(d) The degree of the numerator is greater than the degree of the denominator, so

$$\lim_{x \to -\infty} \frac{4 + 3x^2}{1 - 7x} = \infty \qquad \text{(limit does not exist)}$$

since $\frac{4+3x^2}{1-7x}$ behaves like $\frac{3x^2}{-7x} = -\frac{3}{7}x$ for x large, which tends to $+\infty$ as $x \to -\infty$. ■

Rational functions are not the only functions that involve limits as $x \to \infty$ (or $x \to -\infty$). Many important applications in biology involve exponential functions. We will use the following result repeatedly—it is one of the most important limits:

$$\lim_{x \to \infty} e^{-x} = 0$$

The graph of $f(x) = e^{-x}$ is given in Figure 3.15. You should familiarize yourself with the basic shape of the function $f(x) = e^{-x}$ and its behavior as $x \to \infty$.

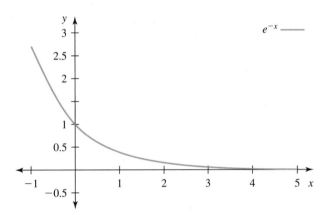

Figure 3.15 The graph of $f(x) = e^{-x}$.

EXAMPLE 3 **Logistic Growth** The logistic curve describes the density of a population over time, where the rate of growth depends on the population size. We will discuss this function in more detail in coming chapters. It suffices here to say that the per capita rate of growth decreases with increasing population size. If $N(t)$ denotes the size of the population at time t, then the logistic curve is given by

$$N(t) = \frac{K}{1 + \left(\frac{K}{N(0)} - 1\right) e^{-rt}} \qquad \text{for } t \geq 0$$

The parameters K and r are positive numbers that describe the population dynamics. We can check that $N(0)$ on the right-hand side is indeed the population size at time 0 [evaluate $N(t)$ at $t = 0$], and we assume that $N(0)$ is positive. The graph of $N(t)$ is shown in Figure 3.16. We will interpret K now; the interpretation of r must wait until the next chapter.

If we are interested in the long-term behavior of the population as it evolves in accordance with the logistic growth curve, we need to investigate what happens to $N(t)$ as $t \to \infty$. We find that

$$\lim_{t \to \infty} \frac{K}{1 + \left(\frac{K}{N(0)} - 1\right) e^{-rt}} = K$$

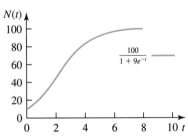

Figure 3.16 The graph of the logistic curve with $K = 100$, $N_0 = 10$, and $r = 1$.

since $\lim_{t \to \infty} e^{-rt} = 0$ for $r > 0$. That is, as $t \to \infty$, the population size approaches K, which is called the **carrying capacity** of the population. You will encounter logistic growth repeatedly in this text; it is one of the most fundamental equations describing population growth. ■

Section 3.3 Problems

Evaluate the limits in Problems 1–24.

1. $\lim\limits_{x \to \infty} \dfrac{2x^2 - 3x + 5}{x^4 - 2x + 1}$

2. $\lim\limits_{x \to \infty} \dfrac{x^2 + 3}{5x^2 - 2x + 1}$

3. $\lim\limits_{x \to -\infty} \dfrac{x^3 + 3}{x - 2}$

4. $\lim\limits_{x \to -\infty} \dfrac{2x - 1}{3 - 4x}$

5. $\lim\limits_{x \to \infty} \dfrac{1 - x^3 + 2x^4}{2x^2 + x^4}$

6. $\lim\limits_{x \to \infty} \dfrac{1 - 5x^3}{1 + 3x^4}$

7. $\lim\limits_{x \to \infty} \dfrac{x^2 - 2}{2x + 1}$

8. $\lim\limits_{x \to -\infty} \dfrac{3 - x^2}{1 - 2x^2}$

9. $\lim\limits_{x \to -\infty} \dfrac{x^2 - 3x + 1}{4 - x}$

10. $\lim\limits_{x \to -\infty} \dfrac{1 - x^3}{2 + x}$

11. $\lim\limits_{x \to -\infty} \dfrac{2 + x^2}{1 - x^2}$

12. $\lim\limits_{x \to -\infty} \dfrac{2x + x^2}{3x + 1}$

13. $\lim\limits_{x \to \infty} \dfrac{4}{1 + e^{-2x}}$

14. $\lim\limits_{x \to \infty} \dfrac{e^{-x}}{1 - e^{-x}}$

15. $\lim\limits_{x \to \infty} \dfrac{2e^x}{e^x + 3}$

16. $\lim\limits_{x \to \infty} \dfrac{e^x}{2 - e^x}$

17. $\lim\limits_{x \to -\infty} \exp[x]$

18. $\lim\limits_{x \to \infty} \exp[-\ln x]$

19. $\lim\limits_{x \to \infty} \dfrac{3e^{2x}}{2e^{2x} - e^x}$

20. $\lim\limits_{x \to \infty} \dfrac{3e^{2x}}{2e^{2x} - e^{3x}}$

21. $\lim\limits_{x \to \infty} \dfrac{3}{2 + e^{-x}}$

22. $\lim\limits_{x \to -\infty} \dfrac{4}{1 + e^{-x}}$

23. $\lim\limits_{x \to -\infty} \dfrac{e^x}{1 + x}$

24. $\lim\limits_{x \to \infty} \dfrac{2}{e^x(1 + x)}$

25. In Section 1.2.3, Example 6, we introduced the Monod growth function

$$r(N) = a \frac{N}{k + N}, \quad N \geq 0$$

Find $\lim\limits_{N \to \infty} r(N)$.

26. In Problem 86 of Section 1.3, we discussed the Michaelis–Menten equation, which describes the initial velocity of an enzymatic reaction (v_0) as a function of the substrate concentration (s_0). The equation was given by

$$v_0 = \frac{v_{max} s_0}{s_0 + K_m}$$

Find $\lim\limits_{s_0 \to \infty} v_0$.

27. Suppose the size of a population at time t is given by

$$N(t) = \frac{500t}{3 + t}, \quad t \geq 0$$

(a) Use a graphing calculator to sketch the graph of $N(t)$.

(b) Determine the size of the population as $t \to \infty$. We call this the **limiting population size**.

(c) Show that, at time $t = 3$, the size of the population is half its limiting size.

28. Logistic Growth Suppose that the size of a population at time t is given by

$$N(t) = \frac{100}{1 + 9e^{-t}}$$

for $t \geq 0$.

(a) Use a graphing calculator to sketch the graph of $N(t)$.

(b) Determine the size of the population as $t \to \infty$, using the basic rules for limits. Compare your answer with the graph that you sketched in (a).

29. Logistic Growth Suppose that the size of a population at time t is given by

$$N(t) = \frac{50}{1 + 3e^{-t}}$$

for $t \geq 0$.

(a) Use a graphing calculator to sketch the graph of $N(t)$.

(b) Determine the size of the population as $t \to \infty$, using the basic rules for limits. Compare your answer with the graph that you sketched in (a).

■ 3.4 The Sandwich Theorem and Some Trigonometric Limits

What happens during bungee jumping? The jumper is tied to an elastic rope, jumps off a bridge, and experiences damped oscillations until she comes to rest and will be hauled in to safety. The trajectory over time might resemble the function (Figure 3.17)

$$g(x) = e^{-x} \cos(10x), \quad x \geq 0$$

We suspect from the graph that

$$\lim_{x \to \infty} e^{-x} \cos(10x) = 0$$

If we wanted to calculate this limit, we would quickly see that none of the rules we have learned so far apply. Although $\lim_{x \to \infty} e^{-x} = 0$, we find that $\lim_{x \to \infty} \cos(10x)$ does not exist: The function $\cos(10x)$ oscillates between -1 and 1. Still, this property allows us to sandwich the function $g(x) = e^{-x} \cos(10x)$ between $f(x) = -e^{-x}$ and $h(x) = e^{-x}$. To do so, we note that from

$$-1 \leq \cos(10x) \leq 1$$

it follows that

$$-e^{-x} \leq e^{-x} \cos(10x) \leq e^{-x}$$

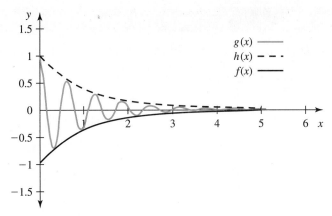

Figure 3.17 The graph of $f(x) = e^{-x} \cos x$, together with the two functions $g(x) = e^{-x}$ and $h(x) = -e^{-x}$.

Then, since

$$\lim_{x \to \infty} (-e^{-x}) = \lim_{x \to \infty} e^{-x} = 0$$

our function $g(x) = e^{-x} \cos(10x)$ gets squeezed in between the two functions $f(x) = -e^{-x}$ and $h(x) = e^{-x}$, which both go to 0 as x tends to infinity. Therefore,

$$\lim_{x \to \infty} e^{-x} \cos(10x) = 0$$

This useful method is known as the sandwich theorem. We will not prove it.

> **Sandwich Theorem** If $f(x) \leq g(x) \leq h(x)$ for all x in an open interval that contains c (except possibly at c) and
>
> $$\lim_{x \to c} f(x) = \lim_{x \to c} h(x) = L$$
>
> then
>
> $$\lim_{x \to c} g(x) = L$$

The theorem is called the sandwich theorem because we "sandwich" the function $g(x)$ between the two functions $f(x)$ and $h(x)$. Since $f(x)$ and $h(x)$ converge to the same value as $x \to c$, $g(x)$ also must converge to that value as $x \to c$, because it is squeezed in between $f(x)$ and $h(x)$. The sandwich theorem also applies to one-sided limits. We demonstrate how to use the sandwich theorem in the next example.

EXAMPLE 1   Show that

$$\lim_{x \to 0} x^2 \sin \frac{1}{x} = 0$$

Solution   First, note that we cannot use Rule 3—which says that the limit of a product is equal to the product of the limits—because it requires that the limits of both factors exist. The limit of $\sin(1/x)$ as $x \to 0$ does not exist; instead, it diverges by oscillating. (See Example 8 of Section 3.1 for a similar limit.) However, we know that

$$-1 \leq \sin \frac{1}{x} \leq 1$$

for all $x \neq 0$. To go from this set of inequalities to one that involves $x^2 \sin \frac{1}{x}$, we need to multiply all three parts by x^2. Performing the multiplication, we find that

$$-x^2 \leq x^2 \sin \frac{1}{x} \leq x^2$$

Since $\lim_{x\to 0}(-x^2) = \lim_{x\to 0} x^2 = 0$, we can apply the sandwich theorem to obtain

$$\lim_{x\to 0} x^2 \sin\frac{1}{x} = 0$$

This limit is illustrated in Figure 3.18.   ■

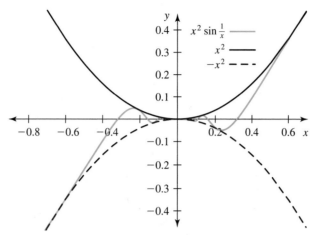

Figure 3.18 The graph of $f(x) = x^2 \sin\frac{1}{x}$.

EXAMPLE 2

Show that

$$\lim_{x\to 0} x \sin\frac{1}{x} = 0$$

Solution

As in Example 1, note that we cannot use Rule 3—which, again, says that the limit of a product is equal to the product of the limits—because it requires that the limits of both factors exist. The limit of $\sin(1/x)$ as $x \to 0$ does not exist; instead, it diverges by oscillating. (See Example 8 of Section 3.1 for a similar limit.) However, we know that

$$-1 \le \sin\frac{1}{x} \le 1$$

for all $x \neq 0$. To go from this set of inequalities to one that involves $x \sin\frac{1}{x}$, we need to multiply all three parts by x. Since multiplying an inequality by x reverses inequality signs when $x < 0$, we need to split the discussion into two cases, one involving $x > 0$, the other $x < 0$.

Multiplying all three parts by $x > 0$, we find that

$$-x \le x \sin\frac{1}{x} \le x$$

Since $\lim_{x\to 0^+}(-x) = \lim_{x\to 0^+} x = 0$, we can apply the sandwich theorem to obtain

$$\lim_{x\to 0^+} x \sin\frac{1}{x} = 0$$

We can repeat the same steps when we multiply by $x < 0$, except we now need to reverse the inequality signs. That is, for $x < 0$,

$$-x \ge x \sin\frac{1}{x} \ge x$$

Because $\lim_{x\to 0^-}(-x) = \lim_{x\to 0^-} x = 0$, we can again apply the sandwich theorem and get

$$\lim_{x\to 0^-} x \sin\frac{1}{x} = 0$$

The left-hand and right-hand limits are the same. Therefore, combining the two results, we find that

$$\lim_{x \to 0} x \sin \frac{1}{x} = 0$$

This limit is illustrated in Figure 3.19. ■

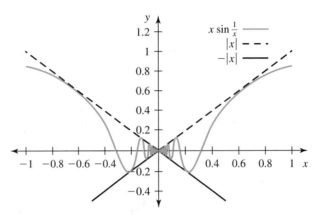

Figure 3.19 The sandwich theorem illustrated on $\lim_{x \to 0} x \sin(1/x)$.

The following two trigonometric limits are important for developing the differential calculus for trigonometric functions:

$$\lim_{x \to 0} \frac{\sin x}{x} = 1 \quad \text{and} \quad \lim_{x \to 0} \frac{1 - \cos x}{x} = 0$$

You should memorize these two limits, noting that the angle x is measured in radians. We will prove both statements. The proof of the first statement uses a nice geometric argument and the sandwich theorem; the second statement follows from the first.

Proof that $\lim_{x \to 0} \frac{\sin x}{x} = 1$ We will need to divide an inequality by $\sin x$. Since dividing an inequality by a negative number reverses the inequality sign (see Example 1), we will split the proof into two cases, one in which $0 < x < \pi/2$, the other in which $-\pi/2 < x < 0$. In the former case, both x and $\sin x$ are positive; in the latter, both x and $\sin x$ are negative. (Since we are interested in the limit as $x \to 0$, we can restrict the values of x to values close to 0.) We start with the case $0 < x < \pi/2$. In Figure 3.20, we draw the unit circle together with the triangles OAD and OBC. The angle x is measured in radians. Since $\overline{OB} = 1$, we find that

$$\text{arc length of } BD = x$$
$$\overline{OA} = \cos x$$
$$\overline{AD} = \sin x$$
$$\overline{BC} = \tan x$$

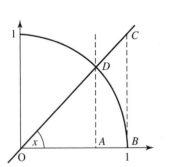

Figure 3.20 The unit circle with the triangles OAD and OBC.

Furthermore, using the symbol $\triangle$ to denote a triangle, we obtain

$$\text{area of } \triangle OAD \leq \text{area of sector } OBD \leq \text{area of } \triangle OBC$$

The area of a sector of central angle x (measured in radians) and radius r is $\frac{1}{2}r^2 x$. Therefore,

$$\frac{1}{2}\overline{OA} \cdot \overline{AD} \leq \frac{1}{2}\overline{OB}^2 \cdot x \leq \frac{1}{2}\overline{OB} \cdot \overline{BC}$$

or

$$\frac{1}{2}\cos x \sin x \le \frac{1}{2} \cdot 1^2 \cdot x \le \frac{1}{2} \cdot 1 \cdot \tan x$$

Dividing this pair of inequalities by $\frac{1}{2}\sin x$ (and noting that $\frac{1}{2}\sin x > 0$ for $0 < x < \pi/2$) yields

$$\cos x \le \frac{x}{\sin x} \le \frac{1}{\cos x}$$

On the rightmost part, we used the fact that $\tan x = \frac{\sin x}{\cos x}$. Taking reciprocals and reversing the inequality signs gives

$$\frac{1}{\cos x} \ge \frac{\sin x}{x} \ge \cos x$$

We can now take the limit as $x \to 0^+$. (Remember, we assumed that $0 < x < \pi/2$, so we can approach 0 only from the right.) We find that

$$\lim_{x \to 0^+} \cos x = 1 \quad \text{and} \quad \lim_{x \to 0^+} \frac{1}{\cos x} = \frac{1}{\lim_{x \to 0^+} \cos x} = 1$$

We now apply the sandwich theorem, which yields

$$\lim_{x \to 0^+} \frac{\sin x}{x} = 1$$

We have shown only that $\lim_{x \to 0^+} \frac{\sin x}{x} = 1$, but a similar argument can be carried out when $-\frac{\pi}{2} < x < 0$. In this case, $\lim_{x \to 0^-} \frac{\sin x}{x} = 1$. The left-hand and the right-hand limits are the same, and we conclude that

$$\lim_{x \to 0} \frac{\sin x}{x} = 1$$

■

Proof that $\lim_{x \to 0} \frac{1 - \cos x}{x} = 0$ Multiplying both numerator and denominator of $f(x) = (1 - \cos x)/x$ by $1 + \cos x$, we can reduce the second statement to the first:

$$\lim_{x \to 0} \frac{1 - \cos x}{x} = \lim_{x \to 0} \frac{1 - \cos x}{x} \frac{1 + \cos x}{1 + \cos x}$$

$$= \lim_{x \to 0} \frac{1 - \cos^2 x}{x(1 + \cos x)}$$

Using the identity $\sin^2 x + \cos^2 x = 1$, we write this as

$$\lim_{x \to 0} \frac{\sin^2 x}{x(1 + \cos x)}$$

Rewriting again, we obtain

$$\lim_{x \to 0} \frac{\sin x}{x} \frac{\sin x}{1 + \cos x}$$

and we can determine the limit. First, we note that $\lim_{x \to 0} \frac{\sin x}{x}$ exists by the first statement, and $\lim_{x \to 0} \frac{\sin x}{1 + \cos x}$ exists because $1 + \cos x \ne 0$ for x close to 0. Then, by Rule 3 of the limit laws, the limit of a product is the product of the limits. We therefore find that

$$\lim_{x \to 0} \frac{\sin x}{x} \frac{\sin x}{1 + \cos x} = \lim_{x \to 0} \frac{\sin x}{x} \lim_{x \to 0} \frac{\sin x}{1 + \cos x} = 1 \cdot 0 = 0$$

■

EXAMPLE 3 Find the following limits.

(a) $\lim\limits_{x\to0} \dfrac{\sin 3x}{5x}$ (b) $\lim\limits_{x\to0} \dfrac{\sin^2 x}{x^2}$ (c) $\lim\limits_{x\to0} \dfrac{\sec x - 1}{x \sec x}$

Solution (a) We cannot apply the first trigonometric limit directly. The trick is to substitute $z = 3x$ and observe that $z \to 0$ as $x \to 0$. Then

$$\lim_{x\to0} \frac{\sin 3x}{5x} = \lim_{z\to0} \frac{\sin z}{5z/3} = \frac{3}{5} \lim_{z\to0} \frac{\sin z}{z} = \frac{3}{5}$$

(b) We note that

$$\lim_{x\to0} \frac{\sin^2 x}{x^2} = \lim_{x\to0} \left(\frac{\sin x}{x} \right)^2 = \left(\lim_{x\to0} \frac{\sin x}{x} \right)^2 = 1$$

Here, we used the fact that the limit of a product is the product of the limits, provided that the individual limits exist.

(c) We first write $\sec x = 1/\cos x$ and then multiply both numerator and denominator by $\cos x$:

$$\lim_{x\to0} \frac{\sec x - 1}{x \sec x} = \lim_{x\to0} \frac{\frac{1}{\cos x} - 1}{\frac{x}{\cos x}}$$

$$= \lim_{x\to0} \frac{\left(\frac{1}{\cos x} - 1 \right) \cos x}{\frac{x}{\cos x} \cos x} = \lim_{x\to0} \frac{1 - \cos x}{x} = 0 \qquad ■$$

Section 3.4 Problems

1. Let

$$f(x) = x^2 \cos \frac{1}{x}, \quad x \neq 0$$

(a) Use a graphing calculator to sketch the graph of $y = f(x)$.

(b) Show that

$$-x^2 \leq x^2 \cos \frac{1}{x} \leq x^2$$

holds for $x \neq 0$.

(c) Use your result in (b) and the sandwich theorem to show that

$$\lim_{x\to0} x^2 \cos \frac{1}{x} = 0$$

2. Let

$$f(x) = x \cos \frac{1}{x}, \quad x \neq 0$$

(a) Use a graphing calculator to sketch the graph of $y = f(x)$.

(b) Use the sandwich theorem to show that

$$\lim_{x\to0} x \cos \frac{1}{x} = 0$$

3. Let

$$f(x) = \frac{\ln x}{x}, \quad x > 0$$

(a) Use a graphing calculator to graph $y = f(x)$.

(b) Use a graphing calculator to investigate the values of x for which

$$\frac{1}{x} \leq \frac{\ln x}{x} \leq \frac{1}{\sqrt{x}}$$

holds.

(c) Use your result in (b) to explain why the following is true:

$$\lim_{x\to\infty} \frac{\ln x}{x} = 0$$

4. Let

$$f(x) = \frac{\sin x}{x}, \quad x > 0$$

(a) Use a graphing calculator to graph $y = f(x)$.

(b) Explain why you cannot use the basic rules for finding limits to compute

$$\lim_{x\to\infty} \frac{\sin x}{x}$$

(c) Show that

$$-\frac{1}{x} \leq \frac{\sin x}{x} \leq \frac{1}{x}$$

holds for $x > 0$, and use the sandwich theorem to compute

$$\lim_{x\to\infty} \frac{\sin x}{x}$$

In Problems 5–20, evaluate the trigonometric limits.

5. $\lim\limits_{x\to 0} \dfrac{\sin(2x)}{2x}$

6. $\lim\limits_{x\to 0} \dfrac{\sin(2x)}{3x}$

7. $\lim\limits_{x\to 0} \dfrac{\sin(5x)}{x}$

8. $\lim\limits_{x\to 0} \dfrac{\sin x}{-x}$

9. $\lim\limits_{x\to 0} \dfrac{\sin(\pi x)}{x}$

10. $\lim\limits_{x\to 0} \dfrac{\sin(-\pi x/2)}{2x}$

11. $\lim\limits_{x\to 0} \dfrac{\sin(\pi x)}{\sqrt{x}}$

12. $\lim\limits_{x\to 0} \dfrac{\sin^2 x}{x}$

13. $\lim\limits_{x\to 0} \dfrac{\sin x \cos x}{x(1-x)}$

14. $\lim\limits_{x\to 0} \dfrac{1-\cos^2 x}{x^2}$

15. $\lim\limits_{x\to 0} \dfrac{1-\cos x}{2x}$

16. $\lim\limits_{x\to 0} \dfrac{1-\cos(2x)}{3x}$

17. $\lim\limits_{x\to 0} \dfrac{1-\cos(5x)}{2x}$

18. $\lim\limits_{x\to 0} \dfrac{1-\cos(x/2)}{x}$

19. $\lim\limits_{x\to 0} \dfrac{\sin x(1-\cos x)}{x^2}$

20. $\lim\limits_{x\to 0} \dfrac{\csc x - \cot x}{x \csc x}$

21. (a) Use a graphing calculator to sketch the graph of

$$f(x) = e^{ax}\sin x, \quad x \geq 0$$

for $a = -0.1, -0.01, 0, 0.01,$ and 0.1.

(b) Which part of the function $f(x)$ produces the oscillations that you see in the graphs sketched in (a)?

(c) Describe in words the effect that the value of a has on the shape of the graph of $f(x)$.

(d) Graph $f(x) = e^{ax}\sin x$, $g(x) = -e^{ax}$, and $h(x) = e^{ax}$ together in one coordinate system for **(i)** $a = 0.1$ and **(ii)** $a = -0.1$. [Use separate coordinate systems for (i) and (ii).] Explain what you see in each case. Show that

$$-e^{ax} \leq e^{ax}\sin x \leq e^{ax}$$

Use this pair of inequalities to determine the values of a for which

$$\lim\limits_{x\to\infty} f(x)$$

exists, and find the limiting value.

3.5 Properties of Continuous Functions

■ 3.5.1 The Intermediate-Value Theorem

As you hike up a mountain, the temperature decreases with increasing elevation. Suppose the temperature at the bottom of the mountain is 70°F and the temperature at the top of the mountain is 40°F. How do you know that at some time during your hike you must have crossed a point where the temperature was exactly 50°F? Your answer will probably be something like the following: "To go from 70°F to 40°F, I must have passed through 50°F, since 50°F is between 40°F and 70°F and the temperature changed continuously as I hiked up the mountain." This statement represents the content of the intermediate-value theorem.

> **The Intermediate-Value Theorem** Suppose that f is continuous on the closed interval $[a, b]$. If L is any real number with $f(a) < L < f(b)$ or $f(b) < L < f(a)$, then there exists at least one number c on the open interval (a, b) such that $f(c) = L$.

We will not prove this theorem, but Figure 3.21 should convince you that it is true. In the figure, f is continuous and defined on the closed interval $[a, b]$ with $f(a) < L < f(b)$. Therefore, the graph of $f(x)$ must intersect the line $y = L$ at least once on the open interval (a, b).

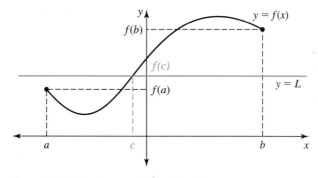

Figure 3.21 The intermediate-value theorem.

EXAMPLE 1   Let

$$f(x) = 3 + \sin x \quad \text{for } 0 \le x \le \frac{3\pi}{2}$$

Show that there exists at least one point c in $(0, 3\pi/2)$ such that $f(c) = 5/2$.

Solution   The graph of $f(x)$ is shown in Figure 3.22. First, note that $f(x)$ is defined on a closed interval and is continuous on $[0, 3\pi/2]$. Furthermore, we find that

$$f(0) = 3 + \sin 0 = 3 + 0 = 3$$

$$f\left(\frac{3\pi}{2}\right) = 3 + \sin \frac{3\pi}{2} = 3 + (-1) = 2$$

Given that

$$2 < \frac{5}{2} < 3$$

we conclude from the intermediate-value theorem that there exists a number c such that $f(c) = 5/2$. Note that the theorem does not tell us where c is or whether there is more than one such number.   ■

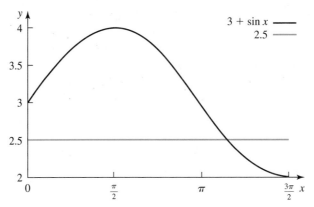

Figure 3.22 The intermediate-value theorem for $f(x) = 3 + \sin x, 0 \le x \le 3\pi/2$, and $L = 2.5$.

In applying the intermediate-value theorem, it is important to check that f is continuous. Discontinuous functions can easily miss values; for example, the floor function in Example 3 of Section 3.2 misses all numbers that are not integers.

As mentioned in Example 1, the intermediate-value theorem gives us only the existence of a number c; it does not tell us how many such points there are or where they are located.

You might wonder how such a result can be of any use. One important application is that the theorem can be used to find approximate roots (or solutions) of equations of the form $f(x) = 0$. We show how in the next example.

EXAMPLE 2   Find a root of the equation $x^5 - 7x^2 + 3 = 0$.

Solution   Let $f(x) = x^5 - 7x^2 + 3 = 0$. Because $f(x)$ is a polynomial, it is continuous for all $x \in \mathbf{R}$. Furthermore,

$$\lim_{x \to -\infty} f(x) = -\infty \quad \text{and} \quad \lim_{x \to \infty} f(x) = \infty$$

That is, if we choose a large enough interval $[a, b]$, then $f(a) < 0$ and $f(b) > 0$ and, therefore, there must be a number $c \in (a, b)$ such that $f(c) = 0$. This number c is a root of the equation $f(x) = 0$. The existence of c is guaranteed by the intermediate-value theorem.

To find a number c for which $f(c) = 0$, we use the **bisection method**. We start by finding a and b such that $f(a) < 0$ and $f(b) > 0$. For example,

$$f(-1) = -5 \quad \text{and} \quad f(2) = 7$$

The intermediate-value theorem then tells us that there must be a number in $(-1, 2)$ for which $f(c) = 0$. To locate this root with more precision, we take the midpoint of $(-1, 2)$, which is 0.5, and evaluate the function at $x = 0.5$. [The midpoint of the interval (a, b) is $(a + b)/2$.] Now, $f(0.5) \approx 1.28$ (rounded to two decimals). We thus have

$$f(-1) = -5 \quad f(0.5) \approx 1.28 \quad f(2) = 7$$

Using the intermediate-value theorem again, we can now guarantee a root in $(-1, 0.5)$, since $f(-1) < 0$ and $f(0.5) > 0$. Bisecting the new interval and computing the respective values of $f(x)$, we find that

$$f(-1) = -5 \quad f(-0.25) \approx 2.562 \quad f(0.5) \approx 1.28$$

Using the intermediate-value theorem yet again, we can guarantee a root in $(-1, -0.25)$, since $f(-1) < 0$ and $f(-0.25) > 0$. Repeating this procedure of bisecting and selecting a new (smaller) interval will eventually produce an interval that is small enough that we can locate the root to any desired accuracy. The first several steps are summarized in Table 3-1.

TABLE 3-1 Bisection Method

a	$\frac{a+b}{2}$	b	$f(a)$	$f(\frac{a+b}{2})$	$f(b)$
-1	0.5	2	-5	1.28	7
-1	0.5	2	-5	1.28	7
-1	-0.25	0.5	-5	2.562	1.28
-1	-0.625	-0.25	-5	0.170	2.562
-1	-0.8125	-0.625	-5	-1.975	0.170
-0.8125	-0.71875	-0.625	-1.975	-0.808	0.170
-0.71875	-0.671875	-0.625	-0.808	-0.297	0.170
-0.671875	-0.6484375	-0.625	-0.297	-0.0579	0.170
-0.6484375	-0.63671875	-0.625	-0.0579	0.0575	0.170
-0.6484375	-0.642578125	-0.63671875	-0.0579	9.9×10^{-5}	0.0575
-0.6484375		-0.642578125			

After nine steps, we find that there exists a root in

$$(-0.6484375, -0.642578125)$$

The length of this interval is 0.005859375. If we are satisfied with that level of precision, we can stop here and choose, for instance, the midpoint of the last interval as an approximate value for a root of the equation $x^5 - 7x^2 + 3 = 0$. The midpoint is

$$\frac{-0.642578125 + (-0.6484375)}{2} = -0.6455078125$$

$$\approx -0.646$$

(rounded to three decimals).

Note that the length of the interval decreases by a factor of $1/2$ at each step. That is, after nine steps, the length of the interval is $(1/2)^9$ of the length of the original interval. In this example, the length of the original interval was 3; hence, the length of the interval after nine steps is

$$3 \cdot \left(\frac{1}{2}\right)^9 = \frac{3}{512} = 0.005859375$$

as we saw. The bisection method is fairly slow when we need high accuracy. For instance, to reduce the length of the interval to 10^{-6}, we would need at least 22 steps, since

$$3 \cdot \left(\frac{1}{2}\right)^{21} > 10^{-6} > 3 \cdot \left(\frac{1}{2}\right)^{22}$$

In Section 5.7, we will learn a faster method.

Figure 3.23 shows the graph of $f(x) = x^5 - 7x^2 + 3$. We see that the graph intersects the x-axis three times. We found an approximation of the leftmost root of the equation $x^5 - 7x^2 + 3$. If we had used another starting interval—say, $[1, 2]$—we would have located an approximation of the rightmost root of the equation. ■

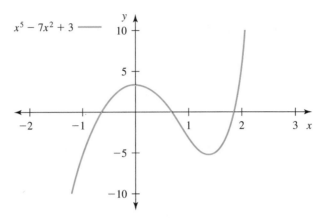

Figure 3.23 The graph of $f(x) = x^5 - 7x^2 + 3$.

■ 3.5.2 A Final Remark on Continuous Functions

Many functions in biology are in fact discontinuous. For example, if we measure the size of a population over time, we find that it takes on discrete values only (namely, nonnegative integers) and therefore changes discontinuously. However, if the population size is sufficiently large, an increase or decrease by 1 changes the population size so slightly that it might be justified to approximate it by a continuous function. For example, if we measure the number of bacteria, in millions, in a petri dish, then the number 2.1 would correspond to 2,100,000 bacteria. An increase by 1 results in 2,100,001 bacteria, or, if we measure the size in millions, in 2.100001, an increase of 10^{-6}.

Section 3.5 Problems

■ 3.5.1, 3.5.2

1. Let

$$f(x) = x^2 - 1, \quad 0 \le x \le 2$$

(a) Graph $y = f(x)$ for $0 \le x \le 2$.

(b) Show that

$$f(0) < 0 < f(2)$$

and use the intermediate-value theorem to conclude that there exists a number $c \in (0, 2)$ such that $f(c) = 0$.

2. Let

$$f(x) = x^3 - 2x + 3, \quad -3 \le x \le -1$$

(a) Graph $y = f(x)$ for $-3 \le x \le -1$.

(b) Use the intermediate-value theorem to conclude that

$$x^3 - 2x + 3 = 0$$

has a solution in $(-3, -1)$.

3. Let

$$f(x) = \sqrt{x^2 + 2}, \quad 1 \le x \le 2$$

(a) Graph $y = f(x)$ for $1 \le x \le 2$.

(b) Use the intermediate-value theorem to conclude that

$$\sqrt{x^2 + 2} = 2$$

has a solution in $(1, 2)$.

4. Let

$$f(x) = \sin x - x, \quad -1 \le x \le 1$$

(a) Graph $y = f(x)$ for $-1 \le x \le 1$.

(b) Use the intermediate-value theorem to conclude that

$$\sin x = x$$

has a solution in $(-1, 1)$.

5. Use the intermediate-value theorem to show that

$$e^{-x} = x$$

has a solution in $(0, 1)$.

6. Use the intermediate-value theorem to show that

$$\cos x = x$$

has a solution in $(0, 1)$.

7. Use the bisection method to find a solution of

$$e^{-x} = x$$

that is accurate to two decimal places.

8. Use the bisection method to find a solution of

$$\cos x = x$$

that is accurate to two decimal places.

9. (a) Use the bisection method to find a solution of $3x^3 - 4x^2 - x + 2 = 0$ that is accurate to two decimal places.

(b) Graph the function $f(x) = 3x^3 - 4x^2 - x + 2$.

(c) Which solution did you locate in (a)? Is it possible in this case to find the other solution by using the bisection method together with the intermediate-value theorem?

10. In Example 2, how many steps are required to guarantee that the approximate root is within 0.0001 of the true value of the root?

11. Suppose that the number of individuals in a population at time t is given by

$$N(t) = \frac{54t}{13 + t}, \quad t \geq 0 \qquad (3.7)$$

(a) Use a calculator to confirm that $N(10)$ is approximately 23.47826. Considering that the number of individuals in a population is an integer, how should you report your answer?

(b) Now suppose that $N(t)$ is given by the same function (3.7), but that the size of the population is measured in millions. How should you report the population size at time $t = 10$? Make some reasonable assumptions about the accuracy of a measurement for the size of such a large population.

(c) Discuss the use of continuous functions in both (a) and (b).

12. Suppose that the biomass of a population at time t is given by

$$B(t) = \frac{32.00t}{17.00 + t}, \quad t \geq 0 \qquad (3.8)$$

(a) Use a calculator to confirm that $B(10)$ is approximately 1.185185. Considering the function $B(t)$, how many significant figures should you report in your answer?

(b) Discuss the use of continuous functions in this problem.

13. Explain why a polynomial of degree 3 has at least one root.

14. Explain why a polynomial of degree n, where n is an odd number, has at least one root.

15. Explain why $y = x^2 - 4$ has at least two roots.

16. On the basis of the intermediate-value theorem, what can you say about the number of roots of a polynomial of even degree?

■ 3.6 A Formal Definition of Limits (Optional)

The ancient Greeks used limiting procedures to compute areas, such as the area of a circle, by the "method of exhaustion." In this method, a region was covered (or "exhausted") as closely as possible by triangles. Adding the areas of the triangles then yielded an approximation of the area of the region of interest. Newton and Leibniz, the inventors of calculus, were aware of the importance of taking limits in their development of the subject; however, they did not give a rigorous definition of the procedure. The French mathematician Augustin-Louis Cauchy (1789–1857) was the first to develop a rigorous definition of limits; the definition we will use goes back to the German mathematician Karl Weierstrass (1815–1897).

Before we write the formal definition, let's return to the informal one. In that definition, we stated that $\lim_{x \to c} f(x) = L$ means that the value of $f(x)$ can be made arbitrarily close to L whenever x is sufficiently close to c. But just how close is sufficient? Take Example 1 from Section 3.1: Suppose we wish to show that

$$\lim_{x \to 2} x^2 = 4$$

without using the continuity of $y = x^2$, which itself was based on $\lim_{x \to c} x = c$ [Equation (3.3)]. What would we have to do? We would need to show that x^2 can be made arbitrarily close to 4 for all values of x sufficiently close, but not equal, to 2. (In what follows, we will always exclude $x = 2$ from the discussion, since the value of x^2 at $x = 2$ is irrelevant in finding the limit.) Suppose we wish to make x^2 within 0.01 of 4; that is, we want $|x^2 - 4| < 0.01$. Does this inequality hold for all x sufficiently close, but not equal, to 2? We begin with

$$|x^2 - 4| < 0.01$$

which is equivalent to

$$-0.01 < x^2 - 4 < 0.01$$
$$3.99 < x^2 < 4.01$$
$$\sqrt{3.99} < |x| < \sqrt{4.01}$$

Now, $\sqrt{3.99} = 1.997498\ldots$ and $\sqrt{4.01} = 2.002498\ldots$. We therefore find that values of $x \neq 2$ in the interval $(1.998, 2.002)$ satisfy $|x^2 - 4| < 0.01$. (We chose a somewhat smaller interval than indicated, to get an interval that is symmetric about 2.) That is, for all values of x within 0.002 of 2 but not equal to 2 (i.e., $0 < |x - 2| < 0.002$), x^2 is within the prescribed precision—that is, within 0.01 of 4.

You might think about this example in the following way: Suppose that you wish to stake out a square of area 4 m^2. Each side of your square is 2 m long. You bring along a stick, which you cut to a length of 2 m. We can then ask: How accurately do we need to cut the stick so that the area will be within a prescribed precision? Our prescribed precision was 0.01, and we found that if we cut the stick within 0.002 of 2 m, we would be able to obtain the prescribed precision.

There is nothing special about 0.01; we could have chosen any other degree of precision and would have found a corresponding interval of x-values. We translate this procedure into a formal definition of limits. (See Figure 3.24.)

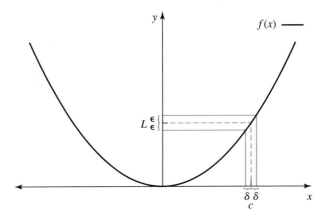

Figure 3.24 The ϵ–δ definition of limits.

Definition The statement

$$\lim_{x \to c} f(x) = L$$

means that, for every $\epsilon > 0$, there exists a number $\delta > 0$ such that

$$|f(x) - L| < \epsilon \quad \text{whenever} \quad 0 < |x - c| < \delta$$

Note that, as in the informal definition of limits, we exclude the value $x = c$ from the statement. (This is done in the inequality $0 < |x - c|$.) To apply the formal definition, we first need to guess the limiting value L. We then choose an $\epsilon > 0$, the prescribed precision, and try to find a $\delta > 0$ such that $f(x)$ is within ϵ of L whenever x is within δ of c but not equal to c. [In our example, $f(x) = x^2$, $c = 2$, $L = 4$, $\epsilon = 0.01$, and $\delta = 0.002$.]

EXAMPLE 1   Show that

$$\lim_{x \to 1} (2x - 3) = -1$$

Solution   We let $f(x) = 2x - 3$. Our guess for the limiting value is $L = -1$. Then

$$|f(x) - L| = |2x - 3 - (-1)|$$
$$= |2x - 2|$$
$$= 2|x - 1|$$

We now choose $\epsilon > 0$. (ϵ is arbitrary, and we do not specify it because our statement needs to hold for all $\epsilon > 0$.) Our goal is to find a $\delta > 0$ such that $2|x - 1| < \epsilon$ whenever x is within δ of 1 but not equal to 1; that is, $0 < |x - 1| < \delta$. The value of δ will typically depend on our choice of ϵ. Since $|x - 1| < \delta$ implies that $2|x - 1| < 2\delta$, we should try $2\delta = \epsilon$. If we choose $\delta = \epsilon/2$, then, indeed,

$$|f(x) - L| = 2|x - 1| < 2\delta = 2\frac{\epsilon}{2} = \epsilon$$

This means that, for every $\epsilon > 0$, we can find a number $\delta > 0$ (namely, $\delta = \epsilon/2$) such that

$$|f(x) - (-1)| < \epsilon \qquad \text{whenever} \qquad 0 < |x - 1| < \delta$$

But this is exactly the definition of

$$\lim_{x \to 1} (2x - 3) = -1$$ ■

EXAMPLE 2   We promised in Section 3.2 that we would show that

$$\lim_{x \to c} x = c$$

Solution   Let $f(x) = x$. We need to show that, for every $\epsilon > 0$, there corresponds a number $\delta > 0$ such that

$$|x - c| < \epsilon \qquad \text{whenever} \qquad 0 < |x - c| < \delta \qquad (3.9)$$

This immediately suggests that we should choose $\delta = \epsilon$, and, indeed, if $\delta = \epsilon$, then (3.9) holds. ■

Let's look at an example in which $f(x)$ is not linear.

EXAMPLE 3   Use the formal definition of limits to show that

$$\lim_{x \to 0} x^3 = 0$$

Solution   We need to show that, for every $\epsilon > 0$, there corresponds a number $\delta > 0$ such that

$$|x^3| < \epsilon \quad \text{whenever} \quad 0 < |x| < \delta \qquad (3.10)$$

Now, $|x^3| < \epsilon$ is equivalent to

$$-\epsilon < x^3 < \epsilon$$
$$-\epsilon^{1/3} < x < \epsilon^{1/3}$$

This pair of inequalities suggests that we set $\delta = \epsilon^{1/3}$. Accordingly, if $0 < |x| < \epsilon^{1/3}$, then

$$-\epsilon^{1/3} < x < \epsilon^{1/3}$$

or

$$-\epsilon < x^3 < \epsilon$$

which is the same as $|x^3| < \epsilon$. ■

We can also use the formal definition to show that a limit does not exist.

EXAMPLE 4   Show that

$$\lim_{x \to 0} \frac{|x|}{x}$$

does not exist.

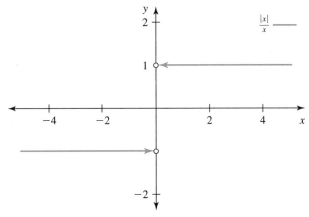

Figure 3.25 The graph of $f(x) = \frac{|x|}{x}$ in Example 4: The limit of $\frac{|x|}{x}$ as x tends to 0 does not exist.

Solution   Showing that this limit does not exist is tricky. (See Figure 3.25.) The approach is as follows: First, we set $f(x) = |x|/x$, $x \neq 0$. Then we assume that the limit exists and try to find a contradiction.[1] Suppose, then, that there exists an L such that

$$\lim_{x \to 0} \frac{|x|}{x} = L$$

If we look at Figure 3.25, we see that if, for instance, we choose $L = 1$, then we cannot get close to L when x is less than 0. Similarly, we see that, for any value of L, either the distance to $+1$ exceeds 1 or the distance to -1 exceeds 1. That is, regardless of the value of L, if $\epsilon < 1$, we will not be able to find a value of δ such that if $0 < |x| < \delta$, then $|f(x) - L| < \epsilon$, since $f(x)$ takes on both the values $+1$ and -1 for $0 < |x| < \delta$. Therefore, $\lim_{x \to 0} \frac{|x|}{x}$ does not exist.   ■

In the previous section, we considered an example in which $\lim_{x \to c} f(x) = \infty$. This statement can be made precise as well.

> **Definition** The statement
> $$\lim_{x \to c} f(x) = \infty$$
> means that, for every $M > 0$, there exists a $\delta > 0$ such that
> $$f(x) > M \quad \text{whenever} \quad 0 < |x - c| < \delta$$

Similar definitions hold for the case when $f(x)$ decreases without bound as $x \to c$ and for one-sided limits. We will not give definitions for all possible cases; rather, we illustrate how we would use such a definition.

---

(1) This approach is called "indirect proof" or "*reductio ad absurdum*." We assume the opposite of what we wish to prove, and then we show that assuming the opposite leads to a contradiction. Therefore, what we originally sought to prove must be true.

EXAMPLE 5   Show that

$$\lim_{x \to 0} \frac{1}{x^2} = \infty$$

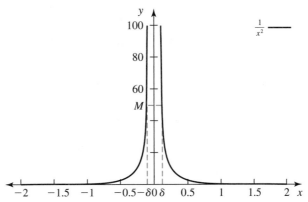

Figure 3.26 The function $f(x) = \frac{1}{x^2}$ in Example 5: The limit of $\frac{1}{x^2}$ as x tends to 0 does not exist.

Solution   The graph of $f(x) = 1/x^2$, $x \neq 0$, is shown in Figure 3.26. We fix $M > 0$. (Again, M is arbitrary, because our solution must hold for all $M > 0$.) We need to find a $\delta > 0$ such that $f(x) > M$ whenever $0 < |x| < \delta$. (Note that $c = 0$.) We start with the inequality $f(x) > M$ and try to determine how to choose δ. We have

$$\frac{1}{x^2} > M \qquad \text{is the same as} \qquad x^2 < \frac{1}{M}$$

Taking square roots on both sides, we find that

$$|x| < \frac{1}{\sqrt{M}}$$

This suggests that we should choose $\delta = 1/\sqrt{M}$. Let's try that value: Given $M > 0$, we choose $\delta = 1/\sqrt{M}$. If $0 < |x| < \delta$, then

$$x^2 < \delta^2, \qquad \text{or} \qquad \frac{1}{x^2} > \frac{1}{\delta^2} = M$$

That is, $1/x^2 > M$ whenever $0 < |x| < \delta = 1/\sqrt{M}$.   ■

There is also a formal definition when $x \to \infty$ (and a similar one for $x \to -\infty$). This definition is analogous to that in Chapter 2.

> **Definition** The statement
> $$\lim_{x \to \infty} f(x) = L$$
> means that, for every $\epsilon > 0$, there exists an $x_0 > 0$ such that
> $$|f(x) - L| < \epsilon \quad \text{whenever } x > x_0$$

Note that, in the definition, x_0 is a real number.

EXAMPLE 6   Show that

$$\lim_{x \to \infty} \frac{x}{0.5 + x} = 1$$

Solution   This limit is illustrated in Figure 3.27. You can see that $f(x) = x/(0.5 + x)$, $x \geq 0$, is in the strip of width 2ϵ and centered at the limiting value $L = 1$ for all values of x greater than x_0. (We assume that $0 < \epsilon < 1$, since, when $\epsilon \geq 1$, the choice $x_0 = 1$ works.) We now determine x_0 when $\epsilon < 1$. To do this, we try to solve

$$\left| \frac{x}{0.5 + x} - 1 \right| < \epsilon$$

for $\epsilon > 0$. This inequality is equivalent to the pair of inequalities

$$-\epsilon < \frac{x}{0.5 + x} - 1 < \epsilon$$

or, after adding 1 to all three parts,

$$1 - \epsilon < \frac{x}{0.5 + x} < 1 + \epsilon$$

Since $\frac{x}{0.5+x} < 1$ for $x > 0$, the right-hand inequality always holds. We therefore need only consider

$$1 - \epsilon < \frac{x}{0.5 + x}$$

Because we are interested in the behavior of $f(x)$ as $x \to \infty$, we need only look at large values of x. Multiplying by $0.5 + x$ (and noticing that we can assume that $0.5 + x > 0$, because we let $x \to \infty$), we obtain

$$(1 - \epsilon)(0.5 + x) < x$$

Solving for x yields

$$(1 - \epsilon)(0.5) < x - x(1 - \epsilon)$$
$$(1 - \epsilon)(0.5) < \epsilon x$$
$$\frac{1 - \epsilon}{2\epsilon} < x$$

For instance, if $\epsilon = 0.1$ (as in Figure 3.27), then

$$x > \frac{0.9}{0.2} = 4.5$$

That is, we would set $x_0 = 4.5$ and conclude that, for $x > 4.5$, $|f(x) - 1| < 0.1$.

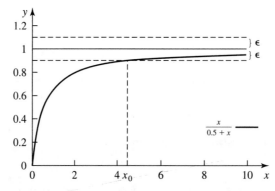

Figure 3.27 The function $f(x) = \frac{x}{0.5+x}$ in Example 6: The limit of $f(x)$ as x tends to infinity is 1.

More generally, we find that, for every $0 < \epsilon < 1$, there exists an

$$x_0 = \frac{1 - \epsilon}{2\epsilon}$$

such that

$$|f(x) - 1| < \epsilon \quad \text{whenever} \quad x > x_0$$

Section 3.6 Problems

1. Find the values of x such that

$$|2x - 1| < 0.01$$

2. Find the values of x such that

$$|3x - 9| < 0.01$$

3. Find the values of x such that

$$|x^2 - 9| < 0.1$$

4. Find the values of x such that

$$|2\sqrt{x} - 5| < 0.1$$

5. Let

$$f(x) = 2x - 1, \quad x \in \mathbf{R}$$

(a) Graph $y = f(x)$ for $-3 \leq x \leq 5$.
(b) For which values of x is $y = f(x)$ within 0.1 of 3? [*Hint:* Find values of x such that $|(2x - 1) - 3| < 0.1$.]
(c) Illustrate your result in (b) on the graph that you obtained in (a).

6. Let

$$f(x) = \sqrt{x}, \quad x \geq 0$$

(a) Graph $y = f(x)$ for $0 \leq x \leq 6$.
(b) For which values of x is $y = f(x)$ within 0.2 of 1? (*Hint:* Find values of x such that $|\sqrt{x} - 1| < 0.2$.)
(c) Illustrate your result in (b) on the graph that you obtained in (a).

7. Let

$$f(x) = \frac{1}{x}, \quad x > 0$$

(a) Graph $y = f(x)$ for $0 < x \leq 4$.
(b) For which values of x is $y = f(x)$ greater than 4?
(c) Illustrate your result in (b) on the graph that you obtained in (a).

8. Let

$$f(x) = e^{-x}, \quad x \geq 0$$

(a) Graph $y = f(x)$ for $0 \leq x \leq 6$.
(b) For which values of x is $y = f(x)$ less than 0.1?
(c) Illustrate your result in (b) on the graph that you obtained in (a).

In Problems 9–22, use the formal definition of limits to prove each statement.

9. $\lim_{x \to 2} (2x - 1) = 3$

10. $\lim_{x \to 0} x^2 = 0$

11. $\lim_{x \to 0} x^5 = 0$

12. $\lim_{x \to 1} \frac{1}{x} = 1$

13. $\lim_{x \to 0} \frac{4}{x^2} = \infty$

14. $\lim_{x \to 0} \frac{-2}{x^2} = -\infty$

15. $\lim_{x \to 0} \frac{1}{x^4} = \infty$

16. $\lim_{x \to 3} \frac{1}{(x - 3)^2} = \infty$

17. $\lim_{x \to \infty} \frac{2}{x^2} = 0$

18. $\lim_{x \to \infty} e^{-x} = 0$

19. $\lim_{x \to \infty} \frac{x}{x + 1} = 1$

20. $\lim_{x \to -\infty} \frac{x}{x + 1} = 1$

21. $\lim_{x \to c} (mx) = mc$, where m is a constant

22. $\lim_{x \to c} (mx + b) = mc + b$, where m and b are constants

Chapter 3 Key Terms

Discuss the following definitions and concepts:

1. Limit of $f(x)$ as x approaches c
2. One-sided limits
3. Infinite limits
4. Divergence by oscillations
5. Convergence
6. Divergence
7. Limit laws
8. Continuity
9. One-sided continuity
10. Continuous function
11. Removable discontinuity
12. Sandwich theorem
13. Trigonometric limits
14. Intermediate-value theorem
15. Bisection method
16. ϵ–δ definition of limits

Chapter 3 Review Problems

In Problems 1–4, determine where each function is continuous. Investigate the behavior as $x \to \pm\infty$. Use a graphing calculator to sketch the corresponding graphs.

1. $f(x) = e^{-|x|}$

2. $f(x) = \begin{cases} \dfrac{\sin x}{x} & \text{if } x \neq 0 \\ 1 & \text{if } x = 0 \end{cases}$

3. $f(x) = \dfrac{2}{e^x + e^{-x}}$

4. $f(x) = \dfrac{1}{\sqrt{x^2 - 1}}$

5. Sketch the graph of a function that is discontinuous from the left and continuous from the right at $x = 1$.

6. Sketch the graph of a function $f(x)$ that is continuous on $[0, 2]$, except at $x = 1$, where $f(1) = 4$, $\lim_{x \to 1^-} f(x) = 2$, and $\lim_{x \to 1^+} f(x) = 3$.

7. Sketch the graph of a continuous function on $[0, \infty)$ with $f(0) = 0$ and $\lim_{x \to \infty} f(x) = 1$.

8. Sketch the graph of a continuous function on $(-\infty, \infty)$ with $f(0) = 1$, $f(x) \geq 0$ for all $x \in \mathbf{R}$, and $\lim_{x \to \pm\infty} f(x) = 0$.

9. Show that the floor function

$$f(x) = \lfloor x \rfloor$$

is continuous from the right, but discontinuous from the left at $x = -2$.

10. Suppose $f(x)$ is continuous on the interval $[1, 3]$. If $f(1) = 0$ and $f(3) = 2$, explain why there must be a number $c \in (1, 3)$ such that $f(c) = 1$.

11. Population Size Assume that the size of a population at time t is

$$N(t) = \frac{at}{k + t}, \quad t \geq 0$$

where a and k are positive constants. Suppose that the limiting population size is

$$\lim_{t \to \infty} N(t) = 1.24 \times 10^6$$

and that, at time $t = 5$, the population size is half the limiting population size. Use the preceding information to determine the constants a and k.

12. Population Size Suppose that

$$N(t) = 10 + 2e^{-0.3t} \sin t, \quad t \geq 0$$

describes the size of a population (in millions) at time t (measured in weeks).

(a) Use a graphing calculator to sketch the graph of $N(t)$, and describe in words what you see.

(b) Give lower and upper bounds on the size of the population; that is, find N_1 and N_2 such that, for all $t \geq 0$,

$$N_1 \leq N(t) \leq N_2$$

(c) Find $\lim_{t \to \infty} N(t)$. Interpret this expression.

13. Physiology Suppose that an organism reacts to a stimulus only when the stimulus exceeds a certain threshold. Assume that the stimulus is a function of time t and that it is given by

$$s(t) = \sin(\pi t), \quad t \geq 0$$

The organism reacts to the stimulus and shows a certain reaction when $s(t) \geq 1/2$. Define a function $g(t)$ such that $g(t) = 0$ when the organism shows no reaction at time t and $g(t) = 1$ when the organism shows the reaction.

(a) Plot $s(t)$ and $g(t)$ in the same coordinate system.

(b) Is $s(t)$ continuous? Is $g(t)$ continuous?

14. Tree Height The following function describes the height of a tree as a function of age:

$$f(x) = 132e^{-20/x}, \quad x \geq 0$$

Find $\lim_{x \to \infty} f(x)$.

15. Predator–Prey Model There are a number of mathematical models that describe predator–prey interactions. Typically, they share the feature that the number of prey eaten per predator increases with the density of the prey. In the simplest version, the number of encounters with prey per predator is proportional to the product of the total number of prey and the period over which the predators search for prey. That is, if we let N be the number of prey, P be the number of predators, T be the period available for searching, and N_e be the number of encounters with prey, then

$$\frac{N_e}{P} = aTN \tag{3.11}$$

where a is a positive constant. The quantity N_e/P is the number of prey encountered per predator.

(a) Set $f(N) = aTN$, and sketch the graph of $f(N)$ when $a = 0.1$ and $T = 2$ for $N \geq 0$.

(b) Predators usually spend some time eating the prey that they find. Therefore, not all of the time T can be used for searching. The actual searching time is reduced by the per-prey handling time T_h and can be written as

$$T - T_h \frac{N_e}{P}$$

Show that if $T - T_h \frac{N_e}{P}$ is substituted for T in (3.11), then

$$\frac{N_e}{P} = \frac{aTN}{1 + aT_h N} \tag{3.12}$$

Define

$$g(N) = \frac{aTN}{1 + aT_h N}$$

and graph $g(N)$ for $N \geq 0$ when $a = 0.1$, $T = 2$, and $T_h = 0.1$.

(c) Show that (3.12) reduces to (3.11) when $T_h = 0$.

(d) Find

$$\lim_{N \to \infty} \frac{N_e}{P}$$

in the cases when $T_h = 0$ and when $T_h > 0$. Explain, in words, the difference between the two cases.

16. Community Respiration Duarte and Agustí (1998) investigated the CO_2 balance of aquatic ecosystems. They related the community respiration rates (R) to the gross primary production rates (P) of aquatic ecosystems. (Both quantities were measured in the same units.) They made the following statement:

> Our results confirm the generality of earlier reports that the relation between community respiration rate and gross production is not linear. Community respiration is scaled as the approximate two-thirds power of gross production.

(a) Use the preceding quote to explain why

$$R = aP^b$$

can be used to describe the relationship between the community respiration rates (R) and the gross primary production rates (P). What value would you assign to b on the basis of their quote?

(b) Suppose that you obtained data on the gross production and respiration rates of a number of freshwater lakes. How would you display your data graphically to quickly convince an audience that the exponent b in the power equation relating R and P is indeed approximately 2/3? (*Hint:* Use an appropriate log transformation.)

(c) The ratio R/P for an ecosystem is important in assessing the global CO_2 budget. If respiration exceeds production (i.e., $R > P$), then the ecosystem acts as a carbon dioxide source, whereas if production exceeds respiration (i.e., $P > R$), then the ecosystem acts as a carbon dioxide sink. Assume now that the exponent in the power equation relating R and P is 2/3. Show that the ratio R/P, as a function of P, is continuous for $P > 0$. Furthermore, show that

$$\lim_{P \to 0+} \frac{R}{P} = \infty$$

and

$$\lim_{P \to \infty} \frac{R}{P} = 0$$

Use a graphing calculator to sketch the graph of the ratio R/P as a function of P for $P > 0$. (Experiment with the graphing calculator to see how the value of a affects the graph.)

(d) Use your results in (c) and the intermediate-value theorem to conclude that there exists a value P^* such that the ratio R/P at P^* is equal to 1. On the basis of your graph in (c), is there more than one such value P^*?

(e) Use your results in (d) to identify production rates P where the ratio $R/P > 1$ (i.e., where respiration exceeds production).

(f) Use your results in (a)–(e) to explain the following quote from Duarte and Agustí:

> Unproductive aquatic ecosystems ... tend to be heterotrophic ($R > P$), and act as carbon dioxide sources.

17. Hyperbolic functions are used in the sciences. We take a look at the following three examples: the hyperbolic sine, $\sinh x$; the hyperbolic cosine, $\cosh x$; and the hyperbolic tangent, $\tanh x$, defined respectively as

$$\sinh x = \frac{e^x - e^{-x}}{2}, \quad x \in \mathbf{R}$$

$$\cosh x = \frac{e^x + e^{-x}}{2}, \quad x \in \mathbf{R}$$

$$\tanh x = \frac{e^x - e^{-x}}{e^x + e^{-x}}, \quad x \in \mathbf{R}$$

(a) Show that these three hyperbolic functions are continuous for all $x \in \mathbf{R}$. Use a graphing calculator to sketch the graphs of all three functions.

(b) Find

$$\lim_{x \to \infty} \sinh x \qquad \lim_{x \to -\infty} \sinh x$$

$$\lim_{x \to \infty} \cosh x \qquad \lim_{x \to -\infty} \cosh x$$

$$\lim_{x \to \infty} \tanh x \qquad \lim_{x \to -\infty} \tanh x$$

(c) Show that the two identities

$$\cosh^2 x - \sinh^2 x = 1$$

and

$$\tanh x = \frac{\sinh x}{\cosh x}$$

are valid.

(d) Show that $\sinh x$ and $\tanh x$ are odd functions and that $\cosh x$ is even.

(*Note*: It can be shown that if a flexible cable is suspended between two points at equal heights, the shape of the resulting curve is given by the hyperbolic cosine function. This curve is called a *catenary*.)

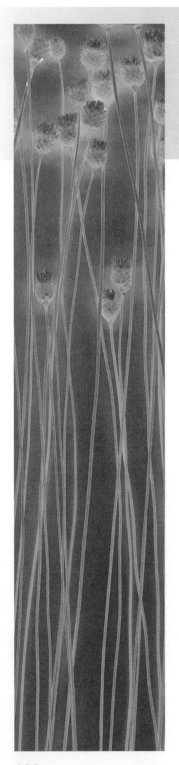

4

Differentiation

LEARNING OBJECTIVES

This chapter presents the fundamentals of differentiation. Specifically, we will learn how to
- formally define a derivative;
- differentiate specific functions;
- approximate a function by a linear function;
- calculate how a measurement error propagates.

Differential calculus allows us to solve two of the basic problems that we mentioned in Chapter 1: constructing a tangent line to a curve (Figure 4.1) and finding maxima and minima of a curve (Figure 4.2). The solutions to these two problems, by themselves, cannot explain the impact calculus has had on the sciences. Calculus is one of the most important analytical tools for investigating dynamic problems. Applications of differential calculus in the life sciences include simple growth models, interactions between organisms, invasions of organisms, the working of neurons, enzymatic reactions, harvesting models in fishery, epidemiological modeling, changes of gene frequencies under random mating, evolutionary strategies, and many others.

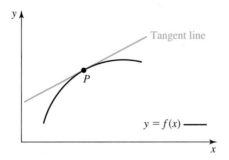

Figure 4.1 Tangent line to a curve at a point.

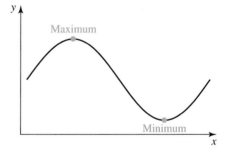

Figure 4.2 Maxima and minima of a curve.

Growth models will be of particular interest to us. Let's revisit the example at the beginning of Chapter 3, in which we looked at a population whose size at time t is given by $N(t)$. The average growth rate during the time interval $[t, t + h]$ is equal to

$$[\text{average growth rate}] = \frac{[\text{change in population size}]}{[\text{length of time interval}]} = \frac{\Delta N}{\Delta t}$$

where

$$\Delta N = N(t + h) - N(t) \quad \text{and} \quad \Delta t = (t + h) - t = h$$

Thus,

$$\frac{\Delta N}{\Delta t} = \frac{N(t + h) - N(t)}{h}$$

The instantaneous rate of growth is defined as the limit of $\Delta N / \Delta t$ as $\Delta t \to 0$ (or $h \to 0$), or

$$\lim_{\Delta t \to 0} \frac{\Delta N}{\Delta t} = \lim_{h \to 0} \frac{N(t+h) - N(t)}{h}$$

provided that this limit exists.

We are interested in the geometric interpretation of the limit when it exists. When we draw a straight line through the points $(t, N(t))$ and $(t+h, N(t+h))$, we obtain the **secant line**. The slope of this line is given by the quantity $\Delta N / \Delta t$ (Figure 4.3). In the limit as $\Delta t \to 0$, the secant line converges to the line that touches the graph at the point $(t, N(t))$. This line is called the **tangent line** at the point $(t, N(t))$ (Figure 4.4). The limit of $\Delta N / \Delta t$ as the length of the time interval $[t, t+h]$ goes to 0 (i.e., $\Delta t \to 0$ or $h \to 0$) will therefore be equal to the slope of the tangent line at $(t, N(t))$. We denote the limiting value of $\Delta N / \Delta t$ as $\Delta t \to 0$ by $N'(t)$ (read "N prime of t") and call this quantity the **derivative** of $N(t)$. That is,

$$N'(t) = \lim_{\Delta t \to 0} \frac{\Delta N}{\Delta t} = \lim_{h \to 0} \frac{N(t+h) - N(t)}{h}$$

provided that this limit exists.

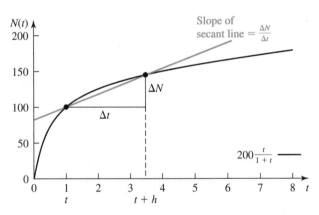

Figure 4.3 The average growth rate $\Delta N / \Delta t$ is equal to the slope of the secant line.

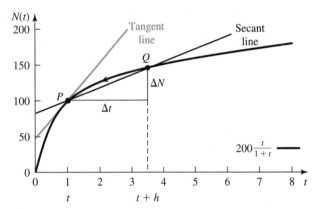

Figure 4.4 The instantaneous growth rate is the limit $\Delta N / \Delta t$ as $\Delta t \to 0$. Geometrically, the point Q moves toward the point P on the graph of $N(t)$, and the secant line through P and Q becomes the tangent line at P. The instantaneous growth rate is then equal to the slope of the tangent line.

Finding derivatives is the topic of this chapter.

4.1 Formal Definition of the Derivative

> **Definition** The derivative of a function f at x, denoted by $f'(x)$, is
>
> $$f'(x) = \lim_{h \to 0} \frac{f(x+h) - f(x)}{h}$$
>
> provided that the limit exists.

If the limit exists, then we say that f is differentiable at x. The phrase "provided that the limit exists" is crucial: If we take an arbitrary function f, the limit may not exist. In fact, we saw many examples in the previous chapter in which limits did not exist. The geometric interpretation will help us to understand when the limit exists and under which conditions we cannot expect the limit to exist. Notice that $\lim_{h \to 0}$ is a two-sided limit (i.e., we approach 0 from both the negative and the positive side). The quotient

$$\frac{f(x+h) - f(x)}{h}$$

is called the **difference quotient**, and we denote it by $\frac{\Delta f}{\Delta x}$. (See Figure 4.5.)

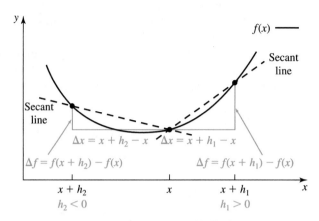

Figure 4.5 The difference quotient $\frac{f(x+h)-f(x)}{h}$ when $h = h_1 > 0$ and $h = h_2 < 0$.

We say that f is differentiable on (a, b) if f is differentiable at every $x \in (a, b)$. (Since the limit in the definition is two sided, we exclude the endpoints of the interval. At endpoints, only one-sided limits can be computed, which yield one-sided derivatives.)

If we want to compute the derivative at $x = c$, we can also write

$$f'(c) = \lim_{x \to c} \frac{f(x) - f(c)}{x - c}$$

which emphasizes that the point $(x, f(x))$ converges to the point $(c, f(c))$ as we take the limit as $x \to c$ (Figure 4.6). This approach will be important when we discuss the geometric interpretation of the derivative in the next subsection.

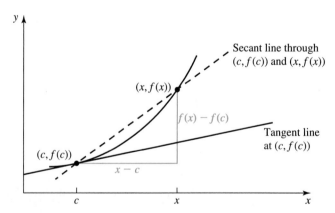

Figure 4.6 The derivative $f'(c) = \lim_{x \to c} \frac{f(x)-f(c)}{x-c}$ is the slope of the tangent line at $(c, f(c))$.

There is more than one way to write the derivative of a function $y = f(x)$. The following expressions are equivalent:

$$y' = \frac{dy}{dx} = f'(x) = \frac{df}{dx} = \frac{d}{dx} f(x)$$

The notation $\frac{df}{dx}$ goes back to Leibniz and is called **Leibniz notation**. (Leibniz had a real talent for finding good notation.) It should remind you that we take the limit of $\Delta f / \Delta x$ as Δx approaches 0.

If we wish to emphasize that we evaluate the derivative of $f(x)$ at $x = c$, we write

$$f'(c) = \frac{df}{dx}\bigg|_{x=c}$$

Newton used different notation to denote the derivative of a function. He wrote $\dot{y}$ (read "y dot") for the derivative of y. This notation is still common in physics when derivatives are taken with respect to a variable that denotes time. We will use either Leibniz notation or the notation $f'(x)$.

■ 4.1.1 Geometric Interpretation and Using the Definition

Let's look at $f(x) = x^2$, $x \in \mathbf{R}$. (Refer to Figures 4.7 and 4.8 as we go along.) To compute the derivative of f at, say, $x = 1$ from the definition, we first compute the difference quotient at $x = 1$. For $h \neq 0$,

$$\frac{\Delta f}{\Delta x} = \frac{f(1 + h) - f(1)}{h} = \frac{(1 + h)^2 - 1^2}{h}$$

$$= \frac{1 + 2h + h^2 - 1}{h} = \frac{2h + h^2}{h} = \frac{h(2 + h)}{h}$$

$$= 2 + h$$

The difference quotient $\Delta f/\Delta x$ is the slope of the secant line through the points $(1, 1)$ and $(1 + h, (1 + h)^2)$ (Figure 4.7).

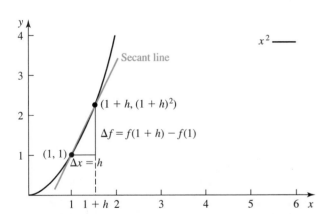

Figure 4.7 The slope of the secant line through $(1, 1)$ and $(1 + h, (1 + h)^2)$ is $\Delta f/\Delta x$.

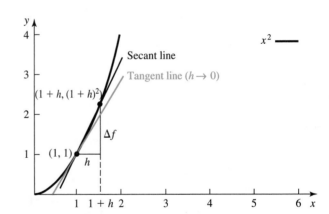

Figure 4.8 Taking the limit $h \to 0$, the secant line converges to the tangent line at $(1, 1)$.

To find the derivative $f'(1)$, we need to take the limit as $h \to 0$ (Figure 4.8):

$$f'(1) = \lim_{h\to 0} \frac{f(1 + h) - f(1)}{h} = \lim_{h\to 0}(2 + h) = 2$$

Taking the limit as $h \to 0$ means that the point $(1+h, (1+h)^2)$ approaches the point $(1, 1)$. [The limit as $h \to 0$ is a two-sided limit; in Figure 4.8, we only drew one point $(1 + h, (1 + h)^2)$ for some $h > 0$.] As $h \to 0$, the secant lines through the points $(1, 1)$ and $(1 + h, (1 + h)^2)$ converge to the line that touches the graph at $(1, 1)$. As mentioned earlier, the limiting line is called the tangent line. Since $f'(1)$ is the limiting value of the slope of the secant line as the point $(1+h, (1+h)^2)$ approaches $(1, 1)$, we find that $f'(1) = 2$ is the slope of the tangent line at the point $(1, 1)$.

Motivated by this example, we define the tangent line formally:

Definition of the Tangent Line If the derivative of a function f exists at $x = c$, then the tangent line at $x = c$ is the line going through the point $(c, f(c))$ with slope

$$f'(c) = \lim_{h \to 0} \frac{f(c + h) - f(c)}{h}$$

Knowing the derivative at a point (which is the slope of the tangent line at that point) and the coordinates of that point allows us to find the equation of the tangent line at the point by using the point–slope form of a straight line, namely,

$$y - y_0 = m(x - x_0)$$

where (x_0, y_0) is the point and m is the slope. Going back to the function $y = x^2$, we see that the point at $c = x_0 = 1$ has coordinates $(x_0, y_0) = (1, 1)$ and its derivative at $c = 1$ is $m = 2$. The equation of the tangent line is then given by

$$y - 1 = 2(x - 1), \qquad \text{or} \qquad y = 2x - 1$$

(Figure 4.9).

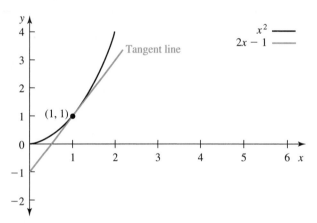

Figure 4.9 The slope of $f(x) = x^2$ at $(1, 1)$ is $m = 2$. The equation of the tangent line at $(1, 1)$ is $y = 2x - 1$.

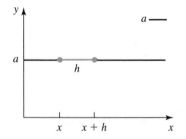

Figure 4.10 The slope of a horizontal line is $m = 0$.

Equation of the Tangent Line If the derivative of a function f exists at $x = c$, then $f'(c)$ is the slope of the tangent line at the point $(c, f(c))$. The equation of the tangent line is given by

$$y - f(c) = f'(c)(x - c)$$

The geometric interpretation will help us to compute derivatives in the next two examples.

EXAMPLE 1

The Derivative of a Constant Function The graph of $f(x) = a$ is a horizontal line that intersects the y-axis at $(0, a)$ (Figure 4.10). Since the graph is a straight line, the tangent line at x coincides with the graph of $f(x)$ and, therefore, the slope of the tangent line at x is equal to the slope of the straight line. The slope of a horizontal line is 0; we thus expect that $f'(x) = 0$. Using the formal definition with $f(x) = a$ and $f(x + h) = a$, we find that

$$f'(x) = \lim_{h \to 0} \frac{f(x + h) - f(x)}{h} = \lim_{h \to 0} \frac{a - a}{h} = \lim_{h \to 0} \frac{0}{h} = \lim_{h \to 0} 0 = 0$$

Here again, it is important to remember that when we take the limit as $h \to 0$, h approaches 0 (from both sides) but is not equal to 0. Since $h \neq 0$, the expression $0/h = 0$. This property was used in going from $\lim_{h\to 0} \frac{0}{h}$ to $\lim_{h\to 0} 0$. ■

The Derivative of a Linear Function The graph of $f(x) = mx + b$ is a straight line with slope m and y-intercept b (Figure 4.11). The derivative of $f(x)$ is the slope of the tangent line at x. Since the graph is a straight line, the tangent line at x coincides with the graph of $f(x)$ and, therefore, the slope of the tangent line at x is equal to the slope of the straight line. We thus expect that $f'(x) = m$. Using the formal definition, we can confirm this expectation:

$$f'(x) = \lim_{h\to 0} \frac{f(x+h) - f(x)}{h} = \lim_{h\to 0} \frac{m(x+h) + b - (mx + b)}{h}$$

$$= \lim_{h\to 0} \frac{mx + mh + b - mx - b}{h} = \lim_{h\to 0} \frac{mh}{h} = \lim_{h\to 0} m = m$$

In going from $\lim_{h\to 0} \frac{mh}{h}$ to $\lim_{h\to 0} m$, we were able to cancel h because $h \neq 0$.

The preceding reasoning yields the following: If $f(x) = mx + b$, then $f'(x) = m$. This includes the special case of a constant function, for which $m = 0$ (Example 1). ■

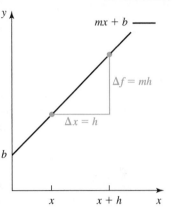

Figure 4.11 The slope of the line $y = mx + b$ is m.

EXAMPLE 3

Using the Definition Find the derivative of

$$f(x) = \frac{1}{x} \quad \text{for } x \neq 0$$

Solution   We will use the formal definition of the derivative to compute $f'(x)$ (Figure 4.12).

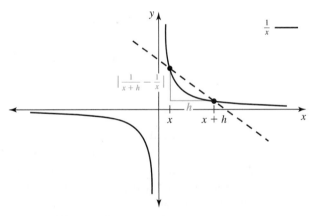

Figure 4.12 The graph of $f(x) = 1/x$ for Example 3.

The main algebraic step is the computation of $f(x+h) - f(x)$; we will do this first. With $f(x+h) = \frac{1}{x+h}$, we find that

$$f(x+h) - f(x) = \frac{1}{x+h} - \frac{1}{x}$$

$$= \frac{x - (x+h)}{x(x+h)} = \frac{-h}{x(x+h)}$$

To compute $f'(x)$, we need to divide both sides of this equation by h and take the limit as $h \to 0$:

$$f'(x) = \lim_{h\to 0} \frac{f(x+h) - f(x)}{h} = \lim_{h\to 0} \frac{\frac{-h}{x(x+h)}}{h}$$

$$= \lim_{h\to 0} \left(-\frac{h}{x(x+h)} \frac{1}{h} \right) = \lim_{h\to 0} \left(-\frac{1}{x(x+h)} \right) = -\frac{1}{x^2}$$

That is, if $f(x) = \frac{1}{x}, x \neq 0$, then

$$f'(x) = -\frac{1}{x^2}, \ x \neq 0$$

Looking back at the first three examples, we see that in order to compute $f'(x)$ from the formal definition of the derivative, we evaluate the limit

$$\lim_{h \to 0} \frac{f(x+h) - f(x)}{h}$$

Since both $\lim_{h \to 0}[f(x+h) - f(x)]$ and $\lim_{h \to 0} h$ are equal to 0, we cannot simply evaluate the limits in the numerator and the denominator separately, because this would result in the undefined expression $0/0$. It is important to simplify the difference quotient before we take the limit.

■ 4.1.2 The Derivative as an Instantaneous Rate of Change: A First Look at Differential Equations

Velocity Suppose that you ride your bike on a straight road. Your position (in miles) at time t (in hours) is given by (Figure 4.13)

$$s(t) = -t^3 + 6t^2 \quad \text{for } 0 \leq t \leq 6$$

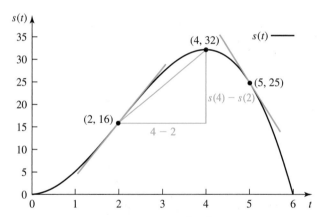

Figure 4.13 The average velocity $\frac{s(4)-s(2)}{4-2}$ is the slope of the secant line through (2, 16) and (4, 32). The velocity at time t is the slope of the tangent line at t: At $t = 2$, the velocity is positive; at $t = 5$, the velocity is negative.

You might ask what the average velocity during the interval (say) [2, 4] is. This velocity is defined as the net change in position during the interval, divided by the length of the interval. To compute the average velocity, find the position at time 2 and at time 4, and take the difference of these two quantities. Then divide this difference by the time that it took you to travel that distance. At time $t = 2$, $s(2) = -8 + 24 = 16$, and at time $t = 4$, $s(4) = -64 + 96 = 32$. Hence, the average velocity is

$$\frac{s(4) - s(2)}{4 - 2} = \frac{32 - 16}{4 - 2} = 8 \text{ mph}$$

We recognize this ratio as the difference quotient

$$\frac{\Delta s}{\Delta t} = \frac{s(t+h) - s(t)}{h}$$

and call the difference quotient $\Delta s / \Delta t$ the **average velocity**, which is an average rate of change.

The **instantaneous velocity** at time t is defined as the limit of $\frac{\Delta s}{\Delta t}$ as $\Delta t \to 0$, or

$$\lim_{\Delta t \to 0} \frac{\Delta s}{\Delta t} = \lim_{h \to 0} \frac{s(t+h) - s(t)}{h}$$

provided that the limit exists. This quantity is the derivative of $s(t)$ at time t, which we denote by

$$\frac{ds}{dt} = \lim_{\Delta t \to 0} \frac{\Delta s}{\Delta t}$$

Note that $\frac{ds}{dt}$ is an instantaneous rate of change. The instantaneous velocity (or, simply, the velocity) is, then, the slope of the tangent line at a given point of the position function $s(t)$, provided that the derivative at this point exists.

Let's look at two points on the graph of $s(t)$, namely, $(2, 16)$ and $(5, 25)$. We find that the slope of the tangent line is positive at $(2, 16)$ and negative at $(5, 25)$. The velocity is therefore positive at time $t = 2$ and negative at time $t = 5$. At $t = 2$ we move away from our starting point, whereas at $t = 5$ we move toward our starting point. At these two times, we move in opposite directions.

There is a difference between *velocity* and *speed*. If you had a speedometer on your bike, it would tell you the speed and not the velocity. Speed is the absolute value of velocity; it ignores direction.

Interpreting the derivative as an instantaneous rate of change will turn out to be extremely important to us. In fact, when you encounter derivatives in your science courses, this will be the interpretation most often used. This interpretation will allow us to describe a quantity in terms of how quickly it changes with respect to another quantity. To illustrate the point, we revisit two previous examples and introduce one new application.

Population Growth   At the beginning of this chapter, we described the growth of a population at time t by the continuous function $N(t)$. If the derivative of $N(t)$ exists at time t, we can define the instantaneous growth rate of the population by

$$N'(t) = \frac{dN}{dt} = [\text{instantaneous population growth rate at time } t]$$

We are frequently interested in the **instantaneous per capita growth rate**. This is the growth rate per individual, and it can be obtained by dividing the instantaneous growth rate of the population by the population size at that time. That is,

$$\frac{1}{N(t)} \frac{dN}{dt} = [\text{instantaneous per capita growth rate at time } t]$$

In biology textbooks (and in this book), the dependence on t is often not explicitly spelled out, and we write

$$\frac{1}{N} \frac{dN}{dt} \qquad \text{instead of} \qquad \frac{1}{N(t)} \frac{dN}{dt}$$

The Rate of a Chemical Reaction   Another illustration of the use of the derivative as an instantaneous rate of change is in Example 5 of Subsection 1.2.2, where we discussed the reaction rate of the irreversible chemical reaction

$$A + B \to AB$$

which is proportional to the concentrations of A and B. If the concentration of the product AB is denoted by x, then the reaction rate is equal to

$$k(a - x)(b - x)$$

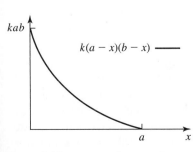

Figure 4.14 The reaction rate for $a \leq b$.

where $a = [A]$ is the initial concentration of A and $b = [B]$ is the initial concentration of B (Figure 4.14). The reaction rate tells us how quickly the concentration of x

changes with time as the reaction proceeds. The concentration x is thus a function of time t: $x = x(t)$. The reaction rate is an instantaneous rate of change, namely,

$$\lim_{\Delta t \to 0} \frac{x(t + \Delta t) - x(t)}{\Delta t}$$

We can identify the limit as $\Delta t \to 0$ as the derivative of the function $x(t)$ with respect to t and therefore write

$$\frac{dx}{dt} = k(a - x)(b - x) \tag{4.1}$$

Equation (4.1) is an example of a **differential equation**—an equation that contains the derivative of a function. We will discuss such equations extensively in later chapters.

From this point on, when we say "rate of change," we will always mean "instantaneous rate of change." When we are interested in the average rate of change, we will always state this explicitly.

The rate of change in a chemical reaction is described by a differential equation. It is sometimes possible to solve such differential equations—that is, to state explicitly a function whose derivative satisfies the given equation. We will discuss this situation in detail later. More often, it is not possible (or not necessary) to explicitly find a solution. Without solving the differential equation, we can still obtain useful information about its behavior. We illustrate this property in the next application.

Tilman's Model for Resource Competition David Tilman (1982) of the University of Minnesota developed a theoretical framework to describe the outcome of competition for limited resources. To test the predictions of his theory, he conducted many experiments on the grassland habitat at Cedar Creek Natural History Area in Minnesota. For this grassland habitat, nitrogen is a limiting resource; that is, adding nitrogen to the soil will result in an increase in biomass. We will discuss the case where one species competes for a single limited resource. We assume that the rate of change of biomass has two components: rate of growth and rate of loss. We write

[rate of biomass change] = [rate of growth] − [rate of loss]

We denote the biomass of the plant population at time t by $B(t)$ and assume that the rate of growth depends on a single resource whose concentration is denoted by R. We will write an equation for the **specific rate of change** of biomass, which is defined as the change of biomass per unit of biomass, or $\frac{1}{B} \frac{dB}{dt}$. We assume that the per-unit rate of loss of biomass is constant and denote this quantity by m. A simple model for how the biomass changes over time is then

$$\frac{1}{B} \frac{dB}{dt} = f(R) - m \tag{4.2}$$

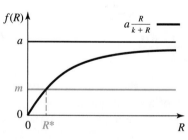

$f(R)$

a

$a\dfrac{R}{k+R}$

m

0

$0 \quad R^*$

R

Figure 4.15 Growth balances loss when $R = R^*$.

where the function $f(R)$ describes the specific growth rate as a function of resource concentration. A common choice for $f(R)$ is the Monod growth function (or Michaelis–Menten equation) that we considered in Example 6 of Subsection 1.2.3, or

$$f(R) = a \frac{R}{k + R} \tag{4.3}$$

where a and k are positive constants. Let's graph $f(R)$ and m together in Figure 4.15. Doing so yields the following observations: When $0 < m < a$, the graphs of the functions $y = f(R)$ and $y = m$ intersect at $R = R^*$ (read "R star"). Consequently, at the resource level R^*, $f(R) = m$, and thus the specific rate of change $\frac{1}{B} \frac{dB}{dt}$ is equal to 0. That is, growth balances loss, and the biomass of the species no longer changes. We say that the biomass is at **equilibrium**. If the resource level R were held at a value less than R^*, then $f(R) - m < 0$, and the specific rate of growth would be negative; that is, biomass would decrease. If $R > R^*$, then $f(R) - m > 0$, and biomass would increase.

We can compute R^* in the case when $f(R)$ is given by (4.3). Since R^* satisfies $f(R^*) = m$, we obtain

$$a\frac{R^*}{k + R^*} = m, \quad \text{or} \quad R^* = \frac{mk}{a - m}$$

■ 4.1.3 Differentiability and Continuity

Using the geometric interpretation, we can find situations in which $f'(c)$ does not exist at one or more values of c.

EXAMPLE 4

A Function with a "Corner" Let

$$f(x) = |x| = \begin{cases} x & \text{for } x \geq 0 \\ -x & \text{for } x < 0 \end{cases}$$

The graph of $f(x)$ is shown in Figure 4.16. Looking at the graph, we realize that there is no tangent line at $x = 0$ and therefore we do not expect that $f'(0)$ exists. We can define the slope of the secant line when we approach 0 from the right and also when we approach 0 from the left; however, the slopes converge to different values in the limit. The former is $+1$, the latter is -1. In this example, we can read off the slopes from the graph. But we can also find the slopes formally by taking appropriate limits. When $h > 0$, $f(h) = |h| = h$ and

$$\lim_{h \to 0+} \frac{f(0 + h) - f(0)}{h} = \frac{h - 0}{h} = 1$$

When $h < 0$, $f(h) = |h| = -h$ and

$$\lim_{h \to 0-} \frac{f(0 + h) - f(0)}{h} = \frac{-h - 0}{h} = -1$$

Since $1 \neq -1$, it follows that

$$\lim_{h \to 0} \frac{f(0 + h) - f(0)}{h}$$

and thus $f'(0)$, do not exist.

At all other points, the derivative exists. We can find the derivative by simply looking at the graph. We see that

$$f'(x) = \begin{cases} +1 & \text{for } x > 0 \\ -1 & \text{for } x < 0 \end{cases}$$

■

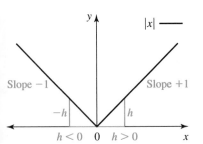

Figure 4.16 f is not differentiable at $x = 0$.

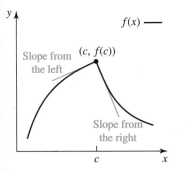

Figure 4.17 $f(x)$ is continuous at $x = c$ but not differentiable at $x = c$: The derivatives from the left and the right are not equal.

Example 4 shows that continuity alone is not enough for a function to be differentiable: The function $f(x) = |x|$ is continuous at all values of x, but it is not differentiable at $x = 0$. To draw the graph of a continuous function that is not differentiable at a point, put in a "corner" at that point (Figure 4.17).

However, if a function is differentiable, it is also continuous. We say that continuity is a necessary, but not a sufficient, condition for differentiability. This result is important enough that we will formulate it as a theorem and prove it:

> **Theorem** If f is differentiable at $x = c$, then f is also continuous at $x = c$.

Proof Since f is differentiable at $x = c$, we know that the limit

$$\lim_{x \to c} \frac{f(x) - f(c)}{x - c} \tag{4.4}$$

exists and is equal to $f'(c)$. To show that f is continuous at $x = c$, we must show that

$$\lim_{x \to c} f(x) = f(c), \qquad \text{or} \qquad \lim_{x \to c}[f(x) - f(c)] = 0$$

First, note that f is defined at $x = c$. [Otherwise, we could not have computed the difference quotient $\frac{f(x)-f(c)}{x-c}$.] Now,

$$\lim_{x \to c}[f(x) - f(c)] = \lim_{x \to c} \frac{f(x) - f(c)}{x - c}(x - c)$$

Given that

$$\lim_{x \to c} \frac{f(x) - f(c)}{x - c}$$

[this is Equation (4.4)] exists and is equal to $f'(c)$, and that

$$\lim_{x \to c}(x - c)$$

exists (it is equal to 0), we can apply the product rule for limits and find that

$$\lim_{x \to c} \frac{f(x) - f(c)}{x - c}(x - c) = \lim_{x \to c} \frac{f(x) - f(c)}{x - c} \lim_{x \to c}(x - c) = f'(c) \cdot 0 = 0$$

This set of equations shows that

$$\lim_{x \to c}[f(x) - f(c)] = 0$$

and consequently that f is continuous at $x = c$. ■

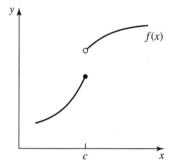

Figure 4.18 The function $y = f(x)$ is not differentiable at $x = c$.

It follows from the preceding theorem that if a function f is not continuous at $x = c$, then f is not differentiable at $x = c$. The function $y = f(x)$ in Figure 4.18 is discontinuous at $x = c$; we cannot draw a tangent line there.

Functions can have vertical tangent lines, but since the slope of a vertical line is not defined, the function would not be differentiable at any point where the tangent line is vertical. This situation is illustrated in the next example.

EXAMPLE 5

Vertical Tangent Line Show that

$$f(x) = x^{1/3}$$

is not differentiable at $x = 0$.

Solution We see from the graph of $f(x)$ in Figure 4.19 that $f(x)$ is continuous at $x = 0$. Using the formal definition, we find that

$$f'(0) = \lim_{h \to 0} \frac{f(h) - f(0)}{h} = \lim_{h \to 0} \frac{h^{1/3} - 0}{h}$$

$$= \lim_{h \to 0} \frac{1}{h^{2/3}} = \infty \qquad \text{does not exist}$$

Since the limit does not exist, $f(x)$ is not differentiable at $x = 0$. We see from the graph that the tangent line at $x = 0$ is vertical. ■

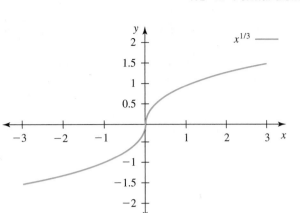

Figure 4.19 The function $f(x) = x^{1/3}$ has a vertical tangent line at $x = 0$. It is therefore not differentiable at $x = 0$.

Section 4.1 Problems

■ 4.1.1

In Problems 1–8, find the derivative at the indicated point from the graph of each function.

1. $f(x) = 5$; $x = 1$

2. $f(x) = -3x$; $x = -2$

3. $f(x) = 4x - 3$; $x = -1$

4. $f(x) = -5x + 1$; $x = 0$

5. $f(x) = 2x^2$; $x = 0$

6. $f(x) = (x + 2)^2$; $x = 1$

7. $f(x) = \cos x$; $x = 0$

8. $f(x) = \sin x$; $x = \dfrac{\pi}{2}$

In Problems 9–16, find c so that $f'(c) = 0$.

9. $f(x) = -3x^2 + 1$

10. $f(x) = -x^2 + 4$

11. $f(x) = (x - 2)^2$

12. $f(x) = (x + 3)^2$

13. $f(x) = x^2 - 6x + 9$

14. $f(x) = x^2 + 4x + 4$

15. $f(x) = \sin\left(\dfrac{\pi}{2}x\right)$

16. $\cos(\pi - x)$

In Problems 17–20, compute $f(c+h) - f(c)$ at the indicated point.

17. $f(x) = -2x + 1$; $c = 2$

18. $f(x) = 3x^2$; $c = 1$

19. $f(x) = \sqrt{x}$; $c = 4$

20. $f(x) = \dfrac{1}{x}$; $c = -2$

21. (a) Use the formal definition of the derivative to find the derivative of $y = 5x^2$ at $x = -1$.

(b) Show that the point $(-1, 5)$ is on the graph of $y = 5x^2$, and find the equation of the tangent line at the point $(-1, 5)$.

(c) Graph $y = 5x^2$ and the tangent line at the point $(-1, 5)$ in the same coordinate system.

22. (a) Use the formal definition to find the derivative of $y = -2x^2$ at $x = 1$.

(b) Show that the point $(1, -2)$ is on the graph of $y = -2x^2$, and find the equation of the tangent line at the point $(1, -2)$.

(c) Graph $y = -2x^2$ and the tangent line at the point $(1, -2)$ in the same coordinate system.

23. (a) Use the formal definition to find the derivative of $y = 1 - x^3$ at $x = 2$.

(b) Show that the point $(2, -7)$ is on the graph of $y = 1 - x^3$, and find the equation of the normal line at the point $(2, -7)$.

(c) Graph $y = 1 - x^3$ and the tangent line at the point $(2, -7)$ in the same coordinate system.

24. (a) Use the formal definition to find the derivative of $y = \dfrac{1}{x}$ at $x = 2$.

(b) Show that the point $(2, \frac{1}{2})$ is on the graph of $y = \frac{1}{x}$, and find the equation of the normal line at the point $(2, \frac{1}{2})$.

(c) Graph $y = \frac{1}{x}$ and the tangent line at the point $(2, \frac{1}{2})$ in the same coordinate system.

25. Use the formal definition to find the derivative of

$$y = \sqrt{x}$$

for $x > 0$.

26. Use the formal definition to find the derivative of

$$f(x) = \frac{1}{x + 1}$$

for $x \neq -1$.

27. Find the equation of the tangent line to the curve $y = 3x^2$ at the point $(1, 3)$.

28. Find the equation of the tangent line to the curve $y = 2/x$ at the point $(2, 1)$.

29. Find the equation of the tangent line to the curve $y = \sqrt{x}$ at the point $(4, 2)$.

30. Find the equation of the tangent line to the curve $y = x^2 - 3x + 1$ at the point $(2, -1)$.

31. Find the equation of the normal line to the curve $y = -3x^2$ at the point $(-1, -3)$.

32. Find the equation of the normal line to the curve $y = 4/x$ at the point $(-1, -4)$.

33. Find the equation of the normal line to the curve $y = 2x^2 - 1$ at the point $(1, 1)$.

34. Find the equation of the normal line to the curve $y = \sqrt{x - 1}$ at the point $(5, 2)$.

35. The following limit represents the derivative of a function f at the point $(a, f(a))$:

$$\lim_{h \to 0} \frac{2(a + h)^2 - 2a^2}{h}$$

Find $f(x)$.

36. The following limit represents the derivative of a function f at the point $(a, f(a))$:

$$\lim_{h \to 0} \frac{4(a+h)^3 - 4a^3}{h}$$

Find $f(x)$.

37. The following limit represents the derivative of a function f at the point $(a, f(a))$:

$$\lim_{h \to 0} \frac{\frac{1}{(2+h)^2+1} - \frac{1}{5}}{h}$$

Find f and a.

38. The following limit represents the derivative of a function f at the point $(a, f(a))$:

$$\lim_{h \to 0} \frac{\sin(\frac{\pi}{6} + h) - \sin \frac{\pi}{6}}{h}$$

Find f and a.

■ **4.1.2**

39. Velocity A car moves along a straight road. Its location at time t is given by

$$s(t) = 20t^2, \quad 0 \le t \le 2$$

where t is measured in hours and $s(t)$ is measured in kilometers.
(a) Graph $s(t)$ for $0 \le t \le 2$.
(b) Find the average velocity of the car between $t = 0$ and $t = 2$. Illustrate the average velocity on the graph of $s(t)$.
(c) Use calculus to find the instantaneous velocity of the car at $t = 1$. Illustrate the instantaneous velocity on the graph of $s(t)$.

40. Velocity A train moves along a straight line. Its location at time t is given by

$$s(t) = \frac{100}{t}, \quad 1 \le t \le 5$$

where t is measured in hours and $s(t)$ is measured in kilometers.
(a) Graph $s(t)$ for $1 \le t \le 5$.
(b) Find the average velocity of the train between $t = 1$ and $t = 5$. Where on the graph of $s(t)$ can you find the average velocity?
(c) Use calculus to find the instantaneous velocity of the train at $t = 2$. Where on the graph of $s(t)$ can you find the instantaneous velocity? What is the speed of the train at $t = 2$?

41. Velocity If $s(t)$ denotes the position of an object that moves along a straight line, then $\Delta s/\Delta t$, called the average velocity, is the average rate of change of $s(t)$, and $v(t) = ds/dt$, called the (instantaneous) velocity, is the instantaneous rate of change of $s(t)$. The speed of the object is the absolute value of the velocity, $|v(t)|$.

Suppose now that a car moves along a straight road. The location at time t is given by

$$s(t) = \frac{160}{3} t^2, \quad 0 \le t \le 1$$

where t is measured in hours and $s(t)$ is measured in kilometers.
(a) Where is the car at $t = 3/4$, and where is it at $t = 1$?
(b) Find the average velocity of the car between $t = 3/4$ and $t = 1$.

(c) Find the velocity and the speed of the car at $t = 3/4$.

42. Velocity Suppose a particle moves along a straight line. The position at time t is given by

$$s(t) = 3t - t^2, \quad t \ge 0$$

where t is measured in seconds and $s(t)$ is measured in meters.
(a) Graph $s(t)$ for $t \ge 0$.
(b) Use the graph in (a) to answer the following questions:
(i) Where is the particle at time 0?
(ii) Is there another time at which the particle visits the location where it was at time 0?
(iii) How far to the right on the straight line does the particle travel?
(iv) How far to the left on the straight line does the particle travel?
(v) Where is the velocity positive? where negative? equal to 0?
(c) Find the velocity of the particle.
(d) When is the velocity of the particle equal to 1 m/s?

43. Tilman's Resource Model In Subsection 4.1.2, we considered Tilman's resource model. Denote the biomass at time t by $B(t)$, and assume that

$$\frac{1}{B} \frac{dB}{dt} = f(R) - m$$

where R denotes the resource level,

$$f(R) = 200 \frac{R}{5+R}$$

and $m = 40$. Use the graphical approach to find the value R^* at which $\frac{1}{B} \frac{dB}{dt} = 0$. Then compute R^* by solving $\frac{1}{B} \frac{dB}{dt} = 0$.

44. Exponential Growth Assume that $N(t)$ denotes the size of a population at time t and that $N(t)$ satisfies the differential equation

$$\frac{dN}{dt} = rN$$

where r is a constant.
(a) Find the per capita growth rate.
(b) Assume that $r < 0$ and that $N(0) = 20$. Is the population size at time 1 greater than 20 or less than 20? Explain your answer.

45. Logistic Growth Assume that $N(t)$ denotes the size of a population at time t and that $N(t)$ satisfies the differential equation

$$\frac{dN}{dt} = 3N \left(1 - \frac{N}{20}\right)$$

Let $f(N) = 3N(1 - \frac{N}{20})$ for $N \ge 0$. Graph $f(N)$ as a function of N and identify all equilibria (i.e., all points where $\frac{dN}{dt} = 0$).

46. Island Model Assume that a species lives in a habitat that consists of many islands close to a mainland. The species occupies both the mainland and the islands, but, although it is present on the mainland at all times, it frequently goes extinct on the islands. Islands can be recolonized by migrants from the mainland. The following model keeps track of the fraction of islands occupied: Denote the fraction of islands occupied at time t by $p(t)$. Assume that each island experiences a constant risk of extinction and that vacant islands (the fraction $1-p$) are colonized from the mainland at a constant rate. Then

$$\frac{dp}{dt} = c(1 - p) - ep$$

where c and e are positive constants.

(a) The gain from colonization is $f(p) = c(1 - p)$ and the loss from extinction is $g(p) = ep$. Graph $f(p)$ and $g(p)$ for $0 \le p \le 1$ in the same coordinate system. Explain why the two graphs intersect whenever e and c are both positive. Compute the point of intersection and interpret its biological meaning.

(b) The parameter c measures how quickly a vacant island becomes colonized from the mainland. The closer the islands, the larger is the value of c. Use your graph in (a) to explain what happens to the point of intersection of the two lines as c increases. Interpret your result in biological terms.

47. Chemical Reaction Consider the chemical reaction

$$A + B \longrightarrow AB$$

If $x(t)$ denotes the concentration of AB at time t, then

$$\frac{dx}{dt} = k(a - x)(b - x)$$

where k is a positive constant and a and b denote the concentrations of A and B, respectively, at time 0. Assume that $k = 3$, $a = 7$, and $b = 4$. For what values of x is $dx/dt = 0$? Interpret the meaning of $dx/dt = 0$.

48. Chemical Reaction Consider the autocatalytic reaction

$$A + X \longrightarrow X$$

which was introduced in Problem 30 of Section 1.2. Find a differential equation that describes the rate of change of the concentration of the product X.

49. Logistic Growth Suppose that the rate of change of the size of a population is given by

$$\frac{dN}{dt} = rN\left(1 - \frac{N}{K}\right)$$

where $N = N(t)$ denotes the size of the population at time t and r and K are positive constants. Find the equilibrium size of the population—that is, the size at which the rate of change is equal to 0. Use your answer to explain why K is called the carrying capacity.

50. Biotic Diversity (Adapted from Valentine, 1985.) Walker and Valentine (1984) suggested a model for species diversity which assumes that species extinction rates are independent of diversity but speciation rates are regulated by competition. Denoting the number of species at time t by $N(t)$, the speciation rate by b, and the extinction rate by a, they used the model

$$\frac{dN}{dt} = N\left[b\left(1 - \frac{N}{K}\right) - a\right]$$

where K denotes the number of "niches," or potential places for species in the ecosystem.

(a) Find possible equilibria under the condition $a < b$.

(b) Use your result in (a) to explain the following statement by Valentine (1985):

> In this situation, ecosystems are never "full," with all potential niches occupied by species so long as the extinction rate is above zero.

(c) What happens when $a \ge b$?

■ **4.1.3**

51. Which of the following statements is true?

(A) If $f(x)$ is continuous, then $f(x)$ is differentiable.

(B) If $f(x)$ is differentiable, then $f(x)$ is continuous.

52. Explain the relationship between continuity and differentiability.

53. Sketch the graph of a function that is continuous at all points in its domain and differentiable in the domain except at one point.

54. Sketch the graph of a periodic function defined on **R** that is continuous at all points in its domain and differentiable in the domain except at $c = k$, $k \in \mathbf{Z}$.

55. If $f(x)$ is differentiable for all $x \in \mathbf{R}$ except at $x = c$, is it true that $f(x)$ must be continuous at $x = c$? Justify your answer.

In Problems 56–69, graph each function and, on the basis of the graph, guess where the function is not differentiable. (Assume the largest possible domain.)

56. $y = |x - 2|$

57. $y = -|x + 5|$

58. $y = 2 - |x - 3|$

59. $y = |x + 2| - 1$

60. $y = \dfrac{1}{2 + x}$

61. $y = \dfrac{1}{x - 3}$

62. $y = \dfrac{3 - x}{3 + x}$

63. $y = \dfrac{x - 1}{x + 1}$

64. $y = |x^2 - 3|$

65. $y = |2x^2 - 1|$

66. $f(x) = \begin{cases} x & \text{for } x \le 0 \\ x + 1 & \text{for } x > 0 \end{cases}$

67. $f(x) = \begin{cases} 2x & \text{for } x \le 1 \\ x + 2 & \text{for } x > 1 \end{cases}$

68. $f(x) = \begin{cases} x^2 & \text{for } x \le -1 \\ 2 - x^2 & \text{for } x > -1 \end{cases}$

69. $f(x) = \begin{cases} x^2 + 1 & \text{for } x \le 0 \\ e^{-x} & \text{for } x > 0 \end{cases}$

70. Suppose the function $f(x)$ is piecewise defined; that is, $f(x) = f_1(x)$ for $x \le a$ and $f(x) = f_2(x)$ for $x > a$. Assume that $f_1(x)$ is continuous and differentiable for $x < a$ and that $f_2(x)$ is continuous and differentiable for $x > a$. Sketch graphs of $f(x)$ for the following three cases:

(a) $f(x)$ is continuous and differentiable at $x = a$.

(b) $f(x)$ is continuous, but not differentiable, at $x = a$.

(c) $f(x)$ is neither continuous nor differentiable at $x = a$.

■ 4.2 The Power Rule, the Basic Rules of Differentiation, and the Derivatives of Polynomials

In this section, we will begin a systematic treatment of the computation of derivatives. Knowing how to differentiate is fundamental to your understanding of the rest of the course. Although computer software is now available to compute derivatives of many functions (such as $y = cx^n$ or $y = e^{\sin x}$), it is nonetheless important that you master the techniques of differentiation.

The power rule is the simplest of the differentiation rules. It allows us to compute the derivative of a function of the form $y = x^n$, where n is a positive integer.

Power Rule Let n be a positive integer; then

$$\frac{d}{dx}(x^n) = nx^{n-1}$$

We found the rule for the constant function $f(x) = a$ in the previous section.

If $f(x)$ is the constant function $f(x) = a$, then

$$\frac{d}{dx}f(x) = 0$$

We prove the power rule first for $n = 2$—that is, for $f(x) = x^2$ (Figure 4.20). In Subsection 4.1.1, we computed the derivative of $y = x^2$ at $x = 1$. In this section, we compute the difference quotient $\frac{\Delta f}{\Delta x}$ at any arbitrary x:

$$\frac{\Delta f}{\Delta x} = \frac{f(x+h) - f(x)}{h} = \frac{(x+h)^2 - x^2}{h}$$

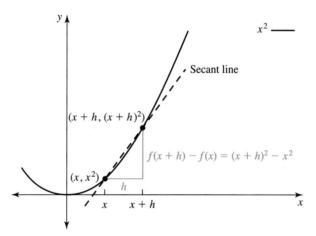

Figure 4.20 The slope of the secant line through (x, x^2) and $(x+h, (x+h)^2)$ is $\frac{(x+h)^2-x^2}{h}$.

Using the expansion $(x+h)^2 = x^2 + 2xh + h^2$, we find that

$$\frac{\Delta f}{\Delta x} = \frac{x^2 + 2xh + h^2 - x^2}{h} = \frac{2xh + h^2}{h} = 2x + h \qquad (4.5)$$

after canceling h in both the numerator and the denominator. To find the derivative, we need to let $h \to 0$:

$$f'(x) = \lim_{\Delta x \to 0} \frac{\Delta f}{\Delta x} = \lim_{h \to 0}(2x + h) = 2x$$

This sequence of steps proves the power rule for $n = 2$. The proof of the rule for other positive integers of n is conceptually no different from the case $n = 2$, but it gets algebraically much more involved. For general n, we need the expansion of $(x+h)^n$, given by the **binomial theorem**, which we will not prove.

> **Binomial Theorem** If n is a positive integer, then
>
> $$(x + y)^n = x^n + nx^{n-1}y + \frac{n(n-1)}{2 \cdot 1}x^{n-2}y^2$$
> $$+ \frac{n(n-1)(n-2)}{3 \cdot 2 \cdot 1}x^{n-3}y^3$$
> $$+ \cdots + \frac{n(n-1)\cdots(n-k+1)}{k(k-1)\cdots 2 \cdot 1}x^{n-k}y^k$$
> $$+ \cdots + nxy^{n-1} + y^n$$

The expansion of $(x + y)^n$ is thus a sum of terms of the form

$$C_{n,k}x^{n-k}y^k, \quad k = 0, 1, \ldots, n$$

where $C_{n,k}$ is a coefficient that depends on n and k. The exact form of the coefficients $C_{n,k}$ will not be important in the proof of the power rule, except for the two terms $C_{n,0} = 1$ and $C_{n,1} = n$, which are the coefficients for x^n and $x^{n-1}y$, respectively.

Proof of the Power Rule We use the binomial theorem to expand and then compute the difference in the numerator of the difference quotient:

$$\Delta f = f(x + h) - f(x) = (x + h)^n - x^n$$
$$= (C_{n,0}x^n + C_{n,1}x^{n-1}h + C_{n,2}x^{n-2}h^2 + C_{n,3}x^{n-3}h^3$$
$$+ \cdots + C_{n,n-1}xh^{n-1} + C_{n,n}h^n) - x^n$$

Since $C_{n,0} = 1$, the x^n terms cancel. We can then factor h out of the remaining terms and find that

$$f(x + h) - f(x) = h \left[C_{n,1}x^{n-1} + C_{n,2}x^{n-2}h + C_{n,3}x^{n-3}h^2 + \cdots + C_{n,n}h^{n-1} \right]$$

When we divide by h and let $h \to 0$, we obtain

$$f'(x) = \lim_{h \to 0} \frac{f(x + h) - f(x)}{h}$$
$$= \lim_{h \to 0} \left[C_{n,1}x^{n-1} + C_{n,2}x^{n-2}h + C_{n,3}x^{n-3}h^2 + \cdots + C_{n,n}h^{n-1} \right]$$

All terms except for the first have h as a factor and thus tend to 0 as $h \to 0$. (The first term does not depend on h.) We find that

$$f'(x) = C_{n,1}x^{n-1}$$

With $C_{n,1} = n$, this is then

$$f'(x) = nx^{n-1}$$

which proves the power rule. ■

EXAMPLE 1

We apply the power rule to various functions and take the opportunity to practice the different notations.

(a) If $f(x) = x^6$, then $f'(x) = 6x^5$.

(b) If $f(x) = x^{300}$, then $f'(x) = 300x^{299}$.

(c) If $g(t) = t^5$, then $\frac{d}{dt}g(t) = 5t^4$.

(d) If $z = s^3$, then $\frac{dz}{ds} = 3s^2$.

(e) If $x = y^4$, then $\frac{dx}{dy} = 4y^3$. ■

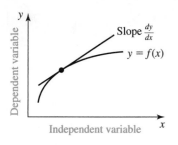

Figure 4.21 If $y = f(x)$, then x is the independent variable and y is the dependent variable.

Example 1 illustrates the importance of knowing how the variables depend on each other (Figure 4.21). If $y = f(x)$, we call x the **independent variable** and y the **dependent variable**, because y depends on the variable x. For instance, in (a), y is a function of x; thus, x is the independent, and y is the dependent, variable. In (e), by contrast, x is a function of y; thus, y is now the independent, and x the dependent, variable. The Leibniz notation $\frac{dy}{dx}$ emphasizes this dependence. When we write $\frac{dy}{dx}$, we consider y to be a function of x (i.e., y is the dependent, and x is the independent, variable) and differentiate y with respect to x.

Since polynomials and rational functions are built up by the basic operations of addition, subtraction, multiplication, and division operating on power functions of the form $y = x^n$, $n = 0, 1, 2, \ldots$, we need differentiation rules for such operations. We begin with the following rules:

Theorem Suppose a is a constant and $f(x)$ and $g(x)$ are differentiable at x. Then the following relationships hold:

1. $\dfrac{d}{dx}[af(x)] = a\dfrac{d}{dx}f(x)$

2. $\dfrac{d}{dx}[f(x) + g(x)] = \dfrac{d}{dx}f(x) + \dfrac{d}{dx}g(x)$

Rule 1 says that a constant factor can be pulled out of the derivative expression; Rule 2 says that the derivative of a sum of two functions is equal to the sum of the derivatives of the functions. Similarly, since $f(x) - g(x) = f(x) + (-1)g(x)$, the derivative of a difference of functions is the difference of the derivatives:

$$\frac{d}{dx}[f(x) - g(x)] = \frac{d}{dx}[f(x) + (-1)g(x)] = \frac{d}{dx}f(x) + \frac{d}{dx}[(-1)g(x)]$$

Using Rule 1 on the rightmost term, we find that $\frac{d}{dx}[(-1)g(x)] = (-1)\frac{d}{dx}g(x)$. Therefore,

$$\frac{d}{dx}[f(x) - g(x)] = \frac{d}{dx}f(x) - \frac{d}{dx}g(x)$$

Rules 1 and 2 allow us to differentiate polynomials, as illustrated in the next three examples.

EXAMPLE 2   Differentiate $y = 2x^4 - 3x^3 + x - 7$.

Solution

$$\frac{d}{dx}(2x^4 - 3x^3 + x - 7) = \frac{d}{dx}(2x^4) - \frac{d}{dx}(3x^3) + \frac{d}{dx}x - \frac{d}{dx}7$$
$$= 2\frac{d}{dx}x^4 - 3\frac{d}{dx}x^3 + \frac{d}{dx}x - \frac{d}{dx}7$$
$$= 2(4x^3) - 3(3x^2) + 1 - 0 = 8x^3 - 9x^2 + 1 \quad ■$$

EXAMPLE 3

(a) $\frac{d}{dx}(-5x^7 + 2x^3 - 10) = -35x^6 + 6x^2$

(b) $\frac{d}{dt}(t^3 - 8t^2 + 3t) = 3t^2 - 16t + 3$

(c) Suppose that n is a positive integer and a is a constant. Then $\frac{d}{ds}(as^n) = ans^{n-1}$.

(d) $\frac{d}{dN}(\ln 5 + N \ln 7) = \ln 7$

(e) $\frac{d}{dr}(r^2 \sin\frac{\pi}{4} - r^3 \cos\frac{\pi}{12} + \sin\frac{\pi}{6}) = 2r\sin\frac{\pi}{4} - 3r^2\cos\frac{\pi}{12} \quad ■$

In the previous section, we related the derivative to the slope of the tangent line; the next example uses this interpretation.

EXAMPLE 4   **Tangent and Normal Lines** If $f(x) = 2x^3 - 3x + 1$, find the tangent and normal lines at $(-1, 2)$.

Solution   The slope of the tangent line at $(-1, 2)$ is $f'(-1)$. We begin calculating this derivative as follows:

$$f'(x) = 6x^2 - 3$$

Evaluating $f'(x)$ at $x = -1$, we get

$$f'(-1) = 6(-1)^2 - 3 = 3$$

Therefore, the equation of the tangent line at $(-1, 2)$ is

$$y - 2 = 3(x - (-1)), \qquad \text{or} \qquad y = 3x + 5$$

To find the equation of the normal line, recall that the normal line is perpendicular to the tangent line; hence, the slope m of the normal line is given by

$$m = -\frac{1}{f'(-1)} = -\frac{1}{3}$$

The normal line goes through the point $(-1, 2)$ as well. The equation of the normal line is therefore

$$y - 2 = -\frac{1}{3}(x - (-1)), \qquad \text{or} \qquad y = -\frac{1}{3}x + \frac{5}{3}$$

The graph of $f(x)$, including the tangent and normal lines at $(-1, 2)$, is shown in Figure 4.22. ■

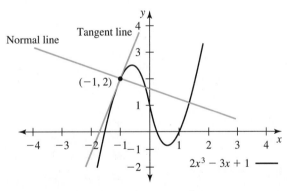

Figure 4.22 The graph of $f(x) = 2x^3 - 3x + 1$, together with the tangent and normal lines at $(-1, 2)$.

Look again at the last example: When we computed $f'(-1)$, we *first* computed $f'(x)$; the *second* step was to evaluate $f'(x)$ at $x = -1$. It makes no sense to plug -1 into $f(x)$ and then differentiate the result. Since $f(-1) = 2$ is a constant, the derivative would be 0, which is obviously not $f'(-1)$. Just look at Figure 4.22 to convince yourself. The notation $f'(-1)$ means that we evaluate the function $f'(x)$ at $x = -1$.

Section 4.2 Problems

Differentiate the functions given in Problems 1–22 with respect to the independent variable.

1. $f(x) = 4x^3 - 7x + 1$

2. $f(x) = -3x^4 + 5x^2$

3. $f(x) = -2x^5 + 7x - 4$

4. $f(x) = -3x^4 + 6x^2 - 2$

5. $f(x) = 3 - 4x - 5x^2$

6. $f(x) = -1 + 3x^2 - 2x^4$

7. $g(s) = 5s^7 + 2s^3 - 5s$

8. $g(s) = 3 - 4s^2 - 4s^3$

9. $h(t) = -\frac{1}{3}t^4 + 4t$

10. $h(t) = \frac{1}{2}t^2 - 3t + 2$

11. $f(x) = x^2 \sin\frac{\pi}{3} + \tan\frac{\pi}{4}$

12. $f(x) = 2x^3 \cos\frac{\pi}{3} + \cos\frac{\pi}{6}$

13. $f(x) = -3x^4 \tan \dfrac{\pi}{6} - \cot \dfrac{\pi}{6}$

14. $f(x) = x^2 \sec \dfrac{\pi}{6} + 3x \sec \dfrac{\pi}{4}$

15. $f(t) = t^3 e^{-2} + t + e^{-1}$

16. $f(x) = \dfrac{1}{2}x^2 e^3 - x^4$

17. $f(s) = s^3 e^3 + 3e$

18. $f(x) = \dfrac{x}{e} + e^2 x + e$

19. $f(x) = 20x^3 - 4x^6 + 9x^8$

20. $f(x) = \dfrac{x^3}{15} - \dfrac{x^4}{20} + \dfrac{2}{15}$

21. $f(x) = \pi x^3 - \dfrac{1}{\pi} + \dfrac{x}{\pi}$

22. $f(x) = \pi x e^2 - \dfrac{x^2 \pi}{e}$

23. Differentiate
$$f(x) = ax^3$$
with respect to x. Assume that a is a constant.

24. Differentiate
$$f(x) = x^3 + a$$
with respect to x. Assume that a is a constant.

25. Differentiate
$$f(x) = ax^2 - 2a$$
with respect to x. Assume that a is a constant.

26. Differentiate
$$f(x) = a^2 x^4 - 2ax^2$$
with respect to x. Assume that a is a constant.

27. Differentiate
$$h(s) = rs^2 - r$$
with respect to s. Assume that r is a constant.

28. Differentiate
$$f(r) = rs^2 - r$$
with respect to r. Assume that s is a constant.

29. Differentiate
$$f(x) = rs^2 x^3 - rx + s$$
with respect to x. Assume that r and s are constants.

30. Differentiate
$$f(x) = \dfrac{r+x}{rs^2} - rsx + (r+s)x - rs$$
with respect to x. Assume that r and s are nonzero constants.

31. Differentiate
$$f(N) = (b-1)N^4 - \dfrac{N^2}{b}$$
with respect to N. Assume that b is a nonzero constant.

32. Differentiate
$$f(N) = \dfrac{bN^2 + N}{K+b}$$
with respect to N. Assume that b and K are positive constants.

33. Differentiate
$$g(t) = a^3 t - at^3$$
with respect to t. Assume that a is a constant.

34. Differentiate
$$h(s) = a^4 s^2 - as^4 + \dfrac{s^2}{a^4}$$
with respect to s. Assume that a is a positive constant.

35. Differentiate
$$V(t) = V_0(1 + \gamma t)$$
with respect to t. Assume that V_0 and γ are positive constants.

36. Differentiate
$$p(T) = \dfrac{NkT}{V}$$
with respect to T. Assume that N, k, and V are positive constants.

37. Differentiate
$$g(N) = N\left(1 - \dfrac{N}{K}\right)$$
with respect to N. Assume that K is a positive constant.

38. Differentiate
$$g(N) = rN\left(1 - \dfrac{N}{K}\right)$$
with respect to N. Assume that K and r are positive constants.

39. Differentiate
$$g(N) = rN^2\left(1 - \dfrac{N}{K}\right)$$
with respect to N. Assume that K and r are positive constants.

40. Differentiate
$$g(N) = rN(a - N)\left(1 - \dfrac{N}{K}\right)$$
with respect to N. Assume that r, a, and K are positive constants.

41. Differentiate
$$R(T) = \dfrac{2\pi^5}{15}\dfrac{k^4}{c^2 h^3}T^4$$
with respect to T. Assume that k, c, and h are positive constants.

In Problems 42–48, find the tangent line, in standard form, to $y = f(x)$ at the indicated point.

42. $y = 3x^2 - 4x + 7$, at $x = 2$

43. $y = 7x^3 + 2x - 1$, at $x = -3$

44. $y = -2x^3 - 3x + 1$, at $x = 1$

45. $y = 2x^4 - 5x$, at $x = 1$

46. $y = -x^3 - 2x^2$, at $x = 0$

47. $y = \dfrac{1}{\sqrt{2}}x^2 - \sqrt{2}$, at $x = 4$

48. $y = 3\pi x^5 - \dfrac{\pi}{2}x^3$, at $x = -1$

In Problems 49–54, find the normal line, in standard form, to $y = f(x)$ at the indicated point.

49. $y = 2 + x^2$, at $x = -1$

50. $y = 1 - 3x^2$, at $x = -2$

51. $y = \sqrt{3}x^4 - 2\sqrt{3}x^2$, at $x = -\sqrt{3}$

52. $y = -2x^2 - x$, at $x = 0$

53. $y = x^3 - 3$, at $x = 1$

54. $y = 1 - \pi x^2$, at $x = -1$

55. Find the tangent line to
$$f(x) = ax^2$$
at $x = 1$. Assume that a is a positive constant.

56. Find the tangent line to
$$f(x) = ax^3 - 2ax$$
at $x = -1$. Assume that a is a positive constant.

57. Find the tangent line to

$$f(x) = \frac{ax^2}{a^2 + 2}$$

at $x = 2$. Assume that a is a positive constant.

58. Find the tangent line to

$$f(x) = \frac{x^2}{a + 1}$$

at $x = a$. Assume that a is a positive constant.

59. Find the normal line to

$$f(x) = ax^3$$

at $x = -1$. Assume that a is a positive constant.

60. Find the normal line to

$$f(x) = ax^2 - 3ax$$

at $x = 2$. Assume that a is a positive constant.

61. Find the normal line to

$$f(x) = \frac{ax^2}{a + 1}$$

at $x = 2$. Assume that a is a positive constant.

62. Find the normal line to

$$f(x) = \frac{x^3}{a + 1}$$

at $x = 2a$. Assume that a is a positive constant.

In Problems 63–70, find the coordinates of all of the points of the graph of $y = f(x)$ that have horizontal tangents.

63. $f(x) = x^2$
64. $f(x) = 2 - x^2$
65. $f(x) = 3x - x^2$
66. $f(x) = 4x + 2x^2$
67. $f(x) = 3x^3 - x^2$
68. $f(x) = -4x^4 + x^3$
69. $f(x) = \frac{1}{2}x^4 - \frac{7}{3}x^3 - 2x^2$
70. $f(x) = 3x^5 - \frac{3}{2}x^4$

71. Find a point on the curve

$$y = 4 - x^2$$

whose tangent line is parallel to the line $y = 2$. Is there more than one such point? If so, find all other points with this property.

72. Find a point on the curve

$$y = (4 - x)^2$$

whose tangent line is parallel to the line $y = -3$. Is there more than one such point? If so, find all other points with this property.

73. Find a point on the curve

$$y = 2x^2 - \frac{1}{2}$$

whose tangent line is parallel to the line $y = x$. Is there more than one such point? If so, find all other points with this property.

74. Find a point on the curve

$$y = 1 - 3x^3$$

whose tangent line is parallel to the line $y = -x$. Is there more than one such point? If so, find all other points with this property.

75. Find a point on the curve

$$y = x^3 + 2x + 2$$

whose tangent line is parallel to the line $3x - y = 2$. Is there more than one such point? If so, find all other points with this property.

76. Find a point on the curve

$$y = 2x^3 - 4x + 1$$

whose tangent line is parallel to the line $y - 2x = 1$. Is there more than one such point? If so, find all other points with this property.

77. Show that the tangent line to the curve

$$y = x^2$$

at the point $(1, 1)$ passes through the point $(0, -1)$.

78. Find all tangent lines to the curve

$$y = x^2$$

that pass through the point $(0, -1)$.

79. Find all tangent lines to the curve

$$y = x^2$$

that pass through the point $(0, -a^2)$, where a is a positive number.

80. How many tangent lines to the curve

$$y = x^2 + 2x$$

pass through the point $(-\frac{1}{2}, -3)$?

81. Suppose that $P(x)$ is a polynomial of degree 4. Is $P'(x)$ a polynomial as well? If yes, what is its degree?

82. Suppose that $P(x)$ is a polynomial of degree k. Is $P'(x)$ a polynomial as well? If yes, what is its degree?

4.3 The Product and Quotient Rules, and the Derivatives of Rational and Power Functions

■ 4.3.1 The Product Rule

The derivative of a sum of differentiable functions is the sum of the derivatives of the functions. The rule for products is not so simple, as can be seen from the following example: Consider $y = x^5 = (x^3)(x^2)$. We know that

$$\frac{d}{dx}x^5 = 5x^4$$
$$\frac{d}{dx}x^3 = 3x^2$$
$$\frac{d}{dx}x^2 = 2x$$

This chain of reasoning shows that

$$\frac{d}{dx}x^5 \quad \text{is not equal to} \quad \left(\frac{d}{dx}x^3\right)\left(\frac{d}{dx}x^2\right)$$

(Leibniz first thought that the multiplication rule was as simple as that, but he quickly realized his mistake and found the correct formula for differentiating products of functions.)

The Product Rule If $h(x) = f(x)g(x)$ and both $f(x)$ and $g(x)$ are differentiable at x, then

$$h'(x) = f'(x)g(x) + f(x)g'(x)$$

If we set $u = f(x)$ and $v = g(x)$, then

$$(uv)' = u'v + uv'$$

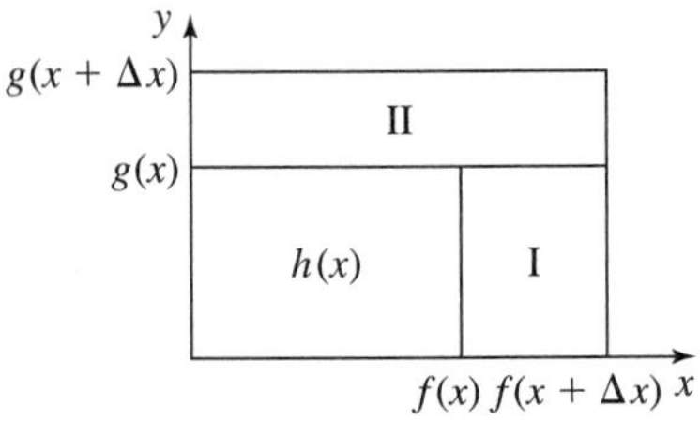

Figure 4.23 The product rule.

Proof Since $h(x) = f(x)g(x)$ is a product of two functions, we can visualize $h(x)$ as the area of a rectangle with sides $f(x)$ and $g(x)$. To compute the derivative, we need $h(x + \Delta x)$; this is given by

$$h(x + \Delta x) = f(x + \Delta x)g(x + \Delta x)$$

To compute $h'(x)$, we must compute $h(x + \Delta x) - h(x)$ (Figure 4.23). We find that

$$\begin{aligned} h(x + \Delta x) - h(x) &= \text{area of I} + \text{area of II} \\ &= [f(x + \Delta x) - f(x)]g(x) \\ &\quad + [g(x + \Delta x) - g(x)]f(x + \Delta x) \end{aligned}$$

Dividing this result by Δx and taking the limit as $\Delta x \to 0$, we obtain

$$\begin{aligned} h'(x) &= \lim_{\Delta x \to 0} \frac{h(x + \Delta x) - h(x)}{\Delta x} \\ &= \lim_{\Delta x \to 0} \frac{[f(x + \Delta x) - f(x)]g(x) + [g(x + \Delta x) - g(x)]f(x + \Delta x)}{\Delta x} \\ &= \lim_{\Delta x \to 0} \left[\frac{f(x + \Delta x) - f(x)}{\Delta x} g(x) + \frac{g(x + \Delta x) - g(x)}{\Delta x} f(x + \Delta x)\right] \end{aligned}$$

Now, we need the assumption that $f'(x)$ and $g'(x)$ exist and that $f(x)$ is continuous at x [which follows from the fact that $f(x)$ is differentiable at x]. These assumptions allow us to use the basic rules for limits, and we write the last expression as

$$\left(\lim_{\Delta x \to 0} \frac{f(x + \Delta x) - f(x)}{\Delta x}\right) g(x) + \left(\lim_{\Delta x \to 0} \frac{g(x + \Delta x) - g(x)}{\Delta x}\right)\left(\lim_{\Delta x \to 0} f(x + \Delta x)\right)$$

The limits of the difference quotients are the respective derivatives. Using the fact that $f(x)$ is continuous at x, we find that $\lim_{\Delta x \to 0} f(x + \Delta x) = f(x)$. Therefore,

$$h'(x) = f'(x)g(x) + g'(x)f(x)$$

as claimed. ■

EXAMPLE 1

Differentiate $f(x) = (3x + 1)(2x^2 - 5)$.

Solution

We write $u = 3x + 1$ and $v = 2x^2 - 5$. The product rule says that $(uv)' = u'v + uv'$. That is, we need the derivatives of both u and v:

$$u = 3x + 1 \qquad v = 2x^2 - 5$$
$$u' = 3 \qquad v' = 4x$$

Then

$$(uv)' = u'v + uv'$$
$$= 3(2x^2 - 5) + (3x + 1)(4x)$$
$$= 6x^2 - 15 + 12x^2 + 4x = 18x^2 + 4x - 15$$

Of course, we could have gotten this result by first multiplying out $(3x + 1)(2x^2 - 5) = 6x^3 - 15x + 2x^2 - 5$, which is simply a polynomial function. We then would have found that

$$\frac{d}{dx}(6x^3 - 15x + 2x^2 - 5) = 18x^2 - 15 + 4x$$

which is the same answer. ■

EXAMPLE 2

Differentiate $f(x) = (3x^3 - 2x)^2$.

Solution

Again, we could simply expand the square and then differentiate the resulting polynomial—but we can also use the product rule. To do so, we write $u = v = 3x^3 - 2x$. Then $f(x) = uv$ and $(uv)' = u'v + uv'$. Since $u = v$, it follows that $u' = v'$, and the formula simplifies to $(uv)' = (u^2)' = u'u + uu' = 2uu'$. Because $u' = 9x^2 - 2$, we have

$$f'(x) = 2(3x^3 - 2x)(9x^2 - 2)$$ ■

EXAMPLE 3

Population Growth In many population models, the population growth rate depends only on the current population size. We can express this quantity by

$$\frac{dN}{dt} = f(N)$$

where $N(t)$ denotes the size of the population at time t and $f(N)$ is the population growth rate, which depends only on the current population size $N = N(t)$. The per capita growth rate $\frac{1}{N}\frac{dN}{dt}$ is then also just a function of N, namely,

$$\frac{1}{N}\frac{dN}{dt} = g(N)$$

with

$$f(N) = Ng(N)$$

Assume that $g(N)$ is differentiable and that $\lim_{N \to 0^+} g(N)$ and $\lim_{N \to 0^+} g'(N)$ exist. Show that

$$g(0) = \lim_{N \to 0^+} \frac{d}{dN} f(N)$$

Solution

Using the product rule, we compute the derivative of the population growth rate $f(N) = Ng(N)$:

$$\frac{d}{dN}(Ng(N)) = g(N) + Ng'(N)$$

Then we take the limit as $N \to 0^+$:

$$\lim_{N \to 0^+} \frac{d}{dN}(Ng(N)) = \lim_{N \to 0^+} \left[g(N) + Ng'(N) \right] = g(0)$$

(Note that we can take only one-sided limits here, since $N \geq 0$ for biological reasons.) ■

EXAMPLE 4

Apply the product rule repeatedly to find the derivative of

$$y = (2x + 1)(x + 1)(3x - 4)$$

Solution

Since the product rule is formulated for products of two factors, we group the terms in our function as follows:

$$u = (2x + 1)(x + 1)$$

Then $y = uv$, with $v = 3x - 4$. Note that any other grouping into two factors would work as well. Now, to differentiate u, we need to use the product rule:

$$w = 2x + 1 \qquad z = x + 1$$
$$w' = 2 \qquad z' = 1$$

Therefore,

$$u' = 2(x + 1) + (2x + 1)(1) = 2x + 2 + 2x + 1 = 4x + 3$$

With $v' = 3$, we find that

$$y' = (4x + 3)(3x - 4) + 3(2x + 1)(x + 1)$$
$$= 12x^2 - 16x + 9x - 12 + 6x^2 + 6x + 3x + 3$$
$$= 18x^2 + 2x - 9$$

■

■ **4.3.2 The Quotient Rule**

The quotient rule will allow us to compute the derivative of a quotient of two functions. In particular, the rule will allow us to compute the derivative of a rational function, because a rational function is the quotient of two polynomial functions.

The Quotient Rule If $h(x) = \frac{f(x)}{g(x)}$, $g(x) \neq 0$, and both $f'(x)$ and $g'(x)$ exist, then

$$h'(x) = \frac{f'(x)g(x) - f(x)g'(x)}{[g(x)]^2}$$

In short, with $u = f(x)$ and $v = g(x)$,

$$\left(\frac{u}{v}\right)' = \frac{u'v - uv'}{v^2}$$

We could prove the quotient rule much as we did the product rule, by using the formal definition of derivatives, but that would not be very exciting. Instead, we will give a different proof of the quotient rule in the next subsection.

Note carefully the exact forms of the product and quotient rules. In the product rule we add $f'g$ and fg', whereas in the quotient rule we subtract fg' from $f'g$. As mentioned, we can use the quotient rule to find the derivative of rational functions. We illustrate this application in the next two examples.

EXAMPLE 5

Differentiate $y = \frac{x^3 - 3x + 2}{x^2 + 1}$. (This function is defined for all $x \in \mathbf{R}$, since $x^2 + 1 \neq 0$.)

Solution

We set $u = x^3 - 3x + 2$ and $v = x^2 + 1$. Both u and v are polynomials, which we know how to differentiate. We find that

$$u = x^3 - 3x + 2 \qquad v = x^2 + 1$$
$$u' = 3x^2 - 3 \qquad v' = 2x$$

Using the quotient rule, we compute y':

$$y' = \frac{u'v - uv'}{v^2} = \frac{(3x^2 - 3)(x^2 + 1) - (x^3 - 3x + 2)2x}{(x^2 + 1)^2}$$

$$= \frac{3x^4 + 3x^2 - 3x^2 - 3 - 2x^4 + 6x^2 - 4x}{(x^2 + 1)^2}$$

$$= \frac{x^4 + 6x^2 - 4x - 3}{(x^2 + 1)^2}$$

■

EXAMPLE 6

Monod Growth Function Differentiate the Monod growth function

$$f(R) = \frac{aR}{k + R}, \quad R \geq 0$$

where a and k are positive constants.

Solution

Since a and k are positive constants, $f(R)$ is defined for all $R \geq 0$. We write $u = aR$ and $v = k + R$ and obtain

$$u = aR \qquad v = k + R$$
$$u' = a \qquad v' = 1$$

Hence,

$$\frac{d}{dR} f(R) = \frac{u'v - uv'}{v^2} = \frac{a(k + R) - aR \cdot 1}{(k + R)^2} = \frac{ak}{(k + R)^2}$$

In Figure 4.24, we graph both $f(R)$ and $f'(R)$. We see that the slope of the tangent line at $(R, f(R))$ is positive for all $R \geq 0$. We can also draw this conclusion from the graph of $f'(R)$, since it is positive for all $R \geq 0$. Furthermore, we see that $f(R)$ becomes less steep as R increases, which is reflected in the fact that $f'(R)$ becomes smaller as R increases. ■

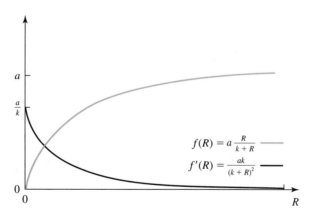

$$f(R) = a\frac{R}{k + R}$$

$$f'(R) = \frac{ak}{(k + R)^2}$$

Figure 4.24 The graph of $f(R)$ and $f'(R)$ in Example 6.

The quotient rule allows us to extend the power rule to the case where the exponent is a negative integer:

Power Rule (Negative Integer Exponents) If $f(x) = x^{-n}$, where n is a positive integer, then

$$f'(x) = -nx^{-n-1}$$

Note that the power rule for negative integer exponents works the same way as the power rule for positive integer exponents: We write the exponent of the original function x^n in front and decrease the exponent by 1. We will now prove the power rule for negative integer exponents.

Proof We write $f(x) = \frac{1}{x^n}$ and set $u = 1$ and $v = x^n$. Then

$$u = 1 \qquad v = x^n$$
$$u' = 0 \qquad v' = nx^{n-1}$$

and, therefore,

$$f'(x) = \frac{u'v - uv'}{v^2} = \frac{0 \cdot x^n - 1 \cdot nx^{n-1}}{(x^n)^2} = -\frac{nx^{n-1}}{x^{2n}} = -nx^{-n-1} \qquad ■$$

EXAMPLE 7

(a) If $y = \frac{1}{x}$, then

$$y' = \frac{d}{dx}(x^{-1}) = (-1)x^{-1-1} = -\frac{1}{x^2}$$

(b) If $g(x) = \frac{3}{x^4}$, then

$$g'(x) = \frac{d}{dx}(3x^{-4}) = 3\frac{d}{dx}x^{-4} = 3(-4)x^{-4-1} = -12x^{-5} = -\frac{12}{x^5} \qquad ■$$

There is a general form of the power rule in which the exponent can be any real number. In the next section, we give the proof for the case when the exponent is rational; we prove the general case in Section 4.7.

Power Rule (General Form) Let $f(x) = x^r$, where r is any real number. Then

$$f'(x) = rx^{r-1}$$

EXAMPLE 8

(a) If $y = \sqrt{x}$, then

$$y' = \frac{d}{dx}\left(x^{1/2}\right) = \frac{1}{2}x^{\frac{1}{2}-1} = \frac{1}{2}x^{-1/2} = \frac{1}{2\sqrt{x}}$$

(b) If $y = \sqrt[5]{x}$, then

$$y' = \frac{d}{dx}\left(x^{1/5}\right) = \frac{1}{5}x^{(1/5)-1} = \frac{1}{5}x^{-4/5} = \frac{1}{5x^{4/5}}$$

(c) If $g(t) = \frac{1}{\sqrt[3]{t}}$, then

$$g'(t) = \frac{d}{dt}\left(t^{-1/3}\right) = \left(-\frac{1}{3}\right)t^{(-1/3)-1} = \left(-\frac{1}{3}\right)t^{-4/3} = -\frac{1}{3t^{4/3}}$$

(d) If $h(s) = s^\pi$, then $h'(s) = \pi s^{\pi-1}$. ■

The function $f(x) = \sqrt{x}$, $x \geq 0$, appears quite frequently. It is therefore worthwhile to memorize its derivative, which is defined only for $x > 0$:

$$\frac{d}{dx}\sqrt{x} = \frac{1}{2\sqrt{x}}$$

EXAMPLE 9

Combining the Rules Differentiate $f(x) = \sqrt{x}(x^2 - 1)$.

Solution 1   We can consider $f(x)$ to be a product of two functions. Let

$$u = \sqrt{x} \qquad v = x^2 - 1$$

$$u' = \frac{1}{2\sqrt{x}} \qquad v' = 2x$$

Hence,

$$f'(x) = u'v + uv' = \frac{1}{2\sqrt{x}}(x^2 - 1) + \sqrt{x}(2x)$$

$$= \frac{x^2 - 1 + \sqrt{x}(2x)2\sqrt{x}}{2\sqrt{x}} = \frac{x^2 - 1 + 4x^2}{2\sqrt{x}} = \frac{5x^2 - 1}{2\sqrt{x}}$$

Solution 2   Since $f(x) = \sqrt{x}(x^2 - 1) = x^{5/2} - x^{1/2}$, we can also use the general version of the power rule. We find that

$$f'(x) = \frac{5}{2}x^{(5/2)-1} - \frac{1}{2}x^{(1/2)-1} = \frac{5}{2}x^{3/2} - \frac{1}{2\sqrt{x}} = \frac{5x^{3/2}\sqrt{x} - 1}{2\sqrt{x}} = \frac{5x^2 - 1}{2\sqrt{x}} \qquad ■$$

EXAMPLE 10   **A Function That Contains a Constant** Differentiate $h(t) = (at)^{1/3}(a+1) - a$, where a is a positive constant.

Solution   Since $h(t)$ is a function of t, we need to differentiate with respect to t, keeping in mind that a is a constant. Rewriting $h(t)$ will make this easier:

$$h(t) = a^{1/3}(a + 1)t^{1/3} - a$$

The factor $a^{1/3}(a + 1)$ in front of $t^{1/3}$ is a constant. Thus,

$$h'(t) = a^{1/3}(a + 1)\frac{1}{3}t^{-2/3} - 0 = \frac{a^{1/3}(a + 1)}{3t^{2/3}} \qquad ■$$

EXAMPLE 11   **Differentiating a Function That Is Not Specified** Suppose $f(2) = 3$ and $f'(2) = 1/4$. Find

$$\frac{d}{dx}[xf(x)]$$

at $x = 2$.

Solution   Since $xf(x)$ is a product, we can use the product rule

$$\frac{d}{dx}[xf(x)] = f(x) + xf'(x)$$

Hence,

$$\frac{d}{dx}[xf(x)]\Big|_{x=2} = f(2) + 2f'(2) = 3 + \frac{1}{2} = \frac{7}{2} \qquad ■$$

EXAMPLE 12   **Differentiating a Function That Is Not Specified** Suppose that $f(x)$ is differentiable. Find an expression for the derivative of

$$y = \frac{f(x)}{x^2}$$

Solution   We set

$$u = f(x) \qquad v = x^2$$

$$u' = f'(x) \qquad v' = 2x$$

and use the quotient rule. We find that

$$y' = \frac{f'(x)x^2 - f(x)2x}{x^4} = \frac{xf'(x) - 2f(x)}{x^3} \qquad ■$$

Section 4.3 Problems

■ 4.3.1

In Problems 1–16, use the product rule to find the derivative with respect to the independent variable.

1. $f(x) = (x + 5)(x^2 - 3)$
2. $f(x) = (2x^3 - 1)(3 + 2x^2)$
3. $f(x) = (3x^4 - 5)(2x - 5x^3)$
4. $f(x) = (3x^4 - x^2 + 1)(2x^2 - 5x^3)$
5. $f(x) = \left(\frac{1}{2}x^2 - 1\right)(2x + 3x^2)$
6. $f(x) = 2(3x^2 - 2x^3)(1 - 5x^2)$
7. $f(x) = \frac{1}{5}(x^2 - 1)(x^2 + 1)$
8. $f(x) = 3(x^2 + 2)(4x^2 - 5x^4) - 3$
9. $f(x) = (3x - 1)^2$ 10. $f(x) = (4 - 2x^2)^2$
11. $f(x) = 3(1 - 2x)^2$ 12. $f(x) = \frac{(2x^2 - 3x + 1)^2}{4} + 2$
13. $g(s) = (2s^2 - 5s)^2$ 14. $h(t) = 4(3t^2 - 1)(2t + 1)$
15. $g(t) = 3(2t^2 - 5t^4)^2$ 16. $h(s) = (4 - 3s^2 + 4s^3)^2$

In Problems 17–20, apply the product rule to find the tangent line, in slope–intercept form, of $y = f(x)$ at the specified point.

17. $f(x) = (3x^2 - 2)(x - 1)$, at $x = 1$
18. $f(x) = (1 - 2x)(1 + 2x)$, at $x = 2$
19. $f(x) = 4(2x^4 + 3x)(4 - 2x^2)$, at $x = -1$
20. $f(x) = (3x^3 - 3)(2 - 2x^2)$, at $x = 0$

In Problems 21–24, apply the product rule to find the normal line, in slope–intercept form, of $y = f(x)$ at the specified point.

21. $f(x) = (1 - x)(2 - x^2)$, at $x = 2$
22. $f(x) = (2x + 1)(3x^2 - 1)$, at $x = 1$
23. $f(x) = 5(1 - 2x)(x + 1) - 3$, at $x = 0$
24. $f(x) = \frac{(2 - x)(3 - x)}{4}$, at $x = -1$

In Problems 25–28, apply the product rule repeatedly to find the derivative of $y = f(x)$.

25. $f(x) = (2x - 1)(3x + 4)(1 - x)$
26. $f(x) = (x - 3)(2 - 3x)(5 - x)$
27. $f(x) = (x - 3)(2x^2 + 1)(1 - x^2)$
28. $f(x) = (2x + 1)(4 - x^2)(1 + x^2)$
29. Differentiate

$$f(x) = a(x - 1)(2x - 1)$$

with respect to x. Assume that a is a positive constant.
30. Differentiate

$$f(x) = (a - x)(a + x)$$

with respect to x. Assume that a is a positive constant.
31. Differentiate

$$f(x) = 2a(x^2 - a)^2 + a$$

with respect to x. Assume that a is a positive constant.
32. Differentiate

$$f(x) = \frac{3(x - 1)^2}{2 + a}$$

with respect to x. Assume that a is a positive constant.

33. Differentiate

$$g(t) = (at + 1)^2$$

with respect to t. Assume that a is a positive constant.
34. Differentiate

$$h(t) = \sqrt{a}(t - a) + a$$

with respect to t. Assume that a is a positive constant.
35. Suppose that $f(2) = -4$, $g(2) = 3$, $f'(2) = 1$, and $g'(2) = -2$. Find

$$(fg)'(2)$$

36. Suppose that $f(2) = -4$, $g(2) = 3$, $f'(2) = 1$, and $g'(2) = -2$. Find

$$(f^2 + g^2)'(2)$$

In Problems 37–40, assume that $f(x)$ is differentiable. Find an expression for the derivative of y at $x = 1$, assuming that $f(1) = 2$ and $f'(1) = -1$.

37. $y = 2xf(x)$ 38. $y = 3x^2 f(x)$
39. $y = -5x^3 f(x) - 2x$ 40. $y = \dfrac{xf(x)}{2}$

In Problems 41–44, assume that $f(x)$ and $g(x)$ are differentiable at x. Find an expression for the derivative of y.

41. $y = 3f(x)g(x)$ 42. $y = [f(x) - 3]g(x)$
43. $y = [f(x) + 2g(x)]g(x)$
44. $y = [-2f(x) - 3g(x)]g(x) + \frac{2g(x)}{3}$
45. Let $B(t)$ denote the biomass at time t with specific growth rate $g(B)$. Show that the specific growth rate at $B = 0$ is given by the slope of the tangent line on the graph of the growth rate at $B = 0$.
46. Let $N(t)$ denote the size of a population at time t. Differentiate

$$f(N) = rN\left(1 - \frac{N}{K}\right)$$

with respect to N, where r and K are positive constants.
47. Let $N(t)$ denote the size of a population at time t. Differentiate

$$f(N) = r\left(aN - N^2\right)\left(1 - \frac{N}{K}\right)$$

with respect to N, where r, K, and a are positive constants.
48. Consider the chemical reaction

$$A + B \longrightarrow AB$$

If x denotes the concentration of AB at time t, then the reaction rate $R(x)$ is given by

$$R(x) = k(a - x)(b - x)$$

where k, a, and b are positive constants. Differentiate $R(x)$.

■ 4.3.2

In Problems 49–70, differentiate with respect to the independent variable.

49. $f(x) = \dfrac{3x - 1}{x + 1}$ 50. $f(x) = \dfrac{1 - 4x^3}{1 - x}$
51. $f(x) = \dfrac{3x^2 - 2x + 1}{2x + 1}$ 52. $f(x) = \dfrac{x^4 + 2x - 1}{5x^2 - 2x + 1}$
53. $f(x) = \dfrac{3 - x^3}{1 - x}$ 54. $f(x) = \dfrac{1 + 2x^2 - 4x^4}{3x^3 - 5x^5}$

55. $h(t) = \dfrac{t^2 - 3t + 1}{t + 1}$

56. $h(t) = \dfrac{3 - t^2}{(t + 1)^2}$

57. $f(s) = \dfrac{4 - 2s^2}{1 - s}$

58. $f(s) = \dfrac{2s^3 - 4s^2 + 5s - 7}{(s^2 - 3)^2}$

59. $f(x) = \sqrt{x}(x - 1)$

60. $f(x) = \sqrt{x}(x^4 - 5x^2)$

61. $f(x) = \sqrt{3x}(x^2 - 1)$

62. $f(x) = \dfrac{\sqrt{5x}(1 + x^2)}{\sqrt{2}}$

63. $f(x) = x^3 - \dfrac{1}{x^3}$

64. $f(x) = x^5 - \dfrac{1}{x^5}$

65. $f(x) = 2x^2 - \dfrac{3x - 1}{x^3}$

66. $f(x) = -x^3 + \dfrac{2x^2 - 3}{4x^4}$

67. $g(s) = \dfrac{s^{1/3} - 1}{s^{2/3} - 1}$

68. $g(s) = \dfrac{s^{1/7} - s^{2/7}}{s^{3/7} + s^{4/7}}$

69. $f(x) = (1 - 2x)\left(\sqrt{2x} + \dfrac{2}{\sqrt{x}}\right)$

70. $f(x) = (x^3 - 3x^2 + 2)\left(\sqrt{x} + \dfrac{1}{\sqrt{x}} - 1\right)$

In Problems 71–74, find the tangent line, in slope–intercept form, of $y = f(x)$ at the specified point.

71. $f(x) = \dfrac{x^2 + 3}{x^3 + 5}$, at $x = -2$

72. $f(x) = \dfrac{3}{x} - \dfrac{4}{\sqrt{x}} + \dfrac{2}{x^2}$, at $x = 1$

73. $f(x) = \dfrac{2x - 5}{x^3}$, at $x = 2$ **74.** $f(x) = \sqrt{x}(x^3 - 1)$, at $x = 1$

75. Differentiate
$$f(x) = \dfrac{ax}{3 + x}$$
with respect to x. Assume that a is a positive constant.

76. Differentiate
$$f(x) = \dfrac{ax}{k + x}$$
with respect to x. Assume that a and k are positive constants.

77. Differentiate
$$f(x) = \dfrac{ax^2}{4 + x^2}$$
with respect to x. Assume that a is a positive constant.

78. Differentiate
$$f(x) = \dfrac{ax^2}{k^2 + x^2}$$
with respect to x. Assume that a and k are positive constants.

79. Differentiate
$$f(R) = \dfrac{R^n}{k^n + R^n}$$
with respect to R. Assume that k is a positive constant and n is a positive integer.

80. Differentiate
$$h(t) = \sqrt{at}(1 - a) + a$$
with respect to t. Assume that a is a positive constant.

81. Differentiate
$$h(t) = \sqrt{at}(t - a) + at$$
with respect to t. Assume that a is a positive constant.

82. Suppose that $f(2) = -4$, $g(2) = 3$, $f'(2) = 1$, and $g'(2) = -2$. Find
$$\left(\dfrac{1}{f}\right)'(2)$$

83. Suppose that $f(2) = -4$, $g(2) = 3$, $f'(2) = 1$, and $g'(2) = -2$. Find
$$\left(\dfrac{f}{2g}\right)'(2)$$

In Problems 84–87, assume that $f(x)$ is differentiable. Find an expression for the derivative of y at $x = 2$, assuming that $f(2) = -1$ and $f'(2) = 1$.

84. $y = \dfrac{f(x)}{x^2 + 1}$

85. $y = \dfrac{x^2 + 4f(x)}{f(x)}$

86. $y = [f(x)]^2 - \dfrac{x}{f(x)}$

87. $y = \dfrac{f(x)}{f(x) + x}$

In Problems 88–91, assume that $f(x)$ and $g(x)$ are differentiable at x. Find an expression for the derivative of y.

88. $y = \dfrac{2f(x) + 1}{3g(x)}$

89. $y = \dfrac{f(x)}{[g(x)]^2}$

90. $y = \dfrac{x^2}{f(x) - g(x)}$

91. $y = \sqrt{x}f(x)g(x)$

92. Assume that $f(x)$ is a differentiable function. Find the derivative of the reciprocal function $g(x) = 1/f(x)$ at those points x where $f(x) \neq 0$.

93. Find the tangent line to the hyperbola $yx = c$, where c is a positive constant, at the point (x_1, y_1) with $x_1 > 0$. Show that the tangent line intersects the x-axis at a point that does not depend on c.

94. *(Adapted from Roff, 1992)* The males in the frog species *Eleutherodactylus coqui* (found in Puerto Rico) take care of their brood. On the other hand, while they protect the eggs, they cannot find other mates and therefore cannot increase their number of offspring. On the other hand, if they do not spend enough time with their brood, then the offspring might not survive. The proportion $w(t)$ of offspring hatching per unit time is given as a function of (1) the probability $f(t)$ of hatching if time t is spent brooding, and (2) the cost C associated with the time spent searching for other mates:
$$w(t) = \dfrac{f(t)}{C + t}$$
Find the derivative of $w(t)$.

4.4 The Chain Rule and Higher Derivatives

■ 4.4.1 The Chain Rule

In Section 1.2, we defined the composition of functions. To find the derivative of composite functions, we need the **chain rule**, the proof of which is given at the end of this section.

Chain Rule If g is differentiable at x and f is differentiable at $y = g(x)$, then the composite function $(f \circ g)(x) = f[g(x)]$ is differentiable at x, and the derivative is given by

$$(f \circ g)'(x) = f'[g(x)]g'(x)$$

This formula looks complicated. Let's take a moment to see what we need to do to find the derivative of the composite function $(f \circ g)(x)$. The function g is the inner function; the function f is the outer function. The expression $f'[g(x)]g'(x)$ thus means that we need to find the derivative of the outer function, evaluated at $g(x)$, and the derivative of the inner function, evaluated at x, and then multiply the two together.

EXAMPLE 1   **A Polynomial** Find the derivative of

$$h(x) = (3x^2 - 1)^2$$

Solution   The inner function is $g(x) = 3x^2 - 1$; the outer function is $f(u) = u^2$. Then

$$g'(x) = 6x \quad \text{and} \quad f'(u) = 2u$$

Evaluating $f'(u)$ at $u = g(x)$ yields

$$f'[g(x)] = 2g(x) = 2(3x^2 - 1)$$

Thus,

$$h'(x) = (f \circ g)'(x) = f'[g(x)]g'(x)$$
$$= 2(3x^2 - 1)6x = 12x(3x^2 - 1) \qquad \blacksquare$$

The derivative of $f \circ g$ can be written in Leibniz notation. If we set $u = g(x)$, then

$$\frac{d}{dx}[(f \circ g)(x)] = \frac{df}{du}\frac{du}{dx}$$

This form of the chain rule emphasizes that, in order to differentiate $f \circ g$, we multiply the derivative of the outer function and the derivative of the inner function, the former evaluated at u, the latter at x.

EXAMPLE 2   **A Polynomial** Find the derivative of

$$h(x) = (2x + 1)^3$$

Solution   If we set $u = g(x) = 2x + 1$ and $f(u) = u^3$, then $h(x) = (f \circ g)(x)$. We need to find both $f'[g(x)]$ and $g'(x)$ to compute $h'(x)$. Now,

$$g'(x) = 2 \quad \text{and} \quad f'(u) = 3u^2$$

Hence, since $f'[g(x)] = 3(g(x))^2 = 3(2x + 1)^2$, it follows that

$$h'(x) = f'[g(x)]g'(x) = 3(2x + 1)^2 \cdot 2$$
$$= 6(2x + 1)^2$$

If we use Leibniz notation, this becomes

$$h'(x) = \frac{df}{du}\frac{du}{dx} = 3u^2 \cdot 2 = 3(2x + 1)^2 \cdot 2$$
$$= 6(2x + 1)^2 \qquad \blacksquare$$

EXAMPLE 3

A Radical Find the derivative of $h(x) = \sqrt{x^2 + 1}$.

Solution If we set $u = g(x) = x^2 + 1$ and $f(u) = \sqrt{u}$, then $h(x) = (f \circ g)(x)$. We find that

$$g'(x) = 2x \quad \text{and} \quad f'(u) = \frac{1}{2\sqrt{u}}$$

We need to evaluate f' at $g(x)$—that is,

$$f'[g(x)] = \frac{1}{2\sqrt{g(x)}} = \frac{1}{2\sqrt{x^2 + 1}}$$

Therefore,

$$h'(x) = f'[g(x)]g'(x) = \frac{1}{2\sqrt{x^2 + 1}} 2x = \frac{x}{\sqrt{x^2 + 1}} \qquad ■$$

EXAMPLE 4

A Radical Find the derivative of

$$h(x) = \sqrt[7]{2x^2 + 3x}$$

Solution We write

$$h(x) = (2x^2 + 3x)^{1/7}$$

The inner function is $u = g(x) = 2x^2 + 3x$ and the outer function is $f(u) = u^{1/7}$. Thus, we find that

$$h'(x) = \frac{df}{du}\frac{du}{dx} = \frac{1}{7}u^{1/7-1}(4x + 3)$$

$$= \frac{1}{7}(2x^2 + 3x)^{-6/7}(4x + 3)$$

$$= \frac{4x + 3}{7(2x^2 + 3x)^{6/7}} \qquad ■$$

EXAMPLE 5

A Rational Function Find the derivative of $h(x) = \left(\frac{x}{x+1}\right)^2$.

Solution If we set $u = g(x) = \frac{x}{x+1}$ and $f(u) = u^2$, then $h(x) = (f \circ g)(x)$. We use the quotient rule to compute the derivative of $g(x)$:

$$g'(x) = \frac{1 \cdot (x + 1) - x \cdot 1}{(x + 1)^2} = \frac{1}{(x + 1)^2}$$

Since $f'(u) = 2u$, we obtain

$$h'(x) = f'[g(x)]g'(x) = 2\frac{x}{x + 1}\frac{1}{(x + 1)^2} = \frac{2x}{(x + 1)^3} \qquad ■$$

The Proof of the Quotient Rule We can use the chain rule to prove the quotient rule. Assume that $g(x) \neq 0$ for all x in the domain of g. If we define $h(x) = \frac{1}{x}$, then

$$(h \circ g)(x) = h[g(x)] = \frac{1}{g(x)}$$

We used the formal definition of the derivative in Example 3 in Section 4.1 to show that $h'(x) = -\frac{1}{x^2}$. This, together with the chain rule, yields

$$(h \circ g)'(x) = -\frac{1}{[g(x)]^2}g'(x), \quad \text{or} \quad \left(\frac{1}{g}\right)' = -\frac{g'}{g^2}$$

Since $\frac{f}{g} = f\frac{1}{g}$, we can use the product rule to find the derivative of $\frac{f}{g}$:

$$\left(\frac{f}{g}\right)' = f'\frac{1}{g} + f\left(\frac{1}{g}\right)' = f'\frac{1}{g} + f\left(-\frac{g'}{g^2}\right)$$
$$= \frac{f'g - fg'}{g^2}$$

Note that we did not use the power rule for negative integer exponents (Subsection 4.3.2) to compute $h'(x)$, but instead used the formal definition of derivatives to compute the derivative of $1/x$. Using the power rule for negative integer exponents would have been circular reasoning: We used the quotient rule to prove the power rule for negative integer exponents, so we cannot use the power rule for negative integer exponents to prove the quotient rule.

EXAMPLE 6

A Function with Parameters Find the derivative of

$$h(x) = (ax^2 - 2)^n$$

where $a > 0$ and n is a positive integer.

Solution If we set $u = g(x) = ax^2 - 2$ and $f(u) = u^n$, then $h(x) = (f \circ g)(x)$. Since

$$g'(x) = 2ax \qquad \text{and} \qquad f'(u) = nu^{n-1}$$

it follows that

$$h'(x) = f'[g(x)]g'(x) = n(ax^2 - 2)^{n-1}2ax$$
$$= 2anx(ax^2 - 2)^{n-1}$$

Looking at $h'(x) = n(ax^2 - 2)^{n-1} \cdot 2ax$, we see that we first differentiated the outer function f, which yielded $n(ax^2 - 2)^{n-1}$ via the power rule, and then multiplied the result by $2ax$, the derivative of the inner function g. ■

EXAMPLE 7

Differentiating a Function That Is Not Specified Suppose $f(x)$ is differentiable. Find

$$\frac{d}{dx}\frac{1}{\sqrt{f(x)}}$$

Solution We set

$$h(x) = \frac{1}{\sqrt{f(x)}} = [f(x)]^{-1/2}$$

Now, $u = f(x)$ is the inner function and $h(u) = u^{-1/2}$ is the outer function; hence,

$$\frac{d}{dx}h(x) = \frac{dh}{du}\frac{du}{dx} = -\frac{1}{2}u^{-3/2}f'(x)$$
$$= -\frac{1}{2u^{3/2}}f'(x) = -\frac{f'(x)}{2[f(x)]^{3/2}}$$ ■

EXAMPLE 8

Generalized Power Rule Suppose $f(x)$ is differentiable and r is a real number. Find

$$\frac{d}{dx}[f(x)]^r$$

Solution Using the general form of the power rule and the chain rule, we find that

$$\frac{d}{dx}[f(x)]^r = r[f(x)]^{r-1}f'(x)$$ ■

EXAMPLE 9　**Differentiating a Function That Is Not Specified**　Suppose that $f'(x) = 3x - 1$. Find

$$\frac{d}{dx} f(x^2) \quad \text{at } x = 3$$

Solution　The inner function is $u = x^2$, the outer function is $f(u)$, and we find that

$$\frac{d}{dx} f(x^2) = 2xf'(x^2)$$

If we substitute $x = 3$ into $f'(x^2)$, we obtain $f'(3^2) = f'(9) = (3)(9) - 1 = 26$. Thus,

$$\frac{d}{dx} f(x^2) \bigg|_{x=3} = (2)(3) f'(9) = (6)(26) = 156 \qquad ■$$

The chain rule can be applied repeatedly, as shown in the next two examples.

EXAMPLE 10　**Nested Chain Rule**　Find the derivative of

$$h(x) = \left(\sqrt{x^2 + 1} + 1 \right)^2$$

Solution　If we set $h(x) = (f \circ g)(x)$, then $g(x) = \sqrt{x^2 + 1} + 1$ and $f(u) = u^2$. We see that $g(x)$ is itself a composition of two functions, with inner function $v = x^2 + 1$ and outer function $\sqrt{v} + 1$. To differentiate $h(x)$, we proceed stepwise. First,

$$h'(x) = \frac{d}{dx} \left(\sqrt{x^2 + 1} + 1 \right)^2 = 2 \left(\sqrt{x^2 + 1} + 1 \right) \frac{d}{dx} \left(\sqrt{x^2 + 1} + 1 \right)$$

Then, since

$$\frac{d}{dx} \left(\sqrt{x^2 + 1} + 1 \right) = \frac{2x}{2\sqrt{x^2 + 1}} = \frac{x}{\sqrt{x^2 + 1}}$$

(where we used the chain rule to differentiate $\sqrt{x^2 + 1}$), we get

$$h'(x) = 2 \left(\sqrt{x^2 + 1} + 1 \right) \frac{x}{\sqrt{x^2 + 1}} \qquad ■$$

EXAMPLE 11　**Nested Chain Rule**　Find the derivative of

$$h(x) = \left(2x^3 - \sqrt{3x^4 - 2} \right)^3$$

Solution　As in the previous example, we proceed stepwise:

$$h'(x) = 3 \left(2x^3 - \sqrt{3x^4 - 2} \right)^2 \frac{d}{dx} \left(2x^3 - \sqrt{3x^4 - 2} \right)$$

$$= 3 \left(2x^3 - \sqrt{3x^4 - 2} \right)^2 \left(6x^2 - \frac{12x^3}{2\sqrt{3x^4 - 2}} \right)$$

$$= 18x^2 \left(2x^3 - \sqrt{3x^4 - 2} \right)^2 \left(1 - \frac{x}{\sqrt{3x^4 - 2}} \right) \qquad ■$$

We conclude this subsection with the proof of the chain rule. The first part of the proof follows along the lines of the argument we sketched out at the beginning of the section, but the second part is much more technical and deals with the problem that Δu could be zero.

Proof of the Chain Rule We will use the definition of the derivative to prove the chain rule. Formally,

$$(f \circ g)'(x) = \lim_{x \to c} \frac{f[g(x)] - f[g(c)]}{x - c}$$

We need to show that the right-hand side is equal to $f'[g(c)]g'(c)$. As long as $g(x) \neq g(c)$, we can write

$$\lim_{x \to c} \frac{f[g(x)] - f[g(c)]}{x - c} = \lim_{x \to c} \frac{\frac{f[g(x)] - f[g(c)]}{g(x) - g(c)}[g(x) - g(c)]}{x - c}$$

$$= \lim_{x \to c} \frac{f[g(x)] - f[g(c)]}{g(x) - g(c)} \frac{g(x) - g(c)}{x - c}$$

Since $g(x)$ is continuous at $x = c$, it follows that $\lim_{x \to c} g(x) = g(c)$, and hence,

$$\lim_{x \to c} \frac{f[g(x)] - f[g(c)]}{g(x) - g(c)} = f'[g(c)]$$

Furthermore,

$$\lim_{x \to c} \frac{g(x) - g(c)}{x - c} = g'(c)$$

Since these limits exist, we can use the fact that the limit of a product is the product of the limits. We find that

$$\lim_{x \to c} \frac{f[g(x)] - f[g(c)]}{x - c} = \lim_{x \to c} \frac{f[g(x)] - f[g(c)]}{g(x) - g(c)} \lim_{x \to c} \frac{g(x) - g(c)}{x - c}$$

$$= f'[g(c)]g'(c)$$

In the preceding calculation, we needed to assume that $g(x) - g(c) \neq 0$. Of course, when we take the limit as $x \to c$, there might be x-values such that $g(x) = g(c)$, and we must deal with this possibility.

We set $y = g(x)$ and $d = g(c)$. The expression

$$f^*(y) \equiv \frac{f(y) - f(d)}{y - d}$$

is defined only for $y \neq d$. Since

$$\lim_{y \to d} \frac{f(y) - f(d)}{y - d} = f'(d)$$

we can extend $f^*[g(x)]$ by defining $f^*[g(x)] = f'[g(x)]$ to make $f^*[g(x)]$ a continuous function:

$$f^*[g(x)] = \begin{cases} \dfrac{f[g(x)] - f[g(c)]}{g(x) - g(c)} & \text{for } g(x) \neq g(c) \\ f'[g(c)] & \text{for } g(x) = g(c) \end{cases}$$

This means that, for all x,

$$f[g(x)] - f[g(c)] = f^*[g(x)][g(x) - g(c)]$$

With this equivalence, we can repeat our calculations to obtain

$$\lim_{x \to c} \frac{f[g(x)] - f[g(c)]}{x - c} = \lim_{x \to c} \frac{f^*[g(x)][g(x) - g(c)]}{x - c}$$

$$\lim_{x \to c} f^*[g(x)] \lim_{x \to c} \frac{g(x) - g(c)}{x - c} = f'[g(c)] \cdot g'(c)$$

Note that in the last step we used the fact that $f^*[g(x)]$ is continuous at $x = c$. ■

■ 4.4.2 Implicit Functions and Implicit Differentiation

So far, we have considered only functions of the form $y = f(x)$, which define y *explicitly* as a function of x. It is also possible to define y *implicitly* as a function of x, as in the following equation:

$$y^5 x^2 - yx + 2y^2 = \sqrt{x}$$

Here, y is still given as a function of x (i.e., y is the dependent variable), but there is no obvious way to solve for y. Fortunately, there is a very useful technique, based on the chain rule, that will allow us to find dy/dx for implicitly defined functions. This technique is called **implicit differentiation**. We explain the procedure in the next example.

EXAMPLE 12   Find $\frac{dy}{dx}$ if $x^2 + y^2 = 1$.

Solution   Remembering that y is a function of x, we differentiate both sides of the equation $x^2 + y^2 = 1$ with respect to x:

$$\frac{d}{dx}\left(x^2 + y^2\right) = \frac{d}{dx}(1)$$

Since the derivative of a sum is the sum of the derivatives, we find that

$$\frac{d}{dx}(x^2) + \frac{d}{dx}(y^2) = \frac{d}{dx}(1)$$

Starting with the left-hand side and using the power rule, we have $\frac{d}{dx}(x^2) = 2x$. To differentiate y^2 with respect to x, we apply the chain rule to get $\frac{d}{dx}(y^2) = 2y\frac{dy}{dx}$. On the right-hand side, we obtain $\frac{d}{dx}(1) = 0$. We therefore have

$$2x + 2y\frac{dy}{dx} = 0$$

We can now solve for $\frac{dy}{dx}$:

$$\frac{dy}{dx} = -\frac{2x}{2y} = -\frac{x}{y}$$

Since $x^2 + y^2 = 1$ is the equation for the unit circle centered at the origin (Figure 4.25), we can use a geometric argument to convince ourselves that we have indeed obtained the correct derivative. The line that connects $(0, 0)$ and (x, y) has slope y/x and is perpendicular to the tangent line at (x, y). Since the slopes of perpendicular lines are negative reciprocals of each other, the slope of the tangent line at (x, y) must be $-x/y$.

We could have solved $x^2 + y^2 = 1$ for y and then differentiated with respect to x; this would have yielded the same answer but would have been more complicated.   ■

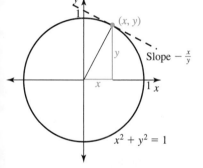

Figure 4.25 The slope of the tangent line at the unit circle $x^2 + y^2 = 1$ at (x, y) is $m = -\frac{x}{y}$.

We summarize the steps we take to find dy/dx when an equation defines y implicitly as a differentiable function of x:

STEP 1. Differentiate both sides of the equation with respect to x, keeping in mind that y is a function of x.

STEP 2. Solve the resulting equation for dy/dx.

Note that differentiating terms involving y typically requires the chain rule. Here is another example; this time, we can neither use a geometric argument nor easily solve for y.

EXAMPLE 13   Find $\frac{dy}{dx}$ when $y^3 x^2 - yx + 2y^2 = x$.

Solution   We differentiate both sides of the equation with respect to x:

$$\frac{d}{dx}(y^3x^2) - \frac{d}{dx}(yx) + \frac{d}{dx}(2y^2) = \frac{d}{dx}(x)$$

To differentiate y^3x^2 and yx with respect to x, we use the product rule:

$$\frac{d}{dx}(y^3x^2) = \left(\frac{d}{dx}y^3\right)x^2 + y^3\left(\frac{d}{dx}x^2\right) = \left(\frac{d}{dx}y^3\right)x^2 + (y^3)(2x)$$

$$\frac{d}{dx}(yx) = \left(\frac{d}{dx}y\right)(x) + y\left(\frac{d}{dx}x\right) = \left(\frac{dy}{dx}\right)x + y$$

To find $\frac{d}{dx}y^3$, we use the chain rule to get

$$\frac{d}{dx}y^3 = 3y^2\frac{dy}{dx}$$

Furthermore,

$$\frac{d}{dx}(2y^2) = 4y\frac{dy}{dx}$$

and

$$\frac{d}{dx}(x) = 1$$

Putting the pieces together, we obtain

$$3y^2\frac{dy}{dx}(x^2) + (y^3)(2x) - \left[\left(\frac{dy}{dx}\right)x + y\right] + 4y\frac{dy}{dx} = 1$$

Factoring $\frac{dy}{dx}$ yields

$$\frac{dy}{dx}[3y^2x^2 - x + 4y] + 2xy^3 - y = 1$$

Solving for $\frac{dy}{dx}$ gives

$$\frac{dy}{dx} = \frac{y + 1 - 2xy^3}{3y^2x^2 - x + 4y}$$

The next example prepares us for the power rule for rational exponents.

EXAMPLE 14   Find $\frac{dy}{dx}$ when $y^2 = x^3$. Assume that $x > 0$ and $y > 0$.

Solution   We differentiate both sides with respect to x:

$$\frac{d}{dx}(y^2) = \frac{d}{dx}(x^3)$$

$$2y\frac{dy}{dx} = 3x^2$$

Therefore,

$$\frac{dy}{dx} = \frac{3}{2}\frac{x^2}{y}$$

Since $y = x^{3/2}$, it follows that

$$\frac{dy}{dx} = \frac{3}{2}\frac{x^2}{y} = \frac{3}{2}\frac{x^2}{x^{3/2}} = \frac{3}{2}x^{1/2}$$

This is the answer we expect from the general version of the power rule:

$$\frac{dy}{dx} = \frac{d}{dx}x^{3/2} = \frac{3}{2}x^{1/2}$$

Power Rule for Rational Exponents We can generalize Example 14 to functions of the form $y = x^r$, where r is a rational number. This will provide a proof of the generalized form of the power rule when the exponent is a rational number, something we promised in the previous section. We write $r = p/q$, where p and q are integers and are in lowest terms. (If q is even, we require x and y to be positive.) Then

$$y = x^{p/q} \quad \Longleftrightarrow \quad y^q = x^p$$

Differentiating both sides of $y^q = x^p$ with respect to x, we find that

$$qy^{q-1}\frac{dy}{dx} = px^{p-1}$$

Hence,

$$\frac{dy}{dx} = \frac{p}{q}\frac{x^{p-1}}{y^{q-1}} = \frac{p}{q}\frac{x^{p-1}}{(x^{p/q})^{q-1}}$$

$$= \frac{p}{q}\frac{x^{p-1}}{x^{p-p/q}} = \frac{p}{q}x^{p-1-p+p/q}$$

$$= \frac{p}{q}x^{p/q-1} = rx^{r-1}$$

We summarize the preceding result:

If r is a rational number, then

$$\frac{d}{dx}(x^r) = rx^{r-1}$$

■ 4.4.3 Related Rates

An important application of implicit differentiation is related-rates problems. We begin with a motivating example.

Consider a parcel of air rising quickly in the atmosphere. The parcel expands without exchanging heat with the surrounding air. Laws of physics tell us that the volume (V) and the temperature (T) of the parcel of air are related via the formula

$$TV^{\gamma-1} = C$$

where γ (lowercase Greek gamma) is approximately 1.4 for sufficiently dry air and C is a constant. The temperature is measured in kelvin,[1] a scale chosen so that the temperature is always positive. (The Kelvin scale is the absolute temperature scale.) Since rising air expands, the volume of the parcel of air increases with time; we express this relationship mathematically as $dV/dt > 0$, where t denotes time.

To determine how the temperature of the air parcel changes as it rises, we implicitly differentiate $TV^{\gamma-1} = C$ with respect to t:

$$\frac{dT}{dt}V^{\gamma-1} + T(\gamma-1)V^{\gamma-2}\frac{dV}{dt} = 0$$

or

$$\frac{dT}{dt} = -\frac{T(\gamma-1)V^{\gamma-2}\frac{dV}{dt}}{V^{\gamma-1}} = -T(\gamma-1)\frac{1}{V}\frac{dV}{dt}$$

---

[1] To compare the Celsius and the Kelvin scales, note that a temperature difference of 1°C is equal to a temperature difference of 1 K, and that 0°C = 273.15 K and 100°C = 373.15 K.

If we use $\gamma = 1.4$, then

$$\frac{dT}{dt} = -T(0.4)\frac{1}{V}\frac{dV}{dt}$$

implying that if air expands (i.e., $dV/dt > 0$), then temperature decreases (i.e., $dT/dt < 0$), since both T and V are positive: The temperature of a parcel of air decreases as the parcel rises, and the temperature of a falling air parcel increases. These phenomena can be observed close to high mountains.

In a typical related-rates problem, one quantity is expressed in terms of another and both quantities change with time. We usually know how one of the quantities changes with time and are interested in finding out how the other quantity changes. For instance, suppose that y is a function of x and both y and x depend on time. If we know how x changes with time (i.e., if we know dx/dt), then we might want to know how y changes with time (i.e, dy/dt). We illustrate this situation in the next example.

EXAMPLE 15 Find $\frac{dy}{dt}$ when $x^2 + y^3 = 1$ and $\frac{dx}{dt} = 2$ for $x = \sqrt{7/8}$.

Solution In this example, both x and y are functions of t. Implicit differentiation with respect to t yields

$$\frac{d}{dt}(x^2 + y^3) = \frac{d}{dt}(1)$$

Hence,

$$2x\frac{dx}{dt} + 3y^2\frac{dy}{dt} = 0$$

Solving for $\frac{dy}{dt}$ gives

$$\frac{dy}{dt} = -\frac{2}{3}\frac{x}{y^2}\frac{dx}{dt}$$

When $x = \sqrt{7/8}$,

$$y^3 = 1 - x^2 = 1 - \frac{7}{8} = \frac{1}{8}$$

Thus, $y = 1/2$. Therefore,

$$\frac{dy}{dt} = -\frac{2}{3}\frac{\sqrt{7/8}}{1/4} \cdot 2 = -\frac{16}{3}\sqrt{\frac{7}{8}} = -\frac{4}{3}\sqrt{14} \qquad ■$$

We present two applications of related rates.

EXAMPLE 16 **Changing Volume** A spherical balloon is being filled with air. When the radius $r = 6$ cm, the radius is increasing at a rate of 2 cm/s. How fast is the volume changing at this time?

Solution The volume V of a sphere of radius r is given by

$$V = \frac{4}{3}\pi r^3 \qquad (4.6)$$

(See Figure 4.26.) Note that V is a function of r. Since r is increasing at a certain rate, we think of r as a function of time t; that is, $r = r(t)$. Because the volume V depends on r, it changes with time t as well. We therefore consider V also as a function of time t. Differentiating both sides of (4.6) with respect to t, we find that

$$\frac{dV}{dt} = \frac{4}{3}\pi 3r^2\frac{dr}{dt} = 4\pi r^2\frac{dr}{dt}$$

When $r = 6$ cm and $dr/dt = 2$ cm/s,

$$\frac{dV}{dt} = 4\pi 6^2 \text{cm}^2 2\frac{\text{cm}}{\text{s}} = 288\pi \frac{\text{cm}^3}{\text{s}}$$

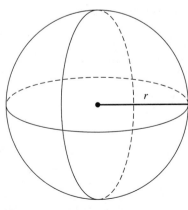

Figure 4.26 The volume of a sphere with radius r is $V = \frac{4}{3}\pi r^3$.

Note that the unit of dV/dt is cm³/s, which is what you should expect, because the unit of the volume is cm³ and time is measured in seconds. ■

EXAMPLE 17   **Allometric Growth (Adapted from Benton and Harper, 1997)** Ichthyosaurs are a group of marine reptiles that were fish shaped and comparable in size to dolphins. They became extinct during the Cretaceous.[2] On the basis of a study of 20 fossil skeletons, it was found that the skull length (in cm) and backbone length (in cm) of an individual ichthyosaur were related through the allometric equation. (We introduced allometric equations in Example 7 of Section 1.2.)

$$[\text{skull length}] = 1.162[\text{backbone length}]^{0.933}$$

How is the growth rate of the backbone related to the growth rate of the skull?

Solution   Let x denote the age of the ichthyosaur, and set

$$S = S(x) = \text{skull length at age } x$$
$$B = B(x) = \text{backbone length at age } x$$

so that

$$S(x) = (1.162)[B(x)]^{0.933}$$

We are interested in the relationship between dS/dx and dB/dx, the growth rates of the skull and the backbone, respectively. Differentiating the equation for $S(x)$ with respect to x, we find that

$$\frac{dS}{dx} = (1.162)(0.933)[B(x)]^{0.933-1}\frac{dB}{dx}$$

Rearranging terms on the right-hand side, we write this as

$$\frac{dS}{dx} = \underbrace{(1.162)[B(x)]^{0.933}}_{S(x)}(0.933)\frac{1}{B(x)}\frac{dB}{dx}$$

Hence,

$$\frac{1}{S(x)}\frac{dS}{dx} = 0.933\frac{1}{B(x)}\frac{dB}{dx}$$

This equation relates the relative growth rates $\frac{1}{S}\frac{dS}{dx}$ and $\frac{1}{B}\frac{dB}{dx}$. The factor 0.933 is less than 1, which indicates that skulls grow less quickly than backbones. This finding should be familiar to us: Relative to their body sizes, juvenile vertebrates often have larger heads than adults.   ■

■ 4.4.4 Higher Derivatives

The derivative of a function f is itself a function. We refer to this derivative as the **first derivative**, denoted f'. If the first derivative exists, we say that the function is once differentiable. Given that the first derivative is a function, we can define its derivative (where it exists). This derivative is called the **second derivative** and is denoted f''. If the second derivative exists, we say that the original function is twice differentiable. This second derivative is again a function; hence, we can define its derivative (where it exists). The result is the **third derivative**, denoted f'''. If the third derivative exists, we say that the original function is three times differentiable. We can continue in this manner; from the fourth derivative on, we denote the derivatives by $f^{(4)}$, $f^{(5)}$, and so on. If the nth derivative exists, we say that the original function is n times differentiable.

Polynomials are functions that can be differentiated as many times as desired. The reason is that the first derivative of a polynomial of degree n is a polynomial of degree $n - 1$. Since the derivative is a polynomial as well, we can find its derivative, and so on. Eventually, the derivative will be equal to 0, as is illustrated in the next example.

---

(2) The Cretaceous period began about 144 million years ago and ended about 65 million years ago.

EXAMPLE 18

Find the nth derivative of $f(x) = x^5$ for $n = 1, 2, \ldots$.

Solution

Differentiating $f(x)$, we find the first derivative to be

$$f'(x) = 5x^4$$

Differentiating $f'(x)$, we find the second derivative to be

$$f''(x) = 5(4x^3) = 20x^3$$

Differentiating $f''(x)$, we obtain the third derivative:

$$f'''(x) = 20(3x^2) = 60x^2$$

Differentiating $f'''(x)$, we find the fourth derivative:

$$f^{(4)}(x) = 60(2x) = 120x$$

Differentiating $f^{(4)}(x)$, we get the fifth derivative:

$$f^{(5)}(x) = 120$$

Differentiating $f^{(5)}(x)$, we find the sixth derivative:

$$f^{(6)}(x) = 0$$

All higher-order derivatives—that is, $f^{(7)}, f^{(8)}, \ldots$—are equal to 0 as well. ■

We can write higher-order derivatives in Leibniz notation: The nth derivative of $f(x)$ is denoted by

$$\frac{d^n f}{dx^n}$$

EXAMPLE 19

Find the second derivative of $f(x) = \sqrt{x}$, $x \geq 0$.

Solution

First, we find the first derivative:

$$\frac{d}{dx}\sqrt{x} = \frac{d}{dx}x^{1/2} = \frac{1}{2}x^{-1/2} \quad \text{for } x > 0$$

To find the second derivative, we differentiate the first derivative

$$\frac{d^2}{dx^2}\sqrt{x} = \frac{d}{dx}\left(\frac{d}{dx}\sqrt{x}\right) = \frac{d}{dx}\left(\frac{1}{2}x^{-1/2}\right) = \frac{1}{2}\left(-\frac{1}{2}\right)x^{(-1/2)-1}$$

$$= -\frac{1}{4}x^{-3/2} \qquad ■$$

When functions are implicitly defined, we can use the technique of implicit differentiation to find higher derivatives.

EXAMPLE 20

Find $\frac{d^2 y}{dx^2}$ when $x^2 + y^2 = 1$.

Solution

We found

$$\frac{dy}{dx} = -\frac{x}{y}$$

in Example 12. Differentiating both sides of this equation with respect to x, we get

$$\frac{d}{dx}\left[\frac{dy}{dx}\right] = \frac{d}{dx}\left[-\frac{x}{y}\right]$$

The left-hand side can be written as

$$\frac{d^2 y}{dx^2}$$

On the right-hand side, we use the quotient rule. Hence,

$$\frac{d^2y}{dx^2} = -\frac{1 \cdot y - x\frac{dy}{dx}}{y^2}$$

Substituting $-\frac{x}{y}$ for $\frac{dy}{dx}$, we obtain

$$\frac{d^2y}{dx^2} = -\frac{y - x(-\frac{x}{y})}{y^2}$$

$$= -\frac{y + \frac{x^2}{y}}{y^2} = -\frac{y^2 + x^2}{y^3}$$

Since $x^2 + y^2 = 1$, we can simplify the rightmost expression further and obtain

$$\frac{d^2y}{dx^2} = -\frac{1}{y^3}$$ ■

We introduced the velocity of an object that moves on a straight line as the derivative of the object's position. The derivative of the velocity is the **acceleration**. If $s(t)$ denotes the position of an object moving on a straight line, $v(t)$ its velocity, and $a(t)$ its acceleration, then the three quantities are related as follows:

$$v(t) = \frac{ds}{dt} \quad \text{and} \quad a(t) = \frac{dv}{dt} = \frac{d^2s}{dt^2}$$

EXAMPLE 21   **Acceleration** Assume that the position of a car moving along a straight line is given by

$$s(t) = 3t^3 - 2t + 1$$

Find the car's velocity and acceleration.

Solution   To find the velocity, we need to differentiate the position:

$$v(t) = \frac{ds}{dt} = 9t^2 - 2$$

To find the acceleration, we differentiate the velocity:

$$a(t) = \frac{dv}{dt} = \frac{d^2s}{dt^2} = 18t$$ ■

EXAMPLE 22   Neglecting air resistance, we find that the distance (in meters) an object falls when dropped from rest from a height is

$$s(t) = \frac{1}{2}gt^2$$

where $g = 9.81 \text{m/s}^2$ is the earth's gravitational constant and t is the time (in seconds) elapsed since the object was released.

(a) Find the object's velocity and acceleration.

(b) If the height is 30 m, how long will it take until the object hits the ground, and what is its velocity at the time of impact?

Solution   **(a)** The velocity is

$$v(t) = \frac{ds}{dt} = gt$$

and the acceleration is

$$a(t) = \frac{dv}{dt} = g$$

Note that the acceleration is constant.

(b) To find the time it takes the object to hit the ground, we set $s(t) = 30$ m and solve for t:

$$30\,\text{m} = \frac{1}{2}(9.81)\frac{\text{m}}{\text{s}^2}t^2$$

This yields

$$t^2 = \frac{60}{9.81}\text{s}^2, \qquad \text{or} \qquad t = \sqrt{\frac{60}{9.81}}\,\text{s} \approx 2.47\,\text{s}$$

(We need consider only the positive solution.) The velocity at the time of impact is then

$$v(t) = gt = (9.81)\frac{\text{m}}{\text{s}^2}\sqrt{\frac{60}{9.81}}\,\text{s} \approx 24.3\frac{\text{m}}{\text{s}}$$

■

Section 4.4 Problems

■ 4.4.1

In Problems 1–28, differentiate the functions with respect to the independent variable.

1. $f(x) = (x - 3)^2$
2. $f(x) = (4x + 5)^3$
3. $f(x) = (1 - 3x^2)^4$
4. $f(x) = (5x^2 - 3x)^3$
5. $f(x) = \sqrt{x^2 + 3}$
6. $f(x) = \sqrt{2x + 7}$
7. $f(x) = \sqrt{3 - x^3}$
8. $f(x) = \sqrt{5x + 3x^4}$
9. $f(x) = \dfrac{1}{(x^3 - 2)^4}$
10. $f(x) = \dfrac{2}{(1 - 5x^2)^3}$
11. $f(x) = \dfrac{3x - 1}{\sqrt{2x^2 - 1}}$
12. $f(x) = \dfrac{(1 - 2x^2)^3}{(3 - x^2)^2}$
13. $f(x) = \dfrac{\sqrt{2x - 1}}{(x - 1)^2}$
14. $f(x) = \dfrac{\sqrt{x^2 - 1}}{2 + \sqrt{x^2 + 1}}$
15. $f(s) = \sqrt{s + \sqrt{s}}$
16. $g(t) = \sqrt{t^2 + \sqrt{t + 1}}$
17. $g(t) = \left(\dfrac{t}{t - 3}\right)^3$
18. $h(s) = \left(\dfrac{2s^2}{s + 1}\right)^4$
19. $f(r) = (r^2 - r)^3(r + 3r^3)^{-4}$
20. $h(s) = \dfrac{2(3 - s)^2}{s^2 + (7s - 1)^2}$
21. $h(x) = \sqrt[5]{3 - x^4}$
22. $h(x) = \sqrt[3]{1 - 2x}$
23. $f(x) = \sqrt[7]{x^2 - 2x + 1}$
24. $f(x) = \sqrt[4]{2 - 4x^2}$
25. $g(s) = (3s^7 - 7s)^{3/2}$
26. $h(t) = (t^4 - 5t)^{5/2}$
27. $h(t) = \left(3t + \dfrac{3}{t}\right)^{2/5}$
28. $h(t) = \left(4t^4 + \dfrac{4}{t^4}\right)^{1/4}$

29. Differentiate

$$f(x) = (ax + 1)^3$$

with respect to x. Assume that a is a positive constant.

30. Differentiate

$$f(x) = \sqrt{ax^2 - 2}$$

with respect to x. Assume that a is a positive constant.

31. Differentiate

$$g(N) = \dfrac{bN}{(k + N)^2}$$

with respect to N. Assume that b and k are positive constants.

32. Differentiate

$$g(N) = \dfrac{N}{(k + bN)^3}$$

with respect to N. Assume that b and k are positive constants.

33. Differentiate

$$g(T) = a(T_0 - T)^3 - b$$

with respect to T. Assume that a, b, and T_0 are positive constants.

34. Suppose that $f'(x) = 2x + 1$. Find the following:

(a) $\dfrac{d}{dx}f(x^2)$ at $x = -1$
(b) $\dfrac{d}{dx}f(\sqrt{x})$ at $x = 4$

35. Suppose that $f'(x) = \frac{1}{x}$. Find the following:

(a) $\dfrac{d}{dx}f(x^2 + 3)$
(b) $\dfrac{d}{dx}f(\sqrt{x - 1})$

In Problems 36–39, assume that $f(x)$ and $g(x)$ are differentiable.

36. Find $\dfrac{d}{dx}\sqrt{f(x) + g(x)}$.
37. Find $\dfrac{d}{dx}\left(\dfrac{f(x)}{g(x)} + 1\right)^2$.
38. Find $\dfrac{d}{dx}f\left[\dfrac{1}{g(x)}\right]$.
39. Find $\dfrac{d}{dx}\dfrac{[f(x)]^2}{g(2x) + 2x}$.

In Problems 40–46, find $\frac{dy}{dx}$ by applying the chain rule repeatedly.

40. $y = (\sqrt{1 - 2x^2} + 1)^2$
41. $y = (\sqrt{x^3 - 3x} + 3x)^4$
42. $y = (1 + 2(x + 3)^4)^2$
43. $y = (1 + (3x^2 - 1)^3)^2$
44. $y = \left(\dfrac{x}{2(x^2 - 1)^2 - 1}\right)^2$
45. $y = \left(\dfrac{2x + 1}{3(x^3 - 1)^3 - 1}\right)^3$
46. $y = \left(\dfrac{(2x + 1)^2 - x}{(3x^3 + 1)^3 - x}\right)^2$

■ 4.4.2

In Problems 47–54, find $\frac{dy}{dx}$ by implicit differentiation.

47. $x^2 + y^2 = 4$
48. $y = x^2 + 3yx$
49. $x^{3/4} + y^{3/4} = 1$
50. $xy - y^3 = 1$
51. $\sqrt{xy} = x^2 + 1$
52. $\dfrac{1}{2xy} - y^3 = 4$
53. $\dfrac{x}{y} = \dfrac{y}{x}$
54. $\dfrac{x}{xy + 1} = 2xy$

In Problems 55–57, find the lines that are (a) tangential and (b) normal to each curve at the given point.

55. $x^2 + y^2 = 25$, $(4, -3)$ (circle)
56. $\dfrac{x^2}{4} + \dfrac{y^2}{9} = 1$, $(1, \frac{3}{2}\sqrt{3})$ (ellipse)
57. $\dfrac{x^2}{25} - \dfrac{y^2}{9} = 1$, $(\frac{25}{3}, 4)$ (hyperbola)

58. Lemniscate

(a) The curve with equation $y^2 = x^2 - x^4$ is shaped like the numeral eight. Find $\frac{dy}{dx}$ at $(\frac{1}{2}, \frac{1}{4}\sqrt{3})$.

(b) Use a graphing calculator to graph the curve in (a). If the calculator cannot graph implicit functions, graph the upper and the lower halves of the curve separately; that is, graph

$$y_1 = \sqrt{x^2 - x^4}$$

$$y_2 = -\sqrt{x^2 - x^4}$$

Choose the viewing rectangle $-2 \le x \le 2, -1 \le y \le 1$.

59. Astroid

(a) Consider the curve with equation $x^{2/3} + y^{2/3} = 4$. Find $\frac{dy}{dx}$ at $(-1, 3\sqrt{3})$.

(b) Use a graphing calculator to graph the curve in (a). If the calculator cannot graph implicit functions, graph the upper and the lower halves of the curve separately. To get the left half of the graph, make sure that your calculator evaluates $x^{2/3}$ in the order $(x^2)^{1/3}$. Choose the viewing rectangle $-10 \le x \le 10$, $-10 \le y \le 10$.

60. Kampyle of Eudoxus

(a) Consider the curve with equation $y^2 = 10x^4 - x^2$. Find $\frac{dy}{dx}$ at $(1, 3)$.

(b) Use a graphing calculator to graph the curve in (a). If the calculator cannot graph implicit functions, graph the upper and the lower halves of the curve separately. Choose the viewing rectangle $-3 \le x \le 3, -10 \le y \le 10$.

■ 4.4.3

61. Assume that x and y are differentiable functions of t. Find $\frac{dy}{dt}$ when $x^2 + y^2 = 1$, $\frac{dx}{dt} = 2$ for $x = \frac{1}{2}$, and $y > 0$.

62. Assume that x and y are differentiable functions of t. Find $\frac{dy}{dt}$ when $y^2 = x^2 - x^4$, $\frac{dx}{dt} = 1$ for $x = \frac{1}{2}$, and $y > 0$.

63. Assume that x and y are differentiable functions of t. Find $\frac{dy}{dt}$ when $x^2 y = 1$ and $\frac{dx}{dt} = 3$ for $x = 2$.

64. Assume that u and v are differentiable functions of t. Find $\frac{du}{dt}$ when $u^2 + v^3 = 12$, $\frac{dv}{dt} = 2$ for $v = 2$, and $u > 0$.

65. Assume that the side length x and the volume $V = x^3$ of a cube are differentiable functions of t. Express dV/dt in terms of dx/dt.

66. Assume that the radius r and the area $A = \pi r^2$ of a circle are differentiable functions of t. Express dA/dt in terms of dr/dt.

67. Assume that the radius r and the surface area $S = 4\pi r^2$ of a sphere are differentiable functions of t. Express dS/dt in terms of dr/dt.

68. Assume that the radius r and the volume $V = \frac{4}{3}\pi r^3$ of a sphere are differentiable functions of t. Express dV/dt in terms of dr/dt.

69. Suppose that water is stored in a cylindrical tank of radius 5 m. If the height of the water in the tank is h, then the volume of the water is $V = \pi r^2 h = (25\text{m}^2)\pi h = 25\pi h \text{ m}^2$. If we drain the water at a rate of 250 liters per minute, what is the rate at which the water level inside the tank drops? (Note that 1 cubic meter contains 1000 liters.)

70. Suppose that we pump water into an inverted right circular conical tank at the rate of 5 cubic feet per minute (i.e., the tank stands with its point facing downward). The tank has a height of 6

ft and the radius on top is 3 ft. What is the rate at which the water level is rising when the water is 2 ft deep? (Note that the volume of a right circular cone of radius r and height h is $V = \frac{1}{3}\pi r^2 h$.)

71. Two people start biking from the same point. One bikes east at 15 mph, the other south at 18 mph. What is the rate at which the distance between the two people is changing after 20 minutes and after 40 minutes?

72. Allometric equations describe the scaling relationship between two measurements, such as skull length versus body length. In vertebrates, we typically find that

$$[\text{skull length}] \propto [\text{body length}]^a$$

for $0 < a < 1$. Express the growth rate of the skull length in terms of the growth rate of the body length.

■ 4.4.4

In Problems 73–82, find the first and the second derivatives of each function.

73. $f(x) = x^3 - 3x^2 + 1$

74. $f(x) = (2x^2 + 4)^3$

75. $g(x) = \dfrac{x - 1}{x + 1}$

76. $h(s) = \dfrac{1}{s^2 + 2}$

77. $g(t) = \sqrt{3t^3 + 2t}$

78. $f(x) = \dfrac{1}{x^2} + x - x^3$

79. $f(s) = \sqrt{s^{3/2} - 1}$

80. $f(x) = \dfrac{2x}{x^2 + 1}$

81. $g(t) = t^{-5/2} - t^{1/2}$

82. $f(x) = x^3 - \dfrac{1}{x^3}$

83. Find the first 10 derivatives of $y = x^5$.

84. Find $f^{(n)}(x)$ and $f^{(n+1)}(x)$ of $f(x) = x^n$.

85. Find a second-degree polynomial $p(x) = ax^2 + bx + c$ with $p(0) = 3$, $p'(0) = 2$, and $p''(0) = 6$.

86. The position at time t of a particle that moves along a straight line is given by the function $s(t)$. The first derivative of $s(t)$ is called the velocity, denoted by $v(t)$; that is, the velocity is the rate of change of the position. The rate of change of the velocity is called **acceleration**, denoted by $a(t)$; that is,

$$\frac{d}{dt}v(t) = a(t)$$

Given that $v(t) = s'(t)$, it follows that

$$\frac{d^2}{dt^2}s(t) = a(t)$$

Find the velocity and the acceleration at time $t = 1$ for the following position functions:

(a) $s(t) = t^2 - 3t$ (b) $s(t) = \sqrt{t^2 + 1}$ (c) $s(t) = t^4 - 2t$

87. Neglecting air resistance, the height h (in meters) of an object thrown vertically from the ground with initial velocity v_0 is given by

$$h(t) = v_0 t - \frac{1}{2}gt^2$$

where $g = 9.81 \text{ m/s}^2$ is the earth's gravitational constant and t is the time (in seconds) elapsed since the object was released.

(a) Find the velocity and the acceleration of the object.

(b) Find the time when the velocity is equal to 0. In which direction is the object traveling right before this time? in which direction right after this time?

■ 4.5 Derivatives of Trigonometric Functions

We will need the trigonometric limits from Section 3.4 to compute the derivatives of the sine and cosine functions. Note that all angles are measured in radians.

> **Theorem** The functions $\sin x$ and $\cos x$ are differentiable for all x, and
>
> $$\frac{d}{dx}\sin x = \cos x \qquad \text{and} \qquad \frac{d}{dx}\cos x = -\sin x$$

Graphs of the derivatives of each of the trigonometric functions, based on the geometric interpretation of a derivative as the slope of the tangent line, confirm these rules. (See Figures 4.27 and 4.28.) Pay particular attention to the points on the graph of $f(x)$ with horizontal tangent lines. These correspond to the points of intersection of the graph of $f'(x)$ with the x-axis.

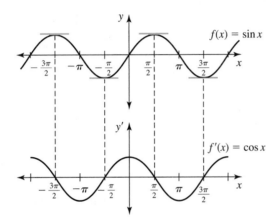

Figure 4.27 The function $f(x) = \sin x$ and its derivative $f'(x) = \cos x$. The derivative $f'(x) = 0$ where $f(x)$ has a horizontal tangent line.

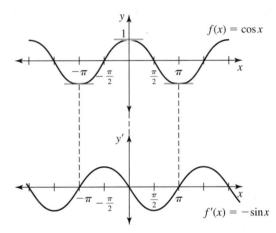

Figure 4.28 The function $f(x) = \cos x$ and its derivative $f'(x) = -\sin x$. The derivative $f'(x) = 0$ where $f(x)$ has a horizontal tangent line.

Proof We prove the first formula; a similar proof of the second formula is discussed in Problem 61. We need the trigonometric identity

$$\sin(\alpha + \beta) = \sin \alpha \cos \beta + \cos \alpha \sin \beta$$

Using the formal definition of derivatives, we find that

$$\frac{d}{dx}\sin x = \lim_{h \to 0} \frac{\sin(x + h) - \sin x}{h}$$

$$= \lim_{h \to 0} \frac{\sin x \cos h + \cos x \sin h - \sin x}{h}$$

$$= \lim_{h \to 0} \left[\sin x \frac{\cos h - 1}{h} + \cos x \frac{\sin h}{h} \right]$$

In Section 3.4, we showed that

$$\lim_{h \to 0} \frac{\cos h - 1}{h} = 0 \qquad \text{and} \qquad \lim_{h \to 0} \frac{\sin h}{h} = 1$$

We can therefore apply the basic rules for limits to obtain

$$\frac{d}{dx}\sin x = \sin x \lim_{h \to 0} \frac{\cos h - 1}{h} + \cos x \lim_{h \to 0} \frac{\sin h}{h}$$

$$= (\sin x)(0) + (\cos x)(1) = \cos x$$

EXAMPLE 1   Find the derivative of $f(x) = -4\sin x + \cos\frac{\pi}{6}$.

Solution

$$f'(x) = \frac{d}{dx}(-4\sin x + \cos\frac{\pi}{6})$$

$$= -4\frac{d}{dx}\sin x + \frac{d}{dx}\cos\frac{\pi}{6}$$

The first term is a trigonometric function and the second term is a constant (namely, $\frac{1}{2}\sqrt{3}$). Differentiating each term, we find that

$$f'(x) = -4(\cos x) + 0 = -4\cos x \qquad\blacksquare$$

EXAMPLE 2   Find the derivative of $y = \cos(x^2 + 1)$.

Solution   We set $u = g(x) = x^2 + 1$ and $f(u) = \cos u$; then $y = f[g(x)]$. Using the chain rule, we then obtain

$$y' = \frac{df}{du}\frac{du}{dx} = \frac{d}{du}(\cos u)\frac{d}{dx}(x^2 + 1) = (-\sin u)(2x)$$

$$= -[\sin(x^2 + 1)]2x = -2x\sin(x^2 + 1) \qquad\blacksquare$$

EXAMPLE 3   Find the derivative of $y = x^2\sin(3x) - \cos(5x)$.

Solution   We will use the product rule for the first term; in addition, we will need the chain rule for both $\sin(3x)$ and $\cos(5x)$:

$$y' = \frac{d}{dx}[x^2\sin(3x) - \cos(5x)]$$

$$= \frac{d}{dx}[x^2\sin(3x)] - \frac{d}{dx}\cos(5x)$$

$$= \left(\frac{d}{dx}x^2\right)\sin(3x) + x^2\frac{d}{dx}\sin(3x) - \frac{d}{dx}\cos(5x)$$

$$= 2x\sin(3x) + x^23\cos(3x) - 5(-\sin(5x))$$

$$= 2x\sin(3x) + 3x^2\cos(3x) + 5\sin(5x) \qquad\blacksquare$$

The derivatives of the other trigonometric functions can be found using the following identities:

$$\tan x = \frac{\sin x}{\cos x} \qquad\qquad \cot x = \frac{\cos x}{\sin x}$$

$$\sec x = \frac{1}{\cos x} \qquad\qquad \csc x = \frac{1}{\sin x}$$

For instance, to find the derivative of the tangent, we use the quotient rule:

$$\frac{d}{dx}\tan x = \frac{d}{dx}\frac{\sin x}{\cos x}$$

$$= \frac{(\frac{d}{dx}\sin x)\cos x - \sin x(\frac{d}{dx}\cos x)}{\cos^2 x}$$

$$= \frac{(\cos x)(\cos x) - (\sin x)(-\sin x)}{\cos^2 x}$$

$$= \frac{\cos^2 x + \sin^2 x}{\cos^2 x} = \frac{1}{\cos^2 x} = \sec^2 x$$

In the penultimate step, we used the identity $\cos^2 x + \sin^2 x = 1$.

The other derivatives can be found in a similar fashion, as explained in Problems 62–64.

We summarize the derivatives of the six fundamental trigonometric functions in the following box:

$$\frac{d}{dx}\sin x = \cos x \qquad\qquad \frac{d}{dx}\cos x = -\sin x$$

$$\frac{d}{dx}\tan x = \sec^2 x \qquad\qquad \frac{d}{dx}\cot x = -\csc^2 x$$

$$\frac{d}{dx}\sec x = \sec x \tan x \qquad\qquad \frac{d}{dx}\csc x = -\csc x \cot x$$

EXAMPLE 4

Compare the derivatives of

(a) $\tan x^2$ **(b)** $\tan^2 x$

Solution

(a) If $y = \tan x^2 = \tan(x^2)$, then, using the chain rule, we find that

$$\frac{dy}{dx} = \frac{d}{dx}\tan(x^2) = (\sec^2(x^2))(2x) = 2x\sec^2(x^2)$$

(b) If $y = \tan^2 x = (\tan x)^2$, then, using the chain rule, we obtain

$$\frac{dy}{dx} = \frac{d}{dx}(\tan x)^2 = 2(\tan x)\frac{d}{dx}\tan x = 2\tan x\sec^2 x$$

The two derivatives are clearly different, and you should look again at $\tan x^2$ and $\tan^2 x$ to make sure that you understand which is the inner and which the outer function. ■

EXAMPLE 5

Repeated Application of the Chain Rule Find the derivative of $f(x) = \sec\sqrt{x^2 + 1}$.

Solution

This is a composite function; the inner function is $\sqrt{x^2 + 1}$ and the outer function is $\sec x$. Applying the chain rule once, we find that

$$\frac{df}{dx} = \frac{d}{dx}\sec\sqrt{x^2 + 1} = \sec\sqrt{x^2 + 1}\tan\sqrt{x^2 + 1}\frac{d}{dx}\sqrt{x^2 + 1}$$

To evaluate $\frac{d}{dx}\sqrt{x^2 + 1}$, we need to apply the chain rule a second time:

$$\frac{d}{dx}\sqrt{x^2 + 1} = \frac{1}{2\sqrt{x^2 + 1}}2x = \frac{x}{\sqrt{x^2 + 1}}$$

Combining the two steps, we obtain

$$\frac{df}{dx} = \left(\sec\sqrt{x^2 + 1}\right)\left(\tan\sqrt{x^2 + 1}\right)\frac{x}{\sqrt{x^2 + 1}}$$

The function $f(x)$ can be thought of as a composition of three functions. The innermost function is $u = g(x) = x^2 + 1$, the middle function is $v = h(u) = \sqrt{u}$, and the outermost function is $f(v) = \sec v$. When we computed the derivative, we applied the chain rule twice in the form

$$\frac{df}{dx} = \frac{df}{dv}\frac{dv}{du}\frac{du}{dx}$$

■

Section 4.5 Problems

In Problems 1–58, find the derivative with respect to the independent variable.

1. $f(x) = 2\sin x - \cos x$ **2.** $f(x) = 3\cos x - 2\sin x$
3. $f(x) = 3\sin x + 5\cos x - 2\sec x$
4. $f(x) = -\sin x + \cos x - 3\csc x$
5. $f(x) = \tan x - \cot x$ **6.** $f(x) = \sec x - \csc x$
7. $f(x) = \sin(3x)$ **8.** $f(x) = \cos(-5x)$
9. $f(x) = 2\sin(3x + 1)$ **10.** $f(x) = -3\cos(1 - 2x)$
11. $f(x) = \tan(4x)$ **12.** $f(x) = \cot(2 - 3x)$
13. $f(x) = 2\sec(1 + 2x)$ **14.** $f(x) = -3\csc(3 - 5x)$
15. $f(x) = 3\sin(x^2)$ **16.** $f(x) = 2\cos(x^3 - 3x)$
17. $f(x) = \sin^3(x^2 - 3)$ **18.** $f(x) = \cos^2(x^2 - 1)$
19. $f(x) = 3\sin^2 x^2$ **20.** $f(x) = -\sin^2(2x^3 - 1)$
21. $f(x) = 4\cos x^2 - 2\cos^2 x$
22. $f(x) = -5\cos(2 - x^3) + 2\cos^3(x - 4)$
23. $f(x) = 4\cos^2 x + 2\cos x^4$ **24.** $f(x) = -3\cos^2(3x^2 - 4)$
25. $f(x) = 2\tan(1 - x^2)$ **26.** $f(x) = -\cot(3x^3 - 4x)$
27. $f(x) = -2\tan^3(3x - 1)$ **28.** $f(x) = \sqrt{\sin x} + \sin\sqrt{x}$
29. $f(x) = \sqrt{\sin(2x^2 - 1)}$ **30.** $g(s) = (\cos^2 s - 3s^2)^2$
31. $g(s) = \sqrt{\cos s} - \cos\sqrt{x}$ **32.** $g(t) = \dfrac{\sin(3t)}{\cos(5t)}$
33. $g(t) = \dfrac{\sin(2t) + 1}{\cos(6t) - 1}$ **34.** $f(x) = \dfrac{\cot(2x)}{\tan(4x)}$
35. $f(x) = \dfrac{\sec(x^2 - 1)}{\csc(x^2 + 1)}$ **36.** $f(x) = \sin x \cos x$
37. $f(x) = \sin(2x - 1)\cos(3x + 1)$
38. $f(x) = \tan x \cot x$
39. $f(x) = \tan(3x^2 - 1)\cot(3x^2 + 1)$
40. $f(x) = \sec x \cos x$
41. $f(x) = \sin x \sec x$ **42.** $f(x) = \dfrac{1}{\sin^2 x + \cos^2 x}$
43. $f(x) = \dfrac{1}{\tan^2 x - \sec^2 x}$ **44.** $g(x) = \dfrac{1}{\sin(3x)}$
45. $g(x) = \dfrac{1}{\sin(3x^2 - 1)}$ **46.** $g(x) = \dfrac{1}{\csc^2(5x)}$
47. $g(x) = \dfrac{1}{\csc^3(1 - 5x^2)}$ **48.** $h(x) = \cot(3x)\csc(3x)$
49. $h(x) = \dfrac{3}{\tan(2x) - x}$ **50.** $g(t) = \left(\dfrac{1}{\sin t^2}\right)^{3/2}$
51. $h(s) = \sin^3 s + \cos^3 s$ **52.** $f(x) = (2x^3 - x)\cos(1 - x^2)$
53. $f(x) = \dfrac{\sin(2x)}{1 + x^2}$ **54.** $f(x) = \dfrac{1 + \cos(3x)}{2x^3 - x}$
55. $f(x) = \tan\dfrac{1}{x}$ **56.** $f(x) = \sec\dfrac{1}{1 + x^2}$
57. $f(x) = \dfrac{\sec x^2}{\sec^2 x}$ **58.** $f(x) = \dfrac{\csc(3 - x^2)}{1 - x^2}$

59. Find the points on the curve $y = \sin(\frac{\pi}{3}x)$ that have a horizontal tangent.
60. Find the points on the curve $y = \cos^2 x$ that have a horizontal tangent.
61. Use the identity
$$\cos(\alpha + \beta) = \cos\alpha\cos\beta - \sin\alpha\sin\beta$$
and the definition of the derivative to show that
$$\frac{d}{dx}\cos x = -\sin x$$

62. Use the quotient rule to show that
$$\frac{d}{dx}\cot x = -\csc^2 x$$
(*Hint*: Write $\cot x = \frac{\cos x}{\sin x}$.)
63. Use the quotient rule to show that
$$\frac{d}{dx}\sec x = \sec x \tan x$$
[*Hint*: Write $\sec x = (\cos x)^{-1}$.]
64. Use the quotient rule to show that
$$\frac{d}{dx}\csc x = -\csc x \cot x$$
[*Hint*: Write $\csc x = (\sin x)^{-1}$.]
65. Find the derivative of
$$f(x) = \sin\sqrt{x^2 + 1}$$
66. Find the derivative of
$$f(x) = \cos\sqrt{x^2 + 1}$$
67. Find the derivative of
$$f(x) = \sin\sqrt{3x^3 + 3x}$$
68. Find the derivative of
$$f(x) = \cos\sqrt{1 - 4x^4}$$
69. Find the derivative of
$$f(x) = \sin^2(x^2 - 1)$$
70. Find the derivative of
$$f(x) = \cos^2(2x^2 + 3)$$
71. Find the derivative of
$$f(x) = \tan^3(3x^3 - 3)$$
72. Find the derivative of
$$f(x) = \sec^2(2x^2 - 2)$$
73. Suppose that the concentration of nitrogen in a lake exhibits periodic behavior. That is, if we denote the concentration of nitrogen at time t by $c(t)$, then we assume that
$$c(t) = 2 + \sin\left(\frac{\pi}{2}t\right)$$
(a) Find
$$\frac{dc}{dt}$$
(b) Use a graphing calculator to graph both $c(t)$ and $\frac{dc}{dt}$ in the same coordinate system.
(c) By inspecting the graph in (b), answer the following questions:
(i) When $c(t)$ reaches a maximum, what is the value of dc/dt?
(ii) When dc/dt is positive, is $c(t)$ increasing or decreasing?
(iii) What can you say about $c(t)$ when $dc/dt = 0$?

■ 4.6 Derivatives of Exponential Functions

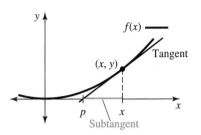

Figure 4.29 The subtangent problem.

Pierre de Fermat (1601–1665) devised a method of finding the tangent line at a given point (x, y) on a curve by constructing the **subtangent**, defined as the line segment between the point where the tangent line intersects the x-axis and the point $(x, 0)$. (See Figure 4.29.)

Fermat's procedure essentially amounted to finding the slope of the tangent line by considering the secant line through two points: (x, y) and a nearby point of the graph of $y = f(x)$. After computing the slope of the secant line, he set the two points he used to compute the slope equal to each other, thus obtaining the slope of the tangent line. This sounds very much like the definition of the derivative that we use today, and, in fact, it is the same idea. Fermat did not, however, develop and formalize a general framework for the differential calculus; that was done by Leibniz and Newton.

Using the definition of derivatives, we can relate the subtangent to the slope of the tangent at the corresponding point of the graph of $y = f(x)$. Suppose the tangent line at (x, y), where $y = f(x)$, intersects the x-axis at $(p(x), 0)$; the location of $p(x)$ depends on x. We set $c(x) = x - p(x)$. This is the equation of the subtangent. We see from Figure 4.29 that the slope of the tangent line at (x, y) is given by $y/c(x)$. Since the slope of the tangent line at (x, y) is the derivative of the function of the curve, evaluated at x [i.e., $f'(x)$], we find that

$$\frac{dy}{dx} = \frac{y}{c(x)}$$

A natural problem (which was posed to Descartes by Debaune in 1639) is to find a curve whose subtangent is a given constant. That is, we wish to find the function $y = f(x)$ that satisfies

$$\frac{dy}{dx} = \frac{y}{c}$$

where c is a constant other than 0. (This problem was solved by Leibniz in 1684, when he published his differential calculus for the first time.) In words, we are looking for a function $y = f(x)$ whose derivative is proportional to the function itself. As we will see next, exponential functions are the solutions to this problem.

Recall from Section 1.2 that the function f is an exponential function with base a if

$$f(x) = a^x, \quad x \in \mathbf{R}$$

where a is a positive constant other than 1. (See Figure 4.30.) We can use the formal definition of the derivative to compute $f'(x)$:

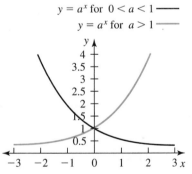

Figure 4.30 The function $y = a^x$.

$$f'(x) = \frac{d}{dx} a^x = \lim_{h \to 0} \frac{f(x+h) - f(x)}{h} = \lim_{h \to 0} \frac{a^{x+h} - a^x}{h}$$

$$= \lim_{h \to 0} \frac{a^x(a^h - 1)}{h} = a^x \lim_{h \to 0} \frac{a^h - 1}{h}$$

In the final step, we were able to write the term a^x in front of the limit because a^x does not depend on h. Thus, we are left with investigating

$$\lim_{h \to 0} \frac{a^h - 1}{h}$$

We first note that this limit does not depend on x. If we assume that the limit exists, then it follows that it is equal to $f'(0)$. To see why, use the formal definition of the derivative to compute $f'(0)$. (It can be formally shown that the limit exists, but doing so is beyond the scope of this course.)

It follows from the preceding calculation that if $f'(0)$ exists, then $f'(x)$ exists and

$$f'(x) = \underbrace{a^x}_{f(x)} f'(0)$$

This equation shows that the exponential function is a function whose derivative is proportional to the function itself, provided that that $f'(0)$ exists. [The constant of proportionality is $f'(0)$.] That is, exponential functions solve the subtangent problems just mentioned. We single out the case where the value of the base a is such that

$$\lim_{h \to 0} \frac{a^h - 1}{h}$$

is equal to 1. We denote this base by e. The number e is thus defined by

$$\lim_{h \to 0} \frac{e^h - 1}{h} = 1 \qquad (4.7)$$

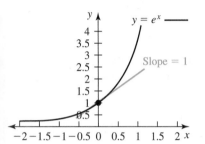

Figure 4.31 The function $y = e^x$. The slope of the tangent line at $x = 0$ is $m = 1$.

We find, for the derivative of $f(x) = e^x$, that

$$\frac{d}{dx} e^x = e^x \qquad (4.8)$$

A graph of $f(x) = e^x$ is shown in Figure 4.31. The domain of this function is **R** and its range is the open interval $(0, \infty)$. (In particular, $e^x > 0$ for all $x \in$ **R**.) Denoting by e the base of the exponential function for which (4.7) and (4.8) hold is no accident; it is indeed the natural exponential base that we introduced in Section 1.2. Although we cannot prove this here, a table should convince you: With $e = 2.71828\ldots$, we find that

h	0.1	0.01	0.001	0.0001
$\frac{e^h - 1}{h}$	1.0517	1.0050	1.00050	1.000050

Now recall that there is an alternative notation for e^x, namely, $\exp[x]$. Using the identity

$$a^x = \exp[\ln a^x]$$

and the fact that $\ln a^x = x \ln a$, we can find the derivative of a^x with the help of the chain rule:

$$\frac{d}{dx} a^x = \frac{d}{dx} \exp[\ln a^x] = \frac{d}{dx} \exp[x \ln a]$$
$$= \exp[x \ln a] \ln a = (\ln a) a^x$$

That is, we have

$$\frac{d}{dx} a^x = (\ln a) a^x \qquad (4.9)$$

which allows us to obtain the following identity:

$$\lim_{h \to 0} \frac{a^h - 1}{h} = \ln a \qquad (4.10)$$

EXAMPLE 1 Find the derivative of $f(x) = e^{-x^2/2}$.

Solution We use the chain rule:

$$f'(x) = e^{-x^2/2} \left(-\frac{2x}{2} \right) = -x e^{-x^2/2} \qquad \blacksquare$$

EXAMPLE 2

Find the derivative of $f(x) = 3^{\sqrt{x}}$.

Solution

We can use (4.9) and the chain rule to get

$$\frac{d}{dx}3^{\sqrt{x}} = (\ln 3)3^{\sqrt{x}}\frac{1}{2\sqrt{x}}$$

However, since every exponential function can be written in terms of the base e, and the differentiation rule for e^x is particularly simple ($\frac{d}{dx}e^x = e^x$), it is often easier to rewrite the exponential function in terms of e and then differentiate. That is, we write

$$3^{\sqrt{x}} = \exp[\ln 3^{\sqrt{x}}] = \exp[\sqrt{x}\ln 3]$$

Then, using the chain rule, we obtain

$$\frac{d}{dx}\exp[\sqrt{x}\ln 3] = \frac{\ln 3}{2\sqrt{x}}\exp[\sqrt{x}\ln 3] = \frac{\ln 3}{2\sqrt{x}}3^{\sqrt{x}}$$ ■

Since we must frequently differentiate functions of the form $y = e^{g(x)}$, we state this differentiation in a separate rule. Using the chain rule, we have

$$\frac{d}{dx}e^{g(x)} = g'(x)e^{g(x)} \qquad (4.11)$$

EXAMPLE 3

Find the derivative of $f(x) = \exp[\sin \sqrt{x}]$.

Solution

We set $g(x) = \sin \sqrt{x}$. To differentiate $g(x)$, we must apply the chain rule:

$$\frac{d}{dx}g(x) = (\cos \sqrt{x})\frac{1}{2\sqrt{x}}$$

Using Equation (4.11), we can now differentiate $f(x)$:

$$\frac{d}{dx}f(x) = (\cos \sqrt{x})\frac{1}{2\sqrt{x}}\exp[\sin \sqrt{x}]$$ ■

Here is an example that shows how (4.10) is used:

EXAMPLE 4

Find

$$\lim_{h\to 0}\frac{3^{2h}-1}{h}$$

Solution

We make the substitution $l = 2h$ and note that $l \to 0$ as $h \to 0$. Then

$$\lim_{h\to 0}\frac{3^{2h}-1}{h} = \lim_{l\to 0}\frac{3^l-1}{l/2}$$

$$= 2\lim_{l\to 0}\frac{3^l-1}{l} = 2\ln 3$$ ■

The exponential function with base e appears in many scientific problems; the next example involves radioactive decay.

EXAMPLE 5

Radioactive Decay Find the derivative of the radioactive decay function, which describes the amount of material left after t units of time. (See Example 10 in Subsection 1.2.5.) The function is

$$W(t) = W_0 e^{-\lambda t}, \quad t \geq 0$$

where W_0 is the amount of material at time 0 and λ is called the *radioactive decay rate*. Show that $W(t)$ satisfies the differential equation

$$\frac{dW}{dt} = -\lambda W(t)$$

Solution   We use the chain rule to find the derivative of $W(t)$:

$$\frac{d}{dt} W(t) = \underbrace{W_0 e^{-\lambda t}}_{W(t)}(-\lambda)$$

That is,

$$\frac{dW}{dt} = -\lambda W(t)$$

In words, the rate of decay is proportional to the amount of material left. This equation should remind you of the subtangent problem; there, we wanted to find a function whose derivative is proportional to the function itself. That is exactly the situation we have in this example: The derivative of $W(t)$ is proportional to $W(t)$. ■

EXAMPLE 6   **Exponential Growth**   Find the per capita growth rate of a population whose size $N(t)$ at time t follows the exponential growth function

$$N(t) = N(0)e^{rt}$$

where $N(0)$ is the population size at time 0 and r is a constant.

Solution   We first find the derivative of $N(t)$:

$$\frac{dN}{dt} = N(0)re^{rt}$$

Since $N(0)e^{rt} = N(t)$, we can write

$$\frac{dN}{dt} = rN(t)$$

Thus, the per capita growth rate of an exponentially growing population is constant; that is,

$$\frac{1}{N}\frac{dN}{dt} = r$$

■

Section 4.6 Problems

Differentiate the functions in Problems 1–52 with respect to the independent variable.

1. $f(x) = e^{3x}$

2. $f(x) = e^{-2x}$

3. $f(x) = 4e^{1-3x}$

4. $f(x) = 3e^{2-5x}$

5. $f(x) = e^{-2x^2+3x-1}$

6. $f(x) = e^{4x^2-2x+1}$

7. $f(x) = e^{7(x^2+1)^2}$

8. $f(x) = e^{-3(x^3-1)^4}$

9. $f(x) = xe^x$

10. $f(x) = 2xe^{-3x}$

11. $f(x) = x^2 e^{-x}$

12. $f(x) = (3x^2 - 1)e^{1-x^2}$

13. $f(x) = \frac{1+e^x}{1+x^2}$

14. $f(x) = \frac{x-e^{-x}}{1+xe^{-x}}$

15. $f(x) = \frac{e^x + e^{-x}}{2+e^x}$

16. $f(x) = \frac{x}{e^x + e^{-x}}$

17. $f(x) = e^{\sin(3x)}$

18. $f(x) = e^{\cos(4x)}$

19. $f(x) = e^{\sin(x^2-1)}$

20. $f(x) = e^{\cos(1-2x^3)}$

21. $f(x) = \sin(e^x)$

22. $f(x) = \cos(e^x)$

23. $f(x) = \sin(e^{2x} + x)$

24. $f(x) = \cos(3x - e^{x^2-1})$

25. $f(x) = \exp[x - \sin x]$

26. $f(x) = \exp[x^2 - 2\cos x]$

27. $g(s) = \exp[\sec s^2]$

28. $g(s) = \exp[\tan s^3]$

29. $f(x) = e^{x \sin x}$

30. $f(x) = e^{1-x \cos x}$

31. $f(x) = -3e^{x^2+\tan x}$

32. $f(x) = 2e^{-x \sec(3x)}$

33. $f(x) = 2^x$

34. $f(x) = 3^x$

35. $f(x) = 2^{x+1}$

36. $f(x) = 3^{x-1}$

37. $f(x) = 5^{\sqrt{2x-1}}$

38. $f(x) = 3^{\sqrt{1-3x}}$

39. $f(x) = 2^{x^2+1}$

40. $f(x) = 3^{x^3-1}$

41. $h(t) = 2^{t^2-1}$

42. $h(t) = 4^{2t^3-t}$

43. $f(x) = 2^{\sqrt{x}}$

44. $f(x) = 3^{\sqrt{x+1}}$

45. $f(x) = 2^{\sqrt{x^2-1}}$

46. $f(x) = 4^{\sqrt{1-2x^3}}$

47. $h(t) = 5^{\sqrt{t}}$

48. $h(t) = 6^{\sqrt{6t^6-6}}$

49. $g(x) = 2^{2\cos x}$

50. $g(r) = 2^{-3\sin r}$

51. $g(r) = 3^{r^{1/5}}$

52. $g(r) = 4^{r^{1/4}}$

Compute the limits in Problems 53–56.

53. $\lim\limits_{h \to 0} \dfrac{e^{2h} - 1}{h}$

54. $\lim\limits_{h \to 0} \dfrac{e^{5h} - 1}{3h}$

55. $\lim\limits_{h \to 0} \dfrac{e^h - 1}{\sqrt{h}}$

56. $\lim\limits_{h \to 0} \dfrac{2^h - 1}{h}$

57. Find the length of the subtangent to the curve $y = 2^x$ at the point $(1, 2)$.

58. Find the length of the subtangent to the curve $y = \exp[x^2]$ at the point $(2, e^4)$.

59. Population Growth Suppose that the population size at time t is

$$N(t) = e^{2t}, \quad t \geq 0$$

(a) What is the population size at time 0?

(b) Show that

$$\frac{dN}{dt} = 2N$$

60. Population Growth Suppose that the population size at time t is

$$N(t) = N_0 e^{rt}, \quad t \geq 0$$

where N_0 is a positive constant and r is a real number.

(a) What is the population size at time 0?

(b) Show that

$$\frac{dN}{dt} = rN$$

61. Bacterial Growth Suppose that a bacterial colony grows in such a way that at time t the population size is

$$N(t) = N(0)2^t$$

where $N(0)$ is the population size at time 0. Find the rate of growth dN/dt. Express your solution in terms of $N(t)$. Show that the growth rate of the population is proportional to the population size.

62. Bacterial Growth Suppose that a bacterial colony grows in such a way that at time t the population size is

$$N(t) = N(0)2^t$$

where $N(0)$ is the population size at time 0. Find the per capita growth rate.

63. Logistic Growth

(a) Find the derivative of the logistic growth curve (see Example 3 in Section 3.3)

$$N(t) = \frac{K}{1 + \left(\frac{K}{N(0)} - 1\right)e^{-rt}}$$

where r and K are positive constants and $N(0)$ is the population size at time 0.

(b) Show that $N(t)$ satisfies the equation

$$\frac{dN}{dt} = rN\left(1 - \frac{N}{K}\right)$$

[*Hint*: Use the function $N(t)$ given in (a) for the right-hand side, and simplify until you obtain the derivative of $N(t)$ that you computed in (a).]

(c) Plot the per capita rate of growth $\frac{1}{N}\frac{dN}{dt}$ as a function of N, and note that it decreases with increasing population size.

64. Fish Recruitment Model The following model is used in the fisheries literature to describe the recruitment of fish as a function of the size of the parent stock: If we denote the number of recruits by R and the size of the parent stock by P, then

$$R(P) = \alpha P e^{-\beta P}, \quad P \geq 0$$

where α and β are positive constants.

(a) Sketch the graph of the function $R(P)$ when $\beta = 1$ and $\alpha = 2$.

(b) Differentiate $R(P)$ with respect to P.

(c) Find all the points on the curve that have a horizontal tangent.

65. Von Bertalanffy Growth Model The growth of fish can be described by the von Bertalanffy growth function

$$L(x) = L_\infty - (L_\infty - L_0)e^{-kx}$$

where x denotes the age of the fish and k, L_∞, and L_0 are positive constants.

(a) Set $L_0 = 1$ and $L_\infty = 10$. Graph $L(x)$ for $k = 1.0$ and $k = 0.1$.

(b) Interpret L_∞ and L_0.

(c) Compare the graphs for $k = 0.1$ and $k = 1.0$. According to which graph do fish reach $L = 5$ more quickly?

(d) Show that

$$\frac{d}{dx}L(x) = k(L_\infty - L(x))$$

That is, $dL/dx \propto L_\infty - L$. What does this proportionality say about how the rate of growth changes with age?

(e) The constant k is the proportionality constant in (d). What does the value of k tell you about how quickly a fish grows?

66. Radioactive Decay Suppose $W(t)$ denotes the amount of a radioactive material left after time t (measured in days). Assume that the radioactive decay rate of the material is 0.2/day. Find the differential equation for the radioactive decay function $W(t)$.

67. Radioactive Decay Suppose $W(t)$ denotes the amount of a radioactive material left after time t (measured in days). Assume that the radioactive decay rate of the material is 4/day. Find the differential equation for the radioactive decay function $W(t)$.

68. Radioactive Decay Suppose $W(t)$ denotes the amount of a radioactive material left after time t (measured in days). Assume that the half-life of the material is 3 days. Find the differential equation for the radioactive decay function $W(t)$.

69. Radioactive Decay Suppose $W(t)$ denotes the amount of a radioactive material left after time t (measured in days). Assume that the half-life of the material is 5 days. Find the differential equation for the radioactive decay function $W(t)$.

70. Radioactive Decay Suppose $W(t)$ denotes the amount of a radioactive material left after time t. Assume that $W(0) = 15$ and that

$$\frac{dW}{dt} = -2W(t)$$

(a) How much material is left at time $t = 2$?

(b) What is the half-life of this material?

71. Radioactive Decay Suppose $W(t)$ denotes the amount of a radioactive material left after time t. Assume that $W(0) = 6$ and that

$$\frac{dW}{dt} = -3W(t)$$

(a) How much material is left at time $t = 4$?

(b) What is the half-life of the material?

72. Radioactive Decay Suppose $W(t)$ denotes the amount of a radioactive material left after time t. Assume that $W(0) = 10$ and $W(1) = 8$.
(a) Find the differential equation that describes this situation.
(b) How much material is left at time $t = 5$?
(c) What is the half-life of the material?

73. Radioactive Decay Suppose $W(t)$ denotes the amount of a radioactive material left after time t. Assume that $W(0) = 5$ and $W(1) = 2$.
(a) Find the differential equation that describes this situation.
(b) How much material is left at time $t = 3$?
(c) What is the half-life of the material?

■ 4.7 Derivatives of Inverse Functions, Logarithmic Functions, and the Inverse Tangent Function

Recall that the logarithmic function is the inverse of the exponential function. To find the derivative of the logarithmic function, we must therefore learn how to compute the derivative of an inverse function.

■ 4.7.1 Derivatives of Inverse Functions

We begin with an example (Figure 4.32). Let $f(x) = x^2$, $x \geq 0$. We computed the inverse function of f in Subsection 1.2.6. First note that $f(x) = x^2$, $x \geq 0$, is one to one (use the horizontal line test from Subsection 1.2.6); hence, we can define its inverse. We repeat the steps from Subsection 1.2.6 to find an inverse function. [Recall that we obtain the graph of the inverse function by reflecting $y = f(x)$ about the line $y = x$.]

1. Write $y = f(x)$:
$$y = x^2$$

2. Solve for x:
$$x = \sqrt{y}$$

3. Interchange x and y:
$$y = \sqrt{x}$$

Since the range of $f(x)$, which is the interval $[0, \infty)$, becomes the domain for the inverse function, it follows that

$$f^{-1}(x) = \sqrt{x} \quad \text{for } x \geq 0$$

We already know the derivative of $\sqrt{x}$, namely, $1/(2\sqrt{x})$. But we will try to find the derivative in a different way that we can generalize to get a formula for finding the derivative of any inverse function. Let $g(x) = f^{-1}(x)$. Then

$$(f \circ g)(x) = f[g(x)] = (\sqrt{x})^2 = x, \quad x \geq 0$$

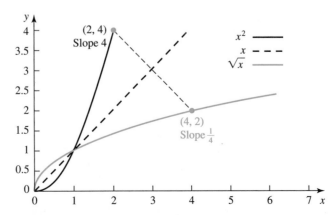

Figure 4.32 The function $y = x^2$, $x \geq 0$, and its inverse function $y = \sqrt{x}$, $x \geq 0$.

Therefore, the derivatives of $(\sqrt{x})^2$ and x must be equal. Applying the chain rule, we find that

$$\frac{d}{dx}(\sqrt{x})^2 = 2\sqrt{x}\,\frac{d}{dx}\sqrt{x}$$

Since $\frac{d}{dx}x = 1$, we obtain

$$2\sqrt{x}\,\frac{d}{dx}\sqrt{x} = 1$$

or, for $x > 0$,

$$\frac{d}{dx}\sqrt{x} = \frac{1}{2\sqrt{x}}$$

To prepare for how the derivatives of a function and its inverse function are related geometrically, look at Figure 4.32, where the slope at the point $(2, 4)$ of $f(x) = x^2$ is $m = 4$ and the slope at the point $(4, 2)$ of $f^{-1}(x) = \sqrt{x}$ is $m = 1/4$. We will also find this reciprocal relationship of slopes at related points in the general case.

The steps that led us to the derivative of $\sqrt{x}$ can be used to find a general formula for the derivatives of inverse functions. We assume that $f(x)$ is one to one in its domain. If $g(x)$ is the inverse function of $f(x)$, then $f[g(x)] = x$. Applying the chain rule, we find that

$$\frac{d}{dx}f[g(x)] = f'[g(x)]g'(x)$$

Since $\frac{d}{dx}x = 1$, we obtain

$$f'[g(x)]g'(x) = 1$$

If $f'[g(x)] \neq 0$, we can divide by $f'[g(x)]$ to get

$$g'(x) = \frac{1}{f'[g(x)]}$$

Because $g(x) = f^{-1}(x)$ and $g'(x) = \frac{d}{dx}g(x) = \frac{d}{dx}f^{-1}(x)$, we obtain the following rule:

Derivative of an Inverse Function If $f(x)$ is one to one and differentiable with inverse function $f^{-1}(x)$ and $f'[f^{-1}(x)] \neq 0$, then $f^{-1}(x)$ is differentiable and

$$\frac{d}{dx}f^{-1}(x) = \frac{1}{f'[f^{-1}(x)]} \qquad (4.12)$$

This reciprocal relationship is illustrated in Figure 4.33.

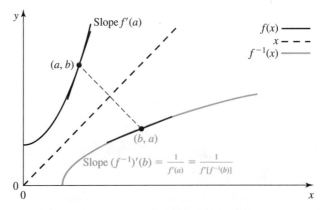

Figure 4.33 The graphs of $y = f(x)$ and its inverse function $y = f^{-1}(x)$ have reciprocal slopes at the points (a, b) and (b, a).

We return to the example of $f(x) = x^2$, $x \geq 0$, where $f^{-1}(x) = \sqrt{x}$, $x \geq 0$, to illustrate how to use (4.12). Now, $f'(x) = 2x$ and we need to evaluate

$$f'[f^{-1}(x)] = f'[\sqrt{x}] = 2\sqrt{x}$$

To apply the formula, we assume that $f'[f^{-1}(x)] \neq 0$. Then

$$\frac{d}{dx}\sqrt{x} = \frac{1}{2\sqrt{x}} \quad \text{for } x > 0$$

Looking at the graphs of $y = x^2$ and $y = \sqrt{x}$, $x \geq 0$, we easily see why $f^{-1}(x)$ is not differentiable at $x = 0$. [Recall that we obtain the graph of the inverse function by reflecting $y = f(x)$ about the line $y = x$.] If we draw the tangent line to the curve $y = x^2$ at $x = 0$, we find that the tangent line is horizontal; that is, its slope is 0. Reflecting a horizontal line about $y = x$ results in a vertical line, for which the slope is not defined (Figure 4.32).

The formula for finding derivatives of inverse functions takes on a particularly easy to remember form when we use Leibniz notation. To see this, note that (without interchanging x and y)

$$y = f(x) \quad \Longleftrightarrow \quad x = f^{-1}(y)$$

and hence

$$\frac{dx}{dy} = \frac{1}{\frac{dy}{dx}}$$

This formula again emphasizes the reciprocal relationship. We illustrate the formula with the example

$$y = x^2 \quad \Longleftrightarrow \quad x = \sqrt{y}$$

for $x > 0$. Since $\frac{dy}{dx} = 2x$, we have

$$\frac{dx}{dy} = \frac{1}{\frac{dy}{dx}} = \frac{1}{2x} = \frac{1}{2\sqrt{y}}$$

That is,

$$\frac{d}{dy}\sqrt{y} = \frac{1}{2\sqrt{y}}$$

The answer is now in terms of y, because we did not interchange x and y when we computed the inverse function. If we now do so, we again find that

$$\frac{d}{dx}\sqrt{x} = \frac{1}{2\sqrt{x}}$$

EXAMPLE 1   Let

$$f(x) = \frac{x}{1+x} \quad \text{for } x \geq 0$$

Find $\frac{d}{dx}f^{-1}(x)\big|_{x=\frac{1}{3}}$.

Solution   To show that $f^{-1}(x)$ exists, we use the horizontal line test and conclude that $f(x)$ is one to one on its domain, since each horizontal line intersects the graph of $f(x)$ at most once. (See Figure 4.34.)

We can actually compute the inverse of $f(x)$. This will give us two different ways to compute the derivative of the inverse of $f(x)$: We can compute the inverse function explicitly and then differentiate the result, or we can use the formula for finding derivatives of inverse functions. We begin with the latter way.

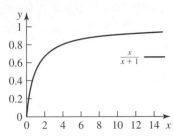

Figure 4.34 The graph of $f(x) = \frac{x}{x+1}$ for $x \geq 0$.

1. To use the formula (4.12), we need to find $f^{-1}(\frac{1}{3})$; this means that we need to find x so that $f(x) = 1/3$. Now,

$$\frac{x}{1+x} = \frac{1}{3} \quad \text{implies that} \quad 2x = 1, \quad \text{or} \quad x = \frac{1}{2}$$

Therefore, $f^{-1}(\frac{1}{3}) = \frac{1}{2}$. Formula (4.12) thus becomes

$$\frac{d}{dx} f^{-1}(x)\Big|_{x=\frac{1}{3}} = \frac{1}{f'[f^{-1}(\frac{1}{3})]} = \frac{1}{f'(\frac{1}{2})}$$

We use the quotient rule to find the derivative of $f(x)$:

$$f'(x) = \frac{(1)(1+x) - (x)(1)}{(1+x)^2} = \frac{1}{(1+x)^2}$$

At $x = 1/2$, $f'(\frac{1}{2}) = \frac{1}{(1+1/2)^2} = \frac{4}{9}$. Therefore,

$$\frac{d}{dx} f^{-1}(x)\Big|_{x=\frac{1}{3}} = \frac{1}{\frac{4}{9}} = \frac{9}{4}$$

2. We can compute the inverse function: Set $y = \frac{x}{1+x}$. Then, solving for x yields

$$x = \frac{y}{1-y}$$

Interchanging x and y, we find that

$$y = \frac{x}{1-x}$$

Since the domain of $f(x)$ is $[0, \infty)$, the range of f is $[0, 1)$. Now, the range of f becomes the domain of the inverse; therefore, the inverse function is

$$f^{-1}(x) = \frac{x}{1-x} \quad \text{for } 0 \leq x < 1$$

We use the quotient rule to find $\frac{d}{dx} f^{-1}(x)$:

$$\frac{d}{dx} f^{-1}(x) = \frac{(1)(1-x) - (x)(-1)}{(1-x)^2} = \frac{1}{(1-x)^2}$$

Therefore,

$$\frac{d}{dx} f^{-1}(x)\Big|_{x=\frac{1}{3}} = \frac{1}{(1-1/3)^2} = \frac{9}{4}$$

which agrees with the answer in part (1).

The inverse cannot always be computed explicitly, as the next example shows.

EXAMPLE 2 Let

$$f(x) = 2x + e^x \quad \text{for } x \in \mathbf{R}$$

Find $\frac{d}{dx} f^{-1}(x)\big|_{x=1}$.

Solution In this case, it is not possible to solve $y = 2x + e^x$ for x. Therefore, we must use (4.12) if we wish to compute the derivative of the inverse function at a particular point. Equation (4.12) becomes

$$\frac{d}{dx} f^{-1}(x)\Big|_{x=1} = \frac{1}{f'[f^{-1}(1)]}$$

We need to find $f'(x)$:

$$f'(x) = 2 + e^x$$

Since $f(0) = 1$, it follows that $f^{-1}(1) = 0$, and, hence,

$$\frac{1}{f'[f^{-1}(1)]} = \frac{1}{f'(0)} = \frac{1}{2+1} = \frac{1}{3}$$

■

The next example, in which we again need to use (4.12), involves finding the derivative of the inverse of a trigonometric function.

EXAMPLE 3   Let $f(x) = \tan x$, $-\frac{\pi}{2} < x < \frac{\pi}{2}$. Find $\frac{d}{dx} f^{-1}(x)\big|_{x=1}$.

Solution   Since $f(\frac{\pi}{4}) = \tan \frac{\pi}{4} = 1$, it follows that $f^{-1}(1) = \frac{\pi}{4}$. Recall that $f'(x) = \sec^2 x$. We therefore have

$$\frac{d}{dx} f^{-1}(x)\bigg|_{x=1} = \frac{1}{f'[f^{-1}(1)]} = \frac{1}{f'(\frac{\pi}{4})} = \frac{1}{\sec^2(\frac{\pi}{4})}$$

$$= \cos^2\left(\frac{\pi}{4}\right) = \left(\frac{1}{2}\sqrt{2}\right)^2 = \frac{1}{2}$$

■

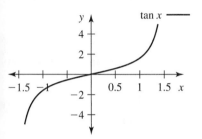

Figure 4.35 The function $f(x) = \tan x$, $(-\frac{\pi}{2}, \frac{\pi}{2})$, is one to one on its domain.

If we define $f(x) = \tan x$ on the domain $(-\frac{\pi}{2}, \frac{\pi}{2})$, then $f(x)$ is one to one, as can be seen from Figure 4.35. (Use the horizontal line test.) The range of $f(x)$ is $(-\infty, \infty)$. We cannot use algebra to solve $y = \tan x$ for x; instead, the inverse of the tangent function gets its own name. It is called $y = \arctan x$ (or $y = \tan^{-1} x$) and its domain is $(-\infty, \infty)$. In the next example, we will find the derivative of $y = \arctan x$, which will turn out to have a surprisingly simple form.

EXAMPLE 4   Let $f(x) = \tan x$, $-\frac{\pi}{2} < x < \frac{\pi}{2}$. Find $\frac{d}{dx} f^{-1}(x)$.

Solution   As mentioned previously, $f^{-1}(x)$ exists, since $f(x)$ is one to one on its domain. Recall that

$$\frac{d}{dx} \tan x = \sec^2 x$$

The inverse of the tangent function is denoted by $\tan^{-1} x$ or $\arctan x$. (Note that $\tan^{-1} x$ is different from $\frac{1}{\tan x}$. The superscript "-1" refers to the function being an inverse function.) We set $y = \arctan x$ (and hence $x = \tan y$). Then

$$\frac{dy}{dx} = \frac{d}{dx} \arctan x = \frac{1}{\frac{dx}{dy}} = \frac{1}{\frac{d}{dy} \tan y} = \frac{1}{\sec^2 y} = \frac{1}{1 + \tan^2 y}$$

where we used the trigonometric identity $\sec^2 y = 1 + \tan^2 y$ to get the denominator in the rightmost term. Since $x = \tan y$, it follows that $x^2 = \tan^2 y$, and, hence,

$$\frac{1}{1 + \tan^2 y} = \frac{1}{1 + x^2}$$

Therefore,

$$\frac{d}{dx} \arctan x = \frac{1}{1 + x^2}$$

■

The result in the preceding example is important, and we summarize it in the following box:

$$\frac{d}{dx} \arctan x = \frac{d}{dx} \tan^{-1} x = \frac{1}{1 + x^2}$$

The derivative of the inverse sine function, $y = \arcsin x$, is discussed in Problem 22 of this section. We list it here:

$$\frac{d}{dx} \arcsin x = \frac{d}{dx} \sin^{-1} x = \frac{1}{\sqrt{1-x^2}}$$

The derivatives of the remaining inverse trigonometric functions are listed in the table of derivatives on the inside back cover of the book.

■ 4.7.2 The Derivative of the Logarithmic Function

We introduced the logarithmic function to the base a, $\log_a x$, as the inverse function of the exponential function a^x (Figures 4.36 and 4.37). We can therefore use the formula for derivatives of inverse functions to find the derivative of $y = \log_a x$. Since

$$\log_a x = \frac{\ln x}{\ln a}$$

and $\ln a$ is a constant, it is enough to find the derivative of $\ln x$ (Figure 4.38). We set $f(x) = e^x$; then $f'(x) = e^x$ and $f^{-1}(x) = \ln x$. Therefore,

$$\frac{d}{dx} \ln x = \frac{d}{dx}[f^{-1}(x)] = \frac{1}{f'[f^{-1}(x)]} = \frac{1}{\exp[\ln x]} = \frac{1}{x}$$

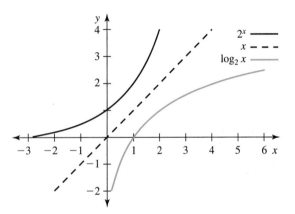

Figure 4.36 The function $y = \log_2 x$ as the inverse function of $y = 2^x$.

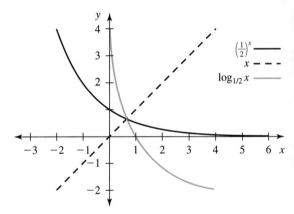

Figure 4.37 The function $y = \log_{1/2} x$ as the inverse function of $y = \left(\frac{1}{2}\right)^x$.

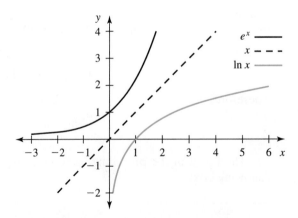

Figure 4.38 The natural logarithm $y = \ln x$ as the inverse function of the natural exponential function $y = e^x$.

We summarize this differentiation rule in the following box:

$$\frac{d}{dx}\ln x = \frac{1}{x}$$

$$\frac{d}{dx}\log_a x = \frac{1}{(\ln a)x}$$

EXAMPLE 5 Find the derivative of $y = \ln(3x)$.

Solution We use the chain rule with $u = g(x) = 3x$ and $f(u) = \ln u$:

$$\frac{dy}{dx} = \frac{dy}{du}\frac{du}{dx} = \frac{1}{u}3 = \frac{3}{3x} = \frac{1}{x}$$

If you are surprised that the factor 3 disappeared, note that

$$y = \ln(3x) = \ln 3 + \ln x$$

Since $\ln 3$ is a constant, its derivative is 0. Hence,

$$\frac{d}{dx}(\ln 3 + \ln x) = \frac{d}{dx}\ln 3 + \frac{d}{dx}\ln x = 0 + \frac{1}{x} = \frac{1}{x}$$ ■

EXAMPLE 6 Find the derivative of $y = \ln(x^2 + 1)$.

Solution We can use the chain rule with $u = g(x) = x^2 + 1$ and $f(u) = \ln u$. We obtain

$$y' = \frac{df}{du}\frac{du}{dx} = \frac{1}{u}2x = \frac{1}{x^2 + 1}2x = \frac{2x}{x^2 + 1}$$ ■

The preceding example is of the form $y = \ln f(x)$. We will frequently encounter such functions; to find their derivatives, we need to use the chain rule, as shown in the following box:

$$\frac{d}{dx}\ln f(x) = \frac{f'(x)}{f(x)}$$

EXAMPLE 7 Differentiate $y = \ln(\sin x)$.

Solution This function is also of the form $y = \ln f(x)$, with $f(x) = \sin x$. Since

$$\frac{d}{dx}\sin x = \cos x$$

it follows that

$$\frac{dy}{dx} = \frac{\cos x}{\sin x} = \cot x$$ ■

EXAMPLE 8 Differentiate

$$y = \ln(\tan x + x)$$

Solution This function is of the form $y = \ln f(x)$ with $f(x) = \tan x + x$. Thus,

$$y' = \frac{\sec^2 x + 1}{\tan x + x}$$ ■

EXAMPLE 9 Differentiate

$$y = \log(2x^3 - 1)$$

Solution This function is of the form $y = \log f(x)$ with $f(x) = 2x^3 - 1$. The logarithm is to base 10. Hence,

$$y' = \frac{1}{\ln 10} \frac{6x^2}{2x^3 - 1}$$

■

■ 4.7.3 Logarithmic Differentiation

In 1695, Leibniz introduced logarithmic differentiation, following Johann Bernoulli's suggestion to find derivatives of functions of the form $y = [f(x)]^x$. Bernoulli generalized this method and published his results two years later. The basic idea is to take logarithms on both sides and then to use implicit differentiation.

EXAMPLE 10 Find $\frac{dy}{dx}$ when $y = x^x$.

Solution We take logarithms on both sides of the equation $y = x^x$:

$$\ln y = \ln x^x$$

Applying properties of the logarithm, we can simplify the right-hand side to $\ln x^x = x \ln x$. We can now differentiate both sides with respect to x. Since y is a function of x, we need to use the chain rule to differentiate $\ln y$ (as we learned in the section on implicit differentiation):

$$\frac{d}{dx}[\ln y] = \frac{d}{dx}[x \ln x]$$

$$\frac{1}{y}\frac{dy}{dx} = 1 \cdot \ln x + x\frac{1}{x}$$

$$\frac{dy}{dx} = y[\ln x + 1]$$

$$\frac{dy}{dx} = (\ln x + 1)x^x$$

■

If the function $y = x^x$ looks strange, write it as

$$y = x^x = \exp[\ln x^x] = \exp[x \ln x]$$

That is, $y = e^{x \ln x}$. We can differentiate this function without using logarithmic differentiation; that is,

$$\frac{dy}{dx} = e^{x \ln x}\frac{d}{dx}(x \ln x)$$

$$= e^{x \ln x}\left(1 \cdot \ln x + x\frac{1}{x}\right)$$

$$= e^{x \ln x}(\ln x + 1)$$

Either approach will give you the correct answer.

EXAMPLE 11 Find the derivative of $y = (\sin x)^x$.

Solution We take logarithms on both sides of the equation and simplify:

$$\ln y = x \ln(\sin x)$$

Differentiating with respect to x yields

$$\frac{d}{dx}[\ln y] = \frac{d}{dx}[x\ln(\sin x)]$$

$$\frac{1}{y}\frac{dy}{dx} = 1\cdot\ln(\sin x) + x\frac{d}{dx}[\ln(\sin x)]$$

$$= \ln(\sin x) + x\frac{\cos x}{\sin x}$$

$$= \ln(\sin x) + x\cot x$$

Hence, after multiplying by y and substituting $(\sin x)^x$ for y, we obtain

$$\frac{dy}{dx} = [\ln(\sin x) + x\cot x](\sin x)^x$$ ■

The next example should convince you that logarithmic differentiation can simplify finding the derivatives of complicated expressions.

EXAMPLE 12   Differentiate

$$y = \frac{e^x x^{3/2}\sqrt{1+x}}{(x^2+3)^4(3x-2)^3}$$

Solution   Without logarithmic differentiation, differentiating y would be rather difficult. Taking logarithms on both sides, however, we can simplify the right-hand side. Note that it is very important that we apply the properties of the logarithm before differentiating, as this will simplify the expressions that we must differentiate. We have

$$\ln y = \ln\frac{e^x x^{3/2}\sqrt{1+x}}{(x^2+3)^4(3x-2)^3}$$

$$= \ln e^x + \ln x^{3/2} + \ln\sqrt{1+x} - \ln(x^2+3)^4 - \ln(3x-2)^3$$

$$= x + \frac{3}{2}\ln x + \frac{1}{2}\ln(1+x) - 4\ln(x^2+3) - 3\ln(3x-2)$$

This no longer looks so daunting, and we can differentiate both sides:

$$\frac{d}{dx}[\ln y] = \frac{d}{dx}\left[x + \frac{3}{2}\ln x + \frac{1}{2}\ln(1+x) - 4\ln(x^2+3) - 3\ln(3x-2)\right]$$

$$\frac{1}{y}\frac{dy}{dx} = 1 + \frac{3}{2}\frac{1}{x} + \frac{1}{2}\frac{1}{1+x} - 4\frac{2x}{x^2+3} - 3\frac{3}{3x-2}$$

Finally, solving for dy/dx yields

$$\frac{dy}{dx} = \left(1 + \frac{3}{2x} + \frac{1}{2(1+x)} - \frac{8x}{x^2+3} - \frac{9}{3x-2}\right)\frac{e^x x^{3/2}\sqrt{1+x}}{(x^2+3)^4(3x-2)^3}$$ ■

We can also use this method to prove the general power rule (as promised in Section 4.3).

Power Rule (General Form) Let $f(x) = x^r$, where r is any real number. Then

$$\frac{d}{dx}(x^r) = rx^{r-1}$$

Proof We set $y = x^r$ and use logarithmic differentiation to obtain

$$\frac{d}{dx}[\ln y] = \frac{d}{dx}[\ln x^r]$$

$$\frac{1}{y}\frac{dy}{dx} = \frac{d}{dx}[r\ln x]$$

$$\frac{1}{y}\frac{dy}{dx} = r\frac{1}{x}$$

Solving for dy/dx yields

$$\frac{dy}{dx} = r\frac{1}{x}y = r\frac{1}{x}x^r = rx^{r-1}$$

■

Section 4.7 Problems

■ 4.7.1

In Problems 1–6, find the inverse of each function and differentiate each inverse in two ways: (i) Differentiate the inverse function directly, and (ii) use (4.12) to find the derivative of the inverse.

1. $f(x) = \sqrt{2x+1}, x \geq -\frac{1}{2}$ **2.** $f(x) = \sqrt{x-1}, x \geq 1$

3. $f(x) = 2x^2 - 1, x \geq 0$ **4.** $f(x) = 3x^2 + 2, x \geq 0$

5. $f(x) = 3 - 2x^3, x \geq 0$ **6.** $f(x) = \dfrac{2x^2 - 1}{x^2 - 1}, x > 1$

In Problems 7–22, use (4.12) to find the derivative of the inverse at the indicated point.

7. Let
$$f(x) = 2x^2 - 2, \quad x \geq 0$$
Find $\frac{d}{dx}f^{-1}(x)\big|_{x=0}$. [Note that $f(1) = 0$.]

8. Let
$$f(x) = -x^3 + 7, \quad x \geq 0$$
Find $\frac{d}{dx}f^{-1}(x)\big|_{x=-1}$. [Note that $f(2) = -1$.]

9. Let
$$f(x) = \sqrt{x+1}, \quad x \geq 0$$
Find $\frac{d}{dx}f^{-1}(x)\big|_{x=2}$. [Note that $f(3) = 2$.]

10. Let
$$f(x) = \sqrt{2+x^2}, \quad x \geq 0$$
Find $\frac{d}{dx}f^{-1}(x)\big|_{x=\sqrt{3}}$. [Note that $f(1) = \sqrt{3}$.]

11. Let
$$f(x) = x + e^x, \quad x \in \mathbb{R}$$
Find $\frac{d}{dx}f^{-1}(x)\big|_{x=1}$. [Note that $f(0) = 1$.]

12. Let
$$f(x) = x + \ln(x+1), \quad x > -1$$
Find $\frac{d}{dx}f^{-1}(x)\big|_{x=0}$. [Note that $f(0) = 0$.]

13. Let
$$f(x) = x - \sin x, \quad x \in \mathbb{R}$$
Find $\frac{d}{dx}f^{-1}(x)\big|_{x=\pi}$. [Note that $f(\pi) = \pi$.]

14. Let
$$f(x) = x - \cos x, \quad x \in \mathbb{R}$$
Find $\frac{d}{dx}f^{-1}(x)\big|_{x=-1}$. [Note that $f(0) = -1$.]

15. Let
$$f(x) = x^2 + \tan x, \quad x \in \left(-\frac{\pi}{2}, \frac{\pi}{2}\right)$$
Find $\frac{d}{dx}f^{-1}(x)\big|_{x=0}$. [Note that $f(0) = 0$.]

16. Let
$$f(x) = x^2 + \tan x, \quad x \in \left(-\frac{\pi}{2}, \frac{\pi}{2}\right)$$
Find $\frac{d}{dx}f^{-1}(x)\big|_{x=\frac{\pi^2}{16}+1}$. [Note that $f(\frac{\pi}{4}) = \frac{\pi^2}{16} + 1$.]

17. Let $f(x) = \ln(\sin x), 0 < x < \pi/2$. Find $\frac{d}{dx}f^{-1}(x)$ at $x = -\ln 2$.

18. Let $f(x) = \ln(\tan x), 0 < x < \pi/2$. Find $\frac{d}{dx}f^{-1}(x)$ at $x = \frac{\ln 3}{2}$.

19. Let $f(x) = x^5 + x + 1, -1 < x < 1$. Find $\frac{d}{dx}f^{-1}(x)$ at $x = 1$.

20. Let $f(x) = e^{-x^2} + x$. Find $\frac{d}{dx}f^{-1}(x)$ at $x = 1$.

21. Let $f(x) = e^{-x^2/2} + 2x$. Find $\frac{d}{dx}f^{-1}(x)$ at $x = 1$.

22. Denote the inverse of $y = \sin x, -\frac{\pi}{2} \leq x \leq \frac{\pi}{2}$, by $y = \arcsin x, -1 \leq x \leq 1$. Show that

$$\frac{d}{dx}\arcsin x = \frac{1}{\sqrt{1-x^2}}, \quad -1 < x < 1$$

■ 4.7.2

In Problems 23–60, differentiate the functions with respect to the independent variable. (Note that log denotes the logarithm to base 10.)

23. $f(x) = \ln(x+1)$ **24.** $f(x) = \ln(3x+4)$

25. $f(x) = \ln(1-2x)$ **26.** $f(x) = \ln(4-3x)$

27. $f(x) = \ln x^2$ **28.** $f(x) = \ln(1-x^2)$

29. $f(x) = \ln(2x^3-x)$ **30.** $f(x) = \ln(1-x^3)$

31. $f(x) = (\ln x)^2$ **32.** $f(x) = (\ln x)^3$

33. $f(x) = (\ln x^2)^2$ **34.** $f(x) = (\ln(1-x^2))^3$

35. $f(x) = \ln\sqrt{x^2+1}$ **36.** $f(x) = \ln\sqrt{2x^2-x}$

37. $f(x) = \ln\dfrac{x}{x+1}$ **38.** $f(x) = \ln\dfrac{2x}{1+x^2}$

39. $f(x) = \ln\dfrac{1-x}{1+2x}$ **40.** $f(x) = \ln\dfrac{x^2-1}{x^3-1}$

41. $f(x) = \exp[x - \ln x]$ **42.** $g(s) = \exp[s^2 + \ln s]$

43. $f(x) = \ln(\sin x)$ **44.** $f(x) = \ln(\cos(1-x))$

45. $f(x) = \ln(\tan x^2)$ **46.** $g(s) = \ln(\sin^2(3s))$

47. $f(x) = x\ln x$ **48.** $f(x) = x^2\ln x^2$

49. $f(x) = \dfrac{\ln x}{x}$ **50.** $h(t) = \dfrac{\ln t}{1+t^2}$

51. $h(t) = \sin(\ln(3t))$ **52.** $h(s) = \ln(\ln s)$

53. $f(x) = \ln|x^2 - 3|$

54. $f(x) = \log(2x^2 - 1)$

55. $f(x) = \log(1 - x^2)$

56. $f(x) = \log(3x^3 - x + 2)$

57. $f(x) = \log(x^3 - 3x)$

58. $f(x) = \log(\sqrt[3]{\tan x^2})$

59. $f(u) = \log_3(3 + u^4)$

60. $g(s) = \log_5(3^s - 2)$

61. Let $f(x) = \ln x$. We know that $f'(x) = \frac{1}{x}$. We will use this fact and the definition of derivatives to show that

$$\lim_{n\to\infty}\left(1 + \frac{1}{n}\right)^n = e$$

(a) Use the definition of the derivative to show that

$$f'(1) = \lim_{h\to 0}\frac{\ln(1 + h)}{h}$$

(b) Show that (a) implies that

$$\ln[\lim_{h\to 0}(1 + h)^{1/h}] = 1$$

(c) Set $h = \frac{1}{n}$ in (b) and let $n \to \infty$. Show that this implies that

$$\lim_{n\to\infty}\left(1 + \frac{1}{n}\right)^n = e$$

62. Assume that $f(x)$ is differentiable with respect to x. Show that

$$\frac{d}{dx}\ln\left[\frac{f(x)}{x}\right] = \frac{f'(x)}{f(x)} - \frac{1}{x}$$

■ **4.7.3**

In Problems 63–74, use logarithmic differentiation to find the first derivative of the given functions.

63. $f(x) = 2x^x$

64. $f(x) = (2x)^{2x}$

65. $f(x) = (\ln x)^x$

66. $f(x) = (\ln x)^{3x}$

67. $f(x) = x^{\ln x}$

68. $f(x) = x^{2\ln x}$

69. $f(x) = x^{1/x}$

70. $f(x) = x^{3/x}$

71. $y = x^{x^x}$

72. $y = (x^x)^x$

73. $y = x^{\cos x}$

74. $y = (\cos x)^x$

75. Differentiate

$$y = \frac{e^{2x}(9x - 2)^3}{\sqrt[4]{(x^2 + 1)(3x^3 - 7)}}$$

76. Differentiate

$$y = \frac{e^{x-1}\sin^2 x}{(x^2 + 5)^{2x}}$$

■ 4.8 Linear Approximation and Error Propagation

Suppose we want to find an approximation to $\ln(1.05)$ without using a calculator. The method for solving this problem will be useful in many other applications. Let's look at the graph of $f(x) = \ln x$ (Figure 4.39). We know that $\ln 1 = 0$, and we see that 1.05 is quite close to 1—so close, in fact, that the curve connecting $(1, 0)$ to $(1.05, \ln 1.05)$ is close to a straight line. This suggests that we should approximate the curve by a straight line—but not just any straight line: We choose the tangent line to the graph of $f(x) = \ln x$ at $x = 1$ (Figure 4.39). We can find the equation of the tangent line without a calculator. We note that the slope of $f(x) = \ln x$ at $x = 1$ is $f'(1) = \frac{1}{x}\big|_{x=1} = 1$. This, together with the point $(1, 0)$, allows us to find the tangent line at $x = 1$:

$$L(x) = f(1) + f'(1)(x - 1) = 0 + (1)(x - 1) = x - 1$$

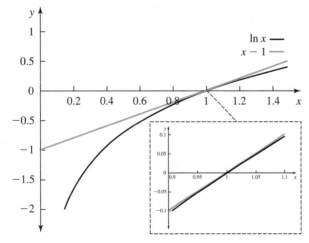

Figure 4.39 The tangent line approximation for $\ln x$ at $x = 1$ to approximate $\ln(1.05)$. When x is close to 1, the tangent line and the graph of $y = \ln x$ are close (see inset).

We call $L(x)$ the **tangent line approximation**, or **the linearization**, of $f(x)$ at $x = 1$. If we evaluate $L(x)$ at $x = 1.05$, we find that $L(1.05) = 1.05 - 1 = 0.05$, which is a good approximation to $\ln 1.05 = 0.048790\ldots$ (Here, we used the calculator to see how close the approximation is to the exact value.)

The Tangent Line Approximation

Assume that $y = f(x)$ is differentiable at $x = a$; then

$$L(x) = f(a) + f'(a)(x - a)$$

is the **tangent line approximation**, or the **linearization**, of f at $x = a$.

Geometrically, the linearization of f at $x = a$, $L(x) = f(a) + f'(a)(x - a)$, is the equation of the tangent line to the graph of $f(x)$ at the point $(a, f(a))$. (See Figure 4.40.)

If $|x - a|$ is sufficiently small, then $f(x)$ can be linearly approximated by $L(x)$; that is,

$$f(x) \approx f(a) + f'(a)(x - a)$$

This approximation is illustrated in Figure 4.41.

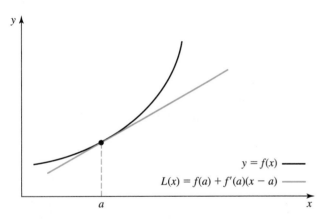

Figure 4.40 The tangent line approximation of $y = f(x)$ at $x = a$.

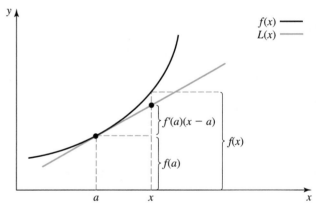

Figure 4.41 The linearization of f at $x = a$ can be used to approximate $f(x)$ for x close to a.

EXAMPLE 1

(a) Find the linear approximation of $f(x) = \sqrt{x}$ at $x = a$, and

(b) use your answer in (a) to find an approximate value of $\sqrt{50}$.

Solution

(a) Since $f(x) = \sqrt{x}$, it follows that $f'(x) = \frac{1}{2\sqrt{x}}$, and the linear approximation at $x = a$ is

$$L(x) = f(a) + f'(a)(x - a)$$
$$= \sqrt{a} + \frac{1}{2\sqrt{a}}(x - a)$$

(See Figure 4.42.)

(b) To find the approximate value of $f(50) = \sqrt{50}$, we need to choose a value for a close to 50 and for which we know $\sqrt{a}$ exactly. Our choice is $a = 49$. We thus approximate $f(50)$ by $L(50)$ with $a = 49$ and find that

$$\sqrt{50} \approx \sqrt{49} + \frac{50 - 49}{2\sqrt{49}} = 7 + \frac{1}{14} \approx 7.0714$$

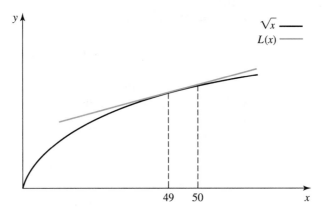

Figure 4.42 The linear approximation of $f(x) = \sqrt{x}$ at $x = 49$ is the line $y = L(x)$.

Using a calculator to compute $\sqrt{50} = 7.0711\ldots$, we see that the error in the linear approximation is quite small. ■

EXAMPLE 2   Find the linear approximation of $f(x) = \sin x$ at $x = 0$.

Solution   Since $f'(x) = \cos x$, it follows that

$$L(x) = f(0) + f'(0)(x - 0)$$
$$= \sin 0 + (\cos 0)x = x$$

(Figure 4.43). That is, for small values of x, we can approximate $\sin x$ by x. This approximation is often used in physics. (Note that x is measured in radians.) ■

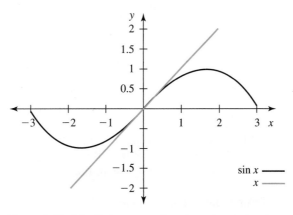

Figure 4.43 The linear approximation of $y = \sin x$ is the line $y = x$.

EXAMPLE 3   Let $N(t)$ be the size of a population at time t, and assume that the growth rate dN/dt of the population is given by

$$\frac{dN}{dt} = f(N)$$

where $f(N)$ is a differentiable function with $f(0) = 0$. Find the linearization of the growth rate at $N = 0$.

Solution   We need to find the tangent line approximation of $f(N)$ at $N = 0$. If we denote the linearization of $f(N)$ by $L(N)$, we obtain

$$L(N) = f(0) + f'(0)N$$

Now, $f(0) = 0$. If we set $r = f'(0)$, we find that, for N close to 0,

$$\frac{dN}{dt} \approx rN$$

The preceding formula shows that the population changes approximately exponentially when its size is small. This behavior is observed, for instance, when bacteria are grown in a nutrient-rich environment at a low population density.

We choose $f(0) = 0$ for biological reasons: When the population size is 0, the growth rate should be 0; otherwise, we would have spontaneous creation if $f(0) > 0$, or the population size would become negative if $f(0) < 0$. ■

EXAMPLE 4

Let $N(t)$ (measured in millions) be the size of a bacterial population at time t, and assume that the per capita growth rate is equal to 2%. We can express this statement in a differential equation, namely,

$$\frac{1}{N}\frac{dN}{dt} = 0.02$$

Suppose we know that at time $t = 10$ the size of the population is 250,000,000; that is, $N(10) = 250$ (since we measure the population size in millions). Use a linear approximation to predict the approximate population size at time $t = 10.1$.

Solution

To predict the population size at time 10.1, we use the following linearization of $N(t)$ at $t = 10$:

$$L(t) = N(10) + N'(10)(t - 10)$$

To evaluate $L(t)$ at $t = 10.1$, we need to find $N'(10)$.

Using the differential equation, we find that

$$N'(t) = (0.02)N(t)$$

When $t = 10$, we obtain

$$N'(10) = (0.02)N(10) = (0.02)(250) = 5$$

Hence,

$$L(10.1) = N(10) + N'(10)(10.1 - 10)$$
$$= 250 + (5)(0.1) = 250.5$$

Thus, we predict that the population size at time 10.1 is approximately 250,500,000. Note that this approximation is good only if the time at which we want to predict the population size is very close to the time at which we know the population size. ■

Error Propagation Linear approximations are used in problems of **error propagation**. Suppose that you wish to determine the surface area of a spherical cell. Since the surface area S of a sphere with radius r is given by

$$S = 4\pi r^2$$

it suffices to measure the radius r of the cell. If your measurement of the radius is accurate within 3%, how does this affect the accuracy of the surface area?

First we must discuss what it means for a measurement to be accurate within a certain percentage. Suppose that x_0 is the true value of an observation and x is the measured value. Then $|\Delta x| = |x - x_0|$ is the **absolute error**, or tolerance, in measurement. The **relative error** is defined as $|\Delta x / x_0|$ and the **percentage error** as $100|\Delta x / x_0|$.

Returning to our example, let's find the error that arises in computing the surface area. We start with the absolute error of the surface area,

$$|\Delta S| = |S(r_0 + \Delta r) - S(r_0)|$$

where r_0 is the true radius and $|\Delta r|$ is the absolute error in the measurement of the radius. We approximate $S(r_0+\Delta r) - S(r_0)$ by its linear approximation $S'(r_0)\Delta r$; that is,

$$\Delta S \approx S'(r_0)\Delta r$$

Since $S'(r) = 8\pi r$, the percentage error in the measurement of the surface area is

$$100\left|\frac{\Delta S}{S(r_0)}\right| \approx 100\left|\frac{S'(r_0)\Delta r}{S(r_0)}\right| = 100\left|\frac{\Delta r}{r_0}\right|\left|\frac{S'(r_0)r_0}{S(r_0)}\right|$$

$$= \underbrace{100\left|\frac{\Delta r}{r_0}\right|}_{=3}\underbrace{\left|\frac{8\pi r_0^2}{4\pi r_0^2}\right|}_{=2} = 6$$

because $100|\Delta r/r_0| = 3$. In other words, the surface area is (approximately) accurate within 6% if the radius is accurate within 3%. Where the doubling of the percentage error comes from can be seen in the next example.

EXAMPLE 5   Suppose that you wish to determine $f(x)$ from a measurement of x. If $f(x)$ is given by a power function, namely, $f(x) = cx^s$, how does an error in the measurement of x propagate?

Solution   Since $f'(x) = csx^{s-1}$, we have

$$\Delta f \approx f'(x)\Delta x = csx^{s-1}\Delta x$$

The percentage error $100\left|\frac{\Delta f}{f}\right|$ is therefore related to the percentage error $100\left|\frac{\Delta x}{x}\right|$ as follows:

$$100\left|\frac{\Delta f}{f}\right| \approx 100\left|\frac{f'(x)\Delta x}{f(x)}\right| = 100\left|\frac{\Delta x}{x}\right|\left|\frac{f'(x)x}{f(x)}\right|$$

$$= 100\left|\frac{\Delta x}{x}\right|\left|\frac{csx^s}{cx^s}\right| = \left(100\left|\frac{\Delta x}{x}\right|\right)|s|$$

In our previous example, $s = 2$; hence, the percentage error in the surface area measurement is twice the percentage error in the radius measurement.   ■

EXAMPLE 6   **Allometric Growth** Suppose that you wish to estimate the total leaf area of a tree in a certain plot. Experimental data obtained from the plot you are studying (Niklas, 1994) indicate that

$$[\text{leaf area}] \propto [\text{stem diameter}]^{1.84}$$

Instead of trying to measure the total leaf area directly, you measure the stem diameter and then use the scaling relationship to estimate the total leaf area. How accurately must you measure the stem diameter if you want to estimate the leaf area within an error of 10%?

Solution   We denote the leaf area by A and stem diameter by d. Then

$$A(d) = cd^{1.84}$$

where c is the constant of proportionality. An error in measurement of d is propagated as

$$\Delta A \approx A'(d)\Delta d = c(1.84)d^{0.84}\Delta d$$

The percentage error $100\left|\frac{\Delta A}{A}\right|$ is related to the percentage error $100\left|\frac{\Delta d}{d}\right|$ as

$$100\left|\frac{\Delta A}{A}\right| \approx 100\left|\frac{A'(d)\Delta d}{A(d)}\right| = 100\left|\frac{\Delta d}{d}\right|\left|\frac{A'(d)d}{A(d)}\right|$$

$$= 100\left|\frac{\Delta d}{d}\right|\left|\frac{c(1.84)d^{0.84}d}{cd^{1.84}}\right| = \left(100\left|\frac{\Delta d}{d}\right|\right)(1.84)$$

We require that $100 \left| \frac{\Delta A}{A} \right| = 10$. Hence,

$$10 = (1.84)\left(100\left|\frac{\Delta d}{d}\right|\right)$$

or

$$100\left|\frac{\Delta d}{d}\right| = \frac{10}{1.84} = 5.4$$

That is, we must measure the stem diameter to within an error of 5.4%.

Using the result of Example 5, we could have found the same error immediately. Since

$$A(d) = cd^{1.84}$$

we get $s = 1.84$, where s is the exponent defined in Example 5. Using

$$100\left|\frac{\Delta A}{A}\right| = |s|\left(100\left|\frac{\Delta d}{d}\right|\right)$$

we obtain

$$100\left|\frac{\Delta d}{d}\right| = \frac{1}{|s|}\left(100\left|\frac{\Delta A}{A}\right|\right) = \frac{10}{1.84} = 5.4$$

as before. ∎

EXAMPLE 7

Suppose that you wish to determine the percentage error of $f(x)$ from a measurement of x, where $f(x) = \ln x$, $x = 10$, and the percentage error for x is equal to 2%. Find the percentage error of $f(x)$.

Solution

The function $f(x)$ is not a power function, so there is no simple rule. We find that

$$100\frac{\Delta f}{f} \approx 100\frac{f'(x)\Delta x}{f(x)}$$

Since we know $100\left|\frac{\Delta x}{x}\right|$, we multiply and divide the right-hand side by x and rearrange terms to get

$$100\frac{f'(x)\Delta x}{f(x)} = 100\frac{\Delta x}{x}\frac{xf'(x)}{f(x)}$$

Since $f'(x) = 1/x$, at $x = 10$ we obtain

$$100\left|\frac{\Delta x}{x}\right|\left|\frac{xf'(x)}{f(x)}\right|\Bigg|_{x=10} = 2\frac{(10)(1/10)}{\ln 10} = \frac{2}{\ln 10} \approx 0.869$$

Thus, the percentage error of f is approximately 0.9%. ∎

Section 4.8 Problems

In Problems 1–10, use the formula

$$f(x) \approx f(a) + f'(a)(x-a)$$

to approximate the value of the given function. Then compare your result with the value you get from a calculator.

1. $\sqrt{65}$; let $f(x) = \sqrt{x}$, $a = 64$, and $x = 65$
2. $\sqrt{35}$; let $f(x) = \sqrt{x}$, $a = 36$, and $x = 35$
3. $\sqrt[3]{124}$
4. $(7.9)^3$
5. $(0.99)^{25}$
6. $\tan(0.01)$

7. $\sin\left(\frac{\pi}{2} + 0.02\right)$
8. $\cos\left(\frac{\pi}{4} - 0.01\right)$
9. $\ln(1.01)$
10. $e^{0.1}$

In Problems 11–30, approximate $f(x)$ at a by the linear approximation

$$L(x) = f(a) + f'(a)(x-a)$$

11. $f(x) = \frac{1}{1+x}$ at $a = 0$
12. $f(x) = \frac{1}{1-x}$ at $a = 0$
13. $f(x) = \frac{2}{1+x}$ at $a = 1$
14. $f(x) = \frac{1}{3-2x}$ at $a = 2$

. $f(x) = \dfrac{1}{(1+x)^2}$ at $a = 0$ **16.** $f(x) = \dfrac{1}{(1-x)^2}$ at $a = 0$

. $f(x) = \ln(1+x)$ at $a = 0$ **18.** $f(x) = \ln(1+2x)$ at $a = 0$

. $f(x) = \log x$ at $a = 1$ **20.** $f(x) = \log(1+x^2)$ at $a = 0$

. $f(x) = e^x$ at $a = 0$ **22.** $f(x) = e^{2x}$ at $a = 0$

. $f(x) = e^{-x}$ at $a = 0$ **24.** $f(x) = e^{-3x}$ at $a = 0$

. $f(x) = e^{x-1}$ at $a = 1$ **26.** $f(x) = e^{2x+1}$ at $a = -1/2$

. $f(x) = (1+x)^{-n}$ at $a = 0$. (Assume that n is a positive integer.)

. $f(x) = (1-x)^{-n}$ at $a = 0$. (Assume that n is a positive integer.)

. $f(x) = \sqrt{1+x^2}$ at $a = 0$

. $f(x) = \left(1+\dfrac{1}{x}\right)^{1/4}$ at $a = 1$

1. Population Growth Suppose that the per capita growth rate of a population is 3%; that is, if $N(t)$ denotes the population size at time t, then

$$\frac{1}{N}\frac{dN}{dt} = 0.03$$

Suppose also that the population size at time $t = 4$ is equal to 00. Use a linear approximation to compute the population size at time $t = 4.1$.

2. Population Growth Suppose that the per capita growth rate of a population is 2%; that is, if $N(t)$ denotes the population size at time t, then

$$\frac{1}{N}\frac{dN}{dt} = 0.02$$

Suppose also that the population size at time $t = 2$ is equal to 0. Use a linear approximation to compute the population size at time $t = 2.1$.

3. Plant Biomass Suppose that the specific growth rate of a plant is 1%; that is, if $B(t)$ denotes the biomass at time t, then

$$\frac{1}{B(t)}\frac{dB}{dt} = 0.01$$

Suppose that the biomass at time $t = 1$ is equal to 5 grams. Use a linear approximation to compute the biomass at time $t = 1.1$.

4. Plant Biomass Suppose that a certain plant is grown along a gradient ranging from nitrogen-poor to nitrogen-rich soil. Experimental data show that the average mass per plant grown in a soil with a total nitrogen content of 1000 mg nitrogen per kg of soil is 2.7 g and the rate of change of the average mass per plant at this nitrogen level is 1.05×10^{-3} g per mg change in total nitrogen per kg soil. Use a linear approximation to predict the average mass per plant grown in a soil with a total nitrogen content of 1100 mg nitrogen per kg of soil.

In Problems 35–40, a measurement error in x affects the accuracy of the value $f(x)$. In each case, determine an interval of the form

$$[f(x) - \Delta f, f(x) + \Delta f]$$

that reflects the measurement error Δx. In each problem, the quantities given are $f(x)$ and $x =$ true value of $x \pm |\Delta x|$.

35. $f(x) = 2x$, $x = 1 \pm 0.1$

36. $f(x) = 1 - 3x$, $x = -2 \pm 0.3$

37. $f(x) = 3x^2$, $x = 2 \pm 0.1$

38. $f(x) = \sqrt{x}$, $x = 10 \pm 0.5$

39. $f(x) = e^x$, $x = 2 \pm 0.2$

40. $f(x) = \sin x$, $x = -1 \pm 0.05$

In Problems 41–44, assume that the measurement of x is accurate within 2%. In each case, determine the error Δf in the calculation of f and find the percentage error $100\frac{\Delta f}{f}$. The quantities $f(x)$ and the true value of x are given.

41. $f(x) = 4x^3$, $x = 1.5$ **42.** $f(x) = x^{1/4}$, $x = 10$

43. $f(x) = \ln x$, $x = 20$ **44.** $f(x) = \dfrac{1}{1+x}$, $x = 4$

45. The volume V of a spherical cell of radius r is given by

$$V(r) = \frac{4}{3}\pi r^3$$

If you can determine the radius to within an accuracy of 3%, how accurate is your calculation of the volume?

46. Poiseuille's Law The speed v of blood flowing along the central axis of an artery of radius R is given by Poiseuille's law,

$$v(R) = cR^2$$

where c is a constant. If you can determine the radius of the artery to within an accuracy of 5%, how accurate is your calculation of the speed?

47. Allometric Growth Suppose that you are studying reproduction in moss. The scaling relation

$$N \propto L^{2.11}$$

has been found (Niklas, 1994) between the number of moss spores (N) and the capsule length (L). This relation is not very accurate, but it turns out that it suffices for your purpose. To estimate the number of moss spores, you measure the capsule length. If you wish to estimate the number of moss spores within an error of 5%, how accurately must you measure the capsule length?

48. Tilman's Resource Model Suppose that the rate of growth of a plant in a certain habitat depends on a single resource—for instance, nitrogen. Assume that the growth rate $f(R)$ depends on the resource level R in accordance with the formula

$$f(R) = a\frac{R}{k+R}$$

where a and k are constants. Express the percentage error of the growth rate, $100\frac{\Delta f}{f}$, as a function of the percentage error of the resource level, $100\frac{\Delta R}{R}$.

49. Chemical Reaction The reaction rate $R(x)$ of the irreversible reaction

$$A + B \rightarrow AB$$

is a function of the concentration x of the product AB and is given by

$$R(x) = k(a-x)(b-x)$$

where k is a constant, a is the concentration of A at the beginning of the reaction, and b is the concentration of B at the beginning of the reaction. Express the percentage error of the reaction rate, $100\frac{\Delta R}{R}$, as a function of the percentage error of the concentration x, $100\frac{\Delta x}{x}$.

Chapter 4 Key Terms

Discuss the following definitions and concepts:

1. Derivative, formal definition
2. Difference quotient
3. Secant line and tangent line
4. Instantaneous rate of change
5. Average rate of change
6. Differential equation
7. Differentiability and continuity
8. Power rule
9. Basic rules of differentiation
10. Product rule
11. Quotient rule
12. Chain rule
13. Implicit function
14. Implicit differentiation
15. Related rates
16. Higher derivatives
17. Derivatives of trigonometric functions
18. Derivatives of exponential function.
19. Derivatives of inverse and logarithmic functions
20. Logarithmic differentiation
21. Tangent line approximation
22. Error propagation
23. Absolute error, relative error, percentage error

Chapter 4 Review Problems

In Problems 1–8, differentiate with respect to the independent variable.

1. $f(x) = -3x^4 + \dfrac{2}{\sqrt{x}} + 1$

2. $g(x) = \dfrac{1}{\sqrt{x^3 + 4}}$

3. $h(t) = \left(\dfrac{1-t}{1+t}\right)^{1/3}$

4. $f(x) = (x^2 + 1)e^{-x}$

5. $f(x) = e^{2x} \sin\left(\dfrac{\pi}{2}x\right)$

6. $g(s) = \dfrac{\sin(3s + 1)}{\cos(3s)}$

7. $f(x) = 2\dfrac{\ln(x+1)}{\ln x^2}$

8. $g(x) = e^{-x} \ln(x + 1)$

In Problems 9–12, find the first and second derivatives of the given functions.

9. $f(x) = e^{-x^2/2}$

10. $g(x) = \tan(x^2 + 1)$

11. $h(x) = \dfrac{x}{x+1}$

12. $f(x) = \dfrac{e^{-x}}{e^{-x} + 1}$

In Problems 13–16, find dy/dx.

13. $x^2 y - y^2 x = \sin x$

14. $e^{x^2 + y^2} = 2x$

15. $\ln(x - y) = 2x$

16. $\tan(x - y) = x^2$

In Problems 17–19, find dy/dx and d^2y/dx^2.

17. $x^2 + y^2 = 16$

18. $x = \tan y$

19. $e^y = \ln x$

20. Assume that x is a function of t. Find $\frac{dy}{dt}$ when $y = \cos x$ and $\frac{dx}{dt} = \sqrt{3}$ for $x = \frac{\pi}{3}$.

21. Velocity A flock of birds passes directly overhead, flying horizontally at an altitude of 100 feet and a speed of 6 feet per second. How quickly is the distance between you and the birds increasing when the distance is 320 feet? (You are on the ground and are not moving.)

22. Find the derivative of

$$y = \ln|\cos x|$$

23. Suppose that $f(x)$ is differentiable. Find an expression for the derivative of each of the following functions:
(a) $y = e^{f(x)}$ **(b)** $y = \ln f(x)$ **(c)** $y = [f(x)]^2$

24. Find the tangent line and the normal line to $y = \ln(x + 1)$ at $x = 1$.

25. Suppose that

$$f(x) = \dfrac{x^2}{1 + x^2}, \quad x \geq 0$$

(a) Use a graphing calculator to graph $f(x)$ for $x \geq 0$. Note that the graph is S shaped.

(b) Find a line through the origin that touches the graph of $f(x)$ at some point $(c, f(c))$ with $c > 0$. This is the tangent line $(c, f(c))$ that goes through the origin. Graph the tangent line the same coordinate system that you used in (a).

In Problems 26–29, find an equation for the tangent line to the curv at the specified point.

26. $y = (\sin x)^{\cos x}$ at $x = \dfrac{\pi}{2}$

27. $y = e^{-x^2} \cos x$ at $x = \dfrac{\pi}{3}$

28. $x^2 + y = e^y$ at $x = \sqrt{e - 1}$

29. $x \ln y = y \ln x$ at $x = 1$

30. In Review Problem 17 of Chapter 2, we introduced the following hyperbolic functions:

$$\sinh x = \dfrac{e^x - e^{-x}}{2}, \quad x \in \mathbf{R}$$

$$\cosh x = \dfrac{e^x + e^{-x}}{2}, \quad x \in \mathbf{R}$$

$$\tanh x = \dfrac{e^x - e^{-x}}{e^x + e^{-x}}, \quad x \in \mathbf{R}$$

(a) Show that

$$\dfrac{d}{dx}\sinh x = \cosh x$$

and

$$\dfrac{d}{dx}\cosh x = \sinh x$$

(b) Use the facts that

$$\tanh x = \dfrac{\sinh x}{\cosh x}$$

and

$$\cosh^2 x - \sinh^2 x = 1$$

together with your results in (a) to show that

$$\dfrac{d}{dx}\tanh x = \dfrac{1}{\cosh^2 x}$$

31. Find a second-degree polynomial

$$p(x) = ax^2 + bx + c$$

with $p(-1) = 6$, $p'(1) = 8$, and $p''(0) = 4$.

32. Use the geometric interpretation of the derivative to find the equations of the tangent lines to the curve

$$x^2 + y^2 = 1$$

at the following points:
(a) $(1, 0)$ **(b)** $\left(\frac{1}{2}, \frac{1}{2}\sqrt{3}\right)$

(c) $\left(-\frac{1}{2}\sqrt{2}, -\frac{1}{2}\sqrt{2}\right)$ **(d)** $(0, -1)$

33. Distance and Velocity Geradedorf[3] and Straightville are connected by a very straight, but rather hilly, road. Biking from Geradedorf to Straightville, your position at time t (measured in hours) is given by the function

$$s(t) = 3\pi t + 3(1 - \cos(\pi t))$$

for $0 \le t \le 5.5$, where $s(t)$ is measured in miles.
(a) Use a graphing calculator to convince yourself that you didn't backtrack during your trip. How can you check this? Assuming that your trip takes 5.5 hours, find the distance between Geradedorf and Straightville.

(b) Find the velocity $v(t)$ and the acceleration $a(t)$.

(c) Use a graphing calculator to graph $s(t)$, $v(t)$, and $a(t)$. In (a), you used the function $s(t)$ to conclude that you didn't backtrack during your trip. Can you use any of the other two functions to answer the question of backtracking? Explain your answer.

(d) Assuming that you slow down going uphill and speed up going downhill, how many peaks and valleys does this road have?

34. Distance and Velocity Suppose your position at time t on a straight road is given by

$$s(t) = \cos(\pi t)$$

for $0 \le t \le 2$, where t is measured in hours.
(a) What is your position at the beginning and end of your trip?

(b) Use a graphing calculator to help describe your trip in words.

(c) What is the total distance you have traveled?

(d) Determine your velocity and your acceleration during the trip. When is your velocity equal to 0? Relate this velocity to your position, and explain what it means.

35. Population Growth In one very simple population model, the growth rate at time t depends on the number of individuals at time $t - T$, where T is a positive constant. (That is, the model incorporates a time delay into the birthrate.) This assumption is useful, for instance, if one wishes to take into account the fact that individuals must mature before reproducing.

---

(3) Those who are curious may look up the words *gerade* and *Dorf* in a German–English dictionary.

Denote the size of the population at time t by $N(t)$, and assume that

$$\frac{dN}{dt} = \frac{\pi}{2T}(K - N(t - T)) \qquad (4.13)$$

where K and T are positive constants.
(a) Show that

$$N(t) = K + A\cos\frac{\pi t}{2T}$$

is a solution of (4.13).
(b) Graph $N(t)$ for $K = 100$, $A = 50$, and $T = 1$.
(c) Explain in words how the size of the population changes over time.

36. Radioactive Decay We denote by $W(t)$ the amount of a radioactive material left at time t if the initial amount present was $W(0) = W_0$.
(a) Show that

$$W(t) = W_0 e^{-\lambda t}$$

solves the differential equation

$$\frac{dW}{dt} = -\lambda W(t)$$

(b) Show that if you graph $W(t)$ on semilog paper, then the result is a straight line.

(c) Use your result in (b) to explain why

$$\frac{d \ln W(t)}{dt} = \text{constant}$$

Determine the constant, and relate it to the graph in (b).
(d) Show that

$$\frac{d \ln W(t)}{dt} = \text{constant}$$

implies that

$$\frac{dW}{dt} \propto W(t)$$

37. Allometric Growth In Example 17 of Subsection 4.4.3, we introduced an allometric relationship between skull length (in cm) and backbone length (in cm) of ichthyosaurs, a group of extinct marine reptiles. The relationship is

$$S = (1.162)B^{0.933}$$

where S and B denote skull length and backbone length, respectively. Suppose that you found only the skull of an individual and that, on the basis of the skull length, you wish to estimate the backbone length of this specimen. How accurately must you measure skull length if you want to estimate backbone length to within an error of 10%?

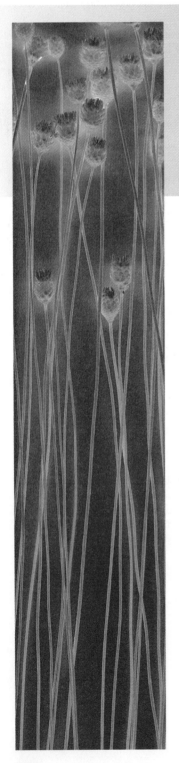

5 | Applications of Differentiation

LEARNING OBJECTIVES

Differentiation is an important tool for understanding the behavior of functions. In this chapter, we will learn how to

- deduce the behavior of functions by using differentiation;
- sketch the graphs of functions on the basis of their behavior;
- apply differentiation for optimization;
- use differentiation to investigate the long-term behavior of difference equations; and
- find antiderivatives.

■ 5.1 Extrema and the Mean-Value Theorem

The primary focus of this chapter is how calculus can help us to understand the behavior of functions. Points where a function is smallest or largest, called extrema, are of particular importance. This section defines extrema, gives conditions that guarantee extrema (via the extreme-value theorem), and provides a characterization of extrema (Fermat's theorem). Fermat's theorem will be crucial in establishing the mean-value theorem, a result that can be understood graphically. The mean-value theorem has far-reaching consequences that arise in later sections, where we learn methods for characterizing the behavior of functions.

■ 5.1.1 The Extreme-Value Theorem

Suppose that you measure the depth of a creek along a transect between two points A and B (see Figure 5.1). Looking at the profile of the creek, you see that there is a location of maximum depth and a location of minimum depth. The existence of such locations is the content of the extreme-value theorem. To formalize the theorem, we must introduce some terminology.

Figure 5.1 A transect of a creek between the points A and B.

> **Definition** Let f be a function defined on the set D that contains the number c. Then
>
> $$f \text{ has a global (or absolute) maximum at } x = c \text{ if}$$
> $$f(c) \geq f(x) \quad \text{for all } x \in D$$
>
> and
>
> $$f \text{ has a global (or absolute) minimum at } x = c \text{ if}$$
> $$f(c) \leq f(x) \quad \text{for all } x \in D$$

The following result gives conditions under which global maxima and global minima, collectively called **global** (or **absolute**) **extrema**, exist:

> **The Extreme-Value Theorem** If f is continuous on a closed interval $[a, b]$, $-\infty < a < b < \infty$, then f has a global maximum and a global minimum on $[a, b]$.

The proof of the extreme-value theorem is beyond the scope of this text and will be omitted. However, the result is quite intuitive, and we illustrate it in Figures 5.2 and 5.3. Figure 5.2 shows that a function may attain its extreme values at the endpoints of the interval $[a, b]$, whereas in Figure 5.3 the extreme values are attained in the interior of the interval $[a, b]$. The function must be continuous and defined on a closed interval in order for it to have global maxima and global minima. But note that the extreme-value theorem tells us only that global extrema exist, not where they are. Furthermore, they need not be unique, meaning that a function can have more than one global maximum or global minimum.

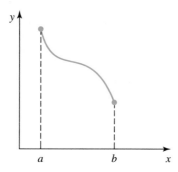

Figure 5.2 Extreme values at the endpoint.

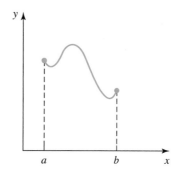

Figure 5.3 Extreme values in the interior.

EXAMPLE 1

Optimal Strategy Suppose a plant has two reproductive strategies, one asexual by clonal reproduction and the other sexual by seed production. The plant's fitness depends on how it allocates its resources to the two strategies. Suppose that the plant allocates a fixed amount of resources to reproduction, a fraction p of which is allocated to clonal reproduction ($0 \le p \le 1$) and a fraction $1 - p$ to sexual reproduction. Denote by $f(p)$ the plant's fitness as a function of p. Assuming that $f(p)$ is a continuous function, why is there a strategy of resource allocation (called an optimal strategy) that maximizes the plant's fitness?

Solution

According to the extreme-value theorem, since $f(p)$ is continuous on the closed interval $[0, 1]$, $f(p)$ has a global maximum (and a global minimum) on $[0, 1]$. The global maximum represents the optimal strategy. Note that the theorem guarantees only the existence of an optimal strategy; it does not tell us *which* strategy is optimal. Furthermore, there could be more than one global maximum, meaning that there could be more than one optimal strategy of resource allocation. ■

Figure 5.2 illustrates the importance of one of the assumptions in the extreme-value theorem, namely, that the interval is *closed*. If the interval from a to b in Figure 5.2 did not include the endpoints, we would have neither a global maximum nor a global minimum.

The next two examples illustrate that the theorem cannot be used if either f is discontinuous or the interval is not closed.

Let

$$f(x) = \begin{cases} 2x & \text{if } 0 \le x < 2 \\ 3 - x & \text{if } 2 \le x \le 3 \end{cases}$$

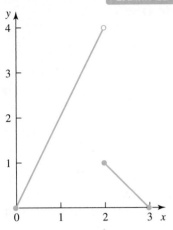

Figure 5.4 The graph of $f(x)$ in Example 2.

Note that $f(x)$ is defined on a *closed* interval, namely, [0, 3]. However, f is discontinuous at $x = 2$, as can be seen in Figure 5.4. The graph of $f(x)$ shows that there is no value $c \in [0, 3]$ where $f(c)$ attains a global maximum. Do not be tempted to say that there should be a global maximum close to $x = 2$: For any candidate for a global maximum that you might come up with, you will be able to find a point whose y-coordinate exceeds the y-coordinate of your previous candidate. Try it! The reason for this is that

$$\lim_{x \to 2^-} f(x) = 4$$

but the function f takes on the value 1 at $x = 2$. We conclude that the function does not have a global maximum. It does, however, have global minima, at $x = 0$ and $x = 3$, where $f(x)$ takes on the value 0. (This is a function that has more than one global minimum.) ■

Let

$$f(x) = x \qquad \text{for } 0 < x < 1$$

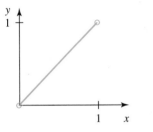

Figure 5.5 The graph of $f(x)$ in Example 3.

Note that $f(x)$ is continuous on its domain, (0, 1), but is *not* defined on a closed interval (Figure 5.5). The function $f(x)$ attains neither a global maximum nor a global minimum. Although

$$\lim_{x \to 0^+} f(x) = 0 \qquad \text{and} \qquad \lim_{x \to 1^-} f(x) = 1$$

and $0 < f(x) < 1$ for all $x \in (0, 1)$, there is no number c in the open interval (0, 1) where $f(c) = 0$ or $f(c) = 1$. ■

■ 5.1.2 Local Extrema

We will now discuss local (or relative) extrema, which are points where a graph is higher or lower than all *nearby* points. This discussion will allow us to identify the peaks and the valleys of the graph of a function. (See Figure 5.6.) The graph of the function in Figure 5.6 has three peaks—at $x = a, c,$ and e—and two valleys—at $x = b$ and d. A peak (or local maximum) has the property that the graph is lower nearby; a valley (or local minimum) has the property that the graph is higher nearby.

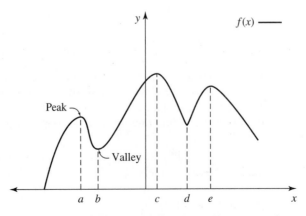

Figure 5.6 The function $y = f(x)$ has valleys at $x = b$ and d and peaks at $x = a, c,$ and e.

The formal definitions follow (see Figures 5.7 and 5.8):

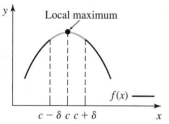

Figure 5.7 The function $y = f(x)$ has a local maximum at $x = c$.

> A function f defined on a set D has a **local** (or **relative**) **maximum** at a point c if there exists a $\delta > 0$ such that
>
> $$f(c) \geq f(x) \qquad \text{for all } x \in (c - \delta, c + \delta) \cap D$$
>
> A function f defined on a set D has a **local** (or **relative**) **minimum** at a point c if there exists a $\delta > 0$ such that
>
> $$f(c) \leq f(x) \qquad \text{for all } x \in (c - \delta, c + \delta) \cap D$$

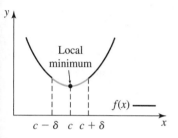

Figure 5.8 The function $y = f(x)$ has a local minimum at $x = c$.

Local maxima and local minima are collectively called local (or relative) extrema. If D is an interval and c is in the interior of D (i.e., not a boundary point), then the definitions simplify: The function f has a local maximum at c if there exists an open interval I such that $f(c) \geq f(x)$ for all $x \in I$; likewise, the function f has a local minimum at c if there exists an open interval I such that $f(c) \leq f(x)$ for all $x \in I$. In the definitions in the preceding box, we wrote $(c - \delta, c + \delta) \cap D$. If c is an interior point of D, δ can be chosen small enough so that $(c - \delta, c + \delta)$ is contained in D and we can set $I = (c - \delta, c + \delta)$. Intersecting the interval $(c - \delta, c + \delta)$ with D becomes important when c is a boundary point, as we will see in Example 4.

We examine local and global extrema in the next two examples; the discussion is based on looking at the graphs of functions. In the first example, we consider a function that is defined on a closed interval; this allows us to compute the value of the function at both endpoints of its domain. In the second example, we consider a function that is defined on a half-open interval; thus, the value of the function can be computed at one endpoint of its domain, but not at the other endpoint.

EXAMPLE 4 Let

$$f(x) = (x - 1)^2(x + 2) \quad \text{for } -2 \leq x \leq 3$$

(a) Use the graph of $f(x)$ to find all local extrema.

(b) Find the global extrema.

Solution **(a)** The graph of $f(x)$ is illustrated in Figure 5.9. The function f is defined on the closed interval $[-2, 3]$. We begin with local extrema that occur at interior points of the domain $D = [-2, 3]$; looking at the figure, we see that a local maximum occurs at $x = -1$, as there are no greater values of f nearby. That is, we can find a small interval I about $x = -1$ so that $f(-1) \geq f(x)$ for all $x \in I$. For instance, we can choose $\delta = 0.1$ in the preceding definition and obtain $I = (-1.1, -0.9)$ (Figure 5.10).

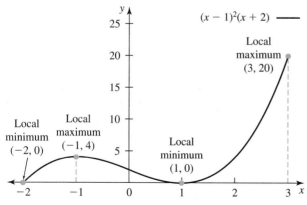

Figure 5.9 The graph of $f(x) = (x - 1)^2(x + 2)$ for $-2 \leq x \leq 3$ in Example 4.

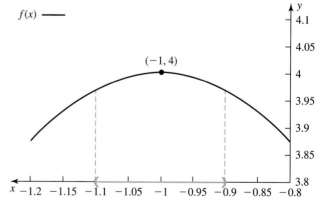

Figure 5.10 The graph of $f(x) = (x - 1)^2(x + 2)$ near $x = -1$. The point $(-1, 4)$ is a local maximum: $f(-1) \geq f(x)$ for all nearby x in the domain of f.

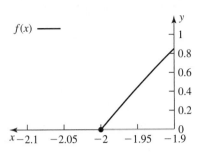

$f(x)$ ——

Figure 5.11 The graph of $f(x) = (x-1)^2(x+2)$ near $x = -2$. The point $(-2, 0)$ is a local minimum: $f(-2) \le f(x)$ for all nearby x in the domain of f.

There is a local minimum at $x = 1$, since there are no smaller values of f nearby. This time, we need to find a small interval about $x = 1$ so that $f(1) \le f(x)$ for all $x \in I$; for example, $I = (0.9, 1.1)$.

A local minimum also occurs at $x = -2$, one of the endpoints of the domain of f. As discussed in the definition of a local minimum, we require an interval I about c such that $f(c) \le f(x)$ for all $x \in I \cap D$, where D is the domain of the function. If c is an interior point, we can always choose I small enough so that $I \subset D$ and, therefore, $I \cap D = I$, but this is not possible at an endpoint. To show that there is a local minimum at $x = -2$, we must find $\delta > 0$ such that $f(-2) \le f(x)$ for all $x \in (-2-\delta, -2+\delta) \cap D = [-2, -2+\delta)$. We can again choose $\delta = 0.1$ and see that $f(-2) \le f(x)$ for all $x \in [-2, -1.9)$ (Figure 5.11).

Similarly, we see that there is a local maximum at $x = 3$, since $f(3) \ge f(x)$ for all $x \in (2.9, 3]$; that is, there is no larger value of f nearby.

(b) Global extrema are points at which a function is either largest or smallest. Since f is defined on a closed interval, it follows from the extreme-value theorem that both a global maximum and a global minimum exist. These global extrema may occur either in the interior or at the endpoints of the domain $D = [-2, 3]$.

To find the global minimum, we compare the local minima. Since $f(-2) = 0$ and $f(1) = 0$, it follows that the global minima occur at $x = -2$ and $x = 1$ (Figure 5.9). To find the global maximum, we compare the local maxima. Since $f(3) = 20$ and $f(-1) = 4$, it follows that $f(3) > f(-1)$; therefore, the global maximum occurs at the endpoint $x = 3$ (Figure 5.9). ∎

EXAMPLE 5   Let

$$f(x) = |x^2 - 4| \quad \text{for} \ -2.5 \le x < 3$$

Find all local and global extrema.

Solution   The graph of $f(x)$, illustrated in Figure 5.12, reveals that local minima occur at $x = -2$ and $x = 2$ and local maxima occur at $x = -2.5$ and $x = 0$. Note that $f(x)$ is not defined at $x = 3$; thus, $x = 3$ cannot be a local maximum. To find the global extrema, we need to look at the function values close to the boundary $x = 3$. Candidates for global extrema are all the local extrema, which must be compared against the value of the function near the boundary $x = 3$. We discuss the global maximum first. Since

$$f(-2.5) = 2.25 \qquad f(0) = 4 \qquad \lim_{x \to 3^-} f(x) = 5$$

the function is largest near the point $x = 3$. But because $f(x)$ is not defined at $x = 3$, the function has no global maximum. (This does not contradict the extreme-value theorem, as the function is not defined on a closed interval, which is an assumption of the theorem.) To find the global minimum, we need only compare $f(-2)$ and $f(2)$.

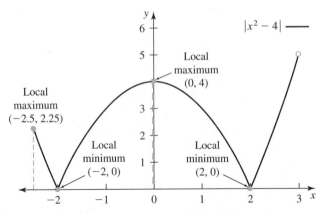

Figure 5.12 The graph of $f(x) = |x^2 - 4|$ for $-2.5 \le x < 3$ in Example 5.

We find that $f(-2) = 0$ and $f(2) = 0$; therefore, global minima occur at $x = -2$ and $x = 2$. ■

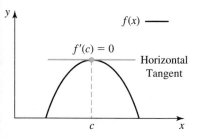

$f(x)$ ——

$f'(c) = 0$

Horizontal Tangent

c

x

Figure 5.13 Fermat's theorem.

Looking at Figures 5.9 and 5.12, we see that if the function f is differentiable at an interior point where f has a local extremum, then there is a horizontal tangent line at that point. This statement is known as Fermat's theorem (see Figure 5.13).

Fermat's Theorem If f has a local extremum at an interior point c and $f'(c)$ exists, then $f'(c) = 0$.

Proof We prove Fermat's theorem for the case where the local extremum is a maximum; the proof where the local extremum is a minimum is similar. We need to show that $f'(c) = 0$. To do so, we use the formal definition of the derivative to compute $f'(c)$:

$$f'(c) = \lim_{x \to c} \frac{f(x) - f(c)}{x - c}$$

To compute the limit, we will separately compute the left-hand limit $(x \to c^-)$ and the right-hand limit $(x \to c^+)$. We begin with the following observation (Figure 5.14): Suppose that f has a local maximum at an interior point c. Then there exists a $\delta > 0$ such that

$$f(x) \leq f(c) \quad \text{for all } x \in (c - \delta, c + \delta)$$

Since $f(x) - f(c) \leq 0$ and $x - c < 0$ if $x < c$, we find that the left-hand limit is

$$\lim_{x \to c^-} \frac{f(x) - f(c)}{x - c} \geq 0 \tag{5.1}$$

and since $f(x) - f(c) \leq 0$ and $x - c > 0$ if $x > c$, we find that the right-hand limit is

$$\lim_{x \to c^+} \frac{f(x) - f(c)}{x - c} \leq 0 \tag{5.2}$$

Now, because f is differentiable at c, it follows that

$$f'(c) = \lim_{x \to c^-} \frac{f(x) - f(c)}{x - c} = \lim_{x \to c^+} \frac{f(x) - f(c)}{x - c}$$

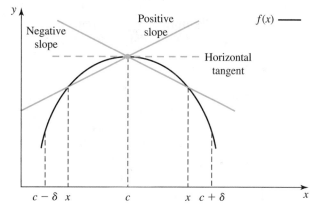

Negative slope

Positive slope

$f(x)$ ——

Horizontal tangent

$c - \delta \quad x \qquad\qquad c \qquad\qquad x \quad c + \delta \qquad\qquad x$

Figure 5.14 An illustration of the proof of Fermat's theorem: For $x < c$, the slope of the secant line is positive; for $x > c$, the slope of the secant line is negative. In the limit $x \to c$, the secant lines converge to the horizontal tangent line.

This, together with Equation (5.1), shows that $f'(c) \geq 0$ and, together with Equation (5.2), that $f'(c) \leq 0$. Now, if you have a number that is simultaneously nonnegative and nonpositive, the number must be 0. Therefore, $f'(c) = 0$. ■

EXAMPLE 6

Explain why $y = \tan x$ does not have a local extremum at $x = 0$.

Solution

$y = \tan x$ is differentiable at $x = 0$, with

$$\frac{d}{dx} \tan x = \sec^2 x$$

Hence, the derivative of $y = \tan x$ at $x = 0$ is equal to 1. Since the derivative is not equal to 0, Fermat's theorem (or, more precisely, its contrapositive) implies that $x = 0$ is not a local extremum. ■

Caution!

1. The condition that $f'(c) = 0$ is a necessary, but not sufficient, condition for the existence of local extrema at interior points where $f'(c)$ exists. In particular, the fact that f is differentiable at c with $f'(c) = 0$ tells us nothing about whether f has a local extremum at $x = c$. For instance, $f(x) = x^3$, $x \in \mathbf{R}$, is differentiable at $x = 0$ and $f'(0) = 0$, but there is no local extremum at $x = 0$. The graph of $y = x^3$ is shown in Figure 5.15. Although there is a horizontal tangent at $x = 0$, there is no local extremum at $x = 0$. Fermat's theorem does tell you, however, that if $x = c$ is an interior point with $f'(c) \neq 0$, then $x = c$ cannot be a local extremum (Example 6). Interior points with horizontal tangents are *candidates* for local extrema.

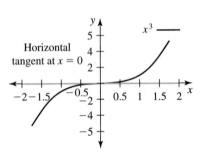

Figure 5.15 The graph of $y = x^3$ has a horizontal tangent at $x = 0$, but $(0, 0)$ is not an extremum.

2. The function f may not be differentiable at a local extremum. For instance, in Example 5, the function $f(x)$ is not differentiable at $x = -2$ and $x = 2$, but both points turned out to be local extrema. This means that, in order to identify candidates for local extrema, it will not be enough simply to look at points with horizontal tangents; you also must look at points where the function $f(x)$ is not differentiable.

3. Local extrema may occur at endpoints of the domain. Since Fermat's theorem says nothing about what happens at endpoints, you will have to look at endpoints separately.

To summarize our discussion, here are guidelines for finding candidates for local extrema:

---

1. Find all numbers c where $f'(c) = 0$.
2. Find all numbers c where $f'(c)$ does not exist.
3. Find the endpoints of the domain of f.

We will return to local extrema in Section 5.3, where we will learn methods for deciding whether candidates for local extrema are indeed local extrema.

■ 5.1.3 The Mean-Value Theorem

The mean-value theorem (MVT) is a very important, yet easily understood, result in calculus. Its consequences are far reaching, and we will use it in every section in this chapter to derive important results that will help us to analyze functions.

Here is an example that explains the MVT: Consider the function

$$f(x) = x^2 \quad \text{for } 0 \leq x \leq 1$$

The secant line connecting the endpoints $(0, 0)$ and $(1, 1)$ of the graph of $f(x)$ has slope

$$m = \frac{f(1) - f(0)}{1 - 0} = \frac{1 - 0}{1 - 0} = 1$$

The graph of $f(x)$ and the secant line are shown in Figure 5.16. Note that $f(x)$ is differentiable in $(0, 1)$; that is, you can draw a tangent line at every point of the graph

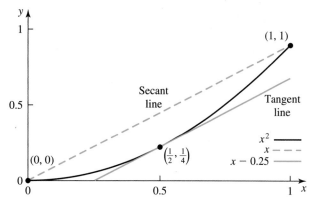

Figure 5.16 The graphs of $f(x) = x^2$, the secant line through $(0, 0)$ and $(1, 1)$, and the tangent line parallel to the secant line.

in the open interval $(0, 1)$. If you look at the graph of $f(x)$, you see that there exists a number $c \in (0, 1)$ such that the slope of the tangent line at $(c, f(c))$ is the same as the slope of the secant line through the points $(0, 0)$ and $(1, 1)$. That is, we claim that there exists a number $c \in (0, 1)$ such that

$$\frac{f(1) - f(0)}{1 - 0} = f'(c)$$

Proving that there exists such a value c is the thrust of the mean-value theorem.

We can compute the value of c in this example. Since $f'(x) = 2x$ and the slope of the secant line is $m = 1$, we must solve

$$1 = 2c, \qquad \text{or} \qquad c = \tfrac{1}{2}$$

Using the point–slope form $[y - y_0 = m(x - x_0)]$, we can find the equation of the tangent line at $(\tfrac{1}{2}, f(\tfrac{1}{2})) = (\tfrac{1}{2}, \tfrac{1}{4})$, namely,

$$y - \tfrac{1}{4} = 1\left(x - \tfrac{1}{2}\right), \qquad \text{or} \qquad y = x - \tfrac{1}{4}$$

(This tangent line is shown in Figure 5.16.)

> **The Mean-Value Theorem (MVT)** If f is continuous on the closed interval $[a, b]$ and differentiable on the open interval (a, b), then there exists at least one number $c \in (a, b)$ such that
>
> $$\frac{f(b) - f(a)}{b - a} = f'(c)$$

The fraction on the left-hand side of the equation in the theorem is the slope of the secant line connecting the points $(a, f(a))$ and $(b, f(b))$, and the quantity on the right-hand side is the slope of the tangent line at $(c, f(c))$ (see Figure 5.17).

Geometrically, the MVT is indeed easily understood: It states that there exists a point on the graph between $(a, f(a))$ and $(b, f(b))$ where the tangent line at this point is parallel to the secant line through $(a, f(a))$ and $(b, f(b))$. [We denoted the point in question by $(c, f(c))$.] The MVT is an "existence" result: It tells us neither how many such points there are nor where they are in the interval (a, b).

Going back to the example $f(x) = x^2, 0 \leq x \leq 1$, we see that $f(x)$ satisfies the assumptions of the MVT, namely, that $f(x)$ is continuous on the closed interval $[0, 1]$ and differentiable on the open interval $(0, 1)$. The MVT then guarantees the

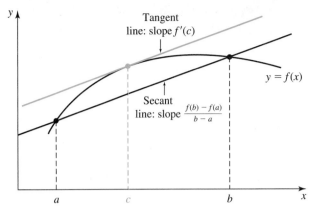

Figure 5.17 The mean value guarantees the existence of a number $c \in (a, b)$ such that the tangent line at $(c, f(c))$ has the same slope as the secant line through $(a, f(a))$ and $(b, f(b))$.

existence of at least one number $c \in (0, 1)$ such that the slope of the secant line through the points $(0, 0)$ and $(1, 1)$ is equal to the slope of the tangent line at $(c, f(c))$.

At this point, you might be wondering how such a seemingly simple theorem can be so important. In the sections that follow, you will encounter the theorem mostly in proofs of other important results that will enable us to understand properties of functions by using calculus. The next example, however, is an application that gives physical meaning to the theorem.

EXAMPLE 7

Velocity A car moves in a straight line. At time t (measured in seconds), its position (measured in meters) is

$$s(t) = \frac{1}{25}t^3, \ 0 \le t \le 10$$

Show that there is a time $t \in (0, 10)$ when the velocity is equal to the average velocity between $t = 0$ and $t = 10$.

Solution The average velocity between $t = 0$ and $t = 10$ is

$$\frac{s(10) - s(0)}{10 - 0} = \frac{\frac{1}{25} \cdot 1000 \, \text{m}}{10 \, \text{s}} = 4\frac{\text{m}}{\text{s}}$$

This is the slope of the secant line connecting the points $(0, 0)$ and $(10, 40)$. Since $s(t)$ is continuous on $[0, 10]$ and differentiable on $(0, 10)$, the MVT tells us that there must exist a number $c \in (0, 10)$ such that $s'(c) = 4\frac{\text{m}}{\text{s}}$. Now, $s'(t)$ is the (instantaneous) velocity. So, at some point during this short trip, the speedometer must have read $4\frac{\text{m}}{\text{s}}$.

■

The rest of this section is devoted to the proof of the MVT, which is typically proved by first showing a special case of the theorem called Rolle's theorem.

> **Rolle's Theorem** If f is continuous on the closed interval $[a, b]$ and differentiable on the open interval (a, b), and if $f(a) = f(b)$, then there exists a number $c \in (a, b)$ such that $f'(c) = 0$.

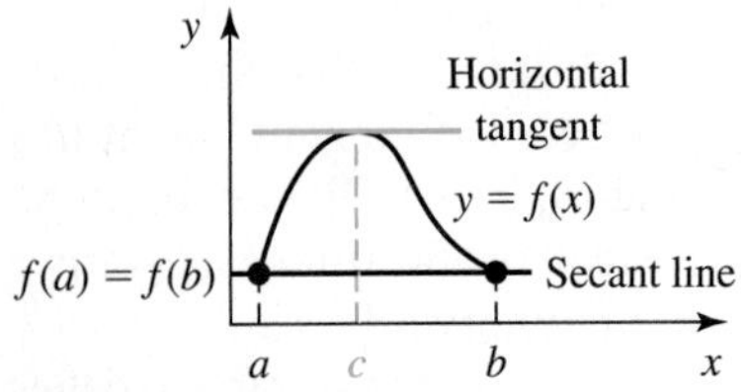

Figure 5.18 An illustration of Rolle's theorem.

Figure 5.18 illustrates Rolle's theorem. The function in the graph is defined on the closed interval $[a, b]$ and takes on the same values at the two endpoints of $[a, b]$ [namely, $f(a) = f(b)$]. Thus, the secant line connecting the two endpoints is a horizontal line. We see, then, that there is a point in (a, b) with a horizontal tangent line.

Before we prove Rolle's theorem, we check why it is a special case of the MVT. If we compare the assumptions in the two theorems, we find that Rolle's theorem has an additional requirement, $f(a) = f(b)$; that is, the function values must agree at the endpoints of the interval on which f is defined. If we apply the MVT to such a function, it says that there exists a number $c \in (a, b)$ such that

$$f'(c) = \frac{f(b) - f(a)}{b - a}$$

But since $f(b) = f(a)$, it follows that the expression on the right-hand side is equal to 0; that is, $f'(c) = 0$, which is the conclusion of Rolle's theorem.

Proof of Rolle's Theorem   If f is the constant function, then $f'(x) = 0$ for all $x \in (a, b)$ and the theorem is true in this particular case. For the more general case, we assume that f is not constant. Since $f(x)$ is continuous on the closed interval $[a, b]$, it follows from the extreme-value theorem that the function has a global maximum and a global minimum in that interval. To see that the function must have a global extremum inside the open interval (a, b), we observe that if f is not constant, then there exists an $x_0 \in (a, b)$ such that either $f(x_0) > f(a) = f(b)$ or $f(x_0) < f(a) = f(b)$. This global extremum is also a local extremum. Suppose that the local extremum is at $c \in (a, b)$; then it follows from Fermat's theorem that $f'(c) = 0$. (In Figure 5.18, the global minima occur at the endpoints of the interval $[a, b]$, but the global maximum occurs in the open interval (a, b), and that's where the horizontal tangent is.) ■

The MVT follows from Rolle's theorem and can be thought of as a "tilted" version of that theorem. (The secant and tangent lines in the MVT are no longer necessarily horizontal [Figure 5.17], as in Rolle's theorem [Figure 5.18], but are "tilted"; they are still parallel, though.)

Proof of the MVT   We define the following function:

$$F(x) = f(x) - \frac{f(b) - f(a)}{b - a}(x - a)$$

The function F is continuous on $[a, b]$ and differentiable on (a, b). Furthermore,

$$F(a) = f(a) - \frac{f(b) - f(a)}{b - a}(a - a) = f(a)$$

$$F(b) = f(b) - \frac{f(b) - f(a)}{b - a}(b - a) = f(a)$$

Therefore, $F(a) = F(b)$. We can apply Rolle's theorem to the function $F(x)$: There exists a $c \in (a, b)$ with $F'(c) = 0$. Since

$$F'(x) = f'(x) - \frac{f(b) - f(a)}{b - a}$$

it follows that, for this value of c,

$$0 = F'(c) = f'(c) - \frac{f(b) - f(a)}{b - a}$$

and hence

$$f'(c) = \frac{f(b) - f(a)}{b - a}$$

■

We next discuss two consequences of the MVT.

Corollary 1 If f is continuous on the closed interval $[a, b]$ and differentiable on the open interval (a, b) such that

$$m \leq f'(x) \leq M \qquad \text{for all } x \in (a, b)$$

then

$$m(b - a) \leq f(b) - f(a) \leq M(b - a)$$

This corollary is useful in obtaining information about a function on the basis of its derivative.

EXAMPLE 8

Population Growth Denote the population size at time t by $N(t)$, and assume that $N(t)$ is continuous on the interval $[0, 10]$ and differentiable on the interval $(0, 10)$ with $N(0) = 100$ and $|dN/dt| \leq 3$ for all $t \in (0, 10)$. What can you say about $N(10)$?

Solution Since $|dN/dt| \leq 3$ implies that $-3 \leq dN/dt \leq 3$, we can set $m = -3$ and $M = 3$ in Corollary 1. With $a = 0$ and $b = 10$, Corollary 1 yields the following estimate:

$$(-3)(10 - 0) \leq N(10) - N(0) \leq (3)(10 - 0)$$

Simplifying and solving for $N(10)$ gives

$$-30 + N(0) \leq N(10) \leq 30 + N(0)$$

Since $N(0) = 100$, we have

$$70 \leq N(10) \leq 130$$

That is, the population size at time $t = 10$ is bounded between 70 and 130. ■

EXAMPLE 9 Show that

$$|\sin b - \sin a| \leq |b - a|$$

Solution If $a = b$, then, trivially, $|\sin a - \sin a| \leq |a - a|$. We therefore assume that $a < b$. (The case $a > b$ is similar.) Let $f(x) = \sin x$, $a \leq x \leq b$. Then $f(x)$ is continuous on $[a, b]$ and differentiable on (a, b). Since $f'(x) = \cos x$, it follows that

$$-1 \leq f'(x) \leq 1$$

for all $x \in (a, b)$. Applying Corollary 1, with $m = -1$ and $M = 1$, to $f(x) = \sin x$, $a < x < b$, we find that

$$-(b - a) \leq \sin b - \sin a \leq (b - a)$$

which is the same as

$$|\sin b - \sin a| \leq |b - a|$$

■

The next corollary is important, and we will see it again in Section 5.8.

Corollary 2 If f is continuous on the closed interval $[a, b]$ and differentiable on the open interval (a, b), with $f'(x) = 0$ for all $x \in (a, b)$, then f is constant on $[a, b]$.

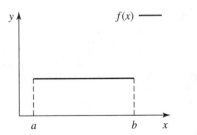

Figure 5.19 An illustration of Corollary 2.

Figure 5.19 explains why Corollary 2 is true: Each point on the graph has a horizontal tangent, so the function must be constant.

EXAMPLE 10

Assume that f is continuous on $[-1, 1]$ and differentiable on $(-1, 1)$, with $f(0) = 2$ and $f'(x) = 0$ for all $x \in (-1, 1)$. Find $f(x)$.

Solution

Corollary 2 tells us that $f(x)$ is a constant. Since we know that $f(0) = 2$, we have $f(x) = 2$ for all $x \in [-1, 1]$. ∎

Proof of Corollary 2 Let $x_1, x_2 \in (a, b), x_1 < x_2$. Then f satisfies the assumptions of the MVT on the closed interval $[x_1, x_2]$. Therefore, there exists a number $c \in (x_1, x_2)$ such that

$$\frac{f(x_2) - f(x_1)}{x_2 - x_1} = f'(c)$$

Since $f'(c) = 0$, it follows that $f(x_2) = f(x_1)$. Finally, because x_1, x_2 are arbitrary numbers from the interval (a, b), we conclude that f is constant. ∎

EXAMPLE 11

Show that

$$\sin^2 x + \cos^2 x = 1 \quad \text{for all } x \in [0, 2\pi]$$

Solution

This identity can be shown without calculus, but let's see what we get if we use Corollary 2. We define $f(x) = \sin^2 x + \cos^2 x, 0 \le x \le 2\pi$. Then $f(x)$ is continuous on $[0, 2\pi]$ and differentiable on $(0, 2\pi)$, with

$$f'(x) = 2 \sin x \cos x - 2 \cos x \sin x = 0$$

Using Corollary 2 now, we conclude that $f(x)$ is equal to a constant on $[0, 2\pi]$. To find the constant, we need only evaluate $f(x)$ at one point in the interval, say, $x = 0$. We find that

$$f(0) = \sin^2 0 + \cos^2 0 = 1$$

This proves the identity. ∎

Section 5.1 Problems

■ **5.1.1**

In Problems 1–8, each function is continuous and defined on a closed interval. It therefore satisfies the assumptions of the extreme-value theorem. With the help of a graphing calculator, graph each function and locate its global extrema. (Note that a function may assume a global extremum at more than one point.)

1. $f(x) = 2x - 1, 0 \le x \le 1$

2. $f(x) = -x^2 + 1, -1 \le x \le 1$

3. $f(x) = \sin(2x), 0 \le x \le \pi$

4. $f(x) = \cos \frac{x}{2}, 0 \le x \le 2\pi$

5. $f(x) = |x|, -1 \le x \le 1$

6. $f(x) = (x - 1)^2(x + 2), -2 \le x \le 2$

7. $f(x) = e^{-|x|}, -1 \le x \le 1$

8. $f(x) = \ln(x + 1), 0 \le x \le 2$

9. Sketch the graph of a function that is continuous on the closed interval $[0, 3]$ and has a global maximum at the left endpoint and a global minimum at the right endpoint.

10. Sketch the graph of a function that is continuous on the closed interval $[-2, 1]$ and has a global maximum and a global minimum in the interior of the domain of the function.

11. Sketch the graph of a function that is continuous on the open interval $(0, 2)$ and has neither a global maximum nor a global minimum in its domain.

12. Sketch the graph of a function that is continuous on the closed interval $[1, 4]$, except at $x = 2$, and has neither a global maximum nor a global minimum in its domain.

■ **5.1.2**

In Problems 13–18, use a graphing calculator to determine all local and global extrema of the functions on their respective domains.

13. $f(x) = 3 - x, x \in [-1, 3)$

14. $f(x) = 5 + 2x, x \in (-2, 1)$

15. $f(x) = x^2 - 2, x \in [-1, 1]$

16. $f(x) = (x - 2)^2, x \in [0, 3]$

17. $f(x) = -x^2 + 1, x \in [-2, 1]$

18. $f(x) = x^2 - x, x \in [0, 1]$

In Problems 19–26, find c such that $f'(c) = 0$ and determine whether $f(x)$ has a local extremum at $x = c$.

19. $f(x) = x^2$

20. $f(x) = (x - 4)^2$

21. $f(x) = -x^2$

22. $f(x) = -(x + 3)^2$

23. $f(x) = x^3$

24. $f(x) = x^5$

25. $f(x) = (x + 1)^3$

26. $f(x) = -(x - 3)^5$

27. Show that $f(x) = |x|$ has a local minimum at $x = 0$ but $f(x)$ is not differentiable at $x = 0$.

28. Show that $f(x) = |x - 1|$ has a local minimum at $x = 1$ but $f(x)$ is not differentiable at $x = 1$.

29. Show that $f(x) = |x^2 - 1|$ has local minima at $x = 1$ and $x = -1$ but $f(x)$ is not differentiable at $x = 1$ or $x = -1$.

30. Show that $f(x) = -|x^2 - 4|$ has local maxima at $x = 2$ and $x = -2$ but $f(x)$ is not differentiable at $x = 2$ or $x = -2$.

31. Graph
$$f(x) = |1 - |x||, \quad -1 \leq x \leq 2$$
and determine all local and global extrema on $[-1, 2]$.

32. Graph
$$f(x) = -||x| - 2|, \quad -3 \leq x \leq 3$$
and determine all local and global extrema on $[-3, 3]$.

33. Suppose the size of a population at time t is $N(t)$ and its growth rate is given by the logistic growth function
$$\frac{dN}{dt} = rN\left(1 - \frac{N}{K}\right), \quad t \geq 0$$

where r and K are positive constants.
(a) Graph the growth rate $\frac{dN}{dt}$ as a function of N for $r = 2$ and $K = 100$, and find the population size for which the growth rate is maximal.
(b) Show that $f(N) = rN(1 - N/K)$, $N \geq 0$, is differentiable for $N > 0$, and compute $f'(N)$.
(c) Show that $f'(N) = 0$ for the value of N that you determined in (a) when $r = 2$ and $K = 100$.

34. Suppose that the size of a population at time t is $N(t)$ and its growth rate is given by the logistic growth function
$$\frac{dN}{dt} = rN\left(1 - \frac{N}{K}\right), \quad t \geq 0$$

where r and K are positive constants. The per capita growth rate is defined by
$$g(N) = \frac{1}{N}\frac{dN}{dt}$$

(a) Show that
$$g(N) = r\left(1 - \frac{N}{K}\right)$$

(b) Graph $g(N)$ as a function of N for $N \geq 0$ when $r = 2$ and $K = 100$, and find the population size for which the per capita growth rate is maximal.

■ **5.1.3**

35. Suppose $f(x) = x^2$, $x \in [0, 2]$.
(a) Find the slope of the secant line connecting the points $(0, 0)$ and $(2, 4)$.
(b) Find a number $c \in (0, 2)$ such that $f'(c)$ is equal to the slope of the secant line you computed in (a), and explain why such a number must exist in $(0, 2)$.

36. Suppose $f(x) = 1/x$, $x \in [1, 2]$.
(a) Find the slope of the secant line connecting the points $(1, 1)$ and $(2, 1/2)$.
(b) Find a number $c \in (1, 2)$ such that $f'(c)$ is equal to the slope of the secant line you computed in (a), and explain why such a number must exist in $(1, 2)$.

37. Suppose that $f(x) = x^2$, $x \in [-1, 1]$.
(a) Find the slope of the secant line connecting the points $(-1, 1)$ and $(1, 1)$.
(b) Find a number $c \in (-1, 1)$ such that $f'(c)$ is equal to the slope of the secant line you computed in (a), and explain why such a number must exist in $(-1, 1)$.

38. Suppose that $f(x) = x^2 - x - 2$, $x \in [-1, 2]$.
(a) Find the slope of the secant line connecting the points $(-1, 0)$ and $(2, 0)$.

(b) Find a number $c \in (-1, 2)$ such that $f'(c)$ is equal to the slope of the secant line you computed in (a), and explain why such a number must exist in $(-1, 2)$.

39. Let $f(x) = x(1 - x)$. Use the MVT to find an interval that contains a number c such that $f'(c) = 0$.

40. Let $f(x) = 1/(1 + x^2)$. Use the MVT to find an interval that contains a number c such that $f'(c) = 0$.

41. Suppose that $f(x) = -x^2 + 2$. Explain why there exists a point c in the interval $(-1, 2)$ such that $f'(c) = -1$.

42. Suppose that $f(x) = x^3$. Explain why there exists a point c in the interval $(-1, 1)$ such that $f'(c) = 1$.

43. Sketch the graph of a function $f(x)$ that is continuous on the closed interval $[0, 1]$ and differentiable on the open interval $(0, 1)$ such that there exists exactly one point $(c, f(c))$ on the graph at which the slope of the tangent line is equal to the slope of the secant line connecting the points $(0, f(0))$ and $(1, f(1))$. Why can you be sure that there is such a point?

44. Sketch the graph of a function $f(x)$ that is continuous on the closed interval $[0, 1]$ and differentiable on the open interval $(0, 1)$ such that there exist exactly two points $(c_1, f(c_1))$ and $(c_2, f(c_2))$ on the graph at which the slope of the tangent lines is equal to the slope of the secant line connecting the points $(0, f(0))$ and $(1, f(1))$. Why can you be sure that there is at least one such point?

45. Suppose that $f(x) = x^2$, $x \in [a, b]$.
(a) Compute the slope of the secant line through the points $(a, f(a))$ and $(b, f(b))$.
(b) Find the point $c \in (a, b)$ such that the slope of the tangent line to the graph of f at $(c, f(c))$ is equal to the slope of the secant line determined in (a). How do you know that such a point exists? Show that c is the midpoint of the interval (a, b); that is, show that $c = (a + b)/2$.

46. Assume that f is continuous on $[a, b]$ and differentiable on (a, b). Show that if $f(a) < f(b)$, then f' is positive at some point between a and b.

47. Assume that f is continuous on $[a, b]$ and differentiable on (a, b). Assume further that $f(a) = f(b) = 0$ but f is not constant on $[a, b]$. Explain why there must be a point $c_1 \in (a, b)$ with $f'(c_1) > 0$ and a point $c_2 \in (a, b)$ with $f'(c_2) < 0$.

48. A car moves in a straight line. At time t (measured in seconds), its position (measured in meters) is
$$s(t) = \frac{1}{10}t^2, \quad 0 \leq t \leq 10$$

(a) Find its average velocity between $t = 0$ and $t = 10$.
(b) Find its instantaneous velocity for $t \in (0, 10)$.
(c) At what time is the instantaneous velocity of the car equal to its average velocity?

49. A car moves in a straight line. At time t (measured in seconds), its position (measured in meters) is
$$s(t) = \frac{1}{100}t^3, \quad 0 \leq t \leq 5$$

(a) Find its average velocity between $t = 0$ and $t = 5$.
(b) Find its instantaneous velocity for $t \in (0, 5)$.
(c) At what time is the instantaneous velocity of the car equal to its average velocity?

50. Denote the population size at time t by $N(t)$, and assume that $N(0) = 50$ and $|dN/dt| \leq 2$ for all $t \in [0, 5]$. What can you say about $N(5)$?

51. Denote the biomass at time t by $B(t)$, and assume that $B(0) = 3$ and $|dB/dt| \leq 1$ for all $t \in [0, 3]$. What can you say about $B(3)$?

52. Suppose that f is differentiable for all $x \in \mathbf{R}$ and, furthermore, that f satisfies $f(0) = 0$ and $1 \leq f'(x) \leq 2$ for all $x > 0$.

(a) Use Corollary 1 of the MVT to show that

$$x \leq f(x) \leq 2x$$

for all $x \geq 0$.

(b) Use your result in (a) to explain why $f(1)$ cannot be equal to 3.

(c) Find an upper and a lower bound for the value of $f(1)$.

53. Suppose that f is differentiable for all $x \in \mathbf{R}$ with $f(2) = 3$ and $f'(x) = 0$ for all $x \in \mathbf{R}$. Find $f(x)$.

54. Suppose that $f(x) = e^{-|x|}$, $x \in [-2, 2]$.

(a) Show that $f(-2) = f(2)$.

(b) Compute $f'(x)$, where defined.

(c) Show that there is no number $c \in (-2, 2)$ such that $f'(c) = 0$.

(d) Explain why your results in (a) and (c) do not contradict Rolle's theorem.

(e) Use a graphing calculator to sketch the graph of $f(x)$.

55. Use Corollary 2 of the MVT to show that if $f(x)$ is differentiable for all $x \in \mathbf{R}$ and satisfies

$$|f(x) - f(y)| \leq |x - y|^2 \qquad (5.3)$$

for all $x, y \in \mathbf{R}$, then $f(x)$ is constant. [*Hint:* Show that (5.3) implies that

$$\lim_{x \to y} \frac{f(x) - f(y)}{x - y} = 0 \qquad (5.4)$$

and use the definition of the derivative to interpret the left-hand side of (5.4).]

56. We have seen that

$$f(x) = f_0 e^{rx}$$

satisfies the differential equation

$$\frac{df}{dx} = rf(x)$$

with $f(0) = f_0$. This exercise will show that $f(x)$ is in fact the only solution. Suppose that r is a constant and f is a differentiable function,

$$\frac{df}{dx} = rf(x) \qquad (5.5)$$

for all $x \in \mathbf{R}$, and $f(0) = f_0$. The following steps will show that $f(x) = f_0 e^{rx}$, $x \in \mathbf{R}$, is the only solution of (5.5).

(a) Define the function

$$F(x) = f(x)e^{-rx}, \quad x \in \mathbf{R}$$

Use the product rule to show that

$$F'(x) = e^{-rx}[f'(x) - rf(x)]$$

(b) Use (a) and (5.5) to show that $F'(x) = 0$ for all $x \in \mathbf{R}$.

(c) Use Corollary 2 to show that $F(x)$ is a constant and, hence, $F(x) = F(0) = f_0$.

(d) Show that (c) implies that

$$f_0 = f(x)e^{-rx}$$

and therefore,

$$f(x) = f_0 e^{rx}$$

5.2 Monotonicity and Concavity

Fish are indeterminate growers; they increase in body size throughout their life. However, as they become older, they grow proportionately more slowly. Their growth is often described mathematically by the von Bertalanffy equation, which fits a large number of both freshwater and marine fishes. This equation is given by

$$L(x) = L_\infty - (L_\infty - L_0)e^{-Kx}$$

where $L(x)$ denotes the length of the fish at age x, L_0 the length at age 0, and L_∞ the asymptotic maximum attainable length. We assume that $L_\infty > L_0$. K is related to how quickly the fish grows. Figure 5.20 shows examples for two different values of K; L_∞ and L_0 are the same in both cases. We see from the graphs that for larger K, the asymptotic length L_∞ is approached more quickly.

The fact that fish increase their body size throughout their life can be expressed mathematically by the first derivative of the function $L(x)$. Looking at the graph, we see that $L(x)$ is an increasing function of x: The tangent line at any point of the graph has a positive slope, or, equivalently, $L'(x) > 0$. We can compute

$$L'(x) = K(L_\infty - L_0)e^{-Kx}$$

Since $L_\infty > L_0$ (by assumption) and $e^{-Kx} > 0$ (this holds for all x, regardless of K), we see that, indeed, $L'(x) > 0$. The graph of $L'(x)$ is shown in Figure 5.21.

The graph of $L'(x)$ shows that $L'(x)$ is a decreasing function of x: Although fish increase their body size throughout their life, they do so at a rate that decreases with age. Mathematically, this relationship can be expressed with the second derivative of

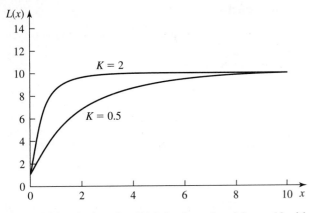

Figure 5.20 The function $L(x)$ for $L_0 = 1$ and $L_\infty = 10$ with $K = 0.5$ and $K = 2$.

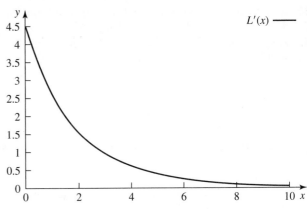

Figure 5.21 The graph of $L'(x)$ with $L_0 = 1$, $L_\infty = 10$, and $K = 0.5$.

$L(x)$—the derivative of the first derivative. The tangent line at any point on the graph of $L'(x)$ has a negative slope; that is, the derivative of $L'(x)$ is negative: $L''(x) < 0$. The fact that the rate of growth decreases with age can also be seen directly from the graph of $L(x)$: It bends downward. The second derivative thus tells us something about which way the graph of $L(x)$ bends.

This section discusses the important concepts of monotonicity—whether a function is decreasing or increasing—and concavity—whether a function bends upward or downward.

■ 5.2.1 Monotonicity

We saw in the motivating example that the first derivative tells us something about whether a function increases or decreases. Not every function is differentiable, however, so we phrase the definitions of increasing and decreasing in terms of the function f alone. (See Figures 5.22 and 5.23.)

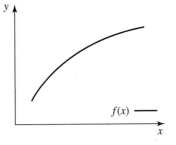

Figure 5.22 An increasing function.

> **Definition** A function f defined on an interval I is called **(strictly) increasing** on I if
>
> $$f(x_1) < f(x_2) \qquad \text{whenever } x_1 < x_2 \text{ in } I$$
>
> and is called **(strictly) decreasing** on I if
>
> $$f(x_1) > f(x_2) \qquad \text{whenever } x_1 < x_2 \text{ in } I$$

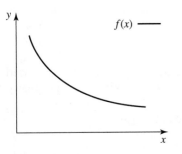

Figure 5.23 A decreasing function.

An increasing or decreasing function is called **monotonic**. The word *strictly* in the preceding definition refers to having a strict inequality ($f(x_1) < f(x_2)$ and $f(x_1) > f(x_2)$). We will frequently drop *strictly*. If, instead of the strict inequality $f(x_1) < f(x_2)$, we have the inequality $f(x_1) \leq f(x_2)$, whenever $x_1 < x_2$ in I, we call f *nondecreasing*. If $f(x_1) \geq f(x_2)$ whenever $x_1 < x_2$ in I, then f is called *nonincreasing*. (See Figures 5.24 and 5.25.)

When the function f is differentiable, there is a useful test to determine whether f is increasing or decreasing. This criterion is a consequence of the MVT.

> **First-Derivative Test for Monotonicity** Suppose f is continuous on $[a, b]$ and differentiable on (a, b).
>
> **(a)** If $f'(x) > 0$ for all $x \in (a, b)$, then f is increasing on $[a, b]$.
>
> **(b)** If $f'(x) < 0$ for all $x \in (a, b)$, then f is decreasing on $[a, b]$.

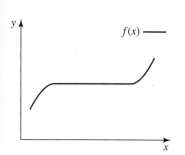

Figure 5.24 A nondecreasing function may have regions where the function is constant.

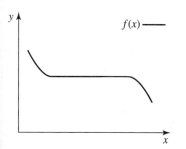

Figure 5.25 A nonincreasing function may have regions where the function is constant.

Proof (See Figure 5.26.) We choose two numbers x_1 and x_2 in $[a, b]$, $x_1 < x_2$. Then f is continuous on $[x_1, x_2]$ and differentiable on (x_1, x_2). We can therefore apply the MVT to f defined on $[x_1, x_2]$: There exists a number $c \in (x_1, x_2)$ such that

$$\frac{f(x_2) - f(x_1)}{x_2 - x_1} = f'(c)$$

In part (a) of the theorem, we assume that $f'(x) > 0$ for all $x \in (a, b)$. Since $c \in (x_1, x_2) \subset (a, b)$, it follows that $f'(c) > 0$. Since, in addition, $x_2 > x_1$, it follows that

$$f(x_2) - f(x_1) = f'(c)(x_2 - x_1) > 0$$

which implies that $f(x_2) > f(x_1)$. Because x_1 and x_2 are arbitrary numbers in $[a, b]$ satisfying $x_1 < x_2$, it follows that f is increasing. The proof of part (b) is similar and relegated to Problem 24. ∎

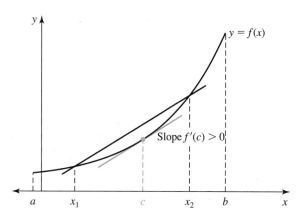

Figure 5.26 An illustration of the proof of "$f'(x) > 0$ for all $x \in (a, b)$ implies that $f(x)$ is increasing on $[a, b]$."

EXAMPLE 1

Determine where the function

$$f(x) = x^3 - \frac{3}{2}x^2 - 6x + 3, \quad x \in \mathbf{R}$$

is increasing and where it is decreasing.

Solution

Since $f(x)$ is continuous and differentiable for all $x \in \mathbf{R}$, we can use the first-derivative test for monotonic functions. We differentiate $f(x)$ and obtain

$$f'(x) = 3x^2 - 3x - 6 = 3(x - 2)(x + 1), \quad x \in \mathbf{R}$$

The graphs of $f(x)$ and $f'(x)$ are shown in Figure 5.27. The graph of $f'(x)$ is a parabola that intersects the x-axis at $x = 2$ and $x = -1$. The function $f'(x)$ therefore changes sign at $x = -1$ and $x = 2$. We find that

$$f'(x) \begin{cases} > 0 & \text{if } x < -1 \text{ or } x > 2 \\ < 0 & \text{if } -1 < x < 2 \end{cases}$$

Thus, $f(x)$ is increasing for $x < -1$ or $x > 2$ and decreasing for $-1 < x < 2$. A look at the graph of $f(x)$ in Figure 5.27 confirms this conclusion. ∎

EXAMPLE 2

Host–Parasitoid Interactions Parasitoids are insects whose larvae develop inside other, host insects. The larvae eventually kill the host. An example is the parasitoid *Macrocentrus grandii*, a wasp, which parasitizes *Ostrinia nubilis*, the European corn

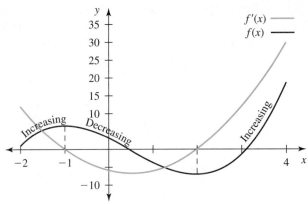

Figure 5.27 The graph of $f(x) = x^3 - \frac{3}{2}x^2 - 6x + 3$ and $f'(x) = 3x^2 - 3x - 6$.

borer. To understand host–parasitoid interactions, a large number of models have been developed. The function

$$f(N) = \left(1 + \frac{a\beta P}{k(\beta + aN)}\right)^{-k}$$

is one example that describes the likelihood of a host escaping parasitism as a function of host density N, where a, β, and k are positive parameters and P is the density of the parasitoid. On the basis of $f(N)$, what is the effect of an increase in host density on the likelihood of escaping parasitism?

Solution   To find the effect of an increase in host density, we compute the derivative of $f(N)$:

$$\frac{df}{dN} = (-k)\left[1 + \frac{a\beta P}{k(\beta + aN)}\right]^{-k-1} \frac{-a^2\beta P}{k(\beta + aN)^2}$$

$$= \left[1 + \frac{a\beta P}{k(\beta + aN)}\right]^{-k-1} \frac{a^2\beta P}{(\beta + aN)^2}$$

Both factors in the final expression are positive; hence, $df/dN > 0$. In words, if the density of the parasitoid is fixed and the host density increases, a host is more likely to escape parasitism in cases where the interaction is described by $f(N)$. ■

■ 5.2.2 Concavity

We saw in the motivating example at the beginning of this section that the second derivative tells us something about whether a function bends upward or downward. We arrived at this conclusion by checking whether the first derivative was increasing or decreasing.

A function is called **concave up** if it bends upward, and **concave down** if it bends downward. Before stating a precise definition of concavity for differentiable functions, we give two examples, in Figure 5.28.

First, look at the graph of the differentiable function $y = x^2$: It bends upward, so we call it concave up. Bending upward means that the slopes of the tangent lines are increasing as x increases. We can check this hypothesis by computing the slope of the tangent line at x, which is given by the first derivative, $y' = 2x$. Since $y' = 2x$ is an increasing function, the slopes of the tangent lines are increasing as x increases.

Looking at the graph of the differentiable function $y = -x^2 + 4$, we see that it bends downward, so we call it concave down. Bending downward means that the slopes of the tangent lines are decreasing as x increases. We can check this hypothesis by computing the first derivative of y, which is $y' = -2x$, a decreasing function.

The following definition pertaining to differentiable functions is based on the preceding discussion (see Figures 5.29 and 5.30):

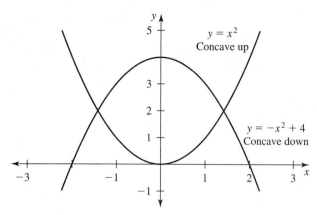

Figure 5.28 The graphs of $f(x) = x^2$ and $g(x) = -x^2 + 4$.

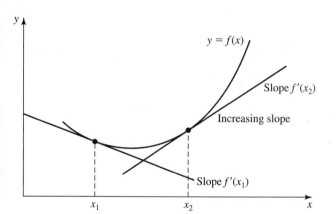

Figure 5.29 A function is concave up if its derivative is increasing.

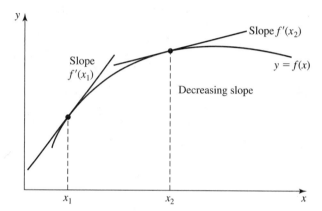

Figure 5.30 A function is concave down if its derivative is decreasing.

> **Definition** A differentiable function $f(x)$ is **concave up** on an interval I if the first derivative $f'(x)$ is an increasing function on I. $f(x)$ is **concave down** on an interval I if the first derivative $f'(x)$ is a decreasing function on I.

Note that the definition assumes that $f(x)$ is differentiable. There is a more general definition that does not require differentiability. (After all, not all functions are differentiable.) The more general definition is more difficult to use, however. The definition given here suffices for our purposes and has the added advantage that it provides the following criterion, which we can use to determine whether a twice-differentiable function is concave up or concave down:

> **Second-Derivative Test for Concavity** Suppose that f is twice differentiable on an open interval I.
>
> **(a)** If $f''(x) > 0$ for all $x \in I$, then f is concave up on I.
> **(b)** If $f''(x) < 0$ for all $x \in I$, then f is concave down on I.

Proof Since f is twice differentiable, we can apply the first-derivative criterion to the function $f'(x)$. The proof of part (a) proceeds, then, as follows: If $f''(x) > 0$ on I, then $f'(x)$ is an increasing function on I. From the definition of *concave up*, it follows that f is concave up on I. The proof of part (b) is similar and relegated to Problem 25. ■

You can use the function $y = x^2$ to remember which functions are concave up: The "u" in "concave up" should remind you of the U-shaped form of the graph of $y = x^2$. You can also use the function $y = x^2$ to remember the second-derivative criterion. You already know that the graph of $y = x^2$ is concave up, and you can easily compute the second derivative of $y = x^2$, namely, $y'' = 2 > 0$.

EXAMPLE 3

Determine where the function

$$f(x) = x^3 - \frac{3}{2}x^2 - 6x + 3, \quad x \in \mathbf{R}$$

is concave up and where it is concave down.

Solution

This is the same function as in Example 1 (redrawn in Figure 5.31). Since $f(x)$ is a polynomial, it is twice differentiable. In Example 1, we found that $f'(x) = 3x^2 - 3x - 6$; differentiating $f'(x)$, we get the second derivative of f:

$$f''(x) = 6x - 3$$

We find that

$$f''(x) \begin{cases} > 0 & \text{if } x > \frac{1}{2} \\ < 0 & \text{if } x < \frac{1}{2} \end{cases}$$

Thus, $f(x)$ is concave up for $x > 1/2$ and concave down for $x < 1/2$. A look at Figure 5.31 confirms this result. ■

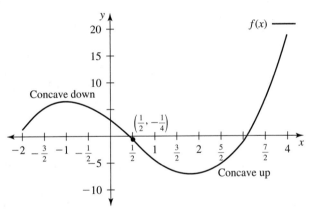

Figure 5.31 The graph of $f(x) = x^3 - \frac{3}{2}x^2 - 6x + 3$.

A very common mistake is to associate monotonicity and concavity. One has nothing to do with the other. For instance, an increasing function can bend downward or upward. (This possibility will be discussed in Problem 21.)

There are many biological examples of increasing functions that have a decreasing derivative and are therefore concave down.

EXAMPLE 4

Crop Yield The response of crop yield Y to soil nitrogen level N can often be described by a function of the form

$$Y(N) = Y_{\max} \frac{N}{K + N}, \quad N \geq 0$$

where $Y_{\max}$ is the maximum attainable yield and K is a positive constant. The graph of $Y(N)$ is shown in Figure 5.32. We see from the graph that $Y(N)$ is an increasing function of N. The graph bends downward and hence is concave down. Before continuing, we will check this conclusion against the results we obtained in this section. Using the quotient rule, we obtain

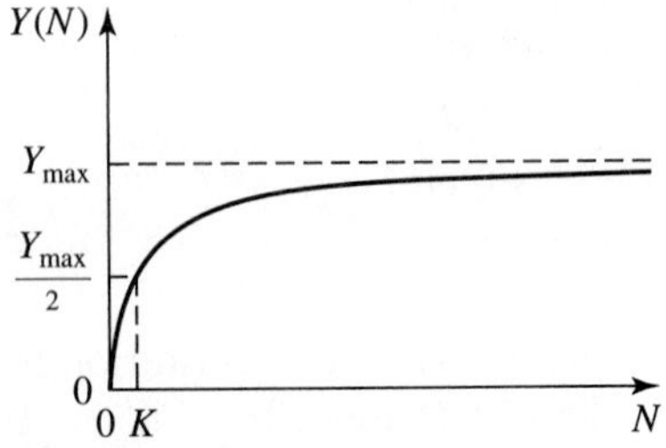

$$Y'(N) = Y_{\max} \frac{K + N - N}{(K + N)^2} = Y_{\max} \frac{K}{(K + N)^2}$$

Figure 5.32 The graph of $Y(N)$ in Example 4.

and using the chain rule, we get

$$Y''(N) = \frac{d}{dN}\left(Y_{\max}K(K+N)^{-2}\right)$$

$$= Y_{\max}K(-2)(K+N)^{-3}(1) = -Y_{\max}\frac{2K}{(K+N)^3}$$

Since $Y_{\max}$ and K are positive constants and $N \geq 0$, it follows that

$$Y'(N) > 0$$

which implies that $Y(N)$ is an increasing function. Furthermore,

$$Y''(N) < 0$$

which implies that $Y(N)$ is concave down. That is, $Y(N)$ is an increasing function, but the rate of increase is decreasing. We say that Y is *increasing at a decelerating rate*. What does this mean? It means that as we increase fertilizer levels, the yield will increase, but at a proportionally lesser rate. This type of curve is called a *diminishing return*. To be concrete, we choose values for $Y_{\max}$ and K:

$$Y(N) = 50\frac{N}{5+N}, \quad N \geq 0$$

The graph of this function is shown in Figure 5.33.

Suppose that initially $N = 5$. If we increase N by 5 (i.e., from 5 to 10), then $Y(N)$ changes from $Y(5) = 25$ to $Y(10) = 33.3$, an increase of 8.3. If we increase N by double the original amount, namely 10 (i.e., from 5 to 15), then $Y(15) = 37.5$ and the increase in yield is only 12.5, less than twice 8.3. Diminishing return can also be understood by comparing successive increments. If we start with $N = 5$ and increase by 5 to $N = 10$, then the change in Y (the Y-increment) is 8.3. Increasing N by the same amount, but starting at 10, we see that the Y-increment changes by $Y(15) - Y(10) = 4.2$. In general, changing N by equal increments has less of an effect for larger values of N; thus, we say that the return is diminishing.

You should compare a function representing a diminishing return with a linear function, say, $f(x) = 2x$, which is neither concave up nor concave down. (See Figure 5.34.) With a linear function, if we increase x from 5 to 10, $f(x)$ changes from 10 to 20. That is, $f(x)$ increases by 10. Then, if we increase x from 10 to 15, $f(x)$ changes from 20 to 30, again an increase of 10. That is, for linear functions, the increase is proportional. ■

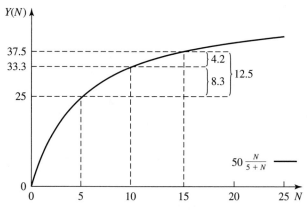

Figure 5.33 The graph of $Y(N)$ in Example 4 for $Y_{\max} = 50$ and $K = 5$.

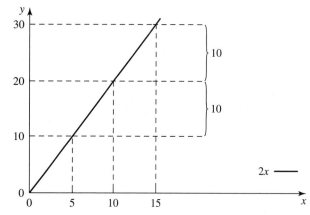

Figure 5.34 The graph of a linear function: Increases are proportional.

Section 5.2 Problems

■ 5.2.1 and 5.2.2

In Problems 1–20, determine where each function is increasing, decreasing, concave up, and concave down. With the help of a graphing calculator, sketch the graph of each function and label the intervals where it is increasing, decreasing, concave up, and concave down. Make sure that your graphs and your calculations agree.

1. $y = 3x - x^2, x \in \mathbf{R}$
2. $y = x^2 + 5x, x \in \mathbf{R}$
3. $y = x^2 + x - 4, x \in \mathbf{R}$
4. $y = x^2 - x + 3, x \in \mathbf{R}$
5. $y = -\frac{2}{3}x^3 + \frac{7}{2}x^2 - 3x + 4, x \in \mathbf{R}$
6. $y = (x - 2)^3 + 3, x \in \mathbf{R}$
7. $y = \sqrt{x + 1}, x \geq -1$
8. $y = (3x - 1)^{1/3}, x \in \mathbf{R}$
9. $y = \frac{1}{x}, x \neq 0$
10. $y = \frac{-2}{x^2 + 3}$
11. $(x^2 + 1)^{1/3}, x \in \mathbf{R}$
12. $y = \frac{5}{x - 2}, x \neq 2$
13. $y = \frac{1}{(1 + x)^2}, x \neq -1$
14. $y = \frac{x^2}{x^2 + 1}, x \geq 0$
15. $y = \sin x, 0 \leq x \leq 2\pi$
16. $y = \cos[\pi(x^2 - 1)], 2 \leq x \leq 3$
17. $y = e^x, x \in \mathbf{R}$
18. $y = \ln x, x > 0$
19. $y = e^{-x^2/2}, x \in \mathbf{R}$
20. $y = \frac{1}{1 + e^{-x}}, x \in \mathbf{R}$

21. Sketch the graph of
(a) a function that is increasing at an accelerating rate; and
(b) a function that is increasing at a decelerating rate.
(c) Assume that your functions in (a) and (b) are twice differentiable. Explain in each case how you could check the respective properties by using the first and the second derivatives. Which of the functions is concave up, and which is concave down?

22. Show that if $f(x)$ is the linear function $y = mx + b$, then increases in $f(x)$ are proportional to increases in x. That is, if we increase x by Δx, then $f(x)$ increases by the same amount Δy, regardless of the value of x. Compute Δy as a function of Δx.

23. We frequently must solve equations of the form $f(x) = 0$. When f is a continuous function on $[a, b]$ and $f(a)$ and $f(b)$ have opposite signs, the intermediate-value theorem guarantees that there exists at least one solution of the equation $f(x) = 0$ in $[a, b]$.
(a) Explain in words why there exists exactly one solution in (a, b) if, in addition, f is differentiable in (a, b) and $f'(x)$ is either strictly positive or strictly negative throughout (a, b).
(b) Use the result in (a) to show that

$$x^3 - 4x + 1 = 0$$

has exactly one solution in $[-1, 1]$.

24. **First-Derivative Test for Monotonicity** Suppose that f is continuous on $[a, b]$ and differentiable on (a, b). Show that if $f'(x) < 0$ for all $x \in (a, b)$, then f is decreasing on $[a, b]$.

25. **Second-Derivative Test for Concavity** Suppose that f is twice differentiable on an open interval I. Show that if $f''(x) < 0$, then f is concave down.

26. Suppose the size of a population at time t is $N(t)$, and the growth rate of the population is given by the logistic growth function

$$\frac{dN}{dt} = rN\left(1 - \frac{N}{K}\right), \quad t \geq 0$$

where r and K are positive constants.

(a) Graph the growth rate $\frac{dN}{dt}$ as a function of N for $r = 3$ and $K = 10$.
(b) The function $f(N) = rN(1 - N/K), N \geq 0$, is differentiable for $N > 0$. Compute $f'(N)$, and determine where the function $f(N)$ is increasing and where it is decreasing.

27. **Logistic Growth** Suppose that the size of a population at time t is $N(t)$ and the growth rate of the population is given by the logistic growth function

$$\frac{dN}{dt} = rN\left(1 - \frac{N}{K}\right), \quad t \geq 0$$

where r and K are positive constants. The per capita growth rate is defined by

$$g(N) = \frac{1}{N}\frac{dN}{dt} = r\left(1 - \frac{N}{K}\right)$$

(a) Graph $g(N)$ as a function of N for $N \geq 0$ when $r = 3$ and $K = 10$.
(b) The function $g(N) = r(1 - N/K), N \geq 0$, is differentiable for $N > 0$. Compute $g'(N)$, and determine where the function $g(N)$ is increasing and where it is decreasing.

28. **Resource-Dependent Growth** The growth rate of a plant depends on the amount of resources available. A simple and frequently used model for resource-dependent growth is the Monod model, according to which the growth rate is equal to

$$f(R) = \frac{aR}{k + R}, \quad R \geq 0$$

where R denotes the resource level and a and k are positive constants. When is the growth rate increasing? When is it decreasing?

29. **Population Growth** Suppose that the growth rate of a population is given by

$$f(N) = N\left(1 - \left(\frac{N}{K}\right)^\theta\right)$$

where N is the size of the population, K is a positive constant denoting the carrying capacity, and θ is a parameter greater than 1. Find $f'(N)$, and determine where the growth rate is increasing and where it is decreasing.

30. **Predation** Spruce budworms are a major pest that defoliates balsam fir. They are preyed upon by birds. A model for the per capita predation rate is given by

$$f(N) = \frac{aN}{k^2 + N^2}$$

where N denotes the density of spruce budworms and a and k are positive constants. Find $f'(N)$, and determine where the predation rate is increasing and where it is decreasing.

31. **Host–Parasitoid Interactions** Parasitoids are insects that lay their eggs in, on, or close to other (host) insects. Parasitoid larvae then devour the host insect. The likelihood of escaping parasitism may depend on parasitoid density. One model expressing this dependence sets the probability of escaping parasitism equal to

$$f(P) = e^{-aP}$$

where P is the parasitoid density and a is a positive constant. Determine whether the probability of escaping parasitism increases or decreases with parasitoid density.

32. Host–Parasitoid Interactions As an alternative to the model set forth in Problem 31, another model sets the probability of escaping parasitism equal to

$$f(P) = \left(1 + \frac{aP}{k}\right)^{-k}$$

where P is the parasitoid density and a and k are positive constants. Determine whether the probability of escaping parasitism increases or decreases with parasitoid density.

33. Tree Growth Suppose that the height y in feet of a tree as a function of the age x in years of the tree is given by

$$y = 117e^{-10/x}, \quad x > 0$$

(a) Show that the height of the tree increases with age. What is the maximum attainable height?

(b) Where is the graph of height versus age concave up, and where is it concave down?

(c) Use a graphing calculator to sketch the graph of height versus age.

(d) Use a graphing calculator to verify that the rate of growth is greatest at the point where the graph in (c) changes concavity.

34. Reproduction Plants employ two basic reproductive strategies: *polycarpy*, in which reproduction occurs repeatedly during the lifetime of the organism, and *monocarpy*, in which reproduction occurs only once during the lifetime of the organism. (Bamboo, for instance, is a monocarpic plant.) The following quote is taken from Iwasa et al. (1995):

> The optimal strategy is polycarpy (repeated reproduction) if reproductive success increases with the investment at a decreasing rate, [or] monocarpy ("big bang" reproduction) or intermittent reproduction if the reproductive success increases at an increasing rate.

(a) Sketch the graph of reproductive success as a function of reproductive investment for the cases of **(i)** polycarpy and **(ii)** monocarpy.

(b) Given that the second derivative describes whether a curve bends upward or downward, explain the preceding quote in terms of the second derivative of the reproductive success function.

35. Pollinator Visits Assume that the formula (Iwasa et al., 1995)

$$X(F) = cF^\gamma$$

where c is a positive constant, expresses the relationship between the number of flowers on a plant, F, and the average number of pollinator visits, $X(F)$. Find the range of values for the parameter γ such that the average number of pollinator visits to a plant increases with the number of flowers F but the rate of increase decreases with F. Explain your answer in terms of appropriate derivatives of the function $X(F)$.

36. Pollinator Visits Assume that the dependence of the average number of pollinator visits to a plant, X, on the number of flowers, F, is given by

$$X(F) = cF^\gamma$$

where γ is a positive constant less than 1 and c is a positive constant (Iwasa et al., 1995). How does the average number of pollen grains exported per flower, $E(F)$, change with the number of flowers on the plant, F, if $E(F)$ is proportional to

$$1 - \exp\left[-k\frac{X(F)}{F}\right]$$

where k is a positive constant?

37. Population Size Denote the size of a population by $N(t)$, and assume that $N(t)$ satisfies

$$\frac{dN}{dt} = Ne^{-aN} - N^2$$

where a is a positive constant.

(a) Show that the nontrivial equilibrium N^* satisfies

$$e^{-aN^*} = N^*$$

(b) Assume now that the nontrivial equilibrium N^* is a function of the parameter a. Use implicit differentiation to show that N^* is a decreasing function of a.

38. Population Size Denote the size of a population by $N(t)$, and assume that $N(t)$ satisfies

$$\frac{dN}{dt} = N\left(1 - \frac{N}{K}\right) - N \ln N$$

where K is a positive constant.

(a) Show that if $K > 1$, then there exists a nontrivial equilibrium $N^* > 0$ that satisfies

$$1 - \frac{N^*}{K} = \ln N^*$$

(b) Assume now that the nontrivial equilibrium N^* is a function of the parameter K. Use implicit differentiation to show that N^* is an increasing function of K.

39. Intraspecific Competition *(Adapted from Bellows, 1981)* Suppose that a study plot contains N annual plants, each of which produces S seeds that are sown within the same plot. The number of surviving plants in the next year is given by

$$A(N) = \frac{NS}{1 + (aN)^b} \tag{5.6}$$

for some positive constants a and b. This mathematical model incorporates density-dependent mortality: The greater the number of plants in the plot, the lower is the number of surviving offspring per plant, which is given by $A(N)/N$ and is called the *net reproductive rate*.

(a) Use calculus to show that $A(N)/N$ is a decreasing function of N.

(b) The following quantity, called the *k-value*, can be used to quantify the effects of intraspecific competition (i.e., competition between individuals of the same species):

$$k = \log[\text{initial density}] - \log[\text{final density}]$$

Here, "log" denotes the logarithm to base 10. The initial density is the product of the number of plants (N) and the number of seeds each plant produces (S). The final density is given by (5.6). Use the expression for k and (5.6) to show that

$$k = \log[NS] - \log\left[\frac{NS}{1 + (aN)^b}\right]$$
$$= \log\left[1 + (aN)^b\right]$$

We typically plot k versus $\log N$; the slope of the resulting curve is then used to quantify the effects of competition.

(i) Show that

$$\frac{d \log N}{dN} = \frac{1}{N \ln 10}$$

where ln denotes the natural logarithm.

(ii) Show that

$$\frac{dk}{d\log N} = (\ln 10)N\frac{dk}{dN} = \frac{b}{1+(aN)^{-b}}$$

(iii) Find

$$\lim_{N\to\infty}\frac{dk}{d\log N}$$

(iv) Show that if

$$\frac{dk}{d\log N} < 1$$

then $A(N)$ is increasing, whereas if

$$\frac{dk}{d\log N} > 1$$

then $A(N)$ is decreasing. [*Hint*: Compute $A'(N)$.] Explain in words what the two inequalities mean with respect to varying the initial density of seeds and observing the number of surviving plants the next year. (*Hint*: The first case is called *undercompensation* and the second case is called *overcompensation*.)

(v) The case

$$\frac{dk}{d\log N} = 1$$

is referred to as *exact compensation*. Suppose that you plot k versus $\log N$ and observe that, over a certain range of values of N, the slope of the resulting curve is equal to 1. Explain what this means.

40. *(Adapted from Reiss, 1989)* Suppose that the rate at which body weight W changes with age x is

$$\frac{dW}{dx} \propto W^a \qquad (5.7)$$

where a is some species-specific positive constant.
(a) The relative growth rate (percentage weight gained per unit of time) is defined as

$$\frac{1}{W}\frac{dW}{dx}$$

What is the relationship between the relative growth rate and body weight? For which values of a is the relative growth rate increasing, and for which values is it decreasing?
(b) As fish grow larger, their weight increases each day but the relative growth rate decreases. If the rate of growth is described by (5.7), what values of a can you exclude on the basis of your results in (a)? Explain how the increase in percentage weight (relative to the current body weight) differs for juvenile fish and for adult fish.

41. Allometric Growth Allometric equations describe the scaling relationship between two measurements, such as tree height versus tree diameter or skull length versus backbone length. These equations are often of the form

$$Y = bX^a \qquad (5.8)$$

where b is some positive constant and a is a constant that can be positive, negative, or zero.
(a) Assume that X and Y are body measurements (and therefore positive) and that their relationship is described by an allometric equation of the form (5.8). For what values of a is Y an increasing function of X, but one such that the ratio Y/X decreases with increasing X? Is Y concave up or concave down in this case?
(b) In vertebrates, we typically find

$$[\text{skull length}] \propto [\text{body length}]^a$$

for some $a \in (0,1)$. Use your answer in (a) to explain what this means for skull length versus body length in juveniles versus adults; that is, at which developmental stage do vertebrates have larger skulls relative to their body length?

42. pH The pH value of a solution measures the concentration of hydrogen ions, denoted by $[\text{H}^+]$, and is defined as

$$\text{pH} = -\log[\text{H}^+]$$

Use calculus to decide whether the pH value of a solution increases or decreases as the concentration of H^+ increases.

43. Allometric Growth The differential equation

$$\frac{dy}{dx} = k\frac{y}{x}$$

describes allometric growth, where k is a positive constant. Assume that x and y are both positive variables and that $y = f(x)$ is twice differentiable. Use implicit differentiation to determine for which values of k the function $y = f(x)$ is concave up.

44. Population Size Let $N(t)$ denote the population size at time t, and assume that $N(t)$ is twice differentiable and satisfies the differential equation

$$\frac{dN}{dt} = rN$$

where r is a real number. Differentiate the differential equation with respect to t, and state whether $N(t)$ is concave up or down.

■ 5.3 Extrema, Inflection Points, and Graphing

■ 5.3.1 Extrema

If f is a continuous function on the closed interval $[a,b]$, then f has a global maximum and a global minimum in $[a,b]$. This is the content of the extreme-value theorem, which is an existence result: It tells us only that global extrema exist under certain conditions, but it does not tell us how to find them.

Our strategy for finding global extrema in the case where f is a continuous function defined on a closed interval will be, first, to identify all local extrema of the function and, then, to select the global extrema from the set of local extrema. If f is a continuous function defined on an open interval or half-open interval, the existence of global extrema is no longer guaranteed, and we must compare the local extrema with the behavior of the function near the open boundaries of the domain. (See Example 5 in Section 5.1.) In particular, if $f(x)$ is defined on $\mathbf{R}$, we need to investigate the behavior of $f(x)$ as $x \to \pm\infty$. For if the function $f(x)$ goes to $+\infty$ (or $-\infty$) as $x \to +\infty$ or $-\infty$, it cannot have a global maximum (global minimum). We discuss this in Example 1 of this section.

Local extrema can be found in a systematic way, using a straightforward recipe to identify candidates. We showed in Section 5.1 that if f has a local extremum at an interior point c and $f'(c)$ exists, then $f'(c) = 0$ (Fermat's theorem). That is, points where f is differentiable and where the first derivative is equal to 0 are certainly candidates for local extrema in the interior of the domain. Of course, these are only candidates, as explained in Section 5.1. (Recall that $y = x^3$ has a horizontal tangent at $x = 0$, but $y = x^3$ does not have a local extremum at $x = 0$.) In addition to points where the first derivative is equal to 0, we must check all points where the function is not differentiable. (For instance, $y = |x|$ has a local minimum at $x = 0$, although it is not differentiable at 0.) Points where the first derivative is equal to 0 or does not exist are called **critical points**. In addition to checking the critical points, we must always check the endpoints of the interval on which f is defined (provided that there are such endpoints).

There are no other points where local extrema can occur. We are thus equipped with a systematic way of searching for *candidates* for local extrema:

---

1. Find all numbers c where $f'(c) = 0$.
2. Find all numbers c where $f'(c)$ does not exist.
3. Find the endpoints of the domain of f.

We illustrate this procedure in the following example: We wish to find all local and global extrema of the function

$$f(x) = |x^2 - 4|, \quad -3 \leq x < 2.5$$

We know from Example 5 of Subsection 5.1.2 what the graph of the function looks like (the domain is different here). We plot it again (Figure 5.35), which will make it easier to understand the procedure for finding relative extrema. But note that very often we do not know what a graph looks like, and we find relative extrema in order to gain a better understanding of the graph!

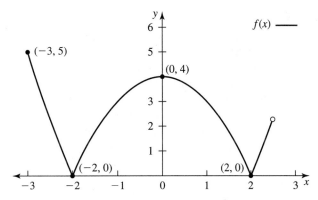

Figure 5.35 The graph of $f(x) = |x^2 - 4|$ for $-3 \leq x < 2.5$.

We will first rewrite $f(x)$ as a piecewise-defined function in order to get rid of the absolute-value sign:

$$f(x) = \begin{cases} x^2 - 4 & \text{for } -3 \leq x \leq -2 \text{ or } 2 \leq x < 2.5 \\ -x^2 + 4 & \text{for } -2 \leq x \leq 2 \end{cases}$$

This piecewise-defined function is differentiable on the open intervals $(-3, -2)$,

(−2, 2), and (2, 2.5). We find that

$$f'(x) = \begin{cases} 2x & \text{for } -3 < x < -2 \text{ or } 2 < x < 2.5 \\ -2x & \text{for } -2 < x < 2 \end{cases}$$

Since $f'(x) = 0$ for $x = 0$ and $0 \in (-2, 2)$, it follows that $(0, f(0))$ is a critical point and is our first candidate for a local extremum. There are no other points where $f'(x) = 0$.

The second step is to identify interior points where the function is not differentiable. Since the function is differentiable on the open intervals $(-3, -2)$, $(-2, 2)$, and $(2, 2.5)$, we must look at the points where the function is pieced together, namely at $x = -2$ and at $x = 2$. We obtain

$$\lim_{x \to -2^-} f'(x) = -4 \qquad \text{and} \qquad \lim_{x \to -2^+} f'(x) = 4$$

and

$$\lim_{x \to 2^-} f'(x) = -4 \qquad \text{and} \qquad \lim_{x \to 2^+} f'(x) = 4$$

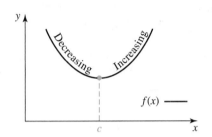

Figure 5.36 The function $y = f(x)$ has a local minimum at $x = c$.

These limits show that the function is not differentiable at $x = -2$ and $x = 2$. Therefore, there are critical points at $x = -2$ and $x = 2$, and those points are also candidates for local extrema.

The third step is to identify endpoints of the domain. Since f is defined on $[-3, 2.5)$, there is an endpoint at $x = -3$. The fourth candidate is thus at $x = -3$. The interval $[-3, 2.5)$ is open at $x = 2.5$; hence, 2.5 is not in the domain of the function. The point $(2.5, f(2.5))$ is therefore not a candidate for an extremum.

Our systematic procedure has provided us with four candidates for local extrema, at $x = -3, -2, 0$, and 2. In each case, we must decide whether the associated point is in fact a local extremum and, if so, whether it is a local maximum or minimum. The following observation, although rather obvious, is the key (see Figures 5.36 and 5.37):

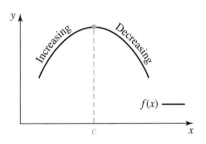

Figure 5.37 The function $y = f(x)$ has a local maximum at $x = c$.

> A continuous function has a local minimum at c if the function is decreasing to the left of c and increasing to the right of c. A continuous function has a local maximum at c if the function is increasing to the left of c and decreasing to the right of c.

If the function is differentiable, as in our example, we can use the first-derivative test to identify regions where the function is increasing and regions where it is decreasing.

Since $f'(x) = 2x$ for $-3 < x < -2$ and $2 < x < 2.5$, it follows that $f'(x) > 0$ for $2 < x < 2.5$ and $f'(x) < 0$ for $-3 < x < -2$. Also, since $f'(x) = -2x$ for $-2 < x < 2$, it follows that $f'(x) > 0$ for $x \in (-2, 0)$ and $f'(x) < 0$ for $x \in (0, 2)$. We illustrate these regions on the following number line for x [the plus (minus) signs show where $f'(x)$ is positive (negative)]:

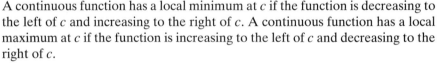

We start with the interior points. At $x = -2$, the function changes from decreasing to increasing; that is, $f(x)$ has a local minimum at $x = -2$. At $x = 0$, the function changes from increasing to decreasing; that is, $f(x)$ has a local maximum at $x = 0$. At $x = 2$, the function changes from decreasing to increasing; that is, $f(x)$ has a local minimum at $x = 2$.

We still need to analyze the endpoint at $x = -3$. We see that the function is decreasing to the right of $x = -3$; that is, $f(x)$ has a local maximum at $x = -3$. You should compare all of our findings with the graph of $f(x)$.

The last step is to select the global extrema from the local extrema, but since the domain of f is not a closed interval, we must compare the values of the local extrema against the value at the boundary $x = 2.5$. We have

$$f(-3) = 5 \qquad f(-2) = 0 \qquad f(0) = 4 \qquad f(2) = 0 \qquad \lim_{x \to 2.5^-} f(x) = 2.25$$

Since 5 is the maximum value and 0 the minimum, the absolute maximum occurs at $x = -3$ and the global minima (there are two) occur at $x = -2$ and $x = 2$.

When a function is twice differentiable at the point where the first derivative is equal to 0, there is a shortcut for determining whether a local maximum or a local minimum exists. (See Figure 5.38.) We assume that the function $f(x)$ is twice differentiable. The graph of $f(x)$ in Figure 5.38 has a local maximum at $x = c$, since the function is increasing to the left of $x = c$ and decreasing to the right of $x = c$. If we look at how the slopes of the tangent lines change as we cross $x = c$ from the left, we see that the slopes are decreasing; that is, $f''(c) < 0$. In other words, the function is concave down at $x = c$ (which is immediately apparent when you look at the graph, but remember that typically you don't have the graph in front of you). There is an analogous result where f has a local minimum at $x = c$. (See Figure 5.39.) This discussion yields the following test:

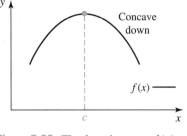

Figure 5.38 The function $y = f(x)$ has a local maximum at $x = c$.

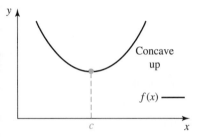

Figure 5.39 The function $y = f(x)$ has a local minimum at $x = c$.

> **The Second-Derivative Test for Local Extrema** Suppose that f is twice differentiable on an open interval containing c.
>
> If $f'(c) = 0$ and $f''(c) < 0$, then f has a local maximum at $x = c$.
> If $f'(c) = 0$ and $f''(c) > 0$, then f has a local minimum at $x = c$.

Note that finding the point c where $f'(c) = 0$ gives us a candidate for a local extremum. If the second derivative $f''(c) \neq 0$, the local extremum is established: Not only does this information tell us whether there is a local extremum, it identifies it. The test is easy to apply, as we have only to check the sign of the second derivative at $x = c$; we do not have to check the behavior of the function in a neighborhood of $x = c$. Still, the second-derivative test will not always work. For instance, if $f(x) = x^4$, then $f'(x) = 4x^3$ and $f''(x) = 12x^2$. On the basis of the graph of $y = f(x)$, we know that $f(x)$ has a local minimum at $x = 0$. We find that $f'(0) = 0$ and $f''(0) = 0$. Thus, the theorem cannot be used to draw any conclusions about $y = f(x)$ at $x = 0$.

We next look at two examples in which the second-derivative test can be applied.

EXAMPLE 1   Find all local and global extrema of

$$f(x) = \frac{3}{2}x^4 - 2x^3 - 6x^2 + 2, \quad x \in \mathbf{R}$$

Solution   Figure 5.40 shows the graph of $f(x)$. Since $f(x)$ is twice differentiable for all $x \in \mathbf{R}$, we begin by finding the first two derivatives of f. The first derivative is

$$f'(x) = 6x^3 - 6x^2 - 12x = 6x(x - 2)(x + 1)$$

Factoring $f'(x)$ will make it easier to find its zeros. The second derivative is

$$f''(x) = 18x^2 - 12x - 12$$

Since $f'(x)$ exists for all $x \in \mathbf{R}$ and the domain has no endpoints, the only candidates for local extrema are points where $f'(x) = 0$:

$$6x(x - 2)(x + 1) = 0$$

We thus find that $x = 0$, $x = 2$, and $x = -1$. Since $f''(x)$ exists, we can use the second-derivative test to determine whether $(0, f(0))$, $(2, f(2))$, and $(-1, f(-1))$

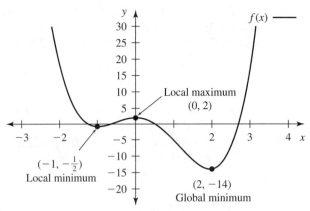

Figure 5.40 The graph of $f(x) = \frac{3}{2}x^4 - 2x^3 - 6x^2 + 2$ in Example 1.

are local extrema and, if so, of what type they are. We need to evaluate the second derivative at each x-coordinate:

$$f''(0) = -12 < 0 \quad \Longrightarrow \quad \text{local maximum at } x = 0$$
$$f''(2) = 36 > 0 \quad \Longrightarrow \quad \text{local minimum at } x = 2$$
$$f''(-1) = 18 > 0 \quad \Longrightarrow \quad \text{local minimum at } x = -1$$

The function $f(x)$ is defined on **R**. As mentioned at the beginning of this section, in order to find global extrema, we must check the local extrema and compare their values against each other and against the function values as $x \to \infty$ and $x \to -\infty$. Thus, we have

$$f(0) = 2 \qquad f(2) = -14 \qquad f(-1) = -\frac{1}{2}$$

and

$$\lim_{x \to \infty} f(x) = \infty \qquad \lim_{x \to -\infty} f(x) = \infty$$

Although the local maximum is 2 at $x = 0$, the point $(0, 2)$ is not a global maximum: Since the function goes to ∞ as $|x| \to \infty$, it certainly exceeds the value 2. In fact, there is no global maximum; there is, however, a global minimum at $x = 2$. ■

EXAMPLE 2   Find all local and global extrema of

$$f(x) = x(1 - x)^{2/3}, \quad x \in \mathbf{R}$$

Solution   The graph of $f(x)$ is shown in Figure 5.41. We differentiate $f(x)$ by the product rule:

$$f'(x) = (1 - x)^{2/3} + x\frac{2}{3}(1 - x)^{-1/3}(-1)$$

$$= (1 - x)^{2/3} - \frac{2x}{3(1 - x)^{1/3}} \quad \text{for } x \neq 1$$

$$f''(x) = \frac{2}{3}(1 - x)^{-1/3}(-1) - \frac{2}{3}\left[(1 - x)^{-1/3} + x\left(-\frac{1}{3}\right)(1 - x)^{-4/3}(-1)\right]$$

$$= -\frac{2}{3(1 - x)^{1/3}} - \frac{2}{3(1 - x)^{1/3}} - \frac{2x}{9(1 - x)^{4/3}}$$

$$= -\frac{4}{3(1 - x)^{1/3}} - \frac{2x}{9(1 - x)^{4/3}} \quad \text{for } x \neq 1$$

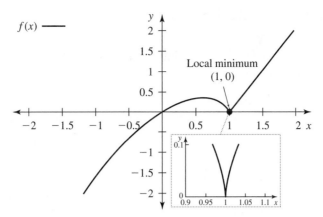

Figure 5.41 The graph of $f(x) = x(1 - x)^{2/3}$.

We first find points where $f'(x) = 0$. If $x \neq 1$, then $f'(x) = 0$ when

$$(1 - x)^{2/3} = \frac{2x}{3(1 - x)^{1/3}}$$

$$3(1 - x) = 2x$$

$$3 = 5x$$

$$x = \frac{3}{5}$$

Next, we check the second derivative at $x = \frac{3}{5}$:

$$f''\left(\frac{3}{5}\right) = -\frac{4}{3(\frac{2}{5})^{1/3}} - \frac{(2)(\frac{3}{5})}{9(\frac{2}{5})^{4/3}} < 0$$

That is, $f(x)$ has a local maximum at $x = \frac{3}{5}$.

The first derivative is not defined at $x = 1$. We therefore must investigate the function in the neighborhood of $x = 1$. Note that $f(x)$ is continuous at $x = 1$. We investigate where the function is increasing and where it is decreasing. The only x-values at which the derivative of the function can change sign are $x = \frac{3}{5}$ and $x = 1$. To determine whether $f'(x)$ is positive or negative in each of the intervals associated with these values, we simply need to evaluate $f'(x)$ at one value in each interval. For instance, $f'(0) = 1 > 0$; that is, $f'(x) > 0$ for $x < 3/5$. A similar computation can be carried out for the other subintervals. We find that $f'(x)$ is positive to the left of $\frac{3}{5}$, negative between $\frac{3}{5}$ and 1, and positive for $x > 1$. The situation is summarized in the following number line:

$$\overset{+++++++\quad -----\quad +++++++}{\underset{\underset{\frac{3}{5}}{|}\qquad\qquad\underset{1}{|}}{\rule{8cm}{0.4pt}}}$$

We conclude that $f(x)$ has a local minimum at $x = 1$. We can say a bit more about what is happening at $x = 1$ (see inset in Figure 5.41):

$$\lim_{x \to 1^-} f'(x) = \lim_{x \to 1^-} \left[(1 - x)^{2/3} - \frac{2x}{3(1 - x)^{1/3}} \right] = -\infty$$

$$\lim_{x \to 1^+} f'(x) = \lim_{x \to 1^+} \left[(1 - x)^{2/3} - \frac{2x}{3(1 - x)^{1/3}} \right] = \infty$$

We see that there is a vertical tangent at $x = 1$; such points are called **cusps**.

Since

$$\lim_{x \to \infty} f(x) = \infty \qquad \text{and} \qquad \lim_{x \to -\infty} f(x) = -\infty$$

there are no absolute extrema.

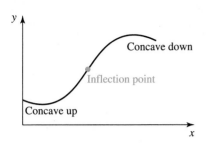

Figure 5.42 Inflection point.

■ 5.3.2 Inflection Points

We begin with a verbal definition of **inflection points** and then give a procedure for locating such points. (See Figure 5.42.)

> Inflection points are points where the concavity of a function changes—that is, where the function changes from concave up to concave down or from concave down to concave up.

If the function is twice differentiable, there is an algebraic condition for finding candidates for inflection points. Recall that if a function f is twice differentiable, it is concave up if $f'' > 0$ and concave down if $f'' < 0$. At an inflection point, f'' must therefore change sign; that is, the second derivative must be 0 at an inflection point. More formally,

> If $f(x)$ is twice differentiable and has an inflection point at $x = c$, then $f''(c) = 0$.

Note that $f''(c) = 0$ is a necessary, but not sufficient, condition for the existence of an inflection point of a twice-differentiable function. For instance, $f(x) = x^4$ has $f''(0) = 0$, but $f(x)$ does not have an inflection point at $x = 0$. The function $f(x) = x^4$ is concave up and has a local minimum at $x = 0$. (See Figure 5.43; we encountered a similar situation in Fermat's theorem, where we had a necessary, but not sufficient, condition for the existence of local extrema.) We can therefore use this test only for finding *candidates* for inflection points. To determine whether a candidate *is* an inflection point, we must check whether the second derivative changes sign.

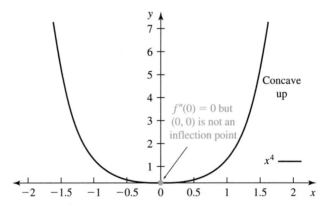

Figure 5.43 The function $f(x) = x^4$ has $f''(0) = 0$ but no inflection point at $x = 0$.

EXAMPLE 3

Show that the function

$$f(x) = \frac{1}{2}x^3 - \frac{3}{2}x^2 + 2x + 1, \quad x \in \mathbf{R}$$

has an inflection point at $x = 1$.

Solution

The graph of $f(x)$ is shown in Figure 5.44. We compute the first two derivatives:

$$f'(x) = \frac{3}{2}x^2 - 3x + 2$$

$$f''(x) = 3x - 3$$

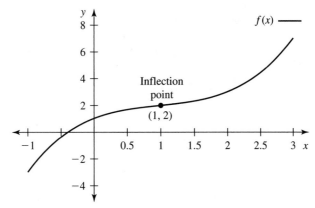

Figure 5.44 The graph of $f(x) = \frac{1}{2}x^3 - \frac{3}{2}x^2 + 2x + 1$ has an inflection point at $x = 1$.

Now, $f''(x) = 0$ if $x = 1$. Therefore, $(1, f(1))$ is a candidate for an inflection point. Since $f''(x)$ is positive for $x > 1$ and negative for $x < 1$, $f''(x)$ changes sign at $x = 1$. We therefore conclude that $f(x)$ has an inflection point at $x = 1$. ■

■ 5.3.3 Graphing and Asymptotes

Using the first and the second derivatives of a twice-differentiable function, we can obtain a fair amount of information about the function. We can determine intervals on which the function is increasing, decreasing, concave up, and concave down. We can identify local and global extrema and find inflection points. To graph the function, we also need to know how the function behaves in the neighborhood of points where either the function or its derivative is not defined, and we need to know how the function behaves at the endpoints of its domain (or, if the function is defined for all $x \in \mathbf{R}$, how the function behaves for $x \to \pm\infty$).

We will need limits again—this time to determine the behavior of a function at points where it is not defined and when $x \to \pm\infty$. We illustrate as follows: Consider

$$f(x) = \frac{1}{x}, \quad x \neq 0$$

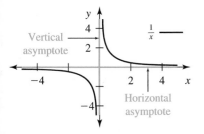

Figure 5.45 The graph of $f(x) = \frac{1}{x}$ with horizontal asymptote $y = 0$ and vertical asymptote $x = 0$.

You are familiar with the graph of $f(x)$. (See Figure 5.45.) You can see that the graph of $f(x)$ approaches the line $y = 0$ when $x \to \infty$ and also when $x \to -\infty$. Such a line is called an **asymptote**, and we say that $f(x)$ approaches the line $y = 0$ asymptotically as $x \to \infty$ and also as $x \to -\infty$. Since $y = 0$ is a horizontal line, it is called a **horizontal asymptote**. We can represent horizontal asymptotes mathematically by the following limits:

$$\lim_{x \to \infty} f(x) = \lim_{x \to \infty} \frac{1}{x} = 0 \quad \text{and} \quad \lim_{x \to -\infty} f(x) = \lim_{x \to -\infty} \frac{1}{x} = 0$$

The function $f(x) = \frac{1}{x}$ is not defined at $x = 0$. Looking at the graph of the function $f(x) = \frac{1}{x}$, we see that it approaches the line $x = 0$ asymptotically. Since $x = 0$ is a vertical line, it is called a **vertical asymptote**. We can also represent vertical asymptotes mathematically by limits:

$$\lim_{x \to 0^-} f(x) = \lim_{x \to 0^-} \frac{1}{x} = -\infty \quad \text{and} \quad \lim_{x \to 0^+} f(x) = \lim_{x \to 0^+} \frac{1}{x} = +\infty$$

Definition A line $y = b$ is a **horizontal** asymptote if either

$$\lim_{x \to -\infty} f(x) = b \quad \text{or} \quad \lim_{x \to \infty} f(x) = b$$

A line $x = c$ is a **vertical** asymptote if

$$\lim_{x \to c^+} f(x) = +\infty \quad \text{or} \quad \lim_{x \to c^+} f(x) = -\infty$$

or

$$\lim_{x \to c^-} f(x) = +\infty \quad \text{or} \quad \lim_{x \to c^-} f(x) = -\infty$$

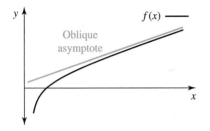

Figure 5.46 The function $y = f(x)$ has an oblique asymptote.

In addition to horizontal and vertical asymptotes, there are **oblique** asymptotes. (See Figure 5.46.) These are straight lines that are neither horizontal nor vertical and are such that the graph of the function approaches them as either $x \to +\infty$ or $x \to -\infty$. Mathematically, we express oblique asymptotes in the following way: If

$$\lim_{x \to +\infty} [f(x) - (mx + b)] = 0 \quad \text{or} \quad \lim_{x \to -\infty} [f(x) - (mx + b)] = 0$$

then the line $y = mx + b$ is an oblique asymptote. The simplest case of an oblique asymptote occurs with a rational function in which the degree of the numerator is one higher than the degree of the denominator.

EXAMPLE 4

Oblique Asymptote Let

$$f(x) = \frac{x^2 - 3}{x - 2}, \quad x \neq 2.$$

To determine whether $f(x)$ has an oblique asymptote, we use long division. We find that

$$\frac{x^2 - 3}{x - 2} = x + 2 + \frac{1}{x - 2}.$$

We see that $f(x)$ is the sum of a linear term $x + 2$ and a remainder term $\frac{1}{x-2}$, the latter of which goes to 0 as $x \to \pm\infty$. To check that $y = x + 2$ is indeed an oblique asymptote, we carry out the following computation:

$$\lim_{x \to \pm\infty} [f(x) - (x + 2)] = \lim_{x \to \pm\infty} \left[\frac{x^2 - 3}{x - 2} - (x + 2) \right]$$

$$= \lim_{x \to \pm\infty} \left[x + 2 + \frac{1}{x - 2} - (x + 2) \right]$$

$$= \lim_{x \to \pm\infty} \frac{1}{x - 2} = 0$$

Hence, $y = x + 2$ is an oblique asymptote. The graph of $f(x) = \frac{x^2-3}{x-2}$, together with its oblique asymptote, is shown in Figure 5.47. [The graph of $f(x)$ also has a vertical asymptote at $x = 2$.] ■

We can now combine the results that we have obtained so far to produce the graph of a given function. We illustrate the steps leading to the graph in the next two examples.

EXAMPLE 5

Sketch the graph of the function

$$f(x) = \frac{2}{3}x^3 - 2x + 1, \quad x \in \mathbf{R}$$

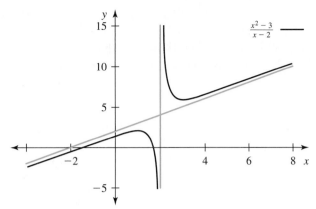

Figure 5.47 The graph of $f(x) = \frac{x^2-3}{x-2}$ with oblique asymptote $g(x) = x + 2$ (and a vertical asymptote at $x = 2$).

Solution

STEP 1. Find $f'(x)$ and $f''(x)$:

$$f'(x) = 2x^2 - 2 = 2(x - 1)(x + 1), \quad x \in \mathbf{R}$$
$$f''(x) = 4x, \quad x \in \mathbf{R}$$

STEP 2. Find the places where $f'(x)$ is positive, negative, zero, or undefined. Identify the intervals where the function is increasing and where it is decreasing. Find local extrema.

We begin by setting $f'(x) = 0$; that is,

$$2(x - 1)(x + 1) = 0$$

We find two solutions, namely $x = 1$ and $x = -1$. The following number line shows where $f'(x)$ is positive and where it is negative. Since $f'(x)$ is a polynomial, it is differentiable for all $x \in \mathbf{R}$; it can change sign only at $x = 1$ and at $x = -1$. These x-values break the number line into three intervals: $x < -1$, $-1 < x < 1$, and $x > 1$. To determine whether $f'(x)$ is positive or negative in each of these intervals, we simply need to evaluate $f'(x)$ at one value in each interval. For instance, $f'(-2) = 2(-3)(-1) = 6 > 0$; that is, $f'(x) > 0$ for $x < -1$. A similar calculation can be carried out for the other subintervals. When we finish calculating, we have the following number line:

$$+ + + + + + + \quad - - - - - \quad + + + + + + +$$
$$\overline{\hspace{2.2cm}\underset{-1}{\vert}\hspace{1.8cm}\underset{1}{\vert}\hspace{2.2cm}}$$

That is, $f(x)$ is increasing for $x < -1$ and $x > 1$ and decreasing for $-1 < x < 1$. The number line also shows that the function has a local maximum at $x = -1$, namely, $(-1, \frac{7}{3})$, and a local minimum at $x = 1$, namely, $(1, -\frac{1}{3})$. (Alternatively, we could have used the second-derivative test.)

STEP 3. Find the places where $f''(x)$ is positive, negative, zero, or undefined. Find inflection points.

We set $f''(x) = 0$; that is,

$$4x = 0$$

We find one solution: $x = 0$. Since $f''(x)$ exists for all $x \in \mathbf{R}$, it can change sign only at $x = 0$. Evaluating $f''(x)$ at a value to the left of 0, say, $x = -1$, shows that $f''(x) < 0$ for $x < 0$. Similarly, evaluating $f''(x)$ at a value to the right of 0, say, $x = 1$, shows that $f''(x) > 0$ for $x > 0$. The situation is illustrated on the following number line:

$$- - - - - - - - - - - \quad + + + + + + + + +$$
$$\overline{\hspace{4.2cm}\underset{0}{\vert}\hspace{4.2cm}}$$

Since $f''(x)$ changes sign at $x = 0$, we conclude that the function has an inflection point at $x = 0$, namely, $(0, 1)$. The function is concave down for $x < 0$ and concave up for $x > 0$.

STEP 4. Determine the behavior at endpoints of the domain.

The domain is $(-\infty, +\infty)$. We therefore need to check the behavior of $f(x)$ as $x \to +\infty$ and as $x \to -\infty$. We find that

$$\lim_{x \to -\infty} f(x) = -\infty \quad \text{and} \quad \lim_{x \to +\infty} f(x) = +\infty$$

Combining the results of these four steps allows us to sketch the graph of the function, as illustrated in Figure 5.48. You should label all extrema and inflection points. ■

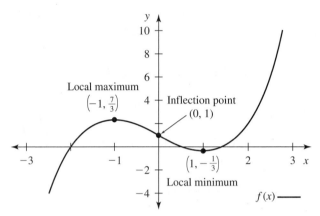

Figure 5.48 The graph of $f(x) = \frac{2}{3}x^3 - 2x + 1$.

EXAMPLE 6

Sketch the graph of the function

$$f(x) = e^{-x^2/2}, \quad x \in \mathbf{R}$$

Solution

STEP 1.

$$f'(x) = -xe^{-x^2/2}, \quad x \in \mathbf{R}$$

and

$$f''(x) = (-1)e^{-x^2/2} + (-x)(-x)e^{-x^2/2}$$

$$= e^{-x^2/2}(x^2 - 1), \quad x \in \mathbf{R}$$

STEP 2. Since $f'(x)$ is defined for all $x \in \mathbf{R}$, we need to identify only those points where $f'(x) = 0$:

$$f'(x) = 0 \quad \text{for } x = 0$$

The sign of $f'(x)$ is illustrated on the following number line for x:

$$\underset{0}{\underline{+ + + + + + + + + + \quad - - - - - - - - - -}}$$

We find that $f(x)$ is increasing for $x < 0$ and decreasing for $x > 0$. Hence, $f(x)$ has a local maximum at $x = 0$, namely, $(0, 1)$.

STEP 3. We have

$$f''(x) = 0 \quad \text{for } x = 1 \text{ and } x = -1$$

The sign of $f''(x)$ is illustrated on the following number line for x:

$$\underset{-1 \qquad\qquad 1}{\underline{+ + + + + + + \quad - - - - - \quad + + + + + + +}}$$

We find that $f(x)$ is concave up for $x < -1$ and $x > 1$ and is concave down for $-1 < x < 1$. There are two inflection points, one at $x = -1$, namely, $(-1, e^{-1/2})$, and the other at $x = 1$, namely, $(1, e^{-1/2})$. There are no other inflection points, since $f''(x)$ is defined for all $x \in \mathbf{R}$.

STEP 4. We have

$$\lim_{x \to -\infty} f(x) = 0 \quad \text{and} \quad \lim_{x \to +\infty} f(x) = 0$$

This shows that $y = 0$ is a horizontal asymptote.
The graph of $f(x)$ is shown in Figure 5.49.

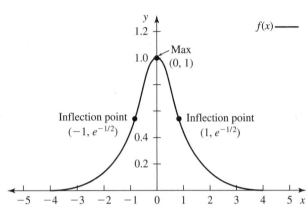

Figure 5.49 The graph of $f(x) = e^{-x^2/2}$.

Section 5.3 Problems

■ 5.3.1

Find the local maxima and minima of each of the functions in Problems 1–16. Determine whether each function has absolute maxima and minima and find their coordinates. For each function, find the intervals on which it is increasing and the intervals on which it is decreasing.

1. $y = (2 - x)^2, -2 \le x \le 3$
2. $y = \sqrt{x - 1}, 1 \le x \le 2$
3. $y = \ln(2x - 1), 1 \le x \le 2$
4. $y = \ln \frac{x}{x+1}, x > 0$
5. $y = xe^{-x}, 0 \le x \le 1$
6. $y = |16 - x^2|, -5 \le x \le 8$
7. $y = (x - 1)^3 + 1, x \in \mathbf{R}$
8. $y = x^3 - 3x + 1, x \in \mathbf{R}$
9. $y = \cos(\pi x^2), -1 \le x \le 1$
10. $y = \sin[2\pi(x - 3)], 2 \le x \le 3$
11. $y = e^{-|x|}, x \in \mathbf{R}$
12. $y = e^{-x^2/4}, x \in \mathbf{R}$
13. $y = \frac{1}{3}x^3 + \frac{1}{2}x^2 - 6x + 2, x \in \mathbf{R}$
14. $y = x^2(1 - x), x \in \mathbf{R}$
15. $y = (x - 1)^{1/3}, x \in \mathbf{R}$
16. $y = \sqrt{1 + x^2}, x \in \mathbf{R}$

17. [This problem illustrates the fact that $f'(c) = 0$ is not a sufficient condition for the existence of a local extremum of a differentiable function.] Show that the function $f(x) = x^3$ has a horizontal tangent at $x = 0$; that is, show that $f'(0) = 0$, but $f'(x)$ does not change sign at $x = 0$ and, hence, $f(x)$ does not have a local extremum at $x = 0$.

18. Suppose that $f(x)$ is twice differentiable on $\mathbf{R}$, with $f(x) > 0$ for $x \in \mathbf{R}$. Show that if $f(x)$ has a local maximum at $x = c$, then $g(x) = \ln f(x)$ also has a local maximum at $x = c$.

■ 5.3.2

In Problems 19–24, determine all inflection points.

19. $f(x) = x^3 - 2, x \in \mathbf{R}$
20. $f(x) = (x - 3)^5, 0 \in \mathbf{R}$
21. $f(x) = e^{-x^2}, x \ge 0$
22. $f(x) = xe^{-x}, x \ge 0$
23. $f(x) = \tan x, -\frac{\pi}{2} < x < \frac{\pi}{2}$
24. $f(x) = \ln x + \frac{1}{x}, x > 0$

25. [This problem illustrates the fact that $f''(c) = 0$ is not a sufficient condition for an inflection point of a twice-differentiable function.] Show that the function $f(x) = x^4$ has $f''(0) = 0$ but that $f''(x)$ does not change sign at $x = 0$ and, hence, $f(x)$ does not have an inflection point at $x = 0$.

26. **Logistic Equation** Suppose that the size of a population at time t is denoted by $N(t)$ and satisfies

$$N(t) = \frac{100}{1 + 3e^{-2t}}$$

for $t \ge 0$.
(a) Show that $N(0) = 25$.
(b) Show that $N(t)$ is strictly increasing.
(c) Show that

$$\lim_{t \to \infty} N(t) = 100$$

(d) Show that $N(t)$ has an inflection point when $N(t) = 50$—that is, when the size of the population is at half its limiting value.
(e) Use your results in (a)–(d) to sketch the graph of $N(t)$.

■ **5.3.3**

Find the local maxima and minima of the functions in Problems 27–34. Determine whether the functions have absolute maxima and minima, and, if so, find their coordinates. Find inflection points. Find the intervals on which the function is increasing, on which it is decreasing, on which it is concave up, and on which it is concave down. Sketch the graph of each function.

27. $y = \frac{2}{3}x^3 - 2x^2 - 6x + 2$ for $-2 \le x \le 5$

28. $y = x^4 - 2x^2$, $x \in \mathbf{R}$

29. $y = |x^2 - 9|$, $-4 \le x \le 5$

30. $y = \sqrt{|x|}$, $x \in \mathbf{R}$

31. $y = x + \cos x$, $x \in \mathbf{R}$

32. $y = \tan x - x$, $x \in \left(-\dfrac{\pi}{2}, \dfrac{\pi}{2}\right)$

33. $y = \dfrac{x^2 - 1}{x^2 + 1}$, $x \in \mathbf{R}$

34. $y = \ln(x^2 + 1)$, $x \in \mathbf{R}$

35. Let
$$f(x) = \frac{x}{x - 1}, \quad x \ne 1$$

(a) Show that
$$\lim_{x \to -\infty} f(x) = 1$$
and
$$\lim_{x \to +\infty} f(x) = 1$$
That is, show that $y = 1$ is a horizontal asymptote of the curve $y = \frac{x}{x-1}$.

(b) Show that
$$\lim_{x \to 1^-} f(x) = -\infty$$
and
$$\lim_{x \to 1^+} f(x) = +\infty$$
That is, show that $x = 1$ is a vertical asymptote of the curve $y = \frac{x}{x-1}$.

(c) Determine where $f(x)$ is increasing and where it is decreasing. Does $f(x)$ have local extrema?

(d) Determine where $f(x)$ is concave up and where it is concave down. Does $f(x)$ have inflection points?

(e) Sketch the graph of $f(x)$ together with its asymptotes.

36. Let
$$f(x) = -\frac{2}{x^2 - 1}, \quad x \ne -1, 1$$

(a) Show that
$$\lim_{x \to +\infty} f(x) = 0$$
and
$$\lim_{x \to -\infty} f(x) = 0$$
That is, show that $y = 0$ is a horizontal asymptote of $f(x)$.

(b) Show that
$$\lim_{x \to -1^-} f(x) = -\infty$$
and
$$\lim_{x \to -1^+} f(x) = +\infty$$
and that
$$\lim_{x \to 1^-} f(x) = +\infty$$

and
$$\lim_{x \to 1^+} f(x) = -\infty$$
That is, show that $x = -1$ and $x = 1$ are vertical asymptotes of $f(x)$.

(c) Determine where $f(x)$ is increasing and where it is decreasing. Does $f(x)$ have local extrema?

(d) Determine where $f(x)$ is concave up and where it is concave down. Does $f(x)$ have inflection points?

(e) Sketch the graph of $f(x)$ together with its asymptotes.

37. Let
$$f(x) = \frac{2x^2 - 5}{x + 2}, \quad x \ne -2$$

(a) Show that $x = -2$ is a vertical asymptote.

(b) Determine where $f(x)$ is increasing and where it is decreasing. Does $f(x)$ have local extrema?

(c) Determine where $f(x)$ is concave up and where it is concave down. Does $f(x)$ have inflection points?

(d) Since the degree of the numerator is one higher than the degree of the denominator, $f(x)$ has an oblique asymptote. Find it.

(e) Sketch the graph of $f(x)$ together with its asymptotes.

38. Let
$$f(x) = \frac{\sin x}{x}, \quad x \ne 0$$

(a) Show that $y = 0$ is a horizontal asymptote.

(b) Since $f(x)$ is not defined at $x = 0$, does this mean that $f(x)$ has a vertical asymptote at $x = 0$? Find $\lim_{x \to 0^+} f(x)$ and $\lim_{x \to 0^-} f(x)$.

(c) Use a graphing calculator to sketch the graph of $f(x)$.

39. Let
$$f(x) = \frac{x^2}{1 + x^2}, \quad x \in \mathbf{R}$$

(a) Determine where $f(x)$ is increasing and where it is decreasing.

(b) Where is the function concave up and where is it concave down? Find all inflection points of $f(x)$.

(c) Find $\lim_{x \to \pm\infty} f(x)$ and decide whether $f(x)$ has a horizontal asymptote.

(d) Sketch the graph of $f(x)$ together with its asymptotes and inflection points (if they exist).

40. Let
$$f(x) = \frac{x^k}{1 + x^k}, \quad x \ge 0$$
where k is a positive integer greater than 1.

(a) Determine where $f(x)$ is increasing and where it is decreasing.

(b) Where is the function concave up and where is it concave down? Find all inflection points of $f(x)$.

(c) Find $\lim_{x \to \infty} f(x)$ and decide whether $f(x)$ has a horizontal asymptote.

(d) Sketch the graph of $f(x)$ together with its asymptotes and inflection points (if they exist).

41. Let
$$f(x) = \frac{x}{a + x}, \quad x \ge 0$$
where a is a positive constant.

(a) Determine where $f(x)$ is increasing and where it is decreasing.

(b) Where is the function concave up and where is it concave down? Find all inflection points of $f(x)$.
(c) Find $\lim_{x \to \infty} f(x)$ and decide whether $f(x)$ has a horizontal asymptote.
(d) Sketch the graph of $f(x)$ together with its asymptotes and inflection points (if they exist).

42. Let

$$f(x) = \frac{2}{1 + e^{-x}}, \quad x \in \mathbb{R}$$

(a) Determine where $f(x)$ is increasing and where it is decreasing.
(b) Where is the function concave up and where is it concave down? Find all inflection points of $f(x)$.
(c) Find $\lim_{x \to \infty} f(x)$ and decide whether $f(x)$ has a horizontal asymptote.
(d) Find $\lim_{x \to -\infty} f(x)$ and decide whether $f(x)$ has a horizontal asymptote.
(e) Sketch the graph of $f(x)$ together with its asymptotes and inflection points (if they exist).

43. Population Growth Suppose that the growth rate of a population is given by

$$f(N) = N \left(1 - \left(\frac{N}{K} \right)^{\theta} \right) \quad N \geq 0$$

where N is the size of the population, K is a positive constant denoting the carrying capacity, and θ is a parameter greater than 1. Find the population size for which the growth rate is maximal.

44. Predation Rate Spruce budworms are a major pest that defoliate balsam fir. They are preyed upon by birds. A model for the per capita predation rate is given by

$$f(N) = \frac{aN}{k^2 + N^2}$$

where N denotes the density of spruce budworm and a and k are positive constants. For which density of spruce budworms is the per capita predation rate maximal?

5.4 Optimization

There are many situations in which we wish to maximize or minimize certain quantities. For instance, in a chemical reaction, you might wish to know under which conditions the reaction rate is maximized. In an agricultural setting, you might be interested in finding the amount of fertilizer that would maximize the yield of some crops. In a medical setting, you might wish to optimize the dosage of a drug for maximum benefit. Optimization problems also arise in the study of the evolution of life histories and involve questions such as when an organism should begin reproduction in order to maximize the number of surviving offspring. In each case, we are interested in finding global extrema.

EXAMPLE 1 **Chemical Reaction** Consider the chemical reaction

$$A + B \to AB$$

In Example 5 of Subsection 1.2.2, we found that the reaction rate is given by the function

$$R(x) = k(a - x)(b - x), \quad 0 \leq x \leq \min(a, b)$$

where x is the concentration of the product AB and $\min(a, b)$ denotes the minimum of the two values of a and b. The constants a and b are the concentrations of the reactants A and B at the beginning of the reaction. To be concrete, we choose $k = 2$, $a = 2$, and $b = 5$. Then

$$R(x) = 2(2 - x)(5 - x) \quad \text{for } 0 \leq x \leq 2$$

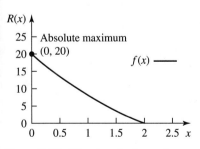

Figure 5.50 The chemical reaction rate $R(x)$ in Example 1. The graph of $R(x) = 2(2 - x)(5 - x), 0 \leq x \leq 2$, has an absolute maximum at $(0, 20)$.

(See Figure 5.50.)

We are interested in finding the concentration x that maximizes the reaction rate; this is the absolute maximum of $R(x)$. Since $R(x)$ is differentiable on $(0, 2)$, we can find all local extrema on $(0, 2)$ by investigating the first derivative. To compute the first derivative of $R(x)$, we multiply $R(x)$ out:

$$R(x) = 20 - 14x + 2x^2 \quad \text{for } 0 \leq x \leq 2$$

Differentiating with respect to x yields

$$R'(x) = -14 + 4x \quad \text{for } 0 < x < 2$$

To find candidates for local extrema, we set $R'(x) = 0$:

$$-14 + 4x = 0 \quad \text{or} \quad x = \frac{7}{2}$$

Since $\frac{7}{2} \notin (0, 2)$, there are no points in the interval $(0, 2)$ with horizontal tangents. Given that

$$R'(x) = -14 + 4x < 0 \quad \text{for } x \in (0, 2)$$

we conclude that $R(x)$ is decreasing in $(0, 2)$. The absolute maximum is therefore attained at the left endpoint of the interval $[0, 2]$, namely, $x = 0$. Thus, the reaction rate is maximal when the concentration of the product AB is equal to 0. You should compare this result with the graph of $R(x)$ in Figure 5.50. Since the reaction rate is proportional to the product of the concentrations of A and B, and since A and B react to form the product AB, their concentrations decrease during the reaction. Hence, we expect the reaction rate to be highest at the beginning of the reaction, when the concentrations of A and B are highest. ■

EXAMPLE 2   Crop Yield Let $Y(N)$ be the yield of an agricultural crop as a function of nitrogen level N in the soil. A model that is used for this relationship is

$$Y(N) = \frac{N}{1 + N^2} \quad \text{for } N \geq 0$$

(where N is measured in appropriate units). Find the nitrogen level that maximizes yield.

Solution   The function $Y(N)$, shown in Figure 5.51, is differentiable for $N > 0$. We find that

$$Y'(N) = \frac{(1 + N^2) - N \cdot 2N}{(1 + N^2)^2} = \frac{1 - N^2}{(1 + N^2)^2}$$

Setting $Y'(N) = 0$, we obtain the x-coordinates of candidates for local extrema:

$$Y'(N) = 0 \quad \text{if } 1 - N^2 = 0 \text{ or } N = \pm 1$$

Since $N = -1$ is not in the domain of $Y(N)$, we can discard it. The other x-coordinate, $N = 1$, is in the domain, and we see that

$$Y'(N) \begin{cases} > 0 & \text{for } 0 < N < 1 \\ < 0 & \text{for } N > 1 \end{cases}$$

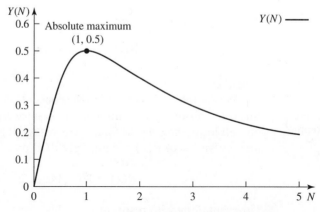

Figure 5.51 Crop yield $Y(N)$ in Example 2. The graph of $Y(N) = \frac{N}{1+N^2}$, $N \geq 0$, has an absolute maximum at $(1, \frac{1}{2})$.

Since $Y(N)$ changes from increasing to decreasing at $N = 1$, $(1, Y(1))$ is a local maximum. To find the global maximum, we still need to check the endpoints of the domain. We obtain

$$Y(0) = 0 \quad \text{and} \quad \lim_{N \to \infty} Y(N) = \lim_{N \to \infty} \frac{N}{1 + N^2} = 0$$

Since $Y(1) = \frac{1}{2}$, we conclude that the global maximum is $(1, \frac{1}{2})$. That is, $N = 1$ is the nitrogen level that maximizes yield.   ■

EXAMPLE 3

Maximizing Area A field biologist wants to enclose a rectangular study plot. She has 1600 ft of fencing. Using this fencing, determine the dimensions of the study plot that will have the largest area.

Solution   Figure 5.52 illustrates the situation. The area A of this study plot is given by

$$A = xy \qquad (5.9)$$

and the perimeter of the study plot is given by

$$1600 = 2x + 2y \qquad (5.10)$$

Solving (5.10) for y yields

$$y = 800 - x$$

We can substitute this value for y in equation (5.9) and obtain

$$A(x) = x(800 - x) = 800x - x^2 \quad \text{for } 0 \le x \le 800$$

It is important to state the domain of the function. Clearly, the smallest value of x is 0, in which case the enclosed area is also 0, since $A(0) = 0$. The largest possible value for x is 800, which will also produce a rectangle with one side of length 0; the corresponding area is $A(800) = 0$.

We wish to maximize the enclosed area $A(x)$. The function $A(x)$ is differentiable for $x \in (0, 800)$:

$$A'(x) = 800 - 2x \quad \text{for } 0 < x < 800$$
$$A''(x) = -2 \qquad \quad \text{for } 0 < x < 800$$

To find candidates for local extrema, we set $A'(x) = 0$ and solve for x:

$$800 - 2x = 0, \quad \text{or} \quad x = 400$$

Since $A''(400) < 0$, the point $(400, 160{,}000)$ is a local maximum. To find the global maximum, we need to check the function $A(x)$ at the endpoints of the interval $[0, 800]$. We have

$$A(0) = A(800) = 0$$

Because $A(400) = 400^2 = 160{,}000$, the area is maximized when $x = 400$, which implies that the study plot is a square. This relationship is true in general: For a rectangle with fixed perimeter, the maximum area occurs when the rectangle is a square. (See Problem 2 in this section.)   ■

EXAMPLE 4

Minimizing Material Aluminum soda cans are shaped like a right circular cylinder and hold about 12 ounces of liquid. The production of aluminum requires a lot of energy, so it is desirable to design soda cans that use the least amount of material. What dimensions would such an optimal soda can have?

Solution   We approximate the soda can by a right circular cylinder in which the cylinder wall and both ends are made of aluminum. We denote the height of the cylinder by h and the radius by r. (See Figure 5.53.)

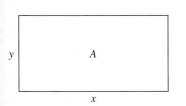

y

A

x

Figure 5.52 The rectangular study plot in Example 3.

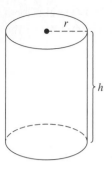

Figure 5.53 A right circular cylinder with height h and radius r.

If we measure h and r in centimeters, we must convert the 12 ounces into a volume measured in cubic centimeters (cm^3). For this, we need to know that 12 ounces are about 0.355 liter and that 1 liter equals 1000 cm^3.

We are now ready to set up the problem. The can with the least amount of material is the cylinder whose surface area is minimal for a given volume. Using formulas from geometry, we find that the surface area A of a right circular cylinder with top and bottom closed is given by

$$A = \underbrace{2\pi r h}_{\text{cylinder wall}} + \underbrace{2(\pi r^2)}_{\text{cylinder ends}}$$

The volume V of a right circular cylinder is given by

$$V = \pi r^2 h$$

We therefore need to minimize A when the volume $V = 12$ ounces $= 355$ cm^3. Solving $\pi r^2 h = 355$ for h yields

$$h = \frac{355}{\pi r^2}$$

Substituting this value for h in the formula for A, we find that

$$A(r) = 2\pi r \frac{355}{\pi r^2} + 2\pi r^2 = \frac{710}{r} + 2\pi r^2 \quad \text{for } r > 0$$

The graph of $A(r)$ is shown in Figure 5.54.

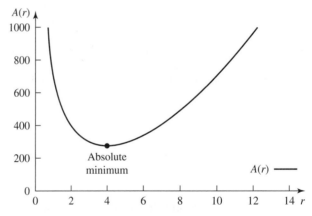

Figure 5.54 The surface area A of a right circular cylinder with given volume as a function of radius r.

To find the global minimum, we differentiate $A = A(r)$ and set the derivative equal to 0:

$$A'(r) = -\frac{710}{r^2} + 4\pi r = 0$$

Solving for r then yields

$$4\pi r = \frac{710}{r^2}, \quad \text{or} \quad r^3 = \frac{710}{4\pi} = \frac{355}{2\pi}$$

We thus find that

$$r = \left(\frac{355}{2\pi}\right)^{1/3} \approx 3.84 \text{ cm} \tag{5.11}$$

To check whether this value of r is indeed where a minimum occurs, we compute the second derivative of $A(r)$:

$$A''(r) = 2\frac{710}{r^3} + 4\pi > 0 \quad \text{for } r > 0$$

Since $A''(r) > 0, r = (\frac{355}{2\pi})^{1/3}$ is where a local minimum occurs. To determine whether this value of r is also where the global minimum occurs, we need to compute the surface area at the boundaries of the domain. Given that

$$\lim_{r \to 0+} A(r) = \infty \quad \text{and} \quad \lim_{r \to \infty} A(r) = \infty$$

it follows that the global minimum is achieved at $r = (\frac{355}{2\pi})^{1/3}$.

To find h, we use

$$h = \frac{355}{\pi r^2} = \frac{355}{\pi(\frac{355}{2\pi})^{2/3}} = \frac{\frac{355}{\pi}}{(\frac{355}{2\pi})^{2/3}}$$

$$= 2\left(\frac{355}{2\pi}\right)^{1/3} = 2r \approx 7.67 \, \text{cm}$$

In the penultimate step, we used (5.11) to simplify the expression. We thus find that the can which uses the least amount of material is one whose height is equal to its diameter.

A real soda can has $h = 12.5$ cm and $r = 3.1$ cm. In our computation, we assumed that the material used to manufacture the can is of equal thickness throughout. The top of a real soda can, however, is of thicker material than the rest of the can, which could explain why soda cans don't have the dimensions we computed in this example.

■

The previous four examples illustrate the basic types of optimization problems. In the first two examples, the functions that we wished to optimize were given; in the third and fourth examples, we needed to set up equations for the functions that we wished to optimize. Once you obtain a function that you wish to optimize, the results from the previous sections in this chapter will help you to find the global extremum. It is important to state the domain of the function, since global extrema may be found at the endpoints of the domain as well as within it.

Life histories of organisms are thought to evolve to some optimal state, within given constraints. Theoretical models can help to find such optimal states. As an example, we will look at clutch size. Suppose an organism can produce more than one offspring at a time. What is the optimal clutch size? The clutch size is determined by the amount of resources the parents can provide to each offspring. On the other hand, if resources are limited (as they usually are), the more offspring per clutch, the less is available to each individual offspring. On the other hand, if the number of offspring is too small, then the chances of having any offspring that survive to reproductive age might be quite small for reasons other than insufficient resources. This trade-off between not enough resources per offspring if there are too many offspring and the chance of losing the entire clutch if there are too few offspring suggests that an intermediate number of offspring might be optimal. We discuss a simple model that addresses the trade-off in the next example.

EXAMPLE 5

(*Adapted from Roff, 1992*) Lloyd (1987) proposed the following model to determine the optimal clutch size: If the clutch size is equal to N and the total amount of resources allocated is R, then the amount of resources allocated to each offspring is $x = R/N$. The chance $f(x)$ of survival for an individual is related to the investment x per individual. Lloyd proposed an S-shaped, or sigmoidal, curve; that is, survival chances are very low when the investment is low, and the curve shows a saturation effect for large investments. With $N = N(x) = R/x$, the success of a clutch, or its **fitness**, can be measured as

$$w(x) = [\text{number of offspring}] \times [\text{probability of survival of offspring}]$$

$$= N(x)f(x) = \frac{R}{x}f(x) \quad \text{for } x > 0$$

where R is a positive constant. We wish to find the value of x that maximizes the fitness $w(x)$. If we assume that $f(x)$ is differentiable for $x > 0$, then differentiating $w(x)$ with respect to x yields

$$\frac{dw}{dx} = R\frac{d}{dx}\left(\frac{f(x)}{x}\right)$$

$$= R\frac{f'(x)x - f(x)}{x^2} = \frac{R}{x}\left(f'(x) - \frac{f(x)}{x}\right) \quad \text{for } x > 0$$

Setting $w'(x) = 0$ gives

$$f'(x) = \frac{f(x)}{x} \tag{5.12}$$

We denote the solution of (5.12) by $\hat{x}$ (read "x hat"). If $f(x)$ is twice differentiable at $\hat{x}$, we can use the second-derivative test to learn whether $\hat{x}$ is a local maximum or minimum. We find that

$$\frac{d^2w}{dx^2} = -\frac{R}{x^2}\left(f'(x) - \frac{f(x)}{x}\right) + \frac{R}{x}\left(f''(x) - \frac{d}{dx}\frac{f(x)}{x}\right)$$

Since $f'(\hat{x}) = f(\hat{x})/\hat{x}$, the first term on the right-hand side is equal to 0 when $x = \hat{x}$. Furthermore, because of (5.12), $\frac{d}{dx}[f(x)/x] = \frac{xf'(x)-f(x)}{x^2} = 0$ when $x = \hat{x}$. Hence,

$$\left.\frac{d^2w}{dx^2}\right|_{x=\hat{x}} = \frac{R}{\hat{x}}f''(\hat{x})$$

If we choose a function $f(x)$ that is concave down at $\hat{x}$, then $f''(\hat{x}) < 0$ and it follows that $w(x)$ has a local maximum at $\hat{x}$.

A common choice for $f(x)$ is

$$f(x) = \frac{x^2}{k^2 + x^2} \quad \text{for } x \geq 0$$

where k is a positive constant. The graph of $f(x)$ is shown in Figure 5.55; the curve is sigmoidal. Differentiating $f(x)$ with respect to x yields

$$f'(x) = \frac{2x(k^2 + x^2) - x^2(2x)}{(k^2 + x^2)^2} = \frac{2k^2x}{(k^2 + x^2)^2}$$

Since

$$\frac{dw}{dx} = 0 \quad \text{for } f'(x) = \frac{f(x)}{x}$$

we obtain

$$\frac{2k^2x}{(k^2 + x^2)^2} = \frac{1}{x}\frac{x^2}{k^2 + x^2}$$

which yields

$$2k^2 = k^2 + x^2 \quad \text{or} \quad k^2 = x^2$$

Because k is a positive constant and $x \geq 0$, we can discard the solution $x = -k$ and find $\hat{x} = k$. To see whether $\hat{x} = k$ is a local maximum for the function $w(x)$, we evaluate $w''(k)$; however, we need to find $f''(x)$ first:

$$f''(x) = \frac{2k^2(k^2 + x^2)^2 - (2k^2x)2(k^2 + x^2)(2x)}{(k^2 + x^2)^4}$$

$$= \frac{2k^2(k^2 + x^2) - 8k^2x^2}{(k^2 + x^2)^3} = \frac{2k^4 - 6k^2x^2}{(k^2 + x^2)^3}$$

Since

$$\left.\frac{d^2w}{dx^2}\right|_{x=k} = \frac{R}{k}f''(k) = \frac{R}{k}\frac{-4k^4}{(2k^2)^3} < 0$$

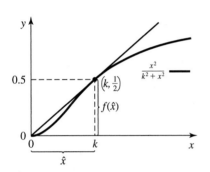

Figure 5.55 The graph of $f(x) = \frac{x^2}{k^2+x^2}$ together with the tangent line at $(k, 1/2)$.

we conclude that there is a local maximum at $\hat{x} = k$. To see whether it is a global maximum, we compare $w(k)$ with $w(0)$ and $\lim_{x \to \infty} w(x)$. We have

$$w(x) = \frac{R}{x} f(x) = \frac{R}{x} \frac{x^2}{k^2 + x^2} = R \frac{x}{k^2 + x^2}$$

so

$$w(0) = 0 \qquad w(k) = \frac{R}{2k} \qquad \lim_{x \to \infty} w(x) = 0$$

Hence, $\hat{x} = k$ is where the absolute maximum occurs; for our choice of $f(x) = \frac{x^2}{k^2+x^2}$, the optimal clutch size N_{opt} satisfies $N_{\text{opt}} = R/k$. [Other choices of $f(x)$ would give a different result.]

There is a geometric way of finding $\hat{x}$. Since

$$f'(\hat{x}) = \frac{f(\hat{x})}{\hat{x}}$$

it follows that the tangent line at $(\hat{x}, f(\hat{x}))$ has slope $\frac{f(\hat{x})}{\hat{x}}$. This line can be obtained by drawing a straight line through the origin that just touches the graph of $y = f(x)$, as illustrated in Figure 5.55. ■

Section 5.4 Problems

1. Find the smallest perimeter possible for a rectangle whose area is 25 in.^{2}.

2. Show that, among all rectangles with a given perimeter, the square has the largest area.

3. A rectangle has its base on the x-axis and its upper two vertices on the parabola $y = 3 - x^2$, as shown in Figure 5.56. What is the largest area the rectangle can have?

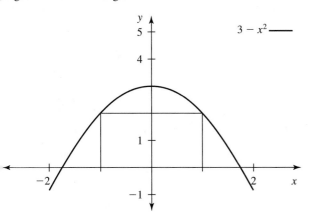

Figure 5.56 The graph of $y = 3 - x^2$ together with the inscribed rectangle in Problem 3.

4. A rectangular study area is to be enclosed by a fence and divided into two equal parts, with the fence running along the division parallel to one of the sides. If the total area is 384 ft^2, find the dimensions of the study area that will minimize the total length of the fence. How much fencing will be required?

5. A rectangular field is bounded on one side by a river and on the other three sides by a fence. Find the dimensions of the field that will maximize the enclosed area if the fence has a total length of 320 ft.

6. Find the largest possible area of a right triangle whose hypotenuse is 4 cm long.

7. Suppose that a and b are the side lengths in a right triangle whose hypotenuse is 5 cm long. What is the largest perimeter possible?

8. Suppose that a and b are the side lengths in a right triangle whose hypotenuse is 10 cm long. Show that the area of the triangle is largest when $a = b$.

9. A rectangle has its base on the x-axis, its lower left corner at $(0, 0)$, and its upper right corner on the curve $y = 1/x$. What is the smallest perimeter the rectangle can have?

10. A rectangle has its base on the x-axis and its upper left and right corners on the curve $y = \sqrt{4 - x^2}$, as shown in Figure 5.57. The left and the right corners are equidistant from the vertical axis. What is the largest area the rectangle can have?

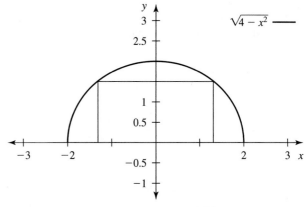

Figure 5.57 The graph of $y = (4 - x^2)^{1/2}$ together with the inscribed rectangle in Problem 10.

11. Denote by (x, y) a point on the straight line $y = 4 - 3x$. (See Figure 5.58.)

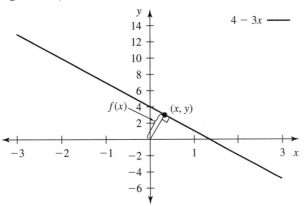

Figure 5.58 The graph of $y = 4 - 3x$ in Problem 11.

(a) Show that the distance from (x, y) to the origin is given by

$$f(x) = \sqrt{x^2 + (4 - 3x)^2}$$

(b) Give the coordinates of the point on the line $y = 4 - 3x$ that is closest to the origin. (*Hint*: Find x so that the distance you computed in (a) is minimized.)

(c) Show that the *square* of the distance between the point (x, y) on the line and the origin is given by

$$g(x) = [f(x)]^2 = x^2 + (4 - 3x)^2$$

and find the minimum of $g(x)$. Show that this minimum agrees with your answer in (b).

12. How close does the line $y = 1 + 2x$ come to the origin?

13. How close does the curve $y = 1/x$ come to the origin? (*Hint*: Find the point on the curve that minimizes the *square* of the distance between the origin and the point on the curve. If you use the square of the distance instead of the distance, you avoid dealing with square roots.)

14. How close does the circle with radius $\sqrt{2}$ and center $(2, 2)$ come to the origin.

15. Show that if $f(x)$ is a positive twice-differentiable function that has a local minimum at $x = c$, then $g(x) = [f(x)]^2$ has a local minimum at $x = c$ as well.

16. Show that if $f(x)$ is a differentiable function with $f(x) < 0$ for all $x \in \mathbf{R}$ and with a local maximum at $x = c$, then $g(x) = [f(x)]^2$ has a local minimum at $x = c$.

17. Find the dimensions of a right circular cylindrical can (with bottom and top closed) that has a volume of 1 liter and that minimizes the amount of material used. (*Note*: One liter corresponds to 1000 cm³.)

18. Find the dimensions of a right circular cylinder that is open on the top, is closed on the bottom, holds 1 liter, and uses the least amount of material.

19. A circular sector with radius r and angle θ has area A. Find r and θ so that the perimeter is smallest when (a) $A = 2$ and (b) $A = 10$. (*Note*: $A = \frac{1}{2}r^2\theta$, and the length of the arc $s = r\theta$, when θ is measured in radians; see Figure 5.59.)

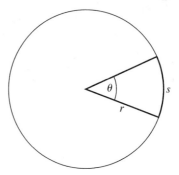

Figure 5.59 The circular sector in Problems 19 and 20.

20. A circular sector with radius r and angle θ has area A. Find r and θ so that the perimeter is smallest for a given area A. (*Note*: $A = \frac{1}{2}r^2\theta$, and the length of the arc $s = r\theta$, when θ is measured in radians; see Figure 5.59.)

21. Repeat Example 4 under the assumption that the top of the can is made out of aluminum that is three times as thick as the aluminum used for the wall and the bottom.

22. Find two positive numbers a and b such that $a + b = 20$ and ab is a maximum.

23. Find two numbers a and b such that $a - b = 4$ and ab is a minimum.

24. Classical Model of Viability Selection Consider a population of diploid organisms (i.e., each individual carries two copies of each chromosome). Genes reside on chromosomes, and we call the location of a gene on a chromosome a **locus**. Different versions of the same gene are called **alleles**. Let us examine the case of one locus with two possible alleles, A_1 and A_2. Since the individuals are diploid, the following types, called **genotypes**, may occur: A_1A_1, A_1A_2, and A_2A_2 (where A_1A_2 and A_2A_1 are considered to be equivalent). If two parents mate and produce an offspring, the offspring receives one gene from each parent. If mating is random, then we can imagine all genes being put into one big gene pool from which we choose two genes at random. If we assume that the frequency of A_1 in the population is p and the frequency of A_2 is $q = 1 - p$, then the combination A_1A_1 is picked with probability p^2, the combination A_1A_2 with probability $2pq$ (the factor 2 appears because A_1 can come from either the father or the mother), and the combination A_2A_2 with probability q^2.

We assume that the survival chances of offspring depend on their genotypes. We define the quantities w_{11}, w_{12}, and w_{22} to describe the differential survival chances of the types A_1A_1, A_1A_2, and A_2A_2, respectively. The ratio $A_1A_1{:}A_1A_2{:}A_2A_2$ among adults is given by

$$p^2w_{11}{:}2pqw_{12}{:}q^2w_{22}$$

The average fitness of this population is defined as

$$\overline{w} = p^2w_{11} + 2pqw_{12} + q^2w_{22}$$

We will investigate the preceding function. Since $q = 1 - p$, $\overline{w}$ is a function of p only; specifically,

$$\overline{w}(p) = p^2w_{11} + 2p(1 - p)w_{12} + (1 - p)^2w_{22}$$

for $0 \le p \le 1$. We consider the following three cases:

(i) Directional selection: $w_{11} > w_{12} > w_{22}$

(ii) Overdominance: $w_{12} > w_{11}, w_{22}$

(iii) Underdominance: $w_{12} < w_{11}, w_{22}$

(a) Show that

$$\overline{w}(p) = p^2(w_{11} - 2w_{12} + w_{22}) + 2p(w_{12} - w_{22}) + w_{22}$$

and graph $\overline{w}(p)$ for each of the three cases, where we choose the parameters as follows:

(i) $w_{11} = 1$, $w_{12} = 0.7$, $w_{22} = 0.3$
(ii) $w_{11} = 0.7$, $w_{12} = 1$, $w_{22} = 0.3$
(iii) $w_{11} = 1$, $w_{12} = 0.3$, $w_{22} = 0.7$

(b) Show that

$$\frac{d\overline{w}}{dp} = 2p(w_{11} - 2w_{12} + w_{22}) + 2(w_{12} - w_{22})$$

(c) Find the global maximum of $\overline{w}(p)$ in each of the three cases considered in (a). (Note that the global maximum may occur at the boundary of the domain of $\overline{w}$.)

(d) We can show that under a certain mating scheme the gene frequencies change until $\overline{w}$ reaches its global maximum. Assume that this is the case, and state what the equilibrium frequency will be for each of the three cases considered in (a).

25. Continuation of Problem 94 from Section 4.3 We discussed the properties of hatching offspring per unit time, $w(t)$, in the species *Eleutherodactylus coqui*. The function $w(t)$ was given by

$$w(t) = \frac{f(t)}{C + t}$$

where $f(t)$ is the proportion of offspring that survive if t is the time spent brooding and where C is the cost associated with the time spent searching for other mates.

We assume now that $f(t)$, $t \geq 0$, is twice differentiable and concave down with $f(0) = 0$ and $0 \leq f \leq 1$. The optimal brooding time is defined as the time that maximizes $w(t)$.

(a) Show that the optimal brooding time can be obtained by finding the point on the curve $f(t)$ where the line through $(-C, 0)$ is tangential to the curve $f(t)$.

(b) Use the procedure in (a) to find the optimal brooding time for $f(t) = \frac{t}{1+t}$ and $C = 2$. Determine the equation of the line through $(-2, 0)$ that is tangential to the curve $f(t) = \frac{t}{1+t}$, and graph both $f(t)$ and the tangent together.

26. Optimal Age of Reproduction *(from Roff, 1992)*
Semelparous organisms breed only once during their lifetime. Examples of this type of reproduction can be found in Pacific salmon and bamboo. The per capita rate of increase, r, can be

thought of as a measure of reproductive fitness. The greater the value of r, the more offspring an individual produces. The intrinsic rate of increase is typically a function of age x. Models for age-structured populations of semelparous organisms predict that the intrinsic rate of increase as a function of x is given by

$$r(x) = \frac{\ln[l(x)m(x)]}{x}$$

where $l(x)$ is the probability of surviving to age x and $m(x)$ is the number of female offspring at age x. The optimal age of reproduction is the age x that maximizes $r(x)$.

(a) Find the optimal age of reproduction for

$$l(x) = e^{-ax}$$

and

$$m(x) = bx^c$$

where a, b, and c are positive constants.

(b) Use a graphing calculator to sketch the graph of $r(x)$ when $a = 0.1$, $b = 4$, and $c = 0.9$.

27. Optimal Age at First Reproduction *(from Lloyd, 1987)*
Iteroparous organisms breed more than once during their lifetime. Consider a model in which the intrinsic rate of increase, r, depends on the age of first reproduction, denoted by x, and satisfies the equation

$$\frac{e^{-x(r(x)+L)}(1 - e^{-kx})^3 c}{1 - e^{-(r(x)+L)}} = 1 \tag{5.13}$$

where k, L, and c are positive constants describing the life history of the organism. The optimal age of first reproduction is the age x for which $r(x)$ is maximized. Since we cannot separate $r(x)$ in the preceding equation, we must use implicit differentiation to find a candidate for the optimal age of reproduction.

(a) Find an equation for $\frac{dr}{dx}$. [*Hint:* Take logarithms of both sides of (5.13) before differentiating with respect to x.]

(b) Set $\frac{dr}{dx} = 0$ and show that this gives

$$r(x) = \frac{3ke^{-kx}}{1 - e^{-kx}} - L$$

[To find the candidate for the optimal age x, you would need to substitute for $r(x)$ in (5.13) and solve the equation numerically. Then you would still need to check that this solution actually gives you the absolute maximum. It can, in fact, be done.]

5.5 L'Hospital's Rule

Guillaume François l'Hospital was born in France in 1661. He became interested in calculus around 1690, when articles on the new calculus by Leibniz and the Bernoulli brothers began to appear. Johann Bernoulli was in Paris in 1691, and l'Hospital asked Bernoulli to teach him some calculus. Bernoulli left Paris a year later, but continued to provide l'Hospital with new material on calculus. Bernoulli received a monthly salary for his service and agreed that he would not give anyone else access to the material. Once l'Hospital thought he understood the material well enough, he decided to write a book on the subject, which was published under his name and met with great success. Bernoulli was not particularly happy about this development, as his contributions were hardly acknowledged in the book; l'Hospital perhaps felt that because he had paid for the course material, he had a right to publish it.

Today, l'Hospital is most famous for his treatment of the limits of fractions in which both the numerator and the denominator tend to 0 in the limit. The rule that bears his name was discovered by Johann Bernoulli but was published in l'Hospital's book. The rule also works when both the numerator and the denominator tend to infinity. We have encountered such examples before—for instance,

$$\lim_{x \to 3} \frac{x^2 - 9}{x - 3} = \lim_{x \to 3} (x + 3) = 6$$

and

$$\lim_{x \to \infty} \frac{kx}{1 + x} = \lim_{x \to \infty} \frac{k}{\frac{1}{x} + 1} = k$$

In both examples, we were able to find the limit by algebraic manipulations.

Using algebraic manipulations, however, is not always possible, as in the following example:

$$\lim_{x \to 0} \frac{e^x - 1}{x}$$

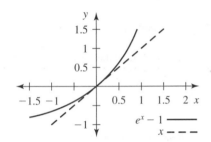

Figure 5.60 The graphs of $y = e^x - 1$ and $y = x$.

Here, both numerator and denominator tend to 0 as $x \to 0$. (See Figure 5.60.) There is no way of algebraically simplifying the ratio. Instead, we linearize both numerator and denominator at $a = 0$, and the linearization serves as an approximation. Recall from Section 4.8 that the linear approximation of a function $f(x)$ at $x = a$ is defined as

$$L(x) = f(a) + f'(a)(x - a)$$

If $f(x) = e^x - 1$, then $f'(x) = e^x$, $f(0) = 0$, and $f'(0) = 1$. That is, the linear approximation of the numerator at $a = 0$ is

$$L(x) = 0 + (1)(x - 0) = x$$

The denominator is already a linear function, namely, $g(x) = x$. We use linearization to approximate $\frac{e^x - 1}{x}$, obtaining the ratio $\frac{x}{x} = 1$. We might then expect that the limiting value of $\frac{e^x - 1}{x}$ as $x \to 0$ is 1, and indeed that can be shown.

To see clearly what we have just done, we look at the general case

$$\lim_{x \to a} \frac{f(x)}{g(x)}$$

and assume that both

$$\lim_{x \to a} f(x) = 0 \qquad \text{and} \qquad \lim_{x \to a} g(x) = 0$$

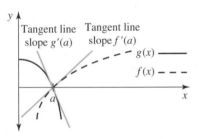

Figure 5.61 L'Hospital's rule.

(See Figure 5.61.) Using a linear approximation as before, we find that, for x close to a,

$$\frac{f(x)}{g(x)} \approx \frac{f(a) + f'(a)(x - a)}{g(a) + g'(a)(x - a)}$$

Since $f(a) = g(a) = 0$ and $x \neq a$, the right-hand side is equal to

$$\frac{f'(a)(x - a)}{g'(a)(x - a)} = \frac{f'(a)}{g'(a)}$$

provided that $\frac{f'(a)}{g'(a)}$ is defined. We therefore hope that something like

$$\lim_{x \to a} \frac{f(x)}{g(x)} = \frac{f'(a)}{g'(a)}$$

holds when $\frac{f(a)}{g(a)}$ is of the form $\frac{0}{0}$ and $\frac{f'(a)}{g'(a)}$ is defined. In fact, something like this does hold; it is called l'Hospital's rule. The rule is more general than what we just did, and its proof would require a generalized version of the mean-value theorem, which is beyond the scope of this book.

> **L'Hospital's Rule** Suppose that f and g are differentiable functions and that
>
> $$\lim_{x \to a} f(x) = \lim_{x \to a} g(x) = 0$$
>
> or
>
> $$\lim_{x \to a} f(x) = \lim_{x \to a} g(x) = \infty$$
>
> If
>
> $$\lim_{x \to a} \frac{f'(x)}{g'(x)} = L$$
>
> then
>
> $$\lim_{x \to a} \frac{f(x)}{g(x)} = L$$

L'Hospital's rule works for $a = +\infty$ or $-\infty$ as well, and it also applies to one-sided limits.

Using l'Hospital's rule, we can redo the three examples we just presented. In each case, the ratio $\frac{f(x)}{g(x)}$ is an **indeterminate expression**: When a is substituted for x, the ratio is of the form $\frac{0}{0}$ or $\frac{\infty}{\infty}$. We apply l'Hospital's rule in each case: We differentiate both numerator and denominator and then take the limit of $\frac{f'(x)}{g'(x)}$ as $x \to a$. If this limit exists, it is equal to the limit of $\frac{f(x)}{g(x)}$ as $x \to a$. L'Hospital's rule then gives

$$\lim_{x \to 3} \frac{x^2 - 9}{x - 3} = \lim_{x \to 3} \frac{2x}{1} = 6$$

$$\lim_{x \to \infty} \frac{kx}{1 + x} = \lim_{x \to \infty} \frac{k}{1} = k$$

$$\lim_{x \to 0} \frac{e^x - 1}{x} = \lim_{x \to 0} \frac{e^x}{1} = 1$$

As we just said, if the limit $\frac{f'(x)}{g'(x)}$ exists as $x \to a$, then we can conclude that the limit of $\frac{f(x)}{g(x)}$ exists as $x \to a$ and the two limits are equal. Thus, each of the first equalities in the three examples are true *because* the second equality holds. This should be kept in mind in the examples that follow. In each one, you might wish to use a graphing calculator to graph the function. The first three examples are straightforward applications of l'Hospital's rule.

EXAMPLE 1 Indeterminate Expression 0/0 Evaluate

$$\lim_{x \to 2} \frac{x^6 - 64}{x^2 - 4}$$

Solution   This limit is of the form $\frac{0}{0}$, since $2^6 - 64 = 0$ and $2^2 - 4 = 0$. Applying l'Hospital's rule yields

$$\lim_{x \to 2} \frac{x^6 - 64}{x^2 - 4} = \lim_{x \to 2} \frac{6x^5}{2x} = \frac{(6)(2^5)}{(2)(2)} = (6)(2^3) = 48 \qquad \blacksquare$$

EXAMPLE 2 Indeterminate Expression 0/0 Evaluate

$$\lim_{x \to 0} \frac{1 - \cos^2 x}{\sin x}$$

Solution This limit is of the form $\frac{0}{0}$, since $1 - \cos^2 0 = 0$ and $\sin 0 = 0$. Applying l'Hospital's rule yields

$$\lim_{x \to 0} \frac{1 - \cos^2 x}{\sin x} = \lim_{x \to 0} \frac{2 \cos x \sin x}{\cos x} = \lim_{x \to 0} 2 \sin x = 0 \qquad \blacksquare$$

EXAMPLE 3   **Indeterminate Expression ∞/∞**   Evaluate

$$\lim_{x \to \infty} \frac{\ln x}{x}$$

Solution This limit is of the form $\frac{\infty}{\infty}$. We can again apply l'Hospital's rule:

$$\lim_{x \to \infty} \frac{\frac{1}{x}}{1} = \lim_{x \to \infty} \frac{1}{x} = 0 \qquad \blacksquare$$

EXAMPLE 4   **Indeterminate Expression ∞/∞, One-Sided Limit**   Evaluate

$$\lim_{x \to (\pi/2)^-} \frac{\tan x}{1 + \tan x}$$

Solution This limit is of the form $\frac{\infty}{\infty}$. We apply l'Hospital's rule and find that

$$\lim_{x \to (\pi/2)^-} \frac{\tan x}{1 + \tan x} = \lim_{x \to (\pi/2)^-} \frac{\sec^2 x}{\sec^2 x} = \lim_{x \to (\pi/2)^-} 1 = 1 \qquad \blacksquare$$

EXAMPLE 5   **Applying L'Hospital's Rule More Than Once**   Evaluate

$$\lim_{x \to \infty} \frac{x^3 - 3x + 1}{3x^3 - 2x^2}$$

Solution This limit is of the form $\frac{\infty}{\infty}$. Applying l'Hospital's rule yields

$$\lim_{x \to \infty} \frac{x^3 - 3x + 1}{3x^3 - 2x^2} = \lim_{x \to \infty} \frac{3x^2 - 3}{9x^2 - 4x}$$

which is still of the form $\frac{\infty}{\infty}$. Applying l'Hospital's rule again, we obtain

$$\lim_{x \to \infty} \frac{3x^2 - 3}{9x^2 - 4x} = \lim_{x \to \infty} \frac{6x}{18x - 4}$$

Since this is still of the form $\frac{\infty}{\infty}$, we can apply l'Hospital's rule yet again. We now find that

$$\lim_{x \to \infty} \frac{6x}{18x - 4} = \lim_{x \to \infty} \frac{6}{18} = \frac{1}{3}$$

In this example, we could have found the answer without using l'Hospital's rule: We just divide both numerator and denominator by x^3 to get

$$\lim_{x \to \infty} \frac{x^3 - 3x + 1}{3x^3 - 2x^2} = \lim_{x \to \infty} \frac{x^3 \left(1 - \frac{3}{x^2} + \frac{1}{x^3}\right)}{x^3 \left(3 - \frac{2}{x}\right)}$$

$$= \lim_{x \to \infty} \frac{1 - \frac{3}{x^2} + \frac{1}{x^3}}{3 - \frac{2}{x}} = \frac{1}{3} \qquad \blacksquare$$

When you apply l'Hospital's rule, it can certainly happen that the limit is infinite, as in the next example.

EXAMPLE 6   **Infinite Limit** Evaluate

$$\lim_{x \to \infty} \frac{e^x}{x}$$

Solution   This limit is of the form $\frac{\infty}{\infty}$. We apply l'Hospital's rule.

$$\lim_{x \to \infty} \frac{e^x}{x} = \lim_{x \to \infty} \frac{e^x}{1} = \infty \qquad \text{(limit does not exist)} \qquad ■$$

L'Hospital's rule can sometimes be applied to limits of the form

$$\lim_{x \to a} f(x)g(x)$$

where

$$\lim_{x \to a} f(x) = 0 \qquad \text{and} \qquad \lim_{x \to a} g(x) = \infty$$

since we can write the limit in the form

$$\lim_{x \to a} f(x)g(x) = \lim_{x \to a} \frac{f(x)}{\frac{1}{g(x)}} = \lim_{x \to a} \frac{g(x)}{\frac{1}{f(x)}}$$

which is again of the form $\frac{0}{0}$ or $\frac{\infty}{\infty}$.

EXAMPLE 7   **Indeterminate Expression $0 \cdot \infty$** Evaluate

$$\lim_{x \to 0^+} x \ln x$$

Solution   This limit is of the form $(0)(-\infty)$. We apply l'Hospital's rule after rewriting it in the form $\frac{\infty}{\infty}$:

$$\lim_{x \to 0^+} x \ln x = \lim_{x \to 0^+} \frac{\ln x}{\frac{1}{x}} = \lim_{x \to 0^+} \frac{\frac{1}{x}}{-\frac{1}{x^2}}$$

$$= \lim_{x \to 0^+} \frac{1}{x}\left(-\frac{x^2}{1}\right) = \lim_{x \to 0^+} (-x) = 0$$

If we had written the limit in the form

$$\lim_{x \to 0^+} \frac{x}{\frac{1}{\ln x}}$$

and then applied l'Hospital's rule, we would have obtained

$$\lim_{x \to 0^+} \frac{x}{\frac{1}{\ln x}} = \lim_{x \to 0^+} \frac{1}{(-1)(\ln x)^{-2}\frac{1}{x}} = \lim_{x \to 0^+} \left[-x(\ln x)^2\right]$$

which is more complicated than the initial expression. Before you apply l'Hospital's rule to expressions of the form $0 \cdot \infty$, you should always determine which way will be easier to evaluate.   ■

EXAMPLE 8   **Indeterminate Expression $0 \cdot \infty$** Evaluate

$$\lim_{x \to 0^+} x \cot x$$

Solution   This limit is of the form $0 \cdot \infty$. We have two choices: We can write

$$\lim_{x \to 0^+} x \cot x = \lim_{x \to 0^+} \frac{x}{\frac{1}{\cot x}} = \lim_{x \to 0^+} \frac{x}{\tan x}$$

where we use the fact that $\cot x = \frac{1}{\tan x}$, or we can write

$$\lim_{x \to 0^+} x \cot x = \lim_{x \to 0^+} \frac{\cot x}{\frac{1}{x}}$$

It is easier to apply l'Hospital's rule to the first form:

$$\lim_{x \to 0^+} x \cot x = \lim_{x \to 0^+} \frac{x}{\tan x} = \lim_{x \to 0^+} \frac{1}{\sec^2 x} = \lim_{x \to 0^+} \cos^2 x = 1$$

In the penultimate step, we used the fact that $\sec x = \frac{1}{\cos x}$. The second form can be evaluated using l'Hospital's rule, but this is more complicated. ■

Limits of the form $\infty - \infty$ sometimes can be evaluated with l'Hospital's rule if we can algebraically transform such limits into the form $\frac{0}{0}$ or $\frac{\infty}{\infty}$.

EXAMPLE 9 **Indeterminate Expression $\infty - \infty$** Evaluate

$$\lim_{x \to (\frac{\pi}{2})^-} (\tan x - \sec x)$$

Solution   This limit is of the form $\infty - \infty$. Note that

$$\tan x = \frac{\sin x}{\cos x} \quad \text{and} \quad \sec x = \frac{1}{\cos x}$$

Using these two identities, we can write the limit as

$$\lim_{x \to (\frac{\pi}{2})^-} (\tan x - \sec x) = \lim_{x \to (\frac{\pi}{2})^-} \left(\frac{\sin x}{\cos x} - \frac{1}{\cos x} \right)$$

$$= \lim_{x \to (\frac{\pi}{2})^-} \frac{\sin x - 1}{\cos x}$$

This is now of the form $\frac{0}{0}$, and we can apply l'Hospital's rule to obtain

$$\lim_{x \to (\frac{\pi}{2})^-} \frac{\sin x - 1}{\cos x} = \lim_{x \to (\frac{\pi}{2})^-} \frac{\cos x}{-\sin x} = \frac{0}{-1} = 0$$ ■

EXAMPLE 10 **Indeterminate Expression $\infty - \infty$** Evaluate

$$\lim_{x \to \infty} (x - \sqrt{x^2 + x})$$

Solution   This limit is of the form $\infty - \infty$. We need to get a product or a ratio. To do so, we can factor x and get

$$\lim_{x \to \infty} (x - \sqrt{x^2 + x}) = \lim_{x \to \infty} x \left(1 - \sqrt{1 + \frac{1}{x}} \right)$$

This is of the form $\infty \cdot 0$. We can transform it to the form $\frac{0}{0}$ and then apply l'Hospital's rule:

$$\lim_{x \to \infty} x \left(1 - \sqrt{1 + \frac{1}{x}} \right) = \lim_{x \to \infty} \frac{1 - \sqrt{1 + \frac{1}{x}}}{\frac{1}{x}}$$

$$= \lim_{x \to \infty} \frac{-\frac{1}{2}(1 + \frac{1}{x})^{-1/2}(-\frac{1}{x^2})}{-\frac{1}{x^2}}$$

$$= \lim_{x \to \infty} \frac{-1}{2\sqrt{1 + \frac{1}{x}}} = -\frac{1}{2}$$ ■

Finally, we consider expressions of the form

$$\lim_{x \to a} [f(x)]^{g(x)}$$

when they are of the type 0^0, ∞^0, or 1^∞. The key to solving such limits is to rewrite them as

$$\lim_{x \to a} [f(x)]^{g(x)} = \lim_{x \to a} \exp \left\{ \ln [f(x)]^{g(x)} \right\}$$
$$= \lim_{x \to a} \exp [g(x) \cdot \ln f(x)]$$
$$= \exp \left[\lim_{x \to a} (g(x) \cdot \ln f(x)) \right]$$

The last step, in which we interchanged lim and exp, uses the fact that the exponential function is continuous. Rewriting the limit in this way transforms

$$0^0 \quad \text{into} \quad \exp [0 \cdot (-\infty)]$$
$$\infty^0 \quad \text{into} \quad \exp [0 \cdot (\infty)]$$
$$1^\infty \quad \text{into} \quad \exp [\infty \cdot \ln 1] = \exp [\infty \cdot 0]$$

Since we know how to deal with limits of the form $0 \cdot \infty$, we are in good shape again. We present a couple of examples.

EXAMPLE 11 Indeterminate Expression 0^0 Evaluate

$$\lim_{x \to 0^+} x^x$$

Solution This limit is of the form 0^0; we rewrite the limit first:

$$\lim_{x \to 0^+} x^x = \lim_{x \to 0^+} \exp[\ln x^x] = \lim_{x \to 0^+} \exp[x \ln x]$$
$$= \exp \left[\lim_{x \to 0^+} (x \ln x) \right]$$

We evaluated this limit in Example 7 and obtained

$$\lim_{x \to 0^+} (x \ln x) = 0$$

Hence,

$$\lim_{x \to 0^+} x^x = \exp \left[\lim_{x \to 0^+} (x \ln x) \right] = \exp[0] = 1$$

(See Figure 5.62.)

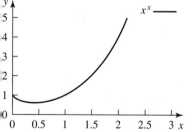

Figure 5.62 The graph of $y = x^x$.

EXAMPLE 12 Indeterminate Expression 1^∞ Evaluate

$$\lim_{x \to (\pi/4)^-} (\tan x)^{\tan(2x)}$$

Solution Since $\tan \frac{\pi}{4} = 1$ and $\tan \left(2\frac{\pi}{4} \right) = \infty$, this limit is of the form 1^∞. We rewrite it as

$$\lim_{x \to (\pi/4)^-} (\tan x)^{\tan(2x)} = \lim_{x \to (\pi/4)^-} \exp[\tan(2x) \cdot \ln \tan x]$$
$$= \exp \left[\lim_{x \to (\pi/4)^-} (\tan(2x) \cdot \ln \tan x) \right]$$

The limit is now of the form $\infty \cdot 0$ (since $\ln \tan \frac{\pi}{4} = \ln 1 = 0$). We evaluate the limit by writing it in the form $\frac{0}{0}$ and then applying l'Hospital's rule:

$$\lim_{x \to (\pi/4)^-} (\tan(2x) \cdot \ln \tan x) = \lim_{x \to (\pi/4)^-} \frac{\ln \tan x}{\frac{1}{\tan(2x)}} = \lim_{x \to (\pi/4)^-} \frac{\ln \tan x}{\cot(2x)}$$

Since

$$\frac{d}{dx} \ln \tan x = \frac{\sec^2 x}{\tan x} = \frac{\cos x}{\cos^2 x \sin x} = \frac{1}{\sin x \cos x}$$

and

$$\frac{d}{dx} \cot(2x) = -(\csc^2(2x)) \cdot 2 = \frac{-2}{\sin^2(2x)}$$

it follows that

$$\lim_{x \to (\pi/4)^-} \frac{\ln \tan x}{\cot(2x)} = \lim_{x \to (\pi/4)^-} \frac{\frac{1}{\sin x \cos x}}{\frac{-2}{\sin^2(2x)}} = \lim_{x \to (\pi/4)^-} \frac{\sin^2(2x)}{-2 \sin x \cos x}$$

$$= \frac{1}{(-2)(\frac{1}{2}\sqrt{2})(\frac{1}{2}\sqrt{2})} = -1$$

Therefore,

$$\lim_{x \to (\pi/4)^-} (\tan x)^{\tan(2x)} = \exp \left[\lim_{x \to (\pi/4)^-} (\tan(2x) \ln \tan x) \right]$$

$$= \exp[-1] = e^{-1}$$

The graph of $f(x) = (\tan x)^{\tan(2x)}$ is shown in Figure 5.63.

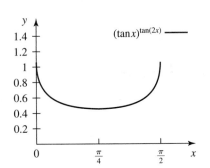

Figure 5.63 The graph of $y = (\tan x)^{\tan(2x)}$.

Section 5.5 Problems

Use l'Hospital's rule to find the limits in Problems 1–50.

1. $\lim\limits_{x \to 5} \dfrac{x^2 - 25}{x - 5}$

2. $\lim\limits_{x \to 2} \dfrac{x - 2}{x^2 - 4}$

3. $\lim\limits_{x \to -2} \dfrac{3x^2 + 5x - 2}{x + 2}$

4. $\lim\limits_{x \to -3} \dfrac{x + 3}{x^2 + 2x - 3}$

5. $\lim\limits_{x \to 0} \dfrac{\sqrt{2x + 4} - 2}{x}$

6. $\lim\limits_{x \to 0} \dfrac{3 - \sqrt{2x + 9}}{2x}$

7. $\lim\limits_{x \to 0} \dfrac{\sin x}{x \cos x}$

8. $\lim\limits_{x \to 0} \dfrac{x \sin x}{1 - \cos x}$

9. $\lim\limits_{x \to 0} \dfrac{1 - \cos x}{x \tan x}$

10. $\lim\limits_{x \to \pi/2} \dfrac{\sin(\frac{\pi}{2} - x)}{\cos x}$

11. $\lim\limits_{x \to 0^+} \dfrac{\sqrt{x}}{\ln(x + 1)}$

12. $\lim\limits_{x \to \infty} \dfrac{\ln x}{\sqrt{x}}$

13. $\lim\limits_{x \to \infty} \dfrac{\ln(\ln x)}{x}$

14. $\lim\limits_{x \to \infty} \dfrac{\ln(\ln x)}{\ln x}$

15. $\lim\limits_{x \to 0} \dfrac{2^x - 1}{3^x - 1}$

16. $\lim\limits_{x \to 0} \dfrac{5^x - 1}{7^x - 1}$

17. $\lim\limits_{x \to 0} \dfrac{3^{-x} - 1}{2^x - 1}$

18. $\lim\limits_{x \to 0} \dfrac{2^{-x} - 1}{5^x - 1}$

19. $\lim\limits_{x \to 0} \dfrac{e^x - 1 - x}{x^2}$

20. $\lim\limits_{x \to 0} \dfrac{e^x - 1 - x - \frac{x^2}{2}}{x^3}$

21. $\lim\limits_{x \to \infty} \dfrac{(\ln x)^2}{x^2}$

22. $\lim\limits_{x \to \infty} \dfrac{x^7}{e^x}$

23. $\lim\limits_{x \to (\pi/2)^-} \dfrac{\tan x}{\sec^2 x}$

24. $\lim\limits_{x \to 0} \dfrac{e^x - 1}{\sin x}$

25. $\lim\limits_{x \to \infty} xe^{-x}$

26. $\lim\limits_{x \to \infty} x^2 e^{-x}$

27. $\lim\limits_{x \to \infty} x^5 e^{-x}$

28. $\lim\limits_{x \to \infty} x^n e^{-x}, n \in \mathbf{N}$

29. $\lim\limits_{x \to 0^+} \sqrt{x} \ln x$

30. $\lim\limits_{x \to 0^+} x^2 \ln x$

31. $\lim\limits_{x \to 0^+} x^5 \ln x$

32. $\lim\limits_{x \to 0^+} x^n \ln x, n \in \mathbf{N}$

33. $\lim\limits_{x \to (\pi/2)^-} \left(\dfrac{\pi}{2} - x \right) \sec x$

34. $\lim\limits_{x \to 1^-} (1 - x) \tan \left(\dfrac{\pi}{2} x \right)$

35. $\lim\limits_{x \to \infty} \sqrt{x} \sin \dfrac{1}{x}$

36. $\lim\limits_{x \to \infty} x^2 \sin \dfrac{1}{x^2}$

37. $\lim\limits_{x \to 0^+} (\cot x - \csc x)$

38. $\lim\limits_{x \to \infty} (x - \sqrt{x^2 - 1})$

39. $\lim\limits_{x \to 0^+} \left(\dfrac{1}{\sin x} - \dfrac{1}{x} \right)$

40. $\lim\limits_{x \to 0^+} \left(\dfrac{1}{\sin^2 x} - \dfrac{1}{x} \right)$

41. $\lim\limits_{x\to 0^+} x^{2x}$

42. $\lim\limits_{x\to 0^+} x^{\sin x}$

43. $\lim\limits_{x\to\infty} x^{1/x}$

44. $\lim\limits_{x\to\infty} (1+e^x)^{1/x}$

45. $\lim\limits_{x\to\infty} \left(1+\dfrac{3}{x}\right)^x$

46. $\lim\limits_{x\to\infty} \left(1+\dfrac{5}{x}\right)^x$

47. $\lim\limits_{x\to\infty} \left(1-\dfrac{2}{x}\right)^x$

48. $\lim\limits_{x\to\infty} \left(1+\dfrac{3}{x^2}\right)^x$

49. $\lim\limits_{x\to\infty} \left(\dfrac{x}{1+x}\right)^x$

50. $\lim\limits_{x\to 0^+} (\cos(2x))^{3/x}$

Find the limits in Problems 51–60. Be sure to check whether you can apply l'Hospital's rule before you evaluate the limit.

51. $\lim\limits_{x\to 0} xe^x$

52. $\lim\limits_{x\to 0^+} \dfrac{e^x}{x}$

53. $\lim\limits_{x\to(\pi/2)^-} (\tan x + \sec x)$

54. $\lim\limits_{x\to(\pi/2)^-} \dfrac{\tan x}{1+\sec x}$

55. $\lim\limits_{x\to 1} \dfrac{x^2-1}{x+1}$

56. $\lim\limits_{x\to 0} \dfrac{1-\cos x}{\sec x}$

57. $\lim\limits_{x\to-\infty} xe^x$

58. $\lim\limits_{x\to 0^+} \left(\dfrac{1}{x}-\dfrac{1}{\sqrt{x}}\right)$

59. $\lim\limits_{x\to 0^+} x^{3x}$

60. $\lim\limits_{x\to\infty} \left(\dfrac{x+1}{x+2}\right)^x$

61. Use l'Hospital's rule to find

$$\lim_{x\to 0} \frac{a^x-1}{b^x-1}$$

where $a, b > 0$.

62. Use l'Hospital's rule to find

$$\lim_{x\to\infty} \left(1+\frac{c}{x}\right)^x$$

where c is a constant.

63. For $p > 0$, determine the values of p for which the following limit is either 1 or ∞ or a constant that is neither 1 nor ∞:

$$\lim_{x\to\infty} \left(1+\frac{c}{x^p}\right)^x$$

64. Show that

$$\lim_{x\to\infty} x^p e^{-x} = 0$$

for any positive number p. Graph $f(x) = x^p e^{-x}$, $x > 0$, for $p = 1/2$, 1, and 2. Since $f(x) = x^p e^{-x} = x^p/e^x$, the limiting behavior ($\lim_{x\to\infty} \frac{x^p}{e^x} = 0$) shows that the exponential function grows faster than any power of x as $x \to \infty$.

65. Show that

$$\lim_{x\to\infty} \frac{\ln x}{x^p} = 0$$

for any number $p > 0$. This shows that the logarithmic function grows more slowly than any positive power of x as $x \to \infty$.

66. When l'Hospital introduced indeterminate limits in his textbook, his *first* example was

$$\lim_{x\to a} \frac{\sqrt{2a^3 x - x^4} - a\sqrt[3]{a^2 x}}{a - \sqrt[4]{ax^3}}$$

where a is a positive constant. (This example was communicated to him by Bernoulli.) Show that this limit is equal to $(16/9)a$.

67. The height y in feet of a tree as a function of the tree's age x in years is given by

$$y = 121e^{-17/x} \quad \text{for } x > 0$$

(a) Determine (1) the rate of growth when $x \to 0^+$ and (2) the limit of the height as $x \to \infty$.

(b) Find the age at which the growth rate is maximal.

(c) Show that the height of the tree is an increasing function of age. At what age is the height increasing at an accelerating rate and at what age at a decelerating rate?

(d) Sketch the graph of both the height and the rate of growth of the tree as functions of age.

■ 5.6 Difference Equations: Stability (Optional)

In Chapter 2, we introduced difference equations and saw that first-order difference equations can be described by recursions of the form

$$x_{t+1} = f(x_t), \quad t = 0, 1, 2, \ldots \tag{5.14}$$

where $f(x)$ is a function. There, we were able to analyze difference equations only numerically (except for equations describing exponential growth, which we were able to solve). We saw that fixed points (or equilibria) played a special role. A fixed point x^* of (5.14) satisfies the equation

$$x^* = f(x^*) \tag{5.15}$$

and has the property that if $x_0 = x^*$, then $x_t = x^*$ for $t = 1, 2, 3, \ldots$. We also saw in a number of applications that, under certain conditions, x_t converged to the fixed point as $t \to \infty$ even if $x_0 \neq x^*$. However, back then, we were not able to predict when this behavior would occur.

In this section, we will return to fixed points and use calculus to come up with a condition that allows us to check whether convergence to a fixed point occurs. We start with the simplest example: exponential growth.

■ 5.6.1 Exponential Growth

Exponential growth in discrete time is given by the recursion

$$N_{t+1} = RN_t, \quad t = 0, 1, 2, \ldots \tag{5.16}$$

where N_t is the population size at time t and $R > 0$ is the growth parameter. We assume throughout that $N_0 \geq 0$, which implies that $N_t \geq 0$.

The fixed point of (5.16) can be found by solving $N = RN$. The only solution of this equation is $N^* = 0$, unless $R = 1$. If $R = 1$, then the population size never changes, regardless of N_0. A consequence of being a fixed point is that if $N_0 = N^*$, then $N_t = N^*$ for $t = 1, 2, 3, \ldots$. That is, with $N^* = 0$, if $N_0 = 0$, then $N_t = 0$ for $t = 1, 2, 3, \ldots$. But what happens if we start with a value that is different from 0? In Chapter 2, we found that $N_t = N_0 R^t$ is a solution of (5.16) with initial condition N_0. Using this fact, we concluded that if $N_0 > 0$ and $0 < R < 1$, then $N_t \to 0$ as $t \to \infty$, whereas if $N_0 > 0$ and $R > 1$, then $N_t \to \infty$ as $t \to \infty$. If $R = 1$, then $N_t = N_0$ for $t = 1, 2, 3, \ldots$.

We can interpret the behavior of N_t as follows: If $0 < R < 1$ and $N_0 > 0$, then N_t will return to the equilibrium $N^* = 0$; if $R \geq 1$ and $N_0 > 0$, then N_t will not return to the equilibrium $N^* = 0$; if $R = 1$, N_t will stay at N_0; if $R > 1$, N_t will go to infinity. We say that $N^* = 0$ is **stable** if $0 < R < 1$ and **unstable** if $R > 1$. The case $R = 1$ is called **neutral**, since, no matter what the value of N_0 is, $N_t = N_0$ for $t = 1, 2, 3, \ldots$.

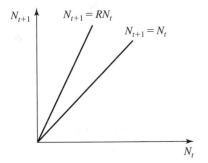

Figure 5.64 The graphs of $N_{t+1} = N_t$ and $N_{t+1} = RN_t$ intersect at $N = 0$ only when $R \neq 1$.

Cobwebbing   There is a graphical approach to determining whether a fixed point is stable or unstable. The fixed points of (5.16) are found graphically where the graphs of $N_{t+1} = RN_t$ and $N_{t+1} = N_t$ intersect, as already pointed out in Chapter 2. We see (Figure 5.64) that the two graphs intersect where $N_t = 0$ only when $R \neq 1$, confirming what we found earlier.

We can use the two graphs in Figure 5.65 to follow successive population sizes ($R > 1$ in the figure). Start at N_0 on the horizontal axis. Since $N_1 = RN_0$, we find N_1 on the vertical axis as shown by the solid horizontal and vertical line segments in Figure 5.65. Using the line $N_{t+1} = N_t$, we can locate N_1 on the horizontal axis, shown in the figure by the dotted horizontal and vertical line segments. Using the line $N_{t+1} = RN_t$ again, we can find N_2 on the vertical axis, shown in the figure by the broken horizontal and vertical line segments. Using the line $N_{t+1} = N_t$ once more, we can locate N_2 on the horizontal axis and then repeat the preceding steps to find N_3 on the vertical axis, and so on (Figure 5.66). This procedure is called **cobwebbing**.

In Figures 5.64–5.66, $R > 1$, and we see that if $N_0 > 0$, then N_t will not converge to the fixed point $N^* = 0$, but instead will move away from 0 (and, in fact, go to infinity as t tends to infinity).

In Figure 5.67, we use the cobwebbing procedure when $0 < R < 1$. We see that if $N_0 > 0$, then N_t will return to the fixed point $N^* = 0$.

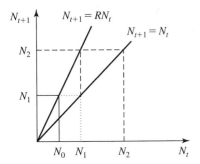

Figure 5.65 The graphs of $N_{t+1} = N_t$ and $N_{t+1} = RN_t$ can be used to determine successive population sizes.

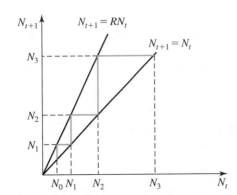

Figure 5.66 The cobwebbing procedure when $R > 1$.

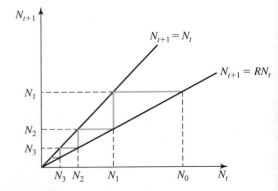

Figure 5.67 The cobwebbing procedure when $0 < R < 1$.

When we discuss the general case, we will find that the slope of the function $N_{t+1} = f(N_t)$ at the fixed point [i.e., $f'(N^*)$] determines whether the solution moves away from the fixed point or converges to it. In the example of exponential growth, $N^* = 0$ and $f'(0) = R$. For $0 < R < 1$, N^* is stable; if $R > 1$, N^* is unstable.

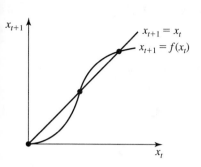

Figure 5.68 Multiple equilibria.

■ 5.6.2 Stability: General Case

The general form of a first-order recursion is

$$x_{t+1} = f(x_t), \quad t = 0, 1, 2, \ldots \tag{5.17}$$

We assume that the function f is differentiable in its domain. To find fixed points algebraically, we solve $x = f(x)$. To find them graphically, we look for points of intersection of the graphs of $x_{t+1} = f(x_t)$ and $x_{t+1} = x_t$ (Figure 5.68). The graphs in Figure 5.68 intersect more than once, which means that there are multiple equilibria or fixed points.

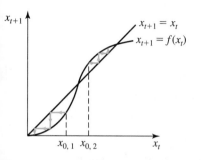

Figure 5.69 Depending on the initial value, the dynamical system converges to different limiting values.

We can use the cobwebbing procedure from the previous subsection to graphically investigate the behavior of the difference equation for different initial values. Two cases are shown in Figure 5.69, one starting at $x_{0,1}$ and the other at $x_{0,2}$. We see that x_t converges to different values, depending on the initial value. This is important to keep in mind in the discussion that follows.

Stability To determine the **stability** of an equilibrium—that is, whether it is stable or unstable—we will proceed as in the previous subsection: We will start at a value that is different from the equilibrium and check whether the solution will return to the equilibrium. There is one important difference, however: We will *not* allow just any initial value that is different from the equilibrium; rather, we allow only initial values that are "close" to the equilibrium. We think of starting at a different value as a **perturbation** of the equilibrium, and since the initial value is close to the equilibrium, we call it a **small perturbation**. The reason for looking only at small perturbations is that if there are multiple equilibria and if we start too far away from the equilibrium of interest, we might end up at a different equilibrium, not because the equilibrium of interest is unstable, but simply because we are drawn to another equilibrium (as in Figure 5.69).

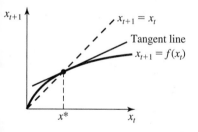

Figure 5.70 Linearizing about the equilibrium.

If we are concerned only with small perturbations, we can approximate the function $f(x)$ by its tangent-line approximation at the equilibrium x^* (Figure 5.70). We will therefore first look at graphs in which we replace $f(x)$ by its tangent-line approximation at x^*.

There are four different cases, which can be divided according to whether the slope of the tangent line at x^* is between 0 and 1 (Figure 5.71a), greater than 1 (Figure 5.71b), between −1 and 0 (Figure 5.72a), and less than −1 (Figure 5.72b).

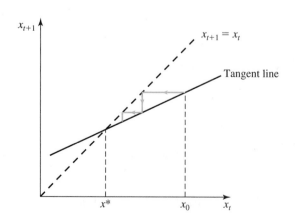

Figure 5.71a A locally stable node.

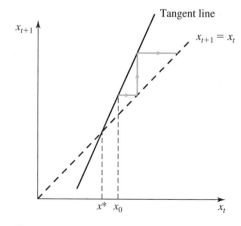

Figure 5.71b An unstable node.

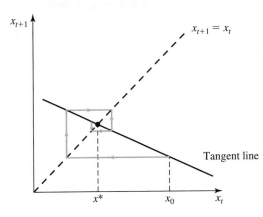

Figure 5.72a A locally stable spiral.

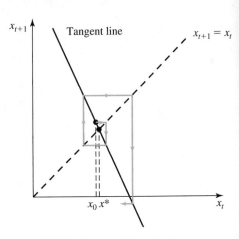

Figure 5.72b An unstable spiral.

We see that when the slope of the tangent line is between -1 and 1, x_t converges to the equilibrium (Figures 5.71a and 5.72a). The difference between Figures 5.71a and 5.72a is that in Figure 5.72a the solution x_t approaches the equilibrium in a spiral (thus exhibiting oscillatory behavior), whereas in Figure 5.71a it approaches it in one direction (thus exhibiting nonoscillatory behavior). Looking at Figure 5.71b, in which the slope is greater than 1, and Figure 5.72b, in which the slope is less than -1, we see that the solution x_t does not return to the equilibrium. In Figure 5.72b the solution moves away from the equilibrium in a spiral (thus exhibiting oscillatory behavior), whereas in Figure 5.71b it moves away in one direction (thus exhibiting nonoscillatory behavior). We call the equilibria in Figures 5.71a and 5.72a **locally stable**, and in Figures 5.71b and 5.72b **unstable**. Note that we added the word *locally* to *stable* to emphasize that this is a local property since we consider only perturbations close to the equilibrium.

Since the slope of the tangent-line approximation of $f(x)$ at x^* is given by $f'(x^*)$, we are led to the following criterion, which we will prove by calculus:

> **Criterion** An equilibrium x^* of $x_{t+1} = f(x_t)$ is locally stable if
>
> $$|f'(x^*)| < 1$$

Proof In Figures 5.71 and 5.72, we looked at the linearization of $f(x)$ about the equilibrium x^* and investigated how a small perturbation affects the future of the solution. Translating this approach into equations, we denote a small perturbation at time t by z_t and write

$$x_t = x^* + z_t$$

Then

$$x_{t+1} = f(x_t) = f(x^* + z_t)$$

Recall that the linear approximation for $f(x)$ at $x = a$ is $L(x) = f(a) + f'(a)(x-a)$. With $x = x^* + z_t$ and $a = x^*$, the linear approximation for $f(x^* + z_t)$ at x^* is

$$L(x^* + z_t) = f(x^*) + f'(x^*)z_t$$

We can approximate $x_{t+1} = x^* + z_{t+1}$ by

$$x^* + z_{t+1} \approx f(x^*) + f'(x^*)z_t$$

Since $f(x^*) = x^*$ (x^* is an equilibrium), we find that

$$z_{t+1} \approx f'(x^*)z_t \tag{5.18}$$

This approximation should remind you of the equation $y_{t+1} = Ry_t$ for exponential growth, where we can identify y_t with z_t and R with $f'(x^*)$. Since the solution of $y_{t+1} = Ry_t$ is equal to $y_t = y_0 R^t$ and $R^t \to 0$ as $t \to \infty$ for $|R| < 1$, we obtain the criterion $|f'(x^*)| < 1$ for local stability. That is, if $|f'(x^*)| < 1$, then the perturbation z_t will converge to $z^* = 0$ or, equivalently, $x_t \to x^*$ as $t \to \infty$. ■

Looking back at Figures 5.71 and 5.72, we can see, in addition, that the equilibrium is approached without oscillations if $f'(x^*) > 0$ and with oscillations if $f'(x^*) < 0$.

EXAMPLE 1

Use the stability criterion to characterize the stability of the equilibria of

$$x_{t+1} = \frac{1}{4} - \frac{5}{4}x_t^2, \quad t = 0, 1, 2, \ldots$$

Solution

To find the equilibria, we need to solve

$$x = \frac{1}{4} - \frac{5}{4}x^2$$

$$\frac{5}{4}x^2 + x - \frac{1}{4} = 0$$

$$5x^2 + 4x - 1 = 0$$

The left-hand side can be factored into $(5x - 1)(x + 1)$, and we find that

$$(5x - 1)(x + 1) = 0 \quad \text{if} \quad x = \frac{1}{5} \quad \text{or} \quad x = -1$$

To determine stability, we need to evaluate the derivative of $f(x) = \frac{1}{4} - \frac{5}{4}x^2$ at the equilibria. Now,

$$f'(x) = -\frac{5}{2}x$$

so if $x = \frac{1}{5}$, then $|f'(\frac{1}{5})| = |-\frac{1}{2}| = \frac{1}{2} < 1$ and if $x = -1$, then $|f'(-1)| = |\frac{5}{2}| = \frac{5}{2} > 1$. Thus, $x = \frac{1}{5}$ is locally stable and $x = -1$ is unstable.

We can say a bit more, namely, that since $f'(\frac{1}{5}) = -\frac{1}{2} < 0$, the equilibrium $x^* = 1/5$ is approached with oscillations. ■

EXAMPLE 2

Use the stability criterion to characterize the stability of the equilibria of

$$x_{t+1} = \frac{x_t}{0.1 + x_t}, \quad t = 0, 1, 2, \ldots$$

Solution

To find the equilibria, we need to solve

$$x = \frac{x}{0.1 + x}$$

This immediately yields $x = 0$ as a solution. If $x \neq 0$, then after dividing by x, we have

$$1 = \frac{1}{0.1 + x} \quad \text{or} \quad 0.1 + x = 1 \quad \text{or} \quad x = 0.9$$

With $f(x) = \frac{x}{0.1+x}$, we find that

$$f'(x) = \frac{0.1 + x - x}{(0.1 + x)^2} = \frac{0.1}{(0.1 + x)^2}$$

Since $f'(0) = \frac{1}{0.1} = 10 > 1$, we conclude that $x^* = 0$ is unstable. Because $f'(0.9) = 0.1 \in (0, 1)$, we conclude that $x^* = 0.9$ is stable and is approached without oscillations. ■

■ 5.6.3 Examples

In the remaining examples in this section, we will revisit three of the growth models we discussed in Chapter 2. There, we analyzed these models by simulations, and you simply had to believe for which parameters a nontrivial locally stable solution existed. We are now in the position to determine stability analytically, using the criterion from the previous subsection.

EXAMPLE 3

Beverton–Holt Recruitment Curve Denote by N_t the size of a population at time $t, t = 0, 1, 2, \ldots$. Find all equilibria and determine their stability for the Beverton–Holt recruitment curve

$$N_{t+1} = \frac{RN_t}{1 + \frac{R-1}{K}N_t}$$

where we assume that the parameters R and K satisfy $R > 1$ and $K > 0$.

Solution To find the equilibria, we set

$$N = \frac{RN}{1 + \frac{R-1}{K}N}$$

and solve for N. This gives immediately the trivial solution $N = 0$ and, after division by $N \neq 0$,

$$1 = \frac{R}{1 + \frac{R-1}{K}N}$$

Solving the latter expression for N yields the nontrivial solution

$$1 + \frac{R-1}{K}N = R, \qquad \text{or} \qquad N = K$$

To determine stability of the two equilibria, we need to differentiate

$$f(N) = \frac{RN}{1 + \frac{R-1}{K}N}$$

Using the quotient rule, we find that

$$f'(N) = \frac{R\left(1 + \frac{R-1}{K}N\right) - RN\frac{R-1}{K}}{\left(1 + \frac{R-1}{K}N\right)^2}$$

$$= \frac{R}{\left(1 + \frac{R-1}{K}N\right)^2}$$

To determine the stability of the trivial equilibrium $N^* = 0$, we compute

$$f'(0) = R > 1$$

(since we assumed that $R > 1$). Thus, $N^* = 0$ is unstable. The stability of the nontrivial equilibrium $N^* = K$ can be determined by computing

$$f'(K) = \frac{R}{\left(1 + \frac{R-1}{K}K\right)^2} = \frac{1}{R}$$

Hence, $|f'(K)| < 1$ because $R > 1$. Consequently, $N^* = K$ is locally stable when $R > 1$, as we found in Chapter 2. Since $f'(K) > 0$, the equilibrium is approached without oscillations. ■

EXAMPLE 4

Logistic Growth   Denote by N_t the size of a population at time $t, t = 0, 1, 2, \ldots$. Find all equilibria and determine their stability for the discrete logistic growth equation

$$N_{t+1} = N_t \left[1 + R \left(1 - \frac{N_t}{K} \right) \right]$$

where we assume that the parameters R and K are both positive.

Solution   To find the equilibria, we set

$$N = N \left[1 + R \left(1 - \frac{N}{K} \right) \right]$$

This yields the trivial solution $N = 0$ and the nontrivial solution $N = K$.

To determine stability, we need to differentiate

$$f(N) = N \left[1 + R \left(1 - \frac{N}{K} \right) \right]$$

Using the product rule, we find that

$$f'(N) = 1 + R \left(1 - \frac{N}{K} \right) + N \left(-\frac{R}{K} \right)$$

$$= 1 + R - \frac{2NR}{K}$$

Since $f'(0) = 1 + R > 1$, we conclude that $N^* = 0$ is unstable. Now,

$$f'(K) = 1 + R - 2R = 1 - R$$

Because $|f'(K)| = |1 - R| < 1$ if $-1 < 1 - R < 1$ or $2 > R > 0$, we conclude that $N^* = K$ is locally stable if $0 < R < 2$, as we saw in Chapter 2. We can say a bit more now: If $0 < R < 1$, then $N^* = K$ is approached without oscillations, since $f'(K) > 0$; if $1 < R < 2$, $N^* = K$ is approached *with* oscillations, since $f'(K) < 0$.   ■

EXAMPLE 5

Ricker's Curve   Denote by N_t the size of a population at time $t, t = 0, 1, 2, \ldots$. Find all equilibria and determine their stability for Ricker's curve,

$$N_{t+1} = N_t \exp \left[R \left(1 - \frac{N_t}{K} \right) \right]$$

where we assume that the parameter R is positive.

Solution   To find the equilibria, we set

$$N = N \exp \left[R \left(1 - \frac{N}{K} \right) \right]$$

This gives the trivial equilibrium $N = 0$ and

$$1 = \exp \left[R \left(1 - \frac{N}{K} \right) \right]$$

Solving the latter equation for N yields

$$R \left(1 - \frac{N}{K} \right) = 0, \quad \text{or} \quad N = K$$

To determine stability, we need to differentiate

$$f(N) = N \exp \left[R \left(1 - \frac{N}{K} \right) \right]$$

Using the product rule and the chain rule, we find that

$$f'(N) = \exp\left[R\left(1 - \frac{N}{K}\right)\right] + N \exp\left[R\left(1 - \frac{N}{K}\right)\right]\left(-\frac{R}{K}\right)$$
$$= \exp\left[R\left(1 - \frac{N}{K}\right)\right]\left(1 - \frac{NR}{K}\right)$$

Now,

$$f'(0) = e^R > 1$$

for $R > 0$, so $N^* = 0$ is unstable. Since

$$f'(K) = 1 - R$$

and $|f'(K)| = |1 - R| < 1$ if $-1 < 1 - R < 1$ or $0 < R < 2$, we conclude that $N^* = K$ is locally stable if $0 < R < 2$. We can say a bit more now: If $0 < R < 1$, then $N^* = K$ is approached without oscillations, since $f'(K) > 0$; if $1 < R < 2$, $N^* = K$ is approached *with* oscillations, since $f'(K) < 0$. ■

Section 5.6 Problems

■ 5.6.1

1. Assume a discrete-time population whose size at generation $t + 1$ is related to the size of the population at generation t by

$$N_{t+1} = (1.03)N_t, \quad t = 0, 1, 2, \ldots$$

(a) If $N_0 = 10$, how large will the population be at generation $t = 5$?

(b) How many generations will it take for the population size to reach double the size at generation 0?

2. Suppose a discrete-time population evolves according to

$$N_{t+1} = (0.9)N_t, \quad t = 0, 1, 2 \ldots$$

(a) If $N_0 = 50$, how large will the population be at generation $t = 6$?

(b) After how many generations will the size of the population be one-quarter of its original size?

(c) What will happen to the population in the long run—that is, as $t \to \infty$?

3. Assume the discrete-time population model

$$N_{t+1} = bN_t, \quad t = 0, 1, 2 \ldots$$

Assume also that the population increases by 2% each generation.

(a) Determine b.

(b) Find the size of the population at generation 10 when $N_0 = 20$.

(c) After how many generations will the population size have doubled?

4. Assume the discrete-time population model

$$N_{t+1} = bN_t, \quad t = 0, 1, 2, \ldots$$

Assume also that the population decreases by 3% each generation.

(a) Determine b.

(b) Find the size of the population at generation 10 when $N_0 = 50$.

(c) How long will it take until the population is one-half its original size?

5. Assume the discrete-time population model

$$N_{t+1} = bN_t, \quad t = 0, 1, 2, \ldots$$

Assume that the population increases by $x\%$ each generation.

(a) Determine b.

(b) After how many generations will the population size have doubled? Compute the doubling time for $x = 0.1, 0.5, 1, 2, 5,$ and 10.

6. (a) Find all equilibria of

$$N_{t+1} = 1.3N_t, \quad t = 0, 1, 2, \ldots$$

(b) Use cobwebbing to determine the stability of the equilibria you found in (a).

7. (a) Find all equilibria of

$$N_{t+1} = 0.9N_t, \quad t = 0, 1, 2, \ldots$$

(b) Use cobwebbing to determine the stability of the equilibria you found in (a).

8. (a) Find all equilibria of

$$N_{t+1} = N_t, \quad t = 0, 1, 2, \ldots$$

(b) How will the population size N_t change over time, starting at time 0 with N_0?

■ 5.6.2

9. Use the stability criterion to characterize the stability of the equilibria of

$$x_{t+1} = \frac{2}{3} - \frac{2}{3}x_t^2, \quad t = 0, 1, 2, \ldots$$

10. Use the stability criterion to characterize the stability of the equilibria of

$$x_{t+1} = \frac{3}{5}x_t^2 - \frac{2}{5}, \quad t = 0, 1, 2, \ldots$$

11. Use the stability criterion to characterize the stability of the equilibria of

$$x_{t+1} = \frac{x_t}{0.5 + x_t}, \quad t = 0, 1, 2, \ldots$$

12. Use the stability criterion to characterize the stability of the equilibria of

$$x_{t+1} = \frac{x_t}{0.3 + x_t}, \quad t = 0, 1, 2, \ldots$$

13. (a) Use the stability criterion to characterize the stability of the equilibria of

$$x_{t+1} = \frac{5x_t^2}{4 + x_t^2}, \quad t = 0, 1, 2, \ldots$$

(b) Use cobwebbing to decide to which value x_t converges as $t \to \infty$ if **(i)** $x_0 = 0.5$ and **(ii)** $x_0 = 2$.

14. (a) Use the stability criterion to characterize the stability of the equilibria of

$$x_{t+1} = \frac{10x_t^2}{9 + x_t^2}, \quad t = 0, 1, 2, \ldots$$

(b) Use cobwebbing to decide to which value x_t converges as $t \to \infty$ if (i) $x_0 = 0.5$ and (ii) $x_0 = 3$.

■ **5.6.3**

15. Ricker's curve is given by

$$R(P) = \alpha P e^{-\beta P}$$

for $P \geq 0$, where P denotes the size of the parental stock and $R(P)$ the number of recruits. The parameters α and β are positive constants.

(a) Show that $R(0) = 0$ and $R(P) > 0$ for $P > 0$.

(b) Find

$$\lim_{P \to \infty} R(P)$$

(c) For what size of the parental stock is the number of recruits maximal?

(d) Does $R(P)$ have inflection points? If so, find them.

(e) Sketch the graph of $f(x)$ when $\alpha = 2$ and $\beta = 1/2$.

16. Suppose that the size of a fish population at generation t is given by

$$N_{t+1} = 1.5N_t e^{-0.001N_t}$$

for $t = 0, 1, 2, \ldots$.

(a) Assume that $N_0 = 100$. Find the size of the fish population at generation t for $t = 1, 2, \ldots, 20$.

(b) Assume that $N_0 = 800$. Find the size of the fish population at generation t for $t = 1, 2, \ldots, 20$.

(c) Determine all fixed points. On the basis of your computations in (a) and (b), make a guess as to what will happen to the population in the long run, starting from **(i)** $N_0 = 100$ and **(ii)** $N_0 = 800$.

(d) Use the cobwebbing method to illustrate your answer in (a).

(e) Explain why the dynamical system converges to the nontrivial fixed point.

17. Suppose that the size of a fish population at generation t is given by

$$N_{t+1} = 10N_t e^{-0.01N_t}$$

for $t = 0, 1, 2, \ldots$.

(a) Assume that $N_0 = 100$. Find the size of the fish population at generation t for $t = 1, 2, \ldots, 20$.

(b) Show that if $N_0 = 100 \ln 10$, then $N_t = 100 \ln 10$ for $t = 1, 2, 3, \ldots$; that is, show that $N^* = 100 \ln 10$ is a nontrivial fixed point, or equilibrium. How would you find N^*? Are there any other equilibria?

(c) On the basis of your computations in (a), make a prediction about the long-term behavior of the fish population when $N_0 = 100$. How does your answer compare with that in (b)?

(d) Use the cobwebbing method to illustrate your answer in (c).

In Problems 18–20, consider the following discrete-time dynamical system, which is called the discrete logistic model and which models the size of a population over time:

$$N_{t+1} = N_t \left[1 + R\left(1 - \frac{N_t}{100}\right)\right]$$

for $t = 0, 1, 2, \ldots$.

18. (a) Find all equilibria when $R = 0.5$.

(b) Investigate the system when $N_0 = 10$ and describe what you see.

19. (a) Find all equilibria when $R = 1.5$.

(b) Investigate the system when $N_0 = 10$ and describe what you see.

20. (a) Find all equilibria when $R = 2.5$.

(b) Investigate the system when $N_0 = 10$ and describe what you see.

In Problems 21–22, we investigate the canonical discrete-time logistic growth model

$$x_{t+1} = rx_t(1 - x_t)$$

for $t = 0, 1, 2, \ldots$.

21. Show that for $r > 1$, there are two fixed points. For which values of r is the nonzero fixed point locally stable?

22. Use a calculator or a spreadsheet to simulate the canonical discrete-time logistic growth model with $x_0 = 0.1$ for $t = 0, 1, 2, \ldots, 100$, and describe the behavior when
(a) $r = 3.20$ **(b)** $r = 3.52$ **(c)** $r = 3.80$
(d) $r = 3.83$ **(e)** $r = 3.828$

In Problems 23–25, we consider density-dependent population growth models of the form

$$N_{t+1} = R(N_t)N_t$$

The function $R(N)$ describes the per capita growth. Various forms have been considered. For each function $R(N)$, find all nontrivial fixed points N^* (i.e., $N^* > 0$) and determine the stability as a function of the parameter values. We assume that the function parameters are $r > 0$, $K > 0$, and $\gamma > 1$.

23. $R(N) = rN^{1-\gamma}$ **24.** $R(N) = \dfrac{r}{1 + N/K}$

25. $R(N) = e^{r(1-N/K)}$

■ 5.7 Numerical Methods: The Newton–Raphson Method (Optional)

Numerical methods are very important in the sciences, where we frequently encounter situations in which exact solutions are impossible. In Section 3.5, we encountered one method, the bisection method, for solving equations of the form $f(x) = 0$. Here we examine another method that is often much more efficient than the bisection method.

The Newton–Raphson method allows us to find solutions of equations of the form

$$f(x) = 0$$

The idea behind the method can be best explained graphically. (See Figure 5.73.)

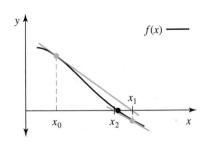

Figure 5.73 The graph of $y = f(x)$ and the first two iterations in the Newton–Raphson method.

Suppose that we wish to find the roots of $f(x) = 0$. We begin by choosing a value x_0 as our initial guess; then we replace the graph of $f(x)$ by its tangent line $y = L(x)$ to our initial guess x_0. Since the slope of the tangent line $y = L(x)$ is equal to $f'(x_0)$, and since $(x_0, f(x_0))$ is a point on the tangent line, we can use the point–slope form by

$$y - f(x_0) = f'(x_0)(x - x_0)$$

to find the equation of the tangent line. This line will intersect the x-axis at some point $x = x_1$, provided that $f'(x_0) \neq 0$. To find x_1, we set $x = x_1$ and $y = 0$ and solve for x_1:

$$0 - f(x_0) = f'(x_0)(x_1 - x_0) \qquad \text{or} \qquad x_1 = x_0 - \frac{f(x_0)}{f'(x_0)}$$

We use x_1 as our next guess and repeat the procedure, which will result in x_2, and so on. The value of x_{n+1} is then given by

$$x_{n+1} = x_n - \frac{f(x_n)}{f'(x_n)} \quad \text{for } n = 0, 1, 2, \ldots \qquad (5.19)$$

This equation produces a sequence of numbers $x_1, x_2, \ldots$. If these values converge to the root of $f(x) = 0$, denoted by r, as $n \to \infty$, or

$$\lim_{n \to \infty} x_n = r$$

then computing $x_1, x_2, \ldots$ provides a numerical way to approximate r. The method will not always converge, but before we discuss situations in which the method fails, we give two examples in which it works.

EXAMPLE 1

Use the Newton–Raphson method to find a numerical approximation to a solution of the equation

$$x^2 - 3 = 0$$

Solution   The equation $x^2 - 3 = 0$ has roots $r = \sqrt{3}$ and $-\sqrt{3}$. Finding a numerical approximation to a root of this equation is therefore the same as finding a numerical approximation to $\sqrt{3}$ or $-\sqrt{3}$. You might ask why we don't just use our calculators and get the numerical value of $\sqrt{3}$. In fact, that is what you would do if you had to solve an equation such as $x^2 - 3 = 0$, but we will use this simple example to illustrate the method.

We will find a numerical approximation to $\sqrt{3}$ by the Newton–Raphson method. As our initial value, we choose a number close to $\sqrt{3}$, say, $x_0 = 2$. The function $f(x)$ is

$$f(x) = x^2 - 3$$

and its derivative is

$$f'(x) = 2x$$

Using (5.19), we find that

$$x_{n+1} = x_n - \frac{x_n^2 - 3}{2x_n}$$

$$= x_n - \frac{x_n}{2} + \frac{3}{2x_n} = \frac{x_n}{2} + \frac{3}{2x_n} \quad \text{for } n = 0, 1, 2, \ldots$$

(See Figure 5.74 for the first step of the approximation.)
The following table shows the results of the procedure:

n	x_n	$x_{n+1} = \dfrac{x_n}{2} + \dfrac{3}{2x_n}$	$\left\lvert\sqrt{3} - x_{n+1}\right\rvert$
0	2	1.75	0.0179
1	1.75	1.7321429	9.2×10^{-5}
2	1.7321429	1.7320508	2.45×10^{-9}

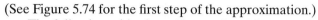

With the starting value $x_0 = 2$, after three steps we obtain the approximation 1.732050. Since a calculator yields the approximation 1.732050080757 for $\sqrt{3}$, our approximation by the Newton–Raphson method is correct to six decimal places. As you can see, the method can converge very quickly. In fact, it is used in many calculators to calculate roots. ■

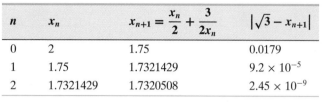

Figure 5.74 The graph of $f(x) = x^2 - 3$ and the first step in the Newton–Raphson method.

In the next example, we cannot simply solve for x by algebraic manipulations. To find a solution of the given equation, we must resort to a numerical method.

EXAMPLE 2 Solve the equation

$$e^x + 1 + x = 0$$

Solution It turns out that this equation can be solved only numerically. We will use the Newton–Raphson method to determine the root of $e^x + 1 + x = 0$. Since $e^x + 1 + x$ is positive for $x = 0$ and negative for $x = -2$, we conclude that there is a root of $e^x + 1 + x = 0$ in the interval $(-2, 0)$. We therefore choose a starting value in this interval, say, $x_0 = -1$. We find that

$$f(x) = e^x + x + 1$$
$$f'(x) = e^x + 1$$

Therefore,

$$x_{n+1} = x_n - \frac{f(x_n)}{f'(x_n)}$$

$$= x_n - \frac{e^{x_n} + x_n + 1}{e^{x_n} + 1} = x_n - 1 - \frac{x_n}{e^{x_n} + 1} \quad \text{for } n = 0, 1, 2, \ldots$$

The first step in the approximation is shown in Figure 5.75.
We summarize the first few steps of the iteration in the following table, where $x_0 = -1$:

n	x_n	$x_{n+1} = x_n - 1 - \dfrac{x_n}{e^{x_n} + 1}$
0	-1	-1.26894142
1	-1.26894142	-1.27845462
2	-1.27845462	-1.27846454
3	-1.27846454	-1.27846454

Note that x_2 and x_3 agree to four decimal places and that x_3 and x_4 agree to eight decimal places. We therefore suspect that $x = -1.278464$ is a root of $e^x + x + 1 = 0$, accurate to six decimal places. This can be confirmed with, for instance, a graphing calculator. ■

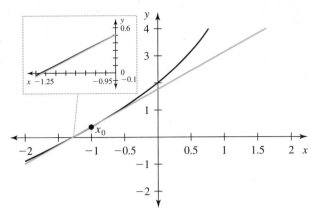

Figure 5.75 The graph of $f(x) = e^x + x + 1$ and the first step of the approximations in the Newton–Raphson method.

It is not our goal here to provide a complete description of the Newton–Raphson method (when it works, how quickly it converges, etc.). Instead, we give a few examples that illustrate some of the problems we can encounter when using the method.

EXAMPLE 3 This example illustrates a situation in which the Newton–Raphson method does not work. Let

$$f(x) = \begin{cases} \sqrt{x - 2.5} & \text{for } x \geq 2.5 \\ -\sqrt{2.5 - x} & \text{for } x \leq 2.5 \end{cases}$$

We wish to solve the equation $f(x) = 0$. We see immediately that $x = 2.5$ is a solution. Given that

$$f'(x) = \begin{cases} \dfrac{1}{2\sqrt{x - 2.5}} & \text{for } x > 2.5 \\ \dfrac{1}{2\sqrt{2.5 - x}} & \text{for } x < 2.5 \end{cases}$$

we apply the Newton–Raphson method and find that

$$x_{n+1} = x_n - \frac{f(x_n)}{f'(x_n)}$$

$$= \begin{cases} x_n - \dfrac{\sqrt{x_n - 2.5}}{\dfrac{1}{2\sqrt{x_n - 2.5}}} & \text{for } x_n > 2.5 \\ x_n - \dfrac{-\sqrt{2.5 - x_n}}{\dfrac{1}{2\sqrt{2.5 - x_n}}} & \text{for } x_n < 2.5 \end{cases}$$

$$= \begin{cases} x_n - 2(x_n - 2.5) = -x_n + 5 & \text{for } x_n > 2.5 \\ x_n + 2(2.5 - x_n) = -x_n + 5 & \text{for } x_n < 2.5 \end{cases}$$

$$= -x_n + 5 \quad \text{for } x_n \neq 2.5$$

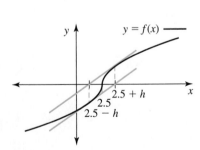

Figure 5.76 The graph of $f(x)$ in Example 3 where the Newton–Raphson method does not converge.

If $x_0 = 2.5 + h$, then $x_1 = 2.5 - h$, $x_2 = 2.5 + h$, $x_3 = 2.5 - h$, and so on; that is, successive approximations oscillate between $2.5 + h$ and $2.5 - h$ and never approach the root $r = 2.5$. A graph of $f(x)$, together with the iterations, is shown in Figure 5.76. Note that the two tangent lines are parallel and are used alternately in the approximation. ■

EXAMPLE 4

This example shows that an initial approximation can get worse. Use the Newton–Raphson method to find the root of

$$x^{1/3} = 0$$

when the starting value is $x_0 = 1$.

Solution

We set $f(x) = x^{1/3}$. Then $f'(x) = \frac{1}{3}x^{-2/3}$, and

$$x_{n+1} = x_n - \frac{f(x_n)}{f'(x_n)} = x_n - \frac{x_n^{1/3}}{\frac{1}{3}x_n^{-2/3}} = x_n - 3x_n = -2x_n$$

The following table shows successive values of x_n:

n	x_n	$x_{n+1} = -2x_n$
0	1	−2
1	−2	4
2	4	−8
3	−8	16

The successive values do not converge to the root $r = 0$. The situation is graphically illustrated in Figure 5.77.

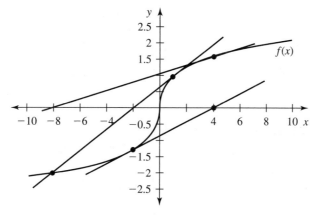

Figure 5.77   The graph of $f(x)$ in Example 4 where the Newton–Raphson method does not converge.

Graphing calculators have an option in the graphing menu that allows you to find roots of equations $f(x) = 0$ if you graph $f(x)$ and put the cursor close to the root. For this example, the calculator cannot produce an answer. ■

EXAMPLE 5

This example shows that our successive approximations do not necessarily converge to the closest root. We wish to find a root of the equation

$$x^4 - x^2 = 0$$

If we set $f(x) = x^4 - x^2$, then $f'(x) = 4x^3 - 2x$ and

$$x_{n+1} = x_n - \frac{f(x_n)}{f'(x_n)}$$

$$= x_n - \frac{x_n^4 - x_n^2}{4x_n^3 - 2x_n} = x_n - \frac{x_n^3 - x_n}{4x_n^2 - 2}$$

We can solve for the roots of $x^4 - x^2 = 0$. Since $x^4 - x^2 = x^2(x^2 - 1)$, there are three roots: $r = 0, -1$, and 1. Suppose that we set $x_0 = -0.7$. The closest root is -1. If we compute x_1, we find that

$$x_1 = (-0.7) - \frac{(-0.7)^3 - (-0.7)}{4(-0.7)^2 - 2} = 8.225$$

Successive values are collected in the following list:

$x_2 = 6.184$	$x_7 = 1.613$
$x_3 = 4.659$	$x_8 = 1.306$
$x_4 = 3.521$	$x_9 = 1.115$
$x_5 = 2.678$	$x_{10} = 1.024$
$x_6 = 2.059$	$x_{11} = 1.001$

We conclude that the method converges to the root $r = 1$. The situation is illustrated in Figure 5.78. ■

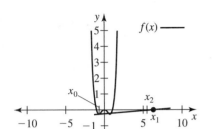

Figure 5.78 The graph of $f(x)$ in Example 5 together with the first two approximations.

Section 5.7 Problems

1. Use the Newton–Raphson method to find a numerical approximation to the solution of

$$x^2 - 7 = 0$$

that is correct to six decimal places.

2. Use the Newton–Raphson method to find a numerical approximation to the solution of

$$e^{-x} = x$$

that is correct to six decimal places.

3. Use the Newton–Raphson method to find a numerical approximation to the solution of

$$x^2 + \ln x = 0$$

that is correct to six decimal places.

4. The equation

$$x^2 - 5 = 0$$

has two solutions. Use the Newton–Raphson method to approximate the two solutions.

5. Use the Newton–Raphson method to solve the equation

$$\sin x = \frac{1}{2}x$$

in the interval $(0, \pi)$.

6. Let

$$f(x) = \begin{cases} \sqrt{x - 1} & \text{for } x \geq 1 \\ -\sqrt{1 - x} & \text{for } x \leq 1 \end{cases}$$

(a) Show that if you use the Newton–Raphson method to solve $f(x) = 0$, then the following statement holds: If $x_0 = 1 + h$, then $x_1 = 1 - h$, and if $x_0 = 1 - h$, then $x_1 = 1 + h$.

(b) Does the Newton–Raphson method converge? Use a graph to explain what happens.

7. In Example 4, we discussed the case of finding the root of $x^{1/3} = 0$.

(a) Given x_0, find a formula for $|x_n|$.

(b) Find

$$\lim_{n \to \infty} |x_n|$$

(c) Graph $f(x) = x^{1/3}$ and illustrate what happens when you apply the Newton–Raphson method.

8. In Example 5, we considered the equation

$$x^4 - x^2 = 0$$

(a) What happens if you choose

$$x_0 = -\frac{1}{2}\sqrt{2}$$

in the Newton–Raphson method? Give a graphical illustration.

(b) Repeat the procedure in (a) for $x_0 = -0.71$, and compare your result with the result we obtained in Example 5 when $x_0 = -0.70$. Give a graphical illustration and explain it in words. What happens when $x_0 = -0.6$? (This is an example in which small changes in the initial value can drastically change the outcome.)

9. Use the Newton–Raphson method to find a numerical approximation to the solution of

$$x^2 - 16 = 0$$

when your initial guess is (a) $x_0 = 3$ and (b) $x_0 = 4$.

10. Suppose that you wish to use the Newton–Raphson method to solve

$$f(x) = 0$$

numerically. It just so happens that your initial guess x_0 satisfies $f(x_0) = 0$. What happens to subsequent iterations? Give a graphical illustration of your results. [Assume that $f'(x_0) \neq 0$.]

■ 5.8 Antiderivatives

Throughout this and the previous chapter, we have repeatedly encountered differential equations. Occasionally, we showed that a certain function would solve a given differential equation. In this section, we will discuss a particular type of differential equation and address two important general questions: First, given a differential equation, how can we find its solutions? Second, given a solution of a differential equation, how do we know if it is the only one?

We will consider differential equations of the form

$$\frac{dy}{dx} = f(x)$$

That is, the rate of change of y with respect to x depends *only* on x. Our goal is to find functions y that satisfy $y' = f(x)$. We will see that if we can find one such function, then there is a whole family of functions with this property, all related by vertical translations. If we want to pick out one of these functions, we need to specify an **initial condition**—a point (x_0, y_0) on the graph of the function. Such a function is called a **solution** of the **initial-value problem**

$$\frac{dy}{dx} = f(x) \quad \text{with } y = y_0 \text{ when } x = x_0 \tag{5.20}$$

Let's look at an example before we begin a systematic treatment of the solution of differential equations of the form (5.20). Consider a population whose size at time t is denoted by $N(t)$, and assume that the growth rate is given by

$$\frac{dN}{dt} = \frac{1}{2\sqrt{t}} \quad \text{for } t > 0 \tag{5.21}$$

and that the size of the population at time 0 is $N(0) = 20$ [i.e., the initial condition is $N(0) = 20$]. Then

$$N(t) = \sqrt{t} + 20 \quad \text{for } t \geq 0 \tag{5.22}$$

is a solution of the differential equation (5.21) that satisfies the initial condition $N(0) = 20$. This is easy to check: First, note that $N(0) = \sqrt{0} + 20 = 20$. Second, differentiating $N(t)$, we find that

$$\frac{dN}{dt} = \frac{d}{dt}\left(\sqrt{t} + 20\right) = \frac{1}{2\sqrt{t}} \quad \text{for } t > 0$$

That is, $N(t) = \sqrt{t} + 20$ satisfies (5.21) with $N(0) = 20$.

This example shows that if we have a solution of a differential equation, we can verify that the solution indeed satisfies the differential equation by differentiating the solution. The method suggests that, in order to find solutions, we reverse the process of differentiation. This leads us to what is called an antiderivative, which is defined as follows:

> **Definition** A function F is called an **antiderivative** of f on an interval I if $F'(x) = f(x)$ for all $x \in I$.

How can we find antiderivatives? Let

$$f(x) = 3x^2 \quad \text{for } x \in \mathbf{R}$$

To find the antiderivative of $f(x) = 3x^2$, we need to find a function whose derivative is $3x^2$. We can guess an answer, namely,

$$F(x) = x^3 \quad \text{for } x \in \mathbf{R}$$

which certainly satisfies $F'(x) = 3x^2$. But this is not the only answer. For example, take $F(x) = x^3 + 4$. Then $F'(x) = 3x^2$; hence, $x^3 + 4$ is also an antiderivative of $3x^2$. In fact, $F(x) = x^3 + C$, $x \in \mathbf{R}$, where C is any constant, is an antiderivative of $3x^2$. [We will soon show that there are no other functions $F(x)$ such that $F'(x) = 3x^2$.] The function $f(x)$ and some of its antiderivatives are shown in Figure 5.79. All of the antiderivatives are related through vertical shifts, since they all have the same derivative.

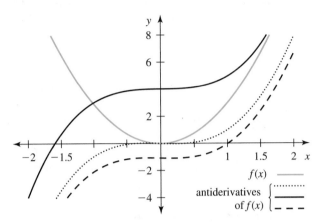

Figure 5.79 The function $f(x) = 3x^2$ and some of its antiderivatives.

Although we will learn rules that allow us to compute antiderivatives, this process is typically much more difficult than finding derivatives, and sometimes it takes ingenuity to come up with the correct answer; in addition, there are even cases where it is impossible to find an expression for an antiderivative.

We begin with two corollaries of the mean-value theorem that will help us in finding antiderivatives. The first of these is Corollary 2 from Section 5.1:

> **Corollary 2** If f is continuous on the closed interval $[a, b]$ and differentiable on the open interval (a, b), with $f'(x) = 0$ for all $x \in (a, b)$, then f is constant on $[a, b]$.

Note that Corollary 2 is the converse of the rule which states that $f'(x) = 0$ when $f(x) = c$, where c is a constant. It tells us that *all* antiderivatives of a function that is identically 0 are constant functions.

The next corollary tells us that functions with identical derivatives differ only by a constant; that is, to find all antiderivatives of a given function, we need only find one.

> **Corollary 3** If $F(x)$ and $G(x)$ are antiderivatives of the continuous function $f(x)$ on an interval I, then there exists a constant C such that
>
> $$G(x) = F(x) + C \quad \text{for all } x \in I$$

Proof Since $F(x)$ and $G(x)$ are both antiderivatives of $f(x)$, it follows that $F'(x) = f(x)$ and $G'(x) = f(x)$; that is, $F'(x) = G'(x)$, or $F'(x) - G'(x) = 0$. Also, since

$$0 = F'(x) - G'(x) = \frac{d}{dx}[F(x) - G(x)]$$

it follows from Corollary 2, applied to the function $F - G$, that $F(x) - G(x) = C$, where C is a constant. ∎

EXAMPLE 1 Find general antiderivatives for the given functions. Assume that all functions are defined for $x \in \mathbf{R}$.

(a) $f(x) = 3x^2$ (b) $f(x) = \cos x$ (c) $f(x) = e^x$

Solution   (a) If $F(x) = x^3$, then $F'(x) = 3x^2$; that is, $F(x) = x^3$ is a particular antiderivative of $3x^2$. Using Corollary 3, we find the general antiderivative simply by adding a constant; that is, the general antiderivative of $f(x) = 3x^2$ is the function $G(x) = x^3 + C$, where C is a constant.

(b) If $F(x) = \sin x$, then $F'(x) = \cos x$. Hence, the general antiderivative of $f(x) = \cos x$ is the function $G(x) = \sin x + C$, where C is a constant.

(c) If $F(x) = e^x$, then $F'(x) = e^x$ and the general antiderivative of $f(x) = e^x$ is the function $G(x) = e^x + C$, where C is a constant. ▪

EXAMPLE 2 Find general antiderivatives for the given functions. (Assume the largest possible domain.)

(a) $f(x) = 3x^5$ (b) $f(x) = x^2 + 2x - 1$
(c) $f(x) = e^{2x}$ (d) $f(x) = \sec^2(3x)$

Solution   (a) Since $\frac{d}{dx}\left(\frac{1}{2}x^6\right) = 3x^5$, $F(x) = \frac{1}{2}x^6 + C$ is the general antiderivative of $f(x) = 3x^5$.

(b) Since $\frac{d}{dx}\left(\frac{1}{3}x^3 + x^2 - x\right) = x^2 + 2x - 1$, $F(x) = \frac{1}{3}x^3 + x^2 - x + C$ is the general antiderivative of $f(x) = x^2 + 2x - 1$.

(c) Since $\frac{d}{dx}\left(\frac{1}{2}e^{2x}\right) = \frac{1}{2}e^{2x}(2) = e^{2x}$, $F(x) = \frac{1}{2}e^{2x} + C$ is the general antiderivative of $f(x) = e^{2x}$.

(d) Since $\frac{d}{dx}\left(\frac{1}{3}\tan(3x)\right) = \frac{1}{3}(\sec^2(3x))(3) = \sec^2(3x)$, $F(x) = \frac{1}{3}\tan(3x) + C$ is the general antiderivative of $f(x) = \sec^2(3x)$. ▪

Table 5-1 summarizes some of the rules for finding antiderivatives. We denote functions by $f(x)$ and $g(x)$ and their particular antiderivatives by $F(x)$ and $G(x)$, respectively. The general antiderivative is then obtained simply by adding a constant. The quantities a and k denote nonzero constants.

TABLE 5-1 A Collection of Antiderivatives

Function	Particular Antiderivative
$kf(x)$	$kF(x)$
$f(x) + g(x)$	$F(x) + G(x)$
$x^n,\ n \neq -1$	$\dfrac{1}{n+1}x^{n+1}$
$\dfrac{1}{x}$	$\ln|x|$
e^{ax}	$\dfrac{1}{a}e^{ax}$
$\sin(ax)$	$-\dfrac{1}{a}\cos(ax)$
$\cos(ax)$	$\dfrac{1}{a}\sin(ax)$
$\sec^2(ax)$	$\dfrac{1}{a}\tan(ax)$

We can now return to our initial question, namely, How do we solve differential equations of the form (5.20)?

EXAMPLE 3 Find the general solution of

$$\frac{dy}{dx} = \frac{3}{x^2} - 2x^2, \quad x \neq 0$$

Solution Finding the general solution of this differential equation means finding the antiderivative of the function $f(x) = \frac{3}{x^2} - 2x^2$. Using Table 5-1, we obtain

$$\frac{3}{-1}x^{-1} - \frac{2}{3}x^3 = -\frac{3}{x} - \frac{2}{3}x^3$$

as a particular antiderivative. That is, the general solution is

$$y = -\frac{3}{x} - \frac{2}{3}x^3 + C, \quad x \neq 0$$ ■

In Example 3, we found the general solution of the given differential equation. Often, we wish to select a particular solution; for instance, we may know that the solution has to pass through a specific point (x_0, y_0). Such a problem is called an *initial-value problem*, as explained at the beginning of this section. We consider the initial-value problem posed in (5.21) again now.

EXAMPLE 4 Solve the initial-value problem

$$\frac{dN}{dt} = \frac{1}{2\sqrt{t}} \quad \text{for } t > 0 \text{ with } N(0) = 20$$

Solution The general antiderivative of $f(t) = \frac{1}{2\sqrt{t}}$ is $F(t) = \sqrt{t} + C$. Since $N(0) = 20$, we have

$$N(0) = \sqrt{0} + C = 20, \quad \text{or} \quad C = 20$$

That is, the function

$$N(t) = \sqrt{t} + 20, \quad t \geq 0$$

solves the initial-value problem, and it is the only solution thereof. (See Figure 5.80.)   ■

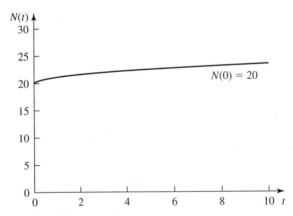

Figure 5.80 The function $N(t)$ solves the initial-value problem with $N(0) = 20$.

EXAMPLE 5 Solve the initial-value problem

$$\frac{dy}{dx} = -2x^2 + 3 \quad \text{for } x \in \mathbf{R} \text{ and } y = 10 \text{ when } x = 3$$

Solution   The general antiderivative of $f(x) = -2x^2 + 3$ is $F(x) = -\frac{2}{3}x^3 + 3x + C$. Since

$$F(3) = -\frac{2}{3}3^3 + (3)(3) + C = -9 + C = 10$$

it follows that $C = 19$. That is,

$$y = -\frac{2}{3}x^3 + 3x + 19, \quad x \in \mathbf{R}$$

solves the initial-value problem, and it is the only solution thereof.   ■

EXAMPLE 6   An object that falls freely in a vacuum, close to the surface of the earth, has a constant acceleration of

$$g = 9.81\frac{m}{s^2}$$

If the object is dropped from rest, find its velocity and the distance it has traveled t seconds after it was released.

Solution   If the distance function is $s(t)$, then the velocity $v(t)$ is given by

$$v(t) = \frac{d}{dt}s(t)$$

and the acceleration is given by

$$a(t) = \frac{d}{dt}v(t) = \frac{d^2}{dt^2}s(t)$$

We wish to solve the initial-value problem

$$\frac{d}{dt}v(t) = 9.81\frac{m}{s^2} \quad \text{when } v(0) = 0$$

A general solution is

$$v(t) = \left(9.81\frac{m}{s^2}\right)t + C$$

Since $v(0) = 0$, it follows that $C = 0$. Hence,

$$v(t) = \left(9.81\frac{m}{s^2}\right)t, \quad t \geq 0$$

To find the distance traveled, note that $s(0) = 0$ and

$$\frac{d}{dt}s(t) = v(t) = \left(9.81\frac{m}{s^2}\right)t, \quad t \geq 0$$

A general solution is

$$s(t) = \frac{1}{2}\left(9.81\frac{m}{s^2}\right)t^2 + C$$

Since $s(0) = 0$, it follows that $C = 0$. Thus,

$$s(t) = \frac{1}{2}\left(9.81\frac{m}{s^2}\right)t^2, \quad t \geq 0$$

Note that if t is measured in seconds, the unit of $v(t)$ is $\frac{m}{s}$ and the unit of $s(t)$ is m.

■

Section 5.8 Problems

In Problems 1–40, find the general antiderivative of the given function.

1. $f(x) = 4x^2 - x$

2. $f(x) = 2 - 5x^2$

3. $f(x) = x^2 + 3x - 4$

4. $f(x) = 3x^2 - x^4$

5. $f(x) = x^4 - 3x^2 + 1$

6. $f(x) = 2x^3 + x^2 - 5x$

7. $f(x) = 4x^3 - 2x + 3$

8. $f(x) = x - 2x^2 - 3x^3 - 4x^4$

9. $f(x) = 1 + \dfrac{1}{x} + \dfrac{1}{x^2}$

10. $f(x) = x^2 - \dfrac{2}{x^2} + \dfrac{3}{x^3}$

11. $f(x) = 1 - \dfrac{1}{x^2}$

12. $f(x) = x^3 - \dfrac{1}{x^3}$

13. $f(x) = \dfrac{1}{1+x}$

14. $f(x) = \dfrac{x}{1+x}$

15. $f(x) = 5x^4 + \dfrac{5}{x^4}$

16. $f(x) = x^7 + \dfrac{1}{x^7}$

17. $f(x) = \dfrac{1}{1+2x}$

18. $f(x) = \dfrac{1}{1+3x}$

19. $f(x) = e^{-3x}$

20. $f(x) = e^{x/2} + e^{-x/2}$

21. $f(x) = 2e^{2x}$

22. $f(x) = -3e^{-4x}$

23. $f(x) = \dfrac{1}{e^{2x}}$

24. $f(x) = \dfrac{3}{e^{-x}}$

25. $f(x) = \sin(2x)$

26. $f(x) = \cos(3x)$

27. $f(x) = \sin\left(\dfrac{x}{3}\right) + \cos\left(\dfrac{x}{3}\right)$

28. $f(x) = \cos\left(\dfrac{x}{5}\right) - \sin\left(\dfrac{x}{5}\right)$

29. $f(x) = 2\sin\left(\dfrac{\pi}{2}x\right) - 3\cos\left(\dfrac{\pi}{2}x\right)$

30. $f(x) = -3\sin\left(\dfrac{\pi}{3}x\right) + 4\cos\left(-\dfrac{\pi}{4}x\right)$

31. $f(x) = \sec^2(2x)$

32. $f(x) = \sec^2(-4x)$

33. $f(x) = \sec^2\left(\dfrac{x}{3}\right)$

34. $f(x) = \sec^2\left(-\dfrac{x}{4}\right)$

35. $f(x) = \dfrac{\sec x + \cos x}{\cos x}$

36. $f(x) = \sin^2 x + \cos^2 x$

37. $f(x) = x^{-7} + 3x^5 + \sin(2x)$

38. $f(x) = 2e^{-3x} + \sec^2\left(-\dfrac{x}{2}\right)$

39. $f(x) = \sec^2(3x - 1) + \dfrac{x^2 - 3}{x}$

40. $f(x) = 5e^{3x} - \sec^2(x - 3)$

In Problems 41–46, assume that a is a positive constant. Find the general antiderivative of the given function.

41. $f(x) = \dfrac{e^{(a+1)x}}{a}$

42. $f(x) = \sin^2(a^2 x + 1)$

43. $f(x) = \dfrac{1}{ax + 3}$

44. $f(x) = \dfrac{a}{a + x}$

45. $f(x) = x^{a+2} - a^{x+2}$

46. $f(x) = \dfrac{e^{-ax} + e^{ax}}{2a}$

In Problems 47–58, find the general solution of the differential equation.

47. $\dfrac{dy}{dx} = \dfrac{2}{x} - x, \ x > 0$

48. $\dfrac{dy}{dx} = \dfrac{2}{x^3} - x^3, \ x > 0$

49. $\dfrac{dy}{dx} = x(1 + x), \ x > 0$

50. $\dfrac{dy}{dx} = e^{-4x}, \ x > 0$

51. $\dfrac{dy}{dt} = t(1 - t), \ t \geq 0$

52. $\dfrac{dy}{dt} = t^2(1 - t^2), \ t \geq 0$

53. $\dfrac{dy}{dt} = e^{-t/2}, \ t \geq 0$

54. $\dfrac{dy}{dt} = 1 - e^{-3t}, \ t \geq 0$

55. $\dfrac{dy}{ds} = \sin(\pi s), \ 0 \leq s \leq 1$

56. $\dfrac{dy}{ds} = \cos(2\pi s), \ 0 \leq s \leq 1$

57. $\dfrac{dy}{dx} = \sec^2\left(\dfrac{x}{2}\right), \ -1 < x < 1$

58. $\dfrac{dy}{dx} = 1 + \sec^2\left(\dfrac{x}{4}\right), \ -1 < x < 1$

In Problems 59–72, solve the initial-value problem.

59. $\dfrac{dy}{dx} = 3x^2$, for $x \geq 0$ with $y = 1$ when $x = 0$

60. $\dfrac{dy}{dx} = \dfrac{x^2}{3}$, for $x \geq 0$ with $y = 2$ when $x = 0$

61. $\dfrac{dy}{dx} = 2\sqrt{x}$, for $x \geq 0$ with $y = 2$ when $x = 1$

62. $\dfrac{dy}{dx} = \dfrac{1}{2\sqrt{x}}$, for $x \geq 1$ with $y = 3$ when $x = 4$

63. $\dfrac{dN}{dt} = \dfrac{1}{t}$, for $t \geq 1$ with $N(1) = 10$

64. $\dfrac{dN}{dt} = \dfrac{t}{t+2}$, for $t \geq 0$ with $N(0) = 2$

65. $\dfrac{dW}{dt} = e^t$, for $t \geq 0$ with $W(0) = 1$

66. $\dfrac{dW}{dt} = e^{-3t}$, for $t \geq 0$ with $W(0) = 2$

67. $\dfrac{dW}{dt} = e^{-3t}$, for $t \geq 0$ with $W(0) = 2/3$

68. $\dfrac{dW}{dt} = e^{-5t}$, for $t \geq 0$ with $W(0) = 1$

69. $\dfrac{dT}{dt} = \sin(\pi t)$, for $t \geq 0$ with $T(0) = 3$

70. $\dfrac{dT}{dt} = \cos(\pi t)$, for $t \geq 0$ with $T(0) = 3$

71. $\dfrac{dy}{dx} = \dfrac{e^{-x} + e^x}{2}$, for $x \geq 0$ with $y = 0$ when $x = 0$

72. $\dfrac{dN}{dt} = t^{-1/3}$, for $t > 0$ with $N(0) = 60$

73. Suppose that the length of a certain organism at age x is given by $L(x)$, which satisfies the differential equation

$$\frac{dL}{dx} = e^{-0.1x}, \quad x \geq 0$$

Find $L(x)$ if the limiting length L_∞ is given by

$$L_\infty = \lim_{x \to \infty} L(x) = 25$$

How big is the organism at age $x = 0$?

74. Fish are indeterminate growers; that is, their length $L(x)$ increases with age x throughout their lifetime. If we plot the growth rate dL/dx versus age x on semilog paper, a straight line with negative slope results. Set up a differential equation that relates growth rate and age. Solve this equation under the assumption that $L(0) = 5$, $L(1) = 10$, and

$$\lim_{x \to \infty} L(x) = 20$$

Graph the solution $L(x)$ as a function of x.

75. An object is dropped from a height of 100 ft. Its acceleration is 32 ft/s^2. When will the object hit the ground, and what will its speed be at impact?

76. Suppose that the growth rate of a population at time t undergoes seasonal fluctuations according to

$$\frac{dN}{dt} = 3 \sin(2\pi t)$$

where t is measured in years and $N(t)$ denotes the size of the population at time t. If $N(0) = 10$ (measured in thousands), find an expression for $N(t)$. How are the seasonal fluctuations in the growth rate reflected in the population size?

77. Suppose that the amount of water contained in a plant at time t is denoted by $V(t)$. Due to evaporation, $V(t)$ changes over time. Suppose that the change in volume at time t, measured over a 24-hour period, is proportional to $t(24 - t)$, measured in grams per hour. To offset the water loss, you water the plant at a constant rate of 4 grams of water per hour.

(a) Explain why

$$\frac{dV}{dt} = -at(24 - t) + 4$$

$0 \le t \le 24$, for some positive constant a, describes this situation.

(b) Determine the constant a for which the net water loss over a 24-hour period is equal to 0.

Chapter 5 Key Terms

Discuss the following definitions and concepts:

1. Global or absolute extrema

2. Local or relative extrema: local minimum and local maximum

3. The extreme-value theorem

4. Fermat's theorem

5. Mean-value theorem

6. Rolle's theorem

7. Increasing and decreasing function

8. Monotonicity and the first derivative

9. Concavity: concave up and concave down

10. Concavity and the second derivative

11. Diminishing return

12. Candidates for local extrema

13. Monotonicity and local extrema

14. The second-derivative test for local extrema

15. Inflection points

16. Inflection points and the second derivative

17. Asymptotes: horizontal, vertical, and oblique

18. Using calculus to graph functions

19. L'Hospital's rule

20. Dynamical systems: cobwebbing

21. Stability of equilibria

22. Newton–Raphson method for finding roots

23. Antiderivative

Chapter 5 Review Problems

1. Suppose that

$$f(x) = xe^{-x}, \quad x \ge 0$$

(a) Show that $f(0) = 0$, $f(x) > 0$ for $x > 0$, and

$$\lim_{x \to \infty} f(x) = 0$$

(b) Find local and absolute extrema.

(c) Find inflection points.

(d) Use the foregoing information to graph $f(x)$.

2. Suppose that

$$f(x) = x \ln x, \quad x > 0$$

(a) Define $f(x)$ at $x = 0$ so that $f(x)$ is continuous for all $x \ge 0$.

(b) Find extrema and inflection points.

(c) Graph $f(x)$.

3. In Review Problem 17 of Chapter 2 we introduced the hyperbolic functions

$$\sinh x = \frac{e^x - e^{-x}}{2}, \quad x \in \mathbf{R}$$

$$\cosh x = \frac{e^x + e^{-x}}{2}, \quad x \in \mathbf{R}$$

$$\tanh x = \frac{e^x - e^{-x}}{e^x + e^{-x}}, \quad x \in \mathbf{R}$$

(a) Show that $f(x) = \tanh x$, $x \in \mathbf{R}$, is a strictly increasing function on $\mathbf{R}$. Evaluate

$$\lim_{x \to -\infty} \tanh x$$

and

$$\lim_{x \to \infty} \tanh x$$

(b) Use your results in (a) to explain why $f(x) = \tanh x$, $x \in \mathbf{R}$, is invertible, and show that its inverse function $f^{-1}(x) = \tanh^{-1} x$ is given by

$$f^{-1}(x) = \frac{1}{2} \ln \frac{1 + x}{1 - x}$$

What is the domain of $f^{-1}(x)$?

(c) Show that

$$\frac{d}{dx} f^{-1}(x) = \frac{1}{1 - x^2}$$

(d) Use your result in (c) and the facts that

$$\tanh x = \frac{\sinh x}{\cosh x}$$

and

$$\cosh^2 x - \sinh^2 x = 1$$

to show that

$$\frac{d}{dx} \tanh x = \frac{1}{\cosh^2 x}$$

4. Let
$$f(x) = \frac{x}{1+e^{-x}}, \quad x \in \mathbb{R}$$

(a) Show that $y = 0$ is a horizontal asymptote as $x \to -\infty$.

(b) Show that $y = x$ is an oblique asymptote as $x \to +\infty$.

(c) Show that
$$f'(x) = \frac{1 + e^{-x}(1+x)}{(1+e^{-x})^2}$$

(d) Use your result in (c) to show that $f(x)$ has exactly one local extremum at $x = c$, where c satisfies the equation
$$1 + c + e^c = 0$$

[*Hint*: Use your result in (c) to show that $f'(x) = 0$ if and only if $1 + e^{-x}(1+x) = 0$. Let $g(x) = 1 + e^{-x}(1+x)$. Show that $g(x)$ is strictly increasing for $x < 0$, that $g(0) > 0$, and $g(-2) < 0$. This implies that $g(x) = 0$ has exactly one solution on $(-2, 0)$. Since $g(-2) < 0$ and $g(x)$ is strictly increasing for $x < 0$, there are no solutions of $g(x) = 0$ for $x < -2$. Furthermore, $g(x) > 0$ for $x > 0$; hence, there are no solutions of $g(x) = 0$ for $x > 0$.]

(e) The equation $1 + c + e^c = 0$ can be solved for c only numerically. With the help of a calculator, find a numerical approximation to c. [*Hint*: From (d), you know that $c \in (-2, 0)$.]

(f) Show that $f(x) < 0$ for $x < 0$. [This implies that, for $x < 0$, the graph of $f(x)$ is below the horizontal asymptote $y = 0$.]

(g) Show that $x - f(x) > 0$ for $x > 0$. [This implies that, for $x > 0$, the graph of $f(x)$ is below the oblique asymptote $y = x$.]

(h) Use your results in (a)–(g) and the fact that $f(0) = 0$ and $f'(0) = \frac{1}{2}$ to sketch the graph of $f(x)$.

5. Recruitment Model Ricker's curve describes the relationship between the size of the parental stock of some fish and the number of recruits. If we denote the size of the parental stock by P and the number of recruits by R, then Ricker's curve is given by
$$R(P) = \alpha P e^{-\beta P} \quad \text{for } P \geq 0$$

where α and β are positive constants. [Note that $R(0) = 0$; that is, without parents there are no offspring. Furthermore, $R(P) > 0$ when $P > 0$.]

We are interested in the size P of the parental stock that maximizes the number $R(P)$ of recruits. Since $R(P)$ is differentiable, we can use its first derivative to solve this problem.

(a) Use the product rule to show that, for $P > 0$,
$$R'(P) = \alpha e^{-\beta P}(1 - \beta P)$$
$$R''(P) = -\alpha\beta e^{-\beta P}(2 - \beta P)$$

(b) Show that $R'(P) = 0$ if $P = 1/\beta$ and that $R''(1/\beta) < 0$. This shows that $R(P)$ has a *local* maximum at $P = \frac{1}{\beta}$. Show that $R(1/\beta) = \frac{\alpha}{\beta}e^{-1} > 0$.

(c) To find the global maximum, you need to check $R(0)$ and $\lim_{P\to\infty} R(P)$. Show that
$$R(0) = 0 \quad \text{and} \quad \lim_{P\to\infty} R(P) = 0$$

and that this implies that there is a global maximum at $P = 1/\beta$.

(d) Show that $R(P)$ has an inflection point at $P = 2/\beta$.

(e) Sketch the graph of $R(P)$ for $\alpha = 2$ and $\beta = 1$.

6. Gompertz Growth Model The *Gompertz growth curve* is sometimes used to study the growth of populations. Its properties are quite similar to the properties of the logistic growth curve. The Gompertz growth curve is given by
$$N(t) = K \exp[-ae^{-bt}]$$

for $t \geq 0$, where K and b are positive constants.

(a) Show that $N(0) = Ke^{-a}$ and, hence,
$$a = \ln\frac{K}{N_0}$$

if $N_0 = N(0)$.

(b) Show that $y = K$ is a horizontal asymptote and that $N(t) < K$ if $N_0 < K$, $N(t) = K$ if $N_0 = K$, and $N(t) > K$ if $N_0 > K$.

(c) Show that
$$\frac{dN}{dt} = bN(\ln K - \ln N)$$

and
$$\frac{d^2N}{dt^2} = b\frac{dN}{dt}[\ln K - \ln N - 1]$$

(d) Use your results in (b) and (c) to show that $N(t)$ is strictly increasing if $N_0 < K$ and strictly decreasing if $N_0 > K$.

(e) When does $N(t)$, $t \geq 0$, have an inflection point? Discuss its concavity.

(f) Graph $N(t)$ when $K = 100$ and $b = 1$ if **(i)** $N_0 = 20$, **(ii)** $N_0 = 70$, and **(iii)** $N_0 = 150$, and compare your graphs with your answers in (b)–(e).

7. Monod Growth Model The Monod growth curve is given by
$$f(x) = \frac{cx}{k+x}$$

for $x \geq 0$, where c and k are positive constants. The equation can be used to describe the specific growth rate of a species as a function of a resource level x.

(a) Show that $y = c$ is a horizontal asymptote for $x \to \infty$. The constant c is called the *saturation value*.

(b) Show that $f(x)$, $x \geq 0$, is strictly increasing and concave down. Explain why this implies that the saturation value is equal to the maximal specific growth rate.

(c) Show that if $x = k$, then $f(x)$ is equal to half the saturation value. (For this reason, the constant k is called the *half-saturation constant*.)

(d) Sketch a graph of $f(x)$ for $k = 2$ and $c = 5$, clearly marking the saturation value and the half-saturation constant. Compare this graph with one where $k = 3$ and $c = 5$.

(e) Without graphing the three curves, explain how you can use the saturation value and the half-saturation constant to decide quickly that
$$\frac{10x}{3+x} > \frac{10x}{5+x} > \frac{8x}{5+x}$$

for $x \geq 0$.

8. Logistic Growth The logistic growth curve is given by
$$N(t) = \frac{K}{1 + (\frac{K}{N_0} - 1)e^{-rt}}$$

for $t \geq 0$, where K, N_0, and r are positive constants and $N(t)$ denotes the population size at time t.

(a) Show that $N(0) = N_0$ and that $y = K$ is a horizontal asymptote as $t \to \infty$.

(b) Show that $N(t) < K$ if $N_0 < K$, $N(t) = K$ if $N_0 = K$, and $N(t) > K$ if $N_0 > K$.

(c) Show that

$$\frac{dN}{dt} = rN\left(1 - \frac{N}{K}\right)$$

and

$$\frac{d^2N}{dt^2} = r\frac{dN}{dt}\left(1 - \frac{2N}{K}\right)$$

(d) Use your results in (b) and (c) to show that $N(t)$ is strictly increasing if $N_0 < K$ and strictly decreasing if $N_0 > K$.

(e) Show that if $N_0 < K/2$, then $N(t)$, $t \geq 0$, has exactly one inflection point $(t^*, N(t^*))$, with $t^* > 0$ and

$$N(t^*) = \frac{K}{2}$$

(i.e., half the carrying capacity). What happens if $K/2 < N_0 < K$? What if $N_0 > K$? Where is the function $N(t)$, $t \geq 0$, concave up, and where is it concave down?

(f) Sketch the graphs of $N(t)$ for $t \geq 0$ when
(i) $K = 100$, $N_0 = 10$, $r = 1$
(ii) $K = 100$, $N_0 = 70$, $r = 1$
(iii) $K = 100$, $N_0 = 150$, $r = 1$

Sketch the respective horizontal asymptotes. Mark the inflection point clearly if it exists.

9. Genetics A population is said to be in Hardy–Weinberg equilibrium, with respect to a single gene with two alleles A and a, if the three genotypes AA, Aa, and aa have respective frequencies $p_{AA} = \theta^2$, $p_{Aa} = 2\theta(1-\theta)$, and $p_{aa} = (1-\theta)^2$ for some $\theta \in [0, 1]$. Suppose that we take a random sample of size n from a population. We can show that the probability of observing n_1 individuals of type AA, n_2 individuals of type Aa, and n_3 individuals of type aa is given by

$$\frac{n!}{n_1! \, n_2! \, n_3!} p_{AA}^{n_1} \, p_{Aa}^{n_2} \, p_{aa}^{n_3}$$

where $n! = n(n-1)(n-2)\cdots 3 \cdot 2 \cdot 1$ (read "n factorial"). Here, $n_1 + n_2 + n_3 = n$. This probability depends on θ. There is a method, called the *maximum likelihood method*, that can be used to estimate θ. The principle is simple: We find the value of θ that maximizes the probability of the observed data. Since the coefficient

$$\frac{n!}{n_1! \, n_2! \, n_3!}$$

does not depend on θ, we need only maximize

$$L(\theta) = p_{AA}^{n_1} \, p_{Aa}^{n_2} \, p_{aa}^{n_3}$$

(a) Suppose $n_1 = 8$, $n_2 = 6$, and $n_3 = 3$. Compute $L(\theta)$.

(b) Show that if $L(\theta)$ is maximal for $\theta = \hat{\theta}$ (read "theta hat"), then $\ln L(\theta)$ is also maximal for $\theta = \hat{\theta}$.

(c) Use your result in (b) to find the value $\hat{\theta}$ that maximizes $L(\theta)$ for the data given in (a). The number $\hat{\theta}$ is the maximum likelihood estimate.

10. Cell Volume Suppose the volume of a cell is increasing at a constant rate of 10^{-12} cm³/s.
(a) If $V(t)$ denotes the cell volume at time t, set up an initial-value problem that describes this situation if the initial volume is 10^{-10} cm³.

(b) Solve the initial-value problem given in (a), and determine the volume of the cell after 10 seconds.

11. Drug Concentration Suppose the concentration $c(t)$ of a drug in the bloodstream at time t satisfies

$$\frac{dc}{dt} = -0.1e^{-0.3t}$$

for $t \geq 0$.
(a) Solve the differential equation under the assumption that there will eventually be no trace of the drug in the blood.

(b) How long does it take until the concentration reaches half its initial value?

12. Resource-Limited Growth Sterner (1997) investigated the effect of food quality on zooplankton dynamics. In his model, zooplankton may be limited by either carbon (C) or phosphorus (P). He argued that when food quantity is low, demand for carbon increases relative to demand for phosphorus in order to to satisfy basic metabolic requirements and that there should be a curve separating C- and P-limited growth when food quantity C_F (measured in amount of carbon per liter) is graphed as a function of the C:P ratio of the food, $f = C_F{:}P_F$. He derived the following equation for the curve separating the two regions:

$$C_F = \frac{m}{a_C g - \frac{C_Z a_P g}{P_Z f}}$$

Here, m denotes the respiration rate, g the ingestion rate, and a_C (a_P) the assimilation rate of carbon (phosphorus). C_Z and P_Z are, respectively, the carbon and the phosphorus content of the zooplankton.
(a) Show that the graph of $y = C_F(f)$ approaches the horizontal line $y = \frac{m}{a_C g}$ as $f \to \infty$.

(b) The graph of $C_F(f)$ has a vertical asymptote. Let $f = C_F{:}P_F$ (the C:P ratio of the food). Show that the vertical asymptote is at

$$\frac{C_F}{P_F} = \frac{C_Z \, a_P}{P_Z \, a_C}$$

(c) Sketch a graph of $C_F(f)$ as a function of f.

(d) The graph of $C_F(f)$ separates C-limited (below the curve) from P-limited (above the curve) growth. Explain why this graph indicates that when food quantity is low, the demand for carbon relative to phosphorus increases.

13. Velocity and Distance Neglecting air resistance, the height (in meters) of an object thrown vertically from the ground with initial velocity v_0 is given by

$$h(t) = v_0 t - \frac{1}{2}gt^2$$

where $g = 9.81$m/s² is the earth's gravitational constant and t is the time (in seconds) elapsed since the object was released
(a) Find the time at which the object reaches its maximum height.

(b) Find the maximum height.

(c) Find the velocity of the object at the time it reaches its maximum height.

(d) At what time $t > 0$ will the object reach the initial height again?

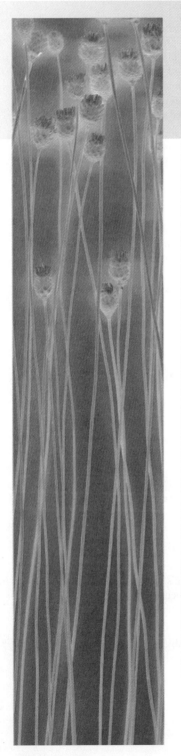

6

Integration

■ 6.1 The Definite Integral

Computing the area of a region bounded by curves is an ancient problem that was solved in certain cases by Greek mathematicians. Foremost among them was Archimedes (circa 287–212 B.C.), who lived more than 2000 years ago. The Greeks used a method called *exhaustion*, which goes back to the Greek mathematician Eudoxus (circa 408–355 B.C.). The basic idea is to divide an area into very small regions consisting mostly of rectilinear figures of known area (such as triangles) so that the total area of the rectilinear figures is close to the area of the region of interest.

Interest in this problem resurfaced in the 17th century, when many new curves had been defined and an attempt was made to determine the areas of regions bounded by such curves. The first curves that were considered were of the form $y = x^n$, where n is a positive integer. In a letter to Roberval on September 22, 1636, Fermat wrote that he had succeeded in computing the area under the curve $y = x^n$. He noted that his method was different from the method employed by the Greeks, notably Archimedes. Whereas Archimedes used triangles to exhaust the area bounded by curved lines, Fermat used rectangles. This sounds like a minor difference, but it enabled Fermat to compute areas bounded by other curves that previously could not have been computed. He found that the area under the curve $y = x^n$ inscribed in a rectangle of width b and height b^n is $1/(n + 1)$ times the area of the rectangle; that is,

$$\frac{1}{n + 1} b \cdot b^n = \frac{1}{n + 1} b^{n+1}$$

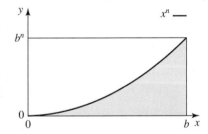

Figure 6.1 The area of the shaded region under the curve $y = x^n$ inscribed in the rectangle is $1/(n + 1)$ times the area of the rectangle.

(See Figure 6.1.) (This problem was independently solved around 1640 by Cavalieri, Pascal, Roberval, and Torricelli as well.)

Augustin-Louis Cauchy (1789–1857) was the first to define areas on the basis of the limit of the sum of areas of approximating rectangles. The definition we will use goes back to Georg Bernhard Riemann (1826–1866). His definition is more general than Cauchy's and allows for a larger class of functions to be used as boundary curves for areas.

■ 6.1.1 The Area Problem

We wish to find the surface area of the lake shown in Figure 6.2; to do so, we overlay a grid and count the number of squares that have a nonempty intersection with the lake. The sum of the areas of these squares will then approximate the area of the lake. The finer the grid, the closer our approximation will be to the true area of the lake.

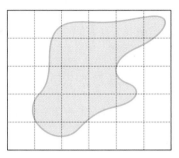 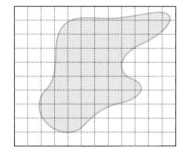

Figure 6.2 The outline of a lake with superimposed grid. The finer the grid, the more accurately the area of the lake can be determined.

Dividing a region into smaller regions of known area is the basic principle we will employ in this section to find the area of a region bounded by curves of continuous functions.

EXAMPLE 1

We will try to find the area of the region below the parabola $f(x) = x^2$ and above the x-axis between 0 and 1. (See Figure 6.3.) To do this, we divide the interval $[0, 1]$ into n subintervals of equal length and approximate the area of interest by a sum of the areas of rectangles, the widths of whose bases are equal to the lengths of the subintervals and whose heights are the values of the function at the left endpoints of these subintervals. This technique is illustrated in Figure 6.4 with $n = 5$.

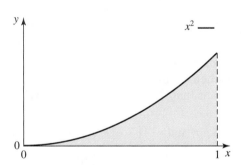 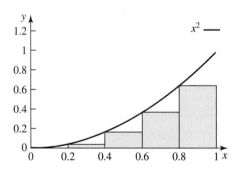

Figure 6.3 The region under the curve $y = x^2$ in Example 1.

Figure 6.4 Approximation of the area under the curve $y = x^2$ from $x = 0$ to $x = 1$ by five rectangles.

In the figure, the base of each rectangle has width $1/5 = 0.2$. The height of the first rectangle is $f(0) = 0$, the height of the second rectangle is $f(0.2) = (0.2)^2$, the height of the third rectangle is $f(0.4) = (0.4)^2$, and so on. The area of a rectangle is the product of its width and height; adding up the areas of the approximating rectangles in Figure 6.4 yields

$$(0.2)(0)^2 + (0.2)(0.2)^2 + (0.2)(0.4)^2 + (0.2)(0.6)^2 + (0.2)(0.8)^2$$
$$= (0.2)\left[0^2 + (0.2)^2 + (0.4)^2 + (0.6)^2 + (0.8)^2\right] = 0.24$$

Thus, an approximation of the area between 0 and 1 is 0.24 when we use five subintervals.

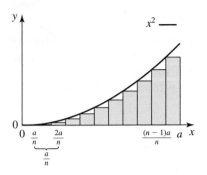

Figure 6.5 Approximation of the area under the curve $y = x^2$ from $x = 0$ to $x = a$ by n rectangles.

We turn now to the general case (illustrated in Figure 6.5), where the interval is $[0, a]$ and the number of subintervals is n. Since the interval $[0, a]$ has length a and the number of subintervals is n, each subinterval has length a/n. The left endpoints of successive subintervals are therefore $0, a/n, 2a/n, 3a/n, \ldots, (n-1)a/n$. The heights of the successive rectangles are then $f(0) = 0$, $f(a/n) = (a/n)^2$, $f(2a/n) = (2a/n)^2, \ldots, f((n-1)a/n) = ((n-1)a/n)^2$. We denote the sum of the areas of the n rectangles by S_n, where S stands for "sum" and the subscript n denotes the number of subintervals. We find that

$$S_n = \frac{a}{n}f(0) + \frac{a}{n}f\left(\frac{a}{n}\right) + \frac{a}{n}f\left(\frac{2a}{n}\right) + \cdots + \frac{a}{n}f\left(\frac{(n-1)a}{n}\right)$$

$$= \frac{a}{n}0^2 + \frac{a}{n}\frac{a^2}{n^2} + \frac{a}{n}\frac{2^2a^2}{n^2} + \cdots + \frac{a}{n}\frac{(n-1)^2a^2}{n^2}$$

$$= \frac{a^3}{n^3}[1^2 + 2^2 + \cdots + (n-1)^2]$$

The sum of the squares of the first k integers can be computed:

$$1^2 + 2^2 + 3^2 + \cdots + k^2 = \frac{k(k+1)(2k+1)}{6} \tag{6.1}$$

(For a proof of this formula, see Problem 31.) Using the preceding formula for $k = n - 1$, we obtain

$$S_n = \frac{a^3}{n^3}\frac{(n-1)(n-1+1)(2(n-1)+1)}{6}$$

$$= \frac{a^3}{n^3}\frac{(n-1)n(2n-1)}{6} = \frac{a^3}{6}\frac{n-1}{n}\frac{n}{n}\frac{2n-1}{n}$$

$$= \frac{a^3}{6}\left(1 - \frac{1}{n}\right) \cdot 1 \cdot \left(2 - \frac{1}{n}\right)$$

The finer the subdivision of $[0, a]$ (i.e., the larger n), the more accurate is the approximation, as illustrated in Figure 6.6, in which we see that the area of the region below the parabola and above the x-axis between 0 and a is more accurately approximated when we use a larger number of rectangles. Choosing finer and finer subdivisions means that we let n go to infinity. We find that

$$\lim_{n\to\infty} S_n = \lim_{n\to\infty} \frac{a^3}{6}\left(1 - \frac{1}{n}\right) \cdot 1 \cdot \left(2 - \frac{1}{n}\right) = \frac{a^3}{6}(1)(1)(2) = \frac{a^3}{3}$$

That is, the area under the parabola $y = x^2$ from 0 to a is equal to $a^3/3$. ∎

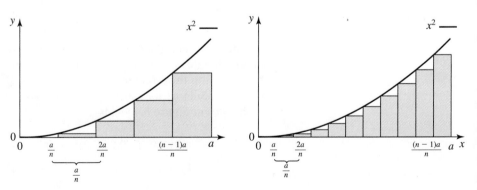

Figure 6.6 Increasing the number of approximating rectangles improves the accuracy of the approximation.

We see from Example 1 that computing areas entails summing a large number of terms. Therefore, before we continue our discussion of the computation of areas, we will spend some time on sums of the type we encountered in Example 1.

It will be convenient to have a shorthand notation for sums that involve a large number of terms:

Sigma Notation for Finite Sums Let $a_1, a_2, \cdots, a_n$ be real numbers and n be a positive integer. Then

$$\sum_{k=1}^{n} a_k = a_1 + a_2 + \cdots + a_n$$

The letter Σ is the capital Greek letter sigma, and the symbol $\sum_{k=1}^{n}$ means that we sum from $k = 1$ to $k = n$, where k is called the *index of summation*, the number 1 is the lower limit of summation, and the number n is the upper limit of summation. In text, instead of $\sum_{k=1}^{n}$ we will write $\sum_{k=1}^{n}$.

EXAMPLE 2

(a) Write each sum in expanded form:

(i) $\displaystyle\sum_{k=1}^{4} k = 1 + 2 + 3 + 4$

(ii) $\displaystyle\sum_{k=3}^{6} k^2 = 3^2 + 4^2 + 5^2 + 6^2$

(iii) $\displaystyle\sum_{k=1}^{n} \frac{1}{k} = 1 + \frac{1}{2} + \frac{1}{3} + \cdots + \frac{1}{n}$

(iv) $\displaystyle\sum_{k=1}^{5} 1 = 1 + 1 + 1 + 1 + 1$

(b) Write each sum in sigma notation:

(i) $2 + 3 + 4 + 5 = \displaystyle\sum_{k=2}^{5} k$

(ii) $1^3 + 2^3 + 3^3 + 4^3 = \displaystyle\sum_{k=1}^{4} k^3$

(iii) $1 + 3 + 5 + 7 + \cdots + (2n + 1) = \displaystyle\sum_{k=0}^{n} (2k + 1)$

(iv) $x + 2x^2 + 3x^3 + \cdots + nx^n = \displaystyle\sum_{k=1}^{n} kx^k$ ■

Occasionally, we will need a formula to sum the first n integers. The next example shows how this is done.

EXAMPLE 3

Show that

$$S_n = \sum_{k=1}^{n} k = 1 + 2 + 3 + \cdots + n = \frac{n(n + 1)}{2}$$

Solution

The following "trick" will enable us to compute the sum S_n: We write the sum in the usual order and in reverse order:

$$S_n = 1 + 2 + 3 + \cdots + n$$
$$S_n = n + (n-1) + (n-2) + \cdots + 2 + 1$$

Adding vertically, we find that

$$2S_n = (1+n) + (2+n-1) + (3+n-2) + \cdots + (n+1)$$
$$= (n+1) + (n+1) + (n+1) + \cdots + (n+1)$$

There are n terms (each $n+1$) on the right-hand side. Hence,

$$2S_n = n(n+1), \qquad \text{or} \qquad S_n = \frac{n(n+1)}{2}$$

This method was used by Karl Friedrich Gauss (1777–1855) when he was 10 years old. One day, to keep the students busy, his teacher asked them to add all the numbers from 1 to 100. To his teacher's astonishment, Karl Friedrich quickly gave the correct answer, 5050. To find the answer, he did not add the numbers in their numerical order, but rather added $1 + 100, 2 + 99, 3 + 98, \ldots, 50 + 51$ (just as we did in the preceding derivation). Each term is equal to 101 and there are 50 such terms; thus, the answer is $50 \cdot 101 = 5050$. (Gauss went on to become one of the greatest mathematicians in history, contributing to geometry, number theory, astronomy, and other areas.) ■

The following rules are useful in evaluating finite sums:

Algebraic Rules

1. Constant-value rule: $\displaystyle\sum_{k=1}^{n} 1 = n$

2. Constant-multiple rule: $\displaystyle\sum_{k=1}^{n} c \cdot a_k = c \sum_{k=1}^{n} a_k$, where c is a constant that does not depend on k

3. Sum rule: $\displaystyle\sum_{k=1}^{n} (a_k + b_k) = \sum_{k=1}^{n} a_k + \sum_{k=1}^{n} b_k$

EXAMPLE 4

Use the algebraic rules to simplify the following sums:

(a) $\displaystyle\sum_{k=2}^{4}(3+k) = \sum_{k=2}^{4} 3 + \sum_{k=2}^{4} k = (3+3+3) + (2+3+4) = 18$

(b) $\displaystyle\sum_{k=1}^{n}(k^2 - 2k) = \sum_{k=1}^{n} k^2 - 2\sum_{k=1}^{n} k$

$$= \frac{n(n+1)(2n+1)}{6} - 2\frac{n(n+1)}{2} = \frac{n(n+1)(2n-5)}{6}$$

[We used (6.1) to evaluate the first sum and Example 3 to evaluate the second sum.]
■

■ 6.1.2 Riemann Integrals

We will now develop a more systematic solution to the area problem. Although our approach will be similar to that in the previous subsection, we will look at a more general situation. We will now allow the function whose graph makes up the boundary of the region of interest to take on negative values as well as positive ones.

Furthermore, we will allow the rectangles that we use to approximate the area to vary in width and the points that we choose to compute the heights of the rectangles to be anywhere in their respective subintervals (which form the bases of the rectangles).

Accordingly, let f be a continuous function on the interval $[a, b]$. (See Figure 6.7.) We partition $[a, b]$ into n subintervals by choosing $n-1$ numbers $x_1, x_2, \ldots, x_{n-1}$ in (a, b) such that

$$a = x_0 < x_1 < x_2 < \cdots < x_{n-1} < x_n = b$$

The n subintervals

$$[x_0, x_1], [x_1, x_2], \ldots, [x_{n-1}, x_n]$$

form a **partition** of $[a, b]$, which we denote by $P = [x_0, x_1, x_2, \ldots, x_n]$. The partition P depends on the number of subintervals n and on the choice of points $x_0, x_1, \ldots, x_n$. For notational convenience, however, we will simply call a partition P. The length of the kth subinterval $[x_{k-1}, x_k]$ is denoted by Δx_k. The length of the longest subinterval is called the **norm** of P and is denoted by $\|P\|$ (read "norm of P"); thus,

$$\|P\| = \max\{\Delta x_1, \Delta x_2, \ldots, \Delta x_n\}$$

where $\max\{\Delta x_1, \Delta x_2, \ldots, \Delta x_n\}$ denotes the largest element of the set $\{\Delta x_1, \Delta x_2, \ldots, \Delta x_n\}$. In each subinterval $[x_{k-1}, x_k]$, we choose a point c_k and construct a rectangle with base Δx_k and height $|f(c_k)|$, as shown in Figure 6.7. If $f(c_k)$ is positive, then $f(c_k)\Delta x_k$ is the area of the rectangle. If $f(c_k)$ is negative, then $f(c_k)\Delta x_k$ is the negative of the rectangle's area. The sum of these products is denoted by S_P; that is,

$$S_P = \sum_{k=1}^{n} f(c_k)\, \Delta x_k$$

The value of the sum depends on the choice of the partition P (hence the subscript P on S) and the choice of the points $c_k \in [x_{k-1}, x_k]$ and is called a **Riemann sum** for f on $[a, b]$.

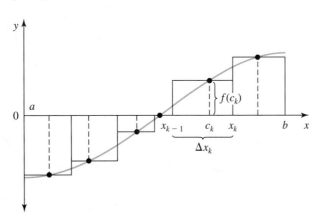

Figure 6.7 An illustration of a Riemann sum.

EXAMPLE 5

Use five equal subintervals with **(a)** left endpoints, **(b)** midpoints, and **(c)** right endpoints to find the Riemann sum for $f(x) = x^2$ on $[0, 1]$.

Solution

We partition $[0, 1]$ into five equal subintervals, each of length 0.2: $[0, 0.2]$, $[0.2, 0.4]$, $[0.4, 0.6]$, $[0.6, 0.8]$, and $[0.8, 1.0]$. The Riemann sum is given by

$$S_P = \sum_{k=1}^{5} f(c_k)\, \Delta x_k$$

where $\Delta x_k = 0.2$ in all three cases (a)–(c).

(a) We use left endpoints; thus, $c_1 = 0, c_2 = 0.2, c_3 = 0.4, c_4 = 0.6,$ and $c_5 = 0.8$. We find that

$$S_P = (0.2)[0^2 + (0.2)^2 + (0.4)^2 + (0.6)^2 + (0.8)^2] = 0.24$$

(b) We use midpoints; hence, $c_1 = 0.1, c_2 = 0.3, c_3 = 0.5, c_4 = 0.7,$ and $c_5 = 0.9$. We get

$$S_P = (0.2)[(0.1)^2 + (0.3)^2 + (0.5)^2 + (0.7)^2 + (0.9)^2] = 0.33$$

(c) We use right endpoints; therefore, $c_1 = 0.2, c_2 = 0.4, c_3 = 0.6, c_4 = 0.8,$ and $c_5 = 1.0$. We obtain

$$S_P = (0.2)[(0.2)^2 + (0.4)^2 + (0.6)^2 + (0.8)^2 + (1.0)^2] = 0.44$$

Comparing S_P in (a)–(c) shows that the Riemann sum depends on the choice of the points $c_k \in [x_{k-1}, x_k]$. ■

To obtain a better approximation, we need to choose finer and finer partitions of $[a, b]$ so that the rectangles fill out the region between the curve and the x-axis more and more accurately. (See Figure 6.8.) A finer partition means that both the number of subintervals becomes larger and the length of the longest subinterval becomes smaller, so the norm of the partition P becomes smaller. One way to do this is to choose a sequence of partitions $P = P(n) = [x_0, x_1, x_2, \ldots, x_n], n = 1, 2, 3, \ldots,$ in such a way that $\|P(n)\| > \|P(n + 1)\|$ for $n = 1, 2, 3, \ldots$. In fact, we will take the limit $\|P(n)\| \to 0$ as $n \to \infty$. For notational convenience, we will omit n and simply write $\|P\| \to 0$, but keep in mind that this means that, simultaneously, the number of subintervals goes to infinity and the length of the longest subinterval goes to 0. The limit of S_P as $\|P\| \to 0$ (if it exists) is called the *definite integral* of f from a to b.

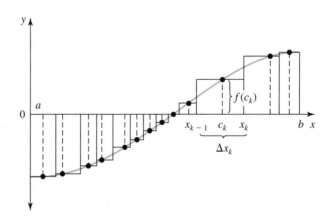

Figure 6.8 A finer partition than in Figure 6.7.

Definite Integral Let $P = [x_0, x_1, x_2, \ldots, x_n], n = 1, 2, \ldots,$ be a sequence of partitions of $[a, b]$ with $\|P\| \to 0$. Set $\Delta x_k = x_k - x_{k-1}$ and $c_k \in [x_{k-1}, x_k]$. The **definite integral** of f from a to b is

$$\int_a^b f(x)\,dx = \lim_{\|P\| \to 0} \sum_{k=1}^{n} f(c_k)\,\Delta x_k$$

if the limit exists, in which case f is said to be (Riemann) **integrable** on the interval $[a, b]$.

The symbol $\int$ is an elongated S (as in "sum") and was introduced by Leibniz. It is called the **integral sign**. In the notation $\int_a^b f(x)\,dx$ [read "the integral from a

to b of $f(x)\,dx$"], $f(x)$ is called the **integrand**, the number a is the **lower limit of integration**, and b is the **upper limit of integration**. Although the symbol dx by itself has no meaning, it should remind you that, as we take the limit, the widths of the subintervals become ever smaller. The x in dx indicates that x is the independent variable and that we integrate with respect to x.

The phrase "if the limit exists" means, in particular, that the value of $\lim_{\|P\|\to 0} S_P$ does not depend on how we choose the partitions and the points $c_k \in [x_{k-1}, x_k]$ as we take the limit. An important result tells us that if f is continuous on $[a, b]$, the definite integral of f on $[a, b]$ exists.

> **Theorem** All continuous functions are Riemann integrable; that is, if $f(x)$ is continuous on $[a, b]$, then
> $$\int_a^b f(x)\,dx$$
> exists.

The class of functions that are Riemann integrable is quite a bit larger than the set of continuous functions; for instance, functions that are both bounded (functions for which there exists an $M < \infty$ such that $|f(x)| < M$ for all x over which we wish to integrate) and piecewise continuous (continuous except for a finite number of discontinuities) are integrable. (See Figure 6.9.) We will be concerned primarily with continuous functions in this text; knowing that continuous functions are Riemann integrable will therefore suffice for the most part.

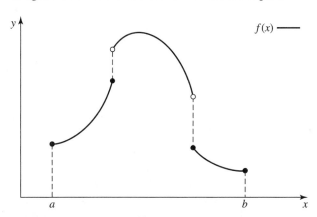

Figure 6.9 The function $y = f(x)$ is piecewise continuous and bounded on $[a, b]$.

Note that $\int_a^b f(x)\,dx$ is a number that does not depend on x. We could have written $\int_a^b f(u)\,du$ (or any other letter in place of x) and meant the same thing.

EXAMPLE 6 Express the definite integral

$$\int_3^7 (x^2 - 1)\,dx$$

as a limit of Riemann sums.

Solution We have

$$\int_3^7 (x^2 - 1)\,dx = \lim_{\|P\|\to 0} \sum_{k=1}^{n} (c_k^2 - 1)\,\Delta x_k$$

where $x_0 = 3 < x_1 < x_2 < \cdots < x_n = 7$, $n = 1, 2, \ldots$, is a sequence of partitions of $[3, 7]$, $c_k \in [x_{k-1}, x_k]$, $\Delta x_k = x_k - x_{k-1}$, and the limit as $\|P\| \to 0$ means that the norm of the partition tends to 0 (and, simultaneously, the number of subintervals goes to infinity). ■

EXAMPLE 7

Express the limit

$$\lim_{\|P\|\to 0} \sum_{k=1}^{n} \sqrt{c_k - 1}\, \Delta x_k$$

as a definite integral, where $P = [x_0, x_1, \ldots, x_n]$, $n = 1, 2, \ldots$, is a sequence of partitions of $[2, 4]$ into n subintervals, $\Delta x_k = x_k - x_{k-1}$, and $c_k \in [x_{k-1}, x_k]$.

Solution

$$\lim_{\|P\|\to 0} \sum_{k=1}^{n} \sqrt{c_k - 1}\, \Delta x_k = \int_2^4 \sqrt{x - 1}\, dx \qquad \blacksquare$$

EXAMPLE 8

Evaluate

$$\int_0^2 x^2\, dx$$

Solution

We evaluated the Riemann sum and its limit for $y = x^2$ from 0 to a in Example 1 and found that

$$\lim_{n\to\infty} S_n = \int_0^a x^2\, dx = \frac{a^3}{3}$$

With $a = 2$, we therefore have

$$\int_0^2 x^2\, dx = \frac{8}{3} \qquad \blacksquare$$

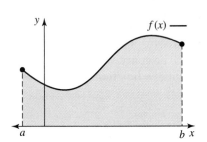

Figure 6.10 The area of a region under the curve of a positive function is given by the definite integral $\int_a^b f(x)\, dx$.

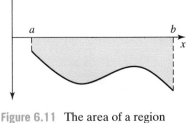

Figure 6.11 The area of a region under the curve of a negative function is given by $-\int_a^b f(x)\, dx$.

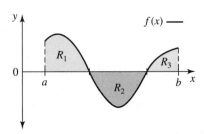

Figure 6.12 A_+ is the combined area of R_1 and R_3, and A_- is the area of R_2. Then $\int_a^b f(x)\, dx = A_+ - A_-$.

Geometric Interpretation of Definite Integrals   In Example 1, we computed the area of the region below the parabola $y = x^2$ and above the x-axis between 0 and a by approximating the region with n rectangles of equal width and then taking the limit as $n \to \infty$. More generally, we can now define the **area** of a region A above the x-axis, as shown in Figure 6.10, as the limiting value (if it exists) of the Riemann sum of approximating rectangles. (Note that an area is always a positive number.) This definition allows us to interpret the definite integral of a nonnegative function as an area.

If $f(x) \le 0$ on $[a, b]$, then the definite integral $\int_a^b f(x)\, dx$ is less than or equal to 0 and its value is the negative of the area of the region above the graph of f and below the x-axis between a and b. (See Figure 6.11.) We refer to the latter region as a "signed area." (A signed area may be either positive or negative.)

In general, a definite integral can thus be interpreted as a difference of areas, as illustrated in Figure 6.12. If A_+ denotes the total area of the region above the x-axis and below the graph of f (where $f \ge 0$) and A_- denotes the total area of the region below the x-axis and above the graph of f (where $f \le 0$), then

$$\int_a^b f(x)\, dx = A_+ - A_-$$

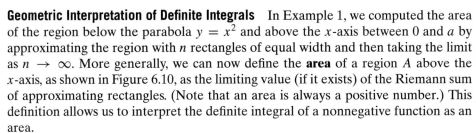

1. If f is integrable on $[a, b]$ and $f(x) \ge 0$ on $[a, b]$, then

$$\int_a^b f(x)\, dx = \left[\begin{array}{c} \text{the area of the region between the} \\ \text{graph of } f \text{ and the } x\text{-axis from } a \text{ to } b \end{array}\right]$$

2. If f is integrable on $[a, b]$, then

$$\int_a^b f(x)\, dx = [\text{area above } x\text{-axis}] - [\text{area below } x\text{-axis}]$$

EXAMPLE 9   Find the value of

$$\int_{-2}^{3} (2x + 1)\, dx$$

by interpreting it as the signed area of an appropriately chosen region.

Solution   We graph $y = 2x + 1$ between -2 and 3. (See Figure 6.13.) The line intersects the x-axis at $x = -1/2$. The area of the region to the left of $-1/2$ between the graph of $y = 2x + 1$ and the x-axis is denoted by A_-; the area of the region to the right of $-1/2$ between the graph of $y = 2x + 1$ and the x-axis is denoted by A_+. Both regions are triangles whose areas can be computed with the formula $A = \frac{1}{2}bh$ from geometry:

$$A_- = \frac{1}{2} \cdot \frac{3}{2} \cdot 3 = \frac{9}{4}$$

$$A_+ = \frac{1}{2} \cdot \frac{7}{2} \cdot 7 = \frac{49}{4}$$

Therefore,

$$\int_{-2}^{3} (2x + 1)\, dx = A_+ - A_- = \frac{49}{4} - \frac{9}{4} = \frac{40}{4} = 10$$

■

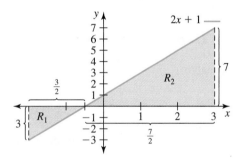

Figure 6.13 The area of R_1 is A_-; the area of R_2 is A_+.

EXAMPLE 10   Find the value of

$$\int_{0}^{2\pi} \sin x\, dx$$

by interpreting it as the signed area of an appropriately chosen region.

Solution   We graph $y = \sin x$ from 0 to 2π. (See Figure 6.14.) The function $f(x) = \sin x$ is symmetric about $x = \pi$. It follows from this symmetry that the area of the region below the graph of f and above the x-axis between 0 and π (denoted by A_+) is the

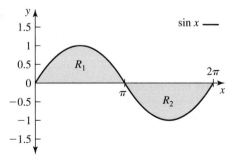

Figure 6.14 The graph of $f(x) = \sin x$, $0 \le x \le 2\pi$, in Example 10. The area of R_1 is A_+; the area of R_2 is A_-.

same as the area of the region above the graph of f and below the x-axis between π and 2π (denoted by A_-). Therefore, $A_+ = A_-$ and

$$\int_0^{2\pi} \sin x \, dx = A_+ - A_- = 0$$

■

EXAMPLE 11 Find the value of

$$\int_0^2 \sqrt{4 - x^2} \, dx$$

by interpreting it as the signed area of an appropriately chosen region.

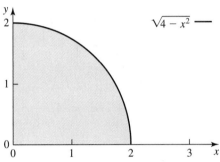

Figure 6.15 The graph of $f(x) = \sqrt{4 - x^2}$ is a quarter-circle. The area of the shaded region is equal to $\int_0^2 \sqrt{4 - x^2} \, dx$.

Solution The graph of $y = \sqrt{4 - x^2}, 0 \leq x \leq 2$, is the quarter-circle with center at $(0, 0)$ and radius 2 in the first quadrant. (See Figure 6.15.) Since the area of a circle with radius 2 is $\pi(2)^2 = 4\pi$, the area of a quarter-circle is $4\pi/4 = \pi$. Hence,

$$\int_0^2 \sqrt{4 - x^2} \, dx = \pi$$

■

■ 6.1.3 Properties of the Riemann Integral

In this subsection, we collect important properties that will help us to evaluate definite integrals.

> **Properties** Assume that f is integrable over $[a, b]$. Then
>
> **1.** $\displaystyle\int_a^a f(x) \, dx = 0$ and
>
> **2.** $\displaystyle\int_b^a f(x) \, dx = -\int_a^b f(x) \, dx$

The first integral says that the signed area between a and a is equal to 0; given that the width of the area is equal to 0, we expect the area to be 0 as well. The second property gives an orientation to the integral; for instance, if $f(x)$ is nonnegative on $[a, b]$, then $\int_a^b f(x) \, dx$ is nonnegative and can be interpreted as the area of the region between the graph of $f(x)$ and the x-axis from a to b. If we reverse the direction of the integration—that is, compute $\int_b^a f(x) \, dx$—we want the integral to be negative.

The next three properties follow immediately from the definition of the definite integral as the limit of a sum of areas of approximating rectangles.

Properties Assume that f and g are integrable over $[a, b]$.

3. If k is a constant, then

$$\int_a^b kf(x)\,dx = k\int_a^b f(x)\,dx$$

4. $\displaystyle\int_a^b [f(x) + g(x)]\,dx = \int_a^b f(x)\,dx + \int_a^b g(x)\,dx$

5. If f is integrable over an interval containing the three numbers a, b, and c, then

$$\int_a^b f(x)\,dx = \int_a^c f(x)\,dx + \int_c^b f(x)\,dx$$

We prove Property (4) to illustrate how the definition of the definite integral can be used to prove its properties.

Proof of (4) We choose a sequence of partitions $P = [x_0, x_1, \ldots, x_n]$ of $[a, b]$ into n subintervals, $n = 1, 2, \ldots$, with $\|P\| \to 0$, $\Delta x_k = x_k - x_{k-1}$, and $c_k \in [x_{k-1}, x_k]$, and we then use the definition of a definite integral:

$$\int_a^b [f(x) + g(x)]\,dx = \lim_{\|P\|\to 0} \sum_{k=1}^n [f(c_k) + g(c_k)]\,\Delta x_k$$

$$= \lim_{\|P\|\to 0} \sum_{k=1}^n [f(c_k)\,\Delta x_k + g(c_k)\,\Delta x_k]$$

Applying the sum rule for finite sums, we find that

$$= \lim_{\|P\|\to 0} \left[\sum_{k=1}^n f(c_k)\,\Delta x_k + \sum_{k=1}^n g(c_k)\,\Delta x_k \right]$$

Since f and g are integrable, the individual limits exist, and we get

$$= \lim_{\|P\|\to 0} \sum_{k=1}^n f(c_k)\,\Delta x_k + \lim_{\|P\|\to 0} \sum_{k=1}^n g(c_k)\,\Delta x_k$$

Using the definition of definite integrals again, we obtain

$$= \int_a^b f(x)\,dx + \int_a^b g(x)\,dx \qquad\blacksquare$$

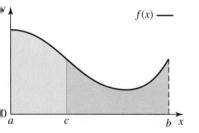

Figure 6.16 Property (5) when $a < c < b$.

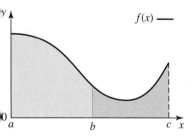

Figure 6.17 Property (5) when $a < b < c$.

Property (5) is an addition property. Rather than proving that it holds, we give two special cases (illustrated in Figures 6.16 and 6.17). In the first case (Figure 6.16), $a < c < b$ and $f(x) \geq 0$ for $x \in [a, b]$. The definite integral $\int_a^b f(x)\,dx$ can then be interpreted as the area between the graph of $f(x)$ and the x-axis from a to b. We see from the figure that this area is composed of two areas: the area between the graph of $f(x)$ and the x-axis from a to c and the area between the graph of $f(x)$ and the x-axis from c to b. We can express this relationship mathematically as

$$\int_a^b f(x)\,dx = \int_a^c f(x)\,dx + \int_c^b f(x)\,dx$$

which is Property (5) in this special case.

In the second case we wish to discuss, $a < b < c$ and $f(x) \geq 0$ for $x \in [a, c]$ (Figure 6.17). From the figure, we see that

$$\int_a^b f(x)\,dx = \int_a^c f(x)\,dx - \int_b^c f(x)\,dx$$

But because of Property (2),

$$\int_b^c f(x)\,dx = -\int_c^b f(x)\,dx$$

Therefore,

$$\int_a^b f(x)\,dx = \int_a^c f(x)\,dx + \int_c^b f(x)\,dx$$

as stated in Property (5).

Property (5) is much more general: The function f need not be positive as in Figures 6.16 and 6.17 (it merely needs to be integrable), and the numbers a, b, and c can be arranged in any order on the number line (not just $a < c < b$, as in Figure 6.16, or $a < b < c$, as in Figure 6.17). The next example shows how to use this property.

EXAMPLE 12   Given that $\int_0^a x^2 = a^3/3$, evaluate

$$\int_1^4 (3x^2 + 2)\,dx$$

Solution

$$\int_1^4 (3x^2 + 2)\,dx = 3\int_1^4 x^2\,dx + \int_1^4 2\,dx$$

To evaluate $\int_1^4 x^2\,dx$, we use the addition property (5) and write

$$\int_1^4 x^2\,dx = \int_1^0 x^2\,dx + \int_0^4 x^2\,dx$$

Since

$$\int_1^0 x^2\,dx = -\int_0^1 x^2\,dx$$

it follows that

$$\int_1^4 x^2\,dx = -\int_0^1 x^2\,dx + \int_0^4 x^2\,dx$$

which can be evaluated with the use of $\int_0^a x^2 = a^3/3$. To evaluate $\int_1^4 2\,dx$, we note that $y = 2$ is a horizontal line that intersects the y-axis at $y = 2$. The region under $y = 2$ from 1 to 4 is therefore a rectangle with base $4 - 1 = 3$ and height 2. Hence,

$$\int_1^4 (3x^2 + 2)\,dx = 3\left[\int_0^4 x^2\,dx - \int_0^1 x^2\,dx\right] + \int_1^4 2\,dx$$

$$= 3\left(\frac{4^3}{3} - \frac{1^3}{3}\right) + (2)(3)$$

$$= 64 - 1 + 6 = 69$$

The next three properties are called order properties. They allow us either to compare definite integrals or say something about how big or small a particular definite integral can be. We first state the properties and then explain what they mean geometrically.

Properties Assume that f and g are integrable over $[a, b]$.

6. If $f(x) \geq 0$ on $[a, b]$, then $\int_a^b f(x)\,dx \geq 0$.

7. If $f(x) \leq g(x)$ on $[a, b]$, then $\int_a^b f(x)\,dx \leq \int_a^b g(x)\,dx$.

8. If $m \leq f(x) \leq M$ on $[a, b]$, then

$$m(b - a) \leq \int_a^b f(x)\,dx \leq M(b - a)$$

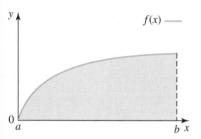

Figure 6.18 An illustration of Property (6).

Property (6), illustrated in Figure 6.18, says that if f is nonnegative over the interval $[a, b]$, then the definite integral over that interval is also nonnegative. We can understand this statement from its geometric interpretation: If $f(x) \geq 0$ for $x \in [a, b]$, then $\int_a^b f(x)\,dx$ is the area between the curve and the x-axis between a and b. But an area must be a nonnegative number.

Property (7) is explained in Figure 6.19 when both f and g are positive functions on $[a, b]$. We use the fact that in this case the definite integral can be interpreted as an area. Looking at the figure, we see that the function f has a smaller area than g has. Property (7) holds without the assumption that both f and g are positive, and we can draw an analogous figure for the general case as well. The definite integral then needs to be interpreted as a signed area.

Property (8) is explained in Figure 6.20 for $f(x) \geq 0$ in $[a, b]$. We see that the rectangle with height m is contained in the area between the graph of f and the x-axis, which in turn is contained in the rectangle with height M. Since (1) $m(b - a)$ is the area of the small rectangle, (2) $\int_a^b f(x)\,dx$ is the area between the graph of f and the x-axis for nonnegative f, and (3) $M(b - a)$ is the area of the big rectangle, the inequalities in (8) follow. Note that the statement does not require that f be nonnegative; you can draw an analogous figure when f is negative on parts or all of $[a, b]$.

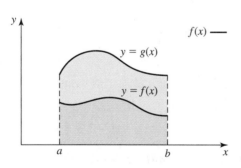

Figure 6.19 An illustration of Property (7).

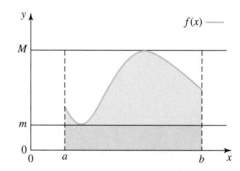

Figure 6.20 An illustration of Property (8).

The next example illustrates how the order properties (6)–(8) are used.

EXAMPLE 13 Show that

$$0 \leq \int_0^\pi \sin x\,dx \leq \pi$$

Solution Note that $0 \leq \sin x \leq 1$ for $x \in [0, \pi]$. Using Property (6), we find that

$$\int_0^\pi \sin x\,dx \geq 0$$

Using Property (8), we obtain

$$\int_0^{\pi} \sin x \, dx \le (1)(\pi) = \pi$$

(See Figure 6.21.)

■

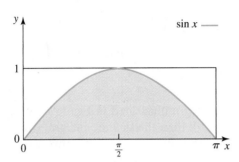

Figure 6.21 An illustration of the integral in Example 13. The shaded area is nonnegative and less than the area of the rectangle with base length π and height 1.

The next example will help us to deepen our understanding of signed areas; it also uses the order properties.

EXAMPLE 14 Find the value of $a \ge 0$ that maximizes

$$\int_0^a (1 - x^2) \, dx$$

Solution

We graph the integrand $f(x) = 1 - x^2$ for $x \ge 0$ in Figure 6.22. Using the interpretation of the definite integral as the signed area, we see from the graph of $f(x)$ that $a = 1$ maximizes the integral, since the graph of $f(x)$ is positive for $x < 1$ and negative for $x > 1$.

We also wish to give a rigorous argument; our goal is to show that

$$\int_0^1 f(x) \, dx > \int_0^a f(x) \, dx$$

for all $a \ge 0$, provided that $a \ne 1$. This would then imply that $a = 1$ maximizes the integral

$$\int_0^a (1 - x^2) \, dx$$

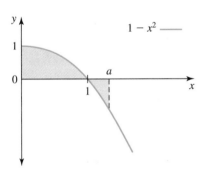

Figure 6.22 An illustration of the integral in Example 14.

First, note that $f(x)$ is continuous for $x \ge 0$ and that

$$f(x) \begin{cases} > 0 & \text{for } 0 \le x < 1 \\ < 0 & \text{for } x > 1 \end{cases}$$

which implies that, for $0 \le a < 1$,

$$\int_a^1 f(x) \, dx > 0$$

and, therefore, for $0 \le a < 1$,

$$\int_0^1 f(x) \, dx = \int_0^a f(x) \, dx + \underbrace{\int_a^1 f(x) \, dx}_{>0} > \int_0^a f(x) \, dx \qquad (6.2)$$

Now, for $a > 1$,

$$\int_1^a f(x)\,dx < 0$$

Therefore,

$$\int_0^a f(x)\,dx = \int_0^1 f(x)\,dx + \underbrace{\int_1^a f(x)\,dx}_{<0} < \int_0^1 f(x)\,dx \qquad (6.3)$$

Combining (6.2) and (6.3) shows that

$$\int_0^a f(x)\,dx < \int_0^1 f(x)\,dx$$

for all $a \geq 0$ and $a \neq 1$. Hence, $a = 1$ maximizes the integral $\int_0^a (1 - x^2)\,dx$. ■

Section 6.1 Problems

■ 6.1.1

1. Approximate the area under the parabola $y = x^2$ from 0 to 1, using four equal subintervals with left endpoints.

2. Approximate the area under the parabola $y = x^2$ from 0 to 1, using five equal subintervals with midpoints.

3. Approximate the area under the parabola $y = x^2$ from 0 to 1, using four equal subintervals with right endpoints.

4. Approximate the area under the parabola $y = 1 - x^2$ from 0 to 1, using five equal subintervals with **(a)** left endpoints and **(b)** right endpoints.

In Problems 5–14, write each sum in expanded form.

5. $\displaystyle\sum_{k=1}^{4} \sqrt{k}$

6. $\displaystyle\sum_{k=3}^{5} (k-1)^2$

7. $\displaystyle\sum_{k=2}^{6} 3^k$

8. $\displaystyle\sum_{k=1}^{3} \frac{k^2}{k^2+1}$

9. $\displaystyle\sum_{k=0}^{3} (x+1)^k$

10. $\displaystyle\sum_{k=0}^{4} k^x$

11. $\displaystyle\sum_{k=0}^{3} (-1)^{k+1}$

12. $\displaystyle\sum_{k=1}^{n} f(c_k)\Delta x_k$

13. $\displaystyle\sum_{k=1}^{n} \left(\frac{k}{n}\right)^2 \frac{1}{n}$

14. $\displaystyle\sum_{k=1}^{n} \cos\left(k\frac{\pi}{n}\right)\frac{\pi}{n}$

In Problems 15–22, write each sum in sigma notation.

15. $2 + 4 + 6 + 8 + \cdots + 2n$

16. $\dfrac{1}{\sqrt{1}} + \dfrac{1}{\sqrt{2}} + \dfrac{1}{\sqrt{3}} + \dfrac{1}{\sqrt{4}}$

17. $\ln 2 + \ln 3 + \ln 4 + \ln 5$

18. $\dfrac{3}{5} + \dfrac{4}{6} + \dfrac{5}{7} + \dfrac{6}{8} + \dfrac{7}{9}$

19. $-\dfrac{1}{4} + \dfrac{1}{6} + \dfrac{2}{7} + \dfrac{3}{8}$

20. $\dfrac{1}{1} + \dfrac{1}{2} + \dfrac{1}{4} + \dfrac{1}{8} + \dfrac{1}{16} + \cdots + \dfrac{1}{2^n}$

21. $1 + q + q^2 + q^3 + q^4 + \cdots + q^{n-1}$

22. $1 - a + a^2 - a^3 + a^4 - a^5 + \cdots + (-1)^n a^n$

In Problems 23–30, use the algebraic rules for sums to evaluate each sum. Recall that

$$\sum_{k=1}^{n} k = \frac{n(n+1)}{2}$$

and

$$\sum_{k=1}^{n} k^2 = \frac{n(n+1)(2n+1)}{6}$$

23. $\displaystyle\sum_{k=1}^{15} (2k+3)$

24. $\displaystyle\sum_{k=1}^{5} (4 - k^2)$

25. $\displaystyle\sum_{k=0}^{6} k(k+1)$

26. $\displaystyle\sum_{k=1}^{n} 4k$

27. $\displaystyle\sum_{k=1}^{n} 4(k-1)^2$

28. $\displaystyle\sum_{k=1}^{n} (k+2)(k-2)$

29. $\displaystyle\sum_{k=1}^{10} (-1)^k$

30. $\displaystyle\sum_{k=0}^{10} (-1)^k$

31. The steps that follow will show that

$$\sum_{k=1}^{n} k^2 = \frac{n(n+1)(2n+1)}{6}$$

(a) Show that

$$\sum_{k=1}^{n} [(1+k)^3 - k^3] = (2^3 - 1^3) + (3^3 - 2^3) + (4^3 - 3^3)$$
$$+ \cdots + [(1+n)^3 - n^3]$$
$$= (1+n)^3 - 1^3$$

(Sums that "collapse" like this due to cancellation of terms are called *telescoping* or *collapsing* sums.)

(b) Use Example 3 and the algebraic rules for sums to show that

$$\sum_{k=1}^{n} [(1+k)^3 - k^3] = 3\sum_{k=1}^{n} k^2 + 3\frac{n(n+1)}{2} + n$$

(c) In (a) and (b), we found two expressions for the sum

$$\sum_{k=1}^{n}[(1+k)^3 - k^3]$$

Those two expressions are therefore equal; that is,

$$(1+n)^3 - 1^3 = 3\sum_{k=1}^{n}k^2 + 3\frac{n(n+1)}{2} + n$$

Solve this equation for $\sum_{k=1}^{n}k^2$, and show that

$$\sum_{k=1}^{n}k^2 = \frac{n(n+1)(2n+1)}{6}$$

■ **6.1.2**

32. Approximate

$$\int_{-1}^{1}(1-x^2)\,dx$$

using five equal subintervals and left endpoints.

33. Approximate

$$\int_{-1}^{1}(1-x^2)\,dx$$

using five equal subintervals and midpoints.

34. Approximate

$$\int_{-1}^{1}(2+x^2)\,dx$$

using five equal subintervals and right endpoints.

35. Approximate

$$\int_{-2}^{2}(2+x^2)\,dx$$

using four equal subintervals and left endpoints.

36. Approximate

$$\int_{-1}^{2}e^{-x}\,dx$$

using three equal subintervals and midpoints.

37. Approximate

$$\int_{0}^{3\pi/2}\sin x\,dx$$

using three equal subintervals and right endpoints.

38. (a) Assume that $a > 0$. Evaluate $\int_{0}^{a} x\,dx$, using the fact that the region bounded by $y = x$ and the x-axis between 0 to a is a triangle. (See Figure 6.23.)

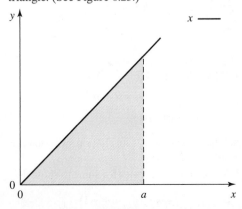

Figure 6.23 The region for Problem 38.

(b) Assume that $a > 0$. Evaluate $\int_{0}^{a} x\,dx$ by approximating the region bounded by $y = x$ and the x-axis from 0 to a with rectangles. Use equal subintervals and take right endpoints. (*Hint*: Use the result in Example 3 to evaluate the sum of the areas of the rectangles.)

39. Assume that $0 < a < b < \infty$. Use a geometric argument to show that

$$\int_{a}^{b} x\,dx = \frac{b^2 - a^2}{2}$$

40. Assume that $0 < a < b < \infty$. Use a geometric argument and Example 1 to show that

$$\int_{a}^{b} x^2\,dx = \frac{b^3 - a^3}{3}$$

Express the limits in Problems 41–47 as definite integrals. Note that (1) $P = [x_0, x_1, \ldots, x_n]$ is a partition of the indicated interval, (2) $c_k \in [x_{k-1}, x_k]$, and (3) $\Delta x_k = x_k - x_{k-1}$.

41. $\lim\limits_{\|P\|\to 0}\sum\limits_{k=1}^{n}2c_k^3\Delta x_k$, where P is a partition of $[1, 2]$

42. $\lim\limits_{\|P\|\to 0}\sum\limits_{k=1}^{n}\sqrt{c_k}\,\Delta x_k$, where P is a partition of $[1, 4]$

43. $\lim\limits_{\|P\|\to 0}\sum\limits_{k=1}^{n}(2c_k - 1)\Delta x_k$, where P is a partition of $[-3, 2]$

44. $\lim\limits_{\|P\|\to 0}\sum\limits_{k=1}^{n}\dfrac{1}{c_k + 1}\Delta x_k$, where P is a partition of $[1, 2]$

45. $\lim\limits_{\|P\|\to 0}\sum\limits_{k=1}^{n}\dfrac{c_k - 1}{c_k + 2}\Delta x_k$, where P is a partition of $[2, 3]$

46. $\lim\limits_{\|P\|\to 0}\sum\limits_{k=1}^{n}(\sin c_k)\Delta x_k$, where P is a partition of $[0, \pi]$

47. $\lim\limits_{\|P\|\to 0}\sum\limits_{k=1}^{n}e^{c_k}\Delta x_k$, where P is a partition of $[-5, 2]$

In Problems 48–53, express the definite integrals as limits of Riemann sums.

48. $\int_{-2}^{-1}\dfrac{x^2}{1+x^2}\,dx$
49. $\int_{2}^{6}(x+1)^{1/3}\,dx$

50. $\int_{1}^{3}e^{-2x}\,dx$
51. $\int_{1}^{e}\ln x\,dx$
52. $\int_{0}^{\pi}\cos\dfrac{2x}{\pi}\,dx$

53. $\int_{0}^{5}g(x)\,dx$, where $g(x)$ is a continuous function on $[0, 5]$

In Problems 54–60, use a graph to interpret the definite integral in terms of areas. Do not compute the integrals.

54. $\int_{0}^{3}(2x+1)\,dx$
55. $\int_{-1}^{2}(x^2 - 1)\,dx$

56. $\int_{-2}^{2}\dfrac{1}{2}x^3\,dx$
57. $\int_{0}^{5}e^{-x}\,dx$

58. $\int_{-\pi}^{\pi}\cos x\,dx$
59. $\int_{1/2}^{4}\ln x\,dx$

60. $\int_{-3}^{2}\left(1 - \dfrac{1}{2}x\right)dx$

In Problems 61–67, use an area formula from geometry to find the value of each integral by interpreting it as the (signed) area under the graph of an appropriately chosen function.

61. $\int_{-2}^{3} |x| \, dx$

62. $\int_{-3}^{3} \sqrt{9 - x^2} \, dx$

63. $\int_{2}^{5} \left(\frac{1}{2}x - 4\right) dx$

64. $\int_{1/2}^{1} \sqrt{1 - x^2} \, dx$

65. $\int_{-2}^{2} (\sqrt{4 - x^2} - 2) \, dx$

66. $\int_{0}^{1} \sqrt{2 - x^2} \, dx$

67. $\int_{-3}^{0} (4 - \sqrt{9 - x^2}) \, dx$

■ **6.1.3**

68. Given that
$$\int_{0}^{a} x^2 \, dx = \frac{1}{3}a^3$$
evaluate the following:

(a) $\int_{0}^{2} \frac{1}{2} x^2 \, dx$

(b) $\int_{-3}^{-2} 3x^2 \, dx$

(c) $\int_{-1}^{3} \frac{1}{3} x^2 \, dx$

(d) $\int_{1}^{1} 3x^2 \, dx$

(e) $\int_{-2}^{3} (x + 1)^2 \, dx$

(f) $\int_{2}^{4} (x - 2)^2 \, dx$

69. Find $\int_{2}^{2} \cos(3x^2) \, dx$.

70. Find $\int_{-3}^{-3} e^{-x^2/2} \, dx$.

71. Find $\int_{-2}^{2} \frac{x^3}{3} \, dx$.

72. Find $\int_{-5}^{5} 2x^5 \, dx$.

73. Find $\int_{-1}^{1} \tan x \, dx$.

74. Explain geometrically why
$$\int_{1}^{2} x^2 \, dx = \int_{0}^{2} x^2 \, dx - \int_{0}^{1} x^2 \, dx \qquad (6.4)$$
and show that (6.4) can be written as
$$\int_{1}^{2} x^2 \, dx = \int_{1}^{0} x^2 \, dx + \int_{0}^{2} x^2 \, dx \qquad (6.5)$$
Relate (6.5) to addition property (5).

In Problems 75–79, verify each inequality without evaluating the integrals.

75. $\int_{0}^{1} x \, dx \geq \int_{0}^{1} x^2 \, dx$

76. $\int_{1}^{2} x \, dx \leq \int_{1}^{2} x^2 \, dx$

77. $0 \leq \int_{0}^{4} \sqrt{x} \, dx \leq 8$

78. $\frac{1}{2} \leq \int_{0}^{1} \sqrt{1 - x^2} \, dx \leq 1$

79. $\frac{\pi}{3} \leq \int_{\pi/6}^{5\pi/6} \sin x \, dx \leq \frac{2\pi}{3}$

80. Find the value of $a \geq 0$ that maximizes $\int_{0}^{a} (4 - x^2) \, dx$.

81. Find the value of $a \in [0, 2\pi]$ that maximizes $\int_{0}^{a} \cos x \, dx$.

82. Find $a \in (0, 2\pi]$ such that
$$\int_{0}^{a} \sin x \, dx = 0$$

83. Find $a > 1$ such that
$$\int_{1}^{a} (x - 2)^3 \, dx = 0$$

84. Find $a > 0$ such that
$$\int_{-a}^{a} (1 - |x|) \, dx = 0$$

85. To determine age-specific mortality, a group of individuals, all born at the same time, is followed over time. If $N(t)$ denotes the number still alive at time t, then $N(t)/N(0)$ is the fraction surviving at time t. The quantity $r(t)$, called the *hazard rate function*, measures the rate at which individuals die at time t; that is, $r(t) \, dt$ is the probability that an individual who is alive at time t dies during the infinitesimal time interval $(t, t + dt)$. The cumulative hazard during the time interval $[0, t]$, $\int_{0}^{t} r(s) \, ds$, can be estimated as $-\ln \frac{N(t)}{N(0)}$. Show that the cumulative hazard during the time interval $[t, t+1]$, $\int_{t}^{t+1} r(s) \, ds$, can be estimated as $-\ln \frac{N(t+1)}{N(t)}$.

■ 6.2 The Fundamental Theorem of Calculus

In Section 6.1, we used the definition of definite integrals to compute $\int_{0}^{a} x^2 \, dx$. This required the summation of a large number of terms, which was facilitated by the explicit summation formula for $\sum_{k=1}^{n} k^2$. Fermat and others were able to carry out similar calculations for the area under curves of the form $y = x^r$, where r was a rational number different from -1. The solution to the case $r = -1$ was found by the Belgian mathematician Gregory of St. Vincent (1584–1667) and published in 1647. At that time, it seemed that methods specific to a given function needed to be developed to compute the area under the curve of that function. Such methods would not have been practical.

Fortunately, it turns out that the area problem is related to the tangent problem. This relationship is not at all obvious; among the first to notice it were Isaac Barrow (1630–1677) and James Gregory (1638–1675). Each presented the relationship in geometrical terms, without realizing the importance of his discovery.

Both Newton and Leibniz are to be credited with systematically developing the connection between the tangent and area problems, which ultimately resulted in a method for computing areas and for solving problems that can be translated into area problems. The result is known as the *fundamental theorem of calculus*, which says that the tangent and area problems are inversely related.

The fundamental theorem of calculus has two parts: The first part links antiderivatives and integrals, and the second part provides a method for computing definite integrals.

■ 6.2.1 The Fundamental Theorem of Calculus (Part I)

Let $f(x)$ be a continuous function on $[a, b]$, and let

$$F(x) = \int_a^x f(u)\, du$$

Geometrically, $F(x) = \int_a^x f(u)\, du$ represents the signed area between the graph of $f(u)$ and the horizontal axis between a and x. (See Figure 6.24.) Note that the independent variable x appears as the upper limit of integration. We can now ask how the signed area $F(x)$ changes as x varies. To answer this question, we compute $\frac{dF}{dx}$, using the definition of the derivative. That is,

$$\frac{d}{dx} F(x) = \lim_{h \to 0} \frac{F(x+h) - F(x)}{h}$$

$$= \lim_{h \to 0} \frac{1}{h} \left[\int_a^{x+h} f(u)\, du - \int_a^x f(u)\, du \right] \tag{6.6}$$

$$= \lim_{h \to 0} \frac{1}{h} \int_x^{x+h} f(u)\, du$$

[In the last step, we used property (5) of Subsection 6.1.3.] To evaluate

$$\lim_{h \to 0} \frac{1}{h} \int_x^{x+h} f(u)\, du$$

we will resort to the geometric interpretation of definite integrals. The following argument is illustrated in Figure 6.25: Note that

$$\int_x^{x+h} f(u)\, du$$

is the signed area of the region bounded by the graph of $f(u)$ and the horizontal axis between x and $x + h$. If h is small, then this area is closely approximated by the area of the inscribed rectangle with height $|f(x)|$. The signed area of this rectangle is $f(x)h$. Hence,

$$\int_x^{x+h} f(u)\, du \approx f(x)h$$

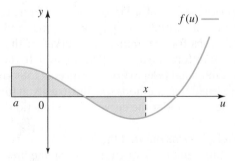

Figure 6.24 The shaded signed area is $F(x)$.

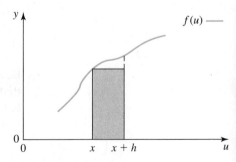

Figure 6.25 The approximate rectangle in the fundamental theorem of calculus.

If we divide both sides by h and let h tend to 0, then

$$\lim_{h \to 0} \frac{1}{h} \int_x^{x+h} f(u)\,du = f(x) \tag{6.7}$$

(as will be shown rigorously at the end of this subsection). Combining (6.6) and (6.7), we arrive at the remarkable result

$$\frac{d}{dx} F(x) = f(x)$$

In addition, we see that $F(x)$ is continuous since it is differentiable.

The preceding argument relies on geometric intuition. To show how we can make the argument mathematically rigorous, we give the complete proof at the end of this subsection. The result is summarized in the following theorem:

The Fundamental Theorem of Calculus (FTC) (Part I) If f is continuous on $[a, b]$, then the function F defined by

$$F(x) = \int_a^x f(u)\,du, \quad a \leq x \leq b$$

is continuous on $[a, b]$ and differentiable on (a, b), with

$$\frac{d}{dx} F(x) = f(x)$$

Simply stated, the FTC (part I) says that if we first integrate $f(x)$ and then differentiate the result, we get $f(x)$ again. In this sense, it shows that integration and differentiation are inverse operations.

We begin with an example that can be immediately solved by using the FTC.

EXAMPLE 1 Compute

$$\frac{d}{dx} \int_0^x (\sin u - e^{-u})\,du$$

for $x > 0$.

Solution First, note that $f(x) = \sin x - e^{-x}$ is continuous for $x \geq 0$. If we set $F(x) = \int_0^x (\sin u - e^{-u})\,du$ and apply the FTC, then

$$\frac{d}{dx} F(x) = \frac{d}{dx} \int_0^x (\sin u - e^{-u})\,du = \sin x - e^{-x}$$
■

EXAMPLE 2 Compute

$$\frac{d}{dx} \int_3^x \frac{1}{1+u^2}\,du$$

for $x > 3$.

Solution First, note that $f(x) = \frac{1}{1+x^2}$ is continuous for $x \geq 3$. If we set $F(x) = \int_3^x \frac{1}{1+u^2}\,du$ and apply the FTC, then ·

$$\frac{d}{dx} F(x) = \frac{d}{dx} \int_3^x \frac{1}{1+u^2}\,du = \frac{1}{1+x^2}$$
■

The remainder of this subsection can be omitted.

Leibniz's Rule (Optional) Combining the chain rule and the FTC (part I), we can differentiate integrals with respect to x when the upper and/or lower limits of integration are functions of x.

In the first example, the upper limit of integration is a function of x.

EXAMPLE 3 Compute

$$\frac{d}{dx} \int_0^{x^2} (u^3 - 2) \, du, \quad x > 0$$

Solution Note that $f(u) = u^3 - 2$ is continuous for all $u \in \mathbf{R}$. We set $F(v) = \int_0^v (u^3 - 2) \, du$, $v > 0$. Then, for $x > 0$,

$$F(x^2) = \int_0^{x^2} (u^3 - 2) \, du$$

We wish to compute $\frac{d}{dx} F(x^2)$. To do so, we need to apply the chain rule. We set $v(x) = x^2$. Then

$$\frac{d}{dx} F(x^2) = \frac{dF(v)}{dv} \frac{dv}{dx}$$

To evaluate $\frac{d}{dv} F(v) = \frac{d}{dv} \int_0^v (u^3 - 2) \, du$, we use the FTC:

$$\frac{d}{dv} \int_0^v (u^3 - 2) \, du = v^3 - 2$$

Since $\frac{dv}{dx} = \frac{d}{dx}(x^2) = 2x$, it follows that

$$\frac{d}{dx} F(x^2) = (v^3 - 2)2x = [(x^2)^3 - 2]2x$$
$$= (x^6 - 2)2x \quad ■$$

Thus far, we have dealt only with the case where the upper limit of integration depends on x. The next example shows what we must do when the lower limit of integration depends on x.

EXAMPLE 4 Compute

$$\frac{d}{dx} \int_{\sin x}^1 u^2 \, du$$

Solution Note that $f(u) = u^2$ is continuous for all $u \in \mathbf{R}$. We use the fact that

$$\int_{\sin x}^1 u^2 \, du = - \int_1^{\sin x} u^2 \, du$$

The upper limit now depends on x, but we introduced a minus sign. Hence

$$\frac{d}{dx} \int_{\sin x}^1 u^2 \, du = -\frac{d}{dx} \int_1^{\sin x} u^2 \, du$$
$$= -(\sin x)^2 \cos x$$

where, as in Example 3, we used the chain rule in the last step. ■

The preceding example makes an important point: We need to be careful about whether the upper or the lower limit of integration depends on x. In the next example, we show what we must do when both limits of integration depend on x.

EXAMPLE 5 For $x \in \mathbf{R}$, compute

$$\frac{d}{dx} \int_{x^2}^{x^3} e^u \, du$$

Solution   Note that $f(u) = e^u$ is continuous for all $u \in \mathbf{R}$. The given integral is the. defined for all $x \in \mathbf{R}$, and we can split it into two integrals at any $a \in \mathbf{R}$. We chu $a = 0$, which yields

$$\int_{x^2}^{x^3} e^u \, du = \int_{x^2}^{0} e^u \, du + \int_{0}^{x^3} e^u \, du = -\int_{0}^{x^2} e^u \, du + \int_{0}^{x^3} e^u \, du$$

The right-hand side is now written in a form that we know how to differentiate, and we find that

$$\frac{d}{dx} \int_{x^2}^{x^3} e^u \, du = -\frac{d}{dx} \int_{0}^{x^2} e^u \, du + \frac{d}{dx} \int_{0}^{x^3} e^u \, du$$

$$= -\left[e^{x^2} \frac{d}{dx} x^2 \right] + \left[e^{x^3} \frac{d}{dx} x^3 \right]$$

$$= -e^{x^2} 2x + e^{x^3} 3x^2 \qquad\qquad ■$$

The preceding example illustrates the most general case that we can encounter, namely, when both limits of integration are functions of x. We summarize this case in the following box, in a property known as Leibniz's rule:

Leibniz's Rule If $g(x)$ and $h(x)$ are differentiable functions and $f(u)$ is continuous for u between $g(x)$ and $h(x)$, then

$$\frac{d}{dx} \int_{g(x)}^{h(x)} f(u) \, du = f[h(x)]h'(x) - f[g(x)]g'(x)$$

We can check that Examples 3–5 can be solved with the preceding formula; for instance, in Example 4, we have $f(u) = u^2$, $g(x) = \sin x$, and $h(x) = 1$. Then $g'(x) = \cos x$ and $h'(x) = 0$. We therefore find that

$$f[h(x)]h'(x) - f[g(x)]g'(x) = 0 - (\sin x)^2 \cos x$$

which is the answer we obtained in Example 4.

Proof of the Fundamental Theorem of Calculus (Part I) (Optional)   At the beginning of this subsection, we found that if

$$F(x) = \int_{a}^{x} f(u) \, du$$

then

$$\frac{d}{dx} F(x) = \lim_{h \to 0} \frac{1}{h} \int_{x}^{x+h} f(u) \, du \qquad\qquad (6.8)$$

We now give a mathematically rigorous argument which will show that

$$\frac{d}{dx} F(x) = f(x)$$

We begin with the observation that, according to the extreme-value theorem, the continuous function $f(u)$ defined on the closed interval $[x, x+h]$ attains an absolute minimum and an absolute maximum on $[x, x+h]$. That is, there exist m and M such that m is the minimum of f on $[x, x+h]$ and M is the maximum of f on $[x, x+h]$, which implies that

$$m \le f(u) \le M \quad \text{for all } u \in [x, x+h] \qquad\qquad (6.9)$$

Of course, m and M depend on both x and h. Applying property (8) from Subsection 6.1.3 to (6.9), we find that

$$\int_x^{x+h} m \, du \le \int_x^{x+h} f(u) \, du \le \int_x^{x+h} M \, du$$

and hence

$$mh \le \int_x^{x+h} f(u) \, du \le Mh$$

Dividing by h, we obtain

$$m \le \frac{1}{h} \int_x^{x+h} f(u) \, du \le M \tag{6.10}$$

We set

$$I = \frac{1}{h} \int_x^{x+h} f(u) \, du$$

Then (6.10) becomes $m \le I \le M$; that is, I is a number between m and M. We compare this inequality with (6.9), which says that $f(u)$ also lies between m, the minimum of f on $[x, x+h]$, and M, the maximum of f on $[x, x+h]$, for all $u \in [x, x+h]$. The intermediate-value theorem applied to $f(u)$ tells us that any value between m and M is attained by $f(u)$ for some number on the interval $[x, x+h]$. Specifically, since I lies between m and M, there must exist a number $c_h \in [x, x+h]$ such that $f(c_h) = I$; that is,

$$f(c_h) = \frac{1}{h} \int_x^{x+h} f(u) \, du \tag{6.11}$$

Because $x \le c_h \le x + h$, it follows that

$$\lim_{h \to 0} c_h = x$$

Since f is continuous,

$$\lim_{h \to 0} f(c_h) = f\left(\lim_{h \to 0} c_h\right) = f(x) \tag{6.12}$$

Combining (6.8), (6.11), and (6.12) yields the result we seek:

$$\frac{d}{dx} F(x) = f(x) \qquad \blacksquare$$

■ 6.2.2 Antiderivatives and Indefinite Integrals

The first part of the fundamental theorem of calculus tells us that if

$$F(x) = \int_a^x f(u) \, du$$

then $F'(x) = f(x)$ [provided that $f(x)$ is continuous over the range of integration]. This statement says that $F(x)$ is an *antiderivative* of $f(x)$. (We introduced antiderivatives in Section 5.8.) Now, if we let

$$F(x) = \int_a^x f(u) \, du \qquad \text{and} \qquad G(x) = \int_b^x f(u) \, du$$

where a and b are two numbers, then both integrals have the same derivative, namely, $F'(x) = G'(x) = f(x)$ [again, provided that $f(x)$ is continuous over the range of integration]. That is, both $F(x)$ and $G(x)$ are antiderivatives of $f(x)$. We saw in

Section 5.8 that antiderivatives of a given function differ only by a constant. We can identify the constant, namely

$$F(x) = \int_a^x f(u)\,du = \int_a^b f(u)\,du + \int_b^x f(u)\,du = C + G(x)$$

where C is a constant denoting the number $\int_a^b f(u)\,du$.

The general antiderivative of a function $f(x)$ is $F(x) + C$, where $F'(x) = f(x)$ and C is a constant. It follows that $C + \int_a^x f(u)\,du$ is the general antiderivative of $f(x)$. We will use the notation $\int f(x)\,dx$ to denote both the general antiderivative of $f(x)$ and the function $C + \int_a^x f(u)\,du$; that is,

$$\int f(x)\,dx = C + \int_a^x f(u)\,du \tag{6.13}$$

We call $\int f(x)\,dx$ an **indefinite integral**. Thus, the first part of the FTC says that indefinite integrals and antiderivatives are the same.

When we write $\int_a^x f(u)\,du$, we use a letter other than x in the integrand because x already appears as the upper limit of integration. However, in the symbolic notation $\int f(x)\,dx$ we write x. This notation is to be interpreted as in (6.13); it is a convenient shorthand for $C + \int_a^x f(u)\,du$. The choice of value of a for the lower limit of integration on the right side of (6.13) is not important, because different indefinite integrals of the same function $f(x)$ differ only by an additive constant that can be absorbed into the constant C.

Examples 6–8 show how to compute indefinite integrals.

EXAMPLE 6　Compute $\int x^4\,dx$.

Solution　We need to find a function $F(x)$ such that $F'(x) = x^4$. The solution is

$$\int x^4\,dx = \frac{1}{5}x^5 + C$$

where C is a constant. We check that, indeed,

$$\frac{d}{dx}\left(\frac{1}{5}x^5 + C\right) = x^4$$

■

EXAMPLE 7　Compute $\int (e^x + \sin x)\,dx$.

Solution　We need to find an antiderivative of $f(x) = e^x + \sin x$. Since

$$\frac{d}{dx}(e^x - \cos x) = e^x - (-\sin x) = e^x + \sin x$$

it follows that

$$\int (e^x + \sin x)\,dx = e^x - \cos x + C$$

■

When we compute the indefinite integral $\int f(x)\,dx$, we want to know the general antiderivative of $f(x)$; this is why we added the constant C in the previous two examples.

EXAMPLE 8　Show that

$$\int \frac{1}{x}\,dx = \ln|x| + C \quad \text{for } x \neq 0$$

Solution　Since the absolute value of x appears on the right-hand side, we split our discussion into two parts, according to whether $x \geq 0$ or $x \leq 0$. Recall that

$$|x| = \begin{cases} x & \text{for } x \geq 0 \\ -x & \text{for } x < 0 \end{cases}$$

Since $\ln x$ is not defined at $x = 0$, we consider the two cases $x > 0$ and $x < 0$.

(i) $x > 0$: Since $\ln |x| = \ln x$ when $x > 0$, we have

$$\frac{d}{dx} \ln x = \frac{1}{x}$$

Hence,

$$\int \frac{1}{x} \, dx = \ln x + C \quad \text{for } x > 0$$

(ii) $x < 0$: Since $\ln |x| = \ln(-x)$ when $x < 0$, it follows that

$$\frac{d}{dx} \ln(-x) = \frac{1}{-x}(-1) = \frac{1}{x}$$

Hence,

$$\int \frac{1}{x} \, dx = \ln(-x) + C \quad \text{for } x < 0$$

Combining (i) and (ii), we obtain

$$\int \frac{1}{x} \, dx = \ln |x| + C \quad \text{for } x \neq 0$$

When we introduced logarithmic and exponential functions in Sections 4.6 and 4.7, we had to resort to the calculator to convince ourselves that e^x and $\ln x$ were indeed the functions we knew from precalculus. To give a mathematically rigorous definition of these functions, we typically start by *defining* $\ln x$ as $\int_1^x \frac{1}{u} \, du$ and then derive the algebraic rules for $\ln x$ from this integral representation. The exponential function e^x is defined as the inverse function of $\ln x$, and the number e is defined so that $\ln e = 1$. This definition is then consistent with the definition in Section 4.6.

We have seen that in order to evaluate indefinite integrals, we must find antiderivatives. Table 6-1 gives a list of indefinite integrals. (The table is a slightly expanded form of the table of antiderivatives from Section 5.8.) Examples 9 and 10 show how to use this list to compute indefinite integrals.

TABLE 6-1 A Collection of Indefinite Integrals

$$\int x^n \, dx = \frac{x^{n+1}}{n+1} + C \quad (n \neq -1) \qquad \int \frac{1}{x} \, dx = \ln |x| + C$$

$$\int e^x \, dx = e^x + C \qquad\qquad \int a^x \, dx = \frac{a^x}{\ln a} + C$$

$$\int \cos x \, dx = \sin x + C \qquad\qquad \int \sin x \, dx = -\cos x + C$$

$$\int \sec^2 x \, dx = \tan x + C \qquad\qquad \int \csc^2 x \, dx = -\cot x + C$$

$$\int \sec x \tan x \, dx = \sec x + C \qquad\qquad \int \csc x \cot x \, dx = -\csc x + C$$

$$\int \tan x \, dx = \ln |\sec x| + C \qquad\qquad \int \cot x \, dx = -\ln |\csc x| + C$$

$$\int \frac{1}{1+x^2} \, dx = \tan^{-1} x + C \qquad\qquad \int \frac{1}{\sqrt{1-x^2}} \, dx = \sin^{-1} x + C$$

EXAMPLE 9 Evaluate

$$\int \frac{1}{\sin^2 x - 1} \, dx$$

Solution We first work on the integrand. Using the fact that $\sin^2 x + \cos^2 x = 1$, we find that

$$\frac{1}{\sin^2 x - 1} = -\frac{1}{\cos^2 x} = -\sec^2 x$$

Hence,

$$\int \frac{1}{\sin^2 x - 1}\, dx = -\int \sec^2 x\, dx = -\tan x + C$$ ■

EXAMPLE 10 Evaluate

$$\int \frac{x^2}{x^2 + 1}\, dx$$

Solution We first rewrite the integrand:

$$\frac{x^2}{x^2 + 1} = \frac{x^2 + 1 - 1}{x^2 + 1} = \frac{x^2 + 1}{x^2 + 1} - \frac{1}{x^2 + 1} = 1 - \frac{1}{x^2 + 1}$$

Then, from Table 6-1,

$$\int \frac{x^2}{x^2 + 1}\, dx = \int \left(1 - \frac{1}{x^2 + 1}\right) dx = x - \tan^{-1} x + C$$ ■

■ **6.2.3 The Fundamental Theorem of Calculus (Part II)**

The first part of the FTC allows us to compute integrals of the form $\int_a^x f(u)\, du$ only up to an additive constant; for instance,

$$F(x) = \int_1^x u^2\, du = \frac{1}{3}x^3 + C$$

To evaluate the definite integral $F(2) = \int_1^2 u^2\, du$, which represents the area under the graph of $f(x) = x^2$ between $x = 1$ and $x = 2$, we would need to know the value of the constant. This value is provided by the second part of the FTC, which allows us to evaluate definite integrals. The calculation that follows shows us how this constant is determined.

We saw in the last subsection that if we set

$$G(x) = \int_a^x f(u)\, du$$

then $G(x)$ is an antiderivative of $f(x)$. Furthermore, if $F(x)$ is another antiderivative of $f(x)$, then $G(x)$ and $F(x)$ differ only by an additive constant. That is,

$$G(x) = F(x) + C$$

where C is a constant. Now,

$$G(a) = \int_a^a f(u)\, du = 0$$

Hence,

$$0 = G(a) = F(a) + C$$

which implies that $C = -F(a)$ and, therefore, $G(x) = F(x) - F(a)$, or, in the integral representation of $G(x)$,

$$\int_a^x f(u)\, du = F(x) - F(a)$$

If we set $x = b$, then

$$\int_a^b f(u)\, du = F(b) - F(a)$$

This formula allows us to evaluate definite integrals and is the content of the second part of the FTC.

> **The Fundamental Theorem of Calculus (Part II)** Assume that f is continuous on $[a, b]$; then
>
> $$\int_a^b f(x)\, dx = F(b) - F(a)$$
>
> where $F(x)$ is an antiderivative of $f(x)$; that is, $F'(x) = f(x)$.

So how do we use this part of the FTC? To compute the definite integral $\int_a^b f(x)\, dx$ when f is continuous on $[a, b]$, we first need to find an antiderivative $F(x)$ of $f(x)$ (any antiderivative will do) and then compute $F(b) - F(a)$. This number is then equal to $\int_a^b f(x)\, dx$. Table 6-1 will help us find the required antiderivative. (Note that an indefinite integral is a function, whereas a definite integral is simply a number.)

Using the FTC (Part II) to Evaluate Definite Integrals

EXAMPLE 11 Evaluate $\int_{-1}^2 (x^2 - 3x)\, dx$.

Solution Note that $f(x) = x^2 - 3x$ is continuous on $[-1, 2]$. We need to find an antiderivative of $f(x) = x^2 - 3x$; for instance, $F(x) = \frac{1}{3}x^3 - \frac{3}{2}x^2$ is an antiderivative of $f(x)$ since $F'(x) = f(x)$. We then must evaluate $F(2) - F(-1)$:

$$F(2) = \frac{1}{3}2^3 - \frac{3}{2}2^2 = \frac{8}{3} - 6 = -\frac{10}{3}$$

$$F(-1) = \frac{1}{3}(-1)^3 - \frac{3}{2}(-1)^2 = -\frac{1}{3} - \frac{3}{2} = -\frac{11}{6}$$

We find that $F(2) - F(-1) = -\frac{10}{3} - (-\frac{11}{6}) = -\frac{9}{6} = -\frac{3}{2}$. Therefore,

$$\int_{-1}^2 (x^2 - 3x)\, dx = F(2) - F(-1) = -\frac{3}{2}$$

In the preceding calculation, we chose the simplest antiderivative—that is, the one in which the constant C is equal to 0. We could have chosen any $C \neq 0$, and the answer would have been the same. Let's see why. The general antiderivative of $f(x)$ is $G(x) = \frac{1}{3}x^3 - \frac{3}{2}x^2 + C$. We can write this as $G(x) = F(x) + C$, where $F(x)$ is the antiderivative we used previously. Then, using $G(x)$ to evaluate the integral, we find that

$$\int_{-1}^2 (x^2 - 3)\, dx = G(2) - G(-1)$$

$$= [F(2) + C] - [F(-1) + C] = F(2) - F(-1)$$

which is the same answer as before, since the constant C cancels out. We thus see that we can use the simplest antiderivative (the one in which $C = 0$), and we will do so from now on. ■

EXAMPLE 12   Evaluate $\int_0^\pi \sin x \, dx$.

Solution   Note that $\sin x$ is continuous on $[0, \pi]$. Since $F(x) = -\cos x$ is an antiderivative of $\sin x$, we have

$$\int_0^\pi \sin x \, dx = F(\pi) - F(0) = -\cos \pi - (-\cos 0) = -(-1) + 1 = 2 \qquad ■$$

EXAMPLE 13   Evaluate

$$\int_{-5}^{-1} \frac{1}{x} \, dx$$

Solution   Note that $\frac{1}{x}$ is continuous on $[-5, -1]$. Now $\ln |x|$ is an antiderivative of $\frac{1}{x}$. We use this antiderivative to evaluate the integral and obtain

$$\int_{-5}^{-1} \frac{1}{x} \, dx = (\ln | -1|) - (\ln | -5|) = -\ln 5$$

since $\ln | -1| = \ln 1 = 0$ and $| -5| = 5$. $\qquad ■$

We next introduce additional notation. If $F(x)$ is an antiderivative of $f(x)$, then we write

$$\int_a^b f(x) \, dx = F(x)]_a^b = F(b) - F(a)$$

For instance,

$$\int_{-5}^{-1} \frac{1}{x} \, dx = \ln |x|]_{-5}^{-1} = \ln | -1| - \ln | -5|$$

The notation $F(x)]_a^b$ indicates that we evaluate the antiderivative $F(x)$ at b and a, respectively, and compute the difference $F(b) - F(a)$.

EXAMPLE 14   Evaluate

$$\int_0^3 2x e^{x^2} \, dx$$

Solution   Observe that $2x e^{x^2}$ is continuous on $[0, 3]$ and that $F(x) = e^{x^2}$ is an antiderivative of $f(x) = 2x e^{x^2}$, since, applying the chain rule, we find that

$$F'(x) = e^{x^2} \left(\frac{d}{dx} x^2 \right) = e^{x^2} 2x$$

Therefore,

$$\int_0^3 2x e^{x^2} \, dx = e^{x^2}]_0^3 = e^9 - e^0 = e^9 - 1 \qquad ■$$

EXAMPLE 15   Evaluate

$$\int_1^4 \frac{2x^2 - 3x + \sqrt{x}}{\sqrt{x}} \, dx$$

Solution   The integrand is continuous on $[1, 4]$. We first simplify the integrand:

$$f(x) = \frac{2x^2 - 3x + \sqrt{x}}{\sqrt{x}} = 2x^{3/2} - 3\sqrt{x} + 1$$

An antiderivative of $f(x)$ is, therefore,

$$F(x) = 2 \cdot \frac{2}{5} x^{5/2} - 3 \cdot \frac{2}{3} x^{3/2} + x = \frac{4}{5} x^{5/2} - 2x^{3/2} + x$$

which can be checked by differentiating $F(x)$. We can now evaluate the integral:

$$\int_1^4 \frac{2x^2 - 3x + \sqrt{x}}{\sqrt{x}} \, dx = \frac{4}{5}x^{5/2} - 2x^{3/2} + x \Big]_1^4$$

$$= \left(\frac{4}{5} \cdot 4^{5/2} - 2 \cdot 4^{3/2} + 4\right) - \left(\frac{4}{5} \cdot 1^{5/2} - 2 \cdot 1^{3/2} + 1\right)$$

$$= \left(\frac{4}{5} \cdot 32 - (2)(8) + 4\right) - \left(\frac{4}{5} - 2 + 1\right)$$

$$= \frac{68}{5} - \left(-\frac{1}{5}\right) = \frac{69}{5}$$ ■

Finding an Integrand

EXAMPLE 16   Suppose that

$$\int_0^x f(t) \, dt = \cos(2x) + a$$

where a is a constant. Find $f(x)$ and a.

Solution   We solve this problem in two steps. First, we use the FTC, part I, to conclude that

$$\frac{d}{dx} \int_0^x f(t) \, dt = f(x)$$

Hence,

$$f(x) = \frac{d}{dx} [\cos(2x) + a] = -2\sin(2x)$$

In the second step, we use the FTC, part II, to determine a:

$$\int_0^x (-2\sin(2t)) \, dt = \cos(2t) \Big]_0^x$$

$$= \cos(2x) - \cos(0) = \cos(2x) - 1$$

We conclude that $a = -1$. ■

Discontinuous Integrand   You might wonder why we always check that the integrand is continuous on the interval between the lower and the upper limit of integration. The next example shows what can go wrong when the integrand is discontinuous.

EXAMPLE 17   Evaluate

$$\int_{-2}^1 \frac{1}{x^2} \, dx$$

Solution   An antiderivative of $f(x) = 1/x^2$ is $F(x) = -\frac{1}{x}$. We find that $F(1) = -1$ and $F(-2) = \frac{1}{2}$. When we compute $F(1) - F(-2)$, we get $-\frac{3}{2}$. This is obviously not equal to $\int_{-2}^1 \frac{1}{x^2} \, dx$, since $f(x) = \frac{1}{x^2}$ is positive on $[-2, 1]$ (see Figure 6.26) and, therefore, the integral of $f(x)$ between -2 and 1 should not be negative. The function $f(x)$ is discontinuous at $x = 0$ (where it has a vertical asymptote). Hence, the second part of the FTC therefore cannot be applied. We will learn how to deal with such discontinuities in Section 7.4. In any case, before you evaluate an integral, always check whether the integrand is continuous between the limits of integration. ■

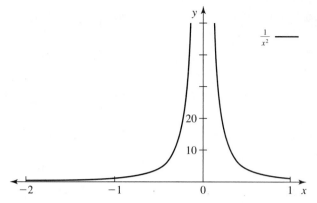

Figure 6.26 The graph of $y = \frac{1}{x^2}$ between $x = -2$ and $x = 1$. The function is discontinuous at $x = 0$.

Section 6.2 Problems

■ 6.2.1

In Problems 1–14, find $\frac{dy}{dx}$.

1. $y = \int_0^x 2u^3 \, du$

2. $y = \int_0^x (1 - \frac{u^4}{2}) \, du$

3. $y = \int_0^x (4u^2 - 3) \, du$

4. $y = \int_0^x (3 + u^4) \, du$

5. $y = \int_0^x \sqrt{1 + 2u} \, du, \; x > 0$

6. $y = \int_0^x \sqrt{1 + u^2} \, du, \; x > 0$

7. $y = \int_0^x \sqrt{1 + \sin^2 u} \, du, \; x > 0$

8. $y = \int_0^x \sqrt{2 + \csc^2 u} \, du, \; x > 0$

9. $y = \int_3^x ue^{4u} \, du$

10. $y = \int_1^x ue^{-u^2} \, du$

11. $y = \int_{-2}^x \frac{1}{u+3} \, du, \; x > -2$

12. $y = \int_{-1}^x \frac{2}{2+u^2} \, du$

13. $y = \int_{\pi/2}^x \sin(u^2 + 1) \, du$

14. $y = \int_{\pi/4}^x \cos^2(u - 3) \, du$

In Problems 15–38, use Leibniz's rule to find $\frac{dy}{dx}$.

15. $y = \int_0^{3x} (1 + t^2) \, dt$

16. $y = \int_0^{2x-1} (t^3 - 2) \, dt$

17. $y = \int_0^{1-4x} (2t^2 + 1) \, dt$

18. $y = \int_0^{3x+2} (1 + t^3) \, dt$

19. $y = \int_4^{x^2+1} \sqrt{t} \, dt, \; x > 0$

20. $y = \int_2^{x^2-2} \sqrt{3 + u} \, du, \; x > 0$

21. $y = \int_0^{3x} (1 + e^t) \, dt$

22. $y = \int_0^{2x^2-1} (e^{-2t} + e^{2t}) \, dt$

23. $y = \int_1^{3x^2+x} (1 + te^t) \, dt$

24. $y = \int_2^{\ln x} e^{-t} \, dt, \; x > 0$

25. $y = \int_x^3 (1 + t) \, dt$

26. $y = \int_x^5 (1 + e^t) \, dt$

27. $y = \int_{2x}^3 (1 + \sin t) \, dt$

28. $y = \int_{2x^2}^6 (1 + \tan t) \, dt$

29. $y = \int_x^5 \frac{1}{u^2} \, du, \; x > 0$

30. $y = \int_{x^2}^3 \frac{1}{1+t} \, dt, \; x > 0$

31. $y = \int_{x^2}^1 \sec t \, dt, \; -1 < x < 1$

32. $y = \int_{2+x^2}^2 \cot t \, dt$

33. $y = \int_x^{2x} (1 + t^2) \, dt$

34. $y = \int_{-x}^x \tan u \, du, \; 0 < x < \frac{\pi}{4}$

35. $y = \int_{x^2}^{x^3} \ln(t - 3) \, dt, \; x > 0$

36. $y = \int_{x^3}^{x^4} \ln(1 + t^2) \, dt, \; x > 0$

37. $y = \int_{2-x^2}^{x+x^3} \sin t \, dt$

38. $y = \int_{1+x^2}^{x^3-2x} \cos t \, dt$

■ 6.2.2

In Problems 39–96, compute the indefinite integrals.

39. $\int (1 + 3x^2) \, dx$

40. $\int (x^3 - 4) \, dx$

41. $\int (\frac{1}{3}x^2 - \frac{1}{2}x) \, dx$

42. $\int (4x^3 + 5x^2) \, dx$

43. $\int \left(\frac{1}{2}x^2 + 3x - \frac{1}{3} \right) dx$

44. $\int \left(\frac{1}{2}x^5 + 2x^3 - 1 \right) dx$

45. $\int \frac{2x^2 - x}{\sqrt{x}} \, dx$

46. $\int \frac{x^3 + 3x}{2\sqrt{x}} \, dx$

47. $\int x^2 \sqrt{x} \, dx$

48. $\int (1 + x^3)\sqrt{x} \, dx$

49. $\int (x^{7/2} + x^{2/7}) \, dx$

50. $\int (x^{3/5} + x^{5/3}) \, dx$

51. $\int \left(\sqrt{x} + \frac{1}{\sqrt{x}} \right) dx$

52. $\int \left(3x^{1/3} + \frac{1}{3x^{1/3}} \right) dx$

53. $\int (x - 1)(x + 1) \, dx$

54. $\int (x - 1)^2 \, dx$

55. $\int (x-2)(3-x)\,dx$

56. $\int (2x+3)^2\,dx$

57. $\int e^{2x}\,dx$

58. $\int 2e^{3x}\,dx$

59. $\int 3e^{-x}\,dx$

60. $\int 2e^{-x/3}\,dx$

61. $\int xe^{-x^2/2}\,dx$

62. $\int e^x(1-e^{-x})\,dx$

63. $\int \sin(2x)\,dx$

64. $\int \sin\dfrac{1-x}{3}\,dx$

65. $\int \cos(3x)\,dx$

66. $\int \cos\dfrac{2-4x}{5}\,dx$

67. $\int \sec^2(3x)\,dx$

68. $\int \csc^2(2x)\,dx$

69. $\int \dfrac{\sin x}{1-\sin^2 x}\,dx$

70. $\int \dfrac{\cos x}{1-\cos^2 x}\,dx$

71. $\int \tan(2x)\,dx$

72. $\int \cot(3x)\,dx$

73. $\int (\sec^2 x + \tan x)\,dx$

74. $\int (\cot x - \csc^2 x)\,dx$

75. $\int \dfrac{4}{1+x^2}\,dx$

76. $\int \left(1 - \dfrac{x^2}{1+x^2}\right)\,dx$

77. $\int \dfrac{1}{\sqrt{1-x^2}}\,dx$

78. $\int \dfrac{5}{\sqrt{1-x^2}}\,dx$

79. $\int \dfrac{1}{x+2}\,dx$

80. $\int \dfrac{1}{x-3}\,dx$

81. $\int \dfrac{2x-1}{3x}\,dx$

82. $\int \dfrac{2x+5}{x}\,dx$

83. $\int \dfrac{x+3}{x^2-9}\,dx$

84. $\int \dfrac{x+4}{x^2-16}\,dx$

85. $\int \dfrac{3-x}{x^2-9}\,dx$

86. $\int \dfrac{4-x}{x^2-16}\,dx$

87. $\int \dfrac{5x^2}{x^2+1}\,dx$

88. $\int \dfrac{2x^2}{1+x^2}\,dx$

89. $\int 3^x\,dx$

90. $\int 2^x\,dx$

91. $\int 3^{-2x}\,dx$

92. $\int 4^{-x}\,dx$

93. $\int (x^2+2^x)\,dx$

94. $\int (x^{-3}+3^{-x})\,dx$

95. $\int (\sqrt{x}+\sqrt{e^x})\,dx$

96. $\int \left(\dfrac{1}{\sqrt{x}}+\dfrac{1}{\sqrt{e^x}}\right)\,dx$

■ **6.2.3**

In Problems 97–122, evaluate the definite integrals.

97. $\int_2^4 (3-2x)\,dx$

98. $\int_{-1}^3 (2x^2-1)\,dx$

99. $\int_0^1 (x^3-x^{1/3})\,dx$

100. $\int_1^2 x^{5/2}\,dx$

101. $\int_1^8 x^{-2/3}\,dx$

102. $\int_4^9 \dfrac{1+\sqrt{x}}{\sqrt{x}}\,dx$

103. $\int_0^2 (2t-1)(t+3)\,dt$

104. $\int_{-1}^2 (2+3t)^2\,dt$

105. $\int_0^{\pi/4} \sin(2x)\,dx$

106. $\int_{-\pi/3}^{\pi/3} 2\cos\left(\dfrac{x}{2}\right)\,dx$

107. $\int_0^{\pi/8} \sec^2(2x)\,dx$

108. $\int_{-\pi/4}^{\pi/4} \tan x\,dx$

109. $\int_0^1 \dfrac{1}{1+x^2}\,dx$

110. $\int_{-\sqrt{3}}^{-1} \dfrac{4}{1+x^2}\,dx$

111. $\int_0^{1/2} \dfrac{1}{\sqrt{1-x^2}}\,dx$

112. $\int_{-1/2}^{1/2} \dfrac{2}{\sqrt{1-x^2}}\,dx$

113. $\int_0^{\pi/6} \tan(2x)\,dx$

114. $\int_{\pi/20}^{\pi/15} \sec(5x)\tan(5x)\,dx$

115. $\int_{-1}^0 e^{3x}\,dx$

116. $\int_0^2 2te^{t^2}\,dt$

117. $\int_{-1}^1 |x|\,dx$

118. $\int_{-1}^1 e^{-|s|}\,ds$

119. $\int_1^e \dfrac{1}{x}\,dx$

120. $\int_2^3 \dfrac{1}{z+1}\,dz$

121. $\int_{-2}^{-1} \dfrac{1}{1-u}\,du$

122. $\int_2^3 \dfrac{2}{t-1}\,dt$

123. Use l'Hospital's rule to compute

$$\lim_{x\to 0} \dfrac{1}{x^2}\int_0^x \sin t\,dt$$

124. Use l'Hospital's rule to compute

$$\lim_{h\to 0} \dfrac{1}{h}\int_0^h e^x\,dx$$

125. Suppose that

$$\int_0^x f(t)\,dt = 2x^2$$

Find $f(x)$.

126. Suppose that

$$\int_0^x f(t)\,dt = \dfrac{1}{2}\tan(2x)$$

Find $f(x)$.

■ 6.3 Applications of Integration

In this section, we will discuss a number of applications of integrals. In the first application, we will revisit the interpretation of integrals as areas; the second application interprets integrals as cumulative (or net) change; the third will allow us to compute averages using integrals; and, finally, we will use integrals to compute volumes. In each application, you will see that integrals can be interpreted as "sums of many small increments."

■ 6.3.1 Areas

The first application is already familiar to us. If f is a nonnegative, continuous function on $[a, b]$, then

$$A = \int_a^b f(x)\, dx$$

represents the area of the region bounded by the graph of $f(x)$ between a and b, the vertical lines $x = a$ and $x = b$, and the x-axis between a and b. In all of the examples we have presented thus far, one of the boundaries of the region whose area we wanted to know has been the x-axis. We will now discuss how to find the geometric area between two arbitrary curves. We emphasize that we want to compute geometric areas; that is, the areas we compute in this subsection will always be positive.

Suppose that $f(x)$ and $g(x)$ are continuous functions on $[a, b]$. We wish to find the area between the graphs of f and g. We start with a simple example. (See Figure 6.27.) We assume for the moment that both f and g are nonnegative on $[a, b]$ and that $f(x) \geq g(x)$ on $[a, b]$. From the figure, we see that

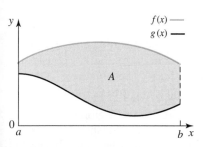

Figure 6.27 Computing the area between the two curves.

$$A = \left[\begin{array}{c} \text{area between} \\ f \text{ and } x\text{-axis} \end{array}\right] - \left[\begin{array}{c} \text{area between} \\ g \text{ and } x\text{-axis} \end{array}\right]$$

$$= \int_a^b f(x)\, dx - \int_a^b g(x)\, dx$$

Using Property (4) of Subsection 6.1.3, we can write this equation as

$$A = \int_a^b [f(x) - g(x)]\, dx$$

We obtained this formula under the assumption that both f and g are nonnegative on $[a, b]$; we now show that this assumption is not necessary. To do so, we use Riemann sums to derive a formula for the area between two curves.

We assume that f and g are continuous on $[a, b]$ and that $f(x) \geq g(x)$ for all $x \in [a, b]$. We approximate the area between the two curves by rectangles: We divide $[a, b]$ into n equal subintervals, each of length Δx; that is, we set $a = x_0 < x_1 < x_2 < \cdots < x_n = b$ with $\Delta x = x_k - x_{k-1} = (b - a)/n$. The kth subinterval is thus between x_{k-1} and x_k. We choose left endpoints to compute the heights of the approximating rectangles. From Figure 6.28, we see that the height of the kth rectangle is equal to $f(x_{k-1}) - g(x_{k-1})$. We therefore obtain

$$A = \lim_{n \to \infty} \sum_{k=1}^n [f(x_{k-1}) - g(x_{k-1})]\, \Delta x$$

$$= \int_a^b [f(x) - g(x)]\, dx$$

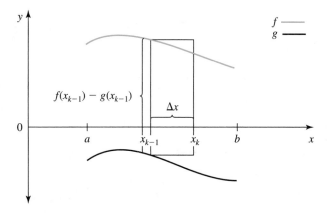

Figure 6.28 The kth rectangle between x_{k-1} and x_k.

The following box expresses this result:

> If f and g are continuous on $[a, b]$, with $f(x) \geq g(x)$ for all $x \in [a, b]$, then the area of the region between the curves $y = f(x)$ and $y = g(x)$ from a to b is equal to
>
> $$\text{Area} = \int_a^b [f(x) - g(x)]\, dx$$

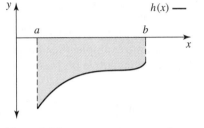

Figure 6.29 The definite integral $\int_a^b h(x)\, dx$ represents a signed area; it is negative here.

Before looking at a number of examples, we point out once more that this area formula always yields a nonnegative number since it computes the geometric area. To contrast this kind of area with the concept of a signed area, let us consider a function $h(x)$ on $[a, b]$, with $h(x) \leq 0$ for all $x \in [a, b]$. (See Figure 6.29.) The definite integral $\int_a^b h(x)\, dx$ represents a signed area and is negative in this case; more precisely, $\int_a^b h(x)\, dx$ is the negative of the geometric area of the region between the x-axis and the graph of $h(x)$ from $x = a$ to $x = b$. That this relationship is consistent with our definition of area can be seen as follows: The region of interest is bounded by the two curves $y = 0$ and $y = h(x)$. Since $h(x) \leq 0$ for $x \in [a, b]$, the area formula yields

$$\text{Area} = \int_a^b [0 - h(x)]\, dx = -\int_a^b h(x)\, dx$$

which is a positive number.

When you compute the area between two curves, you should always graph the bounding curves. This will show you how to set up the appropriate integral(s).

EXAMPLE 1

Find the area between the curves $y = \sec^2 x$ and $y = \cos x$ from $x = 0$ to $x = \pi/4$.

Solution

We first graph the bounding curves, as shown in Figure 6.30. We see that both $\sec^2 x$ and $\cos x$ are continuous on $[0, \pi/4]$ and that $\sec^2 x \geq \cos x$ for $x \in [0, \frac{\pi}{4}]$. Therefore,

$$\text{Area} = \int_0^{\pi/4} [\sec^2 x - \cos x]\, dx$$

$$= \tan x - \sin x \big]_0^{\pi/4}$$

$$= \left(\tan \frac{\pi}{4} - \sin \frac{\pi}{4} \right) - (\tan 0 - \sin 0)$$

$$= \left(1 - \frac{1}{2}\sqrt{2} \right) - (0 - 0) = 1 - \frac{1}{2}\sqrt{2}$$

■

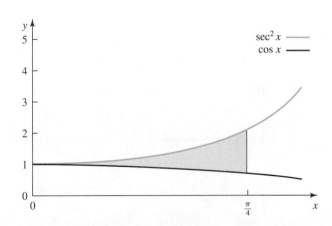

Figure 6.30 The region for Example 1.

EXAMPLE 2   Find the area of the region enclosed by $y = (x - 1)^2 - 1$ and $y = -x + 2$.

Solution   The bounding curves are graphed in Figure 6.31. To find the points where the two curves intersect, we solve

$$(x - 1)^2 - 1 = -x + 2$$
$$x^2 - 2x + 1 - 1 = -x + 2$$
$$x^2 - x - 2 = 0$$
$$(x + 1)(x - 2) = 0$$

Therefore,

$$x = -1 \qquad \text{and} \qquad x = 2$$

are the x-coordinates of the points of intersection. Note that both $y = (x - 1)^2$ and $y = -x + 2$ are continuous on $[-1, 2]$. Since $-x + 2 \geq (x - 1)^2 - 1$ for $x \in [-1, 2]$, the area of the enclosed region is

$$\text{Area} = \int_{-1}^{2} [(-x + 2) - ((x - 1)^2 - 1)]\, dx$$

$$= \int_{-1}^{2} [-x + 2 - x^2 + 2x - 1 + 1]\, dx$$

$$= \int_{-1}^{2} [-x^2 + x + 2]\, dx = -\frac{1}{3}x^3 + \frac{1}{2}x^2 + 2x \Big]_{-1}^{2}$$

$$= \left(-\frac{1}{3}(2)^3 + \frac{1}{2}(2)^2 + (2)(2) \right) - \left(-\frac{1}{3}(-1)^3 + \frac{1}{2}(-1)^2 + (2)(-1) \right)$$

$$= -\frac{8}{3} + 2 + 4 - \frac{1}{3} - \frac{1}{2} + 2 = \frac{9}{2} \qquad ■$$

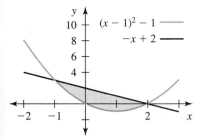

Figure 6.31 The region for Example 2.

EXAMPLE 3   Find the area of the region bounded by $y = \sqrt{x}$, $y = x - 2$, and the x-axis.

Solution   We first graph the bounding curves in Figure 6.32. We see that $y = \sqrt{x}$ and $y = x - 2$ intersect. To find the point of intersection, we solve

$$x - 2 = \sqrt{x}$$

Squaring both sides, we find that

$$(x - 2)^2 = (\sqrt{x})^2 \qquad \text{and thus} \qquad x^2 - 4x + 4 = x$$

or

$$x^2 - 5x + 4 = 0$$

Factoring the preceding equation, we obtain

$$(x - 4)(x - 1) = 0$$

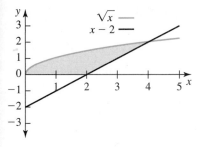

Figure 6.32 The region for Example 3.

which yields the solutions $x = 4$ and $x = 1$. Since squaring an equation can introduce extraneous solutions, we need to check whether the solutions satisfy $x - 2 = \sqrt{x}$. When $x = 4$, we find that $4 - 2 = \sqrt{4}$, which is a true statement; when $x = 1$, we find that $1 - 2 = \sqrt{1}$, which is a false statement. Hence, $x = 4$ is the only solution.

The graph of $y = x - 2$ intersects the x-axis at $x = 2$. To compute the area, we need to split the integral into two parts, because the lower bounding curve is composed of two parts: the x-axis from $x = 0$ to $x = 2$ and the line $y = x - 2$ from $x = 2$ to $x = 4$. We see from the graph that all bounding curves are continuous on their respective intervals. We get

$$\text{Area} = \int_0^2 \sqrt{x}\,dx + \int_2^4 [\sqrt{x} - (x-2)]\,dx$$

$$= \left[\frac{2}{3}x^{3/2}\right]_0^2 + \left[\frac{2}{3}x^{3/2} - \frac{1}{2}x^2 + 2x\right]_2^4$$

$$= \frac{2}{3}\cdot 2^{3/2} + \frac{2}{3}\cdot 4^{3/2} - \frac{1}{2}\cdot 16 + 8 - \frac{2}{3}\cdot 2^{3/2} + 2 - 4 = \frac{10}{3} \qquad ■$$

In the preceding example, we needed to split the integral into two parts because the lower boundary of the area was composed of two different curves that determined the heights of the approximating rectangles in the Riemann integral. Recall that the rectangles are obtained by partitioning the x-axis. It is sometimes more convenient to partition the y-axis. We illustrate this approach in Figure 6.33 for the region of Example 3, where we partition the interval $[0, 2]$ on the y-axis into n equal subintervals, each of length Δy. We need to express the boundary curves as functions of y. In the case of Example 3, the right boundary curve is $x = f(y) = y + 2$ and the left boundary curve is $x = g(y) = y^2$.

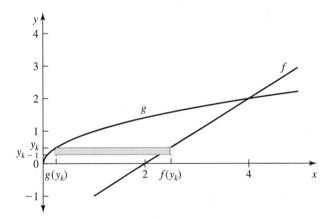

Figure 6.33 The area between $f(y)$ and $g(y)$ in Example 3 together with an approximating rectangle.

We set $y_0 = 0 < y_1 < y_2 < \cdots < y_n = 2$, where $y_k - y_{k-1} = \Delta y$ for $k = 1, 2, \ldots, n$. As shown in Figure 6.33, the kth rectangle has width $y_k - y_{k-1}$ and height $f(y_k) - g(y_k)$. Therefore, the area of the kth rectangle is

$$[f(y_k) - g(y_k)]\,\Delta y$$

If we sum this quantity from $k = 1$ to $k = n$ and let $\Delta y \to 0$, we find that

$$\lim_{\Delta y \to 0} \sum_{k=1}^{n} [f(y_k) - g(y_k)]\,\Delta y = \int_0^2 [f(y) - g(y)]\,dy$$

Since each rectangle is bounded by the same two curves, there is no need to split the integral. Using $f(y) = y + 2$ and $g(y) = y^2$, we obtain, for the total area,

$$\text{Area} = \int_0^2 (y + 2 - y^2)\,dy$$

$$= \frac{1}{2}y^2 + 2y - \frac{1}{3}y^3 \Big]_0^2 = 2 + 4 - \frac{8}{3} = \frac{10}{3}$$

which is the same as the result in Example 3.

To summarize the general case, as illustrated in Figure 6.34, suppose that a region is bounded by $x = f(y)$ and $x = g(y)$, with $g(y) \leq f(y)$ for $c \leq y \leq d$; that is, $f(y)$ is to the right of $g(y)$ for all $y \in [c, d]$. Then the area of the shaded region is given by the following formula:

$$\text{Area} = \int_c^d [f(y) - g(y)]\, dy$$

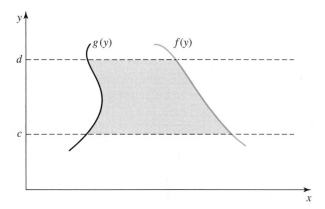

Figure 6.34 The area between $f(y)$ and $g(y)$.

■ 6.3.2 Cumulative Change

Consider a population whose size at time t, $t \geq 0$, is $N(t)$ and whose dynamics are given by the initial-value problem

$$\frac{dN}{dt} = f(t) \quad \text{with } N(0) = N_0$$

for some $f(t)$ that is continuous for $t \geq 0$. To solve this initial-value problem, we must find an antiderivative of $f(t)$ and determine the constant so that $N(0) = N_0$. Using (6.13) (i.e., the FTC, part I), we find that

$$N(t) = \int_0^t f(u)\, du + C$$

is the general antiderivative of $N(t)$. We choose 0 as the lower limit of integration for convenience, because it gives a simple expression for the constant when we take the initial condition into account. That is, with

$$N(0) = \int_0^0 f(u)\, du + C = C$$

it follows that $C = N(0) = N_0$. Therefore,

$$N(t) = N_0 + \int_0^t f(u)\, du$$

or

$$N(t) - N_0 = \int_0^t f(u)\, du \tag{6.14}$$

Since $f(u) = dN/du$ and $N(0) = N_0$, we can write

$$N(t) - N(0) = \int_0^t \frac{dN}{du}\, du$$

which allows us to interpret the definite integral $\int_0^t \frac{dN}{du} \, du$ as the **net**, or **cumulative**, **change** in population size between times 0 and t, since it is a "sum" of instantaneous changes accumulated over time. That is,

$$\left[\begin{array}{c} \text{cumulative} \\ \text{change in } [0, t] \end{array} \right] = \int_0^t \left[\begin{array}{c} \text{instantaneous rate of} \\ \text{change at time } u \end{array} \right] du$$

We now present another example in which we can interpret an integral as the cumulative change in a quantity. Recall that velocity is the instantaneous rate of change of distance. That is, if a particle moves along a straight line, and we denote by $s(t)$ the location of the particle at time t, with $s(0) = s_0$, and by $v(t)$ the velocity at time t, then $s(t)$ and $v(t)$ are related via

$$\frac{ds}{dt} = v(t) \quad \text{for } t > 0 \text{ with } s(0) = s_0$$

To solve this initial-value problem, we must find an antiderivative of $v(t)$ that satisfies $s(0) = s_0$. That is, we must have

$$s(t) = \int_0^t v(u) \, du + C$$

with

$$s_0 = s(0) = \int_0^0 v(u) \, du + C = 0 + C$$

which implies that $C = s_0$. Hence,

$$s(t) = s_0 + \int_0^t v(u) \, du$$

or, with $s(0) = s_0$,

$$s(t) - s(0) = \int_0^t v(u) \, du$$

Again, the cumulative change in distance, $s(t) - s(0)$, can be represented as a "sum" of instantaneous changes.

■ 6.3.3 Average Values

The concentration of soil nitrogen in g/m^3 was measured every meter along a transect in moist tundra and yielded the following data:

Distance from Origin (m)	Concentration (g/m³)
1	589.3
2	602.7
3	618.5
4	667.2
5	641.2
6	658.3
7	672.8
8	661.2
9	652.3
10	669.8

If we denote the concentration at distance x from the origin by $c(x)$, then the average concentration, denoted by $\bar{c}$ (read "c bar"), is the arithmetic average

$$\bar{c} = \frac{1}{10} \sum_{k=1}^{10} c(k) = 643.3 \, g/m^3$$

More generally, to find the average concentration between two points a and b along a transect, we measure the concentration at equal distances. To formulate this notation mathematically, we divide $[a, b]$ into n subintervals of equal lengths $\Delta x = \frac{b-a}{n}$ and measure the concentration at, say, the right endpoint of each subinterval. If the concentration at location x_k is denoted by $c(x_k)$, then the average concentration $\bar{c}$ is

$$\bar{c} = \frac{1}{n} \sum_{k=1}^{n} c(x_k)$$

Since $\Delta x = \frac{b-a}{n}$, we can write $n = \frac{b-a}{\Delta x}$. Hence,

$$\bar{c} = \frac{1}{b-a} \sum_{k=1}^{n} c(x_k) \, \Delta x$$

If we let the number of subintervals grow ($n \to \infty$), then the length of each subinterval goes to 0 ($\Delta x \to 0$) and

$$\bar{c} = \frac{1}{b-a} \lim_{n \to \infty} \sum_{k=1}^{n} c(x_k) \, \Delta x = \frac{1}{b-a} \int_{a}^{b} c(x) \, dx$$

That is, the average concentration can be expressed as an integral over $c(x)$ between a and b, divided by the length of the interval $[a, b]$:

Assume that $f(x)$ is a continuous function on $[a, b]$. The average value of f on the interval $[a, b]$ is

$$f_{\text{avg}} = \frac{1}{b-a} \int_{a}^{b} f(x) \, dx$$

EXAMPLE 4   Find the average value of $f(x) = 4 - x^2$ on the interval $[-2, 2]$.

Solution   We use the formula for computing average values. Note that $f(x) = 4 - x^2$ is continuous on $[-2, 2]$. Then the average value of f on the interval $[-2, 2]$ is

$$f_{\text{avg}} = \frac{1}{2 - (-2)} \int_{-2}^{2} (4 - x^2) \, dx = \frac{1}{4} \left[4x - \frac{1}{3}x^3 \right]_{-2}^{2}$$

$$= \frac{1}{4} \left[8 - \frac{8}{3} + 8 - \frac{8}{3} \right] = \frac{1}{4} \cdot \frac{32}{3} = \frac{8}{3} \qquad ■$$

The following theorem says a bit more about the value of f_{avg}.

The Mean-Value Theorem for Definite Integrals   Assume that $f(x)$ is a continuous function on $[a, b]$. Then there exists a number $c \in [a, b]$ such that

$$f(c)(b - a) = \int_{a}^{b} f(x) \, dx$$

That is, when we compute the average value of a function that is continuous on $[a, b]$, we find that there exists a number c such that $f(c) = f_{\text{avg}}$. We can understand this concept graphically when we look at the graph of a function f and at f_{avg}. For simplicity, let's assume that $f(x) \geq 0$. Since (1) $\int_{a}^{b} f(x) \, dx$ is then equal to the area between the graph of $f(x)$ and the x-axis, (2) $f_{\text{avg}}(b - a)$ is equal to the area of the rectangle with height f_{avg} and width $b - a$, and (3) the two areas are equal, the horizontal line $y = f_{avg}$ must intersect the graph of $f(x)$ at some point on the interval $[a, b]$. (See Figure 6.35.) The x-coordinate of this point of intersection is then the value c in the MVT for definite integrals. (Note that there could be more than one such number.) A similar argument can be made when we do not assume that $f(x)$ is positive. In this case, "area" is replaced by "signed area." The proof of this theorem is short, and we supply it for completeness at the end of this subsection.

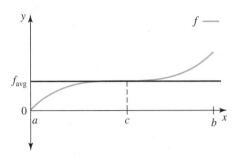

Figure 6.35 An illustration of the average value of a function:
$\int_a^b f(x)\,dx = f_{avg}(b - a)$.

EXAMPLE 5

Find the average value of $f(x) = x^3$ on the interval $[-1, 1]$, and determine $x \in [-1, 1]$ such that $f(x)$ equals the average value.

Solution

The function $f(x) = x^3$ is continuous on $[-1, 1]$. Then

$$f_{avg} = \frac{1}{2} \int_{-1}^{1} x^3\,dx = \frac{1}{2}\left[\frac{1}{4}x^4\right]_{-1}^{1} = \frac{1}{8}(1^4 - (-1)^4) = 0$$

The graph of $y = x^3$ (Figure 6.36) is symmetric about the origin, which explains why the average value is 0. Since $x^3 = 0$ for $x = 0$, the function $f(x)$ takes on its average value at $x = 0$. ■

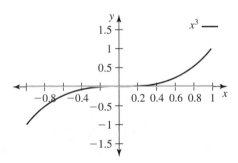

Figure 6.36 The graph of $y = x^3$, $-1 \leq x \leq 1$. The average value is 0.

EXAMPLE 6

The speed of water in a channel varies considerably with depth. Because of friction, the velocity reaches zero at the bottom and along the sides of the channel; the velocity is greatest near the surface of the water. The average velocity of a stream is of interest in characterizing rivers. One way to obtain this average value would be to measure a stream's velocity at various depths along a vertical transect and then average the values obtained. In practice, however, a much simpler method is employed: The speed is measured at 60% of the depth from the surface, because the speed at that depth is very close to the average speed. Explain why it is possible that the measurement at just one depth would yield the average stream velocity.

Solution

Assuming that the velocity profile of the stream along a vertical transect is a continuous function of depth, the MVT for definite integrals guarantees that there exists a depth h at which the velocity is equal to the average stream velocity.

The MVT only gives the existence of such a depth; it does not tell us where the velocity is equal to the average velocity. It is surprising and fortunate that the depth where the velocity reaches its average is quite universal; that is, it does not depend much on the specifics of the river. (The 60%-depth rule is derived in Problems 3–5 of Chapter 6 Review Problems.) ■

Proof of the Mean-Value Theorem for Definite Integrals Since $f(x)$ is continuous on $[a, b]$, we can apply the extreme-value theorem to conclude that f attains an absolute maximum and an absolute minimum in $[a, b]$. If we denote the absolute maximum by M and the absolute minimum by m, then

$$m \leq f(x) \leq M \quad \text{for all } x \in [a, b]$$

and f takes on both m and M for some values in $[a, b]$. We therefore find that

$$m(b - a) \leq \int_a^b f(x)\, dx \leq M(b - a)$$

or

$$m \leq \frac{1}{b - a} \int_a^b f(x)\, dx \leq M$$

We set $I = \frac{1}{b-a} \int_a^b f(x)\, dx$; then $m \leq I \leq M$.

Using the facts that $f(x)$ takes on all values between m and M in the interval $[a, b]$ (this follows from the intermediate-value theorem) and that I is a number between m and M, it follows (also from the intermediate-value theorem) that there must be a number $c \in [a, b]$ such that $f(c) = I$; that is,

$$f(c) = \frac{1}{b - a} \int_a^b f(x)\, dx$$

■

Figure 6.37 A right cylinder with an irregularly shaped base.

■ 6.3.4 The Volume of a Solid (Optional)

From geometry, we know various formulas for computing the volumes of certain regular solids, such as a right circular cylinder. To compute the volume of a less regularly shaped solid, we will use an approach that is similar to that for computing areas of irregularly shaped regions; there, we approximated the areas of such regions by rectangles whose areas were easy to compute with simple formulas from geometry.

We begin with the volume of a generalized cylinder; the volume is the base area times the height. The base can be any arbitrarily shaped region. (See Figure 6.37, for example.)

If we denote the base area by A and the height of the cylinder by h, then the volume of the generalized cylinder is

$$V = Ah$$

As an example, consider the circular cylinder whose base is a disk. If the disk has radius r and the cylinder has height h, then the volume of the circular cylinder is $\pi r^2 h$. We will use cylinders to approximate volumes of more complicated solids.

Suppose that we wish to compute the volume of the solid shown in Figure 6.38. We can slice the solid into small slabs by cutting it perpendicular to the x-axis at points $x_0 = a < x_1 < x_2 < \cdots < x_n = b$ that partition the interval $[a, b]$ and then slice the solid into planes. The intersection of such a plane and the solid is called a *cross section*. We denote the area of the cross section at x_k by $A(x_k)$. By cutting the solid along these planes, we obtain slices, just as we do when we cut bread. We will approximate the volume of a slice between x_{k-1} and x_k by the volume of a cylinder with base area equal to that of the slice at x_k and height $\Delta x_k = x_k - x_{k-1}$. The volume of the slice between x_{k-1} and x_k is then approximately

$$A(x_k)\, \Delta x_k$$

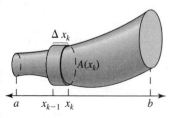

Figure 6.38 The volume of an irregularly shaped solid, found by the disk method.

Adding the volumes of all the slices gives us an approximation for the total volume of the solid:

$$V \approx \sum_{k=1}^{n} A(x_k) \, \Delta x_k$$

By making the partition of $[a, b]$ finer, we can improve the approximation.

Recall that we used $\|P\|$ (the norm of P) as a measure of how fine the partition is; that is, $\|P\| = \max_{k=1,2,\ldots,n} \Delta x_k$. This approach suggests that we should define the volume of the solid as the limit of our approximation as $\|P\| \to 0$. We summarize this concept in the following definition:

Definition The **volume of a solid** of integrable cross-sectional area $A(x)$ between a and b is

$$\int_a^b A(x) \, dx$$

EXAMPLE 7

Find the volume of the sphere of radius r centered at the origin.

Solution

The cross section at x is perpendicular to the x-axis. (See Figure 6.39.) It is a disk of radius $y = \sqrt{r^2 - x^2}$ and whose area is

$$A(x) = \pi y^2 = \pi (r^2 - x^2)$$

Since the solid is between $-r$ and r, it follows that

$$\text{Volume} = \int_{-r}^{r} \pi (r^2 - x^2) \, dx$$

The integrand is continuous on $[-r, r]$. Evaluating the integral yields

$$= \pi \left[r^2 x - \frac{1}{3} x^3 \right]_{-r}^{r}$$

$$= \pi \left[(r^3 - \frac{1}{3} r^3) - (-r^3 + \frac{1}{3} r^3) \right] = \pi \left(\frac{2}{3} r^3 + \frac{2}{3} r^3 \right) = \frac{4}{3} \pi r^3$$

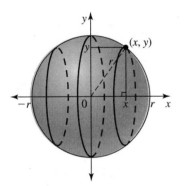

Figure 6.39 The volume of a sphere.

This result agrees with the formula for a sphere that we know from geometry. ■

The cross sections of the sphere in the last example were of a particularly simple form, namely, disks. However, we can think of a sphere as a **solid of revolution**—that is, a solid obtained by revolving a curve about the x-axis (or the y-axis). In this case, we rotate the curve $y = \sqrt{r^2 - x^2}$, $-r \leq x \leq r$, about the x-axis, which creates circular cross sections.

We can use other curves $y = f(x)$, rotate them about the x-axis, and obtain solids in the same way. We illustrate in Figure 6.40, in which we rotate the graph of $y = f(x)$, $a \leq x \leq b$, about the x-axis. A cross section through x perpendicular to the x-axis is then a disk with radius $f(x)$; hence, its cross-sectional area is $A(x) = \pi [f(x)]^2$. If we use the formula $\int_a^b A(x) \, dx$ to compute the volume of the solid, we find that the volume of the solid of revolution is

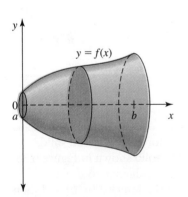

Figure 6.40 The solid of rotation when rotating $f(x)$ about the x-axis.

$$V = \int_a^b \pi [f(x)]^2 \, dx \qquad (6.15)$$

Computing volumes by using (6.15) is called the **disk method**.

EXAMPLE 8

Compute the volume of the solid obtained by rotating $y = x^2, 0 \leq x \leq 2$, about the x-axis.

Solution

We illustrate the solid in Figure 6.41. When we rotate the graph of $y = x^2$ about the x-axis, we find that the cross section at x is a disk with radius $y = f(x) = x^2$. The cross-sectional area at x, $A(x)$, is then $\pi(x^2)^2 = \pi x^4$, which is integrable on $[0, 2]$. Thus, the volume is

$$V = \int_0^2 \pi[f(x)]^2 \, dx = \int_0^2 \pi x^4 \, dx$$

$$= \frac{\pi}{5} x^5 \Big]_0^2 = \frac{32}{5}\pi$$

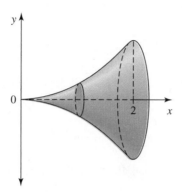

Figure 6.41 The solid of rotation for Example 8.

EXAMPLE 9

Rotate the area bounded by the curves $y = \sqrt{x}$ and $y = x/2$ about the x-axis, and compute the volume of the solid of rotation.

Solution

The curves $y = \sqrt{x}$ and $y = x/2$ are graphed in Figure 6.42, together with a vertical bar to indicate the cross section. We see from the graph that the curves intersect at $x = 0$ and $x = 4$. To find the points of intersection algebraically, we need to equate $\sqrt{x}$ and $x/2$ and solve for x:

$$\sqrt{x} = \frac{x}{2}$$

This equation immediately yields the solution $x = 0$. If $x > 0$, we can divide by $\sqrt{x}$ and find

$$1 = \frac{\sqrt{x}}{2}, \quad \text{or} \quad 2 = \sqrt{x}$$

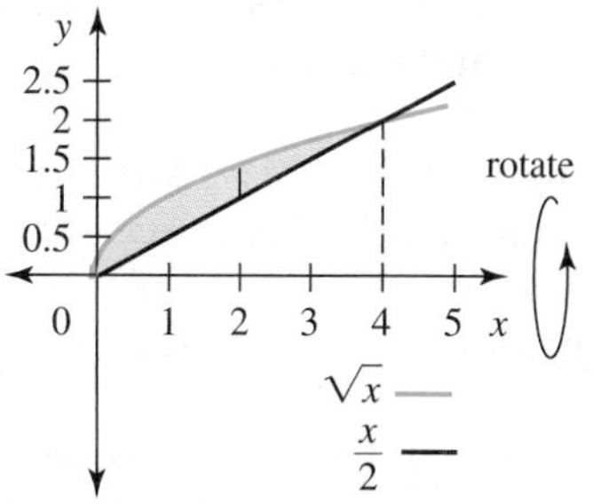

Figure 6.42 The plane region for Example 9.

Squaring yields $x = 4$. Thus, the curves intersect at $x = 0$ and $x = 4$. We can compute the volume of this solid of rotation by first rotating $y = \sqrt{x}, 0 \leq x \leq 4$, about the x-axis and computing the volume of this solid, and then subtracting the volume of the solid obtained by rotating $y = x/2, 0 \leq x \leq 4$. When we do so, we get

$$V = \int_0^4 \pi(\sqrt{x})^2 \, dx - \int_0^4 \pi \left(\frac{1}{2}x\right)^2 dx$$

Both integrands are continuous on $[0, 4]$ and we find that

$$V = \pi \frac{1}{2}x^2 \Big]_0^4 - \pi \frac{1}{12}x^3 \Big]_0^4$$

$$= 8\pi - \frac{16}{3}\pi = \frac{8}{3}\pi$$

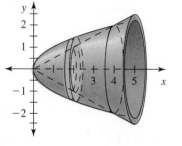

Figure 6.43 The solid of rotation for Example 9.

Looking at Figure 6.43, we see that the cross-sectional area is that of a washer. In this case, the disk method is also referred to as the washer method.

In the next example, we rotate a curve about the y-axis.

EXAMPLE 10 Rotate the region bounded by $y = 2$, $x = 0$, $y = 0$, and $y = \ln x$ about the y-axis, and compute the volume of the resulting solid.

Solution When we rotate about the y-axis, the cross sections are perpendicular to the y-axis. At $y = \ln x$, the radius of the cross-sectional disk is x. (See Figure 6.44.) The solid is shown in Figure 6.45. Since we "sum" the slices along the y-axis, we must integrate with respect to y; because $y = \ln x$, we get $x = e^y$. Therefore, the cross-sectional area at y is $A(y) = \pi(e^y)^2$, which is integrable on $[0, 2]$, and the volume is

$$V = \int_0^2 \pi(e^y)^2 \, dy = \int_0^2 \pi e^{2y} \, dy = \pi \frac{1}{2} e^{2y} \Big]_0^2 = \frac{\pi}{2}(e^4 - 1)$$

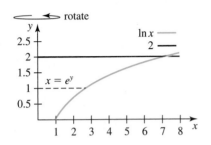

Figure 6.44 The plane region for Example 10.

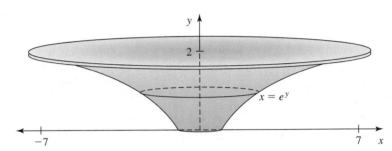

Figure 6.45 The solid of rotation for Example 10.

■ 6.3.5 Rectification of Curves (Optional)

In this subsection, we will study how to compute the lengths of curves in the plane. This is yet another example in which integrals appear as we add up a large number of small increments. The first curve whose length was determined was the semicubical parabola $y^2 = x^3$; this was done by William Neile (1637–1670) in 1657. Interestingly enough, only about 20 years earlier Descartes asserted that there was no rigorous way to determine the exact length of a curve. It turns out that the exact formula is, in essence, an infinitesimal version of the Pythagorean theorem.

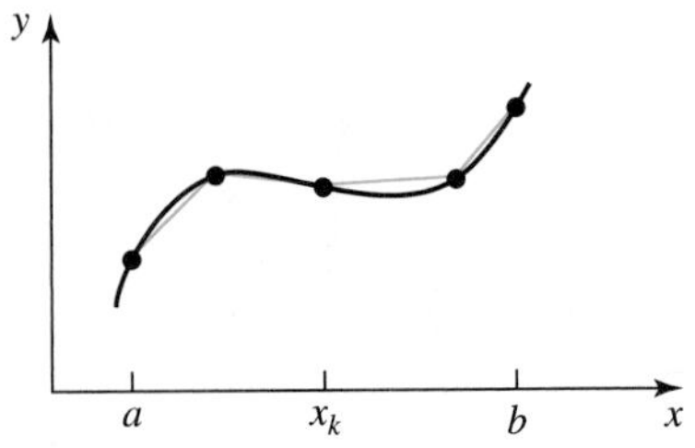

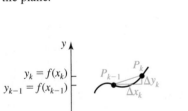

Figure 6.46 The length of a curve in the plane.

How would we *rectify* a curve (i.e., determine its length) with a ruler? We could approximate the curve by short line segments, measure the length of each segment, and add up the measurements, as illustrated in Figure 6.46. By choosing smaller line segments, our approximation would improve. This is precisely the method that we will employ to find an exact formula.

To find the exact formula, assume that the curve whose length we want to find is given by a function $y = f(x)$, $a \le x \le b$, which has a continuous first derivative on (a, b). We partition the interval $[a, b]$ into subintervals by using the partition $P = [x_0, x_1, x_2, \dots, x_n]$, where $a = x_0 < x_1 < x_2 < \cdots < x_n = b$, and approximate the curve by a polygon that consists of the straight-line segments connecting neighboring points on the curve, as shown in Figure 6.46. A typical line segment connecting the points P_{k-1} and P_k is shown in Figure 6.47. Using the Pythagorean theorem, we can find its length. We set $\Delta x_k = x_k - x_{k-1}$ and $\Delta y_k = y_k - y_{k-1}$. Then the length of the line segment is given by

$$\sqrt{(\Delta x_k)^2 + (\Delta y_k)^2}$$

Figure 6.47 A typical line segment.

Using the partition P, we then find that the length of the polygon is

$$L_P = \sum_{k=1}^{n} \sqrt{(\Delta x_k)^2 + (\Delta y_k)^2} \tag{6.16}$$

With finer and finer partitions, the length of the polygon will become a better and better approximation of the length of the corresponding curve. However, before we can take this limit, we need to work on the sum.

The difference Δy_k is equal to $f(x_k) - f(x_{k-1})$. The MVT guarantees that there is a number $c_k \in [x_{k-1}, x_k]$ such that

$$f'(c_k) = \frac{f(x_k) - f(x_{k-1})}{x_k - x_{k-1}}$$

Since $\Delta x_k = x_k - x_{k-1}$, it follows that

$$\Delta y_k = f'(c_k)(x_k - x_{k-1}) = f'(c_k)\,\Delta x_k \tag{6.17}$$

Replacing Δy_k in (6.16) by (6.17), we find that the length of the polygon is given by

$$L_P = \sum_{k=1}^{n} \sqrt{(\Delta x_k)^2 + [f'(c_k)\,\Delta x_k]^2}$$

$$= \sum_{k=1}^{n} \sqrt{1 + [f'(c_k)]^2}\,\Delta x_k$$

This form allows us to take the limit as $\|P\| \to 0$ and obtain

$$L = \lim_{\|P\|\to 0} \sum_{k=1}^{n} \sqrt{1 + [f'(c_k)]^2}\,\Delta x_k$$

$$= \int_a^b \sqrt{1 + [f'(x)]^2}\,dx$$

Thus,

If $f(x)$ is differentiable on (a, b) and $f'(x)$ is continuous on $[a, b]$, then the length of the curve $y = f(x)$ from a to b is given by

$$L = \int_a^b \sqrt{1 + [f'(x)]^2}\,dx$$

As mentioned, the first curve that was rectified was $y = f(x) = x^{3/2}$. We will choose this function for our first example of rectification.

EXAMPLE 11   Determine the length of the curve given by the graph of $y = f(x) = x^{3/2}$ between $a = 5/9$ and $b = 21/9$.

Solution   To determine the length of the curve, we need to find $f'(x)$ first. We have

$$f'(x) = \frac{3}{2}x^{1/2}$$

Then

$$L = \int_{5/9}^{21/9} \sqrt{1 + \left[\frac{3}{2}x^{1/2}\right]^2}\,dx = \int_{5/9}^{21/9} \sqrt{1 + \frac{9}{4}x}\,dx$$

An antiderivative of $\sqrt{1 + \frac{9}{4}x}$ is $\frac{4}{9} \cdot \frac{2}{3}\left(1 + \frac{9}{4}x\right)^{3/2}$, as can be checked by differentiating the latter with respect to x. Thus, the length is

$$L = \left[\frac{4}{9} \cdot \frac{2}{3}\left(1 + \frac{9}{4}x\right)^{3/2}\right]_{5/9}^{21/9} = \frac{8}{27}\left[\left(1 + \frac{9}{4} \cdot \frac{21}{9}\right)^{3/2} - \left(1 + \frac{9}{4} \cdot \frac{5}{9}\right)^{3/2}\right]$$

$$= \frac{8}{27}\left[\left(\frac{5}{2}\right)^3 - \left(\frac{3}{2}\right)^3\right] = \frac{8}{27}\left(\frac{125}{8} - \frac{27}{8}\right) = \frac{98}{27}$$

The length of the curve is therefore 98/27.   ■

Before we present another example, we discuss the formula in more detail. Using

$$\frac{dy}{dx} = f'(x)$$

we can write

$$L = \int_a^b \sqrt{1 + \left(\frac{dy}{dx}\right)^2}\, dx$$

for the length. Treating dy and dx as if they were numbers, we can rewrite this equation as

$$L = \int_a^b \sqrt{(dx)^2 + (dy)^2}$$

We call the expression $\sqrt{(dx)^2 + (dy)^2}$ the **arc length differential** and denote it by ds. We can think of ds as a typical infinitesimal line segment. The Pythagorean theorem in this infinitesimal form then becomes $(ds)^2 = (dx)^2 + (dy)^2$. "Adding up" these line segments (i.e., computing $\int_a^b ds$) then yields the length of the curve.

EXAMPLE 12 Determine the length of

$$f(x) = \frac{1}{4}x^2 - \frac{1}{2}\ln x \quad \text{from } x = 1 \text{ to } x = e$$

Solution Differentiating $f(x)$, we find that

$$f'(x) = \frac{x}{2} - \frac{1}{2x}$$

The length of the curve is then given by

$$L = \int_1^e \sqrt{1 + \left(\frac{x}{2} - \frac{1}{2x}\right)^2}\, dx = \int_1^e \sqrt{1 + \left(\frac{x^2}{4} - \frac{1}{2} + \frac{1}{4x^2}\right)}\, dx$$

$$= \int_1^e \sqrt{\frac{x^2}{4} + \frac{1}{2} + \frac{1}{4x^2}}\, dx$$

We notice that the expression under the square root is a perfect square, namely,

$$\frac{x^2}{4} + \frac{1}{2} + \frac{1}{4x^2} = \left(\frac{x}{2} + \frac{1}{2x}\right)^2$$

Hence, the integral for the length simplifies to

$$L = \int_1^e \sqrt{\left(\frac{x}{2} + \frac{1}{2x}\right)^2}\, dx$$

$$= \int_1^e \left(\frac{x}{2} + \frac{1}{2x}\right) dx = \frac{1}{4}x^2 + \frac{1}{2}\ln|x|\Big]_1^e$$

$$= \frac{1}{4}e^2 + \frac{1}{2} - \frac{1}{4} = \frac{1}{4}(e^2 + 1)$$ ■

Because of the somewhat complicated form of the integrand in the computation of the length, we quickly run into problems when we actually try to compute the integral. In practice, the integrand rarely simplifies enough for easy computation, as it does in Example 12, where it turned out to be a perfect square.

Even seemingly simple looking functions, such as $y = 1/x$, quickly turn into complicated integrals when we compute the length of the curve.

EXAMPLE 13   Set up, but do not evaluate, the length of the curve of the hyperbola $f(x) = \frac{1}{x}$ between $a = 1$ and $b = 2$.

Solution   To determine the length of the curve, we need to find $f'(x)$ first.

$$f'(x) = -\frac{1}{x^2}$$

Then the length of the curve is given by the integral

$$L = \int_1^2 \sqrt{1 + \left(-\frac{1}{x^2}\right)^2}\, dx = \int_1^2 \sqrt{1 + \frac{1}{x^4}}\, dx$$ ■

The antiderivative of the integrand in Example 13 is quite complicated, and we will not be able to find it with the techniques available in this text. In Section 7.5, we will learn numerical methods for evaluating integrals, and some of these methods can be used to evaluate the integral in Example 13. There are also computer software packages that can numerically evaluate such integrals. Using either of these approaches on the integral in Example 13, we would find that the length L is approximately 1.13.

Section 6.3 Problems

■ 6.3.1

Find the areas of the regions bounded by the lines and curves in Problems 1–12.

1. $y = x^2 - 4$, $y = x + 2$

2. $y = 2x^2 - 1$, $y = 2 - x^4$

3. $y = e^{x/2}$, $y = -x$, $x = 0$, $x = 2$

4. $y = \cos x$, $y = 1$, $x = 0$, $x = \frac{\pi}{2}$

5. $y = x^2 + 1$, $y = 4x - 2$ (in the first quadrant)

6. $y = x^2$, $y = 2 - x$, $y = 0$ (in the first quadrant)

7. $y = x^2$, $y = \frac{1}{x}$, $y = 4$ (in the first quadrant)

8. $y = \sin x$, $y = \cos x$ from $x = 0$ to $x = \frac{\pi}{4}$

9. $y = \sin x$, $y = 1$ from $x = 0$ to $x = \frac{\pi}{2}$

10. $y = x^2$, $y = (x - 2)^2$, $y = 0$ from $x = 0$ to $x = 2$

11. $y = x^2$, $y = x^3$ from $x = 0$ to $x = 2$

12. $y = e^{-x}$, $y = x + 1$ from $x = -1$ to $x = 1$

In Problems 13–16, find the areas of the regions bounded by the lines and curves by expressing x as a function of y and integrating with respect to y.

13. $y = x^2$, $y = (x - 2)^2$, $y = 0$ from $x = 0$ to $x = 2$

14. $y = x$, $yx = 1$, $y = \frac{1}{2}$ (in the first quadrant)

15. $x = (y - 1)^2 + 3$, $x = 1 - (y - 1)^2$ from $y = 0$ to $y = 2$ (in the first quadrant)

16. $x = (y - 1)^2 - 1$, $x = (y - 1)^2 + 1$ from $y = 0$ to $y = 2$

■ 6.3.2

17. Consider a population whose size at time t is $N(t)$ and whose dynamics are given by the initial-value problem

$$\frac{dN}{dt} = e^{-t}$$

with $N(0) = 100$.

(a) Find $N(t)$ by solving the initial-value problem.

(b) Compute the cumulative change in population size between $t = 0$ and $t = 5$.

(c) Express the cumulative change in population size between time 0 and time t as an integral. Give a geometric interpretation of this quantity.

18. Suppose that a change in biomass $B(t)$ at time t during the interval $[0, 12]$ follows the equation

$$\frac{d}{dt} B(t) = \cos\left(\frac{\pi}{6}t\right)$$

for $0 \le t \le 12$.

(a) Graph $\frac{dB}{dt}$ as a function of t.

(b) Suppose that $B(0) = B_0$. Express the cumulative change in biomass during the interval $[0, t]$ as an integral. Give a geometric interpretation. What is the value of the biomass at the end of the interval $[0, 12]$ compared with the value at time 0? How are these two quantities related to the cumulative change in the biomass during the interval $[0, 12]$?

19. A particle moves along the x-axis with velocity

$$v(t) = -(t - 2)^2 + 1$$

for $0 \le t \le 5$. Assume that the particle is at the origin at time 0.

(a) Graph $v(t)$ as a function of t.

(b) Use the graph of $v(t)$ to determine when the particle moves to the left and when it moves to the right.

(c) Find the location $s(t)$ of the particle at time t for $0 \le t \le 5$. Give a geometric interpretation of $s(t)$ in terms of the graph of $v(t)$.

(d) Graph $s(t)$ and find the leftmost and rightmost positions of the particle.

20. Recall that the acceleration $a(t)$ of a particle moving along a straight line is the instantaneous rate of change of the velocity $v(t)$; that is,

$$a(t) = \frac{d}{dt}v(t)$$

Assume that $a(t) = 32$ ft/s². Express the cumulative change in velocity during the interval $[0, t]$ as a definite integral, and compute the integral.

21. If $\frac{dl}{dt}$ represents the growth rate of an organism at time t (measured in months), explain what

$$\int_2^7 \frac{dl}{dt}\,dt$$

represents.

22. If $\frac{dw}{dx}$ represents the rate of change of the weight of an organism of age x, explain what

$$\int_3^5 \frac{dw}{dx}\,dx$$

means.

23. If $\frac{dB}{dt}$ represents the rate of change of biomass at time t, explain what

$$\int_1^6 \frac{dB}{dt}\,dt$$

means.

24. Let $N(t)$ denote the size of a population at time t, and assume that

$$\frac{dN}{dt} = f(t)$$

Express the cumulative change of the population size in the interval $[0, 3]$ as an integral.

■ 6.3.3

25. Let $f(x) = x^2 - 2$. Compute the average value of $f(x)$ over the interval $[0, 2]$.

26. Let $g(t) = \sin(\pi t)$. Compute the average value of $g(t)$ over the interval $[-1, 1]$.

27. Suppose that the temperature T (measured in degrees Fahrenheit) in a growing chamber varies over a 24-hour period according to

$$T(t) = 68 + \sin\left(\frac{\pi}{12}t\right)$$

for $0 \leq t \leq 24$.
(a) Graph the temperature T as a function of time t.
(b) Find the average temperature and explain your answer graphically.

28. Suppose that the concentration (measured in gm^{-3}) of nitrogen in the soil along a transect in moist tundra yields data points that follow a straight line with equation

$$y = 673.8 - 34.7x$$

for $0 \leq x \leq 10$, where x is the distance to the beginning of the transect. What is the average concentration of nitrogen in the soil along this transect?

29. Let $f(x) = \tan x$. Give a geometric argument to explain why the average value of $f(x)$ over $[-1, 1]$ is equal to 0.

30. Suppose that you drive from St. Paul to Duluth and you average 50 mph. Explain why there must be a time during your trip at which your speed is exactly 50 mph.

31. Let $f(x) = 2x, 0 \leq x \leq 2$. Use a geometric argument to find the average value of f over the interval $[0, 2]$, and find x such that $f(x)$ is equal to this average value.

32. A particle moves along the x-axis with velocity

$$v(t) = -(t - 3)^2 + 5$$

for $0 \leq t \leq 6$.
(a) Graph $v(t)$ as a function of t for $0 \leq t \leq 6$.
(b) Find the average velocity of this particle during the interval $[0, 6]$.
(c) Find a time $t^* \in [0, 6]$ such that the velocity at time t^* is equal to the average velocity during the interval $[0, 6]$. Is it clear that such a point exists? Is there more than one such point in this case? Use your graph in (a) to explain how you would find t^* graphically.

■ 6.3.4

33. Find the volume of a right circular cone with base radius r and height h.

34. Find the volume of a pyramid with square base of side length a and height h.

In Problems 35–40, find the volumes of the solids obtained by rotating the region bounded by the given curves about the x-axis. In each case, sketch the region and a typical disk element.

35. $y = 4 - x^2, y = 0, x = 0$ (in the first quadrant)
36. $y = \sqrt{2x}, y = 0, x = 2$
37. $y = \sqrt{\sin x}, 0 \leq x \leq \pi, y = 0$
38. $y = e^x, y = 0, x = 0, x = \ln 2$
39. $y = \sec x, -\frac{\pi}{3} \leq x \leq \frac{\pi}{3}, y = 0$
40. $y = \sqrt{1 - x^2}, 0 \leq x \leq 1, y = 0$

In Problems 41–46, find the volumes of the solids obtained by rotating the region bounded by the given curves about the x-axis. In each case, sketch the region together with a typical disk element.

41. $y = x^2, y = x, 0 \leq x \leq 1$
42. $y = 2 - x^3, y = 2 + x^3, 0 \leq x \leq 1$
43. $y = e^x, y = e^{-x}, 0 \leq x \leq 2$
44. $y = \sqrt{1 - x^2}, y = 1, x = 1$ (in the first quadrant)
45. $y = \sqrt{\cos x}, y = 1, x = \frac{\pi}{2}$
46. $y = \frac{1}{x}, x = 0, y = 1, y = 2$ (in the first quadrant)

In Problems 47–52, find the volumes of the solids obtained by rotating the region bounded by the given curves about the y-axis. In each case, sketch the region together with a typical disk element.

47. $y = \sqrt{x}, y = 2, x = 0$
48. $y = x^2, y = 4, x = 0$ (in the first quadrant)
49. $y = \ln(x + 1), y = \ln 3, x = 0$
50. $y = \sqrt{x}, y = x, 0 \leq x \leq 1$
51. $y = x^2, y = \sqrt{x}, 0 \leq x \leq 1$
52. $y = \frac{1}{x}, x = 0, y = \frac{1}{2}, y = 1$

■ 6.3.5

53. Find the length of the straight line

$$y = 2x$$

from $x = 0$ to $x = 2$ by each of the following methods:
(a) planar geometry

(b) the integral formula for the lengths of curves, derived in Subsection 6.3.5

54. Find the length of the straight line

$$y = mx$$

from $x = 0$ to $x = a$, where m and a are positive constants, by each of the following methods:

(a) planar geometry

(b) the integral formula for the lengths of curves, derived in Subsection 6.3.5

55. Find the length of the curve

$$y^2 = x^3$$

from $x = 1$ to $x = 4$.

56. Find the length of the curve

$$2y^2 = 3x^3$$

from $x = 0$ to $x = 1$.

57. Find the length of the curve

$$y = \frac{x^3}{6} + \frac{1}{2x}$$

from $x = 1$ to $x = 3$.

58. Find the length of the curve

$$y = \frac{x^4}{4} + \frac{1}{8x^2}$$

from $x = 2$ to $x = 4$.

In Problems 59–62, set up, but do not evaluate, the integrals for the lengths of the following curves:

59. $y = x^2, -1 \le x \le 1$

60. $y = \sin x, 0 \le x \le \dfrac{\pi}{2}$

61. $y = e^{-x}, 0 \le x \le 1$

62. $y = \ln x, 1 \le x \le e$

63. Find the length of the quarter-circle

$$y = \sqrt{1 - x^2}$$

for $0 \le x \le 1$, by each of the following methods:

(a) a formula from geometry

(b) the integral formula from Subsection 6.3.5

64. A cable that hangs between two poles at $x = -M$ and $x = M$ takes the shape of a catenary, with equation

$$y = \frac{1}{2a}(e^{ax} + e^{-ax})$$

where a is a positive constant. Compute the length of the cable when $a = 1$ and $M = \ln 2$.

65. Show that if

$$f(x) = \frac{e^x + e^{-x}}{2}$$

then the length of the curve $f(x)$ between $x = 0$ and $x = a$ for any $a > 0$ is given by $f'(a)$.

Chapter 6 Key Terms

Discuss the following definitions and concepts:

1. Area

2. Summation notation

3. Algebraic rules for sums

4. A partition of an interval and the norm of a partition

5. Riemann sum

6. Definite integral

7. Riemann integrable

8. Geometric interpretation of definite integrals

9. The constant-value and constant-multiple rules for integrals

10. The definite integral over a union of intervals

11. Comparison rules for definite integrals

12. The fundamental theorem of calculus, part I

13. Leibniz's rule

14. Antiderivatives

15. The fundamental theorem of calculus, part II

16. Evaluating definite integrals by using the FTC, part II

17. Computing the area between curves by using definite integrals

18. Cumulative change and definite integrals

19. The mean-value theorem for definite integrals

20. The volume of a solid and definite integrals

21. Rectification of curves

22. Length of a curve

23. Arc length differential

Chapter 6 Review Problems

1. Discharge of a River In studying the flow of water in an open channel, such as a river in its bed, the amount of water passing through a cross section per second—the discharge (Q)—is of interest. The following formula is used to compute the discharge:

$$Q = \int_0^B \bar{v}(b)h(b)\,db \qquad (6.18)$$

In this formula, b is the distance from one bank of the river to the point where the depth $h(b)$ of the river and the average velocity $\bar{v}(b)$ of the vertical velocity profile of the river at b were measured. The total width of the cross section is B. (See Figure 6.48.)

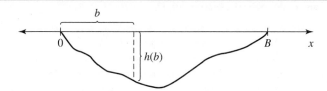

Figure 6.48 The river for Problem 1.

To evaluate the integral in (6.18), we would need to know $\bar{v}(b)$ and $h(b)$ at every location b along the cross section. In practice, the cross section is divided into a finite number of subintervals and measurements of $\bar{v}$ and h are taken at, say, the right endpoints of each subinterval. The following table contains an example of such measurements:

Location	h	$\bar{v}$
0	0	0
1	0.28	0.172
3	0.76	0.213
5	1.34	0.230
7	1.57	0.256
9	1.42	0.241
11	1.21	0.206
13	0.83	0.187
15	0.42	0.116
16	0	0

The location 0 corresponds to the left bank, and the location $B = 16$ to the right bank, of the river. The units of the location and of h are meters, and of $\bar{v}$, meters per second. Approximate the integral in (6.18) by a Riemann sum, using the locations in the table, and find the approximate discharge, using the data from the table.

2. Biomass Growth Suppose that you grow plants in several study plots and wish to measure the response of total biomass to the treatment in each plot. One way to measure this response would be to determine the average specific growth rate of the biomass for each plot over the course of the growing season.

We denote by $B(t)$ the biomass in a given plot at time t. Then the specific growth rate of the biomass at time t is given by

$$\frac{1}{B(t)}\frac{dB}{dt}$$

(a) Explain why

$$\frac{1}{t}\int_0^t \frac{1}{B(s)}\frac{dB(s)}{ds}\,ds$$

is a way to express the average specific growth rate over the interval $[0, t]$.

(b) Use the chain rule to show that

$$\frac{1}{B(t)}\frac{dB}{dt} = \frac{d}{dt}(\ln B(t))$$

(c) Use the results in (a) and (b) to show that the average specific growth rate of $B(s)$ over the interval $[0, t]$ is given by

$$\frac{1}{t}\int_0^t \frac{d}{ds}(\ln(B(s)))\,ds = \frac{1}{t}\ln\frac{B(t)}{B(0)}$$

provided that $B(s) > 0$ for $s \in [0, t]$.

(d) Explain the measurements that you would need to take if you wanted to determine the average specific growth rate of biomass in a given plot over the interval $[0, t]$.

Problems 3–6 discuss stream speed profiles and provide a justification for the two measurement methods described next.

(Adapted from Herschy, 1995) The speed of water in a channel varies considerably with depth. Due to friction, the speed reaches zero at the bottom and along the sides of the channel. The speed is greatest near the surface of the stream. To find the average speed for the vertical speed profile, two methods are frequently employed in practice:

1. The 0.6 depth method: The speed is measured at 0.6 of the depth from the surface, and this value is taken as the average speed.

2. The 0.2 and 0.8 depth method: The speed is measured at 0.2 and 0.8 of the depth from the surface, and the average of the two readings is taken as the average speed.

The theoretical speed distribution of water flowing in an open channel is given approximately by

$$v(d) = \left(\frac{D-d}{a}\right)^{1/c} \tag{6.19}$$

where $v(d)$ is the speed at depth d below the water surface, c is a constant varying from 5 for coarse beds to 7 for smooth beds, D is the total depth of the channel, and a is a constant that is equal to the distance above the bottom of the channel at which the speed has unit value.

3. (a) Sketch the graph of $v(d)$ as a function of d for $D = 3$ m and $a = 1$ m for (i) $c = 5$ and (ii) $c = 7$.

(b) Show that the speed is equal to 0 at the bottom $(d = D)$ and is maximal at the surface $(d = 0)$.

4. (a) Show by integration that the average speed $\bar{v}$ in the vertical profile is given by

$$\bar{v} = \frac{c}{c+1}\left(\frac{D}{a}\right)^{1/c} \tag{6.20}$$

(b) What fraction of the maximum speed is the average speed $\bar{v}$?

(c) If you knew that the maximum speed occurred at the surface of the river [as predicted in the approximate formula for $v(d)$], how could you find $\bar{v}$? (In practice, the maximum speed may occur quite a bit below the surface due to friction between the water on the surface and the atmosphere. Therefore, the speed at the surface would not be an accurate measure of the maximum speed.)

5. Explain why the depth d_1, at which $v = \bar{v}$, is given by the equation

$$\bar{v} = \left(\frac{D-d_1}{a}\right)^{1/c} \tag{6.21}$$

We can find d_1 by equating (6.20) and (6.21). Show that

$$\frac{d_1}{D} = 1 - \left(\frac{c}{c+1}\right)^c$$

and that d_1/D is approximately 0.6 for values of c between 5 and 7, thus resulting in the rule

$$\bar{v} \approx v_{0.6}$$

where $v_{0.6}$ is the speed at depth $0.6D$. (*Hint:* Graph $1-(c/(c+1))^c$ as a function of c for $c \in [5, 7]$, and investigate the range of this function.)

6. We denote by $v_{0.2}$ the speed at depth $0.2D$. We will now find the depth d_2 such that

$$\bar{v} = \tfrac{1}{2}(v_{0.2} + v_{d_2})$$

(a) Show that d_2 satisfies

$$\frac{1}{2}\left[\left(\frac{D-0.2D}{a}\right)^{1/c} + \left(\frac{D-d_2}{a}\right)^{1/c}\right] = \frac{c}{c+1}\left(\frac{D}{a}\right)^{1/c}$$

[*Hint:* Use (6.19) and (6.20).]

(b) Show that

$$\frac{d_2}{D} = 1 - \left[\frac{2c}{c+1} - (0.8)^{1/c}\right]^c$$

and confirm that d_2/D is approximately 0.8 for values of c between 5 and 7, thus resulting in the rule

$$\bar{v} \approx \tfrac{1}{2}(v_{0.2} + v_{0.8})$$

Integration Techniques and Computational Methods

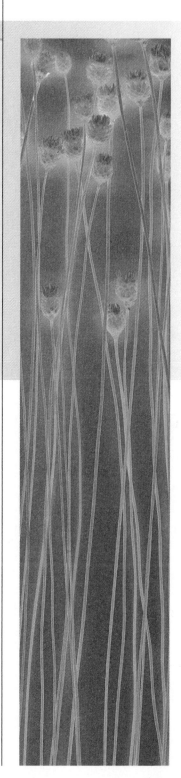

7

The primary focus of this chapter is on integration techniques. Specifically, we will learn how to

- integrate by using the substitution rule and integration by parts;
- integrate rational functions;
- integrate when either the integrand is discontinuous or the limits of integration are infinite;
- integrate numerically; and
- approximate functions by polynomials.

In the first two sections of the chapter, we will learn two important integration techniques that are essentially differentiation rules applied backward. (Because of the connection between differentiation and integration, it should not come as a surprise that some integration techniques are closely related to differentiation rules.) The first technique, called the substitution rule, is the chain rule applied backward; the second, called integration by parts, is the product rule applied backward. The chapter's second section is devoted to these integration techniques. An additional technique called the method of partial fractions is introduced in the third section. The fourth section deals with improper integrals, which are integrals for which the integrand goes to infinity somewhere over the interval of integration or for which the interval of integration is unbounded. Finally, we devote a section to numerical integration, another to the approximation of functions by polynomials, and a last section to the use of tables to evaluate more complicated integrals.

7.1 The Substitution Rule

7.1.1 Indefinite Integrals

The substitution rule is the chain rule in integral form. We therefore begin by recalling the chain rule. Suppose that we wish to differentiate

$$f(x) = \sin(3x^2 + 1)$$

This is clearly a situation in which we need to use the chain rule. We set

$$f(u) = \sin u \qquad \text{and} \qquad u = 3x^2 + 1$$

and find that $f'(u) = \cos u$. To differentiate the inner function $u = 3x^2 + 1$, we use Leibniz notation to get

$$\frac{du}{dx} = 6x$$

or, if we treat du and dx like any other variables,

$$du = 6x \, dx$$

The latter form will be particularly convenient when we reverse the chain rule. But let's first use the chain rule. We obtain

$$\frac{d}{dx} \sin(3x^2 + 1) = \frac{df}{du}\frac{du}{dx} = (\cos u)(6x) = \cos(3x^2 + 1) \cdot 6x$$

Reversing these steps and integrating along the way, we get

$$\int \underbrace{\cos(3x^2 + 1)}_{\cos u} \cdot \underbrace{6x \, dx}_{du} = \int \cos u \, du = \underbrace{\sin u}_{\sin(3x^2+1)} + C = \sin(3x^2 + 1) + C$$

In the first step, we substituted u for $3x^2 + 1$ and used $du = 6x \, dx$. This substitution simplified the integrand. At the end, we substitute back $3x^2 + 1$ for u to get the final answer in terms of x.

To see the general principle behind this technique, we write $u = g(x)$ [and hence $du = g'(x) \, dx$]. Our integral is then of the form

$$\int f[g(x)]g'(x) \, dx$$

If we denote by $F(x)$ an antiderivative of $f(x)$ [i.e., $F'(x) = f(x)$], then, using the chain rule to differentiate $F[g(x)]$, we find that

$$\frac{d}{dx} F[g(x)] = F'[g(x)]g'(x) = f[g(x)]g'(x)$$

which shows that $F[g(x)]$ is an antiderivative of $f[g(x)]g'(x)$. We can therefore write

$$\int f[g(x)]g'(x) \, dx = F[g(x)] + C \tag{7.1}$$

If we set $u = g(x)$, then we can write the right-hand side of (7.1) as $F(u) + C$. But since $F(u)$ is an antiderivative of $f(u)$, it also has the representation

$$\int f(u) \, du = F(u) + C \tag{7.2}$$

which shows that the left-hand side of (7.1) is the same as the left-hand side of (7.2). Equating the left-hand sides of (7.1) and (7.2) results in the substitution rule.

Substitution Rule for Indefinite Integrals If $u = g(x)$, then

$$\int f[g(x)]g'(x) \, dx = \int f(u) \, du$$

We present a number of examples that will illustrate how to use this rule and when the rule can be successfully applied. In the first two examples, we can apply the substitution rule immediately.

EXAMPLE 1   *Using Substitution* Evaluate

$$\int (2x + 1)e^{x^2+x} \, dx$$

Solution   The expression $2x + 1$ is the derivative of $x^2 + x$, which is the inner function of e^{x^2+x}. This suggests the following substitution:

$$u = x^2 + x \quad \text{with } \frac{du}{dx} = 2x + 1 \text{ or } du = (2x + 1) \, dx$$

Hence,

$$\int \underbrace{e^{x^2+x}}_{e^u} \underbrace{(2x + 1) \, dx}_{du} = \int e^u \, du = e^u + C = e^{x^2+x} + C$$

In the last step, we substituted $x^2 + x$ back for u, since we want the final result in terms of x.

■

EXAMPLE 2   **Using Substitution** Evaluate

$$\int \frac{1}{x \ln x}\, dx$$

Solution   We see that $1/x$ is the derivative of $\ln x$. We try

$$u = \ln x \qquad \text{with } \frac{du}{dx} = \frac{1}{x} \text{ or } du = \frac{1}{x}\, dx$$

Then

$$\int \underbrace{\frac{1}{\ln x}}_{\frac{1}{u}} \underbrace{\frac{1}{x}\, dx}_{du} = \int \frac{1}{u}\, du = \ln |u| + C = \ln |\ln x| + C \qquad ■$$

Examples 1 and 2 illustrate types of integrals that are frequently encountered, and we display those integrals as follows for ease of reference:

$$\int g'(x)e^{g(x)}\, dx = e^{g(x)} + C$$

$$\int \frac{g'(x)}{g(x)}\, dx = \ln |g(x)| + C$$

In the previous two examples, the derivative of the inner function appeared exactly in the integrand. This will not always be the case, as shown in the next example, in which the derivative of the inner function appears in the integrand only up to a multiplicative constant.

EXAMPLE 3   **Multiplicative Constant** Evaluate

$$\int 4x\sqrt{x^2 + 1}\, dx$$

Solution   If we set $u = x^2 + 1$, then

$$\frac{du}{dx} = 2x \qquad \text{or} \qquad \frac{du}{2} = x\, dx$$

The integrand contains the derivative of the inner function up to a multiplicative constant. But this is good enough, so we write

$$\int 4x\sqrt{x^2 + 1}\, dx = \int 4 \underbrace{\sqrt{x^2 + 1}}_{\sqrt{u}} \underbrace{x\, dx}_{\frac{du}{2}} = \int 4\sqrt{u}\, \frac{du}{2}$$

$$= \int 2\sqrt{u}\, du = 2 \cdot \frac{2}{3} u^{3/2} + C = \frac{4}{3}(x^2 + 1)^{3/2} + C \qquad ■$$

EXAMPLE 4   **Rewriting the Integrand** Evaluate

$$\int \tan x\, dx$$

Solution   The trick here is to rewrite $\tan x$ as $\frac{\sin x}{\cos x}$ and realize that the derivative of the function in the denominator is the function in the numerator (up to a minus sign). The integral is therefore of the type $\int [g'(x)/g(x)]\, dx$, which we discussed before. We use the substitution

$$u = \cos x \qquad \text{with } \frac{du}{dx} = -\sin x \text{ or } -du = \sin x\, dx$$

Then

$$\int \tan x \, dx = \int \frac{\sin x}{\cos x} \, dx = \int \underbrace{\frac{1}{\cos x}}_{\frac{1}{u}} \underbrace{\sin x \, dx}_{-du}$$

$$= -\int \frac{1}{u} \, du = -\ln|u| + C = -\ln|\cos x| + C$$

In Table 6-1 of Section 6.2, we listed $\int \tan x \, dx = \ln|\sec x| + C$. This is the same result that we have just obtained, since $-\ln|\cos x| = \ln|\cos x|^{-1} = \ln|\sec x|$. ■

In Problem 59, you will evaluate $\int \cot x \, dx$, where the same trick as that in Example 4 is used. That is, both $\int \tan x \, dx$ and $\int \cot x \, dx$ are special cases of $\int [g'(x)/g(x)] \, dx$. We collect both integrals as follows:

$$\int \tan x \, dx = -\ln|\cos x| + C$$

$$\int \cot x \, dx = \ln|\sin x| + C$$

It is not always obvious that substitution will be successful, as in the next example.

EXAMPLE 5

Substitution and Square Roots Evaluate

$$\int x\sqrt{2x - 1} \, dx$$

Solution
Obviously, x is not the derivative of $2x - 1$, so this integral does not seem to fit our scheme. But watch what we do: Set

$$u = 2x - 1 \quad \text{with} \quad \frac{du}{dx} = 2 \text{ or } dx = \frac{du}{2}$$

Since $u = 2x - 1$, we have $x = \frac{1}{2}(u + 1)$. Making all the substitutions, we find that

$$\int x\sqrt{2x - 1} \, dx = \int \frac{1}{2}(u + 1)\sqrt{u} \, \frac{du}{2} = \frac{1}{4} \int (u^{3/2} + u^{1/2}) \, du$$

$$= \frac{1}{4} \left(\frac{2}{5} u^{5/2} + \frac{2}{3} u^{3/2} \right) + C$$

$$= \frac{1}{10} (2x - 1)^{5/2} + \frac{1}{6} (2x - 1)^{3/2} + C \qquad ■$$

Functions in the integrand are not always explicitly given, as in the next example.

EXAMPLE 6

Assume that $g(x)$ is a differentiable function whose derivative $g'(x)$ is continuous. Evaluate

$$\int g'(x) \cos[g(x)] \, dx$$

Solution
If we set

$$u = g(x) \quad \text{with} \quad \frac{du}{dx} = g'(x) \text{ or } du = g'(x) \, dx$$

then

$$\int g'(x) \cos[g(x)] \, dx = \int \cos u \, du = \sin u + C = \sin[g(x)] + C \qquad ■$$

■ 7.1.2 Definite Integrals

Part II of the FTC says that when we evaluate a definite integral, we must find an antiderivative of the integrand and then evaluate the antiderivative at the limits of integration. When we use the substitution $u = g(x)$ to find an antiderivative of an integrand, the antiderivative will be given in terms of u at first. To complete the calculation, we can proceed in either of two ways: (1) We can leave the antiderivative in terms of u and change the limits of integration according to $u = g(x)$, or (2) we can substitute $g(x)$ for u in the antiderivative and then evaluate the antiderivative at the limits of integration in terms of x. We illustrate these two ways by evaluating

$$\int_0^4 2x\sqrt{x^2+1}\,dx$$

Recall that when we compute definite integrals, we need to check whether the integrand is continuous over the interval of integration . This is the case here.

First Way We change the limits of integration along with the substitution. That is, we set

$$u = x^2 + 1 \quad \text{with} \quad \frac{du}{dx} = 2x \text{ or } du = 2x\,dx$$

as before, and note that

$$\text{if } x = 0, \quad \text{then } u = 1$$
$$\text{if } x = 4, \quad \text{then } u = 17$$

Hence,

$$\int_0^4 2x\sqrt{x^2+1}\,dx = \int_1^{17} \sqrt{u}\,du = \frac{2}{3}u^{3/2}\Big]_1^{17} = \frac{2}{3}[(17)^{3/2} - 1]$$

After substitution, the integrand is $\sqrt{u}$, and the limits of integration are $u = 1$ and $u = 17$. The region corresponding to the definite integral after substitution is shown in Figure 7.1.

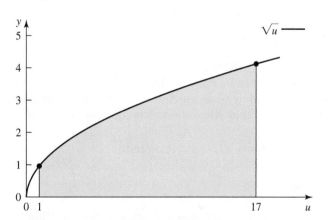

Figure 7.1 The definite integral $\int_0^4 2x\sqrt{x^2+1}\,dx$ becomes $\int_1^{17} \sqrt{u}\,du$ after the substitution $u = x^2 + 1$. The region corresponding to $\int_1^{17} \sqrt{u}\,du$ has an area of $\frac{2}{3}[(17)^{3/2} - 1]$.

This way is the more common one, and we summarize the procedure as follows:

Substitution Rule for Definite Integrals If $u = g(x)$, then

$$\int_a^b f[g(x)]g'(x)\,dx = \int_{g(a)}^{g(b)} f(u)\,du$$

Second Way We can also find the antiderivative of $f(x) = 2x\sqrt{x^2+1}$ first and then use part II of the FTC. To find an antiderivative of $f(x)$, we choose the substitution

$$u = x^2 + 1 \quad \text{with} \quad \frac{du}{dx} = 2x \text{ or } du = 2x\,dx$$

Then

$$\int 2x\sqrt{x^2+1}\,dx = \int \sqrt{u}\,du = \frac{2}{3}u^{3/2} + C = \frac{2}{3}(x^2+1)^{3/2} + C$$

and $F(x) = \frac{2}{3}(x^2+1)^{3/2}$ is an antiderivative of $2x\sqrt{x^2+1}$. Using part II of the FTC, we can now compute the definite integral:

$$\int_0^4 2x\sqrt{x^2+1}\,dx = F(4) - F(0)$$

$$= \frac{2}{3}(17)^{3/2} - \frac{2}{3}(1)^{3/2} = \frac{2}{3}[(17)^{3/2} - 1]$$

The region corresponding to the definite integral before substitution is shown in Figure 7.2.

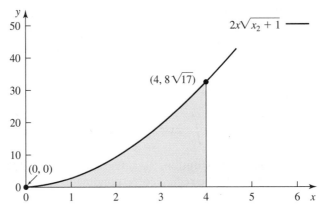

Figure 7.2 The region corresponding to $\int_0^4 2x\sqrt{x^2+1}\,dx$ before substitution has an area of $\frac{2}{3}[(17)^{3/2} - 1]$.

Although we will not use the second way in this section, since the first way turns out to be easier to use when we apply the substitution rule, the second way of first finding an antiderivative will be more convenient in the next section, when we discuss another integration technique (integration by parts).

EXAMPLE 7

Definite Integral Compute

$$\int_1^2 \frac{3x^2 + 1}{x^3 + x}\,dx$$

Solution

The region corresponding to the definite integral is shown in Figure 7.3. The integrand is continuous on $[1, 2]$ and is of the form $\frac{g'(x)}{g(x)}$. We set

$$u = x^3 + x \quad \text{with} \quad \frac{du}{dx} = 3x^2 + 1 \quad \text{or} \quad du = (3x^2 + 1)\,dx$$

and change the limits of integration:

$$\text{if } x = 1, \quad \text{then } u = 2$$
$$\text{if } x = 2, \quad \text{then } u = 10$$

Therefore,

$$\int_1^2 \frac{3x^2 + 1}{x^3 + x}\,dx = \int_2^{10} \frac{1}{u}\,du = \ln|u|\big]_2^{10} = \ln 10 - \ln 2 = \ln\frac{10}{2} = \ln 5 \quad \blacksquare$$

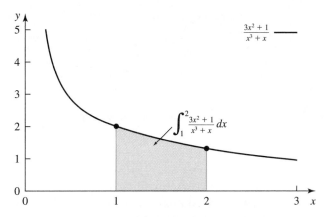

Figure 7.3 The region corresponding to the definite integral in Example 7.

EXAMPLE 8 **Substitution Function Is Decreasing** Compute

$$\int_{1/2}^{1} \frac{1}{x^2} e^{1/x} \, dx$$

Solution The region corresponding to the definite integral is shown in Figure 7.4. The integrand is continuous on $[1/2, 1]$. Since $-1/x^2$ is the derivative of $1/x$, we set

$$u = \frac{1}{x} \quad \text{with} \quad \frac{du}{dx} = -\frac{1}{x^2} \text{ or } -du = \frac{1}{x^2} \, dx$$

and change the limits of integration:

$$\text{if } x = \frac{1}{2}, \quad \text{then } u = 2$$
$$\text{if } x = 1, \quad \text{then } u = 1$$

Therefore,

$$\int_{1/2}^{1} \frac{1}{x^2} e^{1/x} \, dx = -\int_{2}^{1} e^{u} \, du = \int_{1}^{2} e^{u} \, du = e^{u}\big]_{1}^{2} = e^{2} - e$$

Note that because $\frac{1}{x}$ is a decreasing function for $x > 0$, the lower limit is greater than the upper limit of integration after the substitution. When we reversed the order of integration in the second step, we removed the negative sign.

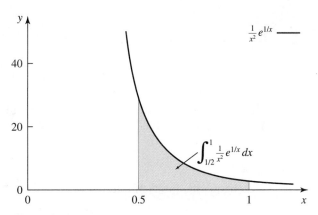

Figure 7.4 The region corresponding to the definite integral in Example 8.

However, you need not reverse the order of integration. Instead, you can compute directly:

$$-\int_2^1 e^u \, du = -e^u]_2^1 = -(e^1 - e^2) = e^2 - e \qquad \blacksquare$$

EXAMPLE 9

Trigonometric Substitution Compute

$$\int_0^{\pi/6} \cos x e^{\sin x} \, dx$$

Solution
The region corresponding to the definite integral is shown in Figure 7.5. The integrand is continuous on the interval $[0, \pi/6]$ and is of the form $g'(x)e^{g(x)}$, which suggests the substitution

$$u = \sin x \quad \text{with} \quad \frac{du}{dx} = \cos x \quad \text{or} \quad du = \cos x \, dx$$

Now we change the limits of integration:

$$\text{if } x = 0, \quad \text{then } u = \sin 0 = 0$$

$$\text{if } x = \frac{\pi}{6}, \quad \text{then } u = \sin \frac{\pi}{6} = \frac{1}{2}$$

Therefore,

$$\int_0^{\pi/6} \cos x e^{\sin x} \, dx = \int_0^{1/2} e^u \, du = e^u]_0^{1/2} = e^{1/2} - 1 \qquad \blacksquare$$

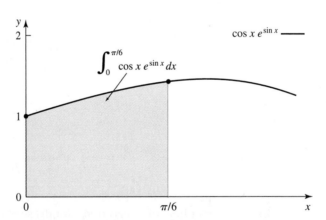

Figure 7.5 The region corresponding to the definite integral in Example 9.

EXAMPLE 10

Rational Function Compute

$$\int_4^9 \frac{2}{x - 3} \, dx$$

Solution
The region corresponding to the definite integral is shown in Figure 7.6. The integrand is continuous on the interval $[4, 9]$. We set

$$u = x - 3 \quad \text{with} \quad \frac{du}{dx} = 1 \text{ or } du = dx$$

and change the limits of integration:

$$\text{if } x = 4, \quad \text{then } u = 1$$

$$\text{if } x = 9, \quad \text{then } u = 6$$

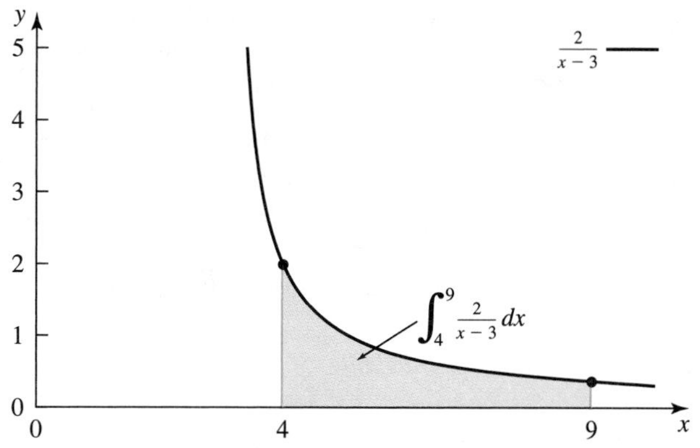

Figure 7.6 The region corresponding to the definite integral in Example 10.

Therefore,

$$\int_4^9 \frac{2}{x-3}\, dx = \int_1^6 \frac{2}{u}\, du = 2\ln|u|\big]_1^6 = 2(\ln 6 - \ln 1) = 2\ln 6 \qquad \blacksquare$$

We can easily spend a great deal of time on integration techniques. The problems can get very involved, and to solve them all, we would need a big bag full of tricks. There are excellent software programs (such as *Mathematica* and MATLAB®) that can integrate symbolically. These programs do not render integration techniques useless; in fact, they use them. Understanding the basic techniques conceptually and being able to apply them in simple situations makes such software packages less of a "black box." Nevertheless, their availability has made it less important to acquire a large number of tricks.

So far, we have learned only one technique: substitution. Unless you can immediately recognize an antiderivative, substitution is the only method you can try at this point.

As we proceed, you will learn other techniques. An additional complication will then be to recognize which technique to use. If you don't see right away what to do, just try something. Don't always expect the first attempt to succeed. With practice, you will see much more quickly whether or not your approach will succeed. If your attempt does not seem to work, try to determine the reason. That way, failed attempts can be quite useful for gaining experience in integration.

Section 7.1 Problems

■ **7.1.1**

In Problems 1–16, evaluate the indefinite integral by making the given substitution.

1. $\int 2x\sqrt{x^2+3}\, dx$, with $u = x^2 + 3$

2. $\int 3x^2\sqrt{x^3+1}\, dx$, with $u = x^3 + 1$

3. $\int 3x(1-x^2)^{1/4}\, dx$, with $u = 1 - x^2$

4. $\int 4x^3(4+x^4)^{1/3}\, dx$, with $u = 4 + x^4$

5. $\int 5\cos(3x)\, dx$, with $u = 3x$

6. $\int 5\sin(1-2x)\, dx$, with $u = 1 - 2x$

7. $\int 7x^2\sin(4x^3)\, dx$, with $u = 4x^3$

8. $\int x\cos(x^2-1)\, dx$, with $u = x^2 - 1$

9. $\int e^{2x+3}\, dx$, with $u = 2x + 3$

10. $\int 3e^{1-x}\, dx$, with $u = 1 - x$

11. $\int xe^{-x^2/2}\, dx$, with $u = -x^2/2$

12. $\int xe^{1-3x^2}\, dx$, with $u = 1 - 3x^2$

13. $\int \dfrac{x+2}{x^2+4x}\,dx$, with $u = x^2 + 4x$

14. $\int \dfrac{2x}{3-x^2}\,dx$, with $u = 3 - x^2$

15. $\int \dfrac{3x}{x+4}\,dx$, with $u = x + 4$

16. $\int \dfrac{x}{5-x}\,dx$, with $u = 5 - x$

In Problems 17–36, use substitution to evaluate the indefinite integrals.

17. $\int \sqrt{x+3}\,dx$

18. $\int (4-x)^{1/7}\,dx$

19. $\int (4x-3)\sqrt{2x^2-3x+2}\,dx$

20. $\int (x^2-2x)(x^3-3x^2+3)^{2/3}\,dx$

21. $\int \dfrac{x-1}{1+4x-2x^2}\,dx$

22. $\int \dfrac{x^2-1}{x^3-3x+1}\,dx$

23. $\int \dfrac{2x}{1+2x^2}\,dx$

24. $\int \dfrac{x^3-1}{x^4-4x}\,dx$

25. $\int 3xe^{x^2}\,dx$

26. $\int \cos x\, e^{\sin x}\,dx$

27. $\int \dfrac{1}{x}\csc^2(\ln x)\,dx$

28. $\int \sec^2 x\, e^{\tan x}\,dx$

29. $\int \sin\left(\dfrac{3\pi}{2}x+\dfrac{\pi}{4}\right)dx$

30. $\int \cos(2x-1)\,dx$

31. $\int \tan x \sec^2 x\,dx$

32. $\int \sin^3 x \cos x\,dx$

33. $\int \dfrac{(\ln x)^2}{x}\,dx$

34. $\int \dfrac{dx}{(x-3)\ln(x-3)}$

35. $\int x^3\sqrt{5+x^2}\,dx$

36. $\int \sqrt{1+\ln x}\,\dfrac{\ln x}{x}\,dx$

In Problems 37–42, a, b, and c are constants and g(x) is a continuous function whose derivative g′(x) is also continuous. Use substitution to evaluate the indefinite integrals.

37. $\int \dfrac{2ax+b}{ax^2+bx+c}\,dx$

38. $\int \dfrac{1}{ax+b}\,dx$

39. $\int g'(x)[g(x)]^n\,dx$

40. $\int g'(x)\sin[g(x)]\,dx$

41. $\int g'(x)e^{-g(x)}\,dx$

42. $\int \dfrac{g'(x)}{[g(x)]^2+1}\,dx$

■ **7.1.2**

In Problems 43–58, use substitution to evaluate the definite integrals.

43. $\int_0^3 x\sqrt{x^2+1}\,dx$

44. $\int_1^2 x^5\sqrt{x^3+2}\,dx$

45. $\int_2^3 \dfrac{2x+3}{(x^2+3x)^3}\,dx$

46. $\int_0^2 \dfrac{2x}{(4x^2+3)^{1/3}}\,dx$

47. $\int_2^5 (x-2)e^{-(x-2)^2/2}\,dx$

48. $\int_{\ln 4}^{\ln 7} \dfrac{e^x}{(e^x-3)^2}\,dx$

49. $\int_0^{\pi/3} \sin x \cos x\,dx$

50. $\int_{-\pi/6}^{\pi/6} \sin^2 x \cos x\,dx$

51. $\int_0^{\pi/4} \tan x \sec^2 x\,dx$

52. $\int_0^{\pi/3} \dfrac{\sin x}{\cos^2 x}\,dx$

53. $\int_5^9 \dfrac{x}{x-3}\,dx$

54. $\int_0^2 \dfrac{x}{x+2}\,dx$

55. $\int_e^{e^2} \dfrac{dx}{x(\ln x)^2}$

56. $\int_1^2 \dfrac{x\,dx}{(x^2+1)\ln(x^2+1)}$

57. $\int_1^9 \dfrac{1}{\sqrt{x}}e^{-\sqrt{x}}\,dx$

58. $\int_0^2 x\sqrt{4-x^2}\,dx$

59. Use the fact that

$$\cot x = \dfrac{\cos x}{\sin x}$$

to evaluate

$$\int \cot x\,dx$$

■ 7.2 Integration by Parts and Practicing Integration

■ 7.2.1 Integration by Parts

As mentioned at the beginning of this chapter, integration by parts is the product rule in integral form. Let $u = u(x)$ and $v = v(x)$ be differentiable functions. Then, differentiating with respect to x yields

$$(uv)' = u'v + uv'$$

or, after rearranging,

$$uv' = (uv)' - u'v$$

Integrating both sides with respect to x, we find that

$$\int uv'\,dx = \int (uv)'\,dx - \int u'v\,dx$$

Since uv is an antiderivative of $(uv)'$, it follows that

$$\int (uv)'\,dx = uv + C$$

Therefore,

$$\int uv' \, dx = uv - \int u'v \, dx$$

(Note that the constant C can be absorbed into the indefinite integral on the right-hand side.) Because $u' = du/dx$ and $v' = dv/dx$, we can write the preceding equation in the short form

$$\int u \, dv = uv - \int v \, du$$

We summarize this result as follows:

Rule for Integration by Parts If $u(x)$ and $v(x)$ are differentiable functions, then

$$\int u(x)v'(x) \, dx = u(x)v(x) - \int u'(x)v(x) \, dx$$

or, in short form,

$$\int u \, dv = uv - \int v \, du$$

You are probably wondering how this technique will help, given that we traded one integral for another one. Here is a first example.

EXAMPLE 1   **Integration by Parts** Evaluate

$$\int x \sin x \, dx$$

Solution   The integrand $x \sin x$ is a product of two functions, one of which will be designated as u, the other as v'. Since integration by parts will result in another integral of the form $\int u'v \, dx$, we must choose u and v' so that $u'v$ is of a simpler form. This suggests the following choices:

$$u = x \quad \text{and} \quad v' = \sin x$$

Because $v = -\cos x$ and $u' = 1$, the integral $\int u'v \, dx$ is of the form $-\int \cos x \, dx$, which is indeed simpler. We obtain

$$\int x \sin x \, dx = (-\cos x)(x) - \int (-\cos x)(1) \, dx$$

$$= -x \cos x + \int \cos x \, dx$$

$$= -x \cos x + \sin x + C$$

If we had chosen $v' = x$ and $u = \sin x$, then we would have had $v = \frac{1}{2}x^2$ and $u' = \cos x$. The integral $\int u'v \, dx$ would have been of the form $\int \frac{1}{2}x^2 \cos x \, dx$, which is even more complicated than $\int x \sin x \, dx$.

If we use the short form $\int u \, dv = uv - \int v \, du$, we would write

$$u = x \quad \text{and} \quad dv = \sin x \, dx$$

Then

$$du = dx \quad \text{and} \quad v = -\cos x$$

and

$$\int \underbrace{x}_{u} \underbrace{\sin x \, dx}_{dv} = \underbrace{x}_{u} \underbrace{(-\cos x)}_{v} - \int \underbrace{(-\cos x)}_{v} \underbrace{dx}_{du}$$

$$= -x \cos x + \sin x + C \qquad \blacksquare$$

EXAMPLE 2   **Integration by Parts** Evaluate

$$\int x \ln x \, dx$$

Solution   Since we do not know an antiderivative of $\ln x$, we try

$$u = \ln x \quad \text{and} \quad v' = x$$

Then

$$u' = \frac{1}{x} \quad \text{and} \quad v = \frac{1}{2}x^2$$

and

$$\int x \ln x \, dx = \frac{1}{2}x^2 \ln x - \int \frac{1}{2}x^2 \cdot \frac{1}{x} \, dx$$

$$= \frac{1}{2}x^2 \ln x - \int \frac{1}{2}x \, dx = \frac{1}{2}x^2 \ln x - \frac{1}{4}x^2 + C \qquad ■$$

Before we present a few more useful "tricks," we show how to evaluate definite integrals with this method.

EXAMPLE 3   **Definite Integral** Compute

$$\int_0^1 xe^{-x} \, dx$$

Solution   The region representing the definite integral is shown in Figure 7.7. The integrand is continuous on $[0, 1]$. We set

$$u = x \quad \text{and} \quad dv = e^{-x} \, dx$$

Then

$$du = dx \quad \text{and} \quad v = -e^{-x}$$

Therefore,

$$\int_0^1 xe^{-x} \, dx = -xe^{-x}\Big]_0^1 - \int_0^1 (-e^{-x}) \, dx$$

$$= -1e^{-1} - (-0e^{-0}) + \int_0^1 e^{-x} \, dx$$

$$= -e^{-1} + \left[-e^{-x}\right]_0^1 = -e^{-1} + (-e^{-1} - (-e^{-0}))$$

$$= -e^{-1} - e^{-1} + 1 = 1 - 2e^{-1} \qquad ■$$

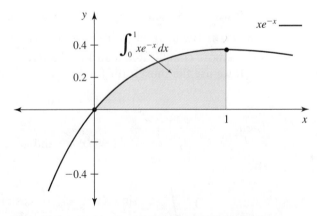

Figure 7.7   The region corresponding to the definite integral in Example 3.

In the next two examples, we demonstrate a "trick" that is sometimes useful in integration by parts. The technique is called "multiplying by 1."

EXAMPLE 4 **Multiplying by 1** Evaluate

$$\int \ln x \, dx$$

Solution   The integrand $\ln x$ is not a product of two functions, but we can write it as $(1)(\ln x)$ and set

$$u = \ln x \quad \text{and} \quad v' = 1$$

Then

$$u' = \frac{1}{x} \quad \text{and} \quad v = x$$

We find that

$$\int \ln x \, dx = \int (1)(\ln x) \, dx = x \ln x - \int x \frac{1}{x} \, dx$$

$$= x \ln x - \int 1 \, dx = x \ln x - x + C$$

Our choices for u and v' might surprise you, as we said that our goal was to make the integral look simpler, which often means that we try to reduce the power of functions of the form x^n. In this case, however, integrating 1 and differentiating $\ln x$ yielded a simpler integral. In fact, if we had chosen $u' = \ln x$ and $v = 1$, we would not have been able to carry out the integration by parts, since we would have needed the antiderivative of $\ln x$ to compute uv and $\int uv' \, dx$.

If you prefer the short-form notation, you don't need to multiply by 1, because

$$u = \ln x \quad \text{and} \quad dv = dx$$

together with

$$du = \frac{1}{x} dx \quad \text{and} \quad v = x$$

immediately produces

$$\int \ln x \, dx = x \ln x - \int x \frac{1}{x} \, dx = x \ln x - \int dx$$

$$= x \ln x - x + C$$ ■

EXAMPLE 5 **Multiplying by 1** Evaluate

$$\int \tan^{-1} x \, dx$$

Solution   We write $\tan^{-1} x = (1)(\tan^{-1} x)$ and

$$u = \tan^{-1} x \quad \text{and} \quad v' = 1$$

Then

$$u' = \frac{1}{x^2 + 1} \quad \text{and} \quad v = x$$

We find that

$$\int \tan^{-1} x \, dx = x \tan^{-1} x - \int \frac{x}{x^2 + 1} \, dx$$

We need to use substitution to evaluate the integral on the right-hand side. With

$$w = x^2 + 1 \quad \text{and} \quad \frac{dw}{dx} = 2x$$

we obtain

$$\int \frac{x}{x^2 + 1}\, dx = \frac{1}{2}\int \frac{dw}{w} = \frac{1}{2}\ln|w| + C_1 = \frac{1}{2}\ln(x^2 + 1) + C_1$$

where C_1 is the constant of integration. Hence,

$$\int \tan^{-1} x\, dx = x \tan^{-1} x - \frac{1}{2}\ln(x^2 + 1) - C_1$$

We write the final answer as

$$\int \tan^{-1} x\, dx = x \tan^{-1} x - \frac{1}{2}\ln(x^2 + 1) + C$$

where C is the constant of integration with $C = -C_1$. Replacing $-C_1$ by C is done for purely aesthetical reasons. ■

EXAMPLE 6 **Using Integration by Parts Repeatedly** Compute

$$\int_0^1 x^2 e^x\, dx$$

Solution When you integrate a definite integral by parts, it is often easier to integrate the indefinite integral first and then to use part II of the FTC to evaluate the definite integral. To evaluate $\int x^2 e^x\, dx$, we set

$$u = x^2 \qquad \text{and} \qquad v' = e^x$$

Then

$$u' = 2x \qquad \text{and} \qquad v = e^x$$

Therefore,

$$\int x^2 e^x\, dx = x^2 e^x - \int 2x e^x\, dx \qquad (7.3)$$

To evaluate the integral $\int x e^x\, dx$, we must use integration by parts a second time. We set

$$u = x \qquad \text{and} \qquad v' = e^x$$

Then

$$u' = 1 \qquad \text{and} \qquad v = e^x$$

Therefore,

$$\int x e^x\, dx = x e^x - \int e^x\, dx = x e^x - e^x + C \qquad (7.4)$$

Combining (7.3) and (7.4), we find that

$$\int x^2 e^x\, dx = x^2 e^x - 2[x e^x - e^x + C]$$

$$= x^2 e^x - 2x e^x + 2e^x - 2C$$

After evaluating the indefinite integral, we can compute the definite integral. Note that the integrand is continuous on $[0, 1]$. We set $F(x) = x^2 e^x - 2x e^x + 2e^x$. Then

$$\int_0^1 x^2 e^x\, dx = F(1) - F(0)$$

$$= (e - 2e + 2e) - (0 - 0 + 2) = e - 2$$

■

EXAMPLE 7   **Using Integration by Parts Repeatedly** Evaluate

$$\int e^x \cos x \, dx$$

Solution   You can check that it does not matter which of the functions you call u and which v'. We set

$$u = \cos x \qquad \text{and} \qquad v' = e^x$$

Then

$$u' = -\sin x \qquad \text{and} \qquad v = e^x$$

Therefore,

$$\int e^x \cos x \, dx = e^x \cos x + \int e^x \sin x \, dx \tag{7.5}$$

We now integrate by parts a second time. This time, the choice matters. We need to set

$$u = \sin x \qquad \text{and} \qquad v' = e^x$$

Then

$$u' = \cos x \qquad \text{and} \qquad v = e^x$$

Therefore,

$$\int e^x \sin x \, dx = e^x \sin x - \int e^x \cos x \, dx \tag{7.6}$$

Combining (7.5) and (7.6) yields

$$\int e^x \cos x \, dx = e^x \cos x + e^x \sin x - \int e^x \cos x \, dx$$

We see that the integral $\int e^x \cos x \, dx$ appears on both sides. Rearranging the equation, we obtain

$$2 \int e^x \cos x \, dx = e^x \cos x + e^x \sin x + C_1$$

or

$$\int e^x \cos x \, dx = \frac{1}{2} e^x (\cos x + \sin x) + C$$

with $C = C_1/2$. [Note that we introduced the constant C_1 (and C) in the final answer.]

We said that the choices for u and v' in the second integration by parts matter. If we had designated $u = e^x$ and $v' = \sin x$, then $u' = e^x$ and $v = -\cos x$, yielding

$$\int e^x \sin x \, dx = -e^x \cos x + \int e^x \cos x \, dx$$

Combining this equation with (7.5), we then obtain

$$\int e^x \cos x \, dx = e^x \cos x - e^x \cos x + \int e^x \cos x \, dx$$

which is a correct, but useless, statement.   ■

We conclude this subsection with a piece of practical advice: In integrals of the form $\int P(x) \sin(ax) \, dx$, $\int P(x) \cos(ax) \, dx$, and $\int P(x) e^{ax} \, dx$, where $P(x)$ is a polynomial and a is a constant, the polynomial $P(x)$ should be considered as u and the expressions $\sin(ax)$, $\cos(ax)$, and e^{ax} as v'. If an integral contains the function $\ln x$, $\tan^{-1} x$, or $\sin^{-1} x$, the function is usually treated as u. After practicing the problems at the end of the section, you can confirm this advice.

■ **7.2.2** Practicing Integration

Thus far in this chapter, we have learned the two main integration techniques: substitution and integration by parts. One of the major difficulties in integration is deciding which rule to use. This subsection is devoted to practicing integration, because such practice aids in making the right decision.

EXAMPLE 8   Find

$$\int \tan x \sec^2 x e^{\tan x} \, dx$$

Solution   Since $\frac{d}{dx} \tan x = \sec^2 x$, we try the substitution $w = \tan x$. Then $dw = \sec^2 x \, dx$ and

$$\int \tan x \sec^2 x e^{\tan x} \, dx = \int w e^w \, dw$$

To continue, we need to use integration by parts, with

$$u = w \quad \text{and} \quad v' = e^w$$

Then

$$u' = 1 \quad \text{and} \quad v = e^w$$

and

$$\int w e^w \, dw = w e^w - \int e^w \, dw = w e^w - e^w + C$$

With $w = \tan x$, we therefore find that

$$\int \tan x \sec^2 x e^{\tan x} \, dx = e^{\tan x} (\tan x - 1) + C \qquad ■$$

Frequently, we must perform algebraic manipulations of the integrand before we can integrate.

EXAMPLE 9   Find

$$\int_0^{\sqrt{3}} \frac{1}{9 + x^2} \, dx$$

Solution   The region corresponding to the definite integral is shown in Figure 7.8. The integrand is continuous on $[0, \sqrt{3}]$. The integrand should remind you of the function $\frac{1}{1+u^2}$, whose antiderivative is $\tan^{-1} u$. However, we have a 9 in the denominator. To get a 1 there, we factor 9 in the denominator to obtain

$$\frac{1}{9 + x^2} = \frac{1}{9(1 + \frac{x^2}{9})} = \frac{1}{9(1 + (\frac{x}{3})^2)}$$

The last expression now suggests that we should try the substitution

$$u = \frac{x}{3} \quad \text{with} \quad dx = 3 \, du$$

Since we wish to evaluate a definite integral, we must change the limits of integration as well. We find that $x = 0$ corresponds to $u = 0$ and $x = \sqrt{3}$ corresponds to $u = \frac{1}{3}\sqrt{3}$. We end up with

$$\int_0^{\sqrt{3}} \frac{1}{9 + x^2} \, dx = \frac{1}{9} \int_0^{\sqrt{3}} \frac{1}{1 + (\frac{x}{3})^2} \, dx = \frac{1}{9} \int_0^{\frac{1}{3}\sqrt{3}} \frac{3}{1 + u^2} \, du$$

$$= \frac{1}{3} \int_0^{\frac{1}{3}\sqrt{3}} \frac{1}{1 + u^2} \, du = \frac{1}{3} \tan^{-1} u \Big]_0^{\frac{1}{3}\sqrt{3}}$$

$$= \frac{1}{3} \left[\tan^{-1} \left(\frac{1}{3}\sqrt{3} \right) - \tan^{-1} 0 \right] = \frac{1}{3} \left(\frac{\pi}{6} - 0 \right) = \frac{\pi}{18} \qquad ■$$

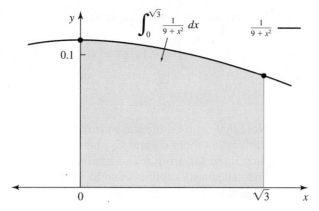

Figure 7.8 The region corresponding to the definite integral in Example 9.

The next example shows that simplifying the integrand first can help greatly.

EXAMPLE 10 Find

$$\int x^{1/2} \ln(x^{1/2} e^x)\, dx$$

Solution Before we try any of our techniques, let's simplify the logarithm first. We find that

$$\ln(x^{1/2} e^x) = \ln x^{1/2} + \ln e^x = \frac{1}{2}\ln x + x$$

The integral now becomes

$$\int x^{1/2} \ln(x^{1/2} e^x)\, dx = \int x^{1/2}\left(\frac{1}{2}\ln x + x\right) dx$$
$$= \frac{1}{2}\int x^{1/2}\ln x\, dx + \int x^{3/2}\, dx$$

We can integrate the first integral by parts, with

$$u = \ln x \qquad \text{and} \qquad v' = x^{1/2}$$

Then

$$u' = \frac{1}{x} \qquad \text{and} \qquad v = \frac{2}{3}x^{3/2}$$

For the first integral, we obtain

$$\int x^{1/2}\ln x\, dx = \frac{2}{3}x^{3/2}\ln x - \int \frac{1}{x}\cdot\frac{2}{3}x^{3/2}\, dx$$
$$= \frac{2}{3}x^{3/2}\ln x - \frac{2}{3}\int x^{1/2}\, dx$$
$$= \frac{2}{3}x^{3/2}\ln x - \frac{2}{3}\cdot\frac{2}{3}x^{3/2} + C$$
$$= \frac{2}{3}x^{3/2}\left(\ln x - \frac{2}{3}\right) + C$$

The other integral is straightforward:

$$\int x^{3/2}\, dx = \frac{2}{5}x^{5/2} + C$$

Combining our results, we find that

$$\int x^{1/2} \ln(x^{1/2}e^x) \, dx = \frac{1}{2} \int x^{1/2} \ln x \, dx + \int x^{3/2} dx$$

$$= \frac{1}{3}x^{3/2} \left(\ln x - \frac{2}{3} \right) + \frac{2}{5}x^{5/2} + C$$

Note that we used the same symbol C to denote the integration constants. We could have called them C_1 and C_2 and then combined them into $C = C_1 + C_2$, but since they stand for arbitrary constants, we need not keep track of how they are related and can simply capture them all by the same symbol. However, we should keep in mind that they are not all the same. ■

Section 7.2 Problems

■ 7.2.1

In Problems 1–30, use integration by parts to evaluate the integrals.

1. $\int x \cos x \, dx$

2. $\int 3x \cos x \, dx$

3. $\int 2x \cos(3x - 1) \, dx$

4. $\int 3x \cos(4 - x) \, dx$

5. $\int 2x \sin(x - 1) \, dx$

6. $\int x \sin(1 - 2x) \, dx$

7. $\int xe^x \, dx$

8. $\int 3xe^{-x/2} \, dx$

9. $\int x^2 e^x \, dx$

10. $\int 2x^2 e^{-x} \, dx$

11. $\int x \ln x \, dx$

12. $\int x^2 \ln x \, dx$

13. $\int x \ln(3x) \, dx$

14. $\int x^2 \ln x^2 \, dx$

15. $\int x \sec^2 x \, dx$

16. $\int x \csc^2 x \, dx$

17. $\int_0^{\pi/3} x \sin x \, dx$

18. $\int_0^{\pi/4} 2x \cos x \, dx$

19. $\int_1^2 \ln x \, dx$

20. $\int_1^e \ln x^2 \, dx$

21. $\int_1^4 \ln \sqrt{x} \, dx$

22. $\int_1^4 \sqrt{x} \ln \sqrt{x} \, dx$

23. $\int_0^1 xe^{-x} \, dx$

24. $\int_0^3 x^2 e^{-x} \, dx$

25. $\int_0^{\pi/3} e^x \sin x \, dx$

26. $\int_0^{\pi/6} e^x \cos x \, dx$

27. $\int e^{-3x} \cos\left(\frac{\pi}{2}x\right) \, dx$

28. $\int e^{-2x} \sin\left(\frac{x}{2}\right) \, dx$

29. $\int \sin(\ln x) \, dx$

30. $\int \cos(\ln x) \, dx$

31. Evaluating the integral

$$\int \cos^2 x \, dx$$

requires two steps.

First, write

$$\cos^2 x = (\cos x)(\cos x)$$

and integrate by parts to show that

$$\int \cos^2 x \, dx = \sin x \cos x + \int \sin^2 x \, dx$$

Then, use $\sin^2 x + \cos^2 x = 1$ to replace $\sin^2 x$ in the integral on the right-hand side, and complete the integration of $\int \cos^2 x \, dx$.

32. Evaluating the integral

$$\int \sin^2 x \, dx$$

requires two steps.
First, write

$$\sin^2 x = (\sin x)(\sin x)$$

and integrate by parts to show that

$$\int \sin^2 x \, dx = -\sin x \cos x + \int \cos^2 x \, dx$$

Then, use $\sin^2 x + \cos^2 x = 1$ to replace $\cos^2 x$ in the integral on the right-hand side, and complete the integration of $\int \sin^2 x \, dx$.

33. Evaluating the integral

$$\int \arcsin x \, dx$$

requires two steps.
(a) Write

$$\arcsin x = 1 \cdot \arcsin x$$

and integrate by parts once to show that

$$\int \arcsin x \, dx = x \arcsin x - \int \frac{x}{\sqrt{1 - x^2}} \, dx$$

(b) Use substitution to compute

$$\int \frac{x}{\sqrt{1 - x^2}} \, dx \qquad (7.7)$$

and combine your result in (a) with (7.7) to complete the computation of $\int \arcsin x \, dx$.

34. Evaluating the integral

$$\int \arccos x \, dx$$

requires two steps.
(a) Write

$$\arccos x = 1 \cdot \arccos x$$

and integrate by parts once to show that

$$\int \arccos x \, dx = x \arccos x + \int \frac{x}{\sqrt{1 - x^2}} \, dx$$

(b) Use substitution to compute

$$\int \frac{x}{\sqrt{1 - x^2}} \, dx \qquad (7.8)$$

and combine your result in (a) with (7.8) to complete the computation of $\int \arccos x \, dx$.

35. (a) Use integration by parts to show that, for $x > 0$,

$$\int \frac{1}{x} \ln x \, dx = (\ln x)^2 - \int \frac{1}{x} \ln x \, dx$$

(b) Use your result in (a) to evaluate

$$\int \frac{1}{x} \ln x \, dx$$

36. (a) Use integration by parts to show that

$$\int x^n e^x \, dx = x^n e^x - n \int x^{n-1} e^x \, dx$$

Such formulas are called **reduction formulas**, since they reduce the exponent of x by 1 each time they are applied.
(b) Apply the reduction formula in (a) repeatedly to compute

$$\int x^3 e^x \, dx$$

37. (a) Use integration by parts to verify the validity of the reduction formula

$$\int x^n e^{ax} \, dx = \frac{1}{a} x^n e^{ax} - \frac{n}{a} \int x^{n-1} e^{ax} \, dx$$

where a is a constant not equal to 0.
(b) Apply the reduction formula in (a) to compute

$$\int x^2 e^{-3x} \, dx$$

38. (a) Use integration by parts to verify the validity of the reduction formula

$$\int (\ln x)^n \, dx = x(\ln x)^n - n \int (\ln x)^{n-1} \, dx$$

(b) Apply the reduction formula in (a) repeatedly to compute

$$\int (\ln x)^3 \, dx$$

In Problems 39–48, first make an appropriate substitution and then use integration by parts to evaluate the indefinite integrals.

39. $\displaystyle\int \cos \sqrt{x} \, dx$ **40.** $\displaystyle\int \sin \sqrt{x} \, dx$

41. $\displaystyle\int x^3 e^{-x^2/2} \, dx$ **42.** $\displaystyle\int x^5 e^{x^2} \, dx$

43. $\displaystyle\int \sin x \cos x e^{\sin x} \, dx$ **44.** $\displaystyle\int \sin x \cos^3 x e^{1-\sin^2 x} \, dx$

45. $\displaystyle\int_0^1 e^{\sqrt{x}} \, dx$ **46.** $\displaystyle\int_1^2 e^{\sqrt{x+1}} \, dx$

47. $\displaystyle\int_1^4 \ln(\sqrt{x} + 1) \, dx$ **48.** $\displaystyle\int_0^1 x^3 \ln(x^2 + 1) \, dx$

■ **7.2.2**

In Problems 49–60, use either substitution or integration by parts to evaluate each integral.

49. $\displaystyle\int x e^{-2x} \, dx$ **50.** $\displaystyle\int x e^{-2x^2} \, dx$

51. $\displaystyle\int \frac{1}{\tan x} \, dx$ **52.** $\displaystyle\int \frac{1}{\csc x \sec x} \, dx$

53. $\displaystyle\int 2x \sin(x^2) \, dx$ **54.** $\displaystyle\int 2x^2 \sin x \, dx$

55. $\displaystyle\int \frac{1}{16 + x^2} \, dx$ **56.** $\displaystyle\int \frac{1}{x^2 + 5} \, dx$

57. $\displaystyle\int \frac{x}{x + 3} \, dx$ **58.** $\displaystyle\int \frac{1}{x^2 + 3} \, dx$

59. $\displaystyle\int \frac{x}{x^2 + 3} \, dx$ **60.** $\displaystyle\int \frac{x + 2}{x^2 + 2} \, dx$

61. The integral

$$\int \ln x \, dx$$

can be evaluated in two ways.
(a) Write $\ln x = 1 \cdot \ln x$ and use integration by parts to evaluate the integral.
(b) Use the substitution $u = \ln x$ and integration by parts to evaluate the integral.

62. Use an appropriate substitution followed by integration by parts to evaluate

$$\int x^3 e^{-x^2/2} \, dx$$

63. Use an appropriate substitution to evaluate

$$\int x(x - 2)^{1/4} \, dx$$

64. Simplify the integrand and then use an appropriate substitution to evaluate

$$\int \frac{\sin^2 x - \cos^2 x}{(\sin x - \cos x)^2} \, dx$$

In Problems 65–70, evaluate each definite integral.

65. $\displaystyle\int_1^4 e^{\sqrt{x}} \, dx$ **66.** $\displaystyle\int_1^2 \ln(x^2 e^x) \, dx$

67. $\displaystyle\int_{-1}^0 \frac{2}{1 + x^2} \, dx$ **68.** $\displaystyle\int_1^2 x^2 \ln x \, dx$

69. $\displaystyle\int_0^{\pi/4} e^x \sin x \, dx$ **70.** $\displaystyle\int_0^{\pi/6} (1 + \tan^2 x) \, dx$

■ 7.3 Rational Functions and Partial Fractions

A rational function f is the quotient of two polynomials. That is,

$$f(x) = \frac{P(x)}{Q(x)} \tag{7.9}$$

where $P(x)$ and $Q(x)$ are polynomials. To integrate rational functions, we use an algebraic technique, called the method of **partial fractions**, to write $f(x)$ as a sum of a polynomial and simpler rational functions. Such a sum is called a **partial-fraction decomposition**. These simpler rational functions, which can be integrated with the methods we have learned, are of the form

$$\frac{A}{(ax+b)^n} \quad \text{or} \quad \frac{Bx+C}{(ax^2+bx+c)^n} \tag{7.10}$$

where A, B, C, a, b, and c are constants and n is a positive integer. In this form, the quadratic polynomial $ax^2 + bx + c$ can no longer be factored into a product of two linear functions with real coefficients. Such polynomials are called **irreducible**. (In other words, $ax^2 + bx + c$ is irreducible if and only if $ax^2 + bx + c = 0$ has no real roots.)

■ 7.3.1 Proper Rational Functions

If the degree of $P(x)$ in (7.9) is greater than or equal to the degree of $Q(x)$, then the first step in the partial-fraction decomposition is to use long division to write $f(x)$ as a sum of a polynomial and a rational function, where the rational function is such that the degree of the polynomial in the numerator is less than the degree of the polynomial in the denominator. (Such rational functions are called **proper**.) We illustrate this step in the next two examples.

EXAMPLE 1 **Long Division before Integration** Find

$$\int \frac{x}{x+2}\, dx$$

Solution The degree of the numerator is equal to the degree of the denominator; using long division or writing the integrand in the form

$$\frac{x}{x+2} = \frac{x+2-2}{x+2} = 1 - \frac{2}{x+2}$$

results in a polynomial of degree 0 and a proper rational function. We can integrate the integrand in this new form:

$$\int \frac{x}{x+2}\, dx = \int \left(1 - \frac{2}{x+2}\right) dx = x - 2\ln|x+2| + C \qquad ■$$

EXAMPLE 2 **Long Division before Integration** Find

$$\int \frac{3x^3 - 7x^2 + 17x - 3}{x^2 - 2x + 5}\, dx$$

Solution Since the degree of the numerator is higher than the degree of the denominator, we use long division to simplify the integrand:

$$
\begin{array}{r}
3x - 1 \\
x^2 - 2x + 5 \overline{)\, 3x^3 - 7x^2 + 17x - 3} \\
\underline{3x^3 - 6x^2 + 15x } \\
-x^2 + 2x - 3 \\
\underline{-x^2 + 2x - 5} \\
2
\end{array}
$$

That is,

$$\frac{3x^3 - 7x^2 + 17x - 3}{x^2 - 2x + 5} = 3x - 1 + \frac{2}{x^2 - 2x + 5}$$

Now, by the quadratic formula, $x^2 - 2x + 5 = 0$ does not have real solutions. This means that it is irreducible, so we will complete the square instead and obtain

$$x^2 - 2x + 5 = (x^2 - 2x + 1) + 4 = (x - 1)^2 + 4$$

The integral we wish to evaluate is therefore

$$\int \left(3x - 1 + \frac{2}{(x - 1)^2 + 4}\right) dx = \int (3x - 1)\, dx + 2 \int \frac{1}{(x - 1)^2 + 4}\, dx \quad (7.11)$$

The first integral on the right-hand side is straightforward since the integrand is a polynomial; we find that

$$\int (3x - 1)\, dx = \frac{3}{2}x^2 - x + C$$

To evaluate the second integral, we use a "trick" similar to the one we used in Example 9 of the previous section—namely, we factor 4 in the denominator:

$$\int \frac{1}{(x - 1)^2 + 4}\, dx = \frac{1}{4} \int \frac{1}{1 + (\frac{x-1}{2})^2}\, dx$$

Setting

$$u = \frac{x - 1}{2} \qquad \text{with} \qquad dx = 2\, du$$

yields

$$\frac{1}{4} \int \frac{1}{1 + (\frac{x-1}{2})^2}\, dx = \frac{1}{4} \int \frac{2\, du}{1 + u^2} = \frac{1}{2} \tan^{-1} u + C = \frac{1}{2} \tan^{-1} \left(\frac{x - 1}{2}\right) + C$$

Putting the pieces together [and remembering that there was a factor 2 in front of the second integral in (7.11)], we find that

$$\int \frac{3x^3 - 7x^2 + 17x - 3}{x^2 - 2x + 5}\, dx = \frac{3}{2}x^2 - x + \tan^{-1} \left(\frac{x - 1}{2}\right) + C \qquad ■$$

Assume now that the rational function is proper. Then, unless the integrand is already of one of the types in (7.10), we need to decompose it further. A result in algebra tells us that every polynomial can be written as the product of linear and irreducible quadratic factors. Factoring the denominator into a product of linear and irreducible quadratic factors is the key to partial-fraction decomposition.

■ 7.3.2 Partial-Fraction Decomposition

Linear Factors   We discuss the cases of distinct and repeated linear factors.

If the linear factor $ax + b$ is contained n times in the factorization of the denominator of a proper rational function, then the partial-fraction decomposition contains terms of the form

$$\frac{A_1}{ax + b} + \frac{A_2}{(ax + b)^2} + \cdots + \frac{A_n}{(ax + b)^n}$$

where $A_1, A_2, \ldots, A_n$ are constants.

We discuss the case of distinct linear factors first.

Case 1a: $Q(x)$ is a product of m distinct linear factors. $Q(x)$ is thus of the form

$$Q(x) = a(x - x_1)(x - x_2) \ldots (x - x_m)$$

where $x_1, x_2, \ldots, x_m$ are the m distinct roots of $Q(x)$. The rational function can then be written as

$$\frac{P(x)}{Q(x)} = \frac{1}{a}\left[\frac{A_1}{x - x_1} + \frac{A_2}{x - x_2} + \cdots + \frac{A_m}{x - x_m}\right]$$

We will see in the next example how the constants $A_1, A_2, \ldots, A_m$ are determined.

EXAMPLE 3   **Distinct Linear Factors**   Find

$$\int \frac{1}{x(x - 1)}\, dx$$

Solution   The integrand is a proper rational function whose denominator is a product of two distinct linear functions. We claim that the integrand can be written in the form

$$\frac{1}{x(x - 1)} = \frac{A}{x} + \frac{B}{x - 1} \tag{7.12}$$

where A and B are constants that we need to determine. To find A and B, we write the right-hand side of (7.12) with a common denominator. That is,

$$\frac{A}{x} + \frac{B}{x - 1} = \frac{A(x - 1) + Bx}{x(x - 1)} = \frac{(A + B)x - A}{x(x - 1)}$$

Since this must be equal to $\frac{1}{x(x-1)}$, we conclude that

$$(A + B)x - A = 1$$

Therefore,

$$A + B = 0 \quad \text{and} \quad -A = 1$$

This yields $A = -1$ and $B = -A = 1$. We thus find that

$$\frac{1}{x(x - 1)} = -\frac{1}{x} + \frac{1}{x - 1}$$

The integrand can now be written as a sum of two rational functions, which can be integrated immediately:

$$\int \frac{1}{x(x - 1)}\, dx = \int \left[\frac{1}{x - 1} - \frac{1}{x}\right] dx = \int \frac{1}{x - 1}\, dx - \int \frac{1}{x}\, dx$$

$$= \ln|x - 1| - \ln|x| + C = \ln\left|\frac{x - 1}{x}\right| + C \qquad ■$$

Case 1b: $Q(x)$ is a product of repeated linear factors. We illustrate how to proceed in the next two examples.

EXAMPLE 4   **Repeated Linear Factors**   Evaluate

$$\int \frac{x}{(x + 1)^2}\, dx$$

Solution   The integrand is a proper rational function whose denominator is a linear factor that is repeated. We therefore write the integrand in the form

$$\frac{x}{(x + 1)^2} = \frac{A}{x + 1} + \frac{B}{(x + 1)^2} \tag{7.13}$$

where A and B are constants. Writing the right-hand side of (7.13) with a common denominator yields

$$\frac{A}{x+1} + \frac{B}{(x+1)^2} = \frac{A(x+1)+B}{(x+1)^2} = \frac{Ax+(A+B)}{(x+1)^2}$$

Equating coefficients on the left-hand side of (7.13), we find that

$$A = 1 \quad \text{and } A + B = 0$$

This implies that $B = -1$. Therefore,

$$\frac{x}{(x+1)^2} = \frac{1}{x+1} - \frac{1}{(x+1)^2}$$

and

$$\int \frac{x}{(x+1)^2}\, dx = \int \left(\frac{1}{x+1} - \frac{1}{(x+1)^2} \right)\, dx$$
$$= \ln |x+1| + \frac{1}{x+1} + C \qquad ■$$

EXAMPLE 5

Repeated Linear Factors Evaluate

$$\int \frac{dx}{x^2(x+1)}$$

Solution

The integrand is a proper rational function whose denominator is a product of three linear functions: x, x (again), and $x+1$. The factor x is repeated, whereas $x+1$ only occurs once. We write the integrand in the form

$$\frac{1}{x^2(x+1)} = \frac{A}{x} + \frac{B}{x^2} + \frac{C}{x+1} \qquad (7.14)$$

where A, B, and C are constants. As in the previous example, we find A, B, and C by writing the right-hand side of (7.14) with a common denominator. This yields

$$\frac{A}{x} + \frac{B}{x^2} + \frac{C}{x+1} = \frac{Ax(x+1)+B(x+1)+Cx^2}{x^2(x+1)}$$
$$= \frac{Ax^2 + Ax + Bx + B + Cx^2}{x^2(x+1)}$$
$$= \frac{(A+C)x^2 + (A+B)x + B}{x^2(x+1)}$$

Comparing the last expression with the left-hand side of (7.14), we conclude that

$$A + C = 0, \quad A + B = 0, \quad \text{and} \quad B = 1$$

This implies that $A = -1$ and $C = 1$. Therefore,

$$\frac{1}{x^2(x+1)} = -\frac{1}{x} + \frac{1}{x^2} + \frac{1}{x+1}$$

and

$$\int \frac{1}{x^2(x+1)}\, dx = \int \left(-\frac{1}{x} + \frac{1}{x^2} + \frac{1}{x+1} \right)\, dx$$
$$= -\ln |x| - \frac{1}{x} + \ln |x+1| + C \qquad ■$$

Irreducible Quadratic Factors Irreducible quadratic factors in the denominator of a proper rational functions are dealt with in the partial-fraction decomposition as follows:

> If the irreducible quadratic factor $ax^2 + bx + c$ is contained n times in the factorization of the denominator of a proper rational function, then the partial-fraction decomposition contains terms of the form
>
> $$\frac{B_1 x + C_1}{ax^2 + bx + c} + \frac{B_2 x + C_2}{(ax^2 + bx + c)^2} + \cdots + \frac{B_n x + C_n}{(ax^2 + bx + c)^n}$$

EXAMPLE 6   **Distinct Irreducible Quadratic Factors** Evaluate

$$\int \frac{2x^3 - x^2 + 2x - 2}{(x^2 + 2)(x^2 + 1)}\, dx$$

Solution   The rational function in the integrand is proper. The denominator is already factored, each factor is an irreducible quadratic polynomial, and the two factors are distinct. We can therefore write the integrand as

$$
\begin{aligned}
\frac{2x^3 - x^2 + 2x - 2}{(x^2 + 2)(x^2 + 1)} &= \frac{Ax + B}{x^2 + 2} + \frac{Cx + D}{x^2 + 1} \\
&= \frac{(Ax + B)(x^2 + 1) + (Cx + D)(x^2 + 2)}{(x^2 + 2)(x^2 + 1)} \\
&= \frac{Ax^3 + Ax + Bx^2 + B + Cx^3 + 2Cx + Dx^2 + 2D}{(x^2 + 2)(x^2 + 1)} \\
&= \frac{(A + C)x^3 + (B + D)x^2 + (A + 2C)x + B + 2D}{(x^2 + 2)(x^2 + 1)}
\end{aligned}
$$

Comparing the last expression with the integrand, we find that

$$A + C = 2, \quad B + D = -1, \quad A + 2C = 2, \quad \text{and} \quad B + 2D = -2$$

which yields $C = 0$ (write $A + 2C = 2$ as $A + C + C = 2$ and use $A + C = 2$) and $D = -1$ (write $B + 2D = -2$ as $B + D + D = -2$ and use $B + D = -1$). Then $A = 2$ and $B = 0$. Therefore,

$$\frac{2x^3 - x^2 + 2x - 2}{(x^2 + 2)(x^2 + 1)} = \frac{2x}{x^2 + 2} - \frac{1}{x^2 + 1}$$

and

$$
\begin{aligned}
\int \frac{2x^3 - x^2 + 2x - 2}{(x^2 + 2)(x^2 + 1)}\, dx &= \int \frac{2x}{x^2 + 2}\, dx - \int \frac{1}{x^2 + 1}\, dx \\
&= \int \frac{du}{u} - \tan^{-1} x + C = \ln|u| - \tan^{-1} x + C \\
&= \ln|x^2 + 2| - \tan^{-1} x + C
\end{aligned}
$$

where we used the substitution $u = x^2 + 2$.   ∎

EXAMPLE 7   **Repeated Irreducible Quadratic Factors** Evaluate

$$\int \frac{x^2 + x + 1}{(x^2 + 1)^2}\, dx$$

Solution   The rational function $\frac{x^2+x+1}{(x^2+1)^2}$ is proper, since the numerator is a polynomial of degree 2 and the denominator is of degree 4 [because $(x^2 + 1)^2 = x^4 + 2x^2 + 1$]. The denominator contains the irreducible quadratic factor x^2+1 twice. We can therefore write the integrand as

$$\frac{x^2 + x + 1}{(x^2 + 1)^2} = \frac{Ax + B}{x^2 + 1} + \frac{Cx + D}{(x^2 + 1)^2} = \frac{(Ax + B)(x^2 + 1) + Cx + D}{(x^2 + 1)^2}$$

$$= \frac{Ax^3 + Ax + Bx^2 + B + Cx + D}{(x^2 + 1)^2}$$

$$= \frac{Ax^3 + Bx^2 + (A + C)x + (B + D)}{(x^2 + 1)^2}$$

Comparing the last expression with the integrand, we conclude that

$$A = 0, \quad B = 1, \quad A + C = 1, \quad \text{and} \quad B + D = 1$$

which implies that $C = 1$ and $D = 0$. Therefore,

$$\frac{x^2 + x + 1}{(x^2 + 1)^2} = \frac{1}{x^2 + 1} + \frac{x}{(x^2 + 1)^2}$$

and

$$\int \frac{x^2 + x + 1}{(x^2 + 1)^2}\, dx = \int \frac{1}{x^2 + 1}\, dx + \int \frac{x}{(x^2 + 1)^2}\, dx$$

The first integral on the right-hand side is $\tan^{-1} x + C$. To evaluate the second integral on the right-hand side, we use substitution: $u = x^2 + 1$ with $du/2 = x\, dx$. This yields

$$\int \frac{x}{(x^2 + 1)^2}\, dx = \frac{1}{2} \int \frac{du}{u^2} = -\frac{1}{2u} + C = -\frac{1}{2(x^2 + 1)} + C$$

Combining the two results, we find that

$$\int \frac{x^2 + x + 1}{(x^2 + 1)^2}\, dx = \tan^{-1} x - \frac{1}{2(x^2 + 1)} + C \qquad \blacksquare$$

EXAMPLE 8   (*Dalzell 1944, 1971*) Show that

$$\int_0^1 \frac{x^4(1 - x)^4}{1 + x^2}\, dx = \frac{22}{7} - \pi$$

In Problem 53, we will show that this equation allows us to find lower and upper bounds on π, namely,

$$3.140 \le \pi \le 3.142$$

Solution   The integrand is an improper rational function. Long division (see Problem 53) yields

$$\frac{x^4(1 - x)^4}{1 + x^2} = x^6 - 4x^5 + 5x^4 - 4x^2 + 4 - \frac{4}{1 + x^2}$$

Therefore,

$$\int_0^1 \frac{x^4(1 - x)^4}{1 + x^2}\, dx = \int_0^1 \left(x^6 - 4x^5 - 4x^2 + 4 - \frac{4}{1 + x^2} \right) dx$$

$$= \left. \frac{x^7}{7} - \frac{2}{3}x^6 + x^5 - \frac{4}{3}x^3 + 4x - 4\tan^{-1} x \right]_0^1$$

$$= \left(\frac{1}{7} - \frac{2}{3} + 1 - \frac{4}{3} + 4 - 4\tan^{-1} 1 \right) - \left(0 - 4\tan^{-1} 0 \right)$$

$$= \left(\frac{22}{7} - \pi \right) - 0 = \frac{22}{7} - \pi \qquad \blacksquare$$

We conclude this section by providing a summary of the two most important cases: when the integrand is a rational function for which the denominator is a polynomial of degree 2 and is either (1) a product of two not necssarily distinct linear factors or (2) an irreducible quadratic polynomial.

The first step is to make sure that the degree of the numerator is less than the degree of the denominator. If not, then we use long division to simplify the integrand.

We will now assume that the degree of the numerator is strictly less than the degree of the denominator (i.e., the integrand is a proper rational function). We write the rational function $f(x)$ as

$$f(x) = \frac{P(x)}{Q(x)}$$

with $Q(x) = ax^2 + bx + c, a \neq 0$, and $P(x) = rx + s$. Either $Q(x)$ can be factored into two linear factors, or it is irreducible (i.e., does not have real roots).

Case 1a: $Q(x)$ is a product of two distinct linear factors. In this case, we write

$$Q(x) = a(x - x_1)(x - x_2)$$

where x_1 and x_2 are the two distinct roots of $Q(x)$. We then use the method of partial fractions to simplify the rational function:

$$\frac{P(x)}{Q(x)} = \frac{rx + s}{ax^2 + bx + c} = \frac{1}{a}\left[\frac{A}{x - x_1} + \frac{B}{x - x_2}\right]$$

The constants A and B must now be determined as in Example 3.

Case 1b: $Q(x)$ is a product of two identical linear factors. In this case, we write

$$Q(x) = a(x - x_1)^2$$

where x_1 is the root of $Q(x)$. We then use the method of partial fractions to simplify the rational function:

$$\frac{P(x)}{Q(x)} = \frac{rx + s}{ax^2 + bx + c} = \frac{1}{a}\left[\frac{A}{x - x_1} + \frac{B}{(x - x_1)^2}\right]$$

The constants A and B must now be determined as in Example 5.

Case 2: $Q(x)$ is an irreducible quadratic polynomial. In this case,

$$Q(x) = ax^2 + bx + c \quad \text{with } b^2 - 4ac < 0$$

and we must complete the square as in Example 2. Doing so then leads to integrals of the form

$$\int \frac{dx}{x^2 + 1} \quad \text{or} \quad \int \frac{x}{x^2 + 1} dx$$

The first integral is $\tan^{-1} x + C$, whereas the second integral can be evaluated by substitution. (See Examples 6 and 7.)

Section 7.3 Problems

■ 7.3.1, 7.3.2

In Problems 1–4, use long division to write $f(x)$ as a sum of a polynomial and a proper rational function.

1. $f(x) = \dfrac{2x^2 + 5x - 1}{x + 2}$

2. $f(x) = -\dfrac{x^2 - 4x - 1}{x - 1}$

3. $f(x) = \dfrac{3x^3 + 5x - 2x^2 - 2}{x^2 + 1}$

4. $f(x) = \dfrac{x^3 - 3x^2 - 15}{x^2 + x + 3}$

In Problems 5–8, write out the partial-fraction decomposition of the function $f(x)$.

5. $f(x) = \dfrac{2x - 3}{x(x + 1)}$

6. $f(x) = -\dfrac{x + 1}{(2x + 1)(x - 1)}$

7. $f(x) = \dfrac{4x^2 - 14x - 6}{x(x - 3)(x + 1)}$

8. $f(x) = \dfrac{16x - 6}{(2x - 5)(3x + 1)}$

In Problems 9–12, write out the partial-fraction decomposition of the function $f(x)$.

9. $f(x) = \dfrac{5x-1}{x^2-1}$ **10.** $f(x) = \dfrac{9x-7}{2x^2-7x+3}$

11. $f(x) = \dfrac{4x+1}{x^2-3x-10}$ **12.** $f(x) = -\dfrac{10}{3x^2+8x-3}$

In Problems 13–18, use partial-fraction decomposition to evaluate the integrals.

13. $\displaystyle\int \frac{1}{x(x-2)}\,dx$ **14.** $\displaystyle\int \frac{1}{x(2x+1)}\,dx$

15. $\displaystyle\int \frac{1}{(x+1)(x-3)}\,dx$ **16.** $\displaystyle\int \frac{1}{(x-1)(x+2)}\,dx$

17. $\displaystyle\int \frac{x^2-2x-2}{x^2(x+2)}\,dx$ **18.** $\displaystyle\int \frac{4x^2-x-1}{(x+1)^2(x-3)}\,dx$

In Problems 19–22, use partial-fraction decomposition to evaluate each integral.

19. $\displaystyle\int \frac{x^3-x^2+x-4}{(x^2+1)(x^2+4)}\,dx$ **20.** $\displaystyle\int \frac{x^3-3x^2+x-6}{(x^2+2)(x^2+1)}\,dx$

21. $\displaystyle\int \frac{2x^2-3x+2}{(x^2+1)^2}\,dx$ **22.** $\displaystyle\int \frac{3x^2+4x+3}{(x^2+1)^2}\,dx$

In Problems 23–26, complete the square in the denominator and evaluate the integral.

23. $\displaystyle\int \frac{1}{x^2-2x+2}\,dx$ **24.** $\displaystyle\int \frac{1}{x^2+4x+5}\,dx$

25. $\displaystyle\int \frac{1}{x^2-4x+13}\,dx$ **26.** $\displaystyle\int \frac{1}{x^2+2x+5}\,dx$

In Problems 27–36, evaluate each integral.

27. $\displaystyle\int \frac{1}{(x-3)(x+2)}\,dx$ **28.** $\displaystyle\int \frac{2x-1}{(x+4)(x+1)}\,dx$

29. $\displaystyle\int \frac{1}{x^2-9}\,dx$ **30.** $\displaystyle\int \frac{1}{x^2+9}\,dx$

31. $\displaystyle\int \frac{1}{x^2-x-2}\,dx$ **32.** $\displaystyle\int \frac{1}{x^2-x+2}\,dx$

33. $\displaystyle\int \frac{x^2+1}{x^2+3x+2}\,dx$ **34.** $\displaystyle\int \frac{x^3+1}{x^2+3}\,dx$

35. $\displaystyle\int \frac{x^2+4}{x^2-4}\,dx$ **36.** $\displaystyle\int \frac{x^4+3}{x^2-4x+3}\,dx$

In Problems 37–44, evaluate each definite integral.

37. $\displaystyle\int_3^5 \frac{x-1}{x}\,dx$ **38.** $\displaystyle\int_3^5 \frac{x}{x-1}\,dx$

39. $\displaystyle\int_0^1 \frac{x}{x^2+1}\,dx$ **40.** $\displaystyle\int_1^2 \frac{x^2+1}{x}\,dx$

41. $\displaystyle\int_2^3 \frac{1}{1-x}\,dx$ **42.** $\displaystyle\int_2^3 \frac{1}{1-x^2}\,dx$

43. $\displaystyle\int_0^1 \tan^{-1}x\,dx$ **44.** $\displaystyle\int_0^1 x\tan^{-1}x\,dx$

In Problems 45–52, evaluate each integral.

45. $\displaystyle\int \frac{1}{(x+1)^2x}\,dx$ **46.** $\displaystyle\int \frac{1}{x^2(x-1)^2}\,dx$

47. $\displaystyle\int \frac{4}{(1-x)(1+x)^2}\,dx$ **48.** $\displaystyle\int \frac{2x^2+2x-1}{x^3(x-3)}\,dx$

49. $\displaystyle\int \frac{1}{(x^2-9)^2}\,dx$ **50.** $\displaystyle\int \frac{1}{(x^2-x-2)^2}\,dx$

51. $\displaystyle\int \frac{1}{x^2(x^2+1)}\,dx$ **52.** $\displaystyle\int \frac{1}{(x+1)^2(x^2+1)}\,dx$

53. (a) To complete Example 8, show that

$$\frac{x^4(1-x)^4}{1+x^2} = x^6 - 4x^5 + 5x^4 - 4x^2 + 4 - \frac{4}{1+x^2}$$

(b) Show that

$$\int_0^1 \frac{x^4(1-x)^4}{2}\,dx \le \int_0^1 \frac{x^4(1-x)^4}{1+x^2}\,dx \le \int_0^1 x^4(1-x)^4\,dx$$

and conclude that

$$\frac{1}{1260} \le \frac{22}{7} - \pi \le \frac{1}{630}$$

Use this result to show that

$$3.140 \le \pi \le 3.142$$

■ 7.4 Improper Integrals

In this section, we discuss definite integrals of two types with the following characteristics:

1. One or both limits of integration are infinite; that is, the integration interval is unbounded; or

2. The integrand becomes infinite at one or more points of the interval of integration.

We call such integrals **improper integrals**.

■ 7.4.1 Type 1: Unbounded Intervals

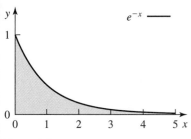

Figure 7.9 The unbounded region between the graph of $y = e^{-x}$ and the x-axis for $x \ge 0$.

Suppose that we wanted to compute the area of the unbounded region below the graph of $f(x) = e^{-x}$ and above the x-axis for $x \ge 0$. (See Figure 7.9.) How would we proceed? We know how to find the area of a region bounded by the graph of a continuous function [here, $f(x) = e^{-x}$] and the x-axis between 0 and z, namely,

$$A(z) = \int_0^z e^{-x}\,dx = -e^{-x}\Big]_0^z = 1 - e^{-z}$$

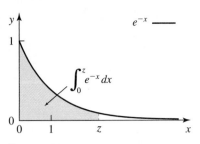

Figure 7.10 The region between 0 and z.

This is the shaded area in Figure 7.10. If we now let z tend to infinity, we may regard the limiting value (if it exists) as the area of the unbounded region below the graph of $f(x) = e^{-x}$ and above the x-axis for $x \geq 0$ (see Figure 7.9):

$$A = \lim_{z \to \infty} A(z) = \lim_{z \to \infty} (1 - e^{-z}) = 1$$

We write

$$\int_0^\infty e^{-x}\, dx = 1$$

Therefore, for functions that are continuous on unbounded intervals (see Figures 7.11 and 7.12), we define

$$\int_a^\infty f(x)\, dx = \lim_{z \to \infty} \int_a^z f(x)\, dx$$

and

$$\int_{-\infty}^a f(x)\, dx = \lim_{z \to -\infty} \int_z^a f(x)\, dx$$

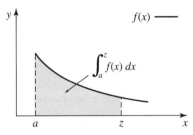

Figure 7.11 The definition of the improper integral $\int_a^\infty f(x)\, dx$ as the limit of $\int_a^z f(x)\, dx$ as $z \to \infty$.

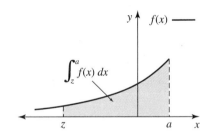

Figure 7.12 The definition of the improper integral $\int_{-\infty}^a f(x)\, dx$ as the limit of $\int_z^a f(x)\, dx$ as $z \to -\infty$.

You might be surprised that the area of an unbounded region can be finite. This need not be the case, and it happens only if the graph of $f(x)$ approaches the x-axis sufficiently fast. We illustrate this property in the next two examples.

EXAMPLE 1   **Finite Area** Compute

$$\int_1^\infty \frac{1}{x^2}\, dx$$

Solution   The function $y = 1/x^2$ is continuous on $[1, \infty)$. We first compute

$$A(z) = \int_1^z \frac{1}{x^2}\, dx = -\frac{1}{x}\Big]_1^z = 1 - \frac{1}{z}$$

(see Figure 7.13) and then let $z \to \infty$. We find that

$$\lim_{z \to \infty} A(z) = \lim_{z \to \infty} \left(1 - \frac{1}{z}\right) = 1$$

Hence,

$$\int_1^\infty \frac{1}{x^2}\, dx = 1$$

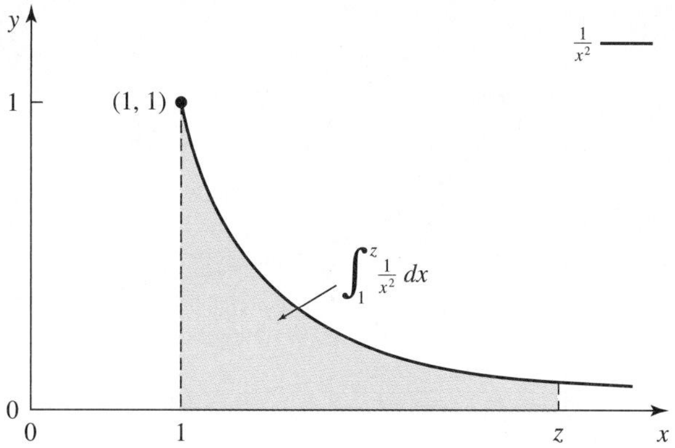

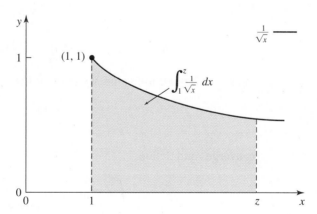

Figure 7.13 The region corresponding to $A(z)$ in Example 1.

EXAMPLE 2

Infinite Area Compute

$$\int_1^\infty \frac{1}{\sqrt{x}} \, dx$$

Solution   The function $f(x) = 1/\sqrt{x}$ is continuous on $[1, \infty)$. We first compute

$$A(z) = \int_1^z \frac{1}{\sqrt{x}} \, dx = 2\sqrt{x} \, \Big]_1^z = 2(\sqrt{z} - 1)$$

(see Figure 7.14) and then let $z \to \infty$. We find that

$$\lim_{z \to \infty} A(z) = \lim_{z \to \infty} 2(\sqrt{z} - 1) = \infty$$

Hence,

$$\int_1^\infty \frac{1}{\sqrt{x}} \, dx$$

does not exist. ■

Figure 7.14 The region corresponding to $A(z)$ in Example 2.

Looking back at Examples 1 and 2, we see that, in both cases, the respective integrands approached the x-axis as $x \to \infty$; that is, both

$$\lim_{x \to \infty} \frac{1}{x^2} = 0 \quad \text{and} \quad \lim_{x \to \infty} \frac{1}{\sqrt{x}} = 0$$

However, $\frac{1}{x^2}$ approaches the x-axis much faster than $\frac{1}{\sqrt{x}}$, as can be seen from the graphs in Figure 7.15. The exponent of x in the denominator determines how fast

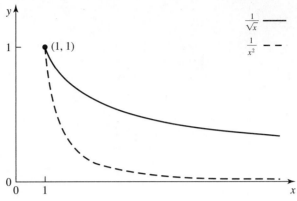

Figure 7.15 The function $y = \frac{1}{x^2}$ approaches the x-axis much faster than the function $y = \frac{1}{\sqrt{x}}$.

the function approaches the x-axis. The area between the graph and the x-axis from $x = 1$ to infinity is finite only if the graph approaches the x-axis fast enough. Indeed, if we tried to compute

$$\int_1^\infty \frac{1}{x^p}\, dx$$

for $0 < p < \infty$, we would find that

$$\int_1^\infty \frac{1}{x^p}\, dx = \begin{cases} \frac{1}{p-1} & \text{for } p > 1 \\ \infty & \text{for } 0 < p \le 1 \end{cases}$$

(Note that $y = 1/x^p$ is continuous on $[1, \infty)$.) For $p > 1$, the function $\frac{1}{x^p}$ approaches the x-axis fast enough as $x \to \infty$ for the area under the graph to be finite. (We investigate this integral further in Problem 33.)

We will use the following terminology to indicate whether an improper integral is finite or infinite:

Let $f(x)$ be continuous on the interval $[a, \infty)$. If

$$\lim_{z \to \infty} \int_a^z f(x)\, dx$$

exists and has a finite value, we say that the improper integral

$$\int_a^\infty f(x)\, dx$$

converges and define

$$\int_a^\infty f(x)\, dx = \lim_{z \to \infty} \int_a^z f(x)\, dx$$

Otherwise, we say that the improper integral **diverges**.

Analogous definitions can be given when the lower limit of integration is infinite.

EXAMPLE 3   **Infinite Lower Limit** Show that the improper integral

$$\int_{-\infty}^0 \frac{1}{(x-1)^2}\, dx$$

converges.

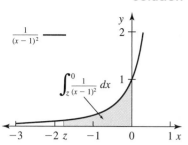

Figure 7.16 The region corresponding to $A(z)$ in Example 3.

Solution

Note that $y = 1/(x-1)^2$ is continuous on $(-\infty, 0]$. To show that the integral converges, we compute its value. We need to find

$$A(z) = \int_z^0 \frac{1}{(x-1)^2}\, dx \quad \text{for } z < 0$$

and then let $z \to -\infty$. (See Figure 7.16.) We find that

$$\int_z^0 (x-1)^{-2}\, dx = -(x-1)^{-1}\Big]_z^0$$

$$= -\frac{1}{x-1}\Big]_z^0 = -\frac{1}{-1} + \frac{1}{z-1} = 1 + \frac{1}{z-1}$$

and

$$\lim_{z \to -\infty}\left(1 + \frac{1}{z-1}\right) = 1$$

Therefore,

$$\int_{-\infty}^0 \frac{1}{(x-1)^2}\, dx = 1 \qquad ■$$

We next discuss the case when both limits of integration are infinite.

> Assume that $f(x)$ is continuous on $(-\infty, \infty)$. Then
>
> $$\int_{-\infty}^{\infty} f(x)\, dx = \int_{-\infty}^{a} f(x)\, dx + \int_{a}^{\infty} f(x)\, dx \qquad (7.15)$$
>
> where a is a real number. If *both* improper integrals on the right-hand side of (7.15) are convergent, then the value of the improper integral on the left-hand side of (7.15) is the sum of the two limiting values on the right-hand side.

Suppose that we wish to compute

$$\int_{-\infty}^{\infty} x^3\, dx$$

We choose a value $a \in (-\infty, \infty)$—for instance, $a = 0$. Then

$$\int_{-\infty}^{\infty} x^3\, dx = \int_{-\infty}^{0} x^3\, dx + \int_{0}^{\infty} x^3\, dx$$

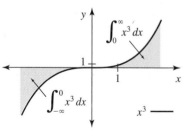

Figure 7.17 The integral $\int_{-\infty}^{\infty} x^3\, dx$ is divergent.

Looking at Figure 7.17, you can see that both improper integrals on the right-hand side are divergent. We check this assertion for the second one: We have

$$\int_{0}^{\infty} x^3\, dx = \lim_{z \to \infty} \int_{0}^{z} x^3\, dx = \frac{1}{4}x^4\Big]_0^z = \frac{1}{4}\lim_{z \to \infty}(z^4 - 0)$$

which does not exist. Hence,

$$\int_{-\infty}^{\infty} x^3\, dx$$

is divergent.

It is important to realize that the definition of $\int_{-\infty}^{\infty} f(x)\, dx$ is different from that of

$$\lim_{b \to \infty} \int_{-b}^{b} f(x)\, dx$$

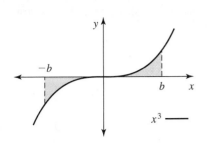

Figure 7.18 Because of symmetry, $\int_{-b}^{b} x^3 \, dx = 0$.

We use $f(x) = x^3$ again to illustrate this difference. For any $b > 0$, we find that

$$\int_{-b}^{b} x^3 \, dx = \frac{1}{4}x^4 \Big]_{-b}^{b} = \frac{1}{4}(b^4 - (-b)^4) = 0$$

(See Figure 7.18.) Therefore,

$$\lim_{b \to \infty} \int_{-b}^{b} x^3 \, dx = 0$$

This limit is not the same as $\int_{-\infty}^{\infty} x^3 \, dx$.

Looking at (7.15), we see that, in order to evaluate $\int_{-\infty}^{\infty} f(x) \, dx$, we need to split up the integral at some $a \in \mathbf{R}$. There are often natural choices for a; we illustrate this in the next example.

EXAMPLE 4　**Infinite Upper and Lower Limit** Compute

$$\int_{-\infty}^{\infty} \frac{1}{1 + x^2} \, dx$$

Solution　The graph of $f(x) = \frac{1}{1+x^2}$ is shown in Figure 7.19. The function $f(x) = 1/(1 + x^2)$ is continuous for all $x \in \mathbf{R}$. It is symmetric about $x = 0$; a good choice for splitting up the integral is therefore $a = 0$. We write

$$\int_{-\infty}^{\infty} \frac{1}{1 + x^2} \, dx = \int_{-\infty}^{0} \frac{1}{1 + x^2} \, dx + \int_{0}^{\infty} \frac{1}{1 + x^2} \, dx$$

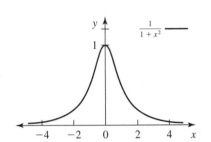

Figure 7.19 The graph of $f(x) = \frac{1}{1+x^2}$ in Example 4.

Now,

$$\lim_{z \to \infty} \int_{0}^{z} \frac{1}{1 + x^2} \, dx = \lim_{z \to \infty} \left[\tan^{-1} x\right]_{0}^{z}$$

$$= \lim_{z \to \infty} (\tan^{-1} z - \tan^{-1} 0) = \frac{\pi}{2}$$

and

$$\lim_{z \to -\infty} \int_{z}^{0} \frac{1}{1 + x^2} \, dx = \lim_{z \to -\infty} \left[\tan^{-1} x\right]_{z}^{0}$$

$$= \lim_{z \to -\infty} (\tan^{-1} 0 - \tan^{-1} z) = \frac{\pi}{2}$$

That $\int_{-\infty}^{0} \frac{1}{1+x^2} \, dx = \frac{\pi}{2}$ is expected because of symmetry. The area of the region to the left of the y-axis is equal to the area of the region to the right of the y-axis. Putting things together, we find that

$$\int_{-\infty}^{\infty} \frac{1}{1 + x^2} \, dx = \frac{\pi}{2} + \frac{\pi}{2} = \pi$$

■

EXAMPLE 5　**Infinite Upper and Lower Limit** Compute

$$\int_{-\infty}^{\infty} \frac{x}{1 + x^2} \, dx$$

Solution　The graph of $f(x) = \frac{x}{1+x^2}$ is shown in Figure 7.20. The function $f(x) = x/(1 + x^2)$ is continuous for all $x \in \mathbf{R}$. Because of the symmetry about the origin, you might be tempted to say that the signed area to the left of 0 is the negative of the area to the

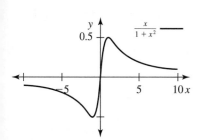

Figure 7.20 The graph of $f(x) = \frac{x}{1+x^2}$ in Example 5.

right of 0 and, therefore, the value of the improper integral should be 0. But this is wrong! We choose $a = 0$, and write

$$\int_{-\infty}^{\infty} \frac{x}{1+x^2} \, dx = \int_{-\infty}^{0} \frac{x}{1+x^2} \, dx + \int_{0}^{\infty} \frac{x}{1+x^2} \, dx$$

We begin by computing

$$\int_{0}^{z} \frac{x}{1+x^2} \, dx$$

Using the substitution $u = 1 + x^2$ and $du = 2x \, dx$, we find that

$$\int_{0}^{z} \frac{x}{1+x^2} \, dx = \int_{1}^{1+z^2} \frac{1}{2u} \, du = \frac{1}{2} \ln |u| \Big]_{1}^{1+z^2}$$

$$= \frac{1}{2}[\ln(1+z^2) - \ln 1] = \frac{1}{2} \ln(1+z^2)$$

Taking the limit as $z \to \infty$, we obtain

$$\int_{0}^{\infty} \frac{x}{1+x^2} \, dx = \lim_{z \to \infty} \frac{1}{2} \ln(1+z^2) = \infty$$

Since one of the integrals is already divergent, we conclude that

$$\int_{-\infty}^{\infty} \frac{x}{1+x^2} \, dx$$

is divergent and therefore cannot be equal to 0. This example has an important take-home message: Before we can use symmetry to compute an improper integral, we need to make sure that the integral exists. ■

■ 7.4.2 Type 2: Unbounded Integrand

So far, when we computed a definite integral, we made sure that the integrand was continuous over the interval of integration . We will now explain what to do when the integrand becomes infinite at one or more points of the interval. Suppose we wish to integrate

$$\int_{0}^{1} \frac{dx}{\sqrt{x}}$$

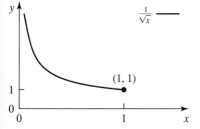

Figure 7.21 The graph of $y = \frac{1}{\sqrt{x}}$.

The graph of $f(x) = \frac{1}{\sqrt{x}}$ is shown in Figure 7.21. We see immediately that $f(x)$ is continuous on $(0, 1]$ and undefined at $x = 0$, and that

$$\lim_{x \to 0^+} \frac{1}{\sqrt{x}} = \infty$$

Let's choose a number $c \in (0, 1)$ and compute

$$\int_{c}^{1} \frac{dx}{\sqrt{x}} = 2\sqrt{x} \Big]_{c}^{1} = 2(1 - \sqrt{c})$$

(See Figure 7.22.) If we now let $c \to 0^+$, we may regard the limiting value (if it exists) as the definite integral $\int_{0}^{1} \frac{1}{\sqrt{x}} \, dx$. That is,

$$\int_{0}^{1} \frac{dx}{\sqrt{x}} = \lim_{c \to 0^+} \int_{c}^{1} \frac{dx}{\sqrt{x}} = \lim_{c \to 0^+} 2(1 - \sqrt{c}) = 2$$

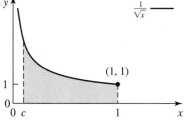

Figure 7.22 The area of the shaded region is $\int_{c}^{1} \frac{1}{\sqrt{x}} \, dx = 2(1 - \sqrt{c})$.

If f is continuous on $(a, b]$ and $\lim_{x \to a^+} f(x) = \pm\infty$ (see Figure 7.23), we define

$$\int_a^b f(x)\,dx = \lim_{c \to a^+} \int_c^b f(x)\,dx$$

provided that this limit exists. If the limit exists, we say that the improper integral on the left-hand side **converges**; if the limit does not exist, we say that the integral **diverges**.

Similarly, if f is continuous on $[a, b)$ and $\lim_{x \to b^-} f(x) = \pm\infty$ (see Figure 7.24), we define

$$\int_a^b f(x)\,dx = \lim_{c \to b^-} \int_a^c f(x)\,dx$$

provided that this limit exists.

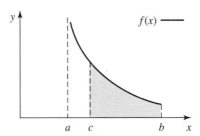

Figure 7.23 The improper integral $\int_a^b f(x)\,dx$ is defined as the limit of $\int_c^b f(x)\,dx$ as $c \to a^+$.

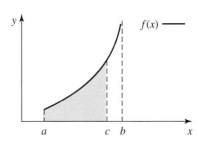

Figure 7.24 The improper integral $\int_a^b f(x)\,dx$ is defined as the limit of $\int_a^c f(x)\,dx$ as $c \to b^-$.

EXAMPLE 6　**Integrand Undefined at Right Endpoint**　Compute

$$\int_0^1 \frac{dx}{(x-1)^{2/3}}$$

Solution　The graph of $f(x) = \frac{1}{(x-1)^{2/3}}$ is shown in Figure 7.25. We see immediately that $f(x)$ is continuous on $[0, 1)$ and undefined at $x = 1$, and that

$$\lim_{x \to 1^-} f(x) = \infty$$

To compute the integral, we choose a number $c \in (0, 1)$ and compute

$$\int_0^c \frac{dx}{(x-1)^{2/3}}$$

(See Figure 7.26.) Letting $c \to 1^-$ will then produce the desired integral. That is,

$$\int_0^1 \frac{dx}{(x-1)^{2/3}} = \lim_{c \to 1^-} \int_0^c \frac{dx}{(x-1)^{2/3}}$$

We first compute the indefinite integral

$$\int \frac{dx}{(x-1)^{2/3}} = 3(x-1)^{1/3} + C$$

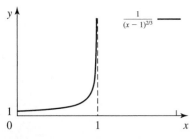

Figure 7.25 The graph of $f(x) = \frac{1}{(x-1)^{2/3}}, 0 \le x < 1$, in Example 6.

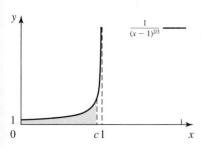

Figure 7.26 The area of the shaded region is $\int_0^c \frac{1}{(x-1)^{2/3}}\,dx$.

If we set $F(x) = 3(x-1)^{1/3}$, then

$$\lim_{c\to1^-}\int_0^c \frac{dx}{(x-1)^{2/3}} = \lim_{c\to1^-}[F(c) - F(0)]$$
$$= \lim_{c\to1^-}\left[3(c-1)^{1/3} - 3(-1)^{1/3}\right] = 3 \qquad (7.16)$$

We therefore find that

$$\int_0^1 \frac{dx}{(x-1)^{2/3}} = 3$$

■

EXAMPLE 7 **Integrand Undefined at Left Endpoint** Compute

$$\int_0^1 \ln x\,dx$$

Solution The graph of $f(x) = \ln x$, $0 < x \le 1$, is shown in Figure 7.27. We immediately see that $f(x)$ is continuous on $(0, 1]$ and not defined at $x = 0$, and that

$$\lim_{x\to0^+} f(x) = -\infty$$

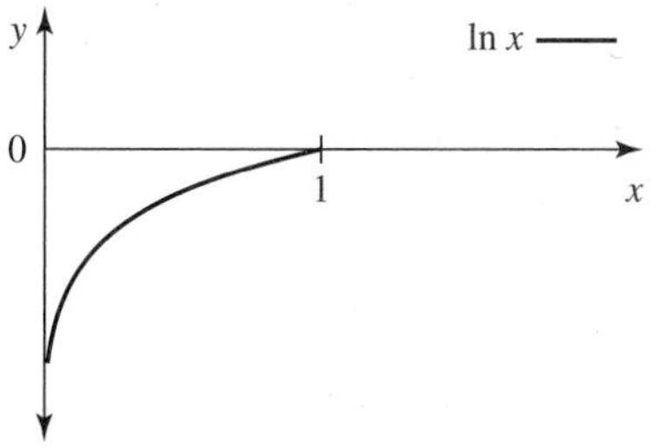

To determine the definite integral, we need to compute

$$\lim_{c\to0^+}\int_c^1 \ln x\,dx$$

Figure 7.27 The graph of $f(x) = \ln x$, $0 < x \le 1$, in Example 7.

Since $F(x) = x \ln x - x$ is an antiderivative of $f(x) = \ln x$, we find that

$$\lim_{c\to0^+}\int_c^1 \ln x\,dx = \lim_{c\to0^+}[F(1) - F(c)]$$
$$= \lim_{c\to0^+}[1\ln 1 - 1 - c\ln c + c]$$

We need to find $\lim_{c\to0^+} c\ln c$. The limit is of the form $0 \cdot \infty$. L'Hospital's rule yields

$$\lim_{c\to0^+} c\ln c = \lim_{c\to0^+}\frac{\ln c}{\frac{1}{c}} = \lim_{c\to0^+}\frac{\frac{1}{c}}{-\frac{1}{c^2}}$$
$$= \lim_{c\to0^+}\left(-\frac{1}{c}\cdot\frac{c^2}{1}\right) = -\lim_{c\to0^+} c = 0$$

Together with $\lim_{c\to0^+} c = 0$, we therefore find that

$$\int_0^1 \ln x\,dx = \lim_{c\to0^+}\int_c^1 \ln x\,dx = -1$$

■

EXAMPLE 8 **Integrand Discontinuous in Interval** Compute

$$\int_{-1}^1 \frac{1}{x^2}\,dx$$

Solution The function $f(x) = \frac{1}{x^2}$ is not defined at $x = 0$. In fact, it has a vertical asymptote at $x = 0$, since

$$\lim_{x\to0^-}\frac{1}{x^2} = \infty \qquad \text{and} \qquad \lim_{x\to0^+}\frac{1}{x^2} = \infty$$

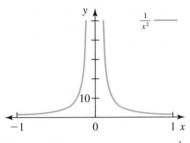

Figure 7.28 The graph of $f(x) = \frac{1}{x^2}$.

The graph of $f(x) = \frac{1}{x^2}, x \neq 0$, is shown in Figure 7.28. We see that $f(x) = 1/x^2$ is continuous, except at $x = 0$. To deal with this discontinuity, we split the integral at $x = 0$. We write

$$\int_{-1}^{1} \frac{1}{x^2}\, dx = \lim_{c \to 0^-} \int_{-1}^{c} \frac{1}{x^2}\, dx + \lim_{c \to 0^+} \int_{c}^{1} \frac{1}{x^2}\, dx$$

(See Figure 7.29.) The function

$$F(x) = -\frac{1}{x}$$

is an antiderivative of $\frac{1}{x^2}$. Therefore,

$$\lim_{c \to 0^-} \int_{-1}^{c} \frac{1}{x^2}\, dx = \lim_{c \to 0^-} [F(c) - F(-1)]$$

$$= \lim_{c \to 0^-} \left[-\frac{1}{c} - 1 \right] = \infty$$

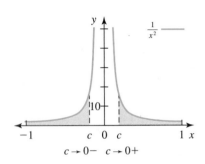

Figure 7.29 The improper integral $\int_{-1}^{1} \frac{1}{x^2}\, dx$.

We can already conclude that the integral is divergent. But to see what the other limit looks like, we will compute it. That is,

$$\lim_{c \to 0^+} \int_{c}^{1} \frac{1}{x^2}\, dx = \lim_{c \to 0^+} [F(1) - F(c)]$$

$$= \lim_{c \to 0^+} \left[-1 + \frac{1}{c} \right] = \infty$$

Therefore,

$$\int_{-1}^{1} \frac{1}{x^2}\, dx$$

is divergent. ■

■ 7.4.3 A Comparison Result for Improper Integrals

In many cases, it is impossible to evaluate an integral exactly. In dealing with improper integrals, we frequently must know whether the integral converges. Instead of computing the value of the improper integral exactly, we can then resort to simpler integrals that either dominate or are dominated by the improper integral of interest. We will explain this idea graphically.

We assume that $f(x) \geq 0$ for $x \geq a$. Suppose we wish to show that $\int_a^\infty f(x)\, dx$ is convergent. Then it is enough to find a function $g(x)$ such that $g(x) \geq f(x)$ for all $x \geq a$ and $\int_a^\infty g(x)\, dx$ is convergent. This is illustrated in Figure 7.30. It is clear from the graph that

$$0 \leq \int_a^\infty f(x)\, dx \leq \int_a^\infty g(x)\, dx$$

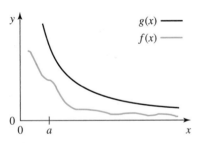

Figure 7.30 The function $g(x)$ lies above the function $f(x)$.

If $\int_a^\infty g(x)\, dx < \infty$, it follows that $\int_a^\infty f(x)\, dx$ is convergent, since $\int_a^\infty f(x)\, dx$ must take on a value between 0 and a finite number, given by $\int_a^\infty g(x)\, dx$.

We again assume that $f(x) \geq 0$ for all $x \geq a$. Suppose we now wish to show that $\int_a^\infty f(x)\, dx$ is divergent. It is then enough to find a function $g(x)$ such that $0 \leq g(x) \leq f(x)$ for all $x \geq a$ and $\int_a^\infty g(x)\, dx$ is divergent. This is illustrated in Figure 7.31. It is clear from the graph that

$$\int_a^\infty f(x)\, dx \geq \int_a^\infty g(x)\, dx \geq 0$$

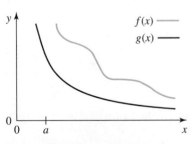

Figure 7.31 The graph of $g(x)$ is below the graph of $f(x)$.

If $\int_a^\infty g(x)\, dx$ is divergent, it follows that $\int_a^\infty f(x)\, dx$ is divergent.

You can see from the preceding discussion that in one case we selected a function that dominated $f(x)$, whereas in the other case we selected a function that was dominated by $f(x)$. This indicates that, before you find a comparison function, you must first guess whether the integral is likely to converge. (With practice, you get better at guessing whether an integral converges or diverges.) Sketching the functions involved can help you convince yourself that you are making the comparison in the right direction. Your comparison function, of course, should be simple enough so that you can integrate it without any problems. We present two examples that illustrate both cases.

EXAMPLE 9   **Convergence** Show that

$$\int_0^\infty e^{-x^2}\, dx$$

is convergent.

Solution   The function $f(x) = e^{-x^2}$ is continuous and positive for $x \in [0, \infty)$. We cannot compute the antiderivative of $f(x) = e^{-x^2}$ with any of the techniques we have learned in this text. In fact, there is no simple way to express the value of $\int_0^z e^{-x^2}\, dx$ for $z > 0$. (It can be expressed as a sum of infinitely many terms.) But we can still determine whether the integral is convergent. To do so, we write $\int_0^\infty e^{-x^2}\, dx$ as a sum of two integrals and then show that each one is finite. We have

$$\int_0^\infty e^{-x^2}\, dx = \int_0^1 e^{-x^2}\, dx + \int_1^\infty e^{-x^2}\, dx$$

Since $0 < e^{-x^2} \leq 1$, it follows that

$$0 < \int_0^1 e^{-x^2}\, dx \leq \int_0^1 dx = 1 < \infty$$

To show that $\int_1^\infty e^{-x^2}\, dx$ is convergent, we use the fact that e^{-x} is a decreasing function and that if $x \geq 1$, then $x \leq x^2$. It then follows that

$$0 \leq e^{-x^2} \leq e^{-x} \quad \text{for } x \geq 1$$

Therefore,

$$0 \leq \int_1^\infty e^{-x^2}\, dx \leq \int_1^\infty e^{-x}\, dx = \lim_{c \to \infty} \left[-e^{-x}\right]_1^c = e^{-1} < \infty$$

Since both integrals are convergent, $\int_0^\infty e^{-x^2}\, dx$ is convergent.

Although for $0 < z < \infty$, $\int_0^z e^{-x^2}\, dx$ can be computed only approximately (e.g., using numerical methods of the sort we will discuss in Section 7.5), we can show with very different tools (which we do not cover in this text) that

$$\int_0^\infty e^{-x^2}\, dx = \frac{\sqrt{\pi}}{2}$$

■

EXAMPLE 10   **Divergence** Show that

$$\int_1^\infty \frac{1}{\sqrt{x + \sqrt{x}}}\, dx$$

is divergent.

Solution The function $f(x) = 1/\sqrt{x + \sqrt{x}}$ is continuous on $[1, \infty)$. The integrand looks rather complicated, but since $x + \sqrt{x} \leq x + x$ for $x \geq 1$, it follows that

$$\frac{1}{\sqrt{x + \sqrt{x}}} \geq \frac{1}{\sqrt{2x}} \quad \text{for } x \geq 1$$

Hence,

$$\int_1^\infty \frac{1}{\sqrt{x + \sqrt{x}}}\, dx \geq \int_1^\infty \frac{1}{\sqrt{2x}}\, dx = \frac{1}{\sqrt{2}} \int_1^\infty \frac{1}{\sqrt{x}}\, dx = \infty$$

as shown in Example 2. Therefore,

$$\int_1^\infty \frac{dx}{\sqrt{x + \sqrt{x}}}$$

is divergent. ■

Section 7.4 Problems

■ 7.4.1, 7.4.2

All the integrals in Problems 1–16 are improper and converge. Explain in each case why the integral is improper, and evaluate each integral.

1. $\int_0^\infty 3e^{-6x}\, dx$

2. $\int_0^\infty xe^{-x}\, dx$

3. $\int_0^\infty \frac{2}{1 + x^2}\, dx$

4. $\int_e^\infty \frac{dx}{x(\ln x)^2}$

5. $\int_1^\infty \frac{1}{x^{3/2}}\, dx$

6. $\int_{-\infty}^{-1} \frac{1}{1 + x^2}\, dx$

7. $\int_{-\infty}^\infty e^{-|x|}\, dx$

8. $\int_{-\infty}^\infty xe^{-x^2/2}\, dx$

9. $\int_{-\infty}^\infty \frac{x}{(1 + x^2)^2}\, dx$

10. $\int_{-\infty}^\infty x^3 e^{-x^4}\, dx$

11. $\int_0^9 \frac{dx}{\sqrt{9 - x}}$

12. $\int_1^e \frac{dx}{x\sqrt{\ln x}}$

13. $\int_0^{\pi/2} \frac{\cos x}{\sqrt{\sin x}}\, dx$

14. $\int_{-2}^0 \frac{dx}{(x + 1)^{1/3}}$

15. $\int_{-1}^1 \ln|x|\, dx$

16. $\int_0^2 \frac{dx}{(x - 1)^{2/5}}$

In Problems 17–28, determine whether each integral is convergent. If the integral is convergent, compute its value.

17. $\int_1^\infty \frac{1}{x^3}\, dx$

18. $\int_1^\infty \frac{1}{x^{1/3}}\, dx$

19. $\int_0^4 \frac{1}{x^4}\, dx$

20. $\int_0^4 \frac{1}{x^{1/4}}\, dx$

21. $\int_0^2 \frac{1}{(x - 1)^{1/3}}\, dx$

22. $\int_0^2 \frac{1}{(x - 1)^4}\, dx$

23. $\int_0^\infty \frac{1}{\sqrt{x + 1}}\, dx$

24. $\int_{-1}^0 \frac{1}{\sqrt{x + 1}}\, dx$

25. $\int_e^\infty \frac{dx}{x \ln x}$

26. $\int_1^e \frac{dx}{x \ln x}$

27. $\int_{-2}^2 \frac{2x\, dx}{(x^2 - 1)^{1/3}}$

28. $\int_{-\infty}^1 \frac{3}{1 + x^2}\, dx$

29. Determine whether

$$\int_{-\infty}^\infty \frac{1}{x^2 - 1}\, dx$$

is convergent. *Hint*: Use the partial-fraction decomposition

$$\frac{1}{x^2 - 1} = \frac{1}{2}\left(\frac{1}{x - 1} - \frac{1}{x + 1}\right)$$

30. Although we cannot compute the antiderivative of $f(x) = e^{-x^2/2}$, it is known that

$$\int_{-\infty}^\infty e^{-x^2/2}\, dx = \sqrt{2\pi}$$

Use this fact to show that

$$\int_{-\infty}^\infty x^2 e^{-x^2/2}\, dx = \sqrt{2\pi}$$

Hint: Write the integrand as

$$x \cdot (xe^{-x^2/2})$$

and use integration by parts.

31. Determine the constant c so that

$$\int_0^\infty ce^{-3x}\, dx = 1$$

32. Determine the constant c so that

$$\int_{-\infty}^\infty \frac{c}{1 + x^2}\, dx = 1$$

33. In this problem, we investigate the integral

$$\int_1^\infty \frac{1}{x^p}\, dx$$

for $0 < p < \infty$.

(a) For $z > 1$, set

$$A(z) = \int_1^z \frac{1}{x^p}\, dx$$

and show that

$$A(z) = \frac{1}{1-p}(z^{-p+1} - 1)$$

for $p \neq 1$ and

$$A(z) = \ln z$$

for $p = 1$.

(b) Use your results in (a) to show that, for $0 < p \leq 1$,

$$\lim_{z \to \infty} A(z) = \infty$$

(c) Use your results in (a) to show that, for $p > 1$,

$$\lim_{z \to \infty} A(z) = \frac{1}{p-1}$$

34. In this problem, we investigate the integral

$$\int_0^1 \frac{1}{x^p}\, dx$$

for $0 < p < \infty$.

(a) Compute

$$\int \frac{1}{x^p}\, dx$$

for $0 < p < \infty$. (*Hint*: Treat the case where $p = 1$ separately.)

(b) Use your result in (a) to compute

$$\int_c^1 \frac{1}{x^p}\, dx$$

for $0 < c < 1$.

(c) Use your result in (b) to show that

$$\int_0^1 \frac{1}{x^p}\, dx = \frac{1}{1-p}$$

for $0 < p < 1$.

(d) Show that

$$\int_0^1 \frac{1}{x^p}\, dx$$

is divergent for $p \geq 1$.

■ **7.4.3**

35. (a) Show that

$$0 \leq e^{-x^2} \leq e^{-x}$$

for $x \geq 1$.

(b) Use your result in (a) to show that

$$\int_1^\infty e^{-x^2}\, dx$$

is convergent.

36. (a) Show that

$$0 \leq \frac{1}{\sqrt{1+x^4}} \leq \frac{1}{x^2}$$

for $x > 0$.

(b) Use your result in (a) to show that

$$\int_1^\infty \frac{1}{\sqrt{1+x^4}}\, dx$$

is convergent.

37. (a) Show that

$$\frac{1}{\sqrt{1+x^2}} \geq \frac{1}{2x} > 0$$

for $x \geq 1$.

(b) Use your result in (a) to show that

$$\int_1^\infty \frac{1}{\sqrt{1+x^2}}\, dx$$

is divergent.

38. (a) Show that

$$\frac{1}{\sqrt{x + \ln x}} \geq \frac{1}{\sqrt{2x}} > 0$$

for $x \geq 1$.

(b) Use your result in (a) to show that

$$\int_1^\infty \frac{1}{\sqrt{x + \ln x}}\, dx$$

is divergent.

In Problems 39–42, find a comparison function for each integrand and determine whether the integral is convergent.

39. $\displaystyle\int_{-\infty}^\infty e^{-x^2/2}\, dx$ **40.** $\displaystyle\int_1^\infty \frac{1}{\sqrt{1+x^6}}\, dx$

41. $\displaystyle\int_1^\infty \frac{1}{\sqrt{1+x}}\, dx$ **42.** $\displaystyle\int_{-\infty}^\infty \frac{1}{e^x + e^{-x}}\, dx$

43. (a) Show that

$$\lim_{x \to \infty} \frac{\ln x}{\sqrt{x}} = 0$$

(b) Use your result in (a) to show that

$$2\ln x \leq \sqrt{x} \tag{7.17}$$

for sufficiently large x. Use a graphing calculator to determine just how large x must be for (7.17) to hold.

(c) Use your result in (b) to show that

$$\int_0^\infty e^{-\sqrt{x}}\, dx \tag{7.18}$$

converges. Use a graphing calculator to sketch the function $f(x) = e^{-\sqrt{x}}$ together with its comparison function(s), and use your graph to explain how you showed that the integral in (7.18) is convergent.

44. (a) Show that

$$\lim_{x \to \infty} \frac{\ln x}{x} = 0$$

(b) Use your result in (a) to show that, for any $c > 0$,

$$cx \geq \ln x$$

for sufficiently large x.

(c) Use your result in (b) to show that, for any $p > 0$,

$$x^p e^{-x} \leq e^{-x/2}$$

provided that x is sufficiently large.

(d) Use your result in (c) to show that, for any $p > 0$,

$$\int_0^\infty x^p e^{-x}\, dx$$

is convergent.

■ 7.5 Numerical Integration

Some integrals, such as

$$\int_0^4 e^{-x^2}\, dx$$

are impossible to evaluate exactly. In such situations, numerical approximations are needed.

One way to approximate an integral numerically should be obvious from our initial approach to the area problem. To solve that problem, we approximated areas by rectangles; that is, we used the Riemann sum approximation. Recall that for f continuous,

$$\int_a^b f(x)\, dx = \lim_{\|P\| \to 0} \sum_{k=1}^n f(c_k)\, \Delta x_k$$

where $P = [x_0, x_1, \ldots, x_n]$, $n = 1, 2, \ldots$, is a sequence of partitions of $[a, b]$ with $x_0 = a$ and $x_n = b$ and $\|P\| \to 0$ as $n \to \infty$. The number c_k is in $[x_{k-1}, x_k]$, and $\Delta x_k = x_k - x_{k-1}$ for $1 \le k \le n$.

In what follows, we will assume that we partition the interval $[a, b]$ into n equal subintervals; that is, each subinterval is of length

$$\Delta x = \frac{b - a}{n}$$

We assume that the function f is continuous on $[a, b]$. We will discuss two methods: the midpoint rule and the trapezoidal rule.

■ 7.5.1 The Midpoint Rule

This is the Riemann sum approximation, where we choose the midpoint of each subinterval for the point c_k. The midpoint of the interval $[x_{k-1}, x_k]$ is

$$c_k = \frac{x_{k-1} + x_k}{2}$$

The rule is defined as follows (see also Figure 7.32):

Midpoint Rule Suppose that $f(x)$ is continuous on $[a, b]$ and that $[x_0, x_1, \ldots, x_n]$ is a partition of $[a, b]$ into n subintervals of equal length. We approximate

$$\int_a^b f(x)\, dx$$

by

$$M_n = \frac{b - a}{n} \sum_{k=1}^n f(c_k)$$

where $c_k = \frac{x_{k-1} + x_k}{2}$ is the midpoint of $[x_{k-1}, x_k]$.

In the next example, we choose an integral that we can evaluate exactly, so that we can see how close the approximation is.

EXAMPLE 1   **Midpoint Rule**   Use the midpoint rule with $n = 4$ to approximate

$$\int_0^1 x^2\, dx$$

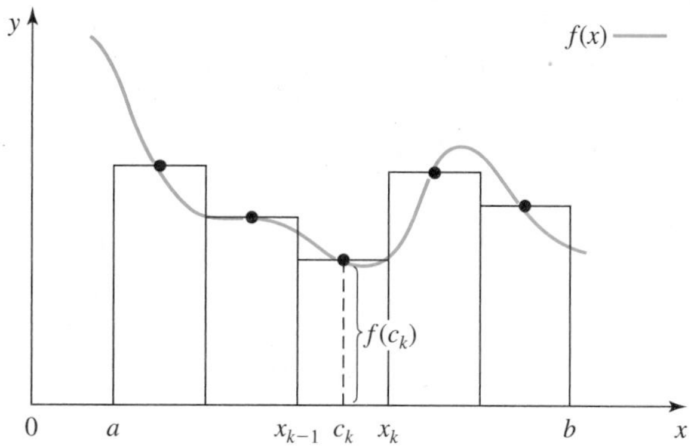

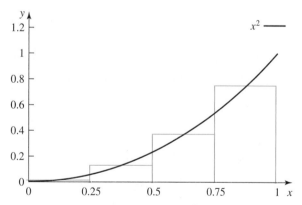

Figure 7.32 The midpoint rule.

Solution   The function $f(x) = x^2$ is continuous on $[0, 1]$. For $n = 4$, we find $\Delta x = \frac{b-a}{4} = \frac{1}{4}$ and we obtain four subintervals, each of length $\frac{1}{4}$ (see Figure 7.33), as given in the following table:

Subinterval $[x_{k-1}, x_k]$	Midpoint c_k	$f(c_k)$	$f(c_k)\,\Delta x$
$\left[0, \dfrac{1}{4}\right]$	$\dfrac{1}{8}$	$\dfrac{1}{64}$	$\dfrac{1}{64}\dfrac{1}{4}$
$\left[\dfrac{1}{4}, \dfrac{1}{2}\right]$	$\dfrac{3}{8}$	$\dfrac{9}{64}$	$\dfrac{9}{64}\dfrac{1}{4}$
$\left[\dfrac{1}{2}, \dfrac{3}{4}\right]$	$\dfrac{5}{8}$	$\dfrac{25}{64}$	$\dfrac{25}{64}\dfrac{1}{4}$
$\left[\dfrac{3}{4}, 1\right]$	$\dfrac{7}{8}$	$\dfrac{49}{64}$	$\dfrac{49}{64}\dfrac{1}{4}$

Figure 7.33 The midpoint rule for $\int_0^1 x^2\,dx$ with $n = 4$.

We find the approximation

$$M_4 = \frac{b-a}{4}\sum_{k=1}^{4} f(c_k) = \frac{1}{4}\left(\frac{1}{64} + \frac{9}{64} + \frac{25}{64} + \frac{49}{64}\right) = \frac{1}{4}\frac{84}{64} = \frac{21}{64} \approx 0.3281$$

We know that $\int_0^1 x^2\,dx = \frac{1}{3}$. Hence, the error is

$$\left|\int_0^1 x^2\,dx - M_4\right| \approx 0.0052$$

Larger values of n improve the approximation.

Instead of memorizing the formula for the midpoint rule, it is easier to keep a picture in mind. We illustrate this heuristic in the next example.

EXAMPLE 2 **Midpoint Rule** Use the midpoint rule with $n = 5$ to approximate

$$\int_1^2 \frac{1}{x}\,dx$$

Solution   The graph of $f(x) = \frac{1}{x}$, together with the five approximating rectangles, is shown in Figure 7.34. We see that $f(x) = 1/x$ is continuous on $[1, 2]$.

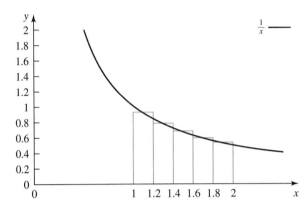

Figure 7.34 The midpoint rule for Example 2.

With $n = 5$, the partition of $[1, 2]$ is given by $P = [1, 1.2, 1.4, 1.6, 1.8, 2]$ and the midpoints are 1.1, 1.3, 1.5, 1.7, and 1.9. Since the width of each rectangle is 0.2 and $f(x) = \frac{1}{x}$, the area of the first rectangle is $(0.2)\frac{1}{1.1}$, the area of the second rectangle is $(0.2)\frac{1}{1.3}$, and so on. We thus find that

$$M_5 = (0.2)\left[\frac{1}{1.1} + \frac{1}{1.3} + \frac{1}{1.5} + \frac{1}{1.7} + \frac{1}{1.9}\right] = 0.6919$$

Note that we factored out 0.2, the width of each rectangle, since it is a common factor of the areas of the five rectangles.

We know that

$$\int_1^2 \frac{1}{x}\,dx = \ln x\Big]_1^2 = \ln 2 - \ln 1 = \ln 2$$

Hence, the error in the approximation is

$$\left|\int_1^2 \frac{1}{x}\,dx - M_5\right| = |\ln 2 - 0.6919| = 0.0012 \qquad ■$$

We typically use an approximation when we cannot evaluate the integral exactly. Thus, we cannot use the exact value to determine how close the approximation is. Fortunately, there are results that allow us to obtain upper bounds for the error:

Error Bound for the Midpoint Rule Suppose that $|f''(x)| \le K$ for all $x \in [a, b]$. Then the error in the midpoint rule is at most

$$\left|\int_a^b f(x)\,dx - M_n\right| \le K\frac{(b-a)^3}{24n^2}$$

Let's check this bound for our two examples. In the first example, $f(x) = x^2$, and therefore $f''(x) = 2$. Hence, with $n = 4$, the error is at most

$$2\frac{(1-0)^3}{24(4^2)} \approx 0.0052$$

This is in fact the error that we obtained.

In the second example, $f(x) = \frac{1}{x}$. Since $f'(x) = -\frac{1}{x^2}$ and $f''(x) = \frac{2}{x^3}$, it follows that

$$|f''(x)| = \left|\frac{2}{x^3}\right| \leq 2 \quad \text{for } 1 \leq x \leq 2$$

Hence, with $n = 5$, the error is at most

$$2\frac{(2-1)^3}{24(5^2)} = 0.0033$$

The actual error was in fact smaller, only 0.0012.

The actual error can be quite a bit smaller than the theoretical error bound, which is the worst-case scenario, but it will never be larger. The advantage of such an error bound is that it allows us to find the number of subintervals required to obtain a certain accuracy. For instance, if we want to numerically approximate $\int_0^1 x^2\,dx$ so that the error is at most 10^{-4}, then we must choose n so that

$$K\frac{(b-a)^3}{24n^2} \leq 10^{-4}$$

$$2\frac{1}{24n^2} \leq 10^{-4}$$

$$\frac{1}{12}10^4 \leq n^2$$

$$28.9 \leq n$$

That is, $n = 29$ would suffice to produce an error of at most 10^{-4}.

Finding a value for K in the estimate is not always easy. A graph of $f''(x)$ over the interval of interest can facilitate finding a bound on the second derivative. We need not find the best possible bound. For instance, if we wanted to integrate $f(x) = e^x$ over the interval $[1, 2]$, we would need to find a bound on $f''(x) = e^x$ over the interval $[1, 2]$. Since $|e^x| \leq e^2$ over that interval, we could use, for instance, $K = 9$. (See Figure 7.35.) This is not the best possible bound, but it is a number that we can find without using a calculator. (The best possible bound would be $K = e^2$.)

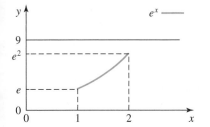

Figure 7.35 An upper bound on $|e^x|$ over [1, 2] is 9.

■ 7.5.2 The Trapezoidal Rule

In this method, we use trapezoids instead of rectangles to approximate integrals, as illustrated in Figure 7.36. We assume again that f is a continuous function on $[a, b]$ and divide $[a, b]$ into n equal subintervals. But this time we approximate the function $f(x)$ by a polygon $P(x)$. To obtain the polygon $P(x)$, we connect the points $(x_k, f(x_k))$, $k = 0, 1, 2, \ldots, n$, by straight lines, as shown in the figure. The integral $\int_a^b P(x)\,dx$ is then the approximation to $\int_a^b f(x)\,dx$.

We see from Figure 7.36 that all this amounts to adding up (signed) areas of trapezoids. Recall from planar geometry that the area of the trapezoid in Figure 7.37 is

$$A = d\frac{h_1 + h_2}{2}$$

The width of each trapezoid in Figure 7.36 is $d = \frac{b-a}{n}$. Adding up the areas of the

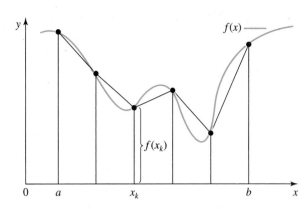

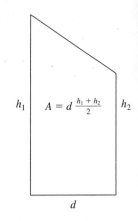

Figure 7.36 The trapezoidal rule.

Figure 7.37 The area of a trapezoid.

trapezoids then yields

$$T_n = \frac{b-a}{n}\left[\frac{f(x_0)+f(x_1)}{2}+\frac{f(x_1)+f(x_2)}{2}+\frac{f(x_2)+f(x_3)}{2}\right.$$

$$\left.+\cdots+\frac{f(x_{n-2})+f(x_{n-1})}{2}+\frac{f(x_{n-1})+f(x_n)}{2}\right]$$

$$=\frac{b-a}{n}\left[\frac{f(x_0)}{2}+f(x_1)+f(x_2)+\cdots+f(x_{n-1})+\frac{f(x_n)}{2}\right]$$

Trapezoidal Rule Suppose that $f(x)$ is continuous on $[a,b]$ and that $P = [x_0, x_1, x_2, \ldots, x_n]$ is a partition of $[a,b]$ into n subintervals of equal length. Then we can approximate

$$\int_a^b f(x)\,dx$$

by

$$T_n = \frac{b-a}{n}\left[\frac{f(x_0)}{2}+f(x_1)+f(x_2)+\cdots+f(x_{n-1})+\frac{f(x_n)}{2}\right]$$

EXAMPLE 3   **Trapezoidal Rule** Use the trapezoidal rule with $n = 4$ to approximate

$$\int_0^1 x^2\,dx$$

Solution   The function $f(x) = x^2$ is continuous on $[0, 1]$. As in Example 1, there are four subintervals, each of length $\frac{1}{4}$. (See Figure 7.38.) We find the following:

k	x_k	$f(x_k)$
0	0	0
1	$\frac{1}{4}$	$\frac{1}{16}$
2	$\frac{1}{2}$	$\frac{1}{4}$
3	$\frac{3}{4}$	$\frac{9}{16}$
4	1	1

The approximation is

$$T_4 = \frac{1}{4}\left[\frac{0}{2} + \frac{1}{16} + \frac{1}{4} + \frac{9}{16} + \frac{1}{2}\right] = 0.34375$$

Since we know that $\int_0^1 x^2\, dx = \frac{1}{3}$, we can compute the error:

$$\left|\int_0^1 x^2\, dx - T_4\right| = 0.0104$$

Note that because $y = x^2$ is concave up, the line segments of the polygon are above the curve $y = x^2$. The area of the trapezoid therefore exceeds the area under the curve $y = x^2$ in each subinterval, and the trapezoidal approximation overestimates the integral. ■

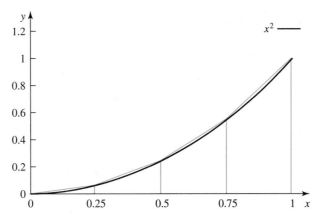

Figure 7.38 The trapezoidal rule for $\int_0^1 x^2\, dx$ with $n = 4$.

EXAMPLE 4

Trapezoidal Rule Use the trapezoidal rule with $n = 5$ to approximate

$$\int_1^2 \frac{1}{x}\, dx$$

Solution   The situation is illustrated in Figure 7.39. The function $1/x$ is continuous on $[1, 2]$. With $n = 5$, the partition of $[1, 2]$ is given by $P = [1.0, 1.2, 1.4, 1.6, 1.8, 2.0]$. The base of each trapezoid has length 0.2. Hence,

$$T_5 = (0.2)\left[\frac{1}{2}\cdot\frac{1}{1.0} + \frac{1}{1.2} + \frac{1}{1.4} + \frac{1}{1.6} + \frac{1}{1.8} + \frac{1}{2}\cdot\frac{1}{2.0}\right] = 0.69563$$

Since we know from Example 2 that $\int_1^2 \frac{1}{x}\, dx = \ln 2$, we can compute the error:

$$\left|\int_1^2 \frac{1}{x}\, dx - T_5\right| = 0.00249$$

■

There is also a theoretical error bound for the trapezoidal rule:

> **Error Bound for the Trapezoidal Rule** Suppose that $|f''(x)| \le K$ for all $x \in [a, b]$. Then the error in the trapezoidal rule is at most
>
> $$\left|\int_a^b f(x)\, dx - T_n\right| \le K\frac{(b - a)^3}{12n^2}$$

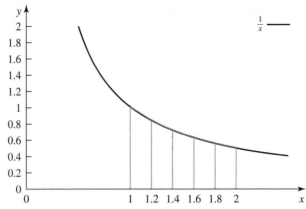

Figure 7.39 The trapezoidal rule for $\int_1^2 \frac{1}{x}\, dx$ with $n = 5$.

In Example 3, since $f(x) = x^2$, it follows that $f''(x) = 2$ and hence $K = 2$. The error is therefore bounded by

$$2\frac{1}{12(4^2)} = 0.0104$$

which is the same as the actual error.

In Example 4, since $f(x) = 1/x$, we have $|f''(x)| = 2/x^3 \le 2$ for $1 \le x \le 2$ (as in Example 2). Hence, with $n = 5$, the error bound is at most

$$2\frac{(2-1)^3}{12(5^2)} = 0.0067$$

The actual error was in fact smaller, only 0.00249. As with the midpoint rule, the theoretical error can be quite a bit larger than the actual error.

Section 7.5 Problems

■ **7.5.1, 7.5.2**

In Problems 1–4, use the midpoint rule to approximate each integral with the specified value of n.

1. $\int_1^2 x^2\, dx, n = 4$

2. $\int_{-1}^0 (x+1)^3\, dx, n = 5$

3. $\int_0^1 e^{-x}\, dx, n = 3$

4. $\int_0^{\pi/2} \sin x\, dx, n = 4$

In Problems 5–8, use the midpoint rule to approximate each integral with the specified value of n. Compare your approximation with the exact value.

5. $\int_2^4 \frac{1}{x}\, dx, n = 4$

6. $\int_{-1}^1 (e^{2x} - 1)\, dx, n = 4$

7. $\int_0^4 \sqrt{x}\, dx, n = 4$

8. $\int_2^4 \frac{2}{\sqrt{x}}\, dx, n = 5$

In Problems 9–12, use the trapezoidal rule to approximate each integral with the specified value of n.

9. $\int_1^2 x^2\, dx, n = 4$

10. $\int_{-1}^0 x^3\, dx, n = 5$

11. $\int_0^1 e^{-x}\, dx, n = 3$

12. $\int_0^{\pi/2} \sin x\, dx, n = 4$

In Problems 13–16, use the trapezoidal rule to approximate each integral with the specified value of n. Compare your approximation with the exact value.

13. $\int_1^3 x^3\, dx, n = 5$

14. $\int_{-1}^1 (1 - e^{-x})\, dx, n = 4$

15. $\int_0^2 \sqrt{x}\, dx, n = 4$

16. $\int_1^2 \frac{1}{x}\, dx, n = 5$

17. How large should n be so that the midpoint rule approximation of

$$\int_0^2 x^2\, dx$$

is accurate to within 10^{-4}?

In Problems 18–24, use the theoretical error bound to determine how large n should be. [Hint: In each case, find the second derivative of the integrand, graph it, and use a graphing calculator to find an upper bound on $|f''(x)|$.]

18. How large should n be so that the midpoint rule approximation of

$$\int_1^2 \frac{1}{x}\, dx$$

is accurate to within 10^{-3}?

19. How large should n be so that the midpoint rule approximation of

$$\int_0^2 e^{-x^2/2}\,dx$$

is accurate to within 10^{-4}?

20. How large should n be so that the midpoint rule approximation of

$$\int_2^8 \frac{1}{\ln t}\,dt$$

is accurate to within 10^{-3}?

21. How large should n be so that the trapezoidal rule approximation of

$$\int_0^1 e^{-x}\,dx$$

is accurate to within 10^{-5}?

22. How large should n be so that the trapezoidal rule approximation of

$$\int_0^2 \sin x\,dx$$

is accurate to within 10^{-4}?

23. How large should n be so that the trapezoidal rule approximation of

$$\int_1^2 \frac{e^t}{t}\,dt$$

is accurate to within 10^{-4}?

24. How large should n be so that the trapezoidal rule approximation of

$$\int_1^2 \frac{\cos x}{x}\,dx$$

is accurate to within 10^{-3}?

25. (a) Show graphically that, for $n = 5$, the trapezoidal rule overestimates, and the midpoint rule underestimates,

$$\int_0^1 x^3\,dx$$

In each case, compute the approximate value of the integral and compare it with the exact value.

(b) The result in (a) has to do with the fact that $y = x^3$ is concave up on $[0, 1]$. To generalize that result to functions with this concavity property, we assume that the function $f(x)$ is continuous, nonnegative, and concave up on the interval $[a, b]$. Denote by M_n the midpoint rule approximation, and by T_n the trapezoidal rule approximation, of $\int_a^b f(x)\,dx$. Explain in words why

$$M_n \le \int_a^b f(x)\,dx \le T_n$$

(c) If we assume that $f(x)$ is continuous, nonnegative, and concave *down* on $[a, b]$, then

$$M_n \ge \int_a^b f(x)\,dx \ge T_n$$

Explain why this is so. Use this result to give an upper and a lower bound on

$$\int_0^1 \sqrt{x}\,dx$$

when $n = 4$ in the approximation.

■ 7.6 The Taylor Approximation

In many ways, polynomials are the easiest functions to work with. Therefore, in this section we will learn how to approximate functions by polynomials. We will see that the approximation typically improves when we use higher-degree polynomials.

■ 7.6.1 Taylor Polynomials

In Section 4.8, we discussed how to linearize a function about a given point. This discussion led to the linear, or tangent, approximation. We found the following:

> The linear approximation of $f(x)$ at $x = a$ is
>
> $$L(x) = f(a) + f'(a)(x - a)$$

As an example, we look at

$$f(x) = e^x$$

and approximate this function by its linearization at $x = 0$. We find that

$$L(x) = f(0) + f'(0)x = 1 + x \qquad (7.19)$$

since $f'(x) = e^x$ and $f(0) = f'(0) = 1$. To see how close the approximation is, we graph both $f(x)$ and $L(x)$ in the same coordinate system. (The result is shown in Figure 7.40.) The approximation is quite good as long as x is close to 0. The figure suggests that it gets gradually worse as we move away from 0. In the approximation, we required only that $f(x)$ and $L(x)$ have in common $f(0) = L(0)$ and $f'(0) = L'(0)$.

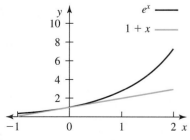

Figure 7.40 The graph of $y = e^x$ and its linear approximation at 0.

To improve the approximation, we may wish to use an approximating function whose higher-order derivatives also agree with those of $f(x)$ at $x = 0$. The function $L(x)$ is a polynomial of degree 1. To improve the approximation, we will continue to work with polynomials, but require that the function and its first n derivatives at $x = 0$ agree with those of the polynomial. To be able to match up the first n derivatives, the polynomial must be of degree n. (If the degree of the polynomial is $k < n$, then all derivatives of degree $k + 1$ or higher are equal to 0.) A polynomial of degree n can be written as

$$P_n(x) = a_0 + a_1 x + a_2 x^2 + \cdots + a_n x^n \tag{7.20}$$

If we want to approximate $f(x)$ at $x = 0$, then we require that

$$\begin{aligned}
f(0) &= P_n(0) \\
f'(0) &= P_n'(0) \\
f''(0) &= P_n''(0) \\
&\vdots \\
f^{(n)}(0) &= P_n^{(n)}(0)
\end{aligned} \tag{7.21}$$

Now,

$$\begin{aligned}
P_n(0) &= a_0 + a_1 x + \cdots + a_n x^n \big|_{x=0} = a_0 \\
P_n'(0) &= a_1 + 2a_2 x + 3a_3 x^2 + \cdots + na_n x^{n-1} \big|_{x=0} = a_1 \\
P_n''(0) &= 2a_2 + (3)(2)a_3 x + \cdots + n(n-1)a_n x^{n-2} \big|_{x=0} = 2a_2 \\
P_n'''(0) &= (3)(2)a_3 + (4)(3)(2)a_4 x + \cdots + n(n-1)(n-2)a_n x^{n-3} \big|_{x=0} \\
&= (3)(2)a_3 \\
&\vdots \\
P_n^{(n)}(0) &= n(n-1)(n-2) \cdots (3)(2)(1)a_n \big|_{x=0} \\
&= n(n-1)(n-2) \cdots (3)(2)(1)a_n
\end{aligned}$$

We introduce the notation

$$k! = k(k-1)(k-2) \cdots (3)(2)(1)$$

where $k!$ is read "k factorial." Solving these equations for a_k, $k = 0, 1, 2, \ldots, n$, and using $f^{(k)}(0) = P^{(k)}(0)$, $k = 0, 1, 2, \ldots, n$, we find that

$$\begin{aligned}
a_0 &= P_n(0) = f(0) \\
a_1 &= P_n'(0) = f'(0) \\
a_2 &= \frac{1}{2}P_n''(0) = \frac{1}{2!}f''(0) \\
a_3 &= \frac{1}{3 \cdot 2}P_n'''(0) = \frac{1}{3!}f'''(0) \\
&\vdots \\
a_n &= \frac{1}{n(n-1)\cdots 2 \cdot 1}P_n^{(n)}(0) = \frac{1}{n!}f^{(n)}(0)
\end{aligned} \tag{7.22}$$

A polynomial of degree n of the form (7.20) and whose coefficients satisfy (7.22) is called a **Taylor polynomial** of degree n. We summarize this definition as follows:

> **Definition** The Taylor polynomial of degree n about $x = 0$ for the function $f(x)$ is given by
>
> $$P_n(x) = f(0) + f'(0)x + \frac{f''(0)}{2!}x^2 + \frac{f'''(0)}{3!}x^3$$
>
> $$+ \frac{f^{(4)}(0)}{4!}x^4 + \cdots + \frac{f^{(n)}(0)}{n!}x^n$$

EXAMPLE 1

Compute the Taylor polynomial of degree 3 about $x = 0$ for the function $f(x) = e^x$.

Solution

To find the Taylor polynomial of degree 3, we need the first three derivatives of $f(x)$ at $x = 0$. We have

$$f(x) = e^x, \qquad \text{so } f(0) = 1$$
$$f'(x) = e^x, \qquad \text{so } f'(0) = 1$$
$$f''(x) = e^x, \qquad \text{so } f''(0) = 1$$
$$f'''(x) = e^x, \qquad \text{so } f'''(0) = 1$$

Therefore,

$$P_3(x) = 1 + x + \frac{x^2}{2!} + \frac{x^3}{3!} = 1 + x + \frac{x^2}{2} + \frac{x^3}{6}$$

since $2! = (2)(1) = 2$ and $3! = (3)(2)(1) = 6$.

Our claim was that this polynomial would provide a better approximation to e^x than the linearization $1 + x$. We check this claim by evaluating e^x, $L(x)$, and $P_3(x)$ at a few values. The results are summarized in the following table:

x	e^x	$1 + x$	$1 + x + \frac{x^2}{2} + \frac{x^3}{6}$
-1	0.36788	0	0.3333
-0.1	0.90484	0.9	0.9048
0	1	1	1.0000
0.1	1.1052	1.1	1.1052
1	2.7183	2	2.6667

We see from the table that the third-degree Taylor polynomial provides a better approximation. Indeed, for x sufficiently close to 0, the values of $f(x)$ and $P_3(x)$ are very close. For instance,

$$f(0.1) = 1.105170918 \qquad \text{and} \qquad P_3(0.1) = 1.105166667$$

That is, their first five digits are identical. The error of approximation is

$$|f(0.1) - P_3(0.1)| = 4.25 \times 10^{-6}$$

which is quite small.

In Figure 7.41, we display the graphs of $f(x)$ and the Taylor polynomials $P_1(x)$, $P_2(x)$, and $P_3(x)$. We see from the graphs that the approximation is good only as long as x is close to 0. We also see that increasing the degree of the Taylor polynomial improves the approximation. ■

When we look at Example 1, we find that the successive Taylor polynomials for $f(x) = e^x$ about $x = 0$ are

$$P_0(x) = 1$$
$$P_1(x) = 1 + x$$
$$P_2(x) = 1 + x + \frac{x^2}{2!}$$
$$P_3(x) = 1 + x + \frac{x^2}{2!} + \frac{x^3}{3!}$$

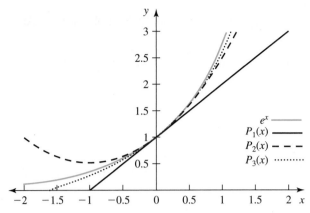

Figure 7.41   The graph of $y = e^x$ and the first three Taylor polynomials.

The first thing we notice is that $P_1(x)$ is the linear approximation $L(x)$ that we found in (7.19).

The next thing we notice is that there is a pattern, and we might be tempted to guess the form of $P_n(x)$ for an arbitrary n. Our guess would be

$$P_n(x) = 1 + x + \frac{x^2}{2!} + \frac{x^3}{3!} + \cdots + \frac{x^n}{n!}$$

and this is indeed the case.

You might wonder why we bother to find an approximation for the function $f(x) = e^x$. To compute $f(1) = e$, for instance, it seems a lot easier simply to use a calculator. However, since $f(x) = e^x$ is not an algebraic function, the values of $f(x)$ cannot be found exactly with only the basic algebraic operations. Taylor polynomials are one way to evaluate such functions on a computer.

We now give additional functions for which we can find the Taylor polynomial of degree n.

EXAMPLE 2   Compute the Taylor polynomial of degree n about $x = 0$ for the function $f(x) = \sin x$.

Solution   We begin by computing successive derivatives of $f(x) = \sin x$ at $x = 0$:

$$f(x) = \sin x \qquad \text{and} \qquad f(0) = 0$$
$$f'(x) = \cos x \qquad \text{and} \qquad f'(0) = 1$$
$$f''(x) = -\sin x \qquad \text{and} \qquad f''(0) = 0$$
$$f'''(x) = -\cos x \qquad \text{and} \qquad f'''(0) = -1$$
$$f^{(4)}(x) = \sin x \qquad \text{and} \qquad f^{(4)}(0) = 0$$

Since $f^{(4)}(x) = f(x)$, we find that $f^{(5)}(x) = f'(x)$, $f^{(6)}(x) = f''(x)$, and so on. We also conclude that all even derivatives are equal to 0 at $x = 0$ and that the odd derivatives alternate between 1 and -1 at $x = 0$. We find that

$$P_1(x) = P_2(x) = x$$

$$P_3(x) = P_4(x) = x - \frac{x^3}{3!}$$

$$P_5(x) = P_6(x) = x - \frac{x^3}{3!} + \frac{x^5}{5!}$$

$$P_7(x) = P_8(x) = x - \frac{x^3}{3!} + \frac{x^5}{5!} - \frac{x^7}{7!}$$

and so on. To find the Taylor polynomial of degree n, we must find out how to write the last term. Note that the sign in front of successive terms alternates between plus and minus. To account for this alternating sign, we introduce the factor

$$(-1)^n = \begin{cases} 1 & \text{if } n \text{ is even} \\ -1 & \text{if } n \text{ is odd} \end{cases}$$

An odd number can be written as $2n + 1$ for any integer n. For a term of the form $\pm\frac{x^k}{k!}$ with k odd, we write

$$(-1)^n \frac{x^{2n+1}}{(2n + 1)!} \tag{7.23}$$

where n is an integer. Inserting successive values of n into (7.23), we find the following:

n	$(-1)^n \dfrac{x^{2n+1}}{(2n + 1)!}$
0	x
1	$-\dfrac{x^3}{3!}$
2	$\dfrac{x^5}{5!}$
3	$-\dfrac{x^7}{7!}$

We see from the table that the term (7.23) produces successive terms in the Taylor polynomial for $f(x) = \sin x$. The Taylor polynomial of degree $2n + 1$ is thus

$$P_{2n+1}(x) = x - \frac{x^3}{3!} + \frac{x^5}{5!} - \frac{x^7}{7!} + \cdots + (-1)^n \frac{x^{2n+1}}{(2n + 1)!} \qquad ■$$

EXAMPLE 3

Compute the Taylor polynomial of degree n about $x = 0$ for the function $f(x) = \frac{1}{1-x}$, $x \neq 1$.

Solution

We begin by computing successive derivatives of $f(x) = \frac{1}{1-x}$ at $x = 0$.

$$f(x) = \frac{1}{1 - x}, \qquad \text{so } f(0) = 1$$

$$f'(x) = \frac{1}{(1 - x)^2}, \qquad \text{so } f'(0) = 1$$

$$f''(x) = \frac{2}{(1 - x)^3}, \qquad \text{so } f''(0) = 2 = 2!$$

$$f'''(x) = \frac{(2)(3)}{(1 - x)^4}, \qquad \text{so } f'''(0) = (2)(3) = 3!$$

$$f^{(4)}(x) = \frac{(2)(3)(4)}{(1 - x)^5}, \qquad \text{so } f^{(4)}(0) = (2)(3)(4) = 4!$$

and so on. Continuing in this way, we find that

$$f^{(k)}(x) = \frac{(2)(3)(4) \cdots (k)}{(1 - x)^{k+1}} \quad \text{so } f^{(k)}(0) = k!$$

For the Taylor polynomial of degree n about $x = 0$, we obtain

$$P_n(x) = 1 + x + \frac{2!}{2!}x^2 + \frac{3!}{3!}x^3 + \frac{4!}{4!}x^4 + \frac{5!}{5!}x^5 + \cdots + \frac{n!}{n!}x^n$$

$$= 1 + x + x^2 + x^3 + \cdots + x^n \qquad ■$$

Taylor approximations are widely used in biology. Here is an example that is already familiar to us.

EXAMPLE 4

Denote the size of a population at time t by $N(t)$. A general model that describes the dynamics of this population is given by

$$\frac{dN}{dt} = f(N) \quad \text{with } f(0) = 0$$

Find the linear and the quadratic approximation of $f(N)$ about $N = 0$.

Solution

The linear approximation of $f(N)$ about $N = 0$ is the Taylor polynomial of degree 1:

$$P_1(N) = \underbrace{f(0)}_{=0} + f'(0)N$$

If we set $r = f'(0)$, then the first-order approximation of this growth model is

$$\frac{dN}{dt} = rN$$

which is the equation that describes exponential growth.

The quadratic approximation of $f(N)$ about $N = 0$ is the Taylor polynomial of degree 2:

$$P_2(N) = \underbrace{f(0)}_{=0} + f'(0)N + \frac{f''(0)}{2}N^2$$

Factoring $f'(0)N$ yields

$$P_2(N) = f'(0)N \left[1 + \frac{f''(0)}{2f'(0)}N \right]$$

If we set $r = f'(0)$ and $K = -\frac{2f'(0)}{f''(0)}$, then the second-order approximation of the growth model is

$$\frac{dN}{dt} = rN \left(1 - \frac{N}{K} \right)$$

which is the equation that describes logistic growth if K and r are positive. In either approximation, $r = f'(0)$ is the intrinsic rate of growth. ■

■ 7.6.2 The Taylor Polynomial about $x = a$

Thus far, we have considered Taylor polynomials about $x = 0$. Because Taylor polynomials typically are good approximations only close to the point of approximation, it is useful to have approximations about points other than $x = 0$. We have already done this for linear approximations. For instance, the tangent-line approximation of $f(x)$ at $x = a$ is

$$L(x) = f(a) + f'(a)(x - a) \tag{7.24}$$

Note that $L(a) = f(a)$ and $L'(a) = f'(a)$. That is, the linear approximation and the original function, together with their first derivatives, agree at $x = a$. If we want to approximate $f(x)$ at $x = a$ by a polynomial of degree n, we then require that the polynomial and the original function, together with their first n derivatives, agree at $x = a$. This leads us to a polynomial of the form

$$P_n(x) = c_0 + c_1(x - a) + c_2(x - a)^2 + \cdots + c_n(x - a)^n \tag{7.25}$$

Comparing (7.25) and (7.24), we conclude that $c_0 = f(a)$ and $c_1 = f'(a)$. To find the remaining coefficients, we proceed as in the case $a = 0$. That is, we differentiate $f(x)$ and $P_n(x)$ and require that their first n derivatives agree at $x = a$. We then arrive at the following formula:

> The Taylor polynomial of degree n about $x = a$ for the function $f(x)$ is given by
>
> $$P_n(x) = f(a) + f'(a)(x - a) + \frac{f''(a)}{2!}(x - a)^2$$
> $$+ \frac{f'''(a)}{3!}(x - a)^3 + \cdots + \frac{f^{(n)}(a)}{n!}(x - a)^n$$

EXAMPLE 5   Find the Taylor polynomial of degree 3 for

$$f(x) = \ln x$$

at $x = 1$.

Solution   We need to evaluate $f(x)$ and its first three derivatives at $x = 1$. We find that

$$f(x) = \ln x, \qquad \text{so } f(1) = 0$$
$$f'(x) = \frac{1}{x}, \qquad \text{so } f'(1) = 1$$
$$f''(x) = -\frac{1}{x^2}, \qquad \text{so } f''(1) = -1$$
$$f'''(x) = \frac{2}{x^3}, \qquad \text{so } f'''(1) = 2$$

Using the definition of the Taylor polynomial, we get

$$P_3(x) = 0 + (1)(x - 1) + \frac{(-1)}{2!}(x - 1)^2 + \frac{2}{3!}(x - 1)^3$$
$$= (x - 1) - \frac{1}{2}(x - 1)^2 + \frac{1}{3}(x - 1)^3$$

Figure 7.42 shows $f(x)$, the linear approximation $P_1(x) = x - 1$, and $P_3(x)$. We see that the approximation is good when x is close to 1 and that the approximation $P_3(x)$ is better than the linear approximation.   ■

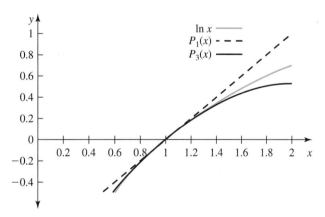

Figure 7.42   The graph of $y = \ln x$, the linear approximation, and the Taylor polynomial of degree 3.

■ 7.6.3 How Accurate Is the Approximation? (Optional)

We saw in Example 1 that the approximation improved when the degree of the polynomial was higher. We will now investigate how accurate the Taylor approximation is. We can assess the accuracy of the approximation directly for the function in Example 3.

In Example 3, we showed that the Taylor polynomial of degree n about $x = 0$ for $f(x) = \frac{1}{1-x}, x \neq 1$, is

$$P_n(x) = 1 + x + x^2 + x^3 + \cdots + x^{n-1} + x^n \tag{7.26}$$

There is a nice "trick" we may use to find an expression for the sum (7.26). Note that

$$x P_n(x) = x + x^2 + x^3 + \cdots + x^n + x^{n+1} \tag{7.27}$$

Subtracting (7.27) from (7.26), we find that

$$P_n(x) - x P_n(x) = 1 + x + x^2 + \cdots + x^n - x - x^2 - \cdots - x^n - x^{n+1}$$
$$= 1 - x^{n+1}$$

That is,

$$(1 - x) P_n(x) = 1 - x^{n+1}$$

or

$$P_n(x) = \frac{1 - x^{n+1}}{1 - x} = \frac{1}{1 - x} - \frac{x^{n+1}}{1 - x}$$

provided that $x \neq 1$. We therefore conclude that

$$|f(x) - P_n(x)| = \left| \frac{x^{n+1}}{1 - x} \right|$$

We can interpret the term $x^{n+1}/(1 - x)$ as the error of approximation. Since

$$\lim_{n \to \infty} \left| \frac{x^{n+1}}{1 - x} \right| = \begin{cases} \infty & \text{if } |x| > 1 \\ 0 & \text{if } |x| < 1 \end{cases}$$

it follows that the error of approximation can be made small only when $|x| < 1$. For $|x| > 1$, the error of approximation increases with increasing n. [When $x = 1$, the function $f(x)$ is not defined.]

In general, it is not straightforward to obtain error estimates. In its general form, the error is given as an integral. Let's first look at the error terms $P_0(x)$ and $P_1(x)$ before stating the error term for arbitrary n.

Using part II of the FTC, we find that

$$f(x) - f(a) = \int_a^x f'(t)\, dt$$

or

$$f(x) = f(a) + \int_a^x f'(t)\, dt$$

Since $f(a) = P_0(x)$, we can interpret $\int_a^x f'(t)\, dt$ as the error term in the Taylor approximation of $f(x)$ about $x = a$ when $n = 0$.

We can use integration by parts to obtain the next-higher approximation:

$$\int_a^x f'(t)\, dt = \int_a^x 1 \cdot f'(t)\, dt$$

We set $u' = 1$ with $u = -(x - t)$ and $v = f'(t)$ with $v' = f''(t)$. [Writing $u = -(x - t)$ turns out to be a more convenient antiderivative of $u' = 1$ than $u = t$, as you will see shortly.] We obtain

$$\int_a^x f'(t)\, dt = -(x - t) f'(t) \Big]_a^x + \int_a^x (x - t) f''(t)\, dt$$
$$= (x - a) f'(a) + \int_a^x (x - t) f''(t)\, dt$$

That is,

$$f(x) = f(a) + f'(a)(x - a) + \int_a^x (x - t)f''(t)\, dt$$

The expression $f(a) + f'(a)(x - a)$ is the linear approximation $P_1(x)$; the integral can then be considered as the error term.

Continuing in this way, we find the general formula:

Taylor's Formula Suppose that $f : I \to \mathbf{R}$, where I is an interval, $a \in I$, and f and its first $n + 1$ derivatives are continuous at $a \in I$. Then, for $x, a \in I$,

$$f(x) = f(a) + \frac{f'(a)}{1!}(x - a) + \frac{f''(a)}{2!}(x - a)^2$$

$$+ \cdots + \frac{f^{(n)}(a)}{n!}(x - a)^n + R_{n+1}(x)$$

where

$$R_{n+1}(x) = \frac{1}{n!} \int_a^x (x - t)^n f^{(n+1)}(t)\, dt$$

We will now examine the error term in Taylor's formula more closely. The error term is given in integral form, and it is often difficult (or impossible) to evaluate the integral. We will first look at the case $n = 0$; that is, we approximate $f(x)$ by the constant function $f(a)$. The error term is then $R_{n+1}(x)$ when $n = 0$; that is,

$$R_1(x) = \int_a^x f'(t)\, dt$$

Using the MVT for integrals, we can find a value c in the interval between a and x such that

$$\int_a^x f'(t)\, dt = f'(c)(x - a)$$

That is, we find

$$R_1(x) = f'(c)(x - a)$$

for some number c between a and x. Although we don't know the value of c, this form is quite useful, for if we set

$$K = \left[\begin{array}{c} \text{largest value of } |f'(t)| \\ \text{for } t \text{ between } a \text{ and } x \end{array} \right]$$

then

$$|R_1(x)| \le K|x - a|$$

Before we give the corresponding results for $R_{n+1}(x)$, we look at one example that illustrates how to find K.

EXAMPLE 6 Estimate the error in the approximation of $f(x) = e^x$ by $P_0(x)$ about $x = 0$ on the interval $[0, 1]$.

Solution Since $f(0) = 1$, it follows that

$$P_0(x) = 1$$

and

$$f(x) = 1 + R_1(x)$$

with

$$R_1(x) = \int_0^x f'(t)\, dt = xf'(c)$$

for some c between 0 and x. Because $f'(t) = e^t$, the largest value of $|f'(t)|$ in the interval $[0, 1]$, namely, $|f'(1)| = e$, occurs when $t = 1$. Since we want to find an approximation of $f(x) = e^x$ for $x \in [0, 1]$, we should not use e in our error estimate, as e is one of the values we want to estimate. Instead, we use $|f'(t)| \le 3$ for $t \in [0, 1]$. We thus have

$$|R_1(x)| \le 3x \quad \text{for } x \in [0, 1]$$

■

The error term for general n can be dealt with in a similar fashion, so that we find the following:

> There exists a c between a and x such that the error term in Taylor's formula is of the form
>
> $$R_{n+1}(x) = \frac{f^{(n+1)}(c)}{(n+1)!}(x-a)^{n+1}$$

As in the case where $n = 0$, this form of the error term is quite useful. Although we don't know what c is, we can try to estimate $f^{(n+1)}(c)$ between a and x as before, when $n = 0$. Let

$$K = \left[\begin{array}{c} \text{largest value of } |f^{(n+1)}(t)| \\ \text{for } t \text{ between } a \text{ and } x \end{array} \right]$$

Then

$$|R_{n+1}(x)| \le \frac{K|x-a|^{n+1}}{(n+1)!}$$

We will use this inequality in the next example to determine in advance what degree of Taylor polynomial will allow us to achieve a given accuracy.

EXAMPLE 7

Suppose that $f(x) = e^x$. What degree of Taylor polynomial about $x = 0$ will allow us to approximate $f(1)$ so that the error is less than 10^{-5}?

Solution

In Example 1, we found that, for any $n \ge 1$,

$$f^{(n+1)}(t) = e^t$$

We need to find out how large $f^{(n+1)}(t)$ can get for $t \in [0, 1]$. We obtain

$$|f^{(n+1)}(t)| = e^t \le e \quad \text{for } 0 \le t \le 1$$

As in Example 6, instead of using e as a bound, we use a slightly larger value, namely, 3. Therefore,

$$|R_{n+1}(1)| \le \frac{3|1|^{n+1}}{(n+1)!} = \frac{3}{(n+1)!} \tag{7.28}$$

We want the error to be less than 10^{-5}; that is, we want

$$|R_{n+1}(1)| < 10^{-5}$$

Inserting different values of n shows that

$$\frac{3}{8!} = 7.44 \times 10^{-5} \quad \text{and} \quad \frac{3}{9!} = 8.27 \times 10^{-6}$$

That is, when $n = 8$,

$$|R_{n+1}(1)| = |R_9(1)| \le 8.27 \times 10^{-6} < 10^{-5}$$

Because the estimate of the error is greater than 10^{-5} when $n = 7$, we conclude that a polynomial of degree 8 would certainly give us the desired accuracy, whereas a polynomial of degree 7 might not. We can easily check this; we find that

$$1 + 1 + \frac{1}{2!} + \frac{1}{3!} + \frac{1}{4!} + \cdots + \frac{1}{7!} = 2.71825396825$$

$$1 + 1 + \frac{1}{2!} + \frac{1}{3!} + \frac{1}{4!} + \cdots + \frac{1}{8!} = 2.71827876984$$

Comparing these with $e = 2.71828182846\ldots$, we see that the error is equal to 2.79×10^{-5} when $n = 7$ and 3.06×10^{-6} when $n = 8$. The error that we computed with (7.28) is a worst-case scenario; that is, the true error can be (and typically is) smaller than the error bound. ■

We have already seen one example in which a Taylor polynomial was useful only for values close to the point at which we approximated the function, regardless of n, the degree of the polynomial. In some situations, the error in the approximation cannot be made small for *any* value close to the point of approximation, regardless of n. One such example is the continuous function

$$f(x) = \begin{cases} e^{-1/x} & \text{for } x > 0 \\ 0 & \text{for } x \leq 0 \end{cases}$$

which is used, for instance, to describe the height of a tree as a function of age. We can show that $f^{(k)}(0) = 0$ for *all* $k \geq 1$, which implies that a Taylor polynomial of degree n about $x = 0$ is

$$P_n(x) = 0$$

for all n. This example clearly shows that it will not help to increase n; the approximation just will not improve.

When we use Taylor polynomials to approximate functions, it is important to know for which values of x the approximation can be made arbitrarily close by choosing n large.

Following are a few of the most important functions, together with their Taylor polynomials about $x = 0$ and the range of x values over which the approximation can be made arbitrarily close by choosing n large enough:

$$e^x = 1 + x + \frac{x^2}{2!} + \frac{x^3}{3!} + \cdots + \frac{x^n}{n!} + R_{n+1}(x), \quad -\infty < x < \infty$$

$$\sin x = x - \frac{x^3}{3!} + \frac{x^5}{5!} - \frac{x^7}{7!} + \frac{x^9}{9!} - \cdots + (-1)^n \frac{x^{2n+1}}{(2n+1)!} + R_{n+1}(x), \quad -\infty < x < \infty$$

$$\cos x = 1 - \frac{x^2}{2!} + \frac{x^4}{4!} - \frac{x^6}{6!} + \frac{x^8}{8!} - \cdots + (-1)^n \frac{x^{2n}}{(2n)!} + R_{n+1}(x), \quad -\infty < x < \infty$$

$$\ln(1+x) = x - \frac{x^2}{2} + \frac{x^3}{3} - \frac{x^4}{4} + \frac{x^5}{5} - \cdots + (-1)^{n+1} \frac{x^n}{n} + R_{n+1}(x), \quad -1 < x \leq 1$$

$$\frac{1}{1-x} = 1 + x + x^2 + x^3 + x^4 + \cdots + x^n + R_{n+1}(x), \quad -1 < x < 1$$

Section 7.6 Problems

■ **7.6.1**

In Problems 1–5, find the linear approximation of $f(x)$ at $x = 0$.

1. $f(x) = e^{2x}$

2. $f(x) = \sin(3x)$

3. $f(x) = \dfrac{1}{1-x}$

4. $f(x) = x^4$

5. $f(x) = \ln(2 + x^2)$

In Problems 6–10, compute the Taylor polynomial of degree n about $a = 0$ for the indicated functions.

6. $f(x) = \dfrac{1}{1+x}, n = 4$

7. $f(x) = \cos x, n = 5$

8. $f(x) = e^{3x}, n = 3$

9. $f(x) = x^5, n = 6$

10. $f(x) = \sqrt{1+x}, n = 3$

In Problems 11–16, compute the Taylor polynomial of degree n about a = 0 for the indicated functions and compare the value of the functions at the indicated point with the value of the corresponding Taylor polynomial.

11. $f(x) = \sqrt{2+x}, n = 3, x = 0.1$

12. $f(x) = \dfrac{1}{1-x}, n = 3, x = 0.1$

13. $f(x) = \sin x, n = 5, x = 1$

14. $f(x) = e^{-x}, n = 4, x = 0.3$

15. $f(x) = \tan x, n = 2, x = 0.1$

16. $f(x) = \ln(1+x), n = 3, x = 0.1$

17. (a) Find the Taylor polynomial of degree 3 about $a = 0$ for $f(x) = \sin x$.

(b) Use your result in (a) to give an intuitive explanation why

$$\lim_{x \to 0} \frac{\sin x}{x} = 1$$

18. (a) Find the Taylor polynomial of degree 2 about $a = 0$ for $f(x) = \cos x$.

(b) Use your result in (a) to give an intuitive explanation why

$$\lim_{x \to 0} \frac{\cos x - 1}{x} = 0$$

■ 7.6.2

In Problems 19–23, compute the Taylor polynomial of degree n about a and compare the value of the approximation with the value of the function at the given point x.

19. $f(x) = \sqrt{x}, a = 1, n = 3; x = 2$

20. $f(x) = \ln x, a = 1, n = 3; x = 2$

21. $f(x) = \cos x, a = \frac{\pi}{6}, n = 3; x = \frac{\pi}{7}$

22. $f(x) = x^{1/5}, a = -1, n = 3; x = -0.9$

23. $f(x) = e^x, a = 2, n = 3; x = 2.1$

24. Show that

$$T^4 \approx T_a^4 + 4T_a^3(T - T_a)$$

for T close to T_a.

25. Show that, for positive constants r and k,

$$rN\left(1 - \frac{N}{K}\right) \approx rN$$

for N close to 0.

26. (a) Show that, for positive constants a and k,

$$f(R) = \frac{aR}{k+R} \approx \frac{a}{k}R$$

for R close to 0.

(b) Show that, for positive constants a and k,

$$f(R) = \frac{aR}{k+R} \approx \frac{a}{2} + \frac{a}{4k}(R-k)$$

for R close to k.

■ 7.6.3

In Problems 27–30, use the following form of the error term

$$R_{n+1}(x) = \frac{f^{(n+1)}(c)}{(n+1)!} x^{n+1}$$

where c is between 0 and x, to determine in advance the degree of Taylor polynomial at a = 0 that would achieve the indicated accuracy in the interval [0, x]. (Do not compute the Taylor polynomial.)

27. $f(x) = e^x, x = 2$, error $< 10^{-3}$

28. $f(x) = \cos x, x = 1$, error $< 10^{-2}$

29. $f(x) = 1/(1+x), x = 0.2$, error $< 10^{-2}$

30. $f(x) = \ln(1+x), x = 0.1$, error $< 10^{-2}$

31. Let $f(x) = e^{-1/x}$ for $x > 0$ and $f(x) = 0$ for $x = 0$. Compute a Taylor polynomial of degree 2 at $x = 0$, and determine how large the error is.

32. We can show that the Taylor polynomial for $f(x) = (1+x)^\alpha$ about $x = 0$, with α a positive constant, converges for $x \in (-1, 1)$. Show that

$$(1+x)^\alpha = 1 + \alpha x + \frac{\alpha(\alpha-1)}{2!}x^2$$

$$+ \frac{\alpha(\alpha-1)(\alpha-2)}{3!}x^3 + \cdots + R_{n+1}(x)$$

33. We can show that the Taylor polynomial for $f(x) = \tan^{-1} x$ about $x = 0$ converges for $|x| \le 1$.

(a) Show that the following is true:

$$\tan^{-1} x = x - \frac{x^3}{3} + \frac{x^5}{5} - \frac{x^7}{7} + \cdots + R_{n+1}(x)$$

(b) Explain why the following holds:

$$\frac{\pi}{4} = 1 - \frac{1}{3} + \frac{1}{5} - \frac{1}{7} + \cdots$$

(This series converges very slowly, as you would see if you used it to approximate π.)

■ 7.7 Tables of Integrals (Optional)

Before the advent of software that could integrate functions, tables of indefinite integrals were useful aids for evaluating integrals. In using a table of integrals, it is still necessary to bring the integrand of interest into a form that is listed in the table— and there are many integrals that simply cannot be evaluated exactly and must be evaluated numerically. We will give a very brief list of indefinite integrals and explain how to use such tables.

I. Basic Functions

1. $\displaystyle\int x^n dx = \frac{1}{n+1}x^{n+1} + C, n \neq -1$

2. $\displaystyle\int \frac{1}{x} dx = \ln|x| + C$

3. $\displaystyle\int e^x dx = e^x + C$

4. $\displaystyle\int a^x dx = \frac{a^x}{\ln a} + C \text{ with } a > 0, a \neq 1$

5. $\displaystyle\int \ln x \, dx = x \ln x - x + C$

6. $\displaystyle\int \sin x \, dx = -\cos x + C$

7. $\displaystyle\int \cos x \, dx = \sin x + C$

8. $\displaystyle\int \tan x \, dx = -\ln|\cos x| + C$

II. Rational Functions

9. $\displaystyle\int \frac{1}{ax+b} dx = \frac{1}{a}\ln|ax+b| + C$

10. $\displaystyle\int \frac{x}{ax+b} dx = \frac{x}{a} - \frac{b}{a^2}\ln|ax+b| + C$

11. $\displaystyle\int \frac{x}{(ax+b)^2} dx = \frac{b}{a^2(ax+b)} + \frac{1}{a^2}\ln|ax+b| + C$

12. $\displaystyle\int \frac{x}{ax^2+bx+c} dx = \frac{1}{2a}\ln|ax^2+bx+c| - \frac{b}{2a}\int \frac{1}{ax^2+bx+c} dx$

13. $\displaystyle\int \frac{1}{a^2+x^2} dx = \frac{1}{a}\arctan\frac{x}{a} + C$

14. $\displaystyle\int \frac{1}{a^2-x^2} dx = \frac{1}{2a}\ln\left|\frac{x+a}{x-a}\right| + C$

III. Integrands Involving $\sqrt{a^2+x^2}$, $\sqrt{a^2-x^2}$, or $\sqrt{x^2-a^2}$

15. $\displaystyle\int \frac{1}{\sqrt{a^2-x^2}} dx = \arcsin\frac{x}{a} + C$

16. $\displaystyle\int \frac{1}{\sqrt{x^2 \pm a^2}} dx = \ln|x + \sqrt{x^2 \pm a^2}| + C$

17. $\displaystyle\int \sqrt{a^2 \pm x^2}\, dx = \frac{1}{2}\left(x\sqrt{a^2 \pm x^2} + a^2\int \frac{1}{\sqrt{a^2 \pm x^2}} dx\right)$

18. $\displaystyle\int \sqrt{x^2 - a^2}\, dx = \frac{1}{2}\left(x\sqrt{x^2 - a^2} - a^2\int \frac{1}{\sqrt{x^2 - a^2}} dx\right)$

IV. Integrands Involving Trigonometric Functions

19. $\displaystyle\int \sin(ax)\, dx = -\frac{1}{a}\cos(ax) + C$

20. $\displaystyle\int \sin^2(ax)\, dx = \frac{1}{2}x - \frac{1}{4a}\sin(2ax) + C$

21. $\displaystyle\int \sin(ax)\sin(bx)\, dx = \frac{\sin(a-b)x}{2(a-b)} - \frac{\sin(a+b)x}{2(a+b)} + C, \text{ for } a^2 \neq b^2$

22. $\displaystyle\int \cos(ax)\, dx = \frac{1}{a}\sin(ax) + C$

23. $\displaystyle\int \cos^2(ax)\,dx = \frac{1}{2}x + \frac{1}{4a}\sin(2ax) + C$

24. $\displaystyle\int \cos(ax)\cos(bx)\,dx = \frac{\sin(a-b)x}{2(a-b)} + \frac{\sin(a+b)x}{2(a+b)} + C,\text{ for } a^2 \neq b^2$

25. $\displaystyle\int \sin(ax)\cos(ax)\,dx = \frac{1}{2a}\sin^2(ax) + C$

26. $\displaystyle\int \sin(ax)\cos(bx)\,dx = -\frac{\cos(a+b)x}{2(a+b)} - \frac{\cos(a-b)x}{2(a-b)} + C,\text{ for } a^2 \neq b^2$

V. Integrands Involving Exponential Functions

27. $\displaystyle\int e^{ax}\,dx = \frac{1}{a}e^{ax} + C$

28. $\displaystyle\int xe^{ax}\,dx = \frac{e^{ax}}{a^2}(ax - 1) + C$

29. $\displaystyle\int x^n e^{ax}\,dx = \frac{1}{a}x^n e^{ax} - \frac{n}{a}\int x^{n-1} e^{ax}\,dx$

30. $\displaystyle\int e^{ax}\sin(bx)\,dx = \frac{e^{ax}}{a^2 + b^2}(a\sin(bx) - b\cos(bx)) + C$

31. $\displaystyle\int e^{ax}\cos(bx)\,dx = \frac{e^{ax}}{a^2 + b^2}(a\cos(bx) + b\sin(bx)) + C$

VI. Integrands Involving Logarithmic Functions

32. $\displaystyle\int \ln x\,dx = x\ln x - x + C$

33. $\displaystyle\int (\ln x)^2\,dx = x(\ln x)^2 - 2x\ln x + 2x + C$

34. $\displaystyle\int x^m \ln x\,dx = x^{m+1}\left[\frac{\ln x}{m+1} - \frac{1}{(m+1)^2}\right] + C, m \neq -1$

35. $\displaystyle\int \frac{\ln x}{x}\,dx = \frac{(\ln x)^2}{2} + C$

36. $\displaystyle\int \frac{1}{x\ln x}\,dx = \ln(\ln x) + C$

37. $\displaystyle\int \sin(\ln x)\,dx = \frac{x}{2}(\sin(\ln x) - \cos(\ln x)) + C$

38. $\displaystyle\int \cos(\ln x)\,dx = \frac{x}{2}(\sin(\ln x) + \cos(\ln x)) + C$

We will now illustrate how to use the preceding table. We begin with examples that fit one of the listed integrals exactly.

EXAMPLE 1   **Square Root** Find

$$\int \sqrt{3 - x^2}\,dx$$

Solution   The integrand involves $\sqrt{a^2 - x^2}$ and is of the form III.17 with $a^2 = 3$. Hence,

$$\int \sqrt{3 - x^2}\,dx = \frac{1}{2}\left(x\sqrt{3 - x^2} + 3\int \frac{1}{\sqrt{3 - x^2}}\,dx\right)$$

To evaluate $\int \frac{1}{\sqrt{3-x^2}}\,dx$, we use III.15 with $a^2 = 3$ and find that

$$\int \frac{1}{\sqrt{3 - x^2}}\,dx = \arcsin\frac{x}{\sqrt{3}} + C$$

Thus,

$$\int \sqrt{3 - x^2}\, dx = \frac{1}{2}\left(x\sqrt{3 - x^2} + 3\arcsin\frac{x}{\sqrt{3}}\right) + C$$ ■

EXAMPLE 2 **Trigonometric Function** Find

$$\int \sin(3x)\cos(4x)\, dx$$

Solution The integrand involves trigonometric functions, and we can find it in IV.26 with $a = 3$ and $b = 4$. Hence,

$$\int \sin(3x)\cos(4x)\, dx = -\frac{\cos(7x)}{14} - \frac{\cos(-x)}{(2)(-1)} + C$$

Since $\cos(-x) = \cos x$, this simplifies to

$$\int \sin(3x)\cos(4x)\, dx = -\frac{\cos(7x)}{14} + \frac{\cos x}{2} + C$$ ■

EXAMPLE 3 **Exponential Function** Find

$$\int x^2 e^{3x}\, dx$$

Solution This integrand is of the form V.29 with $n = 2$ and $a = 3$. Hence,

$$\int x^2 e^{3x}\, dx = \frac{1}{3}x^2 e^{3x} - \frac{2}{3}\int x e^{3x}\, dx$$

We now use V.28 to continue the evaluation of the integral and find that

$$\int x e^{3x}\, dx = \frac{e^{3x}}{9}(3x - 1) + C$$

Thus,

$$\int x^2 e^{3x}\, dx = \frac{1}{3}x^2 e^{3x} - \frac{2}{3}\left[\frac{e^{3x}}{9}(3x - 1)\right] + C$$ ■

Thus far, each of our examples exactly matched one of the integrals in our table. Often, this will not be the case, and the integrand must be manipulated until it matches one of the integrals in the table. Among the manipulations that are used are expansions, long division, completion of the square, and substitution. We give a few examples to illustrate.

EXAMPLE 4 **Exponential Function** Find

$$\int e^{2x}\sin(3x - 1)\, dx$$

Solution This integrand looks similar to V.30. If we use the substitution

$$u = 3x - 1 \quad \text{with } dx = \frac{1}{3}\, du \text{ and } 2x = \frac{2}{3}(u + 1)$$

then the integrand can be transformed so that it matches V.30 exactly, and we have

$$\int e^{2x} \sin(3x - 1)\, dx = \int e^{2(u+1)/3}(\sin u)\frac{1}{3}\, du$$

$$= \frac{e^{2/3}}{3} \int e^{2u/3} \sin u\, du$$

$$= \frac{e^{2/3}}{3} \frac{e^{2u/3}}{\frac{4}{9}+1} \left[\frac{2}{3}\sin u - \cos u\right] + C$$

$$= \frac{e^{2/3}}{3 \cdot \frac{13}{9}} e^{2(3x-1)/3} \left[\frac{2}{3}\sin(3x - 1) - \cos(3x - 1)\right] + C$$

$$= \frac{3}{13} e^{2x} \left[\frac{2}{3}\sin(3x - 1) - \cos(3x - 1)\right] + C \qquad ■$$

EXAMPLE 5 **Rational Function** Find

$$\int \frac{x^2}{9 + x^2}\, dx$$

Solution The integrand is a rational function; we can use long division to simplify it:

$$\frac{x^2}{9 + x^2} = 1 - \frac{9}{9 + x^2}$$

Then, using II.13 with $a = 3$, we obtain

$$\int \frac{x^2}{9 + x^2}\, dx = \int dx - 9 \int \frac{1}{9 + x^2}\, dx$$

$$= x - 9\left(\frac{1}{3}\arctan\frac{x}{3}\right) + C$$

$$= x - 3\arctan\frac{x}{3} + C \qquad ■$$

EXAMPLE 6 **Rational Function** Find

$$\int \frac{1}{x^2 - 2x - 3}\, dx$$

Solution The first step is to complete the square in the denominator:

$$\frac{1}{x^2 - 2x - 3} = \frac{1}{(x^2 - 2x + 1) - 1 - 3}$$

$$= \frac{1}{(x - 1)^2 - 4}$$

Then, using the substitution $u = x - 1$ with $du = dx$, we find that

$$\int \frac{dx}{(x - 1)^2 - 4} = \int \frac{du}{u^2 - 4} = -\int \frac{du}{4 - u^2}$$

which is of the form II.14 with $a = 2$. Therefore,

$$\int \frac{1}{x^2 - 2x - 3}\, dx = -\int \frac{du}{4 - u^2} = -\frac{1}{4}\ln\left|\frac{u + 2}{u - 2}\right| + C$$

$$= -\frac{1}{4}\ln\left|\frac{x + 1}{x - 3}\right| + C \qquad ■$$

■ 7.7.1 A Note on Software Packages That Can Integrate

Mathematicians and scientists use software packages to integrate functions. They are not difficult to use with some practice. Although they will not give you insight into what technique could be used to solve an integration problem, they quickly give you the correct answer. For instance, if we used MATLAB, one of the common software packages, to calculate the integral in Example 8 of Section 7.3, we would enter the following string of commands into our computer:

```
syms x;
f=x^4*(1-x)^4/(1+x^2);
int(f,0,1)
```

MATLAB then returns

```
ans = 22/7-pi
```

Section 7.7 Problems

In Problems 1–8, use the table on pages 383–384 to compute each integral.

1. $\int \dfrac{x}{2x-3}\,dx$

2. $\int \dfrac{dx}{16+x^2}$

3. $\int \sqrt{x^2-16}\,dx$

4. $\int \sin(2x)\cos(2x)\,dx$

5. $\int_0^1 x^3 e^{-x}\,dx$

6. $\int_0^{\pi/4} e^{-x}\cos(2x)\,dx$

7. $\int_1^e x^2 \ln x\,dx$

8. $\int_e^{e^2} \dfrac{dx}{x\ln x}$

In Problems 9–22, use the table on pages 383–384 to compute each integral after manipulating the integrand in a suitable way.

9. $\int_0^{\pi/6} e^x \cos\left(x-\dfrac{\pi}{6}\right) dx$

10. $\int_1^2 x\ln(2x-1)\,dx$

11. $\int (x^2-1)e^{-x/2}\,dx$

12. $\int (x+1)^2 e^{-2x}\,dx$

13. $\int \cos^2(5x-3)\,dx$

14. $\int \dfrac{x^2}{4x^2+4x+1}\,dx$

15. $\int \sqrt{9+4x^2}\,dx$

16. $\int \dfrac{1}{\sqrt{16-9x^2}}\,dx$

17. $\int e^{2x+1}\sin\left(\dfrac{\pi}{2}x\right)dx$

18. $\int (x-1)^2 e^{2x}\,dx$

19. $\int_2^4 \dfrac{1}{x\ln\sqrt{x}}\,dx$

20. $\int_1^e (x+2)^2 \ln x\,dx$

21. $\int \cos(\ln(3x))\,dx$

22. $\int \dfrac{3}{x^2-4x+8}\,dx$

Chapter 7 Key Terms

Discuss the following definitions and concepts:

1. The substitution rule for indefinite integrals

2. The substitution rule for definite integrals

3. Integration by parts

4. The "trick" of "multiplying by 1"

5. Partial-fraction decomposition

6. Partial-fraction method

7. Proper rational function

8. Irreducible quadratic factor

9. Improper integral

10. Integration when the interval is unbounded

11. Integration when the integrand is discontinuous

12. Convergence and divergence of improper integrals

13. Comparison results for improper integrals

14. Numerical integration: midpoint and trapezoidal rule

15. Error bounds for the midpoint and the trapezoidal rule

16. Using tables of integrals for integration

17. Linear approximation

18. Taylor polynomial of degree n

19. Taylor's formula

Chapter 7 Review Problems

In Problems 1–30, evaluate the given indefinite integrals.

1. $\int x^2(1-x^3)^2\,dx$

2. $\int \dfrac{\cos x}{1+\sin^2 x}\,dx$

3. $\int 4xe^{-x^2}\,dx$

4. $\int \dfrac{x\ln(1+x^2)}{1+x^2}\,dx$

5. $\int (1+\sqrt{x})^{1/3}\,dx$

6. $\int x\sqrt{3x+1}\,dx$

7. $\int x\sec^2(3x^2)\,dx$

8. $\int \tan x\sec^2 x\,dx$

9. $\int x\ln x\,dx$

10. $\int x^3 \ln x^2\,dx$

11. $\int \sec^2 x \ln(\tan x)\, dx$

12. $\int \sqrt{x} \ln \sqrt{x}\, dx$

13. $\int \dfrac{1}{4+x^2}\, dx$

14. $\int \dfrac{1}{4-x^2}\, dx$

15. $\int \tan x\, dx$

16. $\int \tan^{-1} x\, dx$

17. $\int e^{2x} \sin x\, dx$

18. $\int x \sin x\, dx$

19. $\int \sqrt{e^x}\, dx$

20. $\int \ln \sqrt{x}\, dx$

21. $\int \sin^2 x\, dx$

22. $\int \sin x \cos x\, e^{\sin x}\, dx$

23. $\int \dfrac{1}{x(x-1)}\, dx$

24. $\int \dfrac{1}{(x+1)(x-2)}\, dx$

25. $\int \dfrac{x}{x+5}\, dx$

26. $\int \dfrac{x}{x^2+5}\, dx$

27. $\int \dfrac{1}{x+5}\, dx$

28. $\int \dfrac{1}{x^2+5}\, dx$

29. $\int \dfrac{(x+1)^2}{x-1}\, dx$

30. $\int \dfrac{2x+1}{\sqrt{1-x^2}}\, dx$

In Problems 31–50, evaluate the given definite integrals.

31. $\int_1^3 \dfrac{x^2+1}{x}\, dx$

32. $\int_0^{\pi/2} x \sin x\, dx$

33. $\int_0^1 x e^{-x^2/2}\, dx$

34. $\int_1^2 \ln x\, dx$

35. $\int_0^2 \dfrac{1}{4+x^2}\, dx$

36. $\int_0^{1/2} \dfrac{2}{\sqrt{1-x^2}}\, dx$

37. $\int_2^6 \dfrac{1}{\sqrt{x-2}}\, dx$

38. $\int_0^2 \dfrac{1}{x-2}\, dx$

39. $\int_0^\infty \dfrac{1}{9+x^2}\, dx$

40. $\int_0^\infty \dfrac{1}{x^2+3}\, dx$

41. $\int_0^\infty \dfrac{1}{x+3}\, dx$

42. $\int_0^\infty \dfrac{1}{(x+3)^2}\, dx$

43. $\int_0^1 \dfrac{1}{x^2}\, dx$

44. $\int_1^\infty \dfrac{1}{x^2}\, dx$

45. $\int_0^1 \dfrac{1}{\sqrt{x}}\, dx$

46. $\int_1^\infty \dfrac{1}{\sqrt{x}}\, dx$

47. $\int_0^1 x \ln x\, dx$

48. $\int_0^1 x 2^x\, dx$

49. $\int_0^{\pi/4} e^{\cos x} \sin x\, dx$

50. $\int_0^{\pi/4} x \sin(2x)\, dx$

In Problems 51–54, use (a) the midpoint rule and (b) the trapezoidal rule to approximate each integral with the specified value of n.

51. $\int_0^2 (x^2-1)\, dx, n=4$

52. $\int_{-1}^1 (x^3-1)\, dx, n=4$

53. $\int_0^1 e^{-x}\, dx, n=5$

54. $\int_0^{\pi/4} \sin(4x)\, dx, n=4$

In Problems 55–58, find the Taylor polynomial of degree n about x = a for each function.

55. $f(x) = \sin(2x), a=0, n=3$

56. $f(x) = e^{-x^2/2}, a=0, n=3$

57. $f(x) = \ln x, a=1, n=3$

58. $f(x) = \dfrac{1}{x-3}, a=4, n=4$

59. Cost of Gene Substitution (*Adapted from Roughgarden, 1996*) Suppose that an advantageous mutation arises in a population. Initially, the gene carrying this mutation is at a low frequency. As the gene spreads through the population, the average fitness of the population increases. We denote by $f_{avg}(t)$ the average fitness of the population at time t, by $f_{avg}(0)$ the average fitness of the population at time 0 (when the mutation arose), and by K the final value of the average fitness after the mutation has spread through the population. Haldane (1957) suggested measuring the *cost of evolution* (now known as the *cost of gene substitution*) by the cumulative difference between the current and the final fitness—that is, by

$$\int_0^\infty (K - f_{avg}(t))\, dt$$

In Figure 7.43, shade the region whose area is equal to the cost of gene substitution.

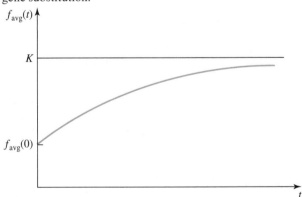

Figure 7.43 The cost of gene substitution. See Problem 59.

Differential Equations

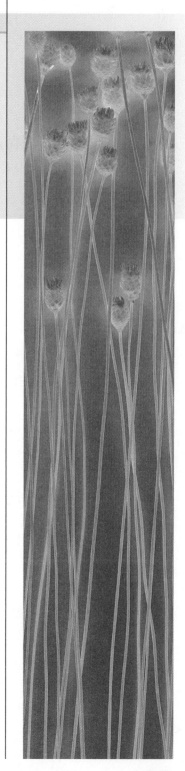

8

In Section 4.6, Example 6, we looked at the exponential growth of a population, given by

$$N(t) = N(0)e^{rt}, \ t \geq 0$$

where $N(t)$ denotes the size of the population at time t and r is a parameter. Differentiating $N(t)$ with respect to t, we found that exponential growth satisfies the differential equation

$$\frac{dN}{dt} = rN(t), \ t \geq 0 \qquad (8.1)$$

We conclude from (8.1) that if a population grows exponentially, then its per capita growth rate $\frac{1}{N}\frac{dN}{dt}$ is a constant—namely, the parameter r. Equation (8.1) contains the derivative of a function, and such equations are therefore called **differential equations**.

While the function $N(t) = N(0)e^{rt}, t \geq 0$, reveals the behavior of the population size over time, it tells us little about what processes lead to exponential growth. In contrast, the differential equation $\frac{1}{N}\frac{dN}{dt} = r$ reveals the process—a constant per capita growth rate—but does not tell us much about the population size trajectory over time. It is therefore important to be able to go back and forth between the two descriptions.

We saw in Example 6 of Section 4.6 that differentiating the function $N(t)$ results in a differential equation describing the rate of change of $N(t)$. On the basis of what we learned in Chapters 6 and 7, we now know that going from the derivative of a function to the function involves integration. In Section 8.1, we will learn how to use integration to go from a differential equation to a function that satisfies the differential equation.

Differential equations can contain derivatives of any order; for example,

$$\frac{d^2y}{dx^2} + \frac{dy}{dx} = xy$$

is a differential equation that contains the first and second derivative of the function $y = y(x)$. If a differential equation, such as (8.1), contains only the first derivative, it is called a **first-order** differential equation.

Throughout this chapter, we will restrict ourselves to first-order differential equations of the form

$$\frac{dy}{dx} = f(x)g(y) \tag{8.2}$$

The right-hand side of (8.2) is the product of two functions, one depending only on x, the other only on y. Such equations are called **separable differential equations**. (The reason for this name will become clear shortly.) This type of differential equation includes two special cases:

$$\frac{dy}{dx} = f(x) \tag{8.3}$$

and

$$\frac{dy}{dx} = g(y) \tag{8.4}$$

We discussed differential equations of the form (8.3) in Section 5.8. Differential equations of the form (8.4) include (8.1) and are frequently used in biological models.

8.1 Solving Differential Equations

Let's return to the growth model in (8.1), and, to be concrete, let's choose $r = 2$. This results in the equation

$$\frac{dN}{dt} = 2N(t), \ t \geq 0 \tag{8.5}$$

We are interested in finding a function $N(t)$ that satisfies (8.5). Such a function is called a **solution** of the differential equation. We already know that, with $N_0 = N(0)$,

$$N(t) = N_0 e^{2t}, \ t \geq 0$$

is a solution of (8.5). To check whether the function $N(t)$ is indeed a solution, we differentiate $N(t)$:

$$\frac{dN}{dt} = 2 \underbrace{N_0 e^{2t}}_{N(t)} = 2N(t)$$

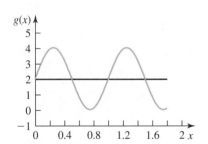

Figure 8.1 The per capita growth rate for the differential equation (8.6) shows oscillations and is described by the function $g(t) = 2(1 + \sin(2\pi t))$.

Modeling biological situations frequently leads to differential equations. A description of the instantaneous rate of change is often a good starting point for building models. As an example, let's look again at (8.5) and let's write it in the form

$$\frac{1}{N}\frac{dN}{dt} = 2$$

In this model, the per capita growth rate is constant. Suppose, however, we observed that the per capita growth rate shows oscillations, as illustrated in Figure 8.1. Then we can immediately modify our original differential equation (8.5) to reflect this observation and obtain

$$\frac{dN}{dt} = 2(1 + \sin(2\pi t))N(t), \ t \geq 0 \tag{8.6}$$

In this section, we will learn how to solve differential equations like (8.6). (See Problem 57 at the end of the section.)

A first-order differential equation tells us what the derivative of a function is. Therefore, in order to find a solution, we must integrate. (Since it is not always possible to integrate a function, it is not always possible to write the solution of a differential equation in explicit form.)

We begin with a general method for solving separable differential equations of the form (8.2), or

$$\frac{dy}{dx} = f(x)g(y) \tag{8.7}$$

We divide both sides of (8.7) by $g(y)$ [assuming that $g(y) \neq 0$]:

$$\frac{1}{g(y)} \frac{dy}{dx} = f(x) \qquad (8.8)$$

Now, if $y = u(x)$ is a solution of (8.8), then $u(x)$ satisfies $\frac{dy}{dx} = u'(x)$, and hence

$$\frac{1}{g[u(x)]} u'(x) = f(x)$$

If we integrate both sides with respect to x, we find that

$$\int \frac{1}{g[u(x)]} u'(x) \, dx = \int f(x) \, dx$$

or

$$\int \frac{1}{g(y)} \, dy = \int f(x) \, dx \qquad (8.9)$$

since $g[u(x)] = g(y)$ and $u'(x) \, dx = dy$.

The preceding analysis suggests the following procedure for solving separable differential equations: We separate the variables x and y so that one side of the equation depends only on y and the other side only on x. To do so, we treat dy and dx as if they were regular numbers. Specifically, separating variables in (8.7) yields

$$\frac{dy}{g(y)} = f(x) \, dx$$

and integrating both sides results in equation (8.9):

$$\int \frac{dy}{g(y)} = \int f(x) \, dx$$

The method of separating the variables x and y works because the right-hand side of (8.7) is of the special form $f(x)g(y)$, which gave this type of differential equation its name. Note that when we divided (8.7) by $g(y)$, we had to be careful, since $g(y)$ might be 0 for some values of y, in which case we cannot divide. We will address this problem in Subsection 8.1.2. In the next two subsections, we discuss how to solve differential equations of the forms (8.3) and (8.4); we give an example of the general type (8.2) in Subsection 8.1.3.

■ 8.1.1 Pure-Time Differential Equations

In many applications, the independent variable represents time. If the rate of change of a function depends only on time, we call the resulting differential equation a **pure-time differential equation**. Such a differential equation is of the form

$$\frac{dy}{dx} = f(x), \quad x \in I \qquad (8.10)$$

where I is an interval and x represents time. We discussed such equations in Section 5.8, where we found that their solution is of the form

$$y(x) = \int_{x_0}^{x} f(u) \, du + C \qquad (8.11)$$

The constant C comes from finding the general antiderivative of $f(x)$; the number x_0 is in the interval I. To determine C, we must phrase the problem as an initial-value problem (see Section 5.8); if we assume that $y(x_0) = y_0$, then plugging x_0 into (8.11) yields $y(x_0) = C$, and thus $C = y_0$. The solution can then be written as

$$y(x) = y_0 + \int_{x_0}^{x} f(u) \, du$$

To solve (8.10) formally, we separate variables; we write the differential equation in the form

$$dy = f(x)\, dx$$

and then integrate both sides:

$$\int dy = \int f(x)\, dx$$

or

$$y(x) = \int f(x)\, dx$$

which is the same as (8.11).

EXAMPLE 1   Suppose that the volume $V(t)$ of a cell at time t changes according to

$$\frac{dV}{dt} = \sin t \quad \text{with } V(0) = 3$$

Find $V(t)$.

Solution   Since

$$V(t) = V(0) + \int_0^t \sin u \, du$$

it follows that

$$V(t) = 3 + [-\cos u]_0^t$$
$$= 3 + (-\cos t + \cos 0)$$
$$= 4 - \cos t$$

because $\cos 0 = 1$. (See Figure 8.2.)   ■

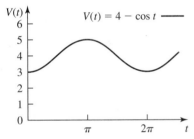

Figure 8.2 The solution $V(t) = 4 - \cos t$ in Example 1.

If we changed the initial condition in Example 1, the graph of the new solution would be obtained from the old solution by shifting the solution vertically so that it would satisfy the new initial condition. (See Figure 8.3; we discussed the situation in Section 5.8.)

■ 8.1.2 Autonomous Differential Equations

Many of the differential equations, such as (8.1), that model biological situations are of the form

$$\frac{dy}{dx} = g(y) \tag{8.12}$$

where the right-hand side does not explicitly depend on x. These equations are called **autonomous differential equations**.

To interpret the biological meaning of *autonomous*, let's return to the growth model

$$\frac{dN}{dt} = 2N(t) \tag{8.13}$$

We will see shortly that the general solution of (8.13) is

$$N(t) = Ce^{2t} \tag{8.14}$$

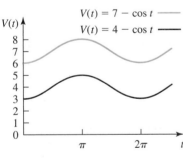

Figure 8.3 The curve $V(t) = 7 - \cos t$ is obtained from $V(t) = 4 - \cos t$ by a vertical shift. The function $V(t) = 7 - \cos t$ solves the differential equation in Example 1 with $V(0) = 6$.

where C is a constant that can be determined if the population size at one time is known. Suppose we conduct an experiment in which we follow a population over time, and suppose the population satisfies (8.13) with $N(0) = 20$. Using (8.14), we find that $N(0) = C = 20$. Then the size of the population at time t is given by

$$N(t) = 20e^{2t}$$

If we repeat the experiment at, say, time $t = 10$ with the exact same initial population size, then, everything else being equal, the population evolves in exactly the same way as the one starting at $t = 0$. Using (8.14) now with $N(10) = 20$, we find that $N(10) = Ce^{20} = 20$, or $C = 20e^{-20}$. The size of the population is then given by

$$N(t) = 20e^{-20}e^{2t} = 20e^{2(t-10)}$$

The graph of this solution can be obtained from the previous graph, where $N(0) = 20$, by shifting the old graph 10 units to the right to the new starting point $(10, 20)$. (See Figure 8.4.)

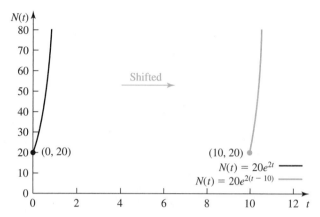

Figure 8.4 The graph of the solution $N(t) = 20e^{2t}$ is shifted to the new starting point $(10, 20)$.

This means that a population starting with $N = 20$ follows the same trajectory, regardless of when we start the experiment. This statement makes sense biologically: If the growth conditions do not depend explicitly on time, the experiment should yield the same outcome, regardless of when the experiment is performed. If the growth conditions for the population do change over time, we would not be able to use an autonomous differential equation to describe the growth of the population; we would need to include the time dependence explicitly in the dynamics.

Formally, we can solve (8.12) by separation of variables. We begin by dividing both sides of (8.12) by $g(y)$ and multiplying both sides of (8.12) by dx, to obtain

$$\frac{dy}{g(y)} = dx$$

Integrating both sides then gives

$$\int \frac{dy}{g(y)} = \int dx$$

We will discuss two cases: $g(y) = k(y - a)$ and $g(y) = k(y - a)(y - b)$. The growth model (8.1) is an example of the first case; the logistic equation, which we saw in Section 3.3 for the first time, is an example of the second case.

Case 1: $g(y) = k(y - a)$. We wish to solve

$$\frac{dy}{dx} = k(y - a) \tag{8.15}$$

where k and a are constants. We assume that $k \neq 0$. Separating variables then yields

$$\frac{dy}{y - a} = k\, dx \tag{8.16}$$

where we need to assume that $y \neq a$ to divide by $y - a$. It is somewhat arbitrary whether we leave k on the right-hand side or move it to the left-hand side; leaving it on the right is more convenient. Integrating both sides of (8.16) results in

$$\int \frac{dy}{y-a} = \int k\,dx$$

or

$$\ln|y-a| = kx + C_1$$

Exponentiating both sides then yields

$$|y-a| = e^{kx+C_1}$$

or

$$|y-a| = e^{C_1}e^{kx}$$

Removing the absolute-value signs, we find

$$y - a = \pm e^{C_1}e^{kx}$$

Renaming the constant by setting $C = \pm e^{C_1}$, we can write the solution as

$$y = Ce^{kx} + a \tag{8.17}$$

(Renaming the constant only serves the purpose of getting the equation in a more readable form.) As in the case of a pure-time differential equation, integration introduces a constant. If we know a point (x_0, y_0) of the solution, then C can be determined. We will refer to such a point as an **initial condition**.

To obtain (8.16), we divided by $y - a$. We are allowed to do this only as long as $y \neq a$. If $y = a$, then $dy/dx = 0$ and the constant function $y = a$ is a solution of (8.15). We *lost* this solution when we divided (8.15) by $y - a$. Note that the constant C in (8.17) is different from 0, since $C = \pm e^{C_1}$ and $e^{C_1} \neq 0$ for any real number C_1. But we can combine the constant solution $y = a$ and the solution in (8.17) by allowing C to be equal to 0 in (8.17).

Before we turn to biological applications, we give an example in which we see how to solve a differential equation such as (8.15) and how to determine the value of C.

EXAMPLE 2   Solve

$$\frac{dy}{dx} = 2 - 3y, \quad \text{where } y_0 = 1 \text{ when } x_0 = 1$$

Solution   Instead of trying to identify the constants C, k, and a in equation (8.17), it is easier to solve the equation directly. We separate variables and then integrate, which results in

$$\int \frac{dy}{2-3y} = \int dx$$

Since an antiderivative of $\frac{1}{2-3y}$ is $-\frac{1}{3}\ln|2-3y|$, we find that

$$-\frac{1}{3}\ln|2-3y| = x + C_1$$

Solving for y yields

$$\ln|2-3y| = -3x - 3C_1$$
$$|2-3y| = e^{-3x-3C_1}$$
$$2-3y = \pm e^{-3C_1}e^{-3x}$$

Setting $C = \pm e^{-3C_1}$, we obtain

$$2 - 3y = Ce^{-3x}$$

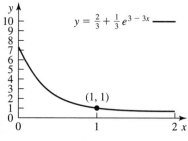

Figure 8.5 The solution to Example 2.

To determine C, we use the initial condition $y_0 = 1$ when $x_0 = 1$. That is,

$$2 - 3 = Ce^{-3}, \quad \text{or} \quad C = -e^3$$

Hence,

$$2 - 3y = -e^3 e^{-3x}$$

or

$$y = \frac{2}{3} + \frac{1}{3}e^{3-3x}$$

(See Figure 8.5.) ■

We now turn to two biological applications that are covered by Case 1.

EXAMPLE 3

Exponential Population Growth This model is given by (8.1) and was introduced in Section 4.6. We denote the population size at time $t \geq 0$ by $N(t)$ and assume that $N(0) = N_0 > 0$. The change in population size is described by the initial-value problem

$$\frac{dN}{dt} = rN, \quad \text{where } N(0) = N_0 \tag{8.18}$$

The parameter r is called the *intrinsic rate of growth* and is the per capita rate of growth, since

$$r = \frac{1}{N}\frac{dN}{dt}$$

When $r > 0$, this model represents a growing population. When $r < 0$, the size of the population decreases. (Note that the per capita growth rate r is independent of the population size.)

We can either solve (8.18) directly, as in Example 2, or use (8.15). Let's use (8.15). If we compare (8.18) with (8.15), we find that $k = r$ and $a = 0$. Hence, using (8.17), we find the solution

$$N(t) = Ce^{rt}$$

Since $N(0) = N_0 = C$, we write the solution as

$$N(t) = N_0 e^{rt} \tag{8.19}$$

Equation (8.19) shows that the population size grows exponentially when $r > 0$. When $r < 0$, the population size decreases exponentially. When $r = 0$, the population size stays constant.

We show solution curves of $N(t) = N_0 e^{rt}$ for $r > 0$, $r = 0$, and $r < 0$ in Figure 8.6. Exponential growth (or decay) is one of the most important growth phenomena in biology. You should therefore memorize both the differential equation (8.18) and its solution (8.19), together with the graphs in Figure 8.6, and know that (8.18) describes a situation in which the per capita growth rate (or intrinsic rate of growth) is a constant.

When $r > 0$, the population size grows without bound ($\lim_{t\to\infty} N(t) = \infty$). This kind of growth can be found when individuals are not limited by the availability of food or by competition. If we start a bacterial colony on a nutrient-rich substrate by inoculating the substrate with a few bacteria, then the bacteria initially can grow and divide unrestrictedly. Subsequently, when the substrate becomes more crowded and the food source depleted, the growth will be restricted and a different differential equation will be required to describe this situation. (We will discuss this scenario in Case 2.) Exponential decay in a population can be seen when the death rate exceeds the birth rate (for instance, in cases of starvation). ■

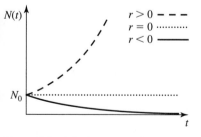

Figure 8.6 Solution curves for $dN/dt = rN$.

The type of growth in Example 3 is referred to as *Malthusian growth*, named after Thomas Malthus (1766–1834), a British clergyman and economist. Malthus wrote about the consequences of unrestricted growth on the welfare of humans. He claimed that populations and food show two fundamentally different growth patterns: Populations grow exponentially and food grows linearly. He concluded that, since exponential growth ultimately overtakes linear growth, populations would eventually experience starvation. (See Problem 56.)

Recall from Section 4.6 that when $r < 0$, (8.18) has the same form as the differential equation that describes radioactive decay. $N(t)$ would then denote the amount of radioactive material left at time t. We will revisit this application in Problem 20.

EXAMPLE 4 **Restricted Growth: von Bertalanffy Equation** This example describes the simplest form of restricted growth and can be used to describe the growth of fish. We denote by $L(t)$ the length of the fish at age t and assume that $L(0) = L_0$. Then

$$\frac{dL}{dt} = k(A - L) \tag{8.20}$$

where A is a positive constant that we will interpret shortly. We assume that $L_0 < A$ and explain this restriction subsequently as well. The constant k is also positive; the equation says that the growth rate dL/dt is proportional to $A - L$, so k should be interpreted as a constant of proportionality. We see that the growth rate dL/dt is positive and decreases linearly with length as long as $L < A$ and that the growth stops (i.e., $dL/dt = 0$) when $L = A$. To solve (8.20), we separate variables and integrate, yielding

$$\int \frac{dL}{A - L} = \int k\, dt$$

Hence,

$$-\ln |A - L| = kt + C_1$$

After multiplying this equation by -1 and exponentiating, we obtain

$$|A - L| = e^{-C_1} e^{-kt}$$

or

$$A - L = C e^{-kt}$$

with $C = \pm e^{-C_1}$. Since $L(0) = L_0$, it follows that

$$A - L_0 = C$$

The solution is then given by

$$A - L(t) = (A - L_0)e^{-kt}$$

or

$$L(t) = A\left[1 - \left(1 - \frac{L_0}{A}\right)e^{-kt}\right] \tag{8.21}$$

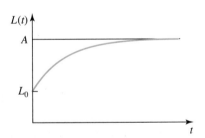

Figure 8.7 The graph of the von Bertalanffy equation.

(See Figure 8.7.)

This is the von Bertalanffy equation that we encountered previously. Since

$$\lim_{t \to \infty} L(t) = A$$

the parameter A denotes the **asymptotic length** of the fish. Mathematically, there are no restrictions on L_0; biologically, however, we require that $0 < L_0 < A$. Otherwise, the growth rate would be negative, meaning that the fish shrinks in size. Note that A is an asymptotic length that is never reached, since there is no finite age T with $L(T) = A$ if $L(0) < A$.

We can now interpret the differential equation (8.16): The growth rate is proportional to the difference of the current length and the asymptotic length, with k representing the constant of proportionality. Since this difference is decreasing over time, (8.16) also shows that the growth rate decreases over time, implying that juveniles grow at a faster rate than adults. Moreover, the growth rate is always positive. This means that fish grow throughout their lives, which is indeed the case. ■

Case 2: $g(y) = k(y - a)(y - b)$. We now turn to differential equations of the form

$$\frac{dy}{dx} = k(y - a)(y - b) \tag{8.22}$$

where k, a, and b are constant. We assume that $k \neq 0$. Separating variables and integrating both sides yields

$$\int \frac{dy}{(y - a)(y - b)} = \int k \, dx \tag{8.23}$$

provided that $y \neq a$ and $y \neq b$. When $a = b$, we must find an antiderivative of $\frac{1}{(y-a)^2}$, which is $-\frac{1}{y-a}$. In this case,

$$-\frac{1}{y - a} = kx + C$$

or

$$y = a - \frac{1}{kx + C}$$

The constant C can then be determined from the initial condition. When $y = a$, $dy/dx = 0$ and, consequently, y is equal to a constant (specifically, $y = a$).

To find the solution when $a \neq b$, we must use the partial-fraction method that we introduced in Section 7.3. Let's first do an example.

EXAMPLE 5   Solve

$$\frac{dy}{dx} = 2(y - 1)(y + 2) \quad \text{with } y_0 = 2 \text{ when } x_0 = 0$$

Solution   Separation of variables yields

$$\int \frac{dy}{(y - 1)(y + 2)} = \int 2 \, dx$$

We use partial fractions to integrate the left-hand side:

$$\frac{1}{(y - 1)(y + 2)} = \frac{A}{y - 1} + \frac{B}{y + 2}$$

$$= \frac{A(y + 2) + B(y - 1)}{(y - 1)(y + 2)}$$

$$= \frac{(A + B)y + 2A - B}{(y - 1)(y + 2)}$$

Comparing the last term with the integrand, we find that

$$A + B = 0 \quad \text{and} \quad 2A - B = 1$$

which yields

$$A = -B \quad \text{and} \quad 2A - B = 3A = 1$$

Thus,

$$A = \frac{1}{3} \quad \text{and} \quad B = -\frac{1}{3}$$

Using the partial-fraction decomposition, we must integrate

$$\frac{1}{3} \int \left(\frac{1}{y - 1} - \frac{1}{y + 2} \right) dy = \int 2 \, dx$$

This produces

$$\frac{1}{3}[\ln |y - 1| - \ln |y + 2|] = 2x + C_1$$

Simplifying the latter equation results in

$$\ln\left|\frac{y-1}{y+2}\right| = 6x + 3C_1$$

$$\left|\frac{y-1}{y+2}\right| = e^{3C_1}e^{6x}$$

$$\frac{y-1}{y+2} = \pm e^{3C_1}e^{6x}$$

$$\frac{y-1}{y+2} = Ce^{6x}$$

Using the initial condition $y_0 = 2$ when $x_0 = 0$, we find that

$$\frac{1}{4} = C$$

The solution is therefore

$$\frac{y-1}{y+2} = \frac{1}{4}e^{6x}$$

If we want the solution in the form $y = f(x)$, we must solve for y:

$$y - 1 = (y+2)\frac{1}{4}e^{6x}$$

$$y\left(1 - \frac{1}{4}e^{6x}\right) = \frac{1}{2}e^{6x} + 1$$

$$y = \frac{\frac{1}{2}e^{6x} + 1}{1 - \frac{1}{4}e^{6x}}$$

$$y = \frac{2e^{6x} + 4}{4 - e^{6x}}$$

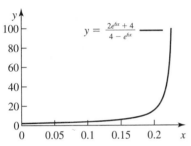

$$y = \frac{2e^{6x}+4}{4 - e^{6x}}$$

Figure 8.8 The solution for Example 5.

(See Figure 8.8.)   ■

We return now to (8.23) when $a \neq b$ and $y \neq a$ and $y \neq b$. We use the partial-fraction method to simplify the integral on the left-hand side. We decompose the integrand into a sum of simpler rational functions that we know how to integrate; that is, we write the integrand in the form

$$\frac{1}{(y-a)(y-b)} = \frac{A}{y-a} + \frac{B}{y-b} \tag{8.24}$$

where A and B are constants that we must find. Next, we do the following algebraic manipulation on the right-hand side of (8.24):

$$\frac{A}{y-a} + \frac{B}{y-b} = \frac{A(y-b) + B(y-a)}{(y-a)(y-b)}$$
$$= \frac{y(A+B) - (Ab+Ba)}{(y-a)(y-b)} \tag{8.25}$$

Comparing the last expression in (8.25) with the left-hand side of (8.24), we conclude that the constants A and B must satisfy

$$A + B = 0 \qquad \text{and} \qquad Ab + Ba = -1$$

Substituting $B = -A$ from the first equation into the second, we find that

$$Ab - Aa = -1, \qquad \text{or} \qquad A(b-a) = -1, \qquad \text{or} \qquad A = \frac{1}{a-b}$$

Therefore,

$$B = -\frac{1}{a - b}$$

That is,

$$\frac{1}{(y - a)(y - b)} = \frac{1}{a - b}\left[\frac{1}{y - a} - \frac{1}{y - b}\right] \tag{8.26}$$

Equation (8.26) allows us to evaluate

$$\int \frac{dy}{(y - a)(y - b)}$$

which is the left-hand side of (8.23). Evaluating yields

$$\int \frac{dy}{(y - a)(y - b)} = \frac{1}{a - b}\int\left(\frac{1}{y - a} - \frac{1}{y - b}\right)dy$$

$$= \frac{1}{a - b}[\ln|y - a| - \ln|y - b|] + C_1$$

Integrating the right-hand side of (8.23) as well, and combining the constants of integration into a new constant, C_2, we find that

$$\frac{1}{a - b}[\ln|y - a| - \ln|y - b|] = kx + C_2$$

or

$$\ln\left|\frac{y - a}{y - b}\right| = k(a - b)x + C_2(a - b)$$

Exponentiating the latter equation yields

$$\left|\frac{y - a}{y - b}\right| = e^{C_2(a - b)}e^{k(a - b)x}$$

or

$$\frac{y - a}{y - b} = \pm e^{C_2(a - b)}e^{k(a - b)x}$$

Defining $C = \pm e^{C_2(a - b)}$, we obtain the solution of (8.22):

$$\frac{y - a}{y - b} = Ce^{k(a - b)x}$$

We solve this for y as follows:

$$y = a + (y - b)Ce^{k(a - b)x}$$
$$y(1 - Ce^{k(a - b)x}) = a - bCe^{k(a - b)x}$$

or

$$y = \frac{a - bCe^{k(a - b)x}}{1 - Ce^{k(a - b)x}} \tag{8.27}$$

The constant C can then be determined from the initial condition. When $y = a$ or $y = b$, $dy/dx = 0$ and, consequently, y is equal to a constant (specifically, $y = a$ or $y = b$).

The next example, of density-dependent growth, is one of the most important applications of this case. In Example 3, we considered unrestricted (or density-*in*dependent) growth, which has the unrealistic feature that if the intrinsic rate of growth is positive, the size of a population grows without bound. Frequently, however, the per capita growth rate decreases as the population size increases. The growth rate thus depends on the population density. The simplest such model for which the growth rate is density dependent is the logistic equation, in which the size of the population cannot grow without bound.

The logistic equation was originally developed around 1835 by Pierre-François Verhulst, who used the term *logistic* to describe the equation. His work was completely forgotten until 1920, when Raymond Pearl and Lowell J. Reed published a series of papers on population growth. They used the same equation as Verhulst. After discovering Verhulst's work, Pearl and Reed adopted the name *logistic* for the equation. Pearl and Reed (1920) used the logistic equation to predict future growth of the U.S. population on the basis of census data from 1790 to 1920. Their equation would have predicted about 185 million people in the United States in the year 2000, which is a gross underestimate of the actual population size (over 260 million people). Although the logistic equation does not seem to fit actual populations very well, it is a useful model for analyzing growth under limiting resources.

EXAMPLE 6

The Logistic Equation The logistic equation describes the change in size of a population for which per capita growth is density dependent. If we denote the population size at time t by $N(t)$, then the change in growth is given by the initial-value problem

$$\frac{dN}{dt} = rN\left(1 - \frac{N}{K}\right) \quad \text{with } N(0) = N_0 \tag{8.28}$$

where r and K are positive constants. This is the simplest way of incorporating density dependence in the per capita growth rate, namely, having it decrease linearly with population size (see Figure 8.9):

$$\frac{1}{N}\frac{dN}{dt} = r\left(1 - \frac{N}{K}\right)$$

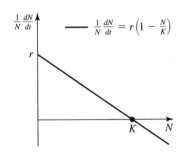

$$\frac{1}{N}\frac{dN}{dt} = r\left(1 - \frac{N}{K}\right)$$

Figure 8.9 The per capita growth rate in the logistic equation is a linearly decreasing function of population size.

We can interpret the parameter r as follows: The per capita growth rate is equal to r when $N = 0$. Therefore, one way to measure r is to grow the organism at a very low density (i.e., when N is much smaller than K), so that the per capita growth rate is close to r. (In Problem 42, we discuss a different way to find r.)

The quantity K is called the **carrying capacity**. Looking at Figure 8.9, we see that the per capita growth rate is 0 when the population size is at the carrying capacity. Since the per capita growth rate is positive below K and negative above K, the size of the population will increase below K and decrease above K. The number K thus determines the population size that can be supported by the environment. To show this claim mathematically, we need to solve (8.28), from whose solution we will then see that, starting from any positive initial population size, the size of the population will eventually reach K [i.e., $\lim_{t\to\infty} N(t) = K$ if $N(0) > 0$].

Let's solve (8.28). We write the right-hand side as

$$g(N) = -\frac{r}{K}(N - 0)(N - K) \tag{8.29}$$

Comparing (8.29) with the right-hand side of (8.22), we find that

$$k = -\frac{r}{K} \qquad a = 0 \qquad b = K \tag{8.30}$$

The solution of (8.28) is given in (8.27) and is, with the use of (8.30),

$$N(t) = \frac{0 - KCe^{-(r/K)(0-K)t}}{1 - Ce^{-(r/K)(0-K)t}}$$

or

$$N(t) = \frac{-CKe^{rt}}{1 - Ce^{rt}} = \frac{CK}{C - e^{-rt}}$$

$$= \frac{K}{1 - e^{-rt}/C} \tag{8.31}$$

Since $N(0) = N_0$, we have

$$N_0 = \frac{CK}{C-1}$$

Solving this equation for C yields

$$N_0(C-1) = CK \qquad \text{or} \qquad C(N_0 - K) = N_0$$

Thus,

$$C = \frac{N_0}{N_0 - K} \tag{8.32}$$

Substituting (8.32) into (8.31), we find that

$$N(t) = \frac{K}{1 - \frac{N_0 - K}{N_0}e^{-rt}}$$

or

$$N(t) = \frac{K}{1 + (\frac{K}{N_0} - 1)e^{-rt}} \tag{8.33}$$

It follows from (8.33) that

$$\lim_{t \to \infty} N(t) = K$$

We see from Figure 8.10, where we plot (8.33) for $N_0 > K$ and $N_0 < K$, that the solution $N(t)$ approaches K, the carrying capacity, as $t \to \infty$. When $N_0 > K$, $N(t)$ approaches K from above; when $0 < N_0 < K$, $N(t)$ approaches K from below. To use separation of variables to solve (8.28), we need to exclude $N = 0$ and $N = K$. When $N(0) = 0$, $dN/dt = 0$ and, consequently, $N(t) = \text{constant} = N(0) = 0$ for all $t \geq 0$. When $N(0) = K$, $dN/dt = 0$, and consequently, $N(t) = \text{constant} = K$ for all $t \geq 0$. [The constant solution $N(t) = K$ is contained in (8.33) if we choose $N_0 = K$.]

The constant solutions K and 0 are called *equilibria*. The constant solution $N(t) = 0$ is not a very interesting one. We call it the *trivial equilibrium*. If $N(0) = 0$, then nothing happens; that is, $N(t)$ stays equal to 0 for all later times. That makes sense: If there aren't any individuals to begin with, then there won't be any later on.

We can show that if $0 < N_0 < \frac{K}{2}$, then the solution curve is S shaped, as seen in Figure 8.10. An S-shaped curve is characteristic of populations that show this type of density-dependent growth. At low densities, the growth is almost like unrestricted growth. At higher densities, the growth is restricted and the curve bends around and eventually levels off at the carrying capacity. If the population size is initially greater than the carrying capacity K, the population size decreases and becomes asymptotically (i.e., when $t \to \infty$) equal to K. ■

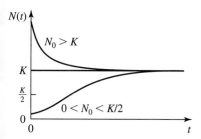

Figure 8.10 Solution curves for different initial values N_0.

■ 8.1.3 Allometric Growth

Solving differential equations of the form (8.2) gets complicated quickly. Before we show the role such differential equations play in biology, we will give an example in which we solve a differential equation of that type.

EXAMPLE 7

Solve

$$\frac{dy}{dx} = \frac{y+1}{x} \qquad \text{with } y_0 = 0 \text{ when } x_0 = 1$$

Solution

To solve this differential equation, we separate variables first and then integrate. We find that

$$\int \frac{dy}{y+1} = \int \frac{dx}{x}$$

Carrying out the integration on both sides, we obtain

$$\ln|y+1| = \ln|x| + C_1 \tag{8.34}$$

Solving for y, we get

$$|y + 1| = e^{C_1}|x|$$
$$y + 1 = \pm e^{C_1}x$$

Setting $C = \pm e^{C_1}$ yields

$$y = Cx - 1$$

Using the initial condition $y_0 = 0$ when $x_0 = 1$ allows us to determine C:

$$0 = C - 1, \quad \text{or} \quad C = 1$$

The solution is therefore

$$y = x - 1$$

■

We now turn to a biological application of equation (8.2): allometric growth. We have seen a number of allometric relationships throughout the earlier chapters of this book—typically, relationships between sizes of parts of an organism (e.g., skull length and body length, or leaf area and stem diameter). We denote by $L_1(t)$ and $L_2(t)$ the respective sizes of two organs of an individual of age t. We say that L_1 and L_2 are related through an allometric law if their specific growth rates are proportional—that is, if

$$\frac{1}{L_1}\frac{dL_1}{dt} = k\frac{1}{L_2}\frac{dL_2}{dt} \tag{8.35}$$

If the constant k is equal to 1, then the growth is called *isometric*; otherwise it is called *allometric*. Cancelling dt on both sides of (8.35) and integrating, we find that

$$\int \frac{dL_1}{L_1} = k\int \frac{dL_2}{L_2}$$

or

$$\ln |L_1| = k \ln |L_2| + C_1 \tag{8.36}$$

Solving for L_1, we obtain

$$L_1 = CL_2^k \tag{8.37}$$

where $C = \pm e^{C_1}$. (Since L_1 and L_2 are typically positive, the constant C will typically be positive.)

EXAMPLE 8

In a study of 45 species of unicellular algae, the relationship between cell volume V and cell biomass B was found to be

$$B \propto V^{0.794}$$

Find a differential equation that relates the relative growth rates of cell biomass and volume.

Solution The relationship between cell biomass and volume can be expressed as

$$B(V) = CV^{0.794} \tag{8.38}$$

where C is the constant of proportionality. Comparing (8.38) with (8.37), we see that $k = 0.794$. It therefore follows from (8.35) that

$$\frac{1}{B}\frac{dB}{dt} = (0.794)\frac{1}{V}\frac{dV}{dt} \tag{8.39}$$

We can also get (8.39) by differentiating (8.38) with respect to V; that is,

$$\frac{dB}{dV} = C(0.794)V^{0.794-1}$$

Equation (8.38) allows us to eliminate C. Solving (8.38) for C, we find that $C = BV^{-0.794}$ and, therefore,

$$\frac{dB}{dV} = BV^{-0.794}(0.794)V^{0.794-1} = (0.794)BV^{-1}$$

Rearranging terms yields

$$\frac{dB}{B} = (0.794)\frac{dV}{V}$$

Dividing both sides by dt, we get

$$\frac{1}{B}\frac{dB}{dt} = (0.794)\frac{1}{V}\frac{dV}{dt}$$

which is the same as (8.39). ■

EXAMPLE 9

Homeostasis The nutrient content of a consumer (e.g., the percent nitrogen of the consumer's biomass) can range from reflecting the nutrient content of its food to being constant. The former is referred to as *absence of homeostasis*, the latter as *strict homeostasis*. A model for homeostatic regulation is provided in Sterner and Elser (2002). The model relates a consumer's nutrient content (denoted by y) to its food's nutrient content (denoted by x) as

$$\frac{dy}{dx} = \frac{1}{\theta}\frac{y}{x} \tag{8.40}$$

where $\theta \geq 1$ is a constant. Solve the differential equation and relate θ to absence of homeostasis and strict homeostasis.

Solution We can solve (8.40) by separation of variables:

$$\int \frac{dy}{y} = \frac{1}{\theta}\int \frac{dx}{x}$$

Integrating and simplifying yields

$$\ln|y| = \frac{1}{\theta}\ln|x| + C_1$$
$$|y| = e^{(1/\theta)\ln|x|+C_1}$$
$$|y| = |x|^{1/\theta}e^{C_1}$$
$$y = \pm e^{C_1}x^{1/\theta}$$

Since x and y are positive (they denote nutrient contents), it follows that

$$y = Cx^{1/\theta}$$

where C is a positive constant.

   Absence of homeostasis means that the consumer reflects the food's nutrient content. This occurs when $y = Cx$ and thus when $\theta = 1$. *Strict homeostasis* means that the nutrient content of the consumer is independent of the nutrient content of the food; that is, $y = C$; this occurs in the limit as $\theta \to \infty$. ■

Section 8.1 Problems

■ **8.1.1**

In Problems 1–8, solve each pure-time differential equation.

1. $\dfrac{dy}{dx} = x + \sin x$, where $y_0 = 0$ for $x_0 = 0$

2. $\dfrac{dy}{dx} = e^{-3x}$, where $y_0 = 10$ for $x_0 = 0$

3. $\dfrac{dy}{dx} = \dfrac{1}{x}$, where $y_0 = 0$ when $x_0 = 1$

4. $\dfrac{dy}{dx} = \dfrac{1}{1+x^2}$, where $y_0 = 1$ when $x_0 = 0$

5. $\dfrac{dx}{dt} = \dfrac{1}{1-t}$, where $x(0) = 2$

6. $\dfrac{dx}{dt} = \cos(2\pi(t-3))$, where $x(3) = 1$

7. $\dfrac{ds}{dt} = \sqrt{3t+1}$, where $s(0) = 1$

8. $\dfrac{dh}{dt} = 5 - 16t^2$, where $h(3) = -11$

9. Suppose that the volume $V(t)$ of a cell at time t changes according to

$$\frac{dV}{dt} = 1 + \cos t \quad \text{with } V(0) = 5$$

Find $V(t)$.

10. Suppose that the amount of phosphorus in a lake at time t, denoted by $P(t)$, follows the equation

$$\frac{dP}{dt} = 3t + 1 \quad \text{with } P(0) = 0$$

Find the amount of phosphorus at time $t = 10$.

■ 8.1.2

In Problems 11–16, solve the given autonomous differential equations.

11. $\dfrac{dy}{dx} = 3y$, where $y_0 = 2$ for $x_0 = 0$

12. $\dfrac{dy}{dx} = 2(1-y)$, where $y_0 = 2$ for $x_0 = 0$

13. $\dfrac{dx}{dt} = -2x$, where $x(1) = 5$

14. $\dfrac{dx}{dt} = 1 - 3x$, where $x(-1) = -2$

15. $\dfrac{dh}{ds} = 2h + 1$, where $h(0) = 4$

16. $\dfrac{dN}{dt} = 5 - N$, where $N(2) = 3$

17. Suppose that a population, whose size at time t is denoted by $N(t)$, grows according to

$$\frac{dN}{dt} = 0.3N(t) \quad \text{with } N(0) = 20$$

Solve this differential equation, and find the size of the population at time $t = 5$.

18. Suppose that you follow the size of a population over time. When you plot the size of the population versus time on a semilog plot (i.e., the horizontal axis, representing time, is on a linear scale, whereas the vertical axis, representing the size of the population, is on a logarithmic scale), you find that your data fit a straight line which intercepts the vertical axis at 1 (on the log scale) and has slope -0.43. Find a differential equation that relates the growth rate of the population at time t to the size of the population at time t.

19. Suppose that a population, whose size at time t is denoted by $N(t)$, grows according to

$$\frac{1}{N}\frac{dN}{dt} = r \tag{8.41}$$

where r is a constant.
(a) Solve (8.41).

(b) Transform your solution in (a) appropriately so that the resulting graph is a straight line. How can you determine the constant r from your graph?

(c) Suppose now that, over time, you followed a population which evolved according to (8.41). Describe how you would determine r from your data.

20. Assume that $W(t)$ denotes the amount of radioactive material in a substance at time t. Radioactive decay is then described by the differential equation

$$\frac{dW}{dt} = -\lambda W(t) \quad \text{with } W(0) = W_0 \tag{8.42}$$

where λ is a positive constant called the *decay constant*.
(a) Solve (8.42).
(b) Assume that $W(0) = 123\,\text{gr}$ and $W(5) = 20\,\text{gr}$ and that time is measured in minutes. Find the decay constant λ and determine the half-life of the radioactive substance.

21. Suppose that a population, whose size at time t is given by $N(t)$, grows according to

$$\frac{dN}{dt} = \frac{1}{100}N^2, \quad \text{with } N(0) = 10 \tag{8.43}$$

(a) Solve (8.43).
(b) Graph $N(t)$ as a function of t for $0 \le t < 10$. What happens as $t \to 10$? Explain in words what this means.

22. Denote by $L(t)$ the length of a fish at time t, and assume that the fish grows according to the von Bertalanffy equation

$$\frac{dL}{dt} = k(34 - L(t)) \quad \text{with } L(0) = 2 \tag{8.44}$$

(a) Solve (8.44).
(b) Use your solution in (a) to determine k under the assumption that $L(4) = 10$. Sketch the graph of $L(t)$ for this value of k.
(c) Find the length of the fish when $t = 10$.
(d) Find the asymptotic length of the fish; that is, find $\lim_{t \to \infty} L(t)$.

23. Denote by $L(t)$ the length of a certain fish at time t, and assume that this fish grows according to the von Bertalanffy equation

$$\frac{dL}{dt} = k(L_\infty - L(t)) \quad \text{with } L(0) = 1 \tag{8.45}$$

where k and L_∞ are positive constants. A study showed that the asymptotic length is equal to 123 in and that it takes this fish 27 months to reach half its asymptotic length.
(a) Use this information to determine the constants k and L_∞ in (8.45). [*Hint*: Solve (8.45).]
(b) Determine the length of the fish after 10 months.
(c) How long will it take until the fish reaches 90% of its asymptotic length?

24. Let $N(t)$ denote the size of a population at time t. Assume that the population exhibits exponential growth.
(a) If you plot $\log N(t)$ versus t, what kind of graph do you get?
(b) Find a differential equation that describes the growth of this population and sketch possible solution curves.

25. Use the partial-fraction method to solve

$$\frac{dy}{dx} = y(1+y)$$

where $y_0 = 2$ for $x_0 = 0$.

26. Use the partial-fraction method to solve

$$\frac{dy}{dx} = y(1 - y)$$

where $y_0 = 2$ for $x_0 = 0$.

27. Use the partial-fraction method to solve

$$\frac{dy}{dx} = y(y - 5)$$

where $y_0 = 1$ for $x_0 = 0$.

28. Use the partial-fraction method to solve

$$\frac{dy}{dx} = (y - 1)(y - 2)$$

where $y_0 = 0$ for $x_0 = 0$.

29. Use the partial-fraction method to solve

$$\frac{dy}{dx} = 2y(3 - y)$$

where $y_0 = 5$ for $x_0 = 1$.

30. Use the partial-fraction method to solve

$$\frac{dy}{dt} = \frac{1}{2}y^2 - 2y$$

where $y_0 = -3$ for $t_0 = 0$.

In Problems 31–34, solve the given differential equations.

31. $\dfrac{dy}{dx} = y(1 + y)$ **32.** $\dfrac{dy}{dx} = (1 + y)^2$

33. $\dfrac{dy}{dx} = (1 + y)^3$ **34.** $\dfrac{dy}{dx} = (3 - y)(2 + y)$

35. (a) Use partial fractions to show that

$$\int \frac{du}{u^2 - a^2} = \frac{1}{2a} \ln \left| \frac{u - a}{u + a} \right| + C$$

(b) Use your result in (a) to find a solution of

$$\frac{dy}{dx} = y^2 - 4$$

that passes through (i) $(0, 0)$, (ii) $(0, 2)$, and (iii) $(0, 4)$.

36. Find a solution of

$$\frac{dy}{dx} = y^2 + 4$$

that passes through $(0, 2)$.

37. Suppose that the size of a population at time t is denoted by $N(t)$ and that $N(t)$ satisfies the differential equation

$$\frac{dN}{dt} = 0.34N \left(1 - \frac{N}{200} \right) \quad \text{with } N(0) = 50$$

Solve this differential equation, and determine the size of the population in the long run; that is, find $\lim_{t \to \infty} N(t)$.

38. Assume that the size of a population, denoted by $N(t)$, evolves according to the logistic equation. Find the intrinsic rate of growth if the carrying capacity is 100, $N(0) = 10$, and $N(1) = 20$.

39. Suppose that $N(t)$ denotes the size of a population at time t and that

$$\frac{dN}{dt} = 1.5N \left(1 - \frac{N}{50} \right)$$

(a) Solve this differential equation when $N(0) = 10$.
(b) Solve this differential equation when $N(0) = 90$.
(c) Graph your solutions in (a) and (b) in the same coordinate system.
(d) Find $\lim_{t \to \infty} N(t)$ for your solutions in (a) and (b).

40. Suppose that the size of a population, denoted by $N(t)$, satisfies

$$\frac{dN}{dt} = 0.7N \left(1 - \frac{N}{35} \right) \tag{8.46}$$

(a) Determine all equilibria by solving $dN/dt = 0$.
(b) Solve (8.46) for **(i)** $N(0) = 10$, **(ii)** $N(0) = 35$, **(iii)** $N(0) = 50$, and **(iv)** $N(0) = 0$. Find $\lim_{t \to \infty} N(t)$ for each of the four initial conditions.
(c) Compare your answer in (a) with the limiting values you found in (b).

41. Let $N(t)$ denote the size of a population at time t. Assume that the population evolves according to the logistic equation. Assume also that the intrinsic growth rate is 5 and that the carrying capacity is 30.
(a) Find a differential equation that describes the growth of this population.
(b) Without solving the differential equation in (a), sketch solution curves of $N(t)$ as a function of t when **(i)** $N(0) = 10$, **(ii)** $N(0) = 20$, and **(iii)** $N(0) = 40$.

42. Logistic growth is described by the differential equation

$$\frac{dN}{dt} = rN \left(1 - \frac{N}{K} \right)$$

The solution of this differential equation with initial condition $N(0) = N_0$ is given by

$$N(t) = \frac{K}{1 + (\frac{K}{N_0} - 1)e^{-rt}} \tag{8.47}$$

(a) Show that

$$r = \frac{1}{t} \ln \left(\frac{K - N_0}{N_0} \right) + \frac{1}{t} \ln \left(\frac{N(t)}{K - N(t)} \right) \tag{8.48}$$

by solving (8.47) for r.
(b) Equation (8.48) can be used to estimate r. Suppose we follow a population that grows according to the logistic equation and find that $N(0) = 10$, $N(5) = 22$, $N(100) = 30$, and $N(200) = 30$. Estimate r.

43. Selection at a Single Locus We consider one locus with two alleles, A_1 and A_2, in a randomly mating diploid population. That is, each individual in the population is either of type A_1A_1, A_1A_2, or A_2A_2. We denote by $p(t)$ the frequency of the A_1 allele and by $q(t)$ the frequency of the A_2 allele in the population at time t. Note that $p(t) + q(t) = 1$. We denote the fitness of the $A_i A_j$ type by w_{ij} and assume that $w_{11} = 1$, $w_{12} = 1 - s/2$, and $w_{22} = 1 - s$, where s is a nonnegative constant less than or equal to 1. That is, the fitness of the heterozygote A_1A_2 is halfway between the fitness of the two homozygotes, and the type A_1A_1 is the fittest. If s is small, we can show that, approximately,

$$\frac{dp}{dt} = \frac{1}{2}sp(1 - p) \quad \text{with } p(0) = p_0 \tag{8.49}$$

(a) Use separation of variables and partial fractions to find the solution of (8.49).
(b) Suppose $p_0 = 0.1$ and $s = 0.01$; how long will take until $p(t) = 0.5$?
(c) Find $\lim_{t \to \infty} p(t)$. Explain in words what this limit means.

■ 8.1.3

In Problems 44–52, solve each differential equation with the given initial condition.

44. $\dfrac{dy}{dx} = 2\dfrac{y}{x}$, with $y_0 = 1$ if $x_0 = 1$

45. $\dfrac{dy}{dx} = \dfrac{x+1}{y}$, with $y_0 = 2$ if $x_0 = 0$

46. $\dfrac{dy}{dx} = \dfrac{y}{x+1}$, with $y_0 = 1$ if $x_0 = 0$

47. $\dfrac{dy}{dx} = (y+1)e^{-x}$, with $y_0 = 2$ if $x_0 = 0$

48. $\dfrac{dy}{dx} = x^2 y^2$, with $y_0 = 1$ if $x_0 = 1$

49. $\dfrac{dy}{dx} = \dfrac{y+1}{x-1}$, with $y_0 = 5$ if $x_0 = 2$

50. $\dfrac{du}{dt} = \dfrac{\sin t}{u^2+1}$, with $u_0 = 3$ if $t_0 = 0$

51. $\dfrac{dr}{dt} = re^{-t}$, with $r_0 = 1$ if $t_0 = 0$

52. $\dfrac{dx}{dy} = \dfrac{1}{2}\dfrac{x}{y}$, with $x_0 = 2$ if $y_0 = 3$

53. *(Adapted from Reiss, 1989)* In a case study by Taylor et al. (1980) in which the maximal rate of oxygen consumption (in ml s^{-1}) for nine species of wild African mammals was plotted against body mass (in kg) on a log–log plot, it was found that the data points fall on a straight line with slope approximately equal to 0.8. Find a differential equation that relates maximal oxygen consumption to body mass.

54. Consider the following differential equation, which is important in population genetics:

$$a(x)g(x) - \frac{1}{2}\frac{d}{dx}[b(x)g(x)] = 0$$

Here, $b(x) > 0$.

(a) Define $y = b(x)g(x)$, and show that y satisfies

$$\frac{a(x)}{b(x)}y - \frac{1}{2}\frac{dy}{dx} = 0 \tag{8.50}$$

(b) Separate variables in (8.50), and show that if $y > 0$, then

$$y = C \exp\left[2\int \frac{a(x)}{b(x)}\,dx\right]$$

55. When phosphorus content in *Daphnia* was plotted against phosphorus content of its algal food on a log–log plot, a straight line with slope $1/7.7$ resulted. (See Sterner and Elser, 2002; data from DeMott et al., 1998.) Find a differential equation that relates the phosphorus content of *Daphnia* to the phosphorus content of its algal food.

56. This problem addresses Malthus's concerns. Assume that a population size grows exponentially according to

$$N(t) = 1000e^t$$

and the food supply grows linearly according to

$$F(t) = 3t$$

(a) Write a differential equation for each of $N(t)$ and $F(t)$.

(b) What assumptions do you need to make to be able to compare whether and, if so, when food supply will be insufficient? Does exponential growth eventually overtake linear growth? Explain.

(c) Do a Web search to determine whether food supply has grown linearly, as claimed by Malthus.

57. At the beginning of this section, we modified the exponential-growth equation to include oscillations in the per capita growth rate. Solve the differential equation we obtained, namely,

$$\frac{dN}{dt} = 2\left(1 + \sin(2\pi t)\right)N(t)$$

with $N(0) = 5$.

■ 8.2 Equilibria and Their Stability

In Subsection 8.1.2, we learned how to solve autonomous differential equations and graphed their solutions as functions of the independent variable for given initial conditions. For instance, logistic growth

$$\frac{dN}{dt} = rN\left(1 - \frac{N}{K}\right) \tag{8.51}$$

with initial condition $N(0) = N_0$ has the solution given in (8.33) and graphed in Figure 8.10 for different initial values.

The solution of a differential equation can inform us about long-term behavior, as we saw in the case of logistic growth. In particular, if $N_0 > 0$, then $N(t) \to K$, the carrying capacity, as $t \to \infty$, and if $N_0 = 0$, then $N(t) = 0$ for all $t > 0$. Also, if $N_0 = K$, then $N(t) = K$ for all $t > 0$. What is so special about $N_0 = K$ or $N_0 = 0$? We see from Equation (8.51) that if $N = K$ or $N = 0$, then $dN/dt = 0$, implying that $N(t)$ is constant.

Constant solutions form a very special class of solutions of autonomous differential equations. These solutions are called **point equilibria** or, simply, equilibria. The constant solutions $N = K$ and $N = 0$ are point equilibria of the logistic equation.

In this section, we will consider autonomous differential equations of the form

$$\frac{dy}{dx} = g(y) \tag{8.52}$$

where we will typically think of x as time. We will learn how to find point equilibria, and we will discuss what they can tell us about the long-term behavior of the solution $y = y(x)$—that is, the behavior of $y(x)$ as $x \to \infty$. If we can solve (8.52), we can study the solution directly to obtain information about its long-term behavior. But what should we do if we cannot solve (8.52)?

Candidates for describing long-term behavior are the constant solutions or equilibria $y = \hat{y}$ (read "y hat") that satisfy $g(\hat{y}) = 0$. Such solutions, of course, need not exist. The following holds, however, if they do exist:

If $\hat{y}$ satisfies

$$g(\hat{y}) = 0$$

then $\hat{y}$ is an equilibrium of

$$\frac{dy}{dx} = g(y)$$

Let's look at equilibria in more detail before we discuss specific examples. The basic property of equilibria is that if, initially (say, at $x = 0$), $y(0) = \hat{y}$ and $\hat{y}$ is an equilibrium, then $y(x) = \hat{y}$ for all $x > 0$.

A physical analogue of equilibria is provided in Figure 8.11. On the left side, a ball rests on top of a hill; on the right side, a ball rests at the bottom of a valley. In either case, the ball is in equilibrium because it does not move.

Of great interest is the **stability** of equilibria. What we mean by this is best explained by our example of a ball on a hill versus a ball in the valley. If we perturb the ball by a small amount—that is, if we move it out of its equilibrium slightly—the ball on the left side will roll down the hill and not return to the top, whereas the ball on the right side will return to the bottom of the valley. We call the situation on the left side *unstable* and the situation on the right side *stable*.

The analogue of stability for equilibria of differential equations is as follows: Suppose that $\hat{y}$ is an equilibrium of $\frac{dy}{dx} = g(y)$; that is, $g(\hat{y}) = 0$. We say that $\hat{y}$ is **locally stable** if the solution returns to $\hat{y}$ after a small perturbation; this means that we look at what happens to the solution when we start close to the equilibrium (i.e., the solution moves away from the equilibrium by a small amount, called a *small perturbation*). If the solution does not return to the equilibrium after a small perturbation, we say that $\hat{y}$ is **unstable**. These concepts will be developed in the next subsection, in which we will discuss a graphical and an analytical method for analyzing stability of equilibria. A number of applications then follow in the subsequent subsections.

■ 8.2.1 A First Look at Stability

Graphical Approach Suppose that $g(y)$ is of the form given in Figure 8.12. To find the equilibria of (8.52), we set $g(y) = 0$. Graphically, this means that if we graph $g(y)$ (i.e., the *derivative* of y with respect to x) as a function of y, then the equilibria are the points of intersection of $g(y)$ with the horizontal axis, which is the y-axis in this case, since y is the independent variable. (Look at the labels of the axes in the figure to see what is graphed there.) We see that, for our choice of $g(y)$, the equilibria are at $y = 0$, y_1, and y_2.

Why does this work? Remember, we are discussing *autonomous* differential equations. This means that the derivative of y (dy/dx) is a function of y; it does *not* depend explicitly on x. This fact allows us to graph the derivative of y as a function of y. Since $dy/dx = g(y)$, we can graph $g(y)$ as a function of y. We can then use the graph of $g(y)$ to say the following about the fate of a solution on the basis of its current value: If the current value y is such that $g(y) > 0$ (i.e., $dy/dx > 0$), then y

Figure 8.11 Stability illustrated with a ball on a hill and in a valley.

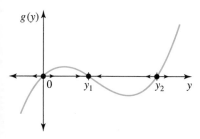

Figure 8.12 The function $g(y)$. The arrows close to the equilibria indicate the type of stability.

will increase as a function of x; if, however, y is such that $g(y) < 0$ (i.e., $dy/dx < 0$), then y will decrease as a function of x. The points y where $g(y) = 0$ are the points where y will not change as a function of x [since $g(y) = dy/dx = 0$]. These points are the equilibria.

Equilibria are characterized by the property that a system in an equilibrium state stays there for all later times (unless some external force disturbs the system). Note that this implies *neither* that the system will necessarily reach a particular equilibrium when starting from some initial value that is different from the equilibrium nor that the system will return to the equilibrium after a small perturbation.

Whether or not the system will return to an equilibrium after a small perturbation depends on the local stability of the equilibrium. By this statement, we mean the following: Suppose that the system is in equilibrium, which we denote by $\hat{y}$. We apply a small perturbation to the system, so that after the perturbation the new state of the system is

$$y = \hat{y} + z \tag{8.53}$$

where z is small and may be positive or negative. We explain what can happen to the system with the use of the function $g(y)$ in Figure 8.12.

Suppose that $\hat{y} = 0$ and we subject this equilibrium to a small perturbation. If the new value $y = \hat{y} + z = z > 0$ for z small, then $dy/dx > 0$; that is, y will increase. If the new value $y = \hat{y} + z = z < 0$ for z small, then $dy/dx < 0$ and y will decrease. In either case, the system will not return to 0. We say that $\hat{y} = 0$ is *unstable*.

We now turn to the equilibrium $\hat{y} = y_1$. We perturb the equilibrium to $y = y_1 + z$ for z small. From Figure 8.12, if $z > 0$, then $dy/dx < 0$ and hence y decreases; if $z < 0$, then $dy/dx > 0$ and y increases. The system will therefore return to the equilibrium y_1 after a small perturbation. We say that y_1 is *locally stable*. The attribute *locally* refers to the fact that the system will return to y_1 if the perturbation is sufficiently small. It does not say anything about what happens when the perturbation is large. For instance, if the perturbation z is large and the new value is less than 0, then $dy/dx < 0$ and the system will not return to y_1.

Analyzing the equilibrium y_2 in the same way shows that it is an unstable equilibrium, just like the equilibrium $\hat{y} = 0$.

The preceding discussion illustrates the fact that it is not necessarily the case that the system will reach an equilibrium value. The only equilibrium in Figure 8.12 that can be reached is y_1: If, initially, $y(0) \in (0, y_2)$, then $y(x)$ will approach y_1; if, however, $y(0) < 0$, then $y(x) \to -\infty$, and if $y > y_2$, then $y(x) \to \infty$.

The preceding discussion also illustrates that we can subject an equilibrium only to a small perturbation if we want to learn something about its stability: If we perturb y_1 too much, so that the value after the perturbation is either less than 0 or greater than y_2, the solution will not return to the equilibrium value y_1.

EXAMPLE 1   Let $N(t)$ denote the size of a population at time t such that the population evolves according to the logistic equation

$$\frac{dN}{dt} = 2N \left(1 - \frac{N}{100} \right) \quad \text{for } N \geq 0$$

Find the equilibria and analyze their stability.

Solution   To find the equilibria, we set $\frac{dN}{dt} = 0$; that is,

$$2N \left(1 - \frac{N}{100} \right) = 0$$

We see that either

$$N_1 = 0 \quad \text{or} \quad N_2 = 100$$

To analyze the stability, we draw the graph of dN/dt versus N in Figure 8.13. Note that $N \geq 0$, since N represents the size of a population. To perturb the trivial equilibrium $N_1 = 0$, we therefore need choose only values that are slightly bigger than 0.

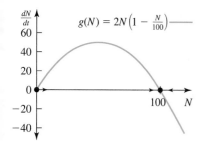

Figure 8.13 The graph of dN/dt versus N in Example 1.

We see from the graph that such small perturbations result in $dN/dt > 0$, and hence N increases. This implies that $N_1 = 0$ is an unstable equilibrium.

To perturb the nontrivial equilibrium $N_2 = 100$, we can either increase or decrease the population size a bit. If we decrease it, then $dN/dt > 0$ and the population size will increase. If we increase it, then $dN/dt < 0$ and the population size will decrease. That is, if the system is subjected to a small perturbation about the nontrivial equilibrium $N_2 = 100$, the population size will return to the equilibrium value of $N_2 = 100$. This implies that $N_2 = 100$ is a locally stable equilibrium. ■

Analytical Approach We assume that $\hat{y}$ is an equilibrium of

$$\frac{dy}{dx} = g(y)$$

[Thus, $\hat{y}$ satisfies $g(\hat{y}) = 0$.] We consider a small perturbation about the equilibrium $\hat{y}$; we express this perturbation as

$$y = \hat{y} + z$$

where z is small and may be either positive or negative. Then

$$\frac{dy}{dx} = \frac{d}{dx}(\hat{y} + z) = \frac{dz}{dx}$$

since $d\hat{y}/dx = 0$ ($\hat{y}$ is a constant). We find that

$$\frac{dz}{dx} = g(\hat{y} + z)$$

If z is sufficiently small, we can approximate $g(\hat{y} + z)$ by its linear approximation. The linear approximation of $g(y)$ about $\hat{y}$ is given by

$$L(y) = g(\hat{y}) + (y - \hat{y})g'(\hat{y})$$

Since $g(\hat{y}) = 0$,

$$L(y) = (y - \hat{y})g'(\hat{y})$$

Therefore, the linear approximation of $g(\hat{y} + z)$ is given by

$$L(\hat{y} + z) = (\hat{y} + z - \hat{y})g'(\hat{y}) = zg'(\hat{y})$$

If we set

$$\lambda = g'(\hat{y})$$

then

$$\frac{dz}{dx} = \lambda z$$

is the first-order approximation of the perturbation. This equation has the solution

$$z(x) = z(0)e^{\lambda x} \tag{8.54}$$

which has the property that

$$\lim_{x \to \infty} z(x) = 0 \quad \text{if } \lambda < 0$$

Now, on the one hand, since $y(x) = \hat{y} + z(x)$, it follows that if $\lambda < 0$, the system returns to the equilibrium $\hat{y}$ after a small perturbation $z(0)$. This means that $\hat{y}$ is locally stable if $\lambda < 0$. On the other hand, if $\lambda > 0$, then $z(x)$ does not go to 0 as $x \to \infty$, implying that the system will *not* return to the equilibrium $\hat{y}$ after a small perturbation, and $\hat{y}$ is unstable. The value $\lambda = g'(\hat{y})$ is called an **eigenvalue** and is the slope of the tangent line of $g(y)$ at $\hat{y}$. This is summarized in the following box:

Stability Criterion   Consider the differential equation

$$\frac{dy}{dx} = g(y)$$

where $g(y)$ is a differentiable function. Assume that $\hat{y}$ is an equilibrium; that is, $g(\hat{y}) = 0$. Then

$$\hat{y} \text{ is locally stable if } g'(\hat{y}) < 0$$
$$\hat{y} \text{ is unstable if } g'(\hat{y}) > 0$$

When the eigenvalue $\lambda = 0$, the first-order approximation $\frac{dz}{dx} = \lambda z$ does not allow us to draw any conclusions about the behavior of $z(x)$, since higher-order terms then become important.

We wish to tie this analytical approach in with the more informal graphical analysis presented at the beginning of this section. Looking at Figure 8.12, we find that the slope of the tangent line at $y = 0$ is positive [i.e., $g'(0) > 0$]; similarly, we find that $g'(y_1) < 0$ and $g'(y_2) > 0$. Hence, the equilibria 0 and y_2 are unstable and the equilibrium y_1 is locally stable, as found in the graphical analysis.

Let's try out the analytical approach on Example 1. There,

$$g(N) = 2N\left(1 - \frac{N}{100}\right)$$

To differentiate $g(N)$, we multiply out:

$$g(N) = 2N - \frac{N^2}{50}$$

Differentiating $g(N)$ yields

$$g'(N) = 2 - \frac{2N}{50}$$

If $N = 0$, then $g'(0) = 2 > 0$; thus, $N = 0$ is an unstable equilibrium. If $N = 100$, then $g'(100) = 2 - 200/50 = -2 < 0$; hence, $N = 100$ is a locally stable equilibrium.

The analytical approach is more powerful than the graphical approach: In addition to determining whether an equilibrium is locally stable or unstable, the analytical approach allows us to say something about how quickly a solution returns to an equilibrium after a small perturbation. This property follows from (8.54). There, we found that the perturbation has the approximate solution

$$z(x) = z(0)e^{\lambda x}$$

If $\lambda > 0$, then the larger λ, the faster the solution moves away from the equilibrium. If $\lambda < 0$, then the more negative λ, the faster the solution will return to the equilibrium after a small perturbation. (See Figure 8.14.)

The preceding derivation of the analytical stability criterion was based on linearizing $g(y)$ about the equilibrium $\hat{y}$. Since the linearization is close only for values close to $\hat{y}$ [unless $g(y)$ is linear], the perturbations about the equilibrium must be small, and hence the stability analysis is always local (i.e., within close vicinity of the equilibrium). When $g(y)$ is linear, the analysis is exact; in particular, we can compute exactly how quickly a solution returns to a locally stable equilibrium (or moves away from an unstable equilibrium) after a perturbation.

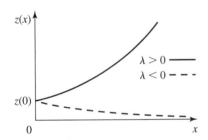

Figure 8.14   The graph of $z(x) = z(0)e^{\lambda x}$ for $\lambda > 0$ and $\lambda < 0$.

EXAMPLE 2 $g(y)$ **Is Linear**   Show that the differential equation

$$\frac{dy}{dx} = 1 - y \tag{8.55}$$

has a locally stable equilibrium at $\hat{y} = 1$, and determine how quickly a solution starting at $y(0) = y_0 \neq 1$ will reach $\hat{y} = 1$.

Solution Since $g(y) = 0$ for $y = 1$, $\hat{y} = 1$ is an equilibrium. Differentiating $g(y) = 1 - y$, we find that $g'(y) = -1$, which is negative regardless of y. Therefore, $\hat{y} = 1$ is a locally stable equilibrium.

We can solve (8.55) exactly by separation of variables:

$$\int \frac{dy}{1 - y} = \int dx$$
$$-\ln |1 - y| = x + C_1$$
$$1 - y = \pm e^{-C_1} e^{-x}$$
$$1 - y = Ce^{-x}$$

Note that we set $\pm e^{-C_1} = C$. Solving for y yields

$$y(x) = 1 - Ce^{-x}$$

If we set $y(0) = y_0$, then $y_0 = 1 - C$, and the solution is

$$y(x) = 1 - (1 - y_0)e^{-x}$$

We see that, for any initial value y_0,

$$\lim_{x \to \infty} y(x) = 1$$

and it takes an infinite amount of time to reach the equilibrium $\hat{y} = 1$ if $y_0 \neq 1$.

Instead of asking how long it takes until the equilibrium is reached (which yielded the uninformative answer "an infinite amount of time"), we compute the time it takes to reduce the initial deviation from the equilibrium, $y_0 - 1$, to a fraction e^{-1}; that is, we wish to determine the number x_R such that

$$\underbrace{y(x_R) - 1}_{\text{deviation from } x = x_R} = \underbrace{e^{-1}(y_0 - 1)}_{\text{initial deviation}}$$

Since $y(x_R) - 1 = -(1 - y_0)e^{-x_R}$, it follows that

$$-(1 - y_0)e^{-x_R} = e^{-1}(y_0 - 1)$$
$$e^{-x_R} = e^{-1}$$
$$x_R = 1$$

(See Figure 8.15.) It takes one unit of time to reduce the initial deviation to a fraction e^{-1}; this does not depend on how large the initial deviation is. ■

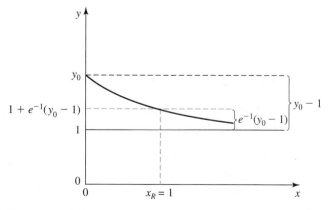

Figure 8.15 An illustration of the time x_R in Example 2.

Using Both Approaches

EXAMPLE 3

Suppose that

$$\frac{dy}{dx} = y(4 - y)$$

Find the equilibria of this differential equation and discuss their stability, using both the graphical and the analytical approach.

Solution

To find the equilibria, we set $dy/dx = 0$. That is,

$$y(4 - y) = 0$$

which yields

$$y_1 = 0 \quad \text{and} \quad y_2 = 4$$

On the one hand, we set $g(y) = y(4 - y)$ and graph $g(y)$ (see Figure 8.16); we see that $y_1 = 0$ is unstable, since, if we perturb $y_1 = 0$ to $y = z > 0$, where z is small, then $g(y) = dy/dx > 0$, and if we perturb $y_1 = 0$ to $y = z < 0$, where z is small, then $g(y) = dy/dx < 0$. That is, in either case, y will not return to 0. On the other hand, y_2 is a locally stable equilibrium: A small perturbation to the right of $y = y_2$ results in $dy/dx < 0$, whereas a small perturbation to the left results in $dy/dx > 0$. In either case, the solution y will return to $y_2 = 4$.

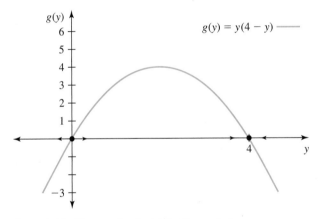

Figure 8.16 The graph of $g(y)$ in Example 3.

If we use the analytical approach, we need to compute the eigenvalues. The eigenvalue associated with $y_1 = 0$ is

$$\lambda_1 = g'(0) = 4 - 2y|_{y=0} = 4 > 0$$

which implies that y_1 is unstable. The eigenvalue associated with $y_2 = 4$ is

$$\lambda_2 = g'(4) = 4 - 2y|_{y=4} = -4 < 0$$

which implies that $y_2 = 4$ is locally stable.

■

■ 8.2.2 Single Compartment or Pool

This example is adapted from DeAngelis (1992). Compartment models are frequently used to model the flow of matter (nutrients, energy, and so forth). The simplest such model consists of one compartment—for instance, a fixed volume V of water (such as a tank or lake) containing a solute (such as phosphorus). Assume that water enters the compartment at a constant rate q and leaves the compartment at the same rate. (See Figure 8.17.) (Having the same input and output rate keeps the volume of the pool constant.) We will investigate the effects of different input concentrations of the solution on the concentration of the solution in the pool.

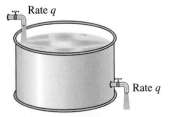

Figure 8.17 Input and output rates are the same: The water in the tank remains at the same level.

We denote by $C(t)$ the concentration of the solution in the compartment at time t. Then the total mass of the solute is $C(t)V$, where V is the volume of the compartment. For instance, if the concentration of the solution is 2 grams per liter and the volume of the compartment is 10 liters, then the total mass of the solute in the compartment is 2 g liter^{-1} times 10 liters, which is equal to 20 g.

If C_I is the concentration of the incoming solution and q is the rate at which water enters, then qC_I, the **input loading**, is the rate at which mass enters. For instance, if the concentration of the incoming solution is 5 g liter^{-1} and the rate at which the solution enters is 0.1 liter s^{-1}, then the input loading—that is, the rate at which mass enters—is 5 g liter^{-1} times 0.1 liter s^{-1}, which is equal to 0.5 g s^{-1}.

If we assume that the solution in the compartment is well mixed, so that the outflowing solution has the same concentration as the solution in the compartment— namely, $C(t)$ at time t—then $qC(t)$ is the rate at which mass leaves the compartment at time t.

Figure 8.18 Flow diagram for the single-compartment model.

These different processes can be schematically illustrated in a flow diagram, as shown in Figure 8.18. Because mass is conserved in the system, we can use the **law of conservation of mass** to derive an equation that describes the flow of matter in this system:

$$\begin{bmatrix} \text{rate of change} \\ \text{of mass of} \\ \text{solute in pool} \end{bmatrix} = \begin{bmatrix} \text{rate at which} \\ \text{mass enters} \end{bmatrix} - \begin{bmatrix} \text{rate at which} \\ \text{mass leaves} \end{bmatrix}$$

Writing C for $C(t)$ (and being careful not to confuse C with a constant), we obtain

$$\frac{d}{dt}(CV) = qC_I - qC \tag{8.56}$$

Since V is constant, we can write (8.56) as

$$\frac{dC}{dt} = \frac{q}{V}(C_I - C) \tag{8.57}$$

This is a linear differential equation of the type discussed in Subsection 8.1.2, Case 1. It can be solved by separation of variables. We skip the steps and instead concentrate on the discussion of the system. If $C(0) = C_0$, then the solution of the differential equation is

$$C(t) = C_I \left[1 - \left(1 - \frac{C_0}{C_I} \right) e^{-(q/V)t} \right] \tag{8.58}$$

Solution curves for different values of C_0 are shown in Figure 8.19. From (8.57), we conclude that C_I is the only equilibrium. Looking at the solution $C(t)$ in (8.58), we see that

$$\lim_{t \to \infty} C(t) = C_I$$

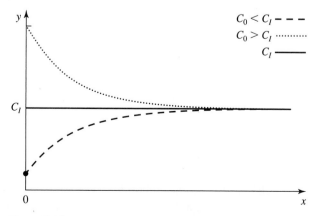

Figure 8.19 The solution curves for the single-compartment model for different values of C_0.

regardless of the initial concentration C_0 in the compartment. This shows that C_I is **globally stable**, which implies that no matter how much we perturb the equilibrium, the system will return to it.

We can also obtain this result by using the eigenvalue method. We write

$$C(t) = C_I + z(t)$$

Then, as before,

$$\frac{dC(t)}{dt} = \frac{d}{dt}[C_I + z(t)] = \frac{dz(t)}{dt}$$

That is,

$$\frac{dz}{dt} = -\frac{q}{V}z(t) \tag{8.59}$$

since $C_I - C(t) = -z(t)$. Note that (8.59) is exact; that is, we need not use a linear approximation for the right-hand side of (8.57), since it is already linear. We see from (8.59) that $-q/V$ is the eigenvalue associated with the equilibrium C_I. Since q and V are both positive, the eigenvalue is negative, and it follows that C_I is locally stable. We can obtain more information here, since (8.59) is exact with solution

$$z(t) = z(0)e^{-(q/V)t} \tag{8.60}$$

which shows that, for *any* perturbation $z(0)$, $z(t) \rightarrow 0$ as $t \rightarrow \infty$. That is, the system returns to the equilibrium C_I [$C(t) \rightarrow C_I$ as $t \rightarrow \infty$] regardless of how much we perturb the system. The reason that the eigenvalue method allows us to show global stability lies in the fact that the differential equation (8.56) is *linear*. In other cases, the eigenvalue method allows us to obtain only local stability, because we must first linearize and, consequently, the linearized differential equation is only an approximation.

Equation (8.60) shows that the system returns to the equilibrium C_I exponentially fast and that the eigenvalue $-(q/V)$ determines the time scale—that is, how quickly the system reaches the equilibrium. The larger q/V, the faster the system recovers from a perturbation. In this context, we can define a return time to equilibrium (just as in Example 2), denoted by T_R. By convention, the return time to equilibrium, T_R, is defined as the amount of time it takes to reduce the initial difference $C_0 - C_I$ to a fraction e^{-1}, or

$$C(T_R) - C_I = e^{-1}(C_0 - C_I) \tag{8.61}$$

Using (8.58), we see that

$$C(T_R) = C_I \left[1 - \left(1 - \frac{C_0}{C_I}\right)e^{-(q/V)T_R}\right]$$

which we can rewrite as

$$C(T_R) - C_I = (C_0 - C_I)e^{-(q/V)T_R} \tag{8.62}$$

Equating (8.61) and (8.62), we find that

$$e^{-1}(C_0 - C_I) = (C_0 - C_I)e^{-(q/V)T_R}$$

which yields

$$1 = \frac{q}{V}T_R, \quad \text{or} \quad T_R = \frac{V}{q}$$

The last equation shows that the return time increases with the volume V and decreases with the flow rate q. This relationship can be understood intuitively: The larger the volume and the smaller the input rate, the longer the system takes to return to equilibrium. It can be shown that T_R is the mean residence time of a molecule of the solute; that is, when the system is in equilibrium, T_R is the average time a molecule of the solute spends in the compartment before leaving.

◼ 8.2.3 The Levins Model

The ecological importance of spatial structure to the maintenance of populations was pointed out by Andrewartha and Birch (1954) on the basis of studies of insect populations. They observed that, although local populations frequently become extinct, their patches of habitat subsequently become recolonized by migrants from other patches occupied by individuals from the same kind of population, thus allowing the population to persist globally. Fifteen years later, Richard Levins introduced the concept of *metapopulations* (Levins, 1969). A major theoretical advance, the concept provided a framework for studying spatially structured populations.

A metapopulation is a collection of subpopulations. Each subpopulation occupies a patch, and different patches are linked via the migration of individuals between patches. (See Figure 8.20.) In this setting, we keep track only of what proportion of patches is occupied by subpopulations. Subpopulations go extinct at a constant rate, denoted by m, which stands for *mortality*. Vacant patches can be colonized at a rate that is proportional to the fraction of occupied patches; the constant of proportionality is denoted by c, which stands for *colonization rate*. If we denote by $p(t)$ the fraction of patches that are occupied at time t, then writing $p = p(t)$, we have

$$\frac{dp}{dt} = cp(1 - p) - mp \qquad (8.63)$$

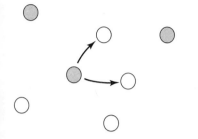

Figure 8.20 A schematic description of a metapopulation model. The shaded patches are occupied; arrows indicate migration events.

The first term on the right-hand side describes the colonization process. Note that an increase in the fraction of occupied patches occurs only if a vacant patch becomes occupied—hence the product $p(1 - p)$ in the first term on the right-hand side. The minus sign in front of m shows that an extinction decreases the fraction of occupied patches.

We will not solve (8.63); instead, we focus on its equilibria. We set

$$cp(1 - p) - mp = 0$$

Isolating the factor cp, we obtain

$$cp\left(1 - \frac{m}{c} - p\right) = 0$$

which has the two solutions

$$p_1 = 0 \qquad \text{and} \qquad p_2 = 1 - \frac{m}{c}$$

We call the solution $p_1 = 0$ a trivial solution, because it corresponds to the situation in which all patches are vacant. Since individuals are not created spontaneously, a vacant patch can be recolonized only through migration from other, occupied patches. Therefore, once a metapopulation is extinct, it stays extinct. The other equilibrium, $p_2 = 1 - m/c$, is relevant only when $p_2 \in (0, 1]$, because p represents a fraction that is a number between 0 and 1. Since m and c are both positive, it follows immediately that $p_2 < 1$ for all choices of m and c. To see when $p_2 > 0$, we check

$$1 - \frac{m}{c} > 0$$

which holds when

$$m < c$$

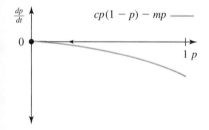

Figure 8.21a The case $m > c$.

That is, the nontrivial equilibrium $p_2 = 1 - m/c$ is in $(0, 1]$ if the extinction rate m is less than the colonization rate c. If $m \geq c$, then there is only one equilibrium in $[0, 1]$, namely, $p_1 = 0$. We illustrate this scenario in Figures 8.21a and 8.22a; looking at the graphs, we can analyze the stability of the equilibria.

Case 1: $m > c$ There is only the trivial equilibrium $p_1 = 0$. For any $p \in (0, 1]$, $dp/dt < 0$; hence, the fraction of occupied patches declines. The equilibrium is locally and globally stable.

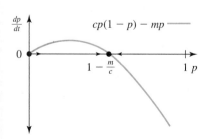

Figure 8.22a The case $m < c$.

Case 2: $m < c$ There are two equilibria: 0 and $1 - m/c$. The trivial equilibrium $p_1 = 0$ is now unstable, since, if we perturb $p_1 = 0$ to some value in $(0, 1 - m/c)$, then $dp/dt > 0$, which implies that $p(t)$ increases. The system will therefore not return to 0.

The other equilibrium, $p_2 = 1 - m/c$, is locally stable. After a small perturbation of this equilibrium to the right of p_2, $dp/dt < 0$; a small perturbation to the left of p_2 gives $dp/dt > 0$. Therefore, the system will return to p_2.

We can also use the eigenvalue approach to analyze the stability of the equilibria. In addition, this approach will allow us to obtain information on how quickly the system returns to the stable equilibrium. We set

$$g(p) = cp(1 - p) - mp$$

To linearize this function about the equilibrium values, we must find

$$g'(p) = c - 2cp - m$$

Now, if $p_1 = 0$, then

$$g'(0) = c - m$$

whereas if $p_2 = 1 - m/c$, then

$$g'\left(1 - \frac{m}{c}\right) = c - 2c\left(1 - \frac{m}{c}\right) - m = c - 2c + 2m - m = m - c$$

From these equations, we see that $c - m$ is the eigenvalue corresponding to $p_1 = 0$ and $m - c$ is the eigenvalue corresponding to $p_2 = 1 - m/c$. We find that

$$\text{if} \quad c - m < 0, \quad \text{then} \quad p_1 = 0 \text{ is locally stable}$$

$$\text{if} \quad m - c < 0, \quad \text{then} \quad p_1 = 0 \text{ is unstable and } p_2 = 1 - \frac{m}{c} \text{ is locally stable}$$

To summarize our results, if $m > c$, then $p_1 = 0$ is the only equilibrium in $[0, 1]$ and $p_1 = 0$ is locally stable. (In fact, the graphical analysis showed that $p_1 = 0$ is *globally* stable.) Figure 8.21b shows a solution curve when $m = 2$ and $c = 1$, starting at $p(0) = 2$. We see that the solution approaches $p_1 = 0$. If $m < c$, then there are two equilibria in $[0, 1]$. The equilibrium $p_1 = 0$ is now unstable, and the equilibrium $p_2 = 1 - m/c$ is locally stable. Figure 8.22b shows solution curves when $m = 1$ and $c = 2$, starting from different initial conditions: $p(0) = 0.1, 0.5$, and 1.5. All solution curves eventually approach $p_2 = 1 - m/c = 0.5$. When $p(0) = p_2 = 0.5$, the solution curve stays at $p_2 = 0.5$.

■ 8.2.4 The Allee Effect

A sexually reproducing species may experience a disproportionately low recruitment rate when the population density falls below a certain level, due to lack of suitable mates. This phenomenon is called an *Allee effect* (Allee, 1931). A simple extension of the logistic equation incorporates the effect. We denote the size of a population at time t by $N(t)$; then, writing $N = N(t)$, we have

$$\frac{dN}{dt} = rN(N - a)\left(1 - \frac{N}{K}\right) \tag{8.64}$$

where r, a, and K are positive constants. We assume that $0 < a < K$. We will see that, as in the logistic equation, K denotes the carrying capacity. The constant a is a threshold population size below which the recruitment rate is negative, meaning that the population will shrink and ultimately go to extinction.

The equilibria of (8.64) are given by $\hat{N} = 0$, a, and K. We set

$$g(N) = rN(N - a)\left(1 - \frac{N}{K}\right) = r\left(N^2 + \frac{a}{K}N^2 - \frac{N^3}{K} - aN\right)$$

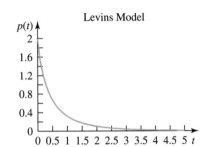

Figure 8.21b Solution curve when $m > c$: $m = 2$, $c = 1$, and $p(0) = 2$. The solution approaches the locally stable equilibrium $p_1 = 0$.

Levins Model

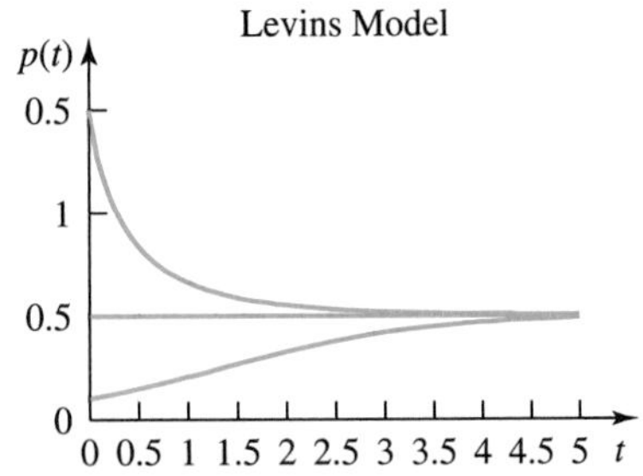

Figure 8.22b Solution curves when $m < c$: $m = 1$, $c = 2$, and $p(0) = 0.1$, 0.5, 1.5. When $p(0) = 0.1$, the solution approaches the locally stable equilibrium $p_2 = 1 - m/c = 0.5$. When $p(0) = 0.5$, the solution remains at the locally stable equilibrium $p_2 = 1 - m/c = 0.5$. When $p(0) = 1.5$, the solution approaches the locally stable equilibrium $p_2 = 1 - m/c = 0.5$.

A graph of $g(N)$ is shown in Figure 8.23a. Differentiating $g(N)$ yields

$$g'(N) = r\left(2N + \frac{2a}{K}N - \frac{3N^2}{K} - a\right) = \frac{r}{K}(2NK + 2aN - 3N^2 - aK)$$

We can compute the eigenvalue $g'(\hat{N})$ associated with the equilibrium $\hat{N}$:

$$\text{if} \quad \hat{N} = 0, \quad \text{then} \quad g'(0) = \frac{r}{K}(-aK) < 0$$

$$\text{if} \quad \hat{N} = a, \quad \text{then} \quad g'(a) = \frac{r}{K}a(K - a) > 0$$

$$\text{if} \quad \hat{N} = K, \quad \text{then} \quad g'(K) = \frac{r}{K}K(a - K) < 0$$

As we continue, you should compare the results from the eigenvalue method with the graph of $g(N)$.

Since $g'(0) < 0$, it follows that $\hat{N} = 0$ is locally stable. Likewise, since $g'(K) < 0$, it follows that $\hat{N} = K$ is locally stable. The equilibrium $\hat{N} = a$ is unstable, because $g'(a) > 0$. This instability is also evident from Figure 8.23a. The Allee effect is an example in which both stable equilibria are locally, but not globally, stable.

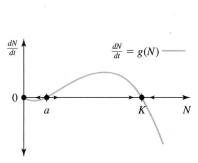

Figure 8.23a The graph of $g(N)$ illustrating the Allee effect.

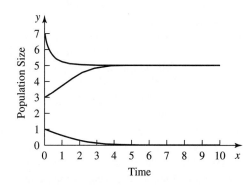

Figure 8.23b Solution curves when $r = 0.5$, $a = 2$, and $K = 5$. When the initial condition $N(0)$ is between 0 and 2, the solution curve approaches the locally stable equilibrium $\hat{N} = 0$. When the initial condition $N(0)$ is greater than 2, the solution curve approaches the locally stable equilibrium $\hat{N} = K = 5$. The approach is from below when $2 < N(0) < 5$ and from above when $N(0) > 5$.

We see from Figures 8.23a and 8.23b that if $0 \le N(0) < a$, then $N(t) \to 0$ as $t \to \infty$. If $a < N(0) \le K$ or $N(0) \ge K$, then $N(t) \to K$ as $t \to \infty$. To interpret our results, we observe that if the initial population $N(0)$ is too small [i.e., $N(0) < a$], then the population goes extinct, and if the initial population is large enough [i.e., $N(0) > a$], then the population persists. That is, the parameter a is a threshold level. The recruitment rate is large enough only when the population size exceeds this level.

Section 8.2 Problems

■ 8.2.1

1. Suppose that

$$\frac{dy}{dx} = y(2 - y)$$

(a) Find the equilibria of this differential equation.

(b) Graph dy/dx as a function of y, and use your graph to discuss the stability of the equilibria.

(c) Compute the eigenvalues associated with each equilibrium, and discuss the stability of the equilibria.

2. Suppose that

$$\frac{dy}{dx} = (4 - y)(5 - y)$$

(a) Find the equilibria of this differential equation.

(b) Graph dy/dx as a function of y, and use your graph to discuss the stability of the equilibria.

(c) Compute the eigenvalues associated with each equilibrium, and discuss the stability of the equilibria.

3. Suppose that

$$\frac{dy}{dx} = y(y-1)(y-2)$$

(a) Find the equilibria of this differential equation.

(b) Graph dy/dx as a function of y, and use your graph to discuss the stability of the equilibria.

(c) Compute the eigenvalues associated with each equilibrium, and discuss the stability of the equilibria.

4. Suppose that

$$\frac{dy}{dx} = y(2-y)(y-3)$$

(a) Find the equilibria of this differential equation.

(b) Graph dy/dx as a function of y, and use your graph to discuss the stability of the equilibria.

(c) Compute the eigenvalues associated with each equilibrium, and discuss the stability of the equilibria.

5. Logistic Equation Assume that the size of a population evolves according to the logistic equation with intrinsic rate of growth $r = 1.5$. Assume that the carrying capacity $K = 100$.
(a) Find the differential equation that describes the rate of growth of this population.

(b) Find all equilibria, and, using the graphical approach, discuss the stability of the equilibria.

(c) Find the eigenvalues associated with the equilibria, and use the eigenvalues to determine the stability of the equilibria. Compare your answers with your results in (b).

6. A Simple Model of Predation Suppose that $N(t)$ denotes the size of a population at time t. The population evolves according to the logistic equation, but, in addition, predation reduces the size of the population so that the rate of change is given by

$$\frac{dN}{dt} = N\left(1-\frac{N}{50}\right) - \frac{9N}{5+N} \qquad (8.65)$$

The first term on the right-hand side describes the logistic growth; the second term describes the effect of predation.
(a) Set

$$g(N) = N\left(1-\frac{N}{50}\right) - \frac{9N}{5+N}$$

and graph $g(N)$.

(b) Find all equilibria of (8.65).

(c) Use your graph in (a) to determine the stability of the equilibria you found in (b).

(d) Use the method of eigenvalues to determine the stability of the equilibria you found in (b).

7. Logistic Equation Assume that the size of a population evolves according to the logistic equation with intrinsic rate of growth $r = 2$. Assume that $N(0) = 10$.
(a) Determine the carrying capacity K if the population grows fastest when the population size is 1000. (*Hint*: Show that the graph of dN/dt as a function of N has a maximum at $K/2$.)

(b) If $N(0) = 10$, how long will it take the population size to reach 1000?

(c) Find $\lim_{t\to\infty} N(t)$.

8. Logistic Equation The logistic curve $N(t)$ is an S-shaped curve that satisfies

$$\frac{dN}{dt} = rN\left(1-\frac{N}{K}\right) \quad \text{with } N(0) = N_0 \qquad (8.66)$$

when $N_0 < K$.
(a) Use the differential equation (8.66) to show that the inflection point of the logistic curve is at exactly half the saturation value of the curve. [*Hint*: Do not solve (8.66); instead, differentiate the right-hand side with respect to t.]
(b) The solution $N(t)$ of (8.66) can be defined for all $t \in \mathbf{R}$. Show that $N(t)$ is symmetric about the inflection point and that $N(0) = N_0$. That is, first use the solution of (8.66) that is given in (8.33), and find the time t_0 so that $N(t_0) = K/2$ (i.e., the inflection point) is at $t = t_0$. Compute $N(t_0 + h)$ and $N(t_0 - h)$ for $h > 0$, and show that

$$N(t_0 + h) - \frac{K}{2} = \frac{K}{2} - N(t_0 - h)$$

Use a sketch of the graph of $N(t)$ to explain why the preceding equation shows that $N(t)$ is symmetric about the inflection point $(t_0, N(t_0))$.

9. Suppose that a fish population evolves according to the logistic equation and that a fixed number of fish per unit time are removed. That is,

$$\frac{dN}{dt} = rN\left(1-\frac{N}{K}\right) - H$$

Assume that $r = 2$ and $K = 1000$.
(a) Find possible equilibria, and discuss their stability when $H = 100$.
(b) What is the maximal harvesting rate that maintains a positive population size?

10. Suppose that a fish population evolves according to a logistic equation and that fish are harvested at a rate proportional to the population size. If $N(t)$ denotes the population size at time t, then

$$\frac{dN}{dt} = rN\left(1-\frac{N}{K}\right) - hN$$

Assume that $r = 2$ and $K = 1000$.
(a) Find possible equilibria, use the graphical approach to discuss their stability when $h = 0.1$, and find the maximal harvesting rate that maintains a positive population size.
(b) Show that if $h < r = 2$, then there is a nontrivial equilibrium. Find the equilibrium.
(c) Use **(i)** the eigenvalue approach and **(ii)** the graphical approach to analyze the stability of the equilibrium found in (b).

■ **8.2.2**

11. Assume the single-compartment model defined in Subsection 8.2.2: If $C(t)$ is the concentration of the solute at time t, then dC/dt is given by (8.57); that is,

$$\frac{dC}{dt} = \frac{q}{V}(C_I - C)$$

where q, V, and C_I are defined as in Subsection 8.2.2. Use the graphical approach to discuss the stability of the equilibrium $\hat{C} = C_I$.

12. Assume the single-compartment model defined in Subsection 8.2.2; that is, denote the concentration of the solute at time t by $C(t)$, and assume that

$$\frac{dC}{dt} = 3(20 - C(t)) \quad \text{for } t \geq 0 \qquad (8.67)$$

(a) Solve (8.67) when $C(0) = 5$.

(b) Find $\lim_{t \to \infty} C(t)$.

(c) Use your answer in (a) to determine t so that $C(t) = 10$.

13. Assume the single-compartment model defined in Subsection 8.2.2; that is, denote the concentration of the solution at time t by $C(t)$, and assume that the concentration of the incoming solution is 3 g liter^{-1} and the rate at which mass enters is 0.2 liter s^{-1}. Assume, further, that the volume of the compartment $V = 400$ liters.

(a) Find the differential equation for the rate of change of the concentration at time t.

(b) Solve the differential equation in (a) when $C(0) = 0$, and find $\lim_{t \to \infty} C(t)$.

(c) Find all equilibria of the differential equation and discuss their stability.

14. Suppose that a tank holds 1000 liters of water, and 2 kg of salt is poured into the tank.

(a) Compute the concentration of salt in g liter^{-1}.

(b) Assume now that you want to reduce the salt concentration. One method would be to remove a certain amount of the salt water from the tank and then replace it by pure water. How much salt water do you have to replace by pure water to obtain a salt concentration of 1 g liter^{-1}?

(c) Another method for reducing the salt concentration would be to hook up an overflow pipe and pump pure water into the tank. That way, the salt concentration would be gradually reduced. Assume that you have two pumps, one that pumps water at a rate of 1 liter s^{-1}, the other at a rate of 2 liter s^{-1}. For each pump, find out how long it would take to reduce the salt concentration from the original concentration to 1 g liter^{-1} and how much pure water is needed in each case. (Note that the rate at which water enters the tank is equal to the rate at which water leaves the tank.) Compare the amount of water needed using the pumps with the amount of water needed in part (b).

15. Assume the single-compartment model introduced in Subsection 8.2.2. Denote the concentration at time t by $C(t)$, measured in mg/L, and assume that

$$\frac{dC}{dt} = 0.37(254 \text{ mg/L} - C(t)) \quad \text{for } t \geq 0$$

(a) Find the equilibrium concentration.

(b) Assume that the concentration is suddenly increased from the equilibrium concentration to 400 mg/L. Find the return time to equilibrium, denoted by T_R, which is the amount of time until the initial difference is reduced to a fraction e^{-1}.

(c) Repeat (b) for the case when the concentration is suddenly increased from the equilibrium concentration to 800 mg/L.

(d) Are the values for T_R computed in (b) and (c) different?

16. Assume the compartment model as in Subsection 8.2.2. Suppose that the equilibrium concentration is C_I and the initial concentration is C_0. Express the time it takes until the initial deviation $C_0 - C_I$ is reduced to a fraction p in terms of T_R.

17. Assume the compartment model as in Subsection 8.2.2. Suppose that the equilibrium concentration is C_I. The time T_R has an integral representation that can be generalized to systems with more than one compartment. Show that

$$T_R = \int_0^\infty \frac{C(t) - C_I}{C(0) - C_I} dt$$

[*Hint*: Use (8.58) to show that

$$\frac{C(t) - C_I}{C(0) - C_I} = e^{-(q/V)t}$$

and integrate both sides with respect to t from 0 to ∞.]

18. Use the compartment model defined in Subsection 8.2.2 to investigate how the size of a lake influences nutrient dynamics in the lake after a perturbation. Mary Lake and Elizabeth Lake are two fictitious lakes in the North Woods that are used as experimental lakes to study nutrient dynamics. Mary Lake has a volume of 6.8×10^3 m^3, and Elizabeth Lake has twice that volume, or 13.6×10^3 m^3. Both lakes have the same inflow/outflow rate $q = 170$ liter s^{-1}. Because both lakes share the same drainage area, the concentration C_I of the incoming solute is the same for both lakes, namely, $C_I = 0.7$ mg liter^{-1}. Assume that at the beginning of the experiment both lakes are in equilibrium; that is, the concentration of the solution in both lakes is 0.7 mg liter^{-1}. Your experiment consists of increasing the concentration of the solution by 10% in each lake at time 0 and then watching how the concentration of the solution in each lake changes with time. Assume the single-compartment model to make predictions about how the concentration of the solution will evolve. (Note that 1 m^3 of water corresponds to 1000 liters of water.)

(a) Find the initial concentration C_0 of the solution in each lake at time 0 (i.e., immediately after the 10% increase in concentration of the solution).

(b) Use Equation (8.58) to determine how the concentration of the solution changes over time in each lake. Graph your results.

(c) Which lake returns to equilibrium faster? Compute the return time to equilibrium, T_R, for each lake, and explain how it is related to the eigenvalues corresponding to the equilibrium concentration C_I for each lake.

19. Use the single-compartment model defined in Subsection 8.2.2 to investigate the effect of an increase in the input concentration C_I on the nutrient concentration in a lake. Suppose a lake in a pristine environment has an equilibrium phosphorus concentration of 0.3 mg^{-1}. The volume V of the lake is 12.3×10^6 m^3, and the inflow/outflow rate q is equal to 220 liter s^{-1}. Conversion of land in the drainage area of the lake to agricultural use has increased the input concentration from 0.3 mg liter^{-1} to 1.1 mg liter^{-1}. Assume that this increase happened instantaneously. Compute the return time to the new equilibrium, denoted by T_R, in days, and find the nutrient concentration in the lake T_R units of time after the change in input concentration. (Note that 1 m^3 of water corresponds to about 1000 liters of water.)

■ **8.2.3**

20. Levins Model Denote by $p = p(t)$ the fraction of occupied patches in a metapopulation model, and assume that

$$\frac{dp}{dt} = 2p(1 - p) - p \quad \text{for } t \geq 0 \tag{8.68}$$

(a) Set $g(p) = 2p(1 - p) - p$. Graph $g(p)$ for $p \in [0, 1]$.

(b) Find all equilibria in (8.68) that are in [0, 1]. Use your graph in (a) to determine their stability.

(c) Use the eigenvalue approach to analyze the stability of the equilibria that you found in (b).

21. Levins Model Denote by $p = p(t)$ the fraction of occupied patches in a metapopulation model, and assume that

$$\frac{dp}{dt} = 0.5p(1 - p) - 1.5p \quad \text{for } t \geq 0 \tag{8.69}$$

(a) Set $g(p) = 0.5p(1 - p) - 1.5p$. Graph $g(p)$ for $p \in [0, 1]$.

(b) Find all equilibria of (8.69) that are in $[0, 1]$. Use your graph in (a) to determine their stability.

(c) Use the eigenvalue approach to analyze the stability of the equilibria that you found in (b).

22. A Metapopulation Model with Density-Dependent Extinction Denote by $p = p(t)$ the fraction of occupied patches in a metapopulation model, and assume that

$$\frac{dp}{dt} = cp(1-p) - p^2 \quad \text{for } t \geq 0 \tag{8.70}$$

where $c > 0$. The term p^2 describes the density-dependent extinction of patches; that is, the per-patch extinction rate is p, and a fraction p of patches are occupied, resulting in an extinction rate of p^2. The colonization of vacant patches is the same as in the Levins model.

(a) Set $g(p) = cp(1-p) - p^2$ and sketch the graph of $g(p)$.

(b) Find all equilibria of (8.70) in $[0, 1]$, and determine their stability.

(c) Is there a nontrivial equilibrium when $c > 0$? Contrast your findings with the corresponding results in the Levins model.

23. Habitat Destruction In Subsection 8.2.3, we introduced the Levins model. To study the effects of habitat destruction on a single species, we modify equation (8.63) in the following way: We assume that a fraction D of patches is permanently destroyed. Consequently, only patches that are vacant and undestroyed can be successfully colonized. These patches have frequency $1 - p(t) - D$ if $p(t)$ denotes the fraction of occupied patches at time t. Then

$$\frac{dp}{dt} = cp(1 - p - D) - mp \tag{8.71}$$

(a) Explain in words the meaning of the different terms in (8.71).

(b) Show that there are two possible equilibria: the trivial equilibrium $p_1 = 0$ and the nontrivial equilibrium $p_2 = 1 - D - \frac{m}{c}$. Sketch the graph of p_2 as a function of D.

(c) Assume that $m < c$ such that the nontrivial equilibrium is stable when $D = 0$. Find a condition for D such that the nontrivial equilibrium is between 0 and 1, and investigate the stability of both the nontrivial equilibrium and the trivial equilibrium under that condition.

(d) Assume the condition that you derived in (c); that is, the nontrivial equilibrium is between 0 and 1. Show that when the system is in equilibrium, the fraction of patches that are

vacant and undestroyed—that is, the sites that are *available* for colonization—is independent of D. Show that the **effective colonization rate** in equilibrium—that is, c times the fraction of available patches—is equal to the extinction rate. This equality shows that the effective birth rate of new colonies balances their extinction rate at equilibrium.

■ **8.2.4**

24. Allee Effect Denote the size of a population at time t by $N(t)$, and assume that

$$\frac{dN}{dt} = 2N(N - 10)\left(1 - \frac{N}{100}\right) \quad \text{for } t \geq 0 \tag{8.72}$$

(a) Find all equilibria of (8.72).

(b) Use the eigenvalue approach to determine the stability of the equilibria you found in (a).

(c) Set

$$g(N) = 2N(N - 10)\left(1 - \frac{N}{100}\right)$$

for $N \geq 0$, and graph $g(N)$. Identify the equilibria of (8.72) on your graph, and use the graph to determine the stability of the equilibria. Compare your results with your findings in (b). Use your graph to give a graphical interpretation of the eigenvalues associated with the equilibria.

25. Allee Effect Denote the size of a population at time t by $N(t)$, and assume that

$$\frac{dN}{dt} = 0.3N(N - 17)\left(1 - \frac{N}{200}\right) \quad \text{for } t \geq 0 \tag{8.73}$$

(a) Find all equilibria of (8.73).

(b) Use the eigenvalue approach to determine the stability of the equilibria you found in (a).

(c) Set

$$g(N) = 0.3N(N - 17)\left(1 - \frac{N}{200}\right)$$

for $N \geq 0$, and graph $g(N)$. Identify the equilibria of (8.73) on your graph, and use the graph to determine the stability of the equilibria. Compare your results with your findings in (b). Use your graph to give a graphical interpretation of the eigenvalues associated with the equilibria.

■ 8.3 Systems of Autonomous Equations (Optional)

In the preceding two sections, we discussed models that could be described by a single differential equation. If we wish to describe models in which several quantities interact, such as a competition model in which various species interact, more than one differential equation is needed. We call this model a *system of differential equations*. We will restrict ourselves again to autonomous systems—that is, systems whose dynamics do not depend explicitly on the independent variable (which typically is time).

This section is a preview of Chapter 11, in which we will discuss systems of differential equations in detail. A thorough analysis of such systems requires a fair amount of theory, which we will develop in Chapters 9 and 10. Since we are not yet equipped with the right tools to analyze systems of differential equations, this section will be rather informal. As with movie previews, you will not know the full story after you finish reading the section, but reading it will (hopefully) convince you that systems of differential equations provide a rich tool for modeling biological systems.

■ 8.3.1 A Simple Model of Epidemics

We begin our discussion of systems of autonomous differential equations with a classical model of an infectious disease: the Kermack–McKendrick model (Kermack & McKendrick, 1927, 1932, 1933). We consider a population of fixed size N that, at time t, can be divided into three classes: the susceptibles, $S(t)$, which can get infected; the infectives, $I(t)$, which are infected and can transmit the disease; and the removed class, $R(t)$, which are immune to the disease. The flow among these classes can be described by

$$S \longrightarrow I \longrightarrow R$$

We assume that the infection spreads according to the mass action law that we encountered in the discussion of chemical reactions. Each susceptible becomes infected at a rate that is proportional to the number of infectives I. Each infected individual recovers at a constant rate. A gain in the class of infectives is a simultaneous loss in the class of susceptibles. Likewise, a gain in the class of recovered individuals is a loss in the class of infectives. We can therefore describe the dynamics by

$$\frac{dS}{dt} = -bSI \tag{8.74}$$

$$\frac{dI}{dt} = bSI - aI \tag{8.75}$$

$$\frac{dR}{dt} = aI \tag{8.76}$$

Note that

$$\frac{dS}{dt} + \frac{dI}{dt} + \frac{dR}{dt} = -bSI + bSI - aI + aI = 0$$

Since

$$\frac{dS}{dt} + \frac{dI}{dt} + \frac{dR}{dt} = \frac{d}{dt}(S + I + R)$$

it follows that $S(t) + I(t) + R(t)$ is a constant that we can identify as the population size N. To analyze the system, we assume that, at time 0,

$$S(0) > 0 \qquad I(0) > 0 \qquad R(0) = 0$$

A question of interest is whether the infection will spread. We say that the infection spreads if

$$I(t) > I(0) \quad \text{for some } t > 0$$

Equation (8.75) allows us to answer the question: If

$$\frac{dI}{dt} = I(bS - a) > 0 \quad \text{at } t = 0$$

then $I(t)$ increases at the beginning, and hence the infection can spread. This condition can be written as

$$\frac{bS(0)}{a} > 1$$

The value $bS(0)/a$ is called the **basic reproductive rate** of the infection and is typically denoted by R_0 [not to be confused with the number $R(0)$ of recovered individuals at time 0]. The quantity R_0 is of great importance in epidemiology, because it tells us whether an infection can spread. R_0 is the key to understanding why vaccination programs work. It explains why it is not necessary to vaccinate everyone against an infectious disease: As long as the number of susceptibles is reduced below a certain threshold, the infection will not spread. The theoretical threshold, based on the Kermack–McKendrick model, is a/b. In practice, there are additional factors (such as the spatial proximity of infected individuals) that influence whether or not an infection will spread. But the basic conclusion is the same: As long as the number of susceptibles is below a certain threshold, the infection will not spread.

To find out how the infection progresses over time, we divide (8.74) by (8.76). For $I > 0$, we obtain

$$\frac{dS/dt}{dR/dt} = \frac{dS}{dR} = -\frac{bSI}{aI} = -\frac{b}{a}S$$

That is,

$$\frac{dS}{dR} = -\frac{b}{a}S$$

Separating variables and integrating yields

$$\int \frac{dS}{S} = -\frac{b}{a}\int dR$$

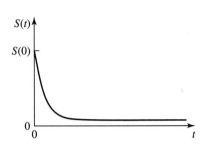

$S(t)$

$S(0)$

Since $S(t) > 0$, we have

$$\ln S(t) = -\frac{b}{a}R(t) + C$$

With $R(0) = 0$, we obtain

$$\ln S(0) = C$$

Hence,

$$S(t) = S(0)e^{-(b/a)R(t)} \qquad (8.77)$$

Figure 8.24 The solution $S(t)$ of the Kermack–McKendrick model.

Since $R(t)$ is nondecreasing (no one can leave the removed class), it follows from (8.77) that $S(t)$ is nonincreasing. (See Figure 8.24.)

Letting $t \to \infty$, we find that

$$S(\infty) = \lim_{t \to \infty} S(t) = \lim_{t \to \infty} S(0)e^{-(b/a)R(t)}$$
$$= S(0)e^{-(b/a)R(\infty)}$$

Since $R(\infty) \leq N$, it follows that

$$S(\infty) \geq S(0)e^{-(b/a)N} > 0$$

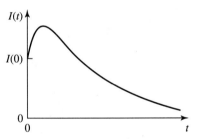

$I(t)$

$I(0)$

That is, not everyone becomes infected. As long as the number of susceptibles is greater than a/b, $dI/dt > 0$ and the number of infected individuals increases. Because the population size is constant, the infection "uses up" susceptibles, and there will be a time when the number of susceptibles falls below a/b. (See Figure 8.25.) From then on, dI/dt is negative, and the number of infected individuals begins to decline. The infection will eventually cease; that is,

$$\lim_{t \to \infty} I(t) = 0$$

Figure 8.25 The solution $I(t)$ of the Kermack–McKendrick model.

Since not everyone becomes infected $[S(\infty) > 0]$, when the infection finally comes to an end, it is because the population runs out of infectives, not because of a lack of susceptibles.

■ 8.3.2 A Compartment Model

In Subsection 8.2.2, we introduced a single-compartment model that led to an autonomous differential equation with one dependent variable. In this subsection, we introduce a model with two compartments that describes the interaction of an *autotroph*[1] and its nutrient pool. (The discussion that follows is partially adapted from DeAngelis, 1992.) A schematic description of the interactions can be found in Figure 8.26.

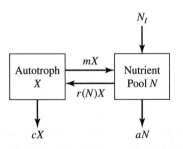

Figure 8.26 A schematic description of the interaction between autotrophs and the nutrient pool.

---

(1) An autotroph is an organism that can manufacture organic compounds entirely from inorganic components. Examples include most chlorophyll-containing plants and blue-green algae.

We assume that the nutrient pool has an external source and denote the input rate of nutrients by N_I. That is, N_I denotes the total mass per unit time that flows into the system. Nutrients may be washed out, and we assume that the output rate is proportional to the total mass of nutrients, N, in the compartment, with proportionality constant a.

The autotroph feeds on the nutrients in the nutrient pool, and its growth rate is proportional to the quantity of autotroph biomass, X. The specific rate of growth, $r(N)$, depends on the amount of available nutrients.

Autotrophs can leave the autotroph compartment in two ways: (1) At rate c, they get completely lost (e.g., through harvesting or by being washed out of their habitat); (2) at rate m, the biomass of the autotroph gets recycled back into the nutrient pool (e.g., after the death of an organism).

This system is then described by the following set of differential equations:

$$\frac{dN}{dt} = N_I - aN - r(N)X + mX \tag{8.78}$$

$$\frac{dX}{dt} = r(N)X - (m + c)X \tag{8.79}$$

You should compare the set of differential equations with the schematic description of the model in Figure 8.26. In particular, you should pay attention to the direction of the arrows. For instance, the term $r(N)X$ shows up in both equations: Because this term corresponds to the nutrient uptake by the autotrophs, it appears as a loss to the nutrient pool, which is indicated by the minus sign in front of the term in equation (8.78); and the same term appears with a plus sign in equation (8.79), because the uptake of nutrients by the autotroph results in an increase in autotroph biomass. Note that the arrow labeled $r(N)X$ goes from the nutrient pool to the autotroph pool. Hence, it represents a loss in the nutrient pool [a minus sign in (8.78) in front of $r(N)X$] and a gain in the autotroph pool [a plus sign in (8.79) in front of $r(N)X$].

It is important to learn how to go from the schematic description to the set of differential equations and back. A schematic description quickly summarizes the flow of matter (such as nutrients), whereas the set of differential equations is indispensable if we want to analyze the system.

To keep the discussion concrete, we assume that the function $r(N)$ is linear; that is,

$$r(N) = bN$$

for some constant $b > 0$.

As in Section 8.2, we can introduce the concept of equilibria. An equilibrium for the system given by (8.78) and (8.79) is characterized by simultaneously requiring that

$$\frac{dN}{dt} = 0 \quad \text{and} \quad \frac{dX}{dt} = 0 \tag{8.80}$$

since, when the rates of change of both quantities are equal to 0, the values for N and X no longer change.

There is a graphical method for finding equilibria: plotting the **zero isoclines**. These curves are obtained by setting $dN/dt = 0$ and $dX/dt = 0$. The curves for which $dX/dt = 0$ are obtained by setting the right-hand side of (8.79) equal to 0; that is, $X(bN - (m + c)) = 0$, yielding

$$N = \frac{m + c}{b} \quad \text{or} \quad X = 0$$

The curve for which $dN/dt = 0$ is obtained by setting the right-hand side of (8.78) equal to 0, yielding

$$X = \frac{N_I - aN}{bN - m}$$

We plot the three curves in the N–X plane, as illustrated in Figure 8.27.

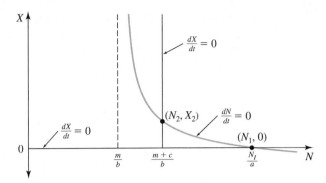

Figure 8.27 The zero isoclines in the N–X plane.

The zero isocline for N intersects the horizontal line $X = 0$ at $(N_1, 0)$, where N_1 satisfies

$$0 = \frac{N_I - aN_1}{bN_1 - m}$$

and thus $N_1 = N_I/a$. We call this a *trivial equilibrium*, since it corresponds to the case in which there is no autotroph in the system. (The system reduces to the single-compartment model we discussed in Section 8.2.)

Depending on where the vertical zero isocline for X is located, there can be another equilibrium (N_1, N_2) for which both N_2 and X_2 are positive. Looking at Figure 8.27, we see that when

$$\frac{m}{b} < \frac{m+c}{b} < \frac{N_I}{a} \tag{8.81}$$

the two zero isoclines $N = (m + c)/b$ and $X = (N_I - aN)/(bN - m)$ intersect in the first quadrant. We call this equilibrium a *nontrivial equilibrium*.

Since $(m + c)/b > m/b$ when $c > 0$, the vertical zero isocline $dX/dt = 0$ is always to the right of the vertical asymptote $N = m/b$. The first inequality in (8.81) therefore always holds. If we solve the second inequality,

$$\frac{m+c}{b} < \frac{N_I}{a}$$

for b, we find that

$$b > \frac{a}{N_I}(m + c)$$

That is, the growth parameter b must exceed a certain threshold in order for the autotroph to survive. This should be intuitively clear, since m and c are the rates at which the autotroph pool is depleted. The depletion must be balanced by an increase in biomass of the autotroph.

Suppose that the ratio m/b is fixed. Then the smaller c (the rate at which autotrophs get lost) is, the farther to the left is the vertical zero isocline $dX/dt = 0$ and, consequently, the larger is the equilibrium value X_2. This should also be intuitively clear, since losing fewer autotrophs should result in a higher equilibrium value.

To find the nontrivial equilibrium (N_2, X_2), we need to solve the system of equations

$$0 = N_I - aN_2 - bN_2X_2 + mX_2 \tag{8.82}$$
$$0 = bN_2X_2 - (m + c)X_2 \tag{8.83}$$

where we now assume that $X_2 \neq 0$. Equation (8.83) yields

$$N_2 = \frac{m+c}{b}$$

Using this relationship in (8.82), we find that

$$0 = N_I - a\frac{m+c}{b} - (m+c)X_2 + mX_2$$

or

$$X_2 = \frac{1}{c}\left(N_I - a\frac{m+c}{b}\right)$$

It can be shown that if the nontrivial equilibrium exists, it is locally stable; that is, the system will return to this equilibrium after a small perturbation. In Chapter 11, we will learn two methods for analyzing the stability of a system of differential equations: a graphical and an analytical method; these are extensions of the methods we developed in Section 8.2.

■ 8.3.3 A Hierarchical Competition Model

We now extend the metapopulation (Levins) model, introduced in Subsection 8.2.3, to a multispecies setting. We recall Levins model but use a somewhat different interpretation. In the model, the dynamics of subpopulations was described. We will now view the Levins model as an occupancy model of sites for single individuals; that is, we suppose that the habitat is divided into patches that are now so small that at most one individual occupies a patch. Using this interpretation, we denote by $p(t)$ the fraction of sites that are occupied by a single individual at time t. Then

$$\frac{dp}{dt} = cp(1-p) - mp$$

where m is the extinction rate (the death rate of an individual) and c is the colonization rate (the rate at which offspring migrate to new sites). Tilman (1994) extended this model to a system in which species are ranked according to their competitiveness. The fraction of sites that are occupied by species i at time t is denoted by $p_i(t)$. We assume that species 1 is the best competitor, species 2 the next best, and so on. A superior competitor can invade a site that is occupied by an inferior competitor. The inferior competitor is displaced upon invasion of the superior competitor. The dynamics are then given by

$$\frac{dp_1}{dt} = c_1 p_1(1-p_1) - m_1 p_1$$

$$\frac{dp_2}{dt} = c_2 p_2(1-p_1-p_2) - m_2 p_2 - c_1 p_1 p_2$$

$$\frac{dp_3}{dt} = c_3 p_3(1-p_1-p_2-p_3) - m_3 p_3 - c_1 p_1 p_3 - c_2 p_2 p_3$$

$$\vdots$$

$$\frac{dp_i}{dt} = c_i\left(1 - \sum_{j=1}^{i} p_j\right) - m_i p_i - \sum_{j=1}^{i-1} c_j p_j p_i$$

$$\vdots$$

The first term describes the colonization by species i of sites that are either occupied by an inferior competitor or vacant, the second term describes the extinction of sites that are occupied by species i, and the remaining terms describe the competitive displacement by superior competitors.

To simplify the discussion, we assume that there are only two species and that $m_1 = m_2 = 1$. The equations are then given by

$$\frac{dp_1}{dt} = c_1 p_1(1-p_1) - p_1$$

$$\frac{dp_2}{dt} = c_2 p_2(1-p_1-p_2) - p_2 - c_1 p_1 p_2$$

The hierarchical structure of the model makes it easy to find possible equilibria. Setting $dp_1/dt = 0$, we find that

$$0 = \hat{p}_1[c_1(1 - \hat{p}_1) - 1]$$

which, aside from the trivial equilibrium 0, gives

$$\hat{p}_1 = 1 - \frac{1}{c_1}$$

The equation for species 1 is identical to the Levins model in Subsection 8.2.3, and we can use the results from that subsection. Thus, $c_1 > 1$, $\hat{p}_1 \in (0, 1)$, and the nontrivial equilibrium is stable. Because we are interested in the coexistence of species, we assume that $c_1 > 1$ in what follows, so that species 1 can survive. Setting $dp_2/dt = 0$ with $\hat{p}_1 = 1 - 1/c_1$ allows us to find $\hat{p}_2$:

$$0 = \hat{p}_2[c_2(1 - \hat{p}_1 - \hat{p}_2) - 1 - c_1\hat{p}_1]$$

This equation yields, aside from the trivial equilibrium 0,

$$\hat{p}_2 = (1 - \hat{p}_1) - \frac{1}{c_2} - \frac{c_1}{c_2}\hat{p}_1$$

$$= \frac{1}{c_1} - \frac{1}{c_2} - \frac{c_1}{c_2} + \frac{1}{c_2}$$

$$= \frac{1}{c_1} - \frac{c_1}{c_2}$$

Coexistence of the two species means that both $\hat{p}_1$ and $\hat{p}_2$ are positive and that their sum $\hat{p}_1 + \hat{p}_2$, which denotes the total fraction of occupied sites, is less than 1. Now, the sum of the two nontrivial equilibria, $\hat{p}_1 + \hat{p}_2 = 1 - c_1/c_2$, is automatically less than 1. Furthermore, since we assumed that $c_1 > 1$, we have $\hat{p}_1 > 0$. Therefore, we need only to find out when $\hat{p}_2 > 0$—that is, when

$$\frac{1}{c_1} - \frac{c_1}{c_2} > 0$$

To satisfy this inequality, we need

$$c_2 > c_1^2$$

So far, we know that there is a nontrivial equilibrium if $c_1 > 1$ and $c_2 > c_1^2$, but this does not tell us anything about stability. Still, even though we cannot yet analyze stability directly, we can take an approach that is very common in the ecological literature: We determine whether species 2 can invade the *monoculture equilibrium* of species 1—that is, the positive equilibrium of species 1 in the absence of species 2. Why does this help us? First, note that species 1 is unaffected by the presence of species 2: As long as species 1 can survive in the absence of species 2, it can also survive in its presence. Therefore, we need only worry about species 2. If species 2 can invade the monoculture equilibrium of species 1, then if species 2 is at a low density, it will be able to increase its density, and it will therefore be able to coexist with species 1. The invasion criterion is then

$$\left. \frac{dp_2}{dt} \right|_{p_1=\hat{p}_1} > 0 \quad \text{when } p_2 \text{ is small}$$

This works as follows:

$$\frac{dp_2}{dt} = p_2[c_2(1 - p_1 - p_2) - 1 - c_1 p_1]$$

We assume that $p_1 = \hat{p}_1 = 1 - 1/c_1$ and that p_2 is very small. Then $1 - \hat{p}_1 - p_2 \approx 1 - \hat{p}_1$. Hence,

$$\frac{dp_2}{dt} \approx p_2\left[c_2\frac{1}{c_1} - 1 - c_1 + 1\right] = p_2\left[\frac{c_2}{c_1} - c_1\right] > 0$$

if

$$\frac{c_2}{c_1} - c_1 > 0, \qquad \text{or} \qquad c_2 > c_1^2$$

Since $dp_2/dt > 0$ when species 1 is in equilibrium and species 2 has a low abundance, it follows that species 2 can invade. We conclude that species 1 and 2 can coexist when $c_2 > c_1^2$.

This mechanism of coexistence is referred to as the **competition–colonization trade-off**. That is, the weaker competitor (species 2) can compensate for its inferior competitiveness by being a superior colonizer ($c_2 > c_1^2$).

Section 8.3 Problems

■ 8.3.1

In Problems 1–4, we will investigate the classical Kermack–McKendrick model for the spread of an infectious disease in a population of fixed size N. (This model was introduced in Subsection 8.3.1, and you should refer to that subsection when working out the problems.) If S(t) denotes the number of susceptibles at time t, I(t) the number of infectives at time t, and R(t) the number of immune individuals at time t, then

$$\frac{dS}{dt} = -bSI$$

$$\frac{dI}{dt} = bSI - aI$$

and $R(t) = N - S(t) - I(t)$.

1. Determine, in each of the following cases, whether or not the disease can spread (*Hint*: Compute R_0.):
(a) $S(0) = 1000$, $a = 200$, $b = 0.3$
(b) $S(0) = 1000$, $a = 200$, $b = 0.1$
2. Assume that $a = 100$ and $b = 0.2$. The **critical number** of susceptibles $S_c(0)$ at time 0 for the spread of a disease that is introduced into a population at time 0 is defined as the minimum number of susceptibles for which the disease can spread. Find $S_c(0)$.
3. Suppose that $a = 100$, $b = 0.01$, and $N = 10,000$. Can the disease spread if, at time 0, there is one infected individual?
4. Refer to the simple model of epidemics in Subsection 8.3.1.
(a) Divide (8.75) by (8.74) to show that when $I > 0$,

$$\frac{dI}{dS} = \frac{a}{b}\frac{1}{S} - 1 \tag{8.84}$$

Also, show that when $R(0) = 0$, $I(0) = I_0$, and $S(0) = S_0$, the solution of (8.84) satisfies

$$I(t) = N - S(t) + \frac{a}{b}\ln\frac{S(t)}{S_0}$$

where $I(t)$ denotes the number of infectives, N the total number of individuals in the population, and $S(t)$ the number of susceptibles at time t.

(b) Since $I(t)$ gives the number of infectives at time t and $dI/dt = bSI - aI$, if $S(0) > a/b$, then $dI/dt > 0$ at time $t = 0$. Also, since $\lim_{t\to\infty} I(t) = 0$, there is a time $t > 0$ at which $I(t)$ is maximal. Show that the number of susceptibles when $I(t)$ is maximal is given by $S = a/b$. [*Hint*: When $I(t)$ attains a maximum, the derivative of $I(t)$ with respect to t, dI/dt, is equal to 0.]
(c) In (a), you expressed $I(t)$ as a function of $S(t)$. Use your result in (b) to show that the maximal number of infectives is given by

$$I_{max} = N - \frac{a}{b} + \frac{a}{b}\ln\left(\frac{a/b}{S_0}\right)$$

(d) Use your result in (c) to show that I_{max} is a decreasing function of the parameter a/b for $a/b < S_0$ (i.e., in the case in which the infection can spread). Use the latter statement to explain how a and b determine the severity (as measured by I_{max}) of the disease. Does this make sense?

■ 8.3.2

5. Assume the compartment model of Subsection 8.3.2, with $a = 5$, $b = 0.02$, $m = 1$, and $c = 1$.
(a) Find the system of differential equations that corresponds to these values.
(b) Determine which values of N_I result in a nontrivial equilibrium, and find the equilibrium values for both the autotroph and the nutrient pool.
6. Assume the compartment model of Subsection 8.2.3, with $a = 1$, $b = 0.01$, $m = 2$, $c = 1$, and $N_I = 500$.
(a) Find the system of differential equations that corresponds to these values.
(b) Plot the zero isoclines corresponding to this system.
(c) Use your graph in (b) to determine whether the system has a nontrivial equilibrium.
7. Assume the compartment model of Subsection 8.3.2, with $a = 1$, $b = 0.01$, $m = 2$, $c = 1$ and $N_I = 200$.
(a) Find the system of differential equations that corresponds to these values.
(b) Plot the zero isoclines corresponding to this system.
(c) Use your graph in (b) to determine whether the system has a nontrivial equilibrium.

■ **8.3.3**

8. Assume the hierarchical competition model introduced in Subsection 8.3.3, and assume that the model describes two species. Specifically, assume that

$$\frac{dp_1}{dt} = 2p_1(1 - p_1) - p_1$$

$$\frac{dp_2}{dt} = 5p_2(1 - p_1 - p_2) - p_2 - 2p_1p_2$$

(a) Find all equilibria.

(b) Determine whether species 2 can invade a monoculture of species 1. (Assume that species 1 is in equilibrium.)

9. Assume the hierarchical competition model introduced in Subsection 8.3.3, and assume that the model describes two species. Specifically, assume that

$$\frac{dp_1}{dt} = 2p_1(1 - p_1) - p_1$$

$$\frac{dp_2}{dt} = 3p_2(1 - p_1 - p_2) - p_2 - 2p_1p_2$$

(a) Find all equilibria.

(b) Determine whether species 2 can invade a monoculture equilibrium of species 1.

10. Assume the hierarchical competition model introduced in Subsection 8.3.3, and assume that the model describes two species. Specifically, assume that

$$\frac{dp_1}{dt} = 2p_1(1 - p_1) - p_1$$

$$\frac{dp_2}{dt} = 6p_2(1 - p_1 - p_2) - p_2 - 2p_1p_2$$

(a) Use the zero-isocline approach to find all equilibria graphically.

(b) Determine the numerical values of all equilibria.

11. Assume the hierarchical competition model introduced in Subsection 8.3.3, and assume that the model describes two species. Specifically, assume

$$\frac{dp_1}{dt} = 3p_1(1 - p_1) - p_1$$

$$\frac{dp_2}{dt} = 5p_2(1 - p_1 - p_2) - p_2 - 3p_1p_2$$

(a) Use the zero-isocline approach to find all equilibria graphically.

(b) Determine the numerical values of all equilibria.

12. *(Adapted from Crawley, 1997)* Denote plant biomass by V, and herbivore number by N. The plant–herbivore interaction is modeled as

$$\frac{dV}{dt} = aV(1 - \frac{V}{K}) - bVN$$

$$\frac{dN}{dt} = cVN - dN$$

(a) Suppose the herbivore number is equal to 0. What differential equation describes the dynamics of the plant biomass? Can you explain the resulting equation? Determine the plant biomass equilibrium in the absence of herbivores.

(b) Now assume that herbivores are present. Describe the effect of herbivores on plant biomass; that is, explain the term $-bVN$ in the first equation. Describe the dynamics of the herbivores— that is, how their population size increases and what contributes to decreases in their population size.

(c) Determine the equilibria (1) by solving

$$\frac{dV}{dt} = 0 \quad \text{and} \quad \frac{dN}{dt} = 0$$

and (2) graphically. Explain why this model implies that "plant abundance is determined solely by attributes of the herbivore," as stated in Crawley (1997).

Chapter 8 Key Terms

Discuss the following definitions and concepts:

1. Differential equation
2. Separable differential equation
3. Solution of a differential equation
4. Pure-time differential equation
5. Autonomous differential equation
6. Exponential growth
7. Von Bertalanffy equation
8. Logistic equation
9. Allometric growth
10. Equilibrium
11. Stability
12. Eigenvalue
13. Single-compartment model
14. Levins model
15. Allee effect
16. Kermack–McKendrick model
17. Zero isocline
18. Hierarchical competition model

Chapter 8 Review Problems

1. Newton's Law of Cooling Suppose that an object has temperature T and is brought into a room that is kept at a constant temperature T_a. Newton's law of cooling states that the rate of temperature change of the object is proportional to the difference between the temperature of the object and the surrounding medium.

(a) Denote the temperature at time t by $T(t)$, and explain why

$$\frac{dT}{dt} = k(T - T_a)$$

is the differential equation that expresses Newton's law of cooling.

(b) Suppose that it takes the object 20 min to cool from 30°C to 28°C in a room whose temperature is 21°C. How long will it take the object to cool to 25°C if it is at 30°C when it is brought into the room? [*Hint*: Solve the differential equation in (a) with the initial condition $T(0) = 30$°C and with $T_a = 21$°C. Use $T(20) = 28$°C to determine the constant k.]

2. *(Adapted from Cain et al., 1995)* In this problem, we discuss a model for clonal growth in the white clover *Trifolium repens*. *T. repens* is a widespread perennial clonal plant species that spreads through stolon growth. (A *stolon* is a horizontal stem.) By mapping the shape of a clone over time, Cain et al. estimated stolon elongation and dieback rates as follows. Denote by $S(t)$ the stolon length of the clone at time t. Cain et al. observed that the change in stolon length was proportional to the stolon length; that is,

$$\frac{dS}{dt} \propto S$$

Introducing the proportionality constant r, called the *net growth rate*, we find that

$$\frac{dS}{dt} = rS \tag{8.85}$$

(a) Suppose that S_f and S_0 are the final and the initial stolon lengths, respectively, and that T denotes the period of observation. Use (8.85) to show that r, the net growth rate, can be estimated from

$$r = \frac{1}{T} \ln \frac{S_f}{S_0}$$

[*Hint*: Solve the differential equation (8.85) with initial condition $S(0) = S_0$, and use the fact that $S(T) = S_f$.]
(b) The net growth rate r is the difference between the stolon elongation rate b and the stolon dieback rate m; that is,

$$r = b - m$$

Let B be the total amount of stolon elongation and D be the total amount of stolon dieback over the observation period of length T. Show that

$$B = \int_0^T bS(t)\, dt = \frac{bS_0}{r}(e^{rT} - 1)$$

$$D = \int_0^T mS(t)\, dt = \frac{mS_0}{r}(e^{rT} - 1)$$

(c) Show that $B - D = S_f - S_0$, and rearrange the equations for B and D in (b) so that you can estimate b and m from r, B, and D; that is, show that

$$b = \frac{rB}{S_f - S_0} = \frac{rB}{B - D}$$

$$m = \frac{rD}{S_f - S_0} = \frac{rD}{B - D}$$

(d) Explain how B and r can be estimated if S_f, S_0, and D are known from field measurements. Use your result in (c) to explain how you would then find estimates for b and m.

3. Diversification of Life (*Adapted from Benton, 1997, and Walker, 1985*) Several models have been proposed to explain the diversification of life during geological periods. According to Benton (1997),

> The diversification of marine families in the past 600 million years (Myr) appears to have followed two or three logistic curves, with equilibrium levels that lasted for up to 200 Myr. In contrast, continental organisms clearly show an exponential pattern of diversification, and although it is not clear whether the empirical diversification patterns are real or are artifacts of a poor fossil record, the latter explanation seems unlikely.

In this problem, we will investigate three models for diversification. They are analogous to models for population growth; however, the quantities involved have a different interpretation. We denote by $N(t)$ the diversification function, which counts the number of taxa as a function of time, and by r the intrinsic rate of diversification.

(a) (*Exponential Model*) This model is described by

$$\frac{dN}{dt} = r_e N \tag{8.86}$$

Solve (8.86) with the initial condition $N(0)$ at time 0, and show that r_e can be estimated from

$$r_e = \frac{1}{t} \ln\left[\frac{N(t)}{N(0)}\right] \tag{8.87}$$

[*Hint*: To find (8.87), solve for r in the solution of (8.86).]
(b) (*Logistic Growth*) This model is described by

$$\frac{dN}{dt} = r_l N\left(1 - \frac{N}{K}\right) \tag{8.88}$$

where K is the equilibrium value. Solve (8.88) with the initial condition $N(0)$ at time 0, and show that r_l can be estimated from

$$r_l = \frac{1}{t} \ln\left[\frac{K - N(0)}{N(0)}\right] + \frac{1}{t} \ln\left[\frac{N(t)}{K - N(t)}\right] \tag{8.89}$$

for $N(t) < K$.
(c) Assume that $N(0) = 1$ and $N(10) = 1000$. Estimate r_e and r_l for both $K = 1001$ and $K = 10,000$.
(d) Use your answer in (c) to explain the following quote from Stanley (1979):

> There must be a general tendency for calculated values of [r] to represent underestimates of exponential rates, because some radiation will have followed distinctly sigmoid paths during the interval evaluated.

(e) Explain why the exponential model is a good approximation to the logistic model when N/K is small compared with 1.

4. A Simple Model for Photosynthesis of Individual Leaves (*Adapted from Horn, 1971*) Photosynthesis is a complex mechanism; the following model is a very simplified caricature: Suppose that a leaf contains a number of traps that can capture light. If a trap captures light, the trap becomes energized. The energy in the trap can then be used to produce sugar, which causes the energized trap to become unenergized. The number of traps that can become energized is proportional to the number of unenergized traps and the intensity of the light. Denote by T the total number of traps (unenergized and energized) in a leaf, by I the light intensity, and by x the number of energized traps. Then the following differential equation describes how the number of energized traps changes over time:

$$\frac{dx}{dt} = k_1(T - x)I - k_2 x$$

Here, k_1 and k_2 are positive constants. Find all equilibria, and use the eigenvalue approach to study their stability.

5. Gompertz Growth Model This model is sometimes used to study the growth of a population for which the per capita growth rate is density dependent. Denote the size of a population at time t by $N(t)$; then, for $N \geq 0$,

$$\frac{dN}{dt} = kN(\ln K - \ln N) \quad \text{with } N(0) = N_0 \tag{8.90}$$

(a) Show that

$$N(t) = K \exp\left[-\left(\ln \frac{K}{N_0}\right) e^{-kt}\right]$$

is a solution of (8.90). To do this, differentiate $N(t)$ with respect to t and show that the derivaive can be written in the form (8.90). Don't forget to show that $N(0) = N_0$. Use a graphing calculator to sketch the graph of $N(t)$ for $N_0 = 100$, $k = 2$, and $K = 1000$. The function $N(t)$ is called the *Gompertz growth curve*.

(b) Use l'Hospital's rule to show that

$$\lim_{N \to 0} N \ln N = 0$$

and use this equation to show that $\lim_{N \to 0} dN/dt = 0$. Are there any other values of N where $dN/dt = 0$?

(c) Sketch the graph of dN/dt as a function of N for $k = 2$ and $K = 1000$. Find the equilibria, and use your graph to and discuss their stability. Explain the meaning of K.

6. Island Biogeography Preston (1962) and MacArthur and Wilson (1963) investigated the effect of area on species diversity in oceanic islands. It is assumed that species can immigrate to an island from a species pool of size P and that species on the island can go extinct. We denote the immigration rate by $I(S)$ and the extinction rate by $E(S)$, where S is the number of species on the island. Then the change in species diversity over time is

$$\frac{dS}{dt} = I(S) - E(S) \tag{8.91}$$

For a fixed island, the simplest functional forms for $I(S)$ and $E(S)$ are

$$I(S) = c\left(1 - \frac{S}{P}\right) \tag{8.92}$$

$$E(S) = m\frac{S}{P} \tag{8.93}$$

where c, m, and P are positive constants.
(a) Find the equilibrium species diversity $\hat{S}$ of (8.91) with $I(S)$ and $E(S)$ given in (8.92) and (8.93).

(b) It is reasonable to assume that the extinction rate is a decreasing function of island size. That is, we assume that if A denotes the area of the island, then m is a function of the island size A, with $dm/dA < 0$. Furthermore, we assume that the immigration rate I does not depend on the size of the island. Use these assumptions to investigate how the equilibrium species diversity changes with island size.

(c) Assume that $S(0) = S_0$. Solve (8.91) with $I(S)$ and $E(S)$ as given in (8.92) and (8.93), respectively.

(d) Assume that $S_0 = 0$. That is, the island is initially void of species. The time constant T for the system is defined as

$$S(T) = (1 - e^{-1})\hat{S}$$

Show that, under the assumption $S_0 = 0$,

$$T = \frac{P}{c + m}$$

(e) Use the assumptions in (b) and your answer in (d) to investigate the effect of island size on the time constant T; that is, determine whether $T(A)$ is an increasing or decreasing function of A.

7. Chemostat A chemostat is an apparatus for growing bacteria in a medium in which all nutrients but one are available in excess. One nutrient, whose concentration can be controlled, is held at a concentration that limits the growth of bacteria. The growth chamber of the chemostat is continually flushed by adding nutrients dissolved in liquid at a constant rate and allowing the liquid in the growth chamber, which contains bacteria, to leave the chamber at the same rate. If X denotes the number of bacteria in

the growth chamber, then the growth dynamics of the bacteria are given by

$$\frac{dX}{dt} = r(N)X - qX \tag{8.94}$$

where $r(N)$ is the growth rate depending on the nutrient concentration N and q is the input and output flow rate. The equation for the nutrient flow is given by

$$\frac{dN}{dt} = qN_0 - qN - r(N)X \tag{8.95}$$

Note that (8.94) is (8.79) with $m = 0$, $N_I = qN_0$, and $a = e = q$ and that (8.95) is (8.78) with $m = 0$.
(a) Explain in words the meaning of the terms in (8.94) and (8.95).
(b) Assume that $r(N)$ is given by the Monod growth function

$$r(N) = b\frac{N}{k + N}$$

where k and b are positive constants. Draw the zero isoclines in the N–X plane, and explain how to find the equilibria $(\hat{N}, \hat{X})$ graphically.
(c) Show that a nontrivial equilibrium (an equilibrium for which $\hat{N}$ and $\hat{X}$ are both positive) satisfies

$$r(\hat{N}) - q = 0 \tag{8.96}$$

$$qN_0 - q\hat{N} - r(\hat{N})\hat{X} = 0 \tag{8.97}$$

Show also that (8.96) has a positive solution $\hat{N}$ if $q < b$, and find an expression for $\hat{N}$. Use this expression and (8.97) to find $\hat{X}$.
(d) Assume that $q < b$. Use your results in (c) to show that $\hat{X} > 0$ if $\hat{N} < N_0$ and $\hat{N} < N_0$ if $q < bN_0/(k + N_0)$. Furthermore, show that $\hat{N}$ is an increasing function of q for $q < b$.
(e) Use your results in (d) to explain why the following is true: As we increase the flow rate q from 0 to $bN_0/(k + N_0)$, the nutrient concentration $\hat{N}$ increases until it reaches the value N_0 and the number of bacteria decreases to 0.

8. *(Adapted from Nee and May, 1992, and Tilman, 1994)* In Subsection 8.3.3, we introduced a hierarchical competition model. We will use this model to investigate the effects of habitat destruction on coexistence. We assume that a fraction D of the sites is permanently destroyed. Furthermore, we restrict our discussion to two species and assume that species 1 is the superior and species 2 the inferior competitor. In the case in which both species have the same mortality ($m_1 = m_2$), which we set equal to 1, the dynamics are described by

$$\frac{dp_1}{dt} = c_1 p_1(1 - p_1 - D) - p_1 \tag{8.98}$$

$$\frac{dp_2}{dt} = c_2 p_2(1 - p_1 - p_2 - D) - p_2 - c_1 p_1 p_2 \tag{8.99}$$

where p_i, $i = 1, 2$, is the fraction of sites occupied by species i.
(a) Explain in words the meanings of the different terms in (8.98) and (8.99).
(b) Show that

$$\hat{p}_1 = 1 - \frac{1}{c_1} - D$$

is an equilibrium for species 1, which is in $(0, 1)$, and is stable if $D < 1 - 1/c_1$ and $c_1 > 1$.
(c) Assume that $c_1 > 1$ and $D < 1 - 1/c_1$. Show that species 2 can invade the nontrivial equilibrium of species 1 [computed in (b)] if

$$c_2 > c_1^2(1 - D)$$

(d) Assume that $c_1 = 2$ and $c_2 = 5$. Then species 1 can survive as long as $D < 1/2$. Show that the fraction of sites that are occupied by species 1 is then

$$\hat{p}_1 = \begin{cases} \dfrac{1}{2} - D & \text{for } 0 \leq D \leq \dfrac{1}{2} \\ 0 & \text{for } \dfrac{1}{2} \leq D \leq 1 \end{cases}$$

Show also that

$$\hat{p}_2 = \frac{1}{10} + \frac{2}{5}D \qquad \text{for} \quad 0 \leq D \leq \frac{1}{2}$$

For $D > 1/2$, species 1 can no longer persist. Explain why the dynamics for species 2 reduce to

$$\frac{dp_2}{dt} = 5p_2(1 - p_2 - D) - p_2$$

in this case. Show, in addition, that the nontrivial equilibrium is of the form

$$\hat{p}_2 = 1 - \frac{1}{5} - D \quad \text{for } \frac{1}{2} \leq D \leq 1 - \frac{1}{5}$$

Plot $\hat{p}_1$ and $\hat{p}_2$ as functions of D in the same coordinate system. What happens for $D > 1 - 1/5$? Use the plot to explain in words how each species is affected by habitat destruction.

(e) Repeat (d) for $c_1 = 2$ and $c_2 = 3$.

9 Linear Algebra and Analytic Geometry

LEARNING OBJECTIVES

The primary focus of this chapter is on tools from linear algebra that are needed to develop multidimensional differential calculus in Chapter 10 and to analyze systems of differential equations in Chapter 11. Specifically, we will learn how to

- solve systems of linear equations;
- define matrices and perform algebraic operations on matrices;
- define and analyze linear maps; and
- define lines and planes in more than two dimensions.

9.1 Linear Systems

Two different species of insects are reared together in a laboratory cage. They are supplied with two different types of food each day. Each individual of species 1 consumes 5 units of food A and 3 units of food B, whereas each individual of species 2 consumes 2 units of food A and 4 units of food B, on average, per day. Each day, a lab technician supplies 900 units of food A and 960 units of food B. How many of each species are reared together?

To solve such a problem, we will set up a system of equations. If

$$x = \text{number of individuals of species 1}$$
$$y = \text{number of individuals of species 2}$$

then the following two equations must be satisfied:

$$\text{food } A: \quad 5x + 2y = 900$$
$$\text{food } B: \quad 3x + 4y = 960$$

We refer to these two equations as a *system of two linear equations in two variables*. This section is devoted to finding solutions of such systems.

Appendices

Appendix A Frequently Used Symbols

A.1 Greek Letters

Lowercase Letters

α	alpha	η	eta	ν	nu	τ	tau
β	beta	θ	theta	ξ	xi	υ	upsilon
γ	gamma	ι	iota	o	omicron	ϕ	phi
δ	delta	κ	kappa	π	pi	χ	chi
ϵ	epsilon	λ	lambda	ρ	rho	ψ	psi
ζ	zeta	μ	mu	σ	sigma	ω	omega

Uppercase Letters

Γ	Gamma	Λ	Lambda	Σ	Sigma
Δ	Delta	Π	Pi	Ω	Omega

A.2 Mathematical Symbols

$<$	less than	$\subset$	subset	$=$	equal to
$\leq$	less than or equal to	$\in$	element of	$\neq$	not equal to
$>$	greater than	$\perp$	perpendicular	$\approx$	approximately
$\geq$	greater than or equal to	$\parallel$	parallel	$\propto$	proportional to
$\cup$	union	$\cap$	intersection	Σ	sum

■ Appendix B Table of the Standard Normal Distribution

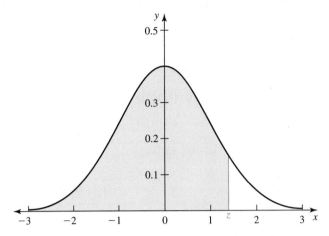

Figure B.1 Areas under the standard normal curve from $-\infty$ to z.

z	0	1	2	3	4	5	6	7	8	9
0.0	.5000	.5040	.5080	.5120	.5160	.5199	.5239	.5279	.5319	.5359
0.1	.5398	.5438	.5478	.5517	.5557	.5596	.5636	.5675	.5714	.5754
0.2	.5793	.5832	.5871	.5910	.5948	.5987	.6026	.6064	.6103	.6141
0.3	.6179	.6217	.6255	.6293	.6331	.6368	.6406	.6443	.6480	.6517
0.4	.6554	.6591	.6628	.6664	.6700	.6736	.6772	.6808	.6844	.6879
0.5	.6915	.6950	.6985	.7019	.7054	.7088	.7123	.7157	.7190	.7224
0.6	.7258	.7291	.7324	.7357	.7389	.7422	.7454	.7486	.7518	.7549
0.7	.7580	.7612	.7642	.7673	.7704	.7734	.7764	.7794	.7823	.7852
0.8	.7881	.7910	.7939	.7967	.7996	.8023	.8051	.8078	.8106	.8133
0.9	.8159	.8186	.8212	.8238	.8264	.8289	.8315	.8340	.8365	.8389
1.0	.8413	.8438	.8461	.8485	.8508	.8531	.8554	.8577	.8599	.8621
1.1	.8643	.8665	.8686	.8708	.8729	.8749	.8770	.8790	.8810	.8830
1.2	.8849	.8869	.8888	.8907	.8925	.8944	.8962	.8980	.8997	.9015
1.3	.9032	.9049	.9066	.9082	.9099	.9115	.9131	.9147	.9162	.9177
1.4	.9192	.9207	.9222	.9236	.9251	.9265	.9279	.9292	.9306	.9319
1.5	.9332	.9345	.9357	.9370	.9382	.9394	.9406	.9418	.9429	.9441
1.6	.9452	.9463	.9474	.9484	.9495	.9505	.9515	.9525	.9535	.9545
1.7	.9554	.9564	.9573	.9582	.9591	.9599	.9608	.9616	.9625	.9633
1.8	.9641	.9649	.9656	.9664	.9671	.9678	.9686	.9693	.9699	.9706
1.9	.9713	.9719	.9726	.9732	.9738	.9744	.9750	.9756	.9761	.9767
2.0	.9772	.9778	.9783	.9788	.9793	.9798	.9803	.9808	.9812	.9817
2.1	.9821	.9826	.9830	.9834	.9838	.9842	.9846	.9850	.9854	.9857
2.2	.9861	.9864	.9868	.9871	.9875	.9878	.9881	.9884	.9887	.9890
2.3	.9893	.9896	.9898	.9901	.9904	.9906	.9909	.9911	.9913	.9916
2.4	.9918	.9920	.9922	.9925	.9927	.9929	.9931	.9932	.9934	.9936
2.5	.9938	.9940	.9941	.9943	.9945	.9946	.9948	.9949	.9951	.9952
2.6	.9953	.9955	.9956	.9957	.9959	.9960	.9961	.9962	.9963	.9964
2.7	.9965	.9966	.9967	.9968	.9969	.9970	.9971	.9972	.9973	.9974
2.8	.9974	.9975	.9976	.9977	.9977	.9978	.9979	.9979	.9980	.9981
2.9	.9981	.9982	.9982	.9983	.9984	.9984	.9985	.9985	.9986	.9986

Answers to Odd-Numbered Problems

Section 1.1

1. (a) $\{-4, 2\}$ **(b)** $\{-4, 2\}$ **3. (a)** $\{-1, 5\}$ **(b)** $\{1, 5\}$ **(c)** $\{-4, 1\}$
(d) no solution **5. (a)** $[-\frac{2}{5}, \frac{6}{5}]$, **(b)** $(-\infty, -\frac{7}{3}) \cup (3, \infty)$,
(c) $(-\infty, -1] \cup [-\frac{1}{7}, \infty)$, **(d)** $(-\frac{1}{5}, \frac{13}{5})$ **7.** $x + 3y - 14 = 0$
9. $3x + y + 2 = 0$ **11.** $7x - 3y + 5 = 0$ **13.** $4x + 3y - 12 = 0$
15. $2y - 3 = 0$ **17.** $x + 1 = 0$ **19.** $3x - y + 2 = 0$
21. $2y - x - 4 = 0$ **23.** $y + 2x - 2 = 0$ **25.** $x + 4y - 3 = 0$
27. $x + 2y + 4 = 0$ **29.** $x + 3y + 4 = 0$ **31.** $2x + 5y - 22 = 0$
33. $y - x + 6 = 0$ **35.** $y = 2$ **37.** $x = -1$ **39.** $x = 1$
41. $y = 3$ **43. (a)** $y = kx$, $[x] = $ ft, $[y] = $ cm, $k = \frac{30.5 \text{ cm}}{1 \text{ ft}}$ implies
$y = (30.5 \frac{\text{cm}}{\text{ft}})x$ **(b)** (i) 183 cm, (ii) $\frac{1159}{12}$ cm, (iii) $\frac{1159}{24}$ cm
(c) (i) $\frac{346}{61}$ ft, (ii) $\frac{150}{61}$ ft, (iii) $\frac{96}{61}$ ft **45.** $s(t) = (40 \text{ mi/hr})t$,
$k = 40 \text{ mi/hr}$ **47.** $\frac{1}{(0.305)^2}$ ft^2 **49. (a)** $[y] = $ liter, $[x] = $ ounces,
$y = \left(\frac{1}{33.81} \frac{\text{liter}}{\text{ounces}}\right)x$ **(b)** $\frac{12}{33.81}$ liters **51. (a)** 88 km/hr, **(b)** 81 mi/hr
53. (a) $C = K - 273.15$, **(b)** $77.4 \text{ K} = -195.75°C = -320.35°F$,
$90.2 \text{ K} = -182.95°C = -297.31°F$; nitrogen gets distilled first,
since it has the lower boiling point. **55.** $(x + 1)^2 + (y - 4)^2 = 9$
57. (a) $(x - 2)^2 + (y - 5)^2 = 9$ **(b)** $y = 5 + \sqrt{5}$ or $y = 5 - \sqrt{5}$
(c) No **59.** center: $(2, 0)$; radius: 4 **61.** center: $(2, -1)$, radius: 4
63. (a) $\frac{5}{12}\pi$, **(b)** $255°$ **65. (a)** $\frac{1}{2}\sqrt{2}$, **(b)** $-\frac{1}{2}\sqrt{3}$, **(c)** $\sqrt{3}$
67. (a) $\alpha = \frac{5\pi}{3}$ or $\alpha = \frac{4\pi}{3}$ **(b)** $\alpha = \frac{\pi}{3}$ or $\alpha = \frac{4\pi}{3}$ **69.** Divide both
left and right side by $\cos^2\theta$. **71.** $\{0, \frac{\pi}{3}, \pi, \frac{5\pi}{3}\}$ **73. (a)** $4^{7/3}$ **(b)** 27
(c) 5^{4k-2} **75. (a)** $x = \frac{1}{16}$ **(b)** $x = 27$ **(c)** $x = \frac{1}{100}$ **77. (a)** $x = -5$
(b) $x = -4$ **(c)** $x = -3$ **79. (a)** $\ln 3$ **(b)** $\log_4(x - 2) + \log_4(x + 2)$
(c) $6x - 2$ **81. (a)** $x = \frac{1}{3}(\ln 2 + 1)$ **(b)** $x = -\frac{1}{2}\ln 10$
(c) $x = \pm\sqrt{1 + \ln 10}$ **83. (a)** $x = 3 + e^5$ **(b)** $x = \sqrt{4 + e}$
(c) $x = 18$ **85.** $5 - 7i$ **87.** $13 + 2i$ **89.** $15 + 9i$ **91.** 37
93. $3 + 2i$ **95.** $6 - 3i$ **97.** $8 - 2i$ **99.** $z + \bar{z} = 2a$, $z - \bar{z} = 2bi$
101. $x_1 = \frac{3}{4} + i\frac{\sqrt{7}}{4}$, $x_2 = \frac{3}{4} - i\frac{\sqrt{7}}{4}$ **103.** $x_1 = -1$, $x_2 = 2$
105. $x_1 = \frac{3}{8} + i\frac{\sqrt{7}}{8}$, $x_2 = \frac{3}{8} - i\frac{\sqrt{7}}{8}$ **107.** $x_1 = \frac{7}{3}$, $x_2 = -1$
109. $x_1 = x_2 = 1$ **111.** $x_1 = \frac{5 + i\sqrt{47}}{6}$, $x_1 = \frac{5 - i\sqrt{47}}{6}$

Section 1.2

1. range: $y \geq 0$

x^2 —

3. range: $y \in [0, 1)$

x^2 —

5. (b) No, their domains are different.

7. $f(x)$ is odd. $f(-x) = -2x - f(x)$

$2x$ —

9. $f(x)$ is even. $f(-x) = |3(-x)| = |3x| = f(x)$

$|3x|$ —

11. $f(x)$ is even. $f(-x) = -|-x| = -|x| = f(x)$

$-|x|$ —

15. (a) $(f \circ g)(x) = 1 - 4x^2$, $x \geq 0$ **(b)** $(g \circ f)(x) = 2(1 - x^2)$, $x \in \mathbf{R}$

17. $(f \circ g)(x) = 3x$, $x \geq 9$

19. $(f \circ g)(x) = x$, $x \geq 0$; $(g \circ f)(x) = x$, $x \geq 0$

21. $x^2 > x^4$ for $0 < x < 1$; $x^2 < x^4$ for $x > 1$

x^4 —
x^2 —

23. They intersect at $x = 0$ or 1.

25. (a)

x^2 —
x^3 —

$n = 4$ $n = 3$
$n = 2$
$n = 1$

27. (a) $f(-x) = f(x)$ **(b)** $f(-x) = -f(x)$

29. (a) $k = \frac{3}{2}$ **(b)** domain: $0 \leq x \leq 3$

$R(x)$ —

A1

31. $s(t) = t$, polynomial of degree 1 **33.** domain: $x \neq 1$;
range: $y \neq 0$ **35.** domain: $x \neq -3, 3$; range: **R**

37. $\frac{1}{x} < \frac{1}{x^2}$ for $0 < x < 1$; $\frac{1}{x} > \frac{1}{x^2}$ for $x > 1$;
they intersect at $x = 1$.

39. (a) **(b)** range of $f(x)$ is $(0, \infty)$ **(c)** $x = -\frac{1}{2}$

(d) exactly one.

41. (a) 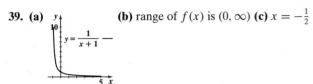 **(b)** range of $f(x)$ is $[0, 3)$, **(c)** $x = 2$,

(d) exactly one, $x = \frac{a}{3-a}$. **43.** 83.3 4.76

45. (a) 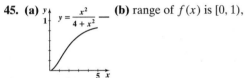 **(b)** range of $f(x)$ is $[0, 1)$,

(c) $f(x)$ approaches 1.

47. 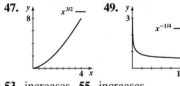 **49.** 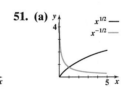 **51. (a)**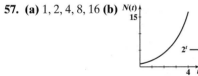

53. increases **55.** increases

57. (a) 1, 2, 4, 8, 16 **(b)**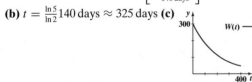

59. $20 \exp\left[-\frac{\ln 2}{5730} 2000\right]$ **61.** $\lambda = \frac{\ln 2}{7 \, \text{days}}$

63. (a) $W(t) = (300 \, \text{gr}) \exp\left[-\frac{\ln 2}{140 \, \text{days}} t\right]$
(b) $t = \frac{\ln 5}{\ln 2} 140 \, \text{days} \approx 325 \, \text{days}$ **(c)**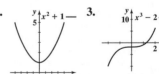

65. $\frac{W(t)}{W(0)} = \exp\left[-\frac{\ln 2}{5730} 15,000\right] \approx 16.3\%$ **67. (a)** $r = 3$
(b) $r = \ln 1.25$ **69. (a)** yes **(b)** no **(c)** yes **(d)** yes **(e)** no **(f)** yes

71. (a) $f^{-1}(x) = \sqrt{x-1}, x \geq 1$ **(b)**

73. $f^{-1}(x) = \sqrt[3]{\frac{1}{x}}, x > 0$

75. $f^{-1}(x) = \log_3 x, x > 0$ **77.** $f^{-1}(x) = \log_{1/4} x, x > 0$

79. $f^{-1}(x) = \log_2(x), x \geq 1$

81. (a) x^5 **(b)** x^4 **(c)** x^{-5} **(d)** x^{-4} **(e)** x^{-3} **(f)** x^2

83. (a) $5 \ln x$ **(b)** $6 \ln x$ **(c)** $\ln(x-1)$ **(d)** $-4 \ln x$

85. (a) $e^{x \ln 3}$ **(b)** $e^{(x^2-1) \ln 4}$ **(c)** $e^{-(x+1) \ln 2}$ **(d)** $e^{(-4x+1) \ln 3}$

87. $\mu = \ln 2$ **89.** $K = -\frac{3}{2} \ln\left(1 - \frac{4}{3} \cdot \frac{47}{300}\right)$

91. Same period; $2 \sin x$ has twice the amplitude of $\sin x$.

93. Same period; $2 \cos x$ has twice the amplitude of $\cos x$.

95. Same period; $y = 2 \tan x$ is stretched by a factor of 2.

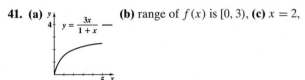

97. amplitude: 3; period: $\frac{\pi}{2}$ **99.** amplitude: 4; period: 1

101. amplitude: 4; period: 8π **103.** amplitude: 3; period: 10

■ **Section 1.3**

1. **3.** **5.**

7. **9.** 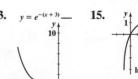 **11.**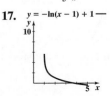

13. **15.** **17.**

19.

$2\sin\left(x + \frac{\pi}{4}\right)$

21. $y = -\sin(\pi x/2)$

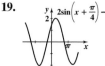

23. **(a)** Shift two units down. **(b)** Shift $y = x^2$ one unit to the right and then one unit up. **(c)** Shift $y = x^2$ two units to the left, stretch by a factor of 2, and reflect about the x-axis. **25.** **(a)** 1. Reflect $\frac{1}{x}$ about the x-axis. 2. Shift up one unit. **(b)** 1. Shift $\frac{1}{x}$ one unit to the right. 2. Reflect about the x-axis. **(c)** 1. Shift $y = \frac{1}{x}$ one unit to the left. 2. Reflect about x-axis. 3. Shift up one unit.

27. **(a)** Stretch $y = e^x$ by a factor of 2, and then shift one unit down. **(b)** Reflect $y = e^x$ about the y-axis, and then reflect about the x-axis. **(c)** Shift $y = e^x$ two units to the right, and then shift one unit up. **29.** **(a)** Shift $y = \ln x$ one unit to the right. **(b)** Reflect $y = \ln x$ about the x-axis, and then shift up one unit. **(c)** Shift $y = \ln x$ three units to the left, then down one unit.

31. **(a)** Reflect $y = \sin x$ about the x-axis, then one unit up. **(b)** Shift $y = \sin x$ by $\pi/4$ units to the right. **(c)** Shift $y = \sin x$ by $\pi/3$ units to the left, and then reflect about the x-axis.

33. Calculate log of each number, for instance, $\log 100 = 2$.

35. **(b)** No **(c)** No **37.** four **39.** one, three **41.** six to seven

43. $y = 5 \times (0.58)^x$ **45.** $y = 3^{1/3} \times (3^{-1/3})^x$

47. $\log y = \log 3 - 2x$ **49.** $\log y = \log 2 - (1.2)(\log e)x$

51. $\log y = \log 5 + (4\log 2)x$ **53.** $\log y = \log 4 + (2\log 3)x$

55. $y = (2)x^{-(\log 2)/\log 5}$ **57.** $y = \frac{1}{8}x^2$ **59.** $\log y = \log 2 + 5\log x$

61. $\log y = 6\log x$ **63.** $\log y = -2\log x$

65. $\log y = \log 4 - 3\log x$ **67.** $\log y = \log 3 + 1.7\log x$, log-log transformation **69.** $\log N(t) = \log 130 + (1.2t)\log 2$, log-linear transformation **71.** $\log R(t) = \log 3.6 + 1.2\log t$, log-log transformation **73.** $y = 1.8x^{0.2}$ **75.** $y = 4 \times 10^x$

77. $y = (5.7)x^{2.1}$ **79.** $\log_2 y = x$ **81.** $\log_2 y = -x$

83. **(a)** $\log N = \log 2 + 3t\log e$ **(b)** slope: $3\log e \approx 1.303$

85. $\log S = \log C + z\log A$, $z =$ slope of straight line

87. $v_{max} =$ horizontal-line intercept, $\frac{v_{max}}{K_m} =$ vertical-line intercept **89.** **(a)** $\log S = \log 1.162 + 0.93\log B$ **91.** **(a)** $\alpha = -\ln 0.9/m$ **(b)** 10% **(c)** 1 m: 90%, 2 m: 81%, 3 m: 72.9% **(e)** slope $= \log 0.9 = -\alpha/\ln 10$ **(f)** $z = -\frac{1}{\alpha}\ln(0.01) = \frac{\ln(0.01)}{\ln(0.9)}$ **(g)** Clear lake: small α; milky lake: large α **93.** $y = (100)(10^{1/3})^x$

95. $y = (2^{1/3})(2^{2/3})^x$ **97.** $y = \log x$

99.
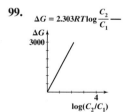
$\Delta G = 2.303RT\log\frac{C_2}{C_1}$

101.

103.
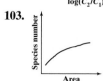

105.

107.

109.
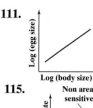

111.
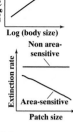

113.
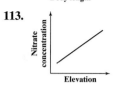

115.
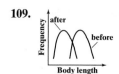

■ **Chapter 1 Review Problems**

1. **(a)** 10^4, 1.1×10^4, 1.22×10^4, 1.35×10^4, 1.49×10^4 **(b)** $t = 10\ln 10 \approx 23.0$

3. **(b)** $R(x) = -4kx^3 + 4k(a+b)x^2 - kb(4a+b)x + kab^2$, polynomial of degree 3

(c) $R(x) = (0.3)(5-x)(6-2x)^2, 0 \le x \le 3$

5. **(a)** $L(t) = 0.69, 2.40, 4.62, 6.91$, $E(t) = 1.72, 2.20 \times 10^4$, 2.69×10^{43}, 1.97×10^{434} **(b)** 20.93 years, 3.09 ft **(c)** $10^{536,000,000}$ years, 21.98 ft **(d)** $L = 19.92$ ft, $E = 10^{195 \times 10^6}$ ft **7.** $T = \frac{\ln 2}{\ln(1 + \frac{q}{100})}$, T goes to infinity as q gets closer to 0. **9.** **(a)**

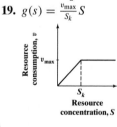

(b) $Y = C^{1.17}10^{-1.92}$ **(c)** $Y_p = 2.25Y_c$ **(d)** 8.5% **11.** **(a)** $21.\overline{8}$ hours per day, 400 days per year **(b)** line through $(0, 24)$ and $(380, 21.\overline{8})$: $y = 4320 - 180x$ **(c)** 376×10^6 to 563×10^6 years ago **13.** **(a)** males: $S(t) = \exp[-(0.019t)^{3.41}]$; females: $S(t) = \exp[-(0.022t)^{3.24}]$ **(b)** males: 47.27 days; females: 40.59 days **(c)** males should live longer **15.** **(a)** $x = k$, $v = \frac{a}{2}$

(b) $x_{0.9} = 81x_{0.1}$ **17.**

19. $g(s) = \frac{v_{max}}{S_k}S$

21. **(a)** $\alpha = -\frac{\ln(0.01)}{18m} \approx 0.25\frac{1}{m}$ **(b)** 4.87 m

■ **Section 2.1**

1. $3, 9, 27, 81, 243, 729$ **3.** $25, 25/4, 25/16, 25/64, 25/256, 25/1024$

5. $N_t = 2 \cdot 2^t$, $t = 0, 1, 2, \dots$ **7.** $N_t = 4^t$, $t = 0, 1, 2, \dots$

9. $N_t = 2 \cdot 2^t$, $t = 0, 1, 2, \dots$ **11.** 1.5 hrs **13.** $1, 2, 4, 8, 16, 32$

15. 161 minutes **17.** 50 minutes **19.** $N(t) = (40)(2^t)$, $t = 0, 1, 2, \dots$ **21.** $N(t) = (20)(3^t)$, $t = 0, 1, 2, \dots$

23. $N(t) = (5)(4^t)$, $t = 0, 1, 2, \dots$ **25.** $N(t+1) = 2N(t)$, $N(0) = 20$ **27.** $N(t+1) = 3N(t)$, $N(0) = 10$

29. $N(t+1) = 4N(t)$, $N(0) = 30$

31. 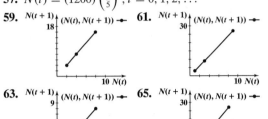 **33.** **35.** 3, 6, 12, 24, 48, 96

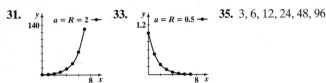

37. 2, 6, 18, 54, 162, 486 **39.** 1, 5, 25, 125, 625, 3125 **41.** 1024,
512, 256, 128, 64, 32 **43.** 729, 243, 81, 27, 9, 3 **45.** 31250, 6250,
1250, 250, 50, 10 **47.** $N(t) = (15)(2^t)$, $t = 0, 1, 2, \ldots$
49. $N(t) = (12)(3^t)$, $t = 0, 1, 2, \ldots$ **51.** $N(t) = (24)(4^t)$,
$t = 0, 1, 2, \ldots$ **53.** $N(t) = (5000)\left(\frac{1}{2}\right)^t$, $t = 0, 1, 2, \ldots$

55. $N(t) = (8000)\left(\frac{1}{3}\right)^t$, $t = 0, 1, 2, \ldots$

57. $N(t) = (1200)\left(\frac{1}{5}\right)^t$, $t = 0, 1, 2, \ldots$

59. **61.** **63.** **65.**

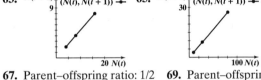

67. Parent–offspring ratio: 1/2 **69.** Parent–offspring ratio: 1/3

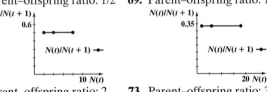

71. Parent–offspring ratio: 2 **73.** Parent–offspring ratio: 3

75. (a) No **(b)** Yes **(c)** Can argue either way. **77.** Limited food
resources; limited habitat; limited nesting sites.

■ **Section 2.2**

1. 0, 1, 2, 3, 4, 5 **3.** $\frac{1}{2}, \frac{1}{3}, \frac{1}{4}, \frac{1}{5}, \frac{1}{6}, \frac{1}{7}$ **5.** 1, 0.25, 0.11, 0.063, 0.04,
0.028 **7.** $-1, 0, 3, 8, 15, 24$ **9.** $0, -1, 2, -3, 4, -5$ **11.** $0, \frac{1}{2}, \frac{4}{3}, \frac{9}{4}$,
$\frac{16}{5}, \frac{25}{6}$ **13.** 1, 2.72, 4.11, 5.65, 7.39, 9.36 **15.** 1, 0.33, 0.11, 0.037,
0.012, 0.0041 **17.** 6, 7, 8, 9 **19.** $\frac{1}{36}, \frac{1}{49}, \frac{1}{64}, \frac{1}{81}$ **21.** $\frac{6}{7}, \frac{7}{8}, \frac{8}{9}, \frac{9}{10}$
23. $\sqrt{6+e^6}, \sqrt{7+e^7}, \sqrt{8+e^8}, \sqrt{9+e^9}$ **25.** $a_n = n$,
$n = 0, 1, 2, \ldots$ **27.** $a_n = 2^n, n = 0, 1, 2, \ldots$ **29.** $a_n = \frac{1}{3^n}$,
$n = 0, 1, 2, \ldots$ **31.** $a_n = (-1)^{n+1}(n + 1), n = 0, 1, 2, \ldots$
33. $a_n = (-1)^{n+1}\frac{1}{(n+2)}, n = 0, 1, 2, \ldots$ **35.** $a_n = \sin[(n + 1)\pi]$,
$n = 0, 1, 2, \ldots$ **37.** $\frac{1}{2}, \frac{1}{3}, \frac{1}{4}, \frac{1}{5}, \frac{1}{6}; 0$ **39.** $0, \frac{1}{2}, \frac{2}{3}, \frac{3}{4}, \frac{4}{5}; 1$ **41.** $1, \frac{1}{2}$,
$\frac{1}{5}, \frac{1}{10}, \frac{1}{17}; 0$ **43.** $1, -\frac{1}{2}, \frac{1}{3}, -\frac{1}{4}, \frac{1}{5}; 0$ **45.** $0, \frac{1}{2}, \frac{4}{3}, \frac{9}{4}, \frac{16}{5}$; limit does
not exist. **47.** $0, 1, \sqrt{2}, \sqrt{3}, \sqrt{4}$; limit does not exist. **49.** 1, 2, 4,
8, 16; limit does not exist. **51.** 1, 3, 9, 27, 64; limit does not exist.
53. $a = 0, N = 100$ **55.** $a = 0, N = 10$ **57.** $a = 0, N = 100$
59. $a = 0, N = 100$ **61.** $a = 1, N = 99$ **63.** $a = 1, N = 9$
65. N is the largest integer less than or equal to $1/\epsilon$. **67.** N is
the largest integer less than or equal to $\sqrt{1/\epsilon}$. **69.** N is the
largest integer less than or equal to $1/\epsilon$. **71.** 0 **73.** 1 **75.** 1
77. 0 **79.** 0 **81.** 1 **83.** 2, 4, 8, 16, 32 **85.** 1, 1, 1, 1, 1

87. $-6, 16, -28, 60, -116$ **89.** $\frac{1}{2}, \frac{1}{3}, \frac{1}{4}, \frac{1}{5}, \frac{1}{6}$ **91.** $2, \frac{5}{2}, \frac{29}{10}, \frac{941}{290}$,
$\frac{969,581}{272,890}$ **93.** 4 **95.** -3 **97.** $2, -2$ **99.** $-1+\sqrt{3}, -1-\sqrt{3}$
101. 0, 5 **103.** 5; 5 **105.** 0, 2; 2 **107.** $0, \frac{1}{2}; \frac{1}{2}$ **109.** $2, -2; 2$

■ **Section 2.3**

1. $N_t = \frac{2N_t}{1+\frac{1}{15}N_t}$ **3.** $N_t = \frac{1.5N_t}{1+\frac{0.5}{40}N_t}$

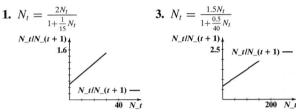

5. $N_t = \frac{2.5N_t}{1+\frac{1.5}{90}N_t}$

7. $R = 2, K = 20$ **9.** $R = 1.5, K = 30$ **11.** $R = 4, K = 450$

13. 0, 90 **15.** 0, 30 **17.** 0, 60 **19.** Limiting population size: 10

21. Limiting population size: 15 **23.** Limiting population size:

40 **25.** $r = 2, x_t = \frac{1}{20}N_t$ **27.** $r = 3, x_t = \frac{2}{45}N_t$ **29.** $r = 3.5$,
$x_t = \frac{2.5}{105}N_t$ **31. (c)** $N_t = 1000M_t, K = 1000L$, **(d)** $M_t = 20$,

$L = 5$ **33.** $z = 6$ **35.**

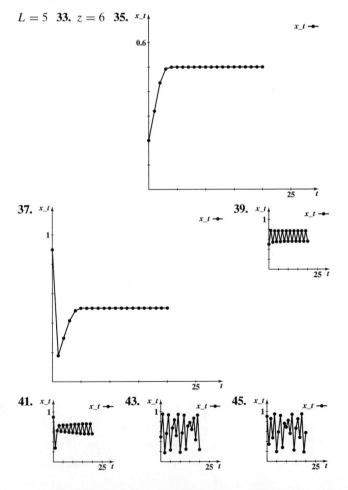

37. **39.** **41.** **43.** **45.**

47. Points of intersection: $N = 0$ and $N = 10$

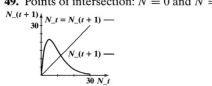

49. Points of intersection: $N = 0$ and $N = 12$

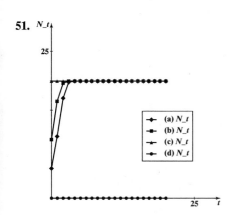

51.

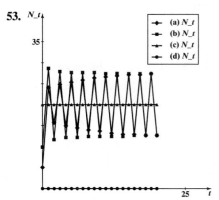

53.

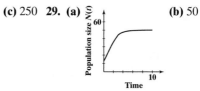

55. $1, 1, 2, 3, 5, 8, 13, \ldots$

57. One-month-old rabbit pairs produce one pair of rabbits; two-month-old rabbit pairs produce two pairs of rabbits.

■ **Chapter 2 Review Problems**

1. 0 **3.** 40 **5.** ∞ **7.** 1 **9.** 0 **11.** $a_n = \frac{2n+1}{2n+2}$, $n = 0, 1, 2, \ldots$

13. $a_n = \frac{n+1}{(n+1)^2+1}$, $n = 0, 1, 2, \ldots$ **15.**

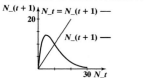

17. $\hat{R}_t \approx 0.8$ for t large; extinction will occur.

19.

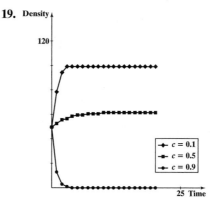

■ **Section 3.1**

1. -3 **3.** -1 **5.** $\frac{3}{2}\sqrt{2}$ **7.** $\frac{4}{3}\sqrt{3}$ **9.** e^{-2} **11.** 0 **13.** 7 **15.** 0
17. 1 **19.** 0 **21.** $-\infty$ **23.** ∞ **25.** ∞ **27.** ∞ **29.** $\frac{1}{6}$ **31.** $\frac{1}{2}$
33. $\lim_{x \to \infty} f(x) = \lim_{x \to -\infty} f(x) = 0$; $\lim_{x \to 0} f(x) = \infty$
35. divergence by oscillations **37.** -9 **39.** 54 **41.** $\frac{53}{3}$ **43.** $\frac{47}{2}$
45. $\frac{28}{3}$ **47.** 2 **49.** 4 **51.** $-\frac{1}{4}$ **53.** -5

■ **Section 3.2**

1. 1 **3.** 5 **5.** $f(2) = 3$ **7.** $a = 6$ **9.** $x = 3$ **11.** $x = 1, x = 2$
13. $f(5/2) = 5/2$. See Example 3 for $k = 3$. **15.** $x \in \mathbf{R}$
17. $x \neq 1$ **19.** $x \in \mathbf{R}$ **21.** $\{x : x < -1 \text{ or } x > 0\}$
23. $\{x \in \mathbf{R} : x \neq \frac{1}{4} + \frac{k}{2}, \ k \in \mathbf{Z}\}$
25. (a) $f(x)$ is not continuous at $x = 0$

(b) $c = 2$ **27. (b)** **(c)** No **29.** $\frac{1}{2}$ **31.** 1 **33.** 3

35. 1 **37.** 1 **39.** 1 **41.** 2 **43.** $\frac{1}{4}$ **45.** $\frac{1}{6}$ **47.** 0

■ **Section 3.3**

1. 0 **3.** ∞ **5.** 2 **7.** ∞ **9.** ∞ **11.** -1 **13.** 4 **15.** 2 **17.** 0
19. $\frac{3}{2}$ **21.** $\frac{3}{2}$ **23.** 0 **25.** a **27. (a)** **(b)** 500

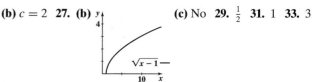

(c) 250 **29. (a)** **(b)** 50

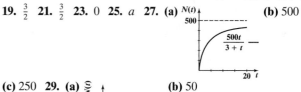

■ **Section 3.4**

1. (a)

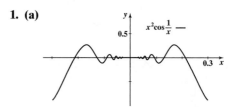

3. (a)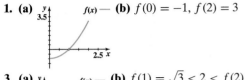

(b) $x \geq e$ **5.** 1 **7.** 5 **9.** π **11.** 0 **13.** 1

15. 0 **17.** 0 **19.** 0

■ Section 3.5

1. (a) 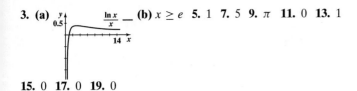 **(b)** $f(0) = -1$, $f(2) = 3$

3. (a) 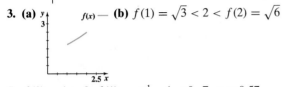 **(b)** $f(1) = \sqrt{3} < 2 < f(2) = \sqrt{6}$

5. $f(0) = 1 > 0$, $f(1) = e^{-1} - 1 < 0$ **7.** $x \approx 0.57$

9. (a) $x \approx -0.67$ **(b)** 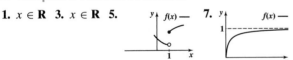 **(c)** No

11. (a) $N(10) = 23$ **(b)** $N(10) = 23$ (in millions)

■ Section 3.6

1. $0.495 < x < 0.505$ **3.** $2.99 < x < 3.01$ or $-3.01 < x < -2.99$
5. (b) $1.95 < x < 2.05$ **7. (a)** 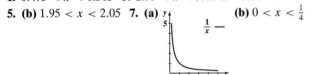 **(b)** $0 < x < \frac{1}{4}$

9. $\delta = \frac{\epsilon}{2}$ **11.** $\delta = \epsilon^{1/5}$ **13.** $\delta = \frac{2}{\sqrt{M}}$ **15.** $\delta = \frac{1}{\sqrt[3]{M}}$ **17.** $x_0 = \sqrt{\frac{2}{\epsilon}}$
19. $x_0 = \frac{1}{\epsilon}$ **21.** $\delta = \frac{\epsilon}{|m|}$

■ Chapter 3 Review Problems

1. $x \in \mathbf{R}$ **3.** $x \in \mathbf{R}$ **5.** 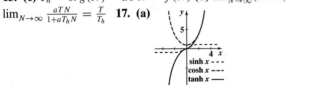 **7.**

9. $f(-2) = -2$, $\lim_{x \to -2^+} f(x) = -2$, $\lim_{x \to -2^-} f(x) = -3$
11. $a = 1.24 \times 10^6$, $k = 5$
13. (a) $g(t) = \begin{cases} 1 & \text{for } \frac{1}{6} + 2k \leq x \leq \frac{5}{6} + 2k,\, k = 0, 1, 2, \ldots \\ 0 & \text{otherwise} \end{cases}$
(b) $s(t)$ is continuous, $g(t)$ is not continuous
15. (c) $T_h = 0$: $g(N) = aTN = f(N)$ **(d)** $\lim_{N \to \infty}(aTN) = \infty$;
$\lim_{N \to \infty} \frac{aTN}{1 + aT_h N} = \frac{T}{T_h}$ **17. (a)**

(b) $\lim_{x \to \infty} \sinh x = \infty$, $\lim_{x \to -\infty} \sinh x = -\infty$,
$\lim_{x \to \infty} \cosh x = \infty$, $\lim_{x \to -\infty} \cosh x = \infty$, $\lim_{x \to \infty} \tanh x = 1$,
$\lim_{x \to -\infty} \tanh x = -1$

■ Section 4.1

1. 0 **3.** 4 **5.** 0 **7.** 0 **9.** 0 **11.** 2 **13.** 3 **15.** $c = 2k + 1$, $k \in \mathbf{Z}$
17. $-2h$ **19.** $\sqrt{4+h} - 2$ **21. (a)** $f'(-1) = -10$
(b) $y = -10x - 5$ **23. (a)** $f'(2) = -12$ **(b)** $y = \frac{1}{12}x - \frac{43}{6}$

25. $f'(x) = \frac{1}{2\sqrt{x}}$ **27.** $y = 6x - 3$ **29.** $y = \frac{1}{4}x + 1$
31. $y = -\frac{1}{6}x - \frac{19}{6}$ **33.** $y = -\frac{1}{4}x + \frac{5}{4}$ **35.** $f(x) = 2x^2$ and
$x = a$ **37.** $f(x) = \frac{1}{x^2+1}$, $a = 2$ **39. (a)**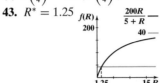

(b) 40 km/hr **(c)** 40 km/hr **41. (a)** $s\left(\frac{3}{4}\right) = 30$, $s(1) = \frac{160}{3}$ **(b)** $\frac{280}{3}$
(c) $v\left(\frac{3}{4}\right) = 80$, $\left|v\left(\frac{3}{4}\right)\right| = 80$
43. $R^* = 1.25$

45. $f(N) = 0$ for $N = 0$ and $N = 20$

47. $x = 7$ or $x = 4$; reaction ceases when $x = 4$.
49. $\frac{dN}{dt} = 0$ for $N = 0$ or $N = K$ **51.** B **53.**

55. No, $f(x)$ could have a discontinuity at $x = c$. **57.** $x = -5$
59. $x = -2$ **61.** $x = 3$ **63.** $x = -1$ **65.** $x = \sqrt{1/2}$ and
$x = -\sqrt{1/2}$ **67.** $x = 1$ **69.** $x = 0$

■ Section 4.2

1. $12x^2 - 7$ **3.** $-10x^4 + 7$ **5.** $-4 - 10x$ **7.** $35s^6 + 6s^2 - 5$
9. $-\frac{4}{3}t^3 + 4$ **11.** $2x \sin \frac{\pi}{3}$ **13.** $-12x^3 \tan \frac{\pi}{6}$ **15.** $3t^2 e^{-2} + 1$
17. $3s^2 e^3$ **19.** $60x^2 - 24x^5 + 72x^7$ **21.** $3\pi x^2 + \frac{1}{\pi}$ **23.** $3ax^2$
25. $2ax$ **27.** $2rs$ **29.** $3rs^2x^2 - r$ **31.** $4(b-1)N^3 - \frac{2N}{b}$
33. $a^3 - 3at^2$ **35.** $V_0\gamma$ **37.** $1 - \frac{2N}{K}$ **39.** $2rN - 3\frac{r}{K}N^2$
41. $4\frac{2\pi^5}{15}\frac{k^4}{c^2h^3}T^3$ **43.** $y - 191x - 377 = 0$ **45.** $y - 3x + 6 = 0$
47. $\sqrt{2}y - 8x + 18 = 0$ **49.** $2y - x - 7 = 0$
51. $24y - x - 73\sqrt{3} = 0$ **53.** $3y + x + 5 = 0$
55. $2ax - y - a = 0$ **57.** $(a^2 + 2)y - 4ax + 4a = 0$
59. $\frac{1}{3a}x + y + a + \frac{1}{3a} = 0$
61. $2a(a+1)y + \frac{1}{2}(a+1)^2x - 8a^2 - (a+1)^2 = 0$ **63.** $(0, 0)$
65. $\left(\frac{3}{2}, \frac{9}{4}\right)$ **67.** $(0, 0)$ and $\left(\frac{2}{9}, -\frac{4}{243}\right)$ **69.** $(0, 0)$, $\left(-\frac{1}{2}, -\frac{17}{96}\right)$, and
$\left(4, -\frac{160}{3}\right)$ **71.** $(0, 4)$; only point **73.** $\left(-\frac{1}{4}, -\frac{3}{8}\right)$; only point
75. $\left(\frac{1}{3}\sqrt{3}, \frac{7}{9}\sqrt{3} + 2\right)$, $\left(-\frac{1}{3}\sqrt{3}, -\frac{7}{9}\sqrt{3} + 2\right)$
77. Tangent line: $y = 2x - 1$ **79.** $y = 2ax - a^2$ and
$y = -2ax - a^2$ **81.** $P'(x)$ is a polynomial of degree 3.

■ Section 4.3

1. $f'(x) = 3x^2 + 10x - 3$ **3.** $f'(x) = -105x^6 + 30x^4 + 75x^2 - 10$
5. $f'(x) = x(2x + 3x^2) + (\frac{1}{2}x^2 - 1)(2 + 6x)$ **7.** $f'(x) = \frac{4}{5}x^3$
9. $f'(x) = 6(3x - 1)$ **11.** $f'(x) = -12(1 - 2x)$
13. $g'(s) = 2(4s - 5)(2s^2 - 5s)$
15. $g'(t) = 6(4t - 20t^3)(2t^2 - 5t^4)$ **17.** $y = x - 1$
19. $y = -56x - 64$ **21.** $y = -\frac{1}{6}x + \frac{7}{3}$ **23.** $y = \frac{1}{5}x + 2$
25. $f'(x) = (12x + 5)(1 - x) - (2x - 1)(3x + 4)$

27. $f'(x) = (6x^2 - 12x + 1)(1 - x^2) - 2x(x - 3)(2x^2 + 1)$

29. $f'(x) = a(4x - 3)$ **31.** $f'(x) = 8ax(x^2 - a)$

33. $g'(t) = 2a(at + 1)$ **35.** 11 **37.** 2 **39.** -27

41. $y' = 3f'(x)g(x) + 3f(x)g'(x)$

43. $y' = f'(x)g(x) + f(x)g'(x) + 4g(x)g'(x)$

45. $f(B) = Bg(B)$ with $f'(0) = g(0)$

47. $f'(N) = r\left[(a - 2N)\left(1 - \frac{N}{K}\right) - \frac{1}{K}(aN - N^2)\right]$

49. $f'(x) = \frac{4}{(x+1)^2}$ **51.** $2\frac{3x^2 + 3x - 2}{(2x+1)^2}$ **53.** $f'(x) = \frac{2x^3 - 3x^2 + 3}{(1-x)^2}$

55. $h'(t) = \frac{t^2 + 2t - 4}{(t+1)^2}$ **57.** $f'(s) = \frac{2s^2 - 4s + 4}{(1-s)^2}$

59. $f'(x) = \frac{1}{2\sqrt{x}}(x - 1) + \sqrt{x}$

61. $f'(x) = \frac{\sqrt{3}}{2\sqrt{x}}(x^2 - 1) + 2x\sqrt{3x}$ **63.** $f'(x) = 3x^2 + \frac{3}{x^4}$

65. $f'(x) = 4x - \frac{3-6x}{x^4}$ **67.** $g'(s) = \frac{2s^{-1/3} - s^{-2/3} - 1}{3(s^{2/3} - 1)^2}$

69. $f'(x) = (-2)\left(\sqrt{2x} + \frac{2}{\sqrt{x}}\right) + (1 - 2x)\left(\frac{1}{\sqrt{2x}} - \frac{1}{x^{3/2}}\right)$

71. $y = -8x - \frac{55}{3}$ **73.** $y = \frac{7}{16}x - 1$ **75.** $f'(x) = \frac{3a}{(3+x)^2}$

77. $f'(x) = \frac{8ax}{(4+x^2)^2}$ **79.** $f'(R) = \frac{nR^{n-1}k^n}{(k^n + R^n)^2}$

81. $h'(t) = \frac{\sqrt{a}}{2\sqrt{t}}(t - a) + \sqrt{at} + a$ **83.** $-\frac{5}{18}$ **85.** -8 **87.** 3

89. $y' = \frac{f'(x)g(x) - 2f(x)g'(x)}{[g(x)]^3}$

91. $y' = \frac{1}{2\sqrt{x}}f(x)g(x) + \sqrt{x}f'(x)g(x) + \sqrt{x}f(x)g'(x)$

93. $y = -\frac{c}{x_1^2}x + 2\frac{c}{x_1}; x = 2x_1$

■ Section 4.4

1. $2(x - 3)$ **3.** $-24x(1 - 3x^2)^3$ **5.** $\frac{x}{\sqrt{x^2+3}}$ **7.** $\frac{-3x^2}{2\sqrt{3-x^3}}$

9. $-\frac{12x^2}{(x^3-2)^5}$ **11.** $\frac{2x-3}{(2x^2-1)^{3/2}}$ **13.** $\frac{1-3x}{\sqrt{2x-1}(x-1)^3}$ **15.** $\frac{2\sqrt{s}+1}{4\sqrt{s}\sqrt{s+\sqrt{s}}}$

17. $\frac{-9t^2}{(t-3)^4}$

19. $(r^2 - r)^2(r + 3r^3)^{-5}[3(2r - 1)(r + 3r^3) - 4(1 + 9r^2)(r^2 - r)]$

21. $-\frac{4}{5}x^3(3 - x^4)^{-4/5}$ **23.** $\frac{2x-2}{7(x^2-2x+1)^{6/7}}$

25. $g'(s) = \frac{3}{2}(3s^7 - 7s)^{1/2}(21s^6 - 7)$ **27.** $\frac{2}{5}(3t + \frac{3}{t})^{-3/5}(3 - \frac{3}{t^2})$

29. $3a(ax + 1)^2$ **31.** $g'(N) = \frac{bk - bN}{(k+N)^3}$ **33.** $g'(T) = -3a(T_0 - T)^2$

35. (a) $\frac{2x}{x^2+3}$ **(b)** $\frac{1}{2(x-1)}$ **37.** $2\left(\frac{f(x)}{g(x)} + 1\right)\frac{f'(x)g(x) - f(x)g'(x)}{[g(x)]^2}$

39. $\frac{2f(x)f'(x)[g(2x)+2x] - [f(x)]^2(g'(2x)\cdot 2 + 2)}{[g(2x)+2x]^2}$

41. $y' = 4(\sqrt{x^3 - 3x} + 3x)^3\left(\frac{3x^2 - 3}{2\sqrt{x^3 - 3x}} + 3\right)$

43. $y' = 36x(3x^2 - 1)(1 + (3x^2 - 1)^3)$

45. $y' = 3\left(\frac{2x+1}{3(x^3-1)^3-1}\right)^2\frac{6(x^3-1)^3 - 2 - 27x^2(2x+1)(x^3-1)^2}{(3(x^3-1)^3-1)^2}$ **47.** $\frac{dy}{dx} = -\frac{x}{y}$

49. $\frac{dy}{dx} = -\left(\frac{y}{x}\right)^{1/4}$ **51.** $\frac{dy}{dx} = 4\sqrt{xy} - \frac{y}{x}$ **53.** $\frac{dy}{dx} = \frac{x}{y}$

55. (a) $y = \frac{4}{3}x - \frac{25}{3}$ **(b)** $y = -\frac{3}{4}x$ **57. (a)** $y = \frac{3}{4}x - \frac{9}{4}$

(b) $y = -\frac{4}{3}x + \frac{136}{9}$ **59. (a)** $(27)^{1/6} = \sqrt{3}$ **(b)**

$x^{2/3} + y^{2/3} = 4$ —

61. $-\frac{2}{3}\sqrt{3}$ **63.** $-\frac{3}{4}$ **65.** $\frac{dV}{dt} = 3x^2\frac{dx}{dt}$ **67.** $\frac{dS}{dt} = 8\pi r\frac{dr}{dt}$

69. $\frac{dh}{dt} = \frac{1}{100\pi}\frac{m}{min}$ **71.** $\frac{183}{\sqrt{61}}\frac{mi}{hr}$ for both $t = 20$ min and $t = 40$ min

73. $f'(x) = 3x^2 - 6x$, $f''(x) = 6x - 6$ **75.** $g'(x) = 2(x + 1)^{-2}$,

$g''(x) = -\frac{4}{(x+1)^3}$ **77.** $g'(t) = \frac{9t^2+2}{2\sqrt{3t^3+2t}}$, $g''(t) = \frac{27t^4 + 36t^2 - 4}{4(3t^3+2t)^{3/2}}$

79. $f'(s) = \frac{3}{4}\left(s^{1/2} - \frac{1}{s}\right)^{-1/2}$, $f''(s) = -\frac{3}{8}\frac{\frac{1}{2}s^{3/2}+1}{\sqrt{s}(s^{3/2}-1)^{3/2}}$

81. $g'(t) = -\frac{5}{2}t^{-7/2} - \frac{1}{2}t^{-1/2}$, $g''(t) = \frac{35}{4}t^{-9/2} + \frac{1}{4}t^{-3/2}$

83. $f(x) = x^5$, $f'(x) = 5x^4$, $f''(x) = 20x^3$, $f'''(x) = 60x^2$,
$f^{(4)}(x) = 120x$, $f^{(5)}(x) = 120$, $f^{(6)} = \cdots = f^{(10)}(x) = 0$

85. $p(x) = 3x^2 + 2x + 3$

87. (a) velocity: $v_0 - gt$, acceleration: $-g$ **(b)** $t = \frac{v_0}{g}$

■ Section 4.5

1. $f'(x) = 2\cos x + \sin x$

3. $f'(x) = 3\cos x - 5\sin x - 2\sec x \tan x$

5. $f'(x) = \sec^2 x + \csc^2 x$ **7.** $f'(x) = 3\cos(3x)$

9. $f'(x) = 6\cos(3x + 1)$ **11.** $f'(x) = 4\sec^2(4x)$

13. $f'(x) = 4\sec(1 + 2x)\tan(1 + 2x)$ **15.** $f'(x) = 6x\cos(x^2)$

17. $f'(x) = 6x\sin^2(x^2 - 3)\cos(x^2 - 3)$

19. $f'(x) = 12x\sin x^2\cos x^2$

21. $f'(x) = -8x\sin x^2 + 4\sin x\cos x$

23. $f'(x) = -8\sin x\cos x - 8x^3\sin x^4$

25. $f'(x) = -4x\sec^2(1 - x^2)$

27. $f'(x) = -18\tan^2(3x - 1)\sec^2(3x - 1)$

29. $f'(x) = \frac{2x\cos(2x^2-1)}{\sqrt{\sin(2x^2-1)}}$ **31.** $g'(s) = \frac{-\sin s}{2\sqrt{\cos s}} + \frac{1}{2\sqrt{s}}\sin\sqrt{s}$

33. $g'(t) = \frac{2\cos(2t)[\cos(6t)-1]+6\sin(6t)[\sin(2t)+1]}{[\cos(6t)-1]^2}$

35. $f'(x) = \frac{2x\sec(x^2-1)[\tan(x^2-1)+\cot(x^2+1)]}{\csc(x^2+1)}$

37. $f'(x) = 2\cos(2x - 1)\cos(3x + 1) - 3\sin(2x - 1)\sin(3x + 1)$

39. $f'(x) = 6x\sec^2(3x^2 - 1)\cot(3x^2 + 1)$
$- 6x\csc^2(3x^2 + 1)\tan(3x^2 - 1)$ **41.** $f'(x) = \sec^2 x$

43. $f'(x) = 0$ **45.** $g'(x) = \frac{-6x\cos(3x^2-1)}{\sin^2(3x^2-1)}$

47. $g'(x) = -30x\sin^2(1 - 5x^2)\cos(1 - 5x^2)$

49. $h'(x) = -\frac{6\sec^2(2x)-3}{(\tan(2x)-x)^2}$ **51.** $h'(s) = 3\sin s\cos s(\sin s - \cos s)$

53. $f'(x) = \frac{2(1+x^2)\cos(2x)-2x\sin(2x)}{(1+x^2)^2}$ **55.** $f'(x) = -\frac{1}{x^2}\sec^2(\frac{1}{x})$

57. $f'(x) = \frac{2(\sec x^2)[x(\tan x^2)-\tan x]}{\sec^2 x}$ **59.** $x = \frac{3}{2} + 3k, k \in \mathbf{Z}$

61. Write $\frac{d}{dx}\cos x = \lim_{h\to 0}\frac{\cos(x+h)-\cos x}{h}$ and use the identity for

$\cos(x + h)$. **63.** Use quotient rule. **65.** $f'(x) = \frac{x\cos\sqrt{x^2+1}}{\sqrt{x^2+1}}$

67. $f'(x) = (\cos\sqrt{3x^3 + 3x})\frac{9x^2+3}{2\sqrt{3x^3+3x}}$

69. $f'(x) = 4x\sin(x^2 - 1)\cos(x^2 - 1)$

71. $f'(x) = 27x^2\tan^2(3x^3 - 3)\sec^2(3x^3 - 3)$

73. (a) $\frac{dc}{dt} = \frac{\pi}{2}\cos(\frac{\pi}{2}t)$ **(b)**

$c(t)$ —
$c'(t)$ —

(c) (i) $\frac{dc}{dt} = 0$ **(ii)** increasing **(iii)** $c(t)$ has a horizontal tangent and either a maximum or a minimum.

■ Section 4.6

1. $f'(x) = 3e^{3x}$ **3.** $f'(x) = -12e^{1-3x}$

5. $f'(x) = (-4x + 3)e^{-2x^2+3x-1}$ **7.** $f'(x) = 28x(x^2 + 1)e^{7(x^2+1)^2}$

9. $f'(x) = e^x(1 + x)$ **11.** $f'(x) = xe^{-x}(2 - x)$

13. $f'(x) = \frac{e^x(1+x^2-2x)-2x}{(1+x^2)^2}$ **15.** $f'(x) = \frac{2e^x - 2e^{-x} - 2}{(2+e^x)^2}$

17. $f'(x) = 3\cos(3x)e^{\sin(3x)}$ **19.** $f'(x) = e^{\sin(x^2-1)}\cos(x^2 - 1)2x$

21. $f'(x) = e^x\cos(e^x)$ **23.** $f'(x) = (2e^{2x} + 1)\cos(e^{2x} + x)$

25. $f'(x) = (1 - \cos x)\exp(x - \sin x)$

27. $g'(s) = \exp[\sec s^2](\sec s^2)(\tan s^2)(2s)$

29. $f'(x) = (\sin x + x\cos x)e^{x\sin x}$

31. $f'(x) = (-3)(2x + \sec^2 x)e^{x^2+\tan x}$ **33.** $f'(x) = (\ln 2)2^x$

35. $f'(x) = (\ln 2)2^{x+1}$ **37.** $f'(x) = \frac{\ln 5}{\sqrt{2x-1}}5^{\sqrt{2x-1}}$

39. $f'(x) = 2x(\ln 2)2^{x^2+1}$ **41.** $h'(t) = (2t)(\ln 2)2^{t^2-1}$

43. $f'(x) = (\ln 2)\frac{1}{2\sqrt{x}}2^{\sqrt{x}}$ **45.** $f'(x) = (\ln 2)\frac{x}{\sqrt{x^2-1}}2^{\sqrt{x^2-1}}$

47. $h'(t) = \frac{\ln 5}{2\sqrt{t}}5^{\sqrt{t}}$ **49.** $g'(x) = -2(\ln 2)(\sin x)2^{2\cos x}$

51. $g'(r) = \frac{\ln 3}{5r^{4/5}}3^{r^{1/5}}$ **53.** 2   **55.** 0   **57.** $\frac{1}{\ln 2}$ **59. (a)** $N(0) = 1$

61. $\frac{dN}{dt} = (\ln 2)N(t)$ which implies that $\frac{dN}{dt}$ is proportional to

$N(t)$ **63. (a)** $\frac{dN}{dt} = \frac{rK(\frac{K}{N(0)}-1)e^{-rt}}{[1+(\frac{K}{N(0)}-1)e^{-rt}]^2}$ **(c)** $dN/(Ndt)$

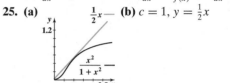

65. (a) $L(x)$

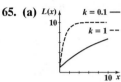

(b) L_∞ is the limiting size and L_0 is the initial size. **(c)** The fish with $k = 1$ reaches $L = 5$ more quickly. **(d)** With age, the rate of growth decreases. **(e)** The larger the value of k, the more quickly the fish grows and reaches its limiting size.

67. $\frac{dW}{dt} = -4W(t)\frac{1}{\text{days}}$ **69.** $\frac{dW}{dt} = -\frac{\ln 2}{5}W(t)\frac{1}{\text{days}}$

71. (a) $W(4) = 6e^{-12}$ **(b)** half-life: $\frac{\ln 2}{3}$

73. (a) $\frac{dW}{dt} = -(\ln\frac{5}{2})W(t)$ **(b)** $W(3) = 5(\frac{5}{2})^{-3}$ **(c)** half-life: $\frac{\ln 2}{\ln 5 - \ln 2}$

■ **Section 4.7**

1. $\frac{d}{dx}f^{-1}(x) = x$ **3.** $\frac{d}{dx}f^{-1}(x) = \frac{1}{\sqrt{8(x+1)}}$

5. $f^{-1}(x) = \left(\frac{3-x}{2}\right)^{1/3}, x \le 3, \frac{d}{dx}f^{-1}(x) = -\frac{1}{6}\left(\frac{2}{3-x}\right)^{2/3}$

7. $\frac{d}{dx}f^{-1}(0) = \frac{1}{4}$ **9.** $\frac{d}{dx}f^{-1}(2) = 4$ **11.** $\frac{d}{dx}f^{-1}(1) = \frac{1}{2}$

13. $\frac{d}{dx}f^{-1}(\pi) = \frac{1}{2}$ **15.** $\frac{d}{dx}f^{-1}(0) = 1$ **17.** $\frac{d}{dx}f^{-1}(-\ln 2) = \frac{1}{\sqrt{3}}$

19. $\frac{d}{dx}f^{-1}(1) = 1$ **21.** $\frac{d}{dx}f^{-1}(1) = \frac{1}{2}$ **23.** $f'(x) = \frac{1}{x+1}$

25. $f'(x) = \frac{-2}{1-2x}$ **27.** $f'(x) = \frac{2}{x}$ **29.** $f'(x) = \frac{6x^2-1}{2x^3-x}$

31. $f'(x) = 2(\ln x)\frac{1}{x}$ **33.** $f'(x) = \frac{8\ln x}{x}$ **35.** $f'(x) = \frac{x}{x^2+1}$

37. $f'(x) = \frac{1}{x(x+1)}$ **39.** $f'(x) = \frac{-1}{1-x} - \frac{2}{1+2x}$

41. $f'(x) = (1 - \frac{1}{x})\exp[x - \ln x]$ **43.** $f'(x) = \cot x$

45. $f'(x) = \frac{2x\sec^2(x^2)}{\tan(x^2)}$ **47.** $f'(x) = \ln x + 1$ **49.** $f'(x) = \frac{1-\ln x}{x^2}$

51. $h'(t)) = \cos(\ln(3t))\frac{1}{t}$ **53.** $f'(x) = \frac{2x}{x^2-3}$ for $|x| \ne \sqrt{3}$

55. $f'(x) = \frac{-2x}{(\ln 10)(1-x^2)}$ **57.** $f'(x) = \frac{3x^2-3}{(\ln 10)(x^3-3x)}$

59. $f'(u) = \frac{4u^3}{(\ln 3)(3+u^4)}$ **63.** $\frac{dy}{dx} = 2x^x(\ln x + 1)$

65. $\frac{dy}{dx} = (\ln x)^x[\ln(\ln x) + \frac{1}{\ln x}]$ **67.** $\frac{dy}{dx} = x^{\ln x}2(\ln x)\frac{1}{x}$

69. $\frac{dy}{dx} = x^{1/x-2}(1 - \ln x)$

71. $\frac{dy}{dx} = [x^x(\ln x + 1)\ln x + x^{x-1}]x^{x^x}$

73. $\frac{dy}{dx} = x^{\cos x}\left[\frac{\cos x}{x} - (\sin x)(\ln x)\right]$

75. $\frac{1}{y}\frac{dy}{dx} = 2 + \frac{27}{9x-2} - \frac{x}{2(x^2+1)} - \frac{9x^2}{4(3x^3-7)}$

■ **Section 4.8**

1. $\sqrt{65} \approx 8.0625$, error $= 2.42 \times 10^{-4}$ **3.** $\sqrt[3]{124} \approx 5 - \frac{1}{75}$,

error $\approx 3.57 \times 10^{-5}$ **5.** $(0.99)^{25} \approx 0.75$, error ≈ 0.0278

7. $\sin\left(\frac{\pi}{2} + 0.02\right) \approx 1$, error $\approx 2.00 \times 10^{-4}$ **9.** $\ln(1.01) \approx 0.01$,

error $\approx 4.97 \times 10^{-5}$ **11.** $L(x) = 1 - x$ **13.** $L(x) = \frac{3}{2} - \frac{1}{2}x$

15. $L(x) = 1 - 2x$ **17.** $L(x) = x$ **19.** $L(x) = \frac{1}{\ln 10}(x - 1)$

21. $L(x) = 1 + x$ **23.** $L(x) = 1 - x$ **25.** $L(x) = x$

27. $L(x) = 1 - nx$ **29.** $L(x) = 1$ **31.** 100.3   **33.** $B(1.1) \approx 5.005$

35. [1.8, 2.2]   **37.** [10.8, 13.2]   **39.** [5.91, 8.87]   **41.** $\pm 6\%$

43. $\pm 0.668\%$ **45.** $\pm 9\%$ **47.** $\pm 2.4\%$ **49.** $\pm\frac{(a+b-2x)x}{(a-x)(b-x)}\left(100\frac{\Delta x}{x}\right)$

■ **Chapter 4 Review Problems**

1. $f'(x) = -12x^3 - \frac{1}{x^{3/2}}$ **3.** $h'(t) = \frac{1}{3}\left(\frac{1+t}{1-t}\right)^{2/3}\frac{-2}{(1+t)^2}$

5. $f'(x) = 2e^{2x}\sin\left(\frac{\pi}{2}x\right) + e^{2x}\frac{\pi}{2}\cos\left(\frac{\pi}{2}x\right)$

7. $f'(x) = \frac{\frac{\ln x}{x+1} - \frac{\ln(x+1)}{x}}{(\ln x)^2}$ **9.** $f'(x) = -xe^{-x^2/2}$,

$f''(x) = e^{-x^2/2}(x^2 - 1)$ **11.** $h'(x) = \frac{1}{(x+1)^2}, h''(x) = -\frac{2}{(x+1)^3}$

13. $\frac{dy}{dx} = \frac{\cos x + y^2 - 2xy}{x^2 - 2xy}$ **15.** $\frac{dy}{dx} = 1 - 2(x - y)$ **17.** $\frac{dy}{dx} = -\frac{x}{y}$,

$\frac{d^2y}{dx^2} = -\frac{16}{y^3}$ **19.** $\frac{dy}{dx} = \frac{1}{x\ln x}, \frac{d^2y}{dx^2} = -\frac{\ln x + 1}{(x\ln x)^2}$ **21.** $5.70\frac{\text{ft}}{\text{sec}}$

23. (a) $\frac{dy}{dx} = f'(x)e^{f(x)}$ **(b)** $\frac{dy}{dx} = \frac{f'(x)}{f(x)}$ **(c)** $\frac{dy}{dx} = 2f(x)f'(x)$

25. (a)

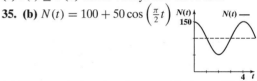

$\frac{1}{2}x$ — **(b)** $c = 1, y = \frac{1}{2}x$

27. $y - \frac{1}{2}e^{-(\pi/3)^2} = -e^{-(\pi/3)^2}\left(\frac{1}{2}\sqrt{3} + \frac{\pi}{3}\right)\left(x - \frac{\pi}{3}\right)$ **29.** $y = x$

31. $p(x) = 2x^2 + 4x + 8$ **33. (a)** $s(5.5) \approx 54.84$ miles

(b) $v(t) = \frac{ds}{dt} = 3\pi + 3\pi\sin(\pi t), a(t) = \frac{dv}{dt} = 3\pi^2\cos(\pi t)$

(c) $v(t) \ge 0$ **(d)** Three valleys and three hills

35. (b) $N(t) = 100 + 50\cos\left(\frac{\pi}{2}t\right)$ $N(t)$

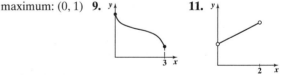

(c) The population size shows oscillations.   **37.** 9.33%

■ **Section 5.1**

1. absolute minimum: $(0, -1)$; absolute maximum: $(1, 1)$

3. absolute minimum: $(\frac{3\pi}{4}, -1)$; absolute maximum: $(\frac{\pi}{4}, 1)$

5. absolute minimum: $(0, 0)$; absolute maximum: $(-1, 1)$ and

$(1, 1)$ **7.** absolute minima: $(1, e^{-1})$ and $(-1, e^{-1})$; absolute

maximum: $(0, 1)$ **9.**   **11.**

13. local maximum = global maximum = $(-1, 4)$, no local and

global minima

15. local minimum = global minimum = $(0, -2)$,

local maximum = global maximum = $(-1, -1)$ and $(1, -1)$

17. local minimum = $(-2, -3)$ and $(1, 0)$,

global minimum = $(-2, -3)$,

local maximum = global maximum = $(0, 1)$ **19.** $f'(0) = 0$;

$f(x)$ has a local minimum at $x = 0$ **21.** $f'(0) = 0$; $f(x) = -x^2$

has a local maximum at $x = 0$ **23.** $f'(0) = 0$, but $x = 0$ is not a

local extremum: $f(x) < 0$ for $x < 0$ and $f(x) > 0$ for $x > 0$

25. $f'(-1) = 0$, but $x = -1$ is not a local extremum: $f(x) < 0$

for $x < -1$ and $f(x) > 0$ for $x > -1$ **27.** $f(0) = 0$ and

$f(x) > 0$ for $x \ne 0$; $\lim_{x\to 0^-} f'(x) = -1, \lim_{x\to 0^+} f'(x) = 1$.

29. $f(1) = f(-1) = 0$ and $f(x) > 0$ for $x \ne 1, -1$;

$\lim_{x\to 1^-} f'(x) = -2 \ne \lim_{x\to 1^+} f'(x) = 2$ and

$\lim_{x\to -1^-} f'(x) = -2 \ne \lim_{x\to -1^+} f'(x) = 2$.

31. loc min = glob min = $(-1, 0)$ and $(1, 0)$; loc max = glob max = $(0, 1)$ and $(2, 1)$

33. (a)

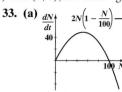

$\frac{dN}{dt}$ is maximal for $N = 50$ **(b)** $f'(N) = r - \frac{2r}{K}N$

35. (a) Slope: 2 **(b)** $c = 1$; guaranteed by the mean-value theorem. **37.** Slope: 0; $c = 0$ **39.** $[0, 1]$

41. $f(-1) = 1$, $f(2) = -2$, $\frac{f(2)-f(-1)}{2-(-1)} = -1$

43. The mean-value theorem guarantees such a point.

45. (a) Slope: $a + b$

(b) Apply the mean-value theorem. Midpoint $= a + \frac{b-a}{2} = \frac{a+b}{2}$.

47. Use the mean-value theorem and argue that the slope of the secant line connecting $(a, f(a))$ and $(c, f(c))$ and the slope of the secant line connecting $(b, f(b))$ and $(c, f(c))$ have opposite signs, where $c \in (a, b)$ with $f(c) \neq 0$. **49. (a)** 0.25 m/s **(b)** $\frac{3}{100}t^2$, $0 < t < 5$ **(c)** $t = \frac{5}{3}\sqrt{3}$ s **51.** $0 \leq B(3) \leq 6$ **53.** $f(x) = 3, x \in \mathbf{R}$

■ **Section 5.2**

1. $y' = 3 - 2x$, $y'' = -2$; $y' > 0$ and y is increasing on $(-\infty, 3/2)$; $y' < 0$ and y is decreasing on $(3/2, \infty)$; $y'' < 0$ and y is concave down.

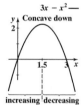

3. $y' = 2x + 1$, $y'' = 2$; $y' > 0$ and y is increasing on $(-1/2, \infty)$; $y' < 0$ and y is decreasing on $(-\infty, -1/2)$; $y'' > 0$ and y is concave up.

5. $y' = -2x^2 + 7x - 3$, $y'' = -4x + 7$; $y' > 0$ and y is increasing on $(1/2, 3)$; $y' < 0$ and y is decreasing on $(-\infty, 1/2) \cup (3, \infty)$; $y'' > 0$ and y is concave up on $(-\infty, 7/4)$; $y'' < 0$ and y is concave down on $(7/4, \infty)$.

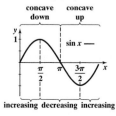

7. $y' = \frac{1}{2\sqrt{x+1}}$, $x > -1$; $y'' = -\frac{1}{4(x-1)^{3/2}}$, $x > -1$; $y' > 0$ and y is increasing; $y'' < 0$ and y is concave down.

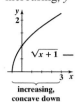

9. $y' = -\frac{1}{x^2}$, $x \neq 0$; $y'' = \frac{2}{x^3}$, $x \neq 0$; $y' < 0$ and y is decreasing for $x \neq 0$; $y'' < 0$ and y is concave down for $x < 0$; $y'' > 0$ and y is concave up for $x > 0$.

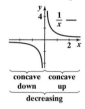

11. $y' = \frac{1}{3}(x^2 + 1)^{-2/3}2x$, $y'' = \frac{6-2x^2}{9(x^2+1)^{5/3}}$; $y' > 0$ and y is increasing on $(0, \infty)$; $y' < 0$ and y is decreasing on $(-\infty, 0)$; $y'' > 0$ and y is concave up on $(-\sqrt{3}, \sqrt{3})$; $y'' < 0$ and y is concave down on $(-\infty, -\sqrt{3}) \cup (\sqrt{3}, \infty)$.

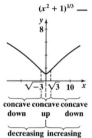

13. $y' = -\frac{2}{(1+x)^3}$, $y'' = \frac{6}{(1+x)^4}$; $y' > 0$ and y is increasing on $(-\infty, -1)$; $y' < 0$ and y is decreasing on $(-1, \infty)$; $y'' > 0$ and y is concave up for $x \neq -1$.

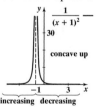

15. $y' = \cos x$, $y'' = -\sin x$; $y' > 0$ and y is increasing on $(0, \pi/2) \cup (3\pi/2, 2\pi)$; $y' < 0$ and y is decreasing on $(\pi/2, 3\pi/2)$; $y'' > 0$ and y is concave up on $(\pi, 2\pi)$; $y'' < 0$ and y is concave down on $(0, \pi)$.

17. $y' = e^x$, $y'' = e^x$; $y' > 0$ and y is increasing for $x \in \mathbf{R}$; $y'' > 0$ and y is concave up for $x \in \mathbf{R}$.

19. $y' = -xe^{-x^2/2}$, $y'' = e^{-x^2/2}(x^2 - 1)$; $y' > 0$ and y is increasing for $x < 0$; $y' < 0$ and y is decreasing for $x > 0$; $y'' > 0$ and y is concave up for $x < -1$ and $x > 1$; $y'' < 0$ and y is concave down for $-1 < x < 1$.

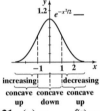

21. (a)
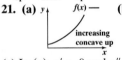

(b)

(c) In (a), $y' > 0$ and $y'' > 0$; in (b), $y' > 0$ and $y'' < 0$.
23. (b) $f(-1) > 0$ and $f(1) < 0$ **25.** $f'(x)$ is decreasing; use the definition of concave down. **27. (a)**

(b) $g'(N) = -\frac{r}{K} < 0$ **29.** $f'(N) = 1 - \left(\frac{N}{K}\right)^\theta (1 + \theta)$; $f(N)$ is increasing for $0 < N < N^*$ and decreasing for $N > N^*$, where $N^* = K\left(\frac{1}{1+\theta}\right)^{1/\theta}$. **31.** The probability of escaping decreases with parasitoid density. **33. (a)** $y' = 117e^{-10/x}\frac{10}{x^2} > 0$; maximum attainable height is 117. **(b)** $y(x)$ is concave up on $(0, 5)$; $y(x)$ is concave down on $(5, \infty)$

(c)
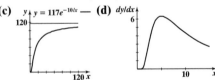

35. For $0 < \gamma < 1$, the average number of pollinator visits increases with the number of flowers on the plant, but at a decelerating rate.
37. (a) $N^* = e^{-aN^*}$ **(b)** $\frac{dN^*}{da} = -N^*e^{-aN^*}/(1 + ae^{-aN^*}) < 0$
39. (a) $\frac{d}{dN}\left(\frac{A}{N}\right) = -S[1 + (aN)^b]^{-2}b(aN)^{b-1}a < 0$ **(b) (v)** The number of surviving plants in the next year is the same as the number of plants this year. **41. (a)** For $0 < a < 1$, Y is an increasing function of X but $\frac{Y}{X}$ is a decreasing function of X. $Y(X)$ is concave down. **(b)** Juveniles have relatively larger heads than adults. **43.** $y = f(x)$ is concave up for $k > 1$ and concave down for $0 < k < 1$.

■ **Section 5.3**

1. local max: $(-2, 16)$ and $(3, 1)$; absolute max: $(-2, 16)$; local min: $(2, 0)$; absolute min: $(2, 0)$; y is increasing on $(2, 3)$ and decreasing on $(-2, 2)$. **3.** local max: $(2, \ln 3)$; absolute max: $(2, \ln 3)$; local min: $(1, 0)$; absolute min: $(1, 0)$; y is increasing on $(1, 2)$. **5.** local min: $(0, 0)$; absolute min $(0, 0)$; local max:

$(1, e^{-1})$; absolute max: $(1, e^{-1})$; y is increasing on $[0, 1]$ **7.** no extrema; y is increasing for all $x \in \mathbf{R}$. **9.** local max: $(0, 1)$; absolute max: $(0, 1)$; local min: $(-1, -1)$ and $(1, -1)$; absolute min: $(-1, -1)$ and $(1, -1)$; y is increasing on $(-1, 0)$ and decreasing on $(0, 1)$. **11.** local max: $(0, 1)$; absolute max: $(0, 1)$; y is increasing on $(-\infty, 0)$, and decreasing on $(0, \infty)$. **13.** local max: $(-3, 15.5)$; local min: $(2, -16/3)$; y is increasing on $(-\infty, -3) \cup (2, \infty)$; y is decreasing on $(-3, 2)$. **15.** y is increasing on $\mathbf{R}$. No extrema. **17.** $f'(x) = 3x^2 > 0$ for $x \neq 0$ **19.** $(0, -2)$ **21.** $(\sqrt{2}/2, e^{-1/2})$ **23.** $(0, 0)$ **25.** $f'(x) = 4x^3$, $f''(x) = 12x^2 > 0$ for all $x \neq 0$ **27.** local min: $(-2, 2/3)$, $(3, -16)$; local max: $(-1, 16/3)$, $(5, 16/3)$; absolute min: $(3, -16)$; absolute max: $(-1, 16/3)$, $(5, 16/3)$; inflection point: $(1, -16/3)$ y is increasing on $(-2, -1) \cup (3, 5)$; y is decreasing on $(-1, 3)$; y is concave up on $(1, 5)$; y is concave down on $(-2, 1)$;

29. local min: $(-3, 0)$, $(3, 0)$; local max: $(-4, 5)$, $(0, 9)$, $(5, 16)$; absolute min: $(-3, 0)$, $(3, 0)$; absolute max: $(5, 16)$; inflection points: $(-3, 0)$, $(3, 0)$; y is increasing on $(-3, 0) \cup (3, 5)$; y is decreasing on $(-4, -3) \cup (0, 3)$; y is concave up on $(-4, -3) \cup (3, 5)$; y is concave down on $(-3, 3)$;

31. no extrema; inflection points: $x = \pi/2 + k\pi, k \in \mathbf{Z}$; y is increasing on $\mathbf{R}$; y is concave up on $(\pi/2 + 2k\pi, 3\pi/2 + 2k\pi)$, $k \in \mathbf{Z}$; y is concave down on $(-\pi/2 + 2k\pi, \pi/2 + 2k\pi), k \in \mathbf{Z}$;

33. local min: $(0, -1)$; absolute min: $(0, -1)$; inflection points at $x = -\frac{\sqrt{3}}{3}$ and $x = \frac{\sqrt{3}}{3}$; y is increasing on $(0, \infty)$; y is decreasing on $(-\infty, 0)$; y is concave up on $(-\frac{\sqrt{3}}{3}, \frac{\sqrt{3}}{3})$; y is concave down on $(-\infty, -\frac{\sqrt{3}}{3}) \cup (\frac{\sqrt{3}}{3}, \infty)$;

35. (c) decreasing for all $x \neq 1$; no extrema **(d)** $f(x)$ is concave down on $(-\infty, 1)$ and concave up on $(1, \infty)$; no inflection points
(e)

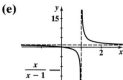

37. (a) $\lim_{x \to -2^+} f(x) = \infty$, $\lim_{x \to -2^-} f(x) = -\infty$ **(b)** $f(x)$ is increasing on $(-\infty, -2 - \sqrt{6}/2) \cup (-2 + \sqrt{6}/2, \infty)$; $f(x)$ is decreasing on $(-2 - \sqrt{6}/2, -2) \cup (-2, -2 + \sqrt{6}/2)$; local max at $x = -2 - \sqrt{6}/2$; local min at $-2 + \sqrt{6}/2$ **(c)** $f(x)$ is concave up on $(-2, \infty)$; $f(x)$ is concave down on $(-\infty, -2)$ **(d)** $y = 2x - 4$
(e)

39. (a) $f'(x) = \frac{2x}{(1+x^2)^2}$ and $f(x)$ is increasing for $x > 0$ and decreasing for $x < 0$ **(b)** $f(x)$ is concave up for $-1/\sqrt{3} < x < 1/\sqrt{3}$ and concave down for $x < -1/\sqrt{3}$ or $x > 1/\sqrt{3}$. $f(x)$ has two inflection points at $x = \pm 1/\sqrt{3}$
(c) $\lim_{x \to \infty} = 1$, $\lim_{x \to -\infty} = 1$ **(d)**

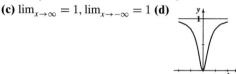

41. (a) $f'(x) = \frac{a}{(a+x)^2}$; $f(x)$ is increasing for $x > 0$
(b) $f''(x) = -\frac{2a}{(a+x)^3} < 0$; f is concave down for all x; there are no inflection points **(c)** $\lim_{x \to \infty} \frac{x}{a+x} = 1$; there is a horizontal asymptote at $y = 1$ **(d)**

43. The growth rate is maximal for $N = K \left(\frac{1}{1+\theta} \right)^{1/\theta}$.

■ **Section 5.4**

1. 20 in. **3.** 4 **5.** The field is 80 ft by 160 ft, where the length along the river is 160 ft. **7.** $5(1 + \sqrt{2})$ **9.** 4 **11. (b)** $(6/5, 2/5)$ **(c)** local minimum at $x = 6/5$ as in (b). **13.** $\sqrt{2}$
15. $g'(x) = 2f(x)f'(x)$ has the same sign change as $f'(x)$.
17. The height is equal to the diameter, namely $2 \left(\frac{500}{\pi} \right)^{1/3}$.
19. (a) $r = \sqrt{2}, \theta = 2$ **(b)** $r = \sqrt{10}, \theta = 2$ **21.** $r = \left(\frac{355}{4\pi} \right)^{1/3}$
23. $a = 2, b = -2$ **25. (a)** Local maximum at t^* satisfies $f'(t^*) = \frac{f(t^*)}{C+t^*}$, which is the slope of the straight line through $(-C, 0)$ and the point with $t = t^*$.
(b) $y = \frac{1}{(1+\sqrt{2})^2} t + \frac{2}{(1+\sqrt{2})^2}$

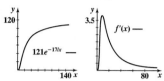

27. (a) $-x\frac{dr}{dx} - r(x) - L + \frac{3ke^{-kx}}{1-e^{-kx}} - \frac{r'(x)e^{-(r(x)+L)}}{1-e^{-(r(x)+L)}} = 0$

■ **Section 5.5**

1. 10 **3.** -7 **5.** $\frac{1}{2}$ **7.** 1 **9.** $\frac{1}{2}$ **11.** ∞ **13.** 0 **15.** $\frac{\ln 2}{\ln 3}$ **17.** $-\frac{\ln 3}{\ln 2}$
19. $\frac{1}{2}$ **21.** 0 **23.** 0 **25.** 0 **27.** 0 **29.** 0 **31.** 0 **33.** 1 **35.** 0
37. 0 **39.** 0 **41.** 1 **43.** 1 **45.** e^3 **47.** e^{-2} **49.** e^{-1} **51.** 0

53. ∞ **55.** 0 **57.** 0 **59.** 1 **61.** $\frac{\ln a}{\ln b}$

63. $\lim_{x \to \infty} \left(1 + \frac{c}{x^p} \right) = \begin{cases} \infty & \text{if } 0 < p < 1 \\ e^c & \text{if } p = 1 \\ 1 & \text{if } p > 1 \end{cases}$

65. Apply l'Hospital's rule. **67.** Let $y = 121e^{-17/x}$.
(a) $\lim_{x \to 0^+} \frac{dy}{dx} = 0$, $\lim_{x \to \infty} \frac{dy}{dx} = 0$ **(b)** $\frac{17}{2}$ **(c)** Height is increasing at an accelerating rate for $0 < x < \frac{17}{2}$ and at a decelerating rate for $x > \frac{17}{2}$. **(d)**

■ **Section 5.6**

1. (a) $N_5 = (10)(1.03)^5$ **(b)** $t = \frac{\ln 2}{\ln 1.03}$ **3. (a)** $b = 1.02$
(b) $N_{10} = (20)(1.02)^{10}$ **(c)** $t = \frac{\ln 2}{\ln 1.02}$ **5. (a)** $b = 1 + \frac{x}{100}$
(b) $t = \frac{\ln 2}{\ln(1+x/100)}$; 693.5, 139.0, 70.0, 35.0, 14.2, 7.3 **7. (a)** 0
(b) stable **9. (a)** $x = 1/2$ and $x = -2$ **(b)** $x = 1/2$ is locally stable, $x = -2$ is unstable. **11.** $x = 0$ is unstable, $x = 0.5$ is locally stable. **13. (a)** $x = 0$ is locally stable, $x = 1$ is unstable, $x = 4$ is locally stable **(b) (i)** 0 **(ii)** 4 **15. (b)** 0 **(c)** $1/\beta$
(d) $P = 2/\beta$ is an inflection point **(e)** R(P)

17. (b) To find equilibria, solve $N = 10Ne^{-0.01N}$; $N = 0$ is another equilibrium. **(c)** Oscillations seem to appear, and the system does not seem to converge to the nontrivial equilibrium.
19. Equilibria: $N = 0$ and $N = 100$. **(b)** Starting from $N = 10$, it appears that the limiting population size is 100. $N = 100$ is locally stable. **21.** Fixed points are 0 and $1 - \frac{1}{r}$. The nonzero fixed point is locally stable for $1 < r < 3$. **23.** $N^* = r^{1/(\gamma-1)}$; locally stable for $1 < r < 3$ **25.** $N^* = K$; locally stable for $0 < r < 2$

■ **Section 5.7**

1. $\sqrt{7} = 2.645751$ **3.** 0.6529186 **5.** 1.895494
7. (a) $|x_n| = 2^n x_0$ **(b)** ∞
9. (a) $x_0 = 3, x_1 = 4.166667, x_2 = 4.003333, x_3 = 4.000001$
(b) $x_0 = x_1 = x_2 = \cdots = 4$

■ **Section 5.8**

1. $F(x) = \frac{4}{3}x^3 - \frac{1}{2}x + C$ **3.** $F(x) = \frac{1}{3}x^3 + \frac{3}{2}x^2 - 4x + C$
5. $F(x) = \frac{1}{5}x^5 - x^3 + x + C$ **7.** $F(x) = x^4 - x^2 + 3x + C$
9. $F(x) = x + \ln|x| - \frac{1}{x} + C$ **11.** $F(x) = x + \frac{1}{x} + C$
13. $F(x) = \ln|1 + x| + C$ **15.** $F(x) = x^5 - \frac{5}{3x^3} + C$
17. $F(x) = \frac{1}{2}\ln|1 + 2x| + C$ **19.** $F(x) = -\frac{1}{3}e^{-3x} + C$
21. $F(x) = e^{2x} + C$ **23.** $F(x) = -\frac{1}{2}e^{-2x} + C$
25. $F(x) = -\frac{1}{2}\cos(2x) + C$
27. $F(x) = -3\cos(x/3) + 3\sin(x/3) + C$
29. $F(x) = -\frac{4}{\pi}\cos(\pi x/2) - \frac{6}{\pi}\sin(\pi x/2) + C$
31. $F(x) = \frac{1}{2}\tan(2x) + C$ **33.** $F(x) = 3\tan(x/3) + C$
35. $F(x) = \tan x + x + C$ **37.** $-\frac{1}{6}x^{-6} + \frac{1}{2}x^6 - \frac{1}{2}\cos(2x) + C$
39. $\frac{1}{3}\tan(3x - 1) + \frac{1}{2}x^2 - 3\ln x + C$ **41.** $\frac{1}{a(a+1)}e^{(a+1)x}$
43. $\frac{1}{a}\ln|ax + 3|$ **45.** $\frac{1}{a+3}x^{a+3} - \frac{1}{\ln a}a^{x+2}$
47. $y = 2\ln|x| - \frac{1}{2}x^2 + C$ **49.** $y = \frac{1}{2}x^2 + \frac{1}{3}x^3 + C$

51. $y = \frac{1}{2}t^2 - \frac{1}{3}t^3 + C$ **53.** $y = -2e^{-t/2} + C$

55. $y = -\frac{1}{\pi}\cos(\pi s) + C$ **57.** $y = 2\tan(x/2) + C$

59. $y = x^3 + 1, x \geq 0$ **61.** $y = \frac{4}{3}x^{3/2} + \frac{2}{3}$

63. $N(t) = \ln t + 10, t \geq 1$ **65.** $W(t) = e^t, t \geq 0$

67. $W(t) = 1 - \frac{1}{3}e^{-3t}$ **69.** $T(t) = 3 + \frac{1}{\pi} - \frac{1}{\pi}\cos(\pi t)$

71. $y = \frac{e^x - e^{-x}}{2}$ **73.** $L(x) = 25 - 10e^{-0.1x}, L(0) = 15$

75. $t = 2.5$ s, $v(2.5) = 80\frac{\text{ft}}{\text{s}}$ **77. (a)** The first term on the right-hand side describes evaporation; the second one describes watering. **(b)** $a = \frac{1}{24}$

■ **Chapter 5 Review Problems**

1. (b) Absolute maximum at $(1, e^{-1})$ **(c)** inflection point at $(2, 2e^{-2})$ **(d)**

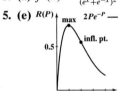

3. (a) $f'(x) = \frac{4}{(e^x + e^{-x})^2} > 0$, hence, $f(x)$ is strictly increasing.

5. (e)

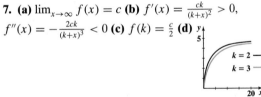

7. (a) $\lim_{x\to\infty} f(x) = c$ **(b)** $f'(x) = \frac{ck}{(k+x)^2} > 0$, $f''(x) = -\frac{2ck}{(k+x)^3} < 0$ **(c)** $f(k) = \frac{c}{2}$ **(d)**

9. (a) $L(\theta) = (\theta^2)^8(2\theta(1-\theta))^6((1-\theta)^2)^3$ **(b)** $\frac{d}{d\theta}\ln L(\theta) = \frac{L'(\theta)}{L(\theta)}$ and $L(\theta) > 0$. **(c)** $\hat{\theta} = \frac{11}{17}$ **11. (a)** $c(t) = \frac{1}{3}e^{-0.3t}, t \geq 0$

(b) $t = \frac{\ln 2}{0.3}$ **13. (a)** $t = v_0/g$ **(b)** $\frac{v_0^2}{2g}$ **(c)** 0 **(d)** $t = \frac{2v_0}{g}$

■ **Section 6.1**

1. 0.21875 **3.** 0.46875 **5.** $\sqrt{1} + \sqrt{2} + \sqrt{3} + \sqrt{4}$

7. $3^2 + 3^3 + 3^4 + 3^5 + 3^6$ **9.** $1 + (x+1) + (x+1)^2 + (x+1)^3$

11. $-1 + 1 - 1 + 1$ **13.** $\left(\frac{1}{n}\right)^2\frac{1}{n} + \left(\frac{2}{n}\right)^2\frac{1}{n} + \left(\frac{3}{n}\right)^2\frac{1}{n} + \cdots + \left(\frac{n}{n}\right)^2\frac{1}{n}$

15. $\sum_{k=1}^{n} 2k$ **17.** $\sum_{k=2}^{5}\ln k$ **19.** $\sum_{k=2}^{6}\frac{k-3}{k+2}$ **21.** $\sum_{k=1}^{n} q^{k-1}$

23. 285 **25.** 112 **27.** $\frac{2n(n-1)(2n-1)}{3}$ **29.** 0 **33.** 1.36 **35.** 14

37. 0 **39.** $\int_a^b x\,dx = \frac{1}{2}b^2 - \frac{1}{2}a^2$

41. $2\int_1^2 x^3\,dx$ **43.** $\int_{-3}^{2}(2x-1)\,dx$ **45.** $\int_2^3 \frac{x-1}{x+2}\,dx$ **47.** $\int_{-5}^{2} e^x\,dx$

49. $\lim_{\|P\|\to 0}\sum_{k=1}^{n}(c_k+1)^{1/3}\Delta x_k$, where $\|P\|$ is a partition of $[2, 6]$, $c_k \in [x_{k-1}, x_k]$, and $\Delta x_k = x_k - x_{k-1}$

51. $\lim_{\|P\|\to 0}\sum_{k=1}^{n}\ln c_k\Delta x_k$, where $\|P\|$ is a partition of $[1, e]$, $c_k \in [x_{k-1}, x_k]$, and $\Delta x_k = x_k - x_{k-1}$

53. $\lim_{\|P\|\to 0}\sum_{k=1}^{n}g(c_k)\Delta x_k$, where $\|P\|$ is a partition of $[0, 5]$, $c_k \in [x_{k-1}, x_k]$, and $\Delta x_k = x_k - x_{k-1}$

55.

$\int_{-1}^{2}(x^2 - 1)\,dx = -A_- + A_+$

57.

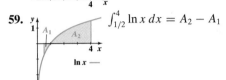

$\int_0^5 e^{-x}\,dx = A$

59.

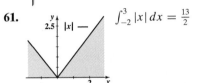

$\int_{1/2}^{4}\ln x\,dx = A_2 - A_1$

61.

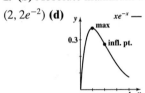

$\int_{-2}^{3}|x|\,dx = \frac{13}{2}$

63.

$\int_2^5(\frac{1}{2}x - 4)\,dx = -\frac{27}{4}$

65. $\int_{-2}^{2}\left(\sqrt{4-x^2} - 2\right)dx = 2\pi - 8$

67. $\int_{-3}^{0}\left(4 - \sqrt{9-x^2}\right)dx = 12 - \frac{9}{4}\pi$ **69.** 0

71. 0 **73.** 0 **75.** $x \geq x^2$ for $0 \leq x \leq 1$ **77.** $\sqrt{x} \geq 0$ for $x \geq 0$ and $\sqrt{x} \leq 2$ for $0 \leq x \leq 4$

79.

The rectangle with height $1/2$ from $\pi/6$ to $5\pi/6$ is contained in the area under $y = \sin x$ from $\pi/6$ to $5\pi/6$, which is contained in the rectangle with height 1 from $\pi/6$ to $5\pi/6$. **81.** $a = \pi/2$

83. $a = 3$

■ **Section 6.2**

1. $\frac{dy}{dx} = 2x^3$ **3.** $\frac{dy}{dx} = 4x^2 - 3$ **5.** $\frac{dy}{dx} = \sqrt{1+2x}$

7. $\frac{dy}{dx} = \sqrt{1 + \sin^2 x}$ **9.** $\frac{dy}{dx} = xe^{4x}$ **11.** $\frac{dy}{dx} = \frac{1}{x+3}$

13. $\frac{dy}{dx} = \sin(x^2 + 1)$ **15.** $\frac{dy}{dx} = 3(1 + 9x^2)$

17. $\frac{dy}{dx} = [2(1-4x)^2 + 1](-4)$ **19.** $\frac{dy}{dx} = 2x\sqrt{x^2 + 1}$

21. $\frac{dy}{dx} = 3(1 + e^{3x})$ **23.** $\frac{dy}{dx} = (6x + 1)[1 + (3x^2 + x)e^{3x^2 + x}]$

25. $\frac{dy}{dx} = -(1+x)$ **27.** $\frac{dy}{dx} = -2[1 + \sin(2x)]$ **29.** $\frac{dy}{dx} = -\frac{1}{x^2}$

31. $\frac{dy}{dx} = -2x\sec(x^2)$ **33.** $\frac{dy}{dx} = 2[1 + (2x)^2] - (1 + x^2)$

35. $\frac{dy}{dx} = 3x^2\ln(x^3 - 3) - 2x\ln(x^2 - 3)$

37. $\frac{dy}{dx} = (1 + 3x^2)\sin(x + x^3) + 2x\sin(2 - x^2)$ **39.** $x + x^3 + C$
41. $\frac{1}{9}x^3 - \frac{1}{4}x^2 + C$ **43.** $\frac{1}{6}x^3 + \frac{3}{2}x^2 - \frac{1}{3}x + C$
45. $x^{3/2}\left(\frac{4}{5}x - \frac{2}{3}\right) + C$ **47.** $\frac{2}{7}x^{7/2} + C$ **49.** $\frac{2}{9}x^{9/2} + \frac{7}{9}x^{9/7} + C$
51. $\frac{2}{3}x^{3/2} + 2\sqrt{x} + C$ **53.** $\frac{1}{3}x^3 - x + C$
55. $-\frac{1}{3}x^3 + \frac{5}{2}x^2 - 6x + C$ **57.** $\frac{1}{2}e^{2x} + C$ **59.** $-3e^{-x} + C$
61. $-e^{-x^2/2} + C$ **63.** $-\frac{1}{2}\cos(2x) + C$ **65.** $\frac{1}{3}\sin(3x) + C$
67. $\frac{1}{3}\tan(3x) + C$ **69.** $\sec x + C$ **71.** $\frac{1}{2}\ln|\sec(2x)| + C$
73. $\tan x + \ln|\sec x| + C$ **75.** $4\tan^{-1}x + C$ **77.** $\sin^{-1}x + C$
79. $\ln|x + 2| + C$ **81.** $\frac{2}{3}x - \frac{1}{3}\ln|x| + C$ **83.** $\ln|x - 3| + C$
85. $-\ln|x + 3| + C$ **87.** $5(x - \tan^{-1}x) + C$ **89.** $\frac{3^x}{\ln 3} + C$
91. $-\frac{9^{-x}}{\ln 9} + C$ **93.** $\frac{1}{3}x^3 + \frac{2^x}{\ln 2} + C$ **95.** $\frac{2}{3}x^{3/2} + 2e^{x/2} + C$
97. -6 **99.** $-\frac{1}{2}$ **101.** 3 **103.** $\frac{28}{3}$ **105.** $\frac{1}{2}$ **107.** $\frac{1}{2}$ **109.** $\frac{\pi}{4}$
111. $\frac{\pi}{6}$ **113.** $\frac{1}{2}\ln 2$ **115.** $\frac{1}{3}(1 - e^{-3})$ **117.** 1 **119.** 1 **121.** $\ln\frac{3}{2}$
123. $\frac{1}{2}$ **125.** $f(x) = 4x$

■ **Section 6.3**

1. $\frac{125}{6}$ **3.** $2e$ **5.** $\frac{4}{3}$ **7.** $\frac{14}{3} - \ln 4$ **9.** $\frac{\pi}{2} - 1$ **11.** $\frac{3}{2}$ **13.** $\frac{2}{3}$ **15.** $\frac{16}{3}$
17. (a) $N(t) = 101 - e^{-t}$ **(b)** $1 - e^{-5}$ **(c)** $N(5) - N(0) = \int_0^5 e^{-t}\,dt$;

shaded area. $N(5) - N(0) = $ Shaded area **19. (a)**

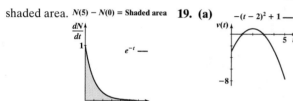

(b) Particle moves to the left for $0 \le t \le 1$ and $3 \le t \le 5$, and to the right for $1 \le t \le 3$. **(c)** $s(t) = 2t^2 - \frac{1}{3}t^3 - 3t$; signed area between $v(u)$ and the horizontal axis from 0 to t.

(d)

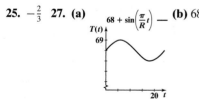

The rightmost position: $s(0) = s(3) = 0$; the leftmost position: $s(5) = -\frac{20}{3}$. **21.** Cumulative growth between $t = 2$ and $t = 7$.

23. Cumulative change in biomass between $t = 1$ and $t = 6$.

25. $-\frac{2}{3}$ **27. (a)**

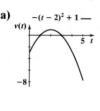

(b) 68

29. $f(x)$ is symmetric about the origin. **31.** average value of $f(x) = 2$; $f(1) = 2$ **33.** $\frac{1}{3}\pi h r^2$ **35.** $\frac{256}{15}\pi$ **37.** 2π **39.** $2\pi\sqrt{3}$
41. $\frac{2}{15}\pi$ **43.** $\frac{\pi}{2}\left(e^4 + e^{-4} - 2\right)$ **45.** $\pi\left(\frac{\pi}{2} - 1\right)$ **47.** $\frac{32}{5}\pi$
49. $\pi\ln 3$ **51.** $\frac{3}{10}\pi$ **53. (a)** $2\sqrt{5}$ **(b)** $2\sqrt{5}$
55. $\frac{8}{27}\left[(10)^{3/2} - \left(\frac{13}{4}\right)^{3/2}\right]$ **57.** $\frac{14}{3}$ **59.** $\int_{-1}^1 \sqrt{1 + 4x^2}\,dx$
61. $\int_0^1 \sqrt{1 + e^{-2x}}\,dx$ **63. (a)** $\frac{\pi}{2}$ **(b)** $\frac{\pi}{2}$ **65.** $f'(a) = \frac{1}{2}(e^a - e^{-a})$

■ **Chapter 6 Review Problems**

1. $3.38\frac{\text{m}^3}{\text{s}}$ **3. (a)**

$v(d)$ $(3 - d)^{1/5}$ — $(3 - d)^{1/7}$ —
1.2

4 d

(b) $v(D) = 0$, $v'(d) < 0$ for $d \in [0, D)$ **5. (a)** $\bar{v} = v(d_1)$

■ **Section 7.1**

1. $\frac{2}{3}(x^2 + 3)^{3/2} + C$ **3.** $-\frac{6}{5}(1 - x^2)^{5/4} + C$ **5.** $\frac{5}{3}\sin(3x) + C$
7. $-\frac{7}{12}\cos(4x^3) + C$ **9.** $\frac{1}{2}e^{2x+3} + C$ **11.** $-e^{-x^2/2} + C$
13. $\frac{1}{2}\ln|x^2 + 4x| + C$ **15.** $3(x + 4) - 12\ln|x + 4| + C$
17. $\frac{2}{3}(x + 3)^{3/2} + C$ **19.** $\frac{2}{3}(2x^2 - 3x + 2)^{3/2} + C$
21. $-\frac{1}{4}\ln|1 + 4x - 2x^2| + C$ **23.** $\frac{1}{2}\ln|1 + 2x^2| + C$
25. $\frac{3}{2}e^{x^2} + C$ **27.** $-\cot(\ln x) + C$ **29.** $-\frac{2}{3\pi}\cos\left(\frac{3\pi}{2}x + \frac{\pi}{4}\right) + C$
31. $\frac{1}{2}\tan^2 x + C$ **33.** $\frac{1}{3}(\ln x)^3 + C$
35. $\frac{1}{15}(5 + x^2)^{3/2}(3x^2 - 10) + C$ **37.** $\ln|ax^2 + bx + c| + C$
39. $\frac{1}{n+1}[g(x)]^{n+1} + C$ **41.** $-e^{-g(x)} + C$ **43.** $\frac{1}{3}(10^{3/2} - 1)$
45. $\frac{7}{2025}$ **47.** $-e^{-9/2} + 1$ **49.** $\frac{3}{8}$ **51.** $\frac{1}{2}$ **53.** $4 + 3\ln 3$ **55.** $\frac{1}{2}$
57. $2(e^{-1} - e^{-3})$ **59.** $\ln|\sin x| + C$

■ **Section 7.2**

1. $x\sin x + \cos x + C$ **3.** $\frac{2}{3}x\sin(3x - 1) + \frac{2}{9}\cos(3x - 1) + C$
5. $-2x\cos(x - 1) + 2\sin(x - 1) + C$ **7.** $xe^x - e^x + C$
9. $x^2e^x - 2xe^x + 2e^x + C$ **11.** $\frac{1}{2}x^2\ln|x| - \frac{1}{4}x^2 + C$
13. $\frac{1}{2}x^2\ln(3x) - \frac{1}{4}x^2 + C$ **15.** $x\tan x + \ln|\cos x| + C$
17. $\frac{1}{2}\left(\sqrt{3} - \frac{\pi}{3}\right)$ **19.** $2\ln 2 - 1$ **21.** $2\ln 4 - \frac{3}{2}$ **23.** $1 - 2e^{-1}$
25. $\frac{1}{2} + \frac{1}{4}(\sqrt{3} - 1)e^{\pi/3}$ **27.** $\frac{2e^{-3x}}{36+\pi^2}\left[\pi\sin\left(\frac{\pi}{2}x\right) - 6\cos\left(\frac{\pi}{2}x\right)\right] + C$
29. $\frac{1}{2}x[\sin(\ln x) - \cos(\ln x)] + C$
31. $\int \cos^2 x\,dx = \frac{1}{2}\sin x\cos x + \frac{1}{2}x + C$
33. (b) $\int \arcsin x\,dx = x\arcsin x + \sqrt{1 - x^2} + C$
35. (b) $\frac{1}{2}(\ln x)^2 + C$ **37. (b)** $-\frac{1}{3}x^2e^{-3x} - \frac{2}{9}xe^{-3x} - \frac{2}{27}e^{-3x} + C$
39. $2\sqrt{x}\sin(\sqrt{x}) + 2\cos(\sqrt{x}) + C$ **41.** $-e^{-x^2/2}(2 + x^2) + C$
43. $\sin xe^{\sin x} - e^{\sin x} + C$ **45.** 2 **47.** $-\frac{1}{2} + 3\ln 3$
49. $-\frac{1}{2}xe^{-2x} - \frac{1}{4}e^{-2x} + C$ **51.** $\ln|\sin x| + C$ **53.** $-\cos(x^2) + C$
55. $\frac{1}{4}\tan^{-1}\left(\frac{x}{4}\right) + C$ **57.** $x - 3\ln|x + 3| + C$
59. $\frac{1}{2}\ln|x^2 + 3| + C$ **61.** $\int \ln x\,dx = x\ln x - x + C$
63. $\frac{4}{9}(x - 2)^{9/4} + \frac{8}{5}(x - 2)^{5/4} + C$ **65.** $2e^2$ **67.** $\frac{\pi}{2}$ **69.** $\frac{1}{2}$

■ **Section 7.3**

1. $2x + 1 - \frac{3}{x+2}$ **3.** $3x - 2 + \frac{2x}{x^2+1}$ **5.** $\frac{5}{x+1} - \frac{3}{x}$ **7.** $\frac{2}{x} - \frac{1}{x-3} + \frac{3}{x+1}$
9. $\frac{2}{x-1} + \frac{3}{x+1}$ **11.** $\frac{3}{x-5} + \frac{1}{x+2}$ **13.** $\frac{1}{2}\ln|x - 2| - \frac{1}{2}\ln|x| + C$
15. $\frac{1}{4}\ln|x - 3| - \frac{1}{4}\ln|x + 1| + C$
17. $\frac{3}{2}\ln|x + 2| + \frac{1}{x} - \frac{1}{2}\ln|x| + C$
19. $-\tan^{-1}x + \frac{1}{2}\ln|x^2 + 4| + C$ **21.** $2\tan^{-1}x + \frac{3}{2(x^2+1)} + C$
23. $\tan^{-1}(x - 1) + C$ **25.** $\frac{1}{3}\tan^{-1}\left(\frac{x-2}{3}\right) + C$ **27.** $\frac{1}{5}\ln\left|\frac{x-3}{x+2}\right| + C$
29. $\frac{1}{6}\ln\left|\frac{x-3}{x+3}\right| + C$ **31.** $\frac{1}{3}\ln\left|\frac{x-2}{x+1}\right| + C$
33. $x - 5\ln|x + 2| + 2\ln|x + 1| + C$ **35.** $x + 2\ln\left|\frac{x-2}{x+2}\right| + C$
37. $2 - \ln 5 + \ln 3$ **39.** $\frac{1}{2}\ln 2$ **41.** $-\ln 2$ **43.** $\frac{\pi}{4} - \frac{1}{2}\ln 2$

45. $\frac{1}{1+x} + \ln\left|\frac{x}{x+1}\right|$ **47.** $-\frac{2}{x+1} + \ln\left|\frac{x+1}{x-1}\right|$

49. $\frac{1}{108}\ln\left|\frac{x+3}{x-3}\right| - \frac{1}{36}\left(\frac{1}{x+3} + \frac{1}{x-3}\right) + C$ **51.** $-\frac{1}{x} - \tan^{-1}x$

■ Section 7.4

1. infinite interval; $\frac{1}{2}$ **3.** infinite interval; π **5.** infinite interval; 2 **7.** infinite interval; 2 **9.** infinite interval; 0 **11.** integrand discontinuous; 6 **13.** integrand discontinuous; 2 **15.** integrand discontinuous at $x = 0$; -2 **17.** infinite interval; $\frac{1}{2}$ **19.** integrand discontinuous at $x = 0$; integral divergent **21.** integrand discontinuous at $x = 1$; 0 **23.** infinite interval; integral divergent **25.** infinite interval; integral divergent **27.** integrand discontinuous at $x = \pm 1$; 0 **29.** integrand discontinuous at $x = \pm 1$; integral divergent **31.** $c = 3$ **35. (b)** $0 \le \int_1^\infty e^{-x^2}\,dx \le \lim_{z \to \infty}\int_1^z e^{-x}\,dx = e < \infty$ **37. (b)** $\int_1^\infty \frac{1}{\sqrt{1+x^2}}\,dx \ge \lim_{z \to \infty}\frac{1}{2}\int_1^z \frac{1}{x}\,dx = \infty$; divergent

39. For $x \ge 1$: $0 \le e^{-x^2/2} \le e^{-x}$; convergent **41.** For $x \ge 1$: $\frac{1}{\sqrt{x+1}} \ge \frac{1}{2\sqrt{x}}$; divergent **43. (a)** Use l'Hospital's rule **(b)** Show that $\lim_{x \to \infty}\frac{\ln x}{\sqrt{x}} = 0$ and use a graphing calculator to show that, for $x > 74.2$, $2\ln x \le \sqrt{x}$ **(c)** For $x > 74.2$, use the fact that $e^{-\sqrt{x}} \le e^{-2\ln x} = \frac{1}{x^2}$ and conclude that the integral is convergent

■ Section 7.5

1. 2.328 **3.** 0.6292 **5.** $M_4 \approx 0.6912$; error ≈ 0.0019 **7.** $M_4 \approx 5.3838$; error ≈ 0.0505 **9.** $T_4 \approx 2.3438$ **11.** $T_3 \approx 0.6380$ **13.** $T_5 = 20.32$; error ≈ 0.32 **15.** $T_4 \approx 1.8195$; error ≈ 0.0661 **17.** $n = 82$ **19.** $n = 58$ **21.** $n = 92$ **23.** $n = 50$ **25. (a)** $M_5 = 0.245$; $T_5 = 0.26$; $|\int_0^1 x^3\,dx - M_5| = 0.005$; $|\int_0^1 x^3\,dx - T_5| = 0.01$ **(c)** $0.6433 \le \int_0^1 \sqrt{x}\,dx \le 0.6730$

■ Section 7.6

1. $L(x) = 1 + 2x$ **3.** $L(x) = 1 + x$ **5.** $L(x) = \ln 2$ **7.** $P_5(x) = 1 - \frac{x^2}{2!} + \frac{x^4}{4!}$ **9.** $P_6(x) = \frac{120}{5!}x^5 = x^5$ **11.** $P_3(x) = \sqrt{2} + \frac{1}{2\sqrt{2}}x - \frac{1}{16\sqrt{2}}x^2 + \frac{1}{64\sqrt{2}}x^3$; $P_3(0.1) \approx 1.4491$; $f(0.1) = \sqrt{2.1}$; $|f(0.1) - P_3(0.1)| \approx 3.34 \times 10^{-7}$ **13.** $P_5(x) = x - \frac{x^3}{3!} + \frac{x^5}{5!}$; $P_5(1) \approx 0.8417$; $f(1) \approx 0.8415$; $|P_5(1) - f(1)| \approx 1.96 \times 10^{-4}$ **15.** $P_2(x) = x$; $P_2(0.1) = 0.1$; $f(0.1) \approx 0.10033$; $|P_2(0.1) - f(0.1)| \approx 3.35 \times 10^{-4}$ **17. (a)** $P_3(x) = x - \frac{x^3}{3!}$ **(b)** $\lim_{x \to 0}\frac{P_3(x)}{x} = 0$ and $P_3(x)$ approximates $f(x) = \sin x$ at $x = 0$ **19.** $P_3(x) = 1 + \frac{1}{2}(x - 1) - \frac{1}{8}(x - 1)^2 + \frac{1}{16}(x - 1)^3$; $P_3(2) \approx 1.4375$; $f(2) \approx 1.4142$; $|P_3(2) - f(2)| \approx 0.023$ **21.** $P_3(x) = \frac{1}{2}\sqrt{3} - \frac{1}{2}(x - \frac{\pi}{6}) - \frac{1}{4}\sqrt{3}(x - \frac{\pi}{6})^2 + \frac{1}{12}(x - \frac{\pi}{6})^3$; $P_3(\frac{\pi}{7}) \approx 0.9010$; $f(\frac{\pi}{7}) \approx 0.9010$; $|P_3(\frac{\pi}{7}) - f(\frac{\pi}{7})| \approx 6.861 \times 10^{-5}$ **23.** $P_3(x) = e^2 + e^2(x - 2) + \frac{e^2}{2}(x - 2)^2 + \frac{e^2}{6}(x - 2)^3$; $P_3(2.1) \approx 8.1661$; $f(2.1) \approx 8.1662$; $|P_3(2.1) - f(2.1)| \approx 3.14 \times 10^{-5}$ **25.** $\int_0^1 x^3\,dx = 0.25$; $M_5 \approx 0.245$; $T_5 \approx 0.26$ **27.** $n = 10$ **29.** $n = 2$ **31.** $P_2(x) = 0$; error term: $f(x) - P_2(x) = f(x)$ **33. (b)** Use $x = 1$: $\tan^{-1} = \frac{\pi}{4}$

■ Section 7.7

1. $\frac{x}{2} + \frac{3}{4}\ln|2x - 3| + C$

3. $\frac{1}{2}\left(x\sqrt{x^2 - 16} - 16\ln|x + \sqrt{x^2 - 16}|\right) + C$ **5.** $6 - 16e^{-1}$ **7.** $\frac{2}{9}e^3 + \frac{1}{9}$ **9.** $\frac{1}{2}e^{\pi/6} - \frac{1}{4}(\sqrt{3} - 1)$ **11.** $-2e^{-x/2}(x^2 + 4x + 7) + C$ **13.** $\frac{1}{20}[10x - 6 + \sin(10x - 6)] + C$

15. $x\sqrt{\frac{9}{4} + x^2} + \frac{9}{4}\left(\ln|x + \sqrt{\frac{9}{4} + x^2}|\right) + C$

17. $\frac{4e^{2x+1}}{16+\pi^2}\left[2\sin\left(\frac{\pi}{2}x\right) - \frac{\pi}{2}\cos\left(\frac{\pi}{2}x\right)\right] + C$ **19.** $2\ln 2$

21. $\frac{x}{2}(\sin(\ln(3x)) + \cos(\ln(3x))) + C$

■ Chapter 7 Review Problems

1. $-\frac{1}{9}(1 - x^3)^3 + C$ **3.** $-2e^{-x^2} + C$

5. $\frac{6}{7}(1 + \sqrt{x})^{7/3} - \frac{3}{2}(1 + \sqrt{x})^{4/3} + C$ **7.** $\frac{1}{6}\tan(3x^2) + C$

9. $\frac{1}{2}x^2\ln x - \frac{1}{4}x^2 + C$ **11.** $\tan x \ln(\tan x) - \tan x + C$

13. $\frac{1}{2}\tan^{-1}\left(\frac{x}{2}\right) + C$ **15.** $-\ln|\cos x| + C$

17. $\frac{e^{2x}}{5}(2\sin x - \cos x) + C$ **19.** $2e^{x/2} + C$

21. $-\frac{1}{2}\sin x \cos x + \frac{x}{2} + C$ **23.** $\ln|\frac{x-1}{x}| + C$

25. $x - 5\ln|x + 5| + C$ **27.** $\ln|x + 5| + C$

29. $\frac{1}{2}x^2 + 3x + 4\ln|x - 1| + C$ **31.** $4 + \ln 3$ **33.** $1 - e^{-1/2}$

35. $\frac{\pi}{8}$ **37.** 4 **39.** $\frac{\pi}{6}$ **41.** divergent **43.** divergent **45.** 2

47. $-\frac{1}{4}$ **49.** $e - e^{\sqrt{2}/2}$ **51. (a)** $M_4 = 0.625$ **(b)** $T_4 = 0.75$

53. (a) $M_5 \approx 0.6311$ **(b)** $T_5 \approx 0.6342$ **55.** $P_3(x) = 2x - \frac{4}{3}x^3$

57. $P_3(x) = (x - 1) - \frac{1}{2}(x - 1)^2 + \frac{1}{3}(x - 1)^3$

59. $f_{avg}(t)$

■ Section 8.1

1. $y = \frac{1}{2}x^2 - \cos x + 1$ **3.** $y = \ln x$ for $x > 0$

5. $x(t) = 2 - \ln(1 - t)$ for $t < 1$ **7.** $s(t) = \frac{2}{9}(3t + 1)^{3/2} + \frac{7}{9}$ for $t \ge -\frac{1}{3}$ **9.** $V(t) = \sin t + 5$ **11.** $y = 2e^{3x}$ **13.** $x(t) = 5e^{2 - 2t}$

15. $h(s) = \frac{1}{2}(9e^{2s} - 1)$ **17.** $N(t) = 20e^{0.3t}$, $N(5) = 20e^{1.5} \approx 90$

19. (a) $N(t) = Ce^{rt}$ **(b)** $\log N(t) = \log C + (r \log e)t$. To determine r, graph $N(t)$ on a semilog graph; the slope is then $r \log e$. **(c)** 1. Obtain data at various points in time. 2. Plot on semilog paper. 3. Determine the slope of the resulting straight line. 4. Divide the slope by $\log e$; this yields r.

21. (a) $N(t) = \frac{100}{10 - t}$ **(b)**

$N(t) - \lim_{t \to 10^-} N(t) = \infty$

23. (a) $L_\infty = 123$; $k = \frac{1}{27}\ln\frac{244}{123} \approx 0.0254$

(b) $L(10) = 123 - 122e^{-0.254} \approx 28.37$ in.

(c) $t = \frac{1}{0.0254}\ln\frac{122}{12.3} \approx 90.33$ months **25.** $y = \frac{2}{3e^{-x} - 2}$

27. $y = \frac{5}{1 + 4e^{5x}}$ **29.** $y = \frac{3}{1 - \frac{5}{3}e^{-6(x-1)}}$ **31.** $y = \frac{1}{\frac{1}{C}e^{-x} - 1}$

33. $y = -1 \pm (-2(x + C))^{-1/2}$ **35. (b) (i)** $y = \frac{2 - 2e^{4x}}{1 + e^{4x}}$ **(ii)** $y = 2$

(iii) $y = \frac{\frac{2}{3}e^{4x} + 2}{1 - \frac{1}{3}e^{4x}}$ **37.** $N(t) = \frac{200}{1 + 3e^{-0.34t}}$, $\lim_{t \to \infty} N(t) = 200$

39. (a) $N(t) = \frac{50}{1 + 4e^{-1.5t}}$ **(b)** $N(t) = \frac{50}{1 - \frac{4}{9}e^{-1.5t}}$ **(c)** $N(t)$

(d) $\lim_{t \to \infty} N(t) = 50$ in both (a) and (b)

41. (a) $\frac{dN}{dt} = 5N\left(1 - \frac{N}{30}\right)$ **(b)** $N(t)$

43. (a) $p(t) = \frac{1}{\frac{1 - p_0}{p_0}e^{-st/2} + 1}$, $t \ge 0$ **(b)** $t = \frac{2}{0.01}\ln 9 \approx 439.4$

(c) $\lim_{t \to \infty} p(t) = 1$, which means that eventually the population will consist only of A_1A_1 types. **45.** $y = \sqrt{x^2 + 2x + 4}$

47. $y = -1 + 3\exp[1 - e^{-x}]$ **49.** $y = 6x - 7$

51. $r(t) = \exp[1 - e^{-t}]$ **53.** $\frac{dc}{c} = k\frac{dm}{m}$ **55.** $\frac{dy}{dx} = \frac{1}{7.7}\frac{y}{x}$

57. $N(t) = 5\exp\left(\frac{1}{\pi} + 2t - \frac{1}{\pi}\cos(2\pi t)\right)$

■ **Section 8.2**

1. (a) $y = 0, 2$ **(b)**

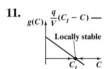

$g(y)$ $y(2 - y)$ — $y = 0$ is unstable;

$y = 2$ is locally stable. **(c)** Eigenvalue associated with $y = 0$ is
$2 > 0$; hence, $y = 0$ is unstable. Eigenvalue associated with $y = 2$
is $-2 < 0$; hence, $y = 2$ is locally stable. **3. (a)** $y = 0, 1, 2$

(b) $y(y - 1)(y - 2)$ —

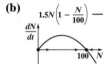

$g(y)$

$y = 0$ and $y = 2$ are unstable; $y = 1$ is locally stable.
(c) Eigenvalue associated with $y = 0$ is $2 > 0$; hence, $y = 0$ is
unstable. Eigenvalue associated with $y = 1$ is $-1 < 0$; hence,
$y = 1$ is locally stable. Eigenvalue associated with $y = 2$ is $2 > 0$;
hence, $y = 2$ is unstable. **5. (a)** $\frac{dN}{dt} = 1.5N\left(1 - \frac{N}{100}\right)$

(b)

$1.5N\left(1 - \frac{N}{100}\right)$ —

$\frac{dN}{dt}$

100 N

$N = 0$ is unstable; $N = 100$ is locally stable **(c)** Eigenvalue
associated with $N = 0$ is $1.5 > 0$; hence, $N = 0$ is unstable.
Eigenvalue associated with $N = 100$ is $-1.5 < 0$; hence,
$N = 100$ is locally stable. Same results as in (b).

7. (a) $K = 2000$ **(b)** $t = \frac{1}{2}\ln 199 \approx 2.65$ **(c)** 2000

9. (a) $N \approx 52.79$ is unstable; $N \approx 947.21$ is locally stable

(b) The maximal harvesting rate is $rK/4$.

11.

$g(C)$ $\frac{q}{V}(C_I - C)$ —

Locally stable

C_I C

The equilibrium C_I is locally stable. **13. (a)** $\frac{dC}{dt} = \frac{0.2}{400}(3 - C)$
(b) $C(t) = 3 - 3e^{-t/2000}, t \geq 0$; $\lim_{t\to\infty} C(t) = 3$ **(c)** $C = 3$ is
locally stable. **15. (a)** Equilibrium concentration: $C_I = 254$
(b) $T_R = \frac{1}{0.37} \approx 2.703$ **(c)** $T_R = \frac{1}{0.37} \approx 2.703$ **(d)** They are the
same. **17.** Use $T_R = \frac{V}{q}$. **19.** $T_R = \frac{12.3 \times 10^9}{220}$ seconds ≈ 647.1 days;
$C(T_R) \approx 0.806\,\frac{mg}{l}$ **21. (a)** $0.5p(1 - p) - 1.5p$ —

$g(p)$

1 p

(b) $p = 0$ is locally stable **(c)** $g'(0) = -1 < 0$, which implies that
0 is locally stable. **23. (a)** $\frac{dp}{dt}$ describes the rate of change of $p(t)$;
$cp(1 - p - D)$ describes the colonization of vacant undestroyed
patches; $-mp$ describes extinction.   **(b)**

p_2

$1 - D - \frac{m}{c}$ —

$1 - \frac{m}{c}$

$1 - \frac{m}{c}$ D

(c) $D < 1 - \frac{m}{c}$; $p_1 = 0$ is unstable; $p_2 = 1 - D - \frac{m}{c}$ is locally
stable. **25. (a)** $N = 0, N = 17,$ and $N = 200$ **(b)** $N = 0$ is locally

stable; $N = 17$ is unstable; $N = 200$ is locally stable.

(c)

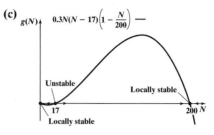

$g(N)$ $0.3N(N - 17)\left(1 - \frac{N}{200}\right)$ —

Unstable   Locally stable

17 200 N

Locally stable

■ **Section 8.3**

1. (a) $R_0 = 1.5 > 1$; the disease will spread. **(b)** $R_0 = \frac{1}{2} < 1$; the
disease will not spread. **3.** $R_0 = 0.9999 < 1$; the disease will not
spread.

5. (a) $\dfrac{dN}{dt} = N_I - 5N - 0.02NX + X$

$\dfrac{dX}{dt} = 0.02NX - 2X$

(b) equilibrium: $(\hat{N}, \hat{X}) = (100, N_I - 500)$; this is a nontrivial
equilibrium, provided that $N_I > 500$.

7. (a) $\dfrac{dN}{dt} = 200 - N - 0.01NX + 2X$ **(b)**

$\dfrac{dX}{dt} = 0.01NX - 3X$

X $\frac{dX}{dt} = 0$

100

300 N

$\frac{dN}{dt} = 0$

(c) No nontrivial equilibria **9. (a)** Equilibria: $(0, 0), (0, 2/3),$
$(1/2, 0)$ **(b)** Since $\frac{dp_2}{dt} < 0$ when $p_1 = 1/2$ and p_2 is small, species
2 cannot invade. **11. (a)**

p_2

$\frac{4}{5}$

$\frac{1}{2}$ $\frac{2}{3}$ p_1

(b) equilibria: $(0, 0), (2/3, 0), (0, 4/5)$

■ **Chapter 8 Review Problems**

1. (a) $\frac{dT}{dt}$ is proportional to the difference between the
temperature of the object and the temperature of the
surrounding medium. **(b)** $t = \frac{1}{0.013}\ln\frac{9}{4} \approx 62.38$ minutes
3. (a) $N(t) = N(0)e^{r_e t}$ **(b)** $N(t) = \dfrac{K}{1 + \left(\frac{K}{N_0} - 1\right)e^{-r_l t}}$ **(c)** $r_e \approx 0.691$;

$K = 1001: r_l \approx 1.382$; $K = 10,000: r_l \approx 0.701$

5. (a) $1000\exp[-(\ln 10)e^{-2t}]$ — **(c)** $2N(\ln 1000 - \ln N)$ —

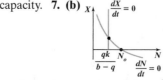

$N(t)$ $g(N)$

1000

100 1000 N

t

$N = 0$ is unstable; $N = 1000$ is locally stable; K is the carrying

capacity. **7. (b)**

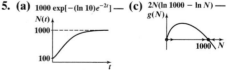

X $\frac{dX}{dt} = 0$

$\frac{qk}{b-q}$ N_0 N

$\frac{dN}{dt} = 0$

(c) $\hat{N} = \frac{qk}{b-q} > 0$ if $b > q$, $\hat{X} = \left(k + \frac{qk}{b-q}\right)\frac{q}{b}\left(\frac{N_0(b-q)}{qk} - 1\right)$

■ Section 9.1

1. $\{(4, 3)\}$

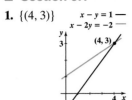

3. No solution; the lines are parallel.

5. (a) $c = 10$ **(b)** $c \neq 10$ **(c)** No

7. Eliminate x_1 from the second equation and solve the system.
9. $x = 2/5$, $y = -11/5$ **11.** $x = 9/17$, $y = -5/17$
13. No solution. **15.** Infinitely many solutions:
$\{(x, y) : x = t, y = \frac{3}{2} - \frac{1}{2}t; t \in R\}$ **17.** Zach bought five fish
and six plants. **19.** Eliminate x_1 from the second equation and
solve the system. **21.** $x = 1$, $y = -1$, $z = 0$ **23.** $x = 2$, $y = 0$,
$z = -3$ **25.** $x = 1$, $y = 1$, $z = -2$
27. $\{(x, y, z) : x = 2 - t, y = 1 + t, z = t, t \in R\}$
29. underdetermined;
$\{(x, y, z) : x = 7 + t, y = t + 2, z = t, t \in R\}$
31. overdetermined; no solution **33.** underdetermined;
$\{(x, y, z) : x = \frac{10}{3} + \frac{13}{9}t, y = \frac{2}{3} + \frac{5}{9}t, z = t, t \in R\}$ **35.** 750 gr of
SL 24–4–8; 1000 gr of SL 21–7–12; $\frac{11,000}{17}$ gr of SL 17–0–0.

■ Section 9.2

1. $\begin{bmatrix} 1 & -3 \\ 0 & -9 \end{bmatrix}$ **3.** $D = \begin{bmatrix} 1 & 0 \\ 4 & 11 \end{bmatrix}$ **5.** Use the rules of matrix
addition to calculate the left-hand side and the right-hand side.
Then compare.

7. $\begin{bmatrix} 19 & 3 & 6 \\ 9 & 11 & 4 \\ 3 & -13 & -7 \end{bmatrix}$ **9.** $D = \begin{bmatrix} -4 & -2 & -7 \\ -5 & -1 & -3 \\ -1 & 5 & -1 \end{bmatrix}$
11. Use the rules of matrix addition to calculate the left-hand
side and the right-hand side. Then compare. **13.** Write A, B,
and C as generic $m \times n$ matrices, and use the rules of matrix
addition and the fact that $a_{ij} + b_{ij} = c_{ij}$ implies $a_{ij} = c_{ij} - b_{ij}$.

15. $A' = \begin{bmatrix} -1 & 2 \\ 0 & 1 \\ 3 & -4 \end{bmatrix}$ **17.** Write A and B as generic $m \times n$
matrices, and use the rules of transposition to show that the
left-hand side is equal to the right-hand side. **19.** Write A as a
generic $m \times n$ matrix, and use the rules of transposition to show
that the left-hand side is equal to the right-hand side.

21. (a) $\begin{bmatrix} -2 & -3 \\ 0 & 5 \end{bmatrix}$ **(b)** $\begin{bmatrix} 1 & 6 \\ 2 & 2 \end{bmatrix}$

23. $AC = \begin{bmatrix} -1 & -2 \\ 1 & 0 \end{bmatrix}$ $CA = \begin{bmatrix} 1 & 4 \\ -1 & -2 \end{bmatrix}$ $AC \neq CA$

25. $(A + B)C = AC + BC = \begin{bmatrix} 1 & -1 \\ 0 & -3 \end{bmatrix}$ **27.** 3×2

29. (a) 1×4 **(b)** 3×3 **(c)** 4×3

31. (a) $\begin{bmatrix} 7 & 5 & 9 & -1 \\ -4 & -2 & -6 & 0 \end{bmatrix}$ **(b)** $\begin{bmatrix} 1 & -1 \\ 2 & 4 \\ 0 & -6 \\ -1 & -3 \end{bmatrix}$

33. $A^2 = \begin{bmatrix} 3 & -1 \\ 1 & 8 \end{bmatrix}$, $A^3 = \begin{bmatrix} 7 & 6 \\ -6 & -23 \end{bmatrix}$, $A^4 = \begin{bmatrix} 8 & -11 \\ 11 & 63 \end{bmatrix}$

35. The powers alternate between B and I_2. **37.** Calculate AI_2
and I_2A. Compare to A.

39. $\begin{bmatrix} 2 & 3 & -1 \\ 0 & 2 & 1 \\ 1 & 0 & -2 \end{bmatrix} \begin{bmatrix} x_1 \\ x_2 \\ x_3 \end{bmatrix} = \begin{bmatrix} 0 \\ 1 \\ 2 \end{bmatrix}$

41. $\begin{bmatrix} 2 & -3 \\ -1 & 1 \\ 3 & 0 \end{bmatrix} \begin{bmatrix} x_1 \\ x_2 \end{bmatrix} = \begin{bmatrix} 4 \\ 3 \\ 4 \end{bmatrix}$

43. $AB = \begin{bmatrix} 1 & 0 \\ 0 & 1 \end{bmatrix}$, $BA = \begin{bmatrix} 1 & 0 \\ 0 & 1 \end{bmatrix}$ **45.** $A^{-1} = \begin{bmatrix} -3/5 & 1/5 \\ 2/5 & 1/5 \end{bmatrix}$

47. $A^{-1} = \begin{bmatrix} -3/5 & 1/5 \\ 2/5 & 1/5 \end{bmatrix}$ and show that $(A^{-1})^{-1} = A$.

49. C does not have an inverse. **51. (a)** $x_1 = 2$, $x_2 = 3$

(b) $A^{-1} = \begin{bmatrix} -1 & 0 \\ -2/3 & -1/3 \end{bmatrix}$, $x_1 = 2$, $x_2 = 3$

53. $\det A = 7$, A is invertible **55.** $\det A = 0$, A is not invertible
57. (a) $\det A = 0$, A is not invertible **(b)** $2x + 4y = b_1$
$$3x + 6y = b_2$$
(c) solution: $\{(x, y) : x = \frac{3}{2} - 2t, y = t, t \in R\}$ **(d)** The system
has no solutions when $\frac{b_1}{2} \neq \frac{b_2}{3}$

59. $A^{-1} = \begin{bmatrix} 1/5 & 1/5 \\ 3/5 & -2/5 \end{bmatrix}$ **61.** $A^{-1} = \begin{bmatrix} -1/21 & 4/21 \\ 5/21 & 1/21 \end{bmatrix}$

63. $\det A = 2$, A is invertible; $A^{-1} = \begin{bmatrix} 1 & 1/2 \\ 0 & 1/2 \end{bmatrix}$, $X = \begin{bmatrix} 0 \\ 0 \end{bmatrix}$

65. C^{-1} does not exist. $\{(x, y) : x = -3t, y = t, t \in R\}$

67. $\begin{bmatrix} 1/4 & 1/4 & 0 \\ -1/8 & 3/8 & 1/2 \\ -3/8 & 1/8 & -1/2 \end{bmatrix}$ **69.** $\begin{bmatrix} -2/3 & -1/6 & -1/3 \\ 0 & -1/2 & 0 \\ -1/3 & 1/6 & 1/3 \end{bmatrix}$

71. $L = \begin{bmatrix} 0 & 3.2 & 1.7 \\ 0.2 & 0 & 0 \\ 0 & 0.7 & 0 \end{bmatrix}$, $N(2) = \begin{bmatrix} 2232 \\ 580 \\ 280 \end{bmatrix}$

73. $L = \begin{bmatrix} 0 & 0 & 4.6 & 3.7 \\ 0.7 & 0 & 0 & 0 \\ 0 & 0.5 & 0 & 0 \\ 0 & 0 & 0.1 & 0 \end{bmatrix}$, $N(2) = \begin{bmatrix} 1242 \\ 934 \\ 525 \\ 25 \end{bmatrix}$

75. four age classes; 60% of one-year olds survive until the end
of the next breeding season; 2 is the average number of female
offspring of a two-year-old. **77.** four age classes; 20% of
two-year olds survive until the end of the next breeding season;
2.5 is the average number of female offspring of a one-year-old.
79. $q_0(t)$ and $q_1(t)$ seem to converge to 2.3; it appears that 74%
of females will be age 0 in the stable age distribution.
81. $q_0(t)$ and $q_1(t)$ oscillate between 0.4 and 3.

■ Section 9.3

1. (a) $\begin{bmatrix} 2(x_1 + y_1) + (x_2 + y_2) \\ 3(x_1 + y_1) + 4(x_2 + y_2) \end{bmatrix}$ **(b)** $\begin{bmatrix} 2\lambda x_1 + \lambda x_2 \\ 3\lambda x_1 + 4\lambda x_2 \end{bmatrix}$

3. length: $2\sqrt{2}$, angle: $\frac{\pi}{4}$

5. length: 3, angle: $\frac{\pi}{2}$

7. 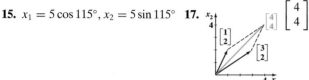 length: 2, angle: $\frac{5\pi}{6}$ **9.** $\begin{bmatrix} \sqrt{3} \\ 1 \end{bmatrix}$

11. $\begin{bmatrix} \cos 120° \\ \sin 120° \end{bmatrix}$ **13.** $x_1 = 3\cos 15°, x_2 = -3\sin 15°$

15. $x_1 = 5\cos 115°, x_2 = 5\sin 115°$ **17.**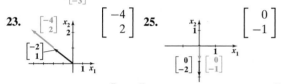

19. 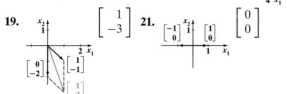 $\begin{bmatrix} 1 \\ -3 \end{bmatrix}$ **21.** $\begin{bmatrix} 0 \\ 0 \end{bmatrix}$

23. 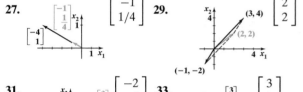 $\begin{bmatrix} -4 \\ 2 \end{bmatrix}$ **25.** $\begin{bmatrix} 0 \\ -1 \end{bmatrix}$

27. 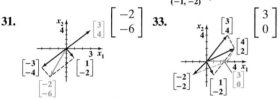 $\begin{bmatrix} -1 \\ 1/4 \end{bmatrix}$ **29.** $\begin{bmatrix} 2 \\ 2 \end{bmatrix}$

31. $\begin{bmatrix} -2 \\ -6 \end{bmatrix}$ **33.** $\begin{bmatrix} 3 \\ 0 \end{bmatrix}$

35. leaves **x** unchanged **37.** counterclockwise rotation by $\theta = \frac{\pi}{2}$

39. counterclockwise rotation by $\theta = \frac{\pi}{6}$ **41.** $\begin{bmatrix} -\frac{1}{2}\sqrt{3} - 1 \\ -\frac{1}{2} + \sqrt{3} \end{bmatrix}$

43. $\begin{bmatrix} 5\cos(\pi/12) - 2\sin(\pi/12) \\ 5\sin(\pi/12) + 2\cos(\pi/12) \end{bmatrix}$ **45.** $\begin{bmatrix} \sqrt{2} + \sqrt{2}/2 \\ -\sqrt{2} + \sqrt{2}/2 \end{bmatrix}$

47. $\begin{bmatrix} 5\cos(-\pi/7) + 3\sin(-\pi/7) \\ 5\sin(-\pi/7) - 3\cos(-\pi/7) \end{bmatrix}$

49. $\lambda_1 = 2, \mathbf{v}_1 = \begin{bmatrix} 1 \\ 0 \end{bmatrix}, \lambda_2 = -1, \mathbf{v}_2 = \begin{bmatrix} -1 \\ 1 \end{bmatrix}$

51. $\lambda_1 = 1, \mathbf{v}_1 = \begin{bmatrix} 1 \\ 0 \end{bmatrix}, \lambda_2 = -1, \mathbf{v}_2 = \begin{bmatrix} 0 \\ 1 \end{bmatrix}$

53. $\lambda_1 = -2, \mathbf{v}_1 = \begin{bmatrix} 1 \\ 1 \end{bmatrix}, \lambda_2 = -1, \mathbf{v}_2 = \begin{bmatrix} 2 \\ 3 \end{bmatrix}$

55. $\lambda_1 = 1, \mathbf{v}_1 = \begin{bmatrix} 1 \\ -1 \end{bmatrix}, \lambda_2 = 4, \mathbf{v}_2 = \begin{bmatrix} 1 \\ 2 \end{bmatrix}$

$x_1 + x_2 = 0$ ——
$2x_1 - x_2 = 0$ ——

57. $\lambda_1 = 4, \lambda_2 = 3$ **59.** $\lambda_1 = 1, \lambda_2 = 2$ **61.** $\lambda_1 = a, \lambda_2 = b$
63. The real parts of both eigenvalues are negative. **65.** The real parts of both eigenvalues are not negative. **67.** The real parts of both eigenvalues are negative. **69. (a)** $l_1: x_2 = 0; l_2:$ $-3x_1 + x_2 = 0$; since l_1 and l_2 are not identical, $\mathbf{u}_1$ and $\mathbf{u}_2$ are linearly independent. **(b)** $\mathbf{x} = 2\mathbf{u}_1 - \mathbf{u}_2$ **(c)** $A^{20}\mathbf{x} = \begin{bmatrix} -1048574 \\ -3145728 \end{bmatrix}$

71. $\begin{bmatrix} -2 \\ 6 \end{bmatrix}$ **73.** $\begin{bmatrix} (-7)3^{20} + 4(-2)^{20} \\ (2)3^{20} - 4(-2)^{20} \end{bmatrix}$

75. (a) $\lambda_1 = 1 + \sqrt{2.2}, \lambda_2 = 1 - \sqrt{2.2}$ **(b)** The larger eigenvalue corresponds to the growth rate. **(c)** 89.2% are in age class 0, and 10.8% are in age class 1 in the stable age distribution.
77. (a) $\lambda_1 = \frac{1}{2}(7 + \sqrt{50.2}), \lambda_2 = \frac{1}{2}(7 - \sqrt{50.2})$ **(b)** The larger eigenvalue corresponds to the growth rate. **(c)** 98.6% are in age class 0, and 1.4% are in age class 1 in the stable age distribution.
79. (a) $\lambda_1 = \sqrt{0.45}, \lambda_2 = -\sqrt{0.45}$ **(b)** The larger eigenvalue corresponds to the growth rate. **(c)** 88.17% are in age class 0, and 11.83% are in age class 1 in the stable age distribution.

■ **Section 9.4**

1. (a) $\begin{bmatrix} -1 \\ 5 \\ -1 \end{bmatrix}$ **(b)** $\begin{bmatrix} 2 \\ 8 \\ -2 \end{bmatrix}$ **(c)** $\begin{bmatrix} 6 \\ -3 \\ 0 \end{bmatrix}$ **3.** $\begin{bmatrix} 2 \\ -2 \end{bmatrix}$ **5.** $\begin{bmatrix} -1 \\ -2 \\ 5 \end{bmatrix}$

7. $\sqrt{10}$ **9.** $\sqrt{26}$ **11.** $\begin{bmatrix} 1/\sqrt{11} \\ 3/\sqrt{11} \\ -1/\sqrt{11} \end{bmatrix}$ **13.** $\begin{bmatrix} 1 \\ 0 \\ 0 \end{bmatrix}$ **15.** 1 **17.** 2

19. $\sqrt{5}$ **21.** $\sqrt{30}$ **23.** $\cos\theta = 1/\sqrt{50}, \theta \approx 1.429$

25. $\cos\theta = 2/\sqrt{110}, \theta \approx 1.379$ **27.** $\begin{bmatrix} 1 \\ 1 \end{bmatrix}$ **29.** $\begin{bmatrix} -2 \\ 1 \\ 1 \end{bmatrix}$

31. (a,b) $\overline{PQ} = 4, \overline{QR} = 3, \overline{PR} = 5$, angle $QPR = \tan^{-1}(3/4) \approx 36.9°$, angle $PRQ = 90° - \tan^{-1}(3/4) \approx 53.1°$, angle $RQP = 90°$. **33. (a)** $\overline{PQ} = \sqrt{10}, \overline{QR} = \sqrt{2}, \overline{PR} = \sqrt{6}$ **(b)** angle $QPR = \cos^{-1}(7/\sqrt{60}) \approx 25.4° = 0.442$, angle $PRQ = \cos^{-1}(-1/\sqrt{12}) \approx 106.8° = 1.864$, angle $RQP = \cos^{-1}(3/\sqrt{20}) \approx 47.9° = 0.835$. **35.** $x + 2y = 4$
37. $4x + y = 2$ **39.** $-y + z = 1$ **41.** $x = 0$ **43.** $x = 1 + 2t$ and $y = -1 + t$ for $t \in \mathbf{R}$ **45.** $x = -1 + t$ and $y = -2 - 3t$ for $t \in \mathbf{R}$
47. $2y - x - 5 = 0$ **49.** $y - x + 4 = 0$

51. $\begin{bmatrix} x \\ y \end{bmatrix} = \begin{bmatrix} 0 \\ 1/4 \end{bmatrix} + t\begin{bmatrix} 1 \\ -3/4 \end{bmatrix}, t \in \mathbf{R}$

53. $\begin{bmatrix} x \\ y \end{bmatrix} = \begin{bmatrix} 0 \\ 3 \end{bmatrix} + t\begin{bmatrix} 1 \\ -2 \end{bmatrix}, t \in \mathbf{R}$

55. $\begin{bmatrix} x \\ y \\ z \end{bmatrix} = \begin{bmatrix} 1 \\ -1 \\ 2 \end{bmatrix} + t\begin{bmatrix} 1 \\ -2 \\ 1 \end{bmatrix}, t \in \mathbf{R}$

57. $\begin{bmatrix} x \\ y \\ z \end{bmatrix} = \begin{bmatrix} -1 \\ 3 \\ -2 \end{bmatrix} + t\begin{bmatrix} -1 \\ -2 \\ 4 \end{bmatrix}, t \in \mathbf{R}$

59. $\begin{bmatrix} x \\ y \\ z \end{bmatrix} = \begin{bmatrix} 5 \\ 4 \\ -1 \end{bmatrix} + t\begin{bmatrix} 3 \\ 4 \\ -4 \end{bmatrix}, t \in \mathbf{R}$

61. $\begin{bmatrix} x \\ y \\ z \end{bmatrix} = \begin{bmatrix} 2 \\ -3 \\ 1 \end{bmatrix} + t \begin{bmatrix} 7 \\ -5 \\ 0 \end{bmatrix}, t \in \mathbf{R}$ **63.** $(-5/2, -1/2, 9/2)$

65. $\begin{bmatrix} x \\ y \\ z \end{bmatrix} = \begin{bmatrix} 5 \\ -1 \\ 0 \end{bmatrix} + t \begin{bmatrix} 1 \\ 1 \\ 0 \end{bmatrix}, t \in \mathbf{R}$

■ **Chapter 9 Review Problems**

1. (a) $A\mathbf{x} = \begin{bmatrix} 0 \\ 2 \end{bmatrix}$

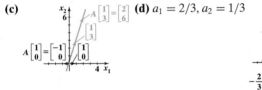

(b) $\lambda_1 = -1, \mathbf{u}_1 = \begin{bmatrix} 1 \\ 0 \end{bmatrix}, \lambda_2 = 2, \mathbf{u}_1 = \begin{bmatrix} 1 \\ 3 \end{bmatrix}$

(c) $A\begin{bmatrix} 1 \\ 0 \end{bmatrix} = \begin{bmatrix} -1 \\ 0 \end{bmatrix}$ **(d)** $a_1 = 2/3, a_2 = 1/3$

3. Growth rate: $\lambda_1 = 1.75$; a stable age distribution: $\begin{bmatrix} 35 \\ 10 \end{bmatrix}$

5. $\begin{bmatrix} -2 & 5 \\ -2 & 9 \end{bmatrix}$ **7.** 1. Gaussian elimination; 2. Write in matrix form $AX = B$ and find the inverse of A. Then compute $X = A^{-1}B$ **9.** $a = -3$ **11.** For $\frac{5}{23} < a \le 1$, the population will grow.

■ **Section 10.1**

1. $CO = HR \times SV$; $[CO] =$ liter; domain: $\{(HR, SV) : HR \ge 0, SV \ge 0\}$; range: $\{CO : CO \ge 0\}$.

3.

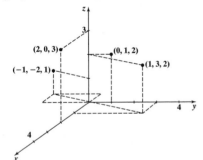

5. $\frac{4}{13}$

7. (a) -14, **(b)** 1 **9.** $e^{-1/10}$ **11.** $-e^2$
13. domain: $\{(x, y) : x \in \mathbf{R}, y \in \mathbf{R}\}$; range: $\{z : z \ge 0\}$; level curves: $x^2 + y^2 = c$, circle with radius $\sqrt{c}$ centered at $(0, 0)$
15. domain: $\{(x, y) : y > x^2, x \in \mathbf{R}\}$; range: $\{z : z \in \mathbf{R}\}$; level curves: $y = e^c + x^2$, parabolas shifted in $y > 0$ direction by e^c
17. domain: $\{(x, y) : x \in \mathbf{R}, y \in \mathbf{R}, x + y \ne 0\}$; range: $\mathbf{R}$; level curves: $y = \frac{1-c}{1+c}x$, straight lines through the origin with slope $(1 - c)/(1 + c)$ for $c \ne -1$. When $c = -1$, level curve: $x = 0$.
19. Figure 10.23 **21.** Figure 10.24 **23. (a)** level curve: $x^2 + y^2 = c$, circle centered at origin with radius $\sqrt{c}$; intersection with x–z plane: $z = x^2$, intersection with y–z plane: $z = y^2$
(b)

$c = 3$ intersection with x–z plane: $z = 4x^2$,
$c = 2$
$c = 1$ intersection with y–z plane: $z = y^2$

(c)

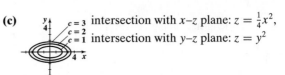

$c = 3$ intersection with x–z plane: $z = \frac{1}{4}x^2$,
$c = 2$
$c = 1$ intersection with y–z plane: $z = y^2$

(d) The intersection with the y–z plane is always $z = y^2$. When $a = 1$, the resulting surface could be obtained by rotating the curve $z = y^2$ about the z-axis. When $0 < a < 1$, the resulting surface is still a paraboloid, but longer along the x-axis than along the y-axis. When $a > 1$, the paraboloid is longer along the y-axis than along the x-axis. **25.** Day 180: 22 m; day 200: 18 m; day 220: 14 m

■ **Section 10.2**

1. 1 **3.** 2 **5.** 18 **7.** $-\frac{1}{2}$ **9.** 1 **11.** $-\frac{3}{2}$ **13.** $\frac{2}{3}$ **15.** Along positive x-axis: 1; along positive y-axis: -2 **17.** Along x-axis: 0; along y-axis: 0; along $y = x$: 2 **19.** Along $y = mx, m \ne 0$: 2; along $y = x^2$: 1; the limit does not exist.
21. 1. $f(x, y)$ is defined at $(0, 0)$. 2. $\lim_{(x,y)\to(0,0)}(x^2 + y^2)$ exists. 3. $f(0, 0) = 0 = \lim_{(x,y)\to(0,0)}(x^2 + y^2)$ **23.** In Problem 17, we showed that $\lim_{(x,y)\to(0,0)}\frac{4xy}{x^2+y^2}$ does not exist. Hence, $f(x, y)$ is discontinuous at $(0, 0)$ **25.** In Problem 19, we showed that $\lim_{(x,y)\to(0,0)}\frac{2xy}{x^3+yx}$ does not exist. Hence, $f(x, y)$ is discontinuous at $(0, 0)$ **27. (a)** $h(x, y) = g[f(x, y)]$ with $f(x, y) = x^2 + y^2$ and $g(z) = \sin z$; **(b)** the function is continuous for all $(x, y) \in \mathbf{R}^2$ **29. (a)** $h(x, y) = g[f(x, y)]$ with $f(x, y) = xy$ and $g(z) = e^z$; **(b)** the function is continuous for all $(x, y) \in \mathbf{R}^2$
31. $\{(x, y) : (x - 1)^2 + (y + 1)^2 < 4\}$

33. The boundary is a circle with radius 3, centered at $(0, 2)$. The boundary is not included. **35.** Choose $2\delta^2 = \epsilon$.

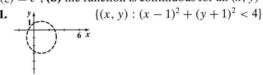

■ **Section 10.3**

1. $\frac{\partial f}{\partial x} = 2xy + y^2$, $\frac{\partial f}{\partial y} = x^2 + 2xy$ **3.** $\frac{\partial f}{\partial x} = \frac{3}{2}y\sqrt{xy} - \frac{2y}{3(xy)^{1/3}}$, $\frac{\partial f}{\partial y} = \frac{3}{2}x\sqrt{xy} - \frac{2x}{3(xy)^{1/3}}$ **5.** $\frac{\partial f}{\partial x} = \cos(x + y)$, $\frac{\partial f}{\partial y} = \cos(x + y)$
7. $\frac{\partial f}{\partial x} = -4x\cos(x^2 - 2y)\sin(x^2 - 2y)$, $\frac{\partial f}{\partial y} = 4\cos(x^2 - 2y)\sin(x^2 - 2y)$ **9.** $\frac{\partial f}{\partial x} = e^{\sqrt{x+y}}\frac{1}{2\sqrt{x+y}}$, $\frac{\partial f}{\partial y} = e^{\sqrt{x+y}}\frac{1}{2\sqrt{x+y}}$ **11.** $\frac{\partial f}{\partial x} = e^x\sin(xy) + ye^x\cos(xy)$, $\frac{\partial f}{\partial y} = xe^x\cos(xy)$ **13.** $\frac{\partial f}{\partial x} = \frac{2}{2x+y}$, $\frac{\partial f}{\partial y} = \frac{1}{2x+y}$
15. $\frac{\partial f}{\partial x} = \frac{-2x}{(\ln 3)(y^2-x^2)}$, $\frac{\partial f}{\partial y} = \frac{2y}{(\ln 3)(y^2-x^2)}$ **17.** 6 **19.** $3e^5$ **21.** 1
23. $\frac{2}{9}$ **25.** $f_x(1, 1) = -2$, $f_y(1, 1) = -2$ **27.** $f_x(-2, 1) = -4$, $f_y(-2, 1) = 4$ **29. (a)** $\frac{\partial P_e}{\partial a} > 0$: the number of prey items eaten increases with increasing attack rate. **(b)** $\frac{\partial P_e}{\partial T} > 0$: the number of prey items eaten increases with increasing T.
31. $\frac{\partial f}{\partial x} = 2xz - y$, $\frac{\partial f}{\partial y} = z^2 - x$, $\frac{\partial f}{\partial z} = 2yz + x^2$
33. $\frac{\partial f}{\partial x} = 3x^2y^2z + \frac{1}{yz}$, $\frac{\partial f}{\partial y} = 2x^3yz - \frac{x}{y^2z}$, $\frac{\partial f}{\partial z} = x^3y^2 - \frac{x}{yz^2}$
35. $\frac{\partial f}{\partial x} = e^{x+y+z}$, $\frac{\partial f}{\partial y} = e^{x+y+z}$, $\frac{\partial f}{\partial z} = e^{x+y+z}$
37. $\frac{\partial f}{\partial x} = \frac{1}{x+y+z}$, $\frac{\partial f}{\partial y} = \frac{1}{x+y+z}$, $\frac{\partial f}{\partial z} = \frac{1}{x+y+z}$
39. $2y$ **41.** e^y **43.** $2\sec^2(u + w)\tan(u + w)$ **45.** $-6x\sin y$
47. $\frac{2}{(x+y)^3}$ **49. (a)** $\frac{\partial f}{\partial N} > 0$: the number of prey encounters per

predator increases as the prey density increases. **(b)** $\frac{\partial f}{\partial T} > 0$: the function increases as the time for search increases. **(c)** $\frac{\partial f}{\partial T_h} < 0$: the function decreases as the handling time T_h increases.

(d)

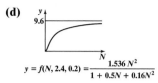

51.

$y = f(N, 2.4, 0.2) = \dfrac{1.536\,N^2}{1 + 0.5N + 0.16N^2}$

■ Section 10.4

1. $8 = 6x + 4y - z$ **3.** $z = -2x - y - 2$ **5.** $z - y = 0$
7. $z - 2ex = -e$ **9.** $z = x + y - 1$ **11.** $f(x, y)$ is defined in an open disk centered at $(1, 1)$ and is continuous at $(1, 1)$.
13. $f(x, y)$ is defined in an open disk centered at $(0, 0)$ and is continuous at $(0, 0)$. **15.** $f(x, y)$ is defined in an open disk centered at $(-1, 2)$ and is continuous at $(-1, 2)$.
17. $L(x, y) = x - 3y$ **19.** $L(x, y) = \frac{1}{2}x + 2y + \frac{1}{2}$
21. $L(x, y) = x + y$ **23.** $L(x, y) = x + \frac{1}{2}y - \frac{3}{2} + \ln 2$
25. $L(x, y) = 1 + x + y$, $L(0.1, 0.05) = 1.15$,
$f(0.1, 0.05) \approx 1.1618$ **27.** $L(x, y) = 2x - 3y - 2$,
$L(1.1, 0.1) = -0.1$, $f(1.1, 0.1) \approx -0.0943$
29. $Df(x, y) = \begin{bmatrix} 1 & 1 \\ 2x & -2y \end{bmatrix}$ **31.** $Df(x, y) = \begin{bmatrix} e^{x-y} & -e^{x-y} \\ e^{x+y} & e^{x+y} \end{bmatrix}$
33. $Df(x, y) = \begin{bmatrix} -\sin(x - y) & \sin(x - y) \\ -\sin(x + y) & -\sin(x + y) \end{bmatrix}$
35. $Df(x, y) = \begin{bmatrix} 4xy + 1 & 2x^2 - 3 \\ e^x \sin y & e^x \cos y \end{bmatrix}$
37. $L(x, y) = \begin{bmatrix} 4x + 2y - 4 \\ -x - y + 3 \end{bmatrix}$ **39.** $L(x, y) = \begin{bmatrix} e(2x - y) \\ 2x - y - 1 \end{bmatrix}$
41. $L(x, y) = \begin{bmatrix} x - y + 1 \\ y - x + 1 \end{bmatrix}$
43. $L(1.1, 1.9) = \begin{bmatrix} -0.9 \\ 9.8 \end{bmatrix}$, $f(1.1, 1.9) \approx \begin{bmatrix} -0.88 \\ 9.83 \end{bmatrix}$
45. $L(1.9, -3.1) = \begin{bmatrix} 25 \\ -22.4 \end{bmatrix}$, $f(1.9, -3.1) \approx \begin{bmatrix} 25 \\ -22.382 \end{bmatrix}$

■ Section 10.5

1. $18 \ln 2 + 8$ **3.** $\dfrac{\frac{\pi}{3} + \frac{\sqrt{3}}{4}}{\sqrt{\frac{\pi^2}{9} + \frac{3}{4}}}$ **5.** 0 **7.** $\frac{dz}{dt} = \frac{\partial f}{\partial x}u'(t) + \frac{\partial f}{\partial y}v'(t)$
9. $-\dfrac{2x}{2y + x^2 + y^2}$ **11.** $-\dfrac{2x - 3y(x^2 + y^2)}{2y - 3x(x^2 + y^2)}$
13. $\frac{dy}{dx} = -\dfrac{1}{\sqrt{1 - x^2}}$ for $-1 \le x \le 1$
15. The growth rate decreases over time.
17. $\operatorname{grad} f = \begin{bmatrix} 3x^2y^2 \\ 2x^3y \end{bmatrix}$ **19.** $\operatorname{grad} f = \dfrac{1}{2\sqrt{x^3 - 3xy}}\begin{bmatrix} 3x^2 - 3y \\ -3x \end{bmatrix}$
21. $\operatorname{grad} f = \dfrac{\exp[\sqrt{x^2 + y^2}]}{\sqrt{x^2 + y^2}}\begin{bmatrix} x \\ y \end{bmatrix}$ **23.** $\operatorname{grad} f = \dfrac{x^2 - y^2}{x^2 + y^2}\begin{bmatrix} \frac{1}{x} \\ -\frac{1}{y} \end{bmatrix}$
25. $\frac{2}{3}\sqrt{3}$ **27.** $-\sqrt{2}$ **29.** $\frac{3}{2}\sqrt{10}$ **31.** $D_{\mathbf{u}}f(2, 1) = \frac{13}{\sqrt{2}}$
33. $D_{\mathbf{u}}f(1, 6) = -\dfrac{1}{4\sqrt{29}}$ **35.** $f(x, y)$ increases most rapidly in the direction $\begin{bmatrix} 5 \\ -3 \end{bmatrix}$ at the point $(-1, 1)$. **37.** $f(x, y)$ increases most rapidly in the direction $\begin{bmatrix} 5/4 \\ -3/4 \end{bmatrix}$ at the point $(5, 3)$.
39. $\begin{bmatrix} 3/5 \\ 4/5 \end{bmatrix}$ **41.** $\dfrac{1}{\sqrt{733}}\begin{bmatrix} 2 \\ -27 \end{bmatrix}$
43. The amoeba will move in the direction $\begin{bmatrix} -4/25 \\ -4/25 \end{bmatrix}$.

■ Section 10.6

1. $f(x, y)$ has a local minimum at $(1, 0)$ **3.** $f(x, y)$ has saddle points at $(2, 4)$ and $(-2, 4)$ **5.** $f(x, y)$ has a saddle point at $(0, 3)$ **7.** $f(x, y)$ has a local maximum at $(0, 0)$. **9.** $f(x, y)$ has saddle points at $(0, \pi/2 + k\pi)$ for $k \in \mathbf{Z}$ **11. (c)** Figure 10.65: $f(x, y)$ stays constant for fixed x; there is neither a maximum nor a minimum at $(0, 0)$. Figure 10.66: saddle point at $(0, 0)$, Figure 10.67: local minimum at $(0, 0)$. **13.** Absolute maximum: $(1, -1)$; absolute minimum: $(-1, 1)$ **15.** Absolute maxima: $(1, 0)$ and $(-1, 0)$; absolute minima: $(0, 1)$ and $(0, -1)$
17. Absolute maxima: $(0, 0)$, $(1, 0)$, $(1, -2)$, and $(0, -2)$; absolute minimum: $(1/2, -1)$ **19.** Absolute maximum at $(2/3, 2/3)$; absolute minima occur at all points along the boundary of the domain. **21.** Absolute minimum: $(-2, 0)$; absolute maximum: $(3, 0)$ **23.** Absolute minimum: $(-1/2, 1/2)$; absolute maximum: $(1/\sqrt{2}, -1/\sqrt{2})$ **25.** Yes. **27.** Absolute maximum at $(N, P) = (1, 1)$. **29.** Maximum volume is $(2\sqrt{2})^3$ m^3. **31.** The minimum surface area is 216 m^2. **33.** The minimum distance is $1/\sqrt{3}$. **35. (a)** Use $p_3 = 1 - p_1 - p_2$ and $0 \le p_3 \le 1$. **37.** Absolute maxima: $(-\sqrt{35}/6, 1/6)$, $(\sqrt{35}/6, 1/6)$; absolute minimum: $(0, -1)$ **39.** Absolute minimum: $(1/4, -1/8)$; no maxima **41.** Absolute minimum: $(12/13, -8/13)$; no maxima. **43.** Local minimum: $(0, 1/3)$; no absolute minima; absolute maxima: $(1/\sqrt{2}, 1/6)$, $(-1/\sqrt{2}, 1/6)$. **45.** Absolute minima: $(1, 0)$ and $(-1, 0)$; no maxima. **47.** Set $f(x, y) = xy$ and $g(x, y) = x + y - c$. Then $y = \lambda$ and $x = \lambda$ implies $x = y$. **49.** The total length of the fence is 96 ft. **51.** Largest possible area is 4. **53.** Smallest perimeter is 4. **55.** $r = \sqrt{A}$, $\theta = 2$, perimeter is $4\sqrt{A}$ **57.** Local minimum at $(2, 2)$; no absolute extrema. **59.** *Hint:* Look at the relative positions of level curves and constraint. **61. (a)** $3x_1 + 3x_2 = 10$,
(b) absolute maximum at $\left(\dfrac{65 - 40\sqrt{2}}{3}, \dfrac{40\sqrt{2} - 55}{3} \right)$.

■ Section 10.7

1. $N_t = 5, 7.5, 11.25, 16.875, 25.31, 37.97, 56.95, 85.43, 128.14, 192.22, 288.33$; $P_t = 0$ for $t = 0, 1, 2, \ldots, 10$ **3.** $N_t = b^t N_0$
5. $N_t = 5, 6.79, 9.89, 14.67, 21.86, 32.59, 48.51, 71.67, 102.92, 128.47, 68.40, 0.71, 0.02, 0.03, 0.04, 0.06$; $P_t = 5, 1.43, 0.57, 0.34, 0.30, 0.39, 0.76, 2.18, 9.18, 51.81, 248.67, 203.69, 2.09, 0.0022, 0, 0$
7. $N_t = 5, 7.5, 11.25, 16.88, 25.31, 37.97, 56.95, 85.43, 128.14, 192.22, 288.33$; $P_t = 0$ for $t = 0, 1, 2, \ldots 10$ **9.** $N_t = b^t N_0$
11. (rounded to the closest integer) $N_t = 100, 79, 37, 16, 10, 10, 13, 17, 24, 34, 47, 61, 67, 54, 32, 18, 13, 13, 16, 20, 27, 36, 45, 51, 48, 36$; $P_t = 50, 141, 164, 80, 27, 10, 5, 3, 3, 4, 8, 19, 49, 94, 99, 59, 27, 13, 8, 6, 7, 10, 17, 33, 58, 72$ **13. (a)**

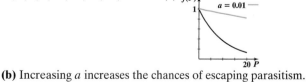

(b) Increasing a increases the chances of escaping parasitism.
15. (a)

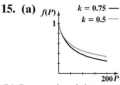

(b) Increasing k increases the chances of escaping parasitism.
17. Stable **19.** Unstable **21.** Unstable **23.** Stable

25. Unstable **27.** Eigenvalues: $1/\sqrt{2}, -1/\sqrt{2}$ **29.** Eigenvalues: $0.5 + i0.5, 0.5 - i0.5$ **31.** For $0 < a < 1/2$, $(0, 0)$ is locally stable. **33.** $(0, 0)$ is unstable; $(1/6, 1/6)$ is locally stable. **35.** $(0, 0)$ is locally stable if $-1 < a < 1$. **37. (a)** If $r > 1/2$, then $(r - 1/2, r - 1/2)$ is an equilibrium. **(b)** For $1/2 < r < 3/2$, the equilibrium $(r - 1/2, r - 1/2)$ is locally stable. **39.** $(0, 0)$ is unstable; $((40 \ln 4)/3, 10 \ln 4)$ is unstable. **41.** $(0, 0)$ is unstable; $(1000, 750)$ is locally stable.

■ Chapter 10 Review Problems

1.

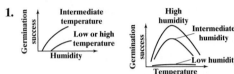

3. (a) $\frac{\partial A_i}{\partial F} > 0$, $\frac{\partial A_i}{\partial D} < 0$ **(b)** $\frac{\partial A_e}{\partial F} > 0$: area covered by introduced species increased with the amount of fertilizer added. $\frac{\partial A_e}{\partial D} > 0$: area covered by introduced species increased with intensity of disturbance [note that this is the opposite of (a)]. **(c)** Fertilization had a positive effect in both cases. That is, fertilization increased the total area covered of both introduced and indigenous species. Intensity of disturbance had a negative effect on indigenous species and a positive effect on introduced species. **5.** $D\mathbf{f}(x, y) = \begin{bmatrix} 2x & -1 \\ 3x^2 & -2y \end{bmatrix}$ **7. (a)**

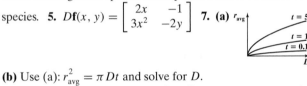

(b) Use (a): $r_{avg}^2 = \pi Dt$ and solve for D.
(c) r_{avg} = arithmetic average = $\frac{1}{N} \sum_{i=1}^{N} d_i$, and use formula for D in (b).

■ Section 11.1

1. $\frac{d\mathbf{x}}{dt} = \begin{bmatrix} 2 & 3 \\ -4 & 1 \end{bmatrix} \mathbf{x}(t)$ **3.** $\frac{d\mathbf{x}}{dt} = \begin{bmatrix} -2 & 0 & 1 \\ -1 & 0 & 0 \\ 1 & 1 & 1 \end{bmatrix} \mathbf{x}(t)$

5. $(1, 0)$: $\begin{bmatrix} -1 \\ 1 \end{bmatrix}$; $(0, 1)$: $\begin{bmatrix} 2 \\ 0 \end{bmatrix}$; $(-1, 0)$: $\begin{bmatrix} 1 \\ -1 \end{bmatrix}$; $(0, -1)$: $\begin{bmatrix} -2 \\ 0 \end{bmatrix}$;
$(1, 1)$: $\begin{bmatrix} 1 \\ 1 \end{bmatrix}$; $(0, 0)$: $\begin{bmatrix} 0 \\ 0 \end{bmatrix}$; $(-2, 1)$: $\begin{bmatrix} 4 \\ -2 \end{bmatrix}$;

7. $(1, 0)$: $\begin{bmatrix} 1 \\ -1 \end{bmatrix}$; $(0, 1)$: $\begin{bmatrix} 3 \\ 2 \end{bmatrix}$; $(-1, 1)$: $\begin{bmatrix} 2 \\ 3 \end{bmatrix}$; $(0, -1)$: $\begin{bmatrix} -3 \\ -2 \end{bmatrix}$;
$(-3, 1)$: $\begin{bmatrix} 0 \\ 5 \end{bmatrix}$; $(0, 0)$: $\begin{bmatrix} 0 \\ 0 \end{bmatrix}$; $(-2, 1)$: $\begin{bmatrix} 1 \\ 4 \end{bmatrix}$;

9. Figure 11.18: (d); Figure 11.19: (c);
Figure 11.20: (b); Figure 11.21: (a)

11.

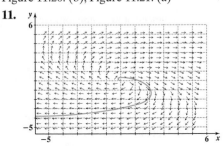

13. $\mathbf{x}(t) = c_1 e^{6t} \begin{bmatrix} 3 \\ 5 \end{bmatrix} + c_2 e^{-2t} \begin{bmatrix} 1 \\ -1 \end{bmatrix}$

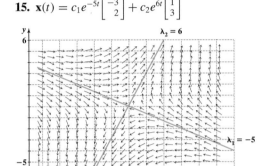

15. $\mathbf{x}(t) = c_1 e^{-5t} \begin{bmatrix} -3 \\ 2 \end{bmatrix} + c_2 e^{6t} \begin{bmatrix} 1 \\ 3 \end{bmatrix}$

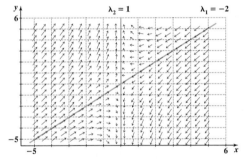

17. $\mathbf{x}(t) = c_1 e^{-2t} \begin{bmatrix} 1 \\ 1 \end{bmatrix} + c_2 e^{t} \begin{bmatrix} 0 \\ 1 \end{bmatrix}$

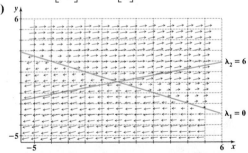

19. $\mathbf{x}(t) = e^{-3t} \begin{bmatrix} -5 \\ 4 \end{bmatrix} + e^{2t} \begin{bmatrix} 0 \\ 1 \end{bmatrix}$ **21.** $\mathbf{x}(t) = e^t \begin{bmatrix} 1 \\ 1 \end{bmatrix}$

23. $\mathbf{x}(t) = 2e^{2t} \begin{bmatrix} 7 \\ 2 \end{bmatrix} - e^{-3t} \begin{bmatrix} 1 \\ 1 \end{bmatrix}$ **25.** $\mathbf{x}(t) = \frac{13}{8} e^{-3t} \begin{bmatrix} 1 \\ -1 \end{bmatrix} - \frac{3}{8} e^{5t} \begin{bmatrix} 7 \\ 1 \end{bmatrix}$
27. (c) Use differentiation to find dx_1/dt and dx_2/dt.

29. unstable node **31.** saddle **33.** saddle **35.** unstable node
37. stable node **39.** saddle **41.** saddle **43.** unstable spiral
45. stable spiral **47.** stable spiral **49.** unstable spiral
51. neutral spiral **53.** neutral spiral **55.** stable spiral
57. saddle **59.** stable spiral **61.** saddle **63.** stable node
65. unstable spiral **67. (a)** $\lambda_1 = 0$, $\mathbf{v}_1 = \begin{bmatrix} 2 \\ -1 \end{bmatrix}$; $\lambda_2 = 6$, $\mathbf{v}_1 = \begin{bmatrix} 4 \\ 1 \end{bmatrix}$

(b) $\mathbf{x}(t) = c_1 \begin{bmatrix} 2 \\ -1 \end{bmatrix} + c_2 e^{6t} \begin{bmatrix} 4 \\ 1 \end{bmatrix}$

(c)

The direction vectors approach the eigenvector associated with the eigenvalue $\lambda_2 = 6$.

Section 11.2

1. $\frac{dx_1}{dt} = -0.55x_1 + 0.1x_2$ $(0, 0)$ is a stable node.

$\frac{dx_2}{dt} = 0.5x_1 - 0.12x_2$

3. $\frac{dx_1}{dt} = -2.5x_1 + 0.7x_2$ $(0, 0)$ is a stable node.

$\frac{dx_2}{dt} = 2.5x_1 - 0.8x_2$

5. $\frac{dx_1}{dt} = 0.1x_2$ All material gets stuck in compartment 1.

$\frac{dx_2}{dt} = -0.4x_2$

7. $\frac{dx_1}{dt} = -0.6x_1 + 1.2x_2$ $(0, 0)$ is a stable node.

$\frac{dx_2}{dt} = 0.1x_1 - 1.25x_2$

9. $a = 0.1, b = 0.3, c = 0.3, d = 0.2$

11. $a = 0, b = 0.1, c = 0.2, d = 0$

13. $a = 0.2, b = 1.1, c = 2.1, d = 1.2$

15. $a = 0.3, b = 0, c = 0.9, d = 0.2$

17. $a = 0, b = 0, c = 0.2, d = 0.3$ **19.** $x_1(t) = 4e^{-0.3t}$,

$x_2(t) = 4(1 - e^{-0.3t})$ **21. (a)** $a = 0.2, b = 0.1, c = 0, d = 0$

(b) The constant is the total area.

(d) $x_2(t) = 20 - x_1(t) = \frac{40}{3} + \frac{14}{3}e^{-0.3t}$, $\lim_{t \to \infty} x_1(t) = \frac{20}{3}$,

$\lim_{t \to \infty} x_2(t) = \frac{40}{3}$ **23.** $x(t) = 3\sin(2t)$ **25.** $\frac{dx}{dt} = v, \frac{dv}{dt} = 3x$

27. $\frac{dx}{dt} = v, \frac{dv}{dt} = x - v$

Section 11.3

1. saddle **3.** saddle **5.** unstable node **7.** $(0, 0)$: unstable node;

$(0, 4/5)$: saddle; $(1/2, 0)$: saddle; $(0.5, 0.3)$: stable node **9.** $(0, 0)$:

unstable node; $(0, 1)$: saddle; $(1, 0)$: saddle; $(1/2, 1)$: stable node

11. $(0, 0)$: saddle; $(1, 1)$: unstable spiral **13.** $a \geq 1/4$. Unstable

spiral for $a > 1/4$. **15. (a)**

(b) $(10/3, 10/3)$ is a stable node. **17.** $\text{tr} < 0, \det = ?$ **19.** $\text{tr} = ?$,

$\det < 0$ **21.** $\text{tr} < 0, \det > 0$; equilibrium is locally stable

23. (a)

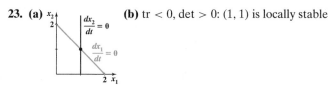

(b) $\text{tr} < 0, \det > 0$: $(1, 1)$ is locally stable

Section 11.4

1. $\frac{dN_1}{dt} = 2N_1\left(1 - \frac{N_1}{20} - \frac{N_2}{100}\right)$

$\frac{dN_2}{dt} = 3N_2\left(1 - \frac{N_2}{15} - \frac{N_1}{75}\right)$

3. Species 2 excludes species 1. **5.** Founder control **7.** $(0, 0)$:

unstable (source); $(18, 0)$: unstable (saddle); $(0, 20)$: stable (sink)

9. $(0, 0)$: unstable (source); $(35, 0)$: stable (sink);

$(0, 40)$: stable (sink); $(85/11, 100/11)$: unstable (saddle)

11. $(\alpha_{12}, \alpha_{21}) = (1/4, 7/18)$

13.

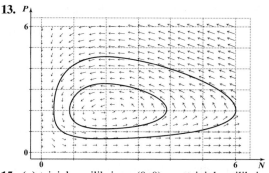

15. (a) trivial equilibrium: $(0, 0)$; nontrivialequilibrium:

$(3/2, 1/4)$ **(b)** $\lambda_1 = 1, \lambda_2 = -3$: $(0, 0)$ is an unstable saddle

(c) $\lambda_1 = i\sqrt{3}, \lambda_2 = -i\sqrt{3}$: purely imaginary eigenvalues, linear

stability analysis cannot be used to infer stability of equilibrium.

(d)

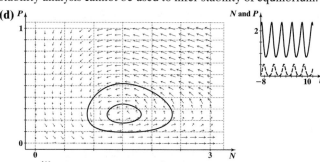

17. (a) $\frac{dN}{dt} = 5N, N(t) = N(0)e^{5t}$; in the absence of the

predator, the insect species grows exponentially fast. **(b)** If

$P(t) > 0$, then $N(t)$ stays bounded.

(c)

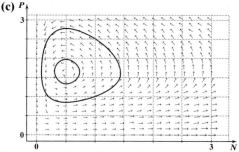

By spraying the field, the solution moves to a different cycle; this

results in a much larger insect outbreak later in the year

compared to before the spraying. **19. (a)** When $P = 0$, then

$\frac{dN}{dt} = 3N\left(1 - \frac{N}{10}\right)$; equilibria: $\hat{N} = 0$ (unstable) and $\hat{N} = 10$

(locally stable). If $N(0) > 0$, then $\lim_{t \to \infty} N(t) = 10$ **(b)** $(0, 0)$:

unstable (saddle); $(10, 0)$: unstable (saddle); $(4, 0.9)$: stable spiral

(c)

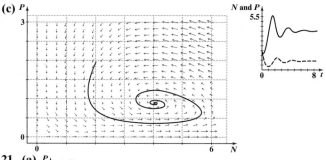

21. (a)

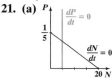

(b) tr $Df(\hat{N}, \hat{P}) < 0$ and det $Df(\hat{N}, \hat{P}) > 0$: the nontrivial equilibrium is locally stable. **23.** $\hat{N} = \frac{d}{c}$ does not depend on a; hence, it remains unchanged if a changes. $\hat{P} = \frac{a}{b}(1 - \frac{d/c}{K})$ is an increasing function of a; hence, the predator equilibrium increases when a increases. **25.** $\hat{N} = \frac{d}{c}$ is a decreasing function of c; hence, the prey abundance decreases as c increases. $\hat{P} = \frac{a}{b}(1 - \frac{d/c}{K})$ is an increasing function of c; hence, the predator abundance increases as c increases. **27.** predation; locally stable **29.** mutualism; locally stable **31.** mutualism; unstable **33.** competition; unstable

35. $\begin{bmatrix} - & - \\ - & - \end{bmatrix}$; trace negative; determinant undetermined

37. $\begin{bmatrix} - & - \\ - & - \end{bmatrix}$; trace negative; determinant undetermined

39. $\begin{bmatrix} - & - \\ - & - \end{bmatrix}$; trace negative; determinant undetermined

41. If $a_{ii} < 0$, then the growth rate of species i is negatively affected by an increase in the density of species i. This is referred to as self regulation. **43. (a)** $(\hat{N}, \hat{P}) = (\frac{d}{c}, \frac{a}{b})$ **(b)** $\begin{bmatrix} 0 & -b\frac{d}{c} \\ c\frac{a}{b} & 0 \end{bmatrix}$ **(c)** $a_{11} = a_{22} = 0$: neither species has an effect on itself; $a_{12} = -b\frac{d}{c} < 0$: prey is affected negatively by predators; $a_{21} = c\frac{a}{b} > 0$: predators are affected positively by prey.

45.

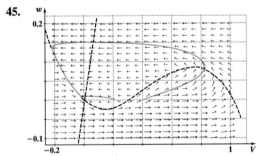

47. $V(0) > 0.3$ **49.** $\frac{dc}{dt} = kab$

51. $e = [E], s = [S], c = [ES], p = [P], \frac{de}{dt} = -k_1 es + k_2 c$, $\frac{ds}{dt} = -k_1 es, \frac{dc}{dt} = k_1 es - k_2 c, \frac{dp}{dt} = k_2 c$ **53.** $\frac{dx}{dt} + \frac{dy}{dt} = 0$, $x(t) + y(t)$ is constant. **55.** $\frac{dx}{dt} + \frac{dy}{dt} + \frac{dz}{dt} = 0, x(t) + y(t) + z(t)$ is constant. **57. (c)** $f(s)$

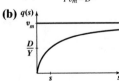

(d) Since $\frac{dp}{dt} = f(s)$, the reaction rate is a function of s and hence, the availability of s determines the reaction rate.

59. (a) $\hat{s} = \frac{DK_m}{Yv_m - D}$; $\hat{s}$ is an increasing function of D.

(b) $q(s)$

The s-coordinate of the point of intersection of the graph of $q(s)$ and the horizontal line $f(s) = D/Y$ is the equilibrium.

61. $(4, 0)$: unstable; $(2, 2)$: stable

■ **Chapter 11 Review Problems**

1. $Z(t) = Z(0)e^{(r_1 - r_2)t}$ **3. (a)**

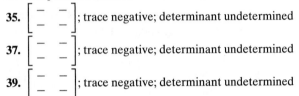

(b) The nontrivial equilibrium is locally stable. **5. (a)** If $c_1 > m_1$, then there exists a nontrivial equilibrium in which species 1 has positive density and species 2 is absent.
7. (a) $\hat{x} = Y(s_0 - \hat{s}) > 0$ when $\hat{s} < s_0$ **(b)** $\frac{\partial \hat{s}}{\partial D} > 0$; $\frac{\partial \hat{s}}{\partial Y} < 0$

■ **Section 12.1**

1. 40 **3.** 120 **5.** 84 **7.** $4^{9749} \approx 3.04 \times 10^{5869}$ **9.** 120 **11.** 5040 **13.** 358,800 **15.** 2730 **17.** 6! **19.** 120 **21.** 120 **23.** 1365 **25.** 126 **27.** $\binom{1000}{20} \approx 3.4 \times 10^{41}$ **29. (a)** exactly two red balls: 10; exactly two blue balls: 6; one of each: 20 **(b)** total: 36 **31.** 168, 168 **33.** $\emptyset, \{a\}, \{b\}, \{c\}, \{a, b\}, \{a, c\}, \{b, c\}, \{a, b, c\}$; to form a subset, for each element, we need to decide whether it should be in the subset. There are $2^3 = 8$ choices. **35.** 12 **37.** 30 **39.** 31 **41.** $\binom{60}{20}\binom{40}{20}\binom{20}{20}$ **43.** $x^4 + 4x^3 y + 6x^2 y^2 + 4xy^3 + y^4$ **45.** $\binom{26}{4}\binom{26}{5}$ **47.** $4\binom{13}{2}\binom{4}{2}\binom{4}{2}\binom{11}{1}$ **49.** $\binom{13}{1}\binom{4}{4}\binom{12}{1}\binom{4}{1}$ **51.** 3!

■ **Section 12.2**

1. $\Omega = \{HHH, HHT, HTH, THH, HTT, THT, TTH, TTT\}$ **3.** $\Omega = \{(i, j) : 1 \le i < j \le 5\}$ **5.** $A \cup B = \{1, 2, 3, 5\}, A \cap B = \{1, 3\}$ **7.** $\{4, 6\}$ **9.** 0.6 **11.** 0.25 **13.** 0.3 **15.** 0.7 **17.** 0.5

19. (a) **(b)**

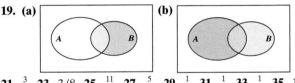

21. $\frac{3}{4}$ **23.** 3/8 **25.** $\frac{11}{36}$ **27.** $\frac{5}{12}$ **29.** $\frac{1}{4}$ **31.** $\frac{1}{2}$ **33.** $\frac{1}{8}$ **35.** 11/16 **37.** 1/4 **39.** 3/5 **41.** $\frac{1}{17}$ **43.** $\frac{12}{55}$ **45.** $1 - \frac{\binom{48}{4}}{\binom{52}{4}}$ **47.** $\frac{\binom{26}{13}}{\binom{52}{13}}$

49. $\frac{\binom{13}{2}\binom{4}{2}\binom{4}{2}\binom{1}{1}\binom{4}{1}}{\binom{52}{5}}$ **51. (a)** $\frac{\binom{N-100}{7}\binom{100}{3}}{\binom{N}{10}}$ **(b)** 333

■ **Section 12.3**

1. $\frac{13}{51}$ **3.** 13/50 **5.** $\frac{3}{5}$ **7.** $\frac{1}{2}$ **9.** $\frac{1}{6}$ **11.** $\frac{4}{7}$ **13.** 1/4 **15.** 0.8425 **17.** 0.7804 **19.** $\frac{5}{9}$ **21.** P(first card is an ace) $= P$(second card is an ace) $= \frac{1}{13}$ **23.** 0.3 **25.** $\frac{3}{4}$ **27.** A and B are independent. **29.** A and B are not independent. **31. (a)** $\frac{1}{8}$ **(b)** $\frac{7}{8}$ **(c)** $\frac{1}{2}$ **(d)** $\frac{7}{8}$ **33.** $\left(\frac{1}{4}\right)^{10}$ **35.** $1 - (0.9)^{10}$ **37.** 0.1624 **39.** $\frac{1}{3}$ **41.** $\frac{1}{3}$ **43. (a)** $\frac{1}{2}$ **(b)** $\frac{1}{2}$ **(c)** $\frac{1}{3}$

■ **Section 12.4**

1. $P(X = 0) = \frac{1}{4}, P(X = 1) = \frac{1}{2}, P(X = 2) = \frac{1}{4}$
3. $P(X = 0) = \frac{6}{36}, P(X = 1) = \frac{10}{36}, P(X = 2) = \frac{8}{36}$, $P(X = 3) = \frac{6}{36}, P(X = 4) = \frac{4}{36}, P(X = 5) = \frac{2}{36}$
5. $P(X = 0) = \frac{\binom{3}{0}\binom{2}{2}}{\binom{5}{2}}, P(X = 1) = \frac{\binom{3}{1}\binom{2}{1}}{\binom{5}{2}}, P(X = 2) = \frac{\binom{3}{2}\binom{2}{0}}{\binom{5}{2}}$
7. $P(X = 0) = \frac{\binom{13}{0}\binom{39}{3}}{\binom{52}{3}}, P(X = 1) = \frac{\binom{13}{1}\binom{39}{2}}{\binom{52}{3}}$, $P(X = 2) = \frac{\binom{13}{2}\binom{39}{1}}{\binom{52}{3}}, P(X = 3) = \frac{\binom{13}{3}\binom{39}{0}}{\binom{52}{3}}$

9. $F(x) = \begin{cases} 0, & x < -3 \\ 0.2, & -3 \le x < -1 \\ 0.5, & -1 \le x < 1.5 \\ 0.9, & 1.5 \le x < 2 \\ 1, & x \ge 2 \end{cases}$

11. $P(X = -1) = 0.2$, $P(X = 0) = 0.1$, $P(X = 1) = 0.4$, $P(X = 2) = 0.3$ **13. (a)** $N = 55$ **(b)** $\frac{28}{55}$

15. (a)

k	12	13	14	15	16	17	18	19	20	21
p_k	1/25	4/25	5/25	3/25	1/25	5/25	2/25	1/25	2/25	1/25

(b) 15.84

17. (a)

k	2	3	4	5	6	7	8	9	10
p_k	1/25	1/25	2/25	3/25	4/25	2/25	6/25	3/25	3/25

(b) 6.84

19. (a) -0.4 **(b)** 1.0 **(c)** 1.4 **21.** $E(X) = -0.1$, $var(X) = 3.39$, s.d. $= \sqrt{3.39}$ **23. (a)** $E(X) = \frac{55}{10}$ **(b)** $var(X) = 8.25$ **27. (a)** 0.1 **(b)** 0.5 **(c)** 0.4 **(d)** 0.2 **29. (a)** $E(X) = 0.75$, $EY = 0.3$ **(b)** $E(X + Y) = 1.05$ **(c)** $var(X) = 1.7875$, $var(Y) = 3.01$ **(d)** $var(X + Y) = var(X) + var(Y) = 4.7975$ **31. (a)** Since $[X - E(X)]^2 \ge 0$, it follows that $E[X - E(X)]^2 \ge 0$; therefore, $var(X) \ge 0$. **(b)** Since $var(X) = E(X^2) - [E(X)]^2 \ge 0$, it follows that $E(X^2) \ge [E(X)]^2$. **33. (a)** $\binom{10}{5}(0.5)^{10}$ **(b)** $(0.5)^{10}\left[\binom{10}{8} + \binom{10}{9} + \binom{10}{10}\right]$ **(c)** $1 - (0.5)^{10}$

35. $P(X = k) = \binom{6}{k}\left(\frac{1}{6}\right)^k\left(\frac{5}{6}\right)^{6-k}$, $k = 0, 1, 2, \ldots, 6$ **37.** 14/64 **39.** $\left(\frac{3}{5}\right)^3 + 3\left(\frac{3}{5}\right)\left(\frac{3}{5}\right)^2$ **41.** $(0.8)^{20}$ **43. (a)** 1 **(b)** $(10)(0.9)^{10}$ **45.** 12.5 **47. (a)** $\frac{\binom{24}{6}\binom{12}{4}}{\binom{36}{10}}$ **(b)** $\binom{10}{6}\left(\frac{2}{3}\right)^6\left(\frac{1}{3}\right)^4$ **49.** $\frac{30!}{10!14!6!}(0.2)^{10}(0.35)^{14}(0.45)^6$ **51.** $\frac{40!}{20!10!8!2!}\left(\frac{9}{16}\right)^{20}\left(\frac{3}{16}\right)^{10}\left(\frac{3}{16}\right)^8\left(\frac{1}{16}\right)^2$ **53.** $\frac{6!}{2!2!2!}\left(\frac{6}{24}\right)^2\left(\frac{8}{24}\right)^2\left(\frac{10}{24}\right)^2$ **55.** $\frac{23!}{5!12!6!}\left(\frac{1}{4}\right)^5\left(\frac{1}{2}\right)^{12}\left(\frac{1}{4}\right)^6$ **57.** 5/16 **59.** $(3/4)^4$ **61.** $1/2, 1/4, 1/8$ **63.** 1/8 **65.** 1/8 **67.** 15/16 **69.** $\left(\frac{14}{15}\right)^{19}$ **71.** $E(T) = 6$, $var(T) = 30$ **73. (a)** $\left(\frac{9}{10}\right)^5\frac{1}{10}$ **(b)** $\frac{9}{10}\frac{8}{9}\frac{7}{8}\frac{6}{7}\frac{5}{6}\frac{1}{5}$ **75. (a)** $(1 - p)^{k-1}p$ **(b)** $\binom{k-1}{1}p^2(1 - p)^{k-2}$

77.

k	0	1	2	3
$P(X = k)$	e^{-2}	$2e^{-2}$	$2e^{-2}$	$\frac{4}{3}e^{-2}$

79. (a) $1 - 2e^{-1}$ **(b)** $e^{-1}\left(1 + \frac{1}{2} + \frac{1}{6}\right)$ **81.** $1 - e^{-1.5}\left[1 + 1.5 + \frac{(1.5)^2}{2} + \frac{(1.5)^3}{6}\right]$ **83.** $1 - 3e^{-2}$ **85.** e^{-7} **87.** $1 - e^{-0.5}$ **89.** $1 - 4e^{-3}$ **91. (a)** $18e^{-6}$ **(b)** $1/4, 1/2, 1/4$ **93.** $(2/3)^2$ **95.** $P(X = 0) \approx e^{-0.5}$ **97. (a)** 0.5819 **(b)** 0.5820 **99.** $e^{-1.5}$

■ **Section 12.5**

1. distribution function: $F(x) = 1 - e^{-3x}$ for $x \ge 0$, $F(x) = 0$ for $x \le 0$ **3.** $c = \frac{1}{\pi}$ **5.** $E(X) = \frac{1}{2}$, $var(X) = \frac{1}{4}$ **7.** $E(X) = \frac{3}{2}$, $var(X) = \frac{3}{4}$ **9. (b)** $E(X) = \frac{a-1}{a-2}$ **11. (d)**

13. 95%: (7.4, 18.2), 99%: (4.7, 20.9) **15.** 50% **17.** 99.5% **19.** 2.5% **21. (a)** 0.6915 **(b)** 0.383 **(c)** 0.1587 **(d)** 0.0668 **23. (a)** $x = 3.56$ **(b)** $x = 1.5$ **(c)** $x = 0.5$ **(d)** $x = 1.34$ **25. (a)** 0.0228 **(b)** $x = 628$ **27.** 0.76% **29.** 0.8185 **33.** $E(|X|) = 2/\sqrt{2\pi}$ **35. (a)** 0.0735 **(b)** 0.6068 **(c)** 88 **(d)** 56 **37.** 0.1 **39.** $a = 1, b = 7$ **41.** $E(Y) = \frac{3}{4}$ **43.** $HHTHHTHHHT$ **45. (a)** $(1 - x)^n$ **(b)** Use l'Hospital's rule on $\lim_{n\to\infty} \ln(1 - \frac{x}{n})^n$. **47.** $E(X) = \frac{1}{\lambda}$ **49.** $e^{-4/3}$ **51. (a)** $e^{-20/27}$ **(b)** $e^{-20/27}$ **53. (a)** e^{-4} **(b)** $8e^{-4}$ **(c)** $32e^{-8}$ **(d)** $\frac{1}{4}$ **55.** 0.25 hour **57. (a)** $1 - e^{-2/3}$ **(b)** $P(N(5) = 1) = \frac{5}{3}e^{-5/3}$ **59. (a)** $1 - e^{-3/5}$ **(b)** $e^{-1/5}$ **61. (a)** 5 years **(b)** $\ln 2/0.2$ years **63. (a)** $\exp\left[-(1.5 + 10e^{0.05} - 10)\right]$ **(b)** $\exp\left[-(2.1 + 10e^{0.07} - 10)\right] - \exp\left[-(3 + 10e^{0.1} - 10)\right]$ **65.** Solution of $1.2x + (0.6)e^{0.5x} - 0.6 - \ln 2 = 0$ is approximately 0.451. **67. (a)** $\exp\left[-(2 \times 10^{-5})\frac{(50)^{2.5}}{2.5}\right]$ **(b)** 0.1477 **69.** $x_m \approx 30.4$

■ **Section 12.6**

1. Exact probability: $e^{-3/2}$; Markov's inequality: $P(X \ge 3) \le \frac{2}{3}$ **5.** Exact: $P(|X| \ge 1) = 1/2$; Chebyshev's inequality: $P(|X| \ge 1) \le \frac{4}{3}$ **7.** $\frac{9}{25}$ **9.** $\frac{1}{n}\sum_{i=1}^n X_i$ converges to 0.9 as $n \to \infty$ **11.** Since $E(|X_i|) = \infty$, we cannot apply the law of large numbers as stated in Section 12.6. **13.** The sample size should be at least 380. **15.** 0.1587 **17. (a)** 0.0023 **(b)** 0.83 **19. (a)** 0.1114 **(b)** 0.1664 **(c)** 0.1679 **21. (a)** -11.2 **(b)** 0.579 **23.** 69 **25.** 385 **27. (a)** 0.3660 **(b)** 0.3679 **(c)** 0.243 **29. (a)** 0.1849 **(b)** 0.1755 **(c)** 0.1896 **31.** Likely not. **33. (a)** 0.6065, 0.3033, 0.0758 **(b)** 0.8391 **35.** 0.1429 **37.** 0.9515

■ **Section 12.7**

1. median: 15; sample mean: 16.2; sample variance: 180.2 **3.** median: 35.5; sample mean: 36; sample variance: 43.1 **5.** $\overline{X} = 11.93$; $S^2 = 3.389$ **7.** $\overline{X} = 5.69$; $S^2 = 3.465$ **9.**

Sample	Sample Mean
(1, 1)	1.0
(1, 6)	3.5
(1, 8)	4.5
(6, 1)	3.5
(6, 6)	6.0
(6, 8)	7.0
(8, 1)	4.5
(8, 6)	7.0
(8, 8)	8.0

15. (a) approximately normal with mean 1/3 and variance 1/450 **(b)** approximately normal **17. (c)** true values: $\mu = 0.5$, $\sigma^2 = \frac{1}{12}$ **19.** $\overline{X} = 16.2$; S.E. $= 4.245$ **21.** $[-0.3993, 0.5213]$ **23.** $\hat{p} = 0.72$; [0.651, 0.789] **25.** $y = 1.92x - 0.92$; $r^2 = 0.9521$ **31.** $y = 0.201x + 0.481$; $r^2 = 0.841$

■ **Chapter 12 Review Problems**

1. (a) 0.431 **3.** 168,168,000 **5. (a)** $E(X) = 4.2$ **(b)** 0.0043 **(c)** 0.0215 **(d)** $1 - (0.0043)^5$ **7. (a)** 0.16 **(b)** 0.2 **9. (a)** $\mu = 170$, $\sigma = 6.098$ **(b)** 0.4013 **11.** 20% **13. (b)** $E(V) = \frac{n-1}{n}\sigma^2$

References

W. C. Allee (1931). *Animal Aggregations: A Study in General Sociology*. University of Chicago Press.

H. G. Andrewartha and L. C. Birch (1954). *The Distribution and Abundance of Animals*. University of Chicago Press.

M. Begon and G. A. Parker (1986). Should egg size and clutch size decrease with age? *Oikos* **47**: 293–302.

T. S. Bellows, Jr. (1981). The descriptive properties of some models for density dependence. *Journal of Animal Ecology* **50**: 139–156.

M. J. Benton (1997). Models for the diversification of life. *TREE* **12**: 490–495.

M. Benton and D. Harper (1997). *Basic Paleontology*. Addison-Wesley and Longman.

William H. Beyer, ed. (1991). *CRC Standard Probability and Statistics Tables and Formulae*. CRC Press.

P. J. Bohlen, P. M. Groffman, C. T. Driscoll, T. J. Fahey, and T. G. Siccama (2001). Plant-soil-microbial interactions in a northern hardwood forest. *Ecology* **82**: 965–978.

R. Borchert (1994). Soil and stem water storage determine phenology and distribution of tropical dry forest trees. *Ecology* **75**: 1437–1449.

T. Boulinier, J. D. Nichols, and J. E. Hines (2001). Forest fragmentation and bird community dynamics: Inference at regional scales. *Ecology* **82**: 1159–1169.

G. E. Briggs and J. B. S. Haldane (1925). A note on the kinematics of enzyme actions. *Biochemical Journal* **19**: 338–339.

J. L. Brooks and S. I. Dodson (1965). Predation, body-size and composition of plankton. *Science* **150**: 28–35.

M. J. W. Burke and J. P. Grime (1996). An experimental study of plant community invasibility. *Ecology* **77**: 776–790.

M. L. Cain, S. W. Pacala, J. A. Silander, Jr., and M.-J. Fortin (1995). Neighborhood models of clonal growth in the white clover *Trifolium repens*. *American Naturalist* **145**: 888–917.

G. S. Campbell (1986). *An Introduction to Environmental Biophysics*. Springer.

M. J. Crawley (1997). Plant-herbivore dynamics. In *Plant Ecology*, ed. M. J. Crawley, pp. 401–474. Blackwell Science.

J. W. Dalling, K. Winter, and J. D. Nason (2001). The unusual life history of *Alseis blackiana*: A shade-persistent pioneer tree? *Ecology* **82**: 933–945.

D. P. Dalzell (1944). On 22/7. *Journal of the London Mathematical Society* **19**: 133–134.

D. P. Dalzell (1971). On 22/7 and 355/113. *Eureka: The Archimedians' Journal* **34**: 1013.

C. Darwin (1859). *On the Origin of Species by Means of Natural Selection*. John Murray.

C. Darwin (1959). *The Origin of Species*. Reprinted by Penguin Classics (1985). Penguin Books.

D. L. DeAngelis (1992). *Dynamics of Nutrient Cycling and Food Webs*. Chapman & Hall.

W. R. DeMott, R. D. Gulati, and K. Siewertsen (1998). Effects of phosphorus-deficient diets on the carbon and phosphorus balance of *Daphnia magna*. *Limnology and Oceanography* **43**: 1147–1161.

A. M. de Roos (1996). A gentle introduction to physiologically structured population models. In *Structured-Population Models in Marine, Terrestrial, and Freshwater Systems*, eds. S. Tuljapurkar and H. Caswell. Chapman & Hall.

R. H. Dott, Jr., and R. L. Batten (1976). *Evolution of the Earth*, 2nd edition. McGraw-Hill.

J. E. Dowd and D. S. Riggs (1965). A comparison of estimates of Michaelis-Menten kinetic constants from various linear transformations. *Journal of Biological Chemistry* **240**: 863–869.

C. M. Duarte and S. Agustí (1998). The CO_2 balance of unproductive aquatic ecosystems. *Science* **281**: 234–236.

P. J. Dyck, J. L. Davies, D. M. Wilson, F. J. Service, L. J. Melton III, and P. C. O'Brien (1999). Risk factors for severity of diabetic polyneuropathy. *Diabetes Care* **22**: 1479–1486.

D. S. Falconer (1989). *Introduction to Quantitative Genetics*. Longman.

D. S. Falconer and T. F. C. Mackay (1996). *Introduction to Quantitative Genetics*, 4th edition. Longman.

R. Fitzhugh (1961). Impulses and physiological states in theoretical models of nerve membrane. *Biophysics Journal* **1**: 445–466.

D. J. Futuyama (1995). *Science on Trial*, 2nd edition. Sinauer.

P. Gaastra (1959). Mededelinger van de Landbouwhogeschool Te Wageningen, The Netherlands. In *Plant Physiology* (1978), eds. F. B. Salisbury and C. W. Ross. Wadsworth.

G. F. Gause (1934). *The Struggle for Existence*. Reprinted by Hafner (1964). Williams & Wilkins.

L. A. Gavrilov and N. S. Gavrilova (2001). The reliability theory of aging and longevity. *Journal of Theoretical Biology* **213**: 527–545.

Z. M. Gliwicz (1990). Food threshold and body size in caldocerans. *Nature* **343**: 683–740.

P. R. Grant (1982). Variation in the size and shape of Darwin's finch eggs. *Auk* **99**: 15–23.

P. R. Grant, I. Abbott, D. Schluter, R. L. Curry, and L. K. Abbott (1985). Variation in the size and shape of Darwin's finches. *Biological Journal of the Linnean Society* **25**: 1–39.

K. J. Griffiths (1969). The importance of coincidence in the functional and numerical responses of two parasites of the European pine sawfly, *Neodiprion sertifer*. *Canadian Entomologist* **101**: 673–713.

J. B. S. Haldane (1957). The cost of natural selection. *Journal of Genetics* **55**: 511–524.

D. J. Hall (1964). An experimental approach to the dynamics of a natural population of *Daphnia galeata mendota*. *Ecology* **45**: 94–111.

D. L. Hartl and A. G. Clark (1989). *Principles of Population Genetics*, 2nd edition. Sinauer.

R. W. Herschy (1995). *Streamflow Measurement*, 2nd edition. Taylor & Francis.

T. Hojo and K. Pearson (1931). Distribution of the median, quartiles and interquartile distance in samples from a normal population. *Biometrika* **23**: 315–363.

L. Holdridge, W. Grenke, W. Hatheway, T. Liang, and J. Tosi, Jr. (1971). *Forest Environments in Tropical Life Zones: A Pilot Study*. Pergamon Press.

C. S. Holling (1959). Some characteristics of simple types of predation and parasitism. *Canadian Entomologist* **91**: 385–398.

H. S. Horn (1971). The adaptive geometry of trees. *Monographs in Population Biology 3*. Princeton University Press.

S. B. Hulley and D. Grady (2004). The WHI estrogen-alone trial— do things look any better? *JAMA* **14**: 1769–1771.

C. E. Iselin, J. E. Robertson, and D. F. Paulson (1999). Radical perineal prostatectomy: Oncological outcome during a 20-year period. *Journal of Urology* **161**: 163–168.

Y. Iwasa, T. J. de Jong and P. G. L. Klinkhamer (1995). Why pollinators visit only a fraction of the open flowers on a plant and its consequence for fitness curves of plants. *Journal of Evolutionary Biology* **8**: 439–453.

T. H. Jukes and C. R. Cantor (1969). Evolution of protein molecules. In *Mammalian Protein Metabolism III*, ed. H. N. Munro, pp. 21–132. Academic Press.

P. M. Kareiva (1983). Local movement in herbivorous insects: Applying a passive diffusion model to mark-recapture field experiments. *Oecologia* **57**: 322–327.

W. O. Kermack and A. G. McKendrick (1927). Contributions to the mathematical theory of epidemics. *Proceedings of the Royal Society A* **115**: 700–721.

W. O. Kermack and A. G. McKendrick (1932). Contributions to the mathematical theory of epidemics. *Proceedings of the Royal Society A* **138**: 55–83.

W. O. Kermack and A. G. McKendrick (1933). Contributions to the mathematical theory of epidemics. *Proceedings of the Royal Society A* **141**: 94–122.

K. B. Krauskopf and D. K. Bird (1995). *Introduction to Geochemistry*, p. 268. McGraw-Hill.

H. E. Landsberg (1969). *Weather and Health, an Introduction to Biometerology*. Doubleday.

A. C. Leopold and P. E. Kriedemann (1975). *Plant Growth and Development*. McGraw-Hill.

P. Leslie (1945). On the use of matrices in certain population mathematics. *Biometrika* **33**: 183–212.

R. Levins (1969). Some demographic and genetic consequences of environmental heterogeneity for biological control. *Bulletin of the Entomological Society of America* **15**: 237–240.

R. Levins (1970). Community equilibria and stability, and an extension of the competitive exclusion principle. *American Naturalist* **104**: 413–423.

D. C. Lloyd (1987). Selection of offspring size at independence and other size-versus-number strategies. *American Naturalist* **129**: 800–817.

A. J. Lotka (1932). The growth of mixed populations: Two species competing for a common food supply. *Journal of the Washington Academy of Sciences* **22**: 461–469.

R. H. MacArthur and E. O. Wilson (1963). An equilibrium theory of insular zoogeography. *Evolution* **17**: 373–387.

T. F. C. Mackey (1984) Jumping genes meet abdominal bristles: Hybrid dysgenesis-induced quantitative variation in *Drosophila melanogaster*. *Genetics Research* **44**: 231–237.

R. M. May (1975). *Stability and Complexity in Model Ecosystems*. Princeton University Press.

R. M. May (1976). Simple mathematical models with very complicated dynamics. *Nature* **261**: 459–461.

R. M. May (1978). Host–parasitoid systems in patchy environments: A phenomenological model. *Journal of Animal Ecology*, **47**: 833–843.

L. Michaelis and M. I. Menten (1913). Die Kinetik der Invertinwirkung. *Biochemische Zeitschrift* **49**: 333–369.

J. L. Monod (1942). *Recherches sur la Croissance des Cultures Bacteriennes*. Hermann.

J. L. Monod (1950). La technique de culture continué: Théorie et applications. *Annales de l'Institut Pasteur* **79**: 390–410.

B. Moss (1980). *Ecology of Freshwaters*. Blackwell Scientific.

J. S. Nagumo, S. Arimoto, and S. Yoshizawa (1962). An active pulse transmission line simulating nerve axon. *Proceedings of the Institute of Radio Engineers* **50**: 2061–2071.

S. Nee and R. M. May (1992). Dynamics of metapopulation: Habitat destruction and competitive coexistence. *Journal of Animal Ecology* **61**: 37–40.

A. J. Nicholson (1933). The balance of animal populations. *Journal of Animal Ecology* **2**: 131–178.

A. J. Nicholson and V. A. Bailey (1935). The balance of animal populations. *Proceedings of the Zoological Society of London* **3**: 551–598.

K. J. Niklas (1994). *Plant Allometry: The Scaling of Form and Process*. University of Chicago Press.

R. T. Oglesby (1977). Relationships of fish yield to lake phytoplankton, standing crop, production, and morphoedaphic factors. *Journal of the Fisheries Reserve Board of Canada* **34**: 2271–2279.

J. G. Owen (1988). On productivity as a predictor of rodent and carnivore density. *Ecology* **69**: 1161–1165.

S. W. Pacala and M. Rees (1998). Models suggesting field experiments to test two hypotheses explaining successional diversity. *American Naturalist* **152**: 729–737.

R. Pearl and L. J. Reed (1920). On the rate of growth of the population of the United States since 1790 and its mathematical representation. *Proceedings of the National Academy of Sciences* **6**: 275–288.

G. W. Pierce (1949). *The Songs of Insects*. Harvard University Press.

A. Pisek, W. Larcher, W. Moser, and I. Pack (1969). Kardinale Temperaturbereiche der Photosynthese und Grenztemperaturen des Lebens der Blätter verschiedener Spermatophyten. III. Temperaturabhängigkeit und optimaler Temperaturbereich der Netto-Photosynthese. *Flora, Jena* **158**: 608–630.

S. D. Pletcher (1998). Mutation and the evolution of age-specific mortality rates: Experimental results and statistical developments. Ph.D. thesis, University of Minnesota.

F. W. Preston (1962). The canonical distribution of commonness and rarity. *Ecology* **43**: 185–215, 410–431.

M. J. Reiss (1989). *The Allometry of Growth and Reproduction*. Cambridge University Press.

D. A. Roff (1992). *The Evolution of Life Histories*. Chapman & Hall.

M. L. Rosenzweig (1971). Paradox of enrichment: Destabilization of exploitation ecosystems in ecological time. *Science* **171**: 385–387.

M. L. Rosenzweig and Z. Abramsky (1993). How are diversity and productivity related? In *Species Diversity in Ecological Communities*, eds. R. E. Ricklefs and D. Schluter, pp. 52–65. University of Chicago Press.

J. Roughgarden (1996). *Theory of Population Genetics and Evolutionary Ecology*, 2nd edition. Prentice Hall.

S. M. Stanley (1979). *Macroevolution: Pattern and Process*, p. 332. W. H. Freeman.

R. W. Sterner (1997). Modeling interactions between food quality and quantity in homeostatic consumers. *Freshwater Biology* **38**: 473–482.

R. W. Sterner and J. J. Elser (2002). *Ecological Stoichiometry: The Biology of Elements from Molecules to the Biosphere*. Princeton University Press.

C. R. Taylor, G. M. O. Maloiy, E. R. Weibel, U. A. Langman, J. M. Z. Kaman, H. J. Seeherman, and B. N. C. Heglund (1980). Design of the mammalian respiratory system. III. Scaling maximum aerobic capacity to body mass: Wild and domestic mammals. *Respiration Physiology* **44**: 25–37.

W. R. Thompson (1924). La théorie mathématique de l'action des parasites entomophages et le facteur du hasard. *Annales de la Faculté des Sciences de Marseille* **2**: 69–89.

D. Tilman (1982). *Resource Competition and Community Structure*. Princeton University Press.

D. Tilman (1994). Competition and biodiversity in spatially structured habitats. *Ecology* **75**: 2–16.

M. M. Tilzer, W. Geller, U. Sommer, and H. H. Stable (1982). Kohlenstoffkreislauf und Nahrungsketten in der Freiwasserzone des Bodensees. *Konstanzer Blätter für Hochschulfragen* **73**: 51.

U.S. Bureau of the Census (1994). *Statistical Abstract of the United States*, 14th edition. Government Printing Office.

J. W. Valentine (1985). Biotic diversity and clade diversity. In *Phanerozoic Diversity Patterns: Profiles in Macroevolution*, ed. J. W. Valentine, pp. 419–424. Princeton University Press.

P. M. Vitousek and H. Farrington (1997). Nutrient limitation and soil development: Experimental test of a biogeochemical theory. *Biogeochemistry* **37**: 63–75.

V. Volterra (1926). Fluctuations in the abundance of species considered mathematically. *Nature* **118**: 558–560.

T. D. Walker (1985). Diversification functions and the rate of taxonomic evolution. In *Phanerozoic Diversity Patterns: Profiles in Macroevolution*, ed. J. W. Valentine, pp. 311–334. Princeton University Press.

T. W. Walker and J. K. Syers (1976). The fate of phosphorus during pedogenesis. *Geoderma* 15: 1–19.

T. D. Walker and J. W. Valentine (1984). Equilibrium models of evolutionary species diversity and the number of empty niches. *American Naturalist* **124**: 887–899.

P. D. Ward (1992). *On Methuselah's Trail—Living Fossils and the Great Extinctions*. Freeman.

Women's Health Initiative Steering Committee (2004). Effects of conjugated equine estrogen in postmenopausal women with hysterectomy: The Women's Health Initiative Randomized Controlled Trial. *JAMA* **291** (14), 1701–1712.

S. Wright (1968). *Evolution of Populations, Vol. 1. Genetics and Biometrik Foundation*. University of Chicago Press.

E. K. Yeargers, R. W. Shonkwiler, and J. V. Herod (1996). *An Introduction to the Mathematics of Biology: With Computer Algebra Models*. Birkhäuser.

Photo Credits

Front Endpapers

About the Author

Chapter Openers

Index

Taken from:

Student's Solutions Manual
by Max Sterelyukhin

to accompany

Calculus for Biology and Medicine

Third Edition
by Claudia Neuhauser

Chapter 1

Preview and Review

1.1 Preliminaries

Prob. 1.

(a) Walking 3 units to the right and to the left from -1 we get the numbers 2 and -4, respectively.

(b) $|x - (-1)| = 3$, so $x + 1 = \pm 3$, yielding, $x = 2$ or $x = -4$.

Prob 3.

(a) $2x - 4 = \pm 6$, so either $2x = 10$ giving the solution $x = 5$ or $2x = -2$ and the other solution is $x = -1$.

(b) $x - 3 = \pm 2$, from which we see that $x = 5$ or $x = 1$.

(c) $2x + 3 = \pm 5$, so $2x = 2$ giving $x = 1$ or $2x = -8$ and $x = -4$.

(d) The equation has no solutions, since the absolute value of a number cannot be negative, and so could never be equal to -2.

Prob. 5.

(a) We can change the absolute value for two inequalities

$$-4 \leq 5x - 2 \leq 4$$

3

which then can be solved to

$$-4 + 2 \le 5x \le 4 + 2$$

and dividing by 5 we get:

$$-\frac{2}{5} \le x \le \frac{6}{5}$$

(b) It will change to the inequalities: $1 - 3x < -8$ or $1 - 3x > 8$. Solving the first we get: $9 < 3x$ or $x > 3$, and solving the second we get $-3x > 7$. Dividing by -3 and reverting the side of the inequality we get $x < -\frac{7}{3}$.

(c) The first inequality will be $7x + 4 \ge 3$, that solves to $x \ge -\frac{1}{7}$. The second inequality will be $7x + 4 \le -3$, and solving this we have $7x \le -7$ or $x \le -1$.

(d) $|6 - 5x| < 7$

$$-7 < 6 - 5x < 7$$

$$-7 - 6 < -5x < 7 - 6$$

$$-13 < -5x < 1$$

$$-\tfrac{1}{5} < x < \tfrac{13}{5}$$

Prob. 7. We use the point-slope formula to get: $y - y_0 = m(x - x_0)$, and in this case: $y - 4 = -\frac{1}{3}(x - 2)$, so multiplying both sides by 3, we get: $3(y - 4) = -(x - 2)$, or $3y - 12 = -x + 2$, and finally writing it into standard form: $x + 3y - 14 = 0$.

Prob. 9. $(x_0, y_0) = (0, -2)$ $m = -3$

$$y - y_0 = m(x - x_0)$$

$$y - (-2) = -3(x - 0)$$

$$y + 2 = -3x$$

Here $3x + y + 2 = 0$ is the Standard Form with $A = 3$, $B = 1$, $C = 2$.

Prob. 11. $(x, y_1) = (-2, -3)$

$(x_2, y_2) = (1, 4)$

First find the slope as

$$m = \frac{y_2 - y_1}{x_2 - x_1} = \frac{(4) - (-3)}{(1) - (-2)} = \frac{4 + 3}{1 + 2}$$

$$m = \frac{7}{3}$$

Second, get Standard Form with point-slope method:

$y - y_0 = m(x - x_0)$

Substitute into (x_0, y_0) either (x_1, y_1) or (x_2, y_2) - the result will be the same.

$y - 4 = \frac{7}{3}(x - 1)$

$3(y - 4) = 7(x - 1)$

$3y - 12 = 7x - 7$

$3y - 7x - 12 + 7 = 0$

$-7x + 3y - 5 = 0$ is Standard Form

or $7x - 3y + 5 = 0$.

Prob. 13. $(x_1, y_1) = (0, 4)$

$(x_2, y_2) = (3, 0)$

$m = \frac{y_2 - y_1}{x_2 - x_1} = \frac{(0) - (4)}{(3) - (0)} = -\frac{4}{3}$

$y - y_0 = m(x - x_0)$

$y - 4 = -\frac{4}{3}(x - 0)$

$3(y - 4) = -4x$

$3y - 12 = -4x$

$4x + 3y - 12 = 0$ is Standard Form.

Prob. 15. Horizontal lines are always $y = k$.

A horizontal line through $(3, \frac{3}{2})$ is $y = \frac{3}{2}$. The Standard Form is $2y - 3 = 0$

Prob. 17. Vertical lines are always $x = h$. A vertical line through $(-1, \frac{7}{2})$ is $x = -1$. Standard form is $x + 1 = 0$.

Prob. 19. Here $m = 3$ and the y-intercept $(0, 2)$. Use slope-intercept form $y = mx + b$.

Here $y = 3x + 2$. Standard form is $3x - y + 2 = 0$.

Prob. 21. Here $m = \frac{1}{2}$ and y-intercept $(0, 2)$.

$y = mx + b$

$y = \frac{1}{2}x + 2$ is slope-intercept form

$x - 2y + 4$ is Standard form.

Prob. 23. Here $m = -2$ and x-intercept $(1, 0)$

$y - y_0 = m(x - x_0)$

$y - 0 = -2(x - 1)$

$y = -2x + 2$ slope-intercept form

$2x + y - 2 = 0$ Standard form

Prob. 25. Here $m = -\frac{1}{4}$ and x-intercept $(3, 0)$

$y - y_0 = m(x - x_0)$

$y - 0 = -\frac{1}{4}(x - 3)$

$y = -\frac{1}{4}x + \frac{3}{4}$ slope-intercept form and $x + 4y - 3 = 0$ is Standard form.

Prob. 27. Line through $(2, -3)$ parallel to $x + 2y - 4 = 0$

$x + 2y - 4 = 0$ is Standard form.

Change to slope-intercept form to find slope of the given line

$x + 2y - 4 = 0$

$2y - 4 = -x$

$2y = -x + 4$

$\frac{2y}{2} = \frac{-x+4}{2}$

$y = -\frac{1}{2}x + 2$, slope is $m = -\frac{1}{2}$.

Thus the line we want has $m = -\frac{1}{2}$, point is $(2, -3)$

$y - y_0 = m(x - x_0)$

$y - (-3) = -\frac{1}{2}(x - 2)$

$y + 3 = -\frac{1}{2}(x - 2)$

$y + 3 = -\frac{1}{2}x + 1$

$2(y + 3) = (-\frac{1}{2}x + 1)2$

$2y + 6 = -x + 2$

$x + 2y + 4 = 0$ is Standard form of the line parallel to $x + 2y - 4 = 0$ passing through $(2, -3)$.

Prob. 29. Line passing through $(-1, -1)$ parallel to line passing through $(0, 1)$ and $(3, 0)$.

First find slope $m = \frac{y_2 - y_1}{x_2 - x_1}$

$m = \frac{(0) - (1)}{(3) - (0)} = -\frac{1}{3}$

Second use point-slope form

$y - y_0 = m(x - x_0)$

$y - (-1) = -\frac{1}{3}(x - (-1))$

$y + 1 = -\frac{1}{3}(x + 1)$

$$-3(y+1) = x+1$$

$$-3y - 3 = x + 1$$

$x + 3y + 4 = 0$ Standard form.

Prob. 31. Line through $(1,4)$ perpendicular to $2y - 5x + 7 = 0$

$$2y - 5x + 7 = 0$$

$$2y = 5x - 7$$

$$\frac{2y}{2} = \frac{5x-7}{2}$$

$y = \frac{5}{2}x - \frac{7}{2},\ m = \frac{5}{2}$

$m_\perp = -\frac{1}{m}$ (recall $m_1 \cdot m_2 = -1$)

$m_\perp = \frac{-1}{\left(\frac{5}{2}\right)} = -\frac{2}{5}$

use pt-slope form with $(1,4)$

$$y - y_0 = m_\perp(x - x_0)$$

$$y - 4 = -\frac{2}{5}(x - 1)$$

$$5(y - 4) = -2(x - 1)$$

$$5y - 20 = -2x + 2$$

$$2x - 2 + 5y - 20 = 0$$

$$2x + 5y - 22 = 0$$

Prob. 33. Line through $(5,-1)$ perpendicular to line passing through $(-2,1)$ and $(1,-2)$

$m = \frac{y_2 - y_1}{x_2 - x_1} = \frac{(-2)-(1)}{(1)-(-2)} = -\frac{3}{3}$

$$m = -1$$

$m_\perp = -\frac{1}{m} = \frac{-1}{-1} = 1$

use pt-slope form with $(5,-1)$

$$y - y_0 = m_\perp(x - x_0)$$

$$y - (-1) = 1(x - 5)$$

$$y + 1 = x - 5$$

$$y = x - 6$$

$$x - y - 6 = 0$$

Prob. 35. So the line is horizontal through $(4,2)$, and the equation is $y = 2$, in standard form the equation is $y - 2 = 0$.

Prob. 37. The line is vertical with equation $x = -1$, so in standard form the equation is $x + 1 = 0$.

Prob. 39. The line is vertical with equation $x = 1$, so in standard form the equation is $x - 1 = 0$.

Prob. 41. The line is horizontal with equation $y = 3$, so in standard form the equation is $y - 3 = 0$.

Prob. 43. $y = 30.5x$ is in the form of $y = mx$ meaning the two quantities x and y are linearly related. Thus y is proportional to x, and m is the constant of proportionality.

(a) To use this relationship, recall that 1 foot $= 30.5$ cm. Therefore let x be the variable for feet, and y be the variable for centimeters.

(b) Convert into centimeters.

  (i) $y = 30.5x$, $x = 6$ft

  $y = 30.5(6) = 183$cm

  (ii) $y = 30.5x$, $x = 3$ft 2in. Note that 2 inches $= \frac{2}{12}$ feet ≈ 0.167ft

  Let $x = 3.167$ feet (approx.)

  $y = 30.5(3.167) = 96.58$cm

  (iii) $y = 30.5x$, $x = 1$ft 7in.

  Note 7in $= \frac{7}{12}$ feet ≈ 0.583ft.

  Let $x = 1.583$ft (approx.)

  $y = 30.5(1.583) = 48.29$cm.

(c) Convert into feet

  (i) $y = 30.5x$, $y = 173$cm

  $173 = 30.5x$

  $x = 5.67$ feet

  (ii) $y = 30.5x$, $y = 75$cm

  $75 = 30.5x$

  $x = 2.459$ feet

(iii) $y = 48$cm

$$y = 30.5x$$

$$48 = 30.5x$$

$$x = 1.574 \text{ feet}$$

Prob. 45. Distance = rate · time (Recall $y = m \cdot x$)

time = 15 mins = $\frac{1}{4}$ hour = 0.25 hrs

distance = 10 mi

Constant of proportionality is miles per hour or "mph"

distance = speed · time

10 mi = speed · 0.25 hrs

$\frac{10mi}{0.25hrs}$ = speed (the constant of proportionality)

Thus speed = 40 $\frac{miles}{hour}$ (or "mph")

Prob. 47. 1 foot = 0.305 meters so 3.279 ft = 1 meter. Now we can convert $1m^2 = (1m)(1m) = (3.279ft)(3.279ft)$
$= 10.75ft^2$ (approx.)

Prob. 49. 1 liter = 33.81 ounces

(a) $y = mx$, $m = \frac{1liter}{33.81ounces}$

y (liters) = $m \cdot x$ (ounces)

$y = \frac{1}{33.81} \cdot x$

(b) $x = 12$ ounces

$y = \frac{1}{33.8}(12) = 0.355$ (approx.)

So 12 ounces is 0.355 liters.

Prob. 51. 1 mile = 1.609 kilometers

(a) $\left(55\frac{miles}{hour}\right) \cdot \left(\frac{1.609kilometers}{1mile}\right) = 88.5\frac{kilometers}{hour}$

(b) $\left(130\frac{kilometers}{hour}\right) \cdot \left(\frac{1mile}{1.609kilometers}\right) = 80.8\frac{miles}{hour}$

Prob. 53.

(a) Denoting the two scales by K and C, they relate by equation

$$K = mC + b$$

and the slope of the line m is equal to 1 because 1 K denotes the same temperature difference as $1°C$, so

$$K = C + b$$

and substituting the two points $(-273.15, 0)$ we get $b = 273.15$ so

$$K = C + 273.15$$

(b) Nitrogen boils at $77.4K$ and oxygen at $90.2K$

So the boiling points will be given in Celsius by the equation

$$C = K - 273.15$$

so they are $77.4 - 273.15 = -195.75°$ for nitrogen and $90.2 - 273.15 = -182.95°$ for oxygen.

Now, $F = \frac{9}{5}C + 32$, and the boiling points in $°$ F are

Nitrogen: $F = \frac{9}{5}(-195.75) + 32 = -320.35°F$

Oxygen: $F = \frac{9}{5}(-182.95) + 32 = -297.31°F$

and the nitrogen will end up being distilled first.

Prob. 55. $r^2 = (x - x_0)^2 + (y - y_0)^2$

$r = 3, \quad (x_0, y_0) = (-1, 4)$

$9 = (x - (-1))^2 + (y - 4)^2$

$9 = (x + 1)^2 + (y - 4)^2$

Prob. 57. $r^2 = (x - x_0)^2 + (y - y_0)^2$

(a) $r = 3, \quad (x_0, y_0) = (2, 5)$

$3^2 = (x - 2)^2 + (y - 5)^2$

$9 = (x - 2)^2 + (y - 5)^2$

(b) where does the circle intersect the y-axis?

When $x = 0$ the circle is on the y-axis.

$$9 = (x - 2)^2 + (y - 5)^2$$

$$9 = (0 - 2)^2 + (y - 5)^2$$

$$9 = 4 + (y - 5)^2$$

$$5 = (y - 5)^2$$

$$\sqrt{5} = y - 5$$

$$5 \pm \sqrt{5} = y$$

(c) Does the circle intersect the x-axis? If $y = 0$ the circle would be on the x-axis.

$$9 = (x - 2)^2 + (y - 5)^2$$

$$9 = (x - 2)^2 + (0 - 5)^2$$

$$9 = (x - 2)^2 + 25$$

$$-16 = (x - 2)^2$$

Since the square of a real number cannot be negative, the circle does not intersect the x-axis.

Prob. 59. Find center and radius.

$$(x - 2)^2 + y^2 = 16$$
$$(x - 2)^2 + (y - 0)^2 = 4^2$$
center $(x_0, y_0) = (2, 0), \quad r = 4$

Prob. 61. $0 = x^2 + y^2 - 4x + 2y - 11$

$$0 = (x^2 - 4x + 4) + (y^2 + 2y + 1) - 11 - 5$$
$$0 = (x - 2)^2 + (y + 1)^2 - 16$$
$$16 = (x - 2)^2 + (y + 1)^2$$
$$16 = (x - 2)^2 + (y - (-1))^2$$
$r = 4$ and center is $(x_0, y_0) = (2, -1)$

Prob. 63.

(a) Convert to radian measure

$$(75°)(\frac{\pi}{180°}) = \frac{5}{12}\pi radians.$$

(b) Convert to degree measure

$$(\frac{17}{12}\pi)(\frac{180°}{\pi}) = \frac{3060°}{12} = 255°$$

Prob. 65.

(a)
$$\sin\left(\frac{-5}{4}\pi\right) = \frac{\sqrt{2}}{2}$$

(b)
$$\cos\left(\frac{5}{6}\pi\right) = \frac{-\sqrt{3}}{2}$$

(c)
$$\tan\left(\frac{\pi}{3}\right) = \sqrt{3}$$

Prob. 67.

(a) Find values of $\alpha \in [0, 2\pi)$

$$\sin\alpha = -\frac{1}{2}\sqrt{3}$$

$$\pi + \frac{\pi}{3} = \frac{4}{3}\pi$$

and

$$2\pi - \frac{\pi}{3} - \frac{5}{3}\pi$$

$$\alpha = \frac{4}{3}\pi \text{ and } \frac{5}{3}\pi$$

(b) Find values of $\alpha \in [0, 2\pi)$

$$\tan\alpha = \sqrt{3}$$

$\frac{\pi}{3}$ and $\pi + \frac{\pi}{3}$

$$\alpha = \frac{\pi}{3} \text{ and } \frac{4}{3}\pi$$

Prob. 69.

$$\sin^2\theta + \cos^2\theta = 1$$

$$\frac{\sin^2\theta + \cos^2\theta}{\cos^2\theta} = \frac{1}{\cos^2\theta} \quad \text{Divide both sides by } \cos^2\theta$$

$$\frac{\sin^2\theta}{\cos^2\theta} + \frac{\cos^2\theta}{\cos^2\theta} = \frac{1}{\cos^2\theta} \quad \text{Distribute}$$

$$\left(\text{Recall} \quad \frac{\sin\theta}{\cos\theta} = \tan\theta, \quad \text{and} \quad \frac{1}{\cos\theta} = \sec\theta \right)$$

$$\tan^2\theta + 1 = \sec^2\theta \quad \text{make substitution}$$

Prob. 71.

$$2\cos\theta\sin\theta = \sin\theta, \quad [0, 2\pi)$$

$$\frac{2\cos\theta\sin\theta}{\sin\theta} = \frac{\sin\theta}{\sin\theta} \quad \text{as long as } \sin\theta \neq 0, \text{ or } \theta \neq 0, \ \theta \neq \pi$$

$$2\cos\theta = 1$$

$$\cos\theta = \frac{1}{2}$$

$$\theta = \frac{\pi}{3} \quad \text{and} \quad 2\pi - \frac{\pi}{3}$$

Hence

$$\theta = 0, \pi, \frac{\pi}{3} \quad \text{and} \quad \frac{5}{3}\pi$$

Prob. 73.

(a) $4^3 4^{-2/3}$ Recall

$$a^r a^s \qquad = a^{r+s}$$
$$4^{3+(-2/3)} \quad = 4^{7/3} = 16\sqrt[3]{4}$$

(b)

$$\frac{3^2 3^{1/2}}{3^{-1/2}} \qquad = \frac{3^{5/2}}{3^{-1/2}} = 3^{5/2} \cdot 3^{1/2}$$
$$= 3^{5/2+1/2} = 3^{6/2} = 3^3 = 27$$

(c)

$$\frac{5^k 5^{2k-1}}{5^{1-k}} \quad = 5^k \cdot 5^{2k-1} \cdot 5^{k-1}$$
$$5^{k+2k-1+k-1} \qquad = 5^{4k-2}$$

Prob. 75.

(a)

$$\log_4 x \qquad = -2$$
$$x \quad = 4^{-2} = \frac{1}{4^2} = \frac{1}{16}$$

(b)

$$\log_{1/3} x \qquad = -3$$
$$x \quad = \left(\tfrac{1}{3}\right)^{-3} = \frac{1}{\left(\tfrac{1}{3}\right)^3} = \frac{1}{\left(\tfrac{1}{27}\right)} = 27$$

(c)

$$\log_{10} x \qquad = -2$$
$$x \quad = 10^{-2} = \frac{1}{10^2} = \frac{1}{100}$$

Prob. 77.

(a)

$$\log_{1/2} 32 = x$$
$$32 = \left(\tfrac{1}{2}\right)^x = \tfrac{1^x}{2^x} = \tfrac{1}{2^x}$$
$$\text{So } 2^x = \tfrac{1}{32}$$
$$2^x = 2^{-5}$$
$$x = -5$$

(b)

$$\log_{1/3} 81 = x$$
$$81 = \left(\tfrac{1}{3}\right)^x = \tfrac{1^x}{3^x}$$
$$3^x = \tfrac{1}{81} = \tfrac{1}{3^4} = 3^{-4}$$
$$x = -4$$

(c)

$$\log_{10} 0.001 = x$$
$$10^x = 0.001 = \tfrac{1}{1000} = \tfrac{1}{10^3}$$
$$10^x = 10^{-3}$$
$$x = -3$$

Prob. 79.

(a) $-\ln\left(\tfrac{1}{3}\right) = \ln\left[\left(\tfrac{1}{3}\right)^{-1}\right] = \ln 3$

(b) $\log_4(x^2 - 4) = \log_4[(x-2)(x+2)] = \log_4(x-2) + \log_4(x+2)$

(c) $\log_2 4^{(3x-1)} = (3x-1)\log_2(2^2) = (3x-1)(2 \cdot \log_2 2) = (3x-1)(2 \cdot 1) = 6x - 2$

Prob. 81.

(a)

$$e^{3x-1} = 2$$

$$\ln e^{(3x-1)} = \ln 2$$

$$(3x-1)(\ln e) = \ln 2 \qquad \text{Recall } \ln e = 1$$

$$3x - 1 = \ln 2$$

$$3x = 1 + \ln 2$$

$$x = \frac{1 + \ln 2}{3}$$

(b)

$$e^{-2x} = 10$$

$$\ln e^{(-2x)} = \ln 10$$

$$(-2x)(\ln e) = \ln 10$$

$$-2x = \ln 10$$

$$x = \frac{\ln 10}{-2} = -\frac{1}{2} \cdot \ln 10$$

$$\text{or } x = \ln 10^{-1/2} = \ln\left(\frac{1}{\sqrt{10}}\right)$$

(c)

$$e^{x^2-1} = 10$$

$$\ln e^{(x^2-1)} = \ln 10$$

$$(x^2 - 1)(\ln e) = \ln 10 \qquad (\ln e = 1)$$

$$x^2 - 1 = \ln 10$$

$$x^2 = 1 + \ln 10$$

$$x = \pm\sqrt{1 + \ln 10}$$

Prob. 83.

(a)

$$\ln(x - 3) = 5$$
$$e^{\ln(x-3)} = e^5, \quad \texttt{Recall } e^{\ln x} = x$$
$$x - 3 = e^5$$
$$x = e^5 + 3$$

(b)

$$\ln(x + 2) + \ln(x - 2) = 1$$
$$\ln(x + 2)(x - 2) = 1$$
$$e^{\ln[(x+2)(x-2)]} = e$$
$$(x + 2)(x - 2) = e$$
$$x^2 - 4 = e$$
$$x^2 = 4 + e$$
$$x = \sqrt{4 + e}$$

(c)

$$\log_3 x^2 - \log_3 2x = 2$$
$$\log_3 \frac{x^2}{2x} = 2$$
$$\frac{x^2}{2x} = 3^2$$
$$\frac{x}{2} = 9$$
$$x = 18$$

Prob. 85. $3 - 2i - (-2 + 5i) = 3 - 2i + 2 - 5i = 5 - 7i$

Prob. 87. $(4 - 2i) + (9 + 4i) = 4 + 9 - 2i + 4i = 13 + 2i$

Prob. 89. $3(5 + 3i) = 15 + 9i$

Prob. 91. $(6 - i)(6 + i) = 36 - i^2 = 36 - (-1) = 37$

Prob. 93.

$$z = 3 - 2i$$

$$\text{conjugate } \overline{z} = 3 + 2i$$

Prob. 95. $\overline{z + v} = \overline{3 - 2i} + \overline{3 + 5i} = 3 + 2i + 3 - 5i = 6 - 3i$

Prob. 97.

$$\overline{vw} = \overline{(3 + 5i)(1 - i)} = \overline{8 + 2i} = 8 - 2i$$

Prob. 99. Let

$$z = a + bi$$

$$z + \overline{z} = a + bi + \overline{a + bi}$$

$$= a + bi + a - bi = 2a$$

and

$$z - \overline{z} = (a + bi) - \overline{(a + bi)}$$

$$= a + bi - (a - bi)$$

$$= a + bi - a + bi = 2bi$$

Prob. 101. $2x^2 - 3x + 2 = 0$. Here $a = 2$, $b = -3$, $c = 2$

Recall

$$x_{1,2} = \frac{-b \pm \sqrt{b^2 - 4ac}}{2a}$$

$$x_{1,2} = \frac{-(-3) \pm \sqrt{(-3)^2 - 4(2)(2)}}{2(2)}$$

$$x_{1,2} = \frac{3 \pm \sqrt{9 - 16}}{4}$$

$$x_{1,2} = \frac{3 \pm \sqrt{-7}}{4} = \frac{3 \pm \sqrt{7i^2}}{4}$$

Recall $i^2 = -1$, and $\sqrt{ab} = \sqrt{a} \cdot \sqrt{b}$

$$x_{1,2} = \frac{3 \pm \sqrt{7} \cdot \sqrt{i^2}}{4} = \frac{3 \pm \sqrt{7}i}{4}$$

$$x_1 = \frac{3 + \sqrt{7}i}{4} \quad \text{and} \quad x_2 = \frac{3 - \sqrt{7}i}{4}$$

Prob. 103. Here $a = -1, b = 1$, and $c = 2$

$$x_{1,2} = \frac{-b \pm \sqrt{b^2 - 4ac}}{2a}$$

$$x_{1,2} = \frac{-(1) \pm \sqrt{(1)^2 - 4(-1)(2)}}{2(-1)}$$

$$x_{1,2} = \frac{-1 \pm \sqrt{1+8}}{-2}$$

$$x_{1,2} = \frac{-1 \pm \sqrt{9}}{-2} = \frac{-1 \pm 3}{-2}$$

$$x_1 = \frac{-1+3}{-2} = \frac{2}{-2} = -1$$

$$x_2 = \frac{-1-3}{-2} = \frac{-4}{-2} = 2$$

Prob. 105. $4x^2 - 3x + 1 = 0$

$$a = 4, \quad b = -3, \quad c = 1$$

$$x_{1,2} = \frac{-b \pm \sqrt{b^2 - 4ac}}{2a}$$

$$x_{1,2} = \frac{-(-3) \pm \sqrt{(-3)^2 - 4(4)(1)}}{2(4)}$$

$$x_{1,2} = \frac{3 \pm \sqrt{9 - 16}}{8}$$

$$x_{1,2} = \frac{3 \pm \sqrt{-7}}{8} = \frac{3 \pm \sqrt{7i^2}}{8} \quad \text{Note } i^2 = -1$$

$$x_{1,2} = \frac{3 \pm \sqrt{7}i}{8}$$

$$x_1 = \frac{3 + \sqrt{7}i}{8}$$

$$x_2 = \frac{3 - \sqrt{7}i}{8}$$

Prob. 107. $3x^2 - 4x - 7 = 0$. Compute the discriminant, $b^2 - 4ac$

$$a = 3, \quad b = -4, \quad c = -7$$

$$(-4)^2 - 4(3)(-7) = 16 + 84 = 100 > 0$$

Hence, two real solutions. These are -1 and $\frac{7}{3}$.

Prob. 109. $-x^2 + 2x - 1 = 0$. Compute the discriminant, $b^2 - 4ac$

$$a = -1, \quad b = 2, \quad c = -1$$

$$(2)^2 - 4(-1)(-1)$$

$$4 - 4 = 0$$

Two identical real solutions, that is, only one real solution. This solution is 1.

Prob. 111. $3x^2 - 5x + 6 = 0$

$$a = 3, \quad b = -5, \quad c = 6$$

Compute the discriminant

$$b^2 - 4ac$$

$$(-5)^2 - 4(3)(6)$$

$$25 - 72 = -47 < 0$$

Hence, two complex solutions which are conjugates of each other. These are $\frac{5+\sqrt{47}i}{6}$ and $\frac{5-\sqrt{47}i}{6}$.

Prob. 113. Let $z = a + bi$. Conjugate $\bar{z} = a - bi$

$$\overline{(\bar{z})} = \overline{(a - bi)} = a + bi = z.$$

Hence $z = \overline{(\bar{z})}$.

Prob. 115. Let

$$z \quad = a + bi$$

$$w \quad = c + di$$

Does $\overline{zw} = \bar{z} \cdot \bar{w}$?

First,

$$\bar{z} \cdot \bar{w} \quad = \overline{(a + bi)(c + di)} = \overline{(ac - bd) + (ad + bc)i}$$

$$= (ac - bd) - (ad + bc)i$$

On the other hand,

$$\overline{z} \cdot \overline{w} \quad = \overline{(a + bi)} \cdot \overline{(c + di)}$$

$$= (a - bi) \cdot (c - di)$$

$$= ac - adi - bci + bdi^2$$

$$= ac - (ad + bc)i - bd$$

$$= (ac - bd) - (ad + bc)i$$

So $\overline{zw} = \overline{z} \cdot \overline{w}$ is true.

1.2 Elementary Functions

Prob. 1. $f(x) = x^2$, $x \in \mathbb{R}$. Range $[0, +\infty)$

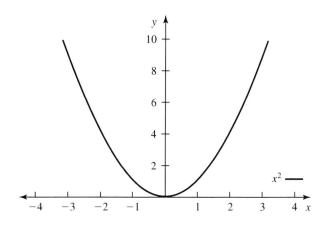

Prob. 3. $f(x) = x^2$, $-1 < x \leq 0$. Range $[0, 1)$

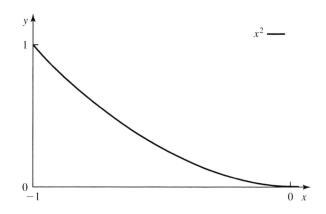

Prob. 5.

(a) Factor $\frac{x^2-1}{x-1} = \frac{(x+1)(x-1)}{x-1} = x+1$ (if $x \neq 1$)

$$f(x) = \frac{x^2 - 1}{x - 1}, \quad x \neq 1$$

(b) No the functions are not equal, they have different domains. The function f is not defined at the point $x = 1$.

Prob. 7. The function is odd, as the tests below indicate.

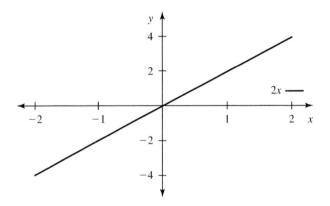

Test for "Even";

$$\text{Does } f(x) \qquad\qquad = f(x)?$$
$$\text{Ask if } ;2x \qquad\qquad = 2(-x)?$$
$$\text{Does } 2x \;= -2x? \quad \text{no, not "even"}$$

Test for "Odd";

$$\text{Does } f(x) \qquad\qquad = -f(-x)$$
$$\text{Ask if } ;2x \qquad\qquad = -2(-x)?$$
$$\text{Does } 2x \;= 2x? \quad \text{yes, hence "odd"}$$

Prob. 9. The function is even, as the tests below indicate.

$$f(x) = |3x|$$

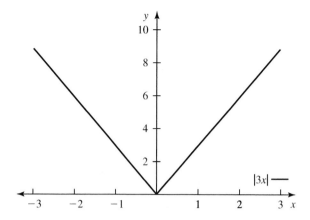

Test for "Even";

$$\text{Does } f(x) \qquad = f(-x)?$$

$$\text{Ask if } ; |3x| \qquad = |3(-x)|?$$

$$\text{Does } |3x| \;\; = |-3x|? \quad \text{yes, hence "even"}$$

Test for "Odd";

$$\text{Does } f(x) \qquad = -f(-x)?$$

$$\text{Ask if } ; |3x| \qquad = -|3(-x)|?$$

$$\text{Does } |3x| \;\; = -|3x|? \quad \text{no, not "odd"}$$

Prob. 11. The function is even, as the tests below indicate.

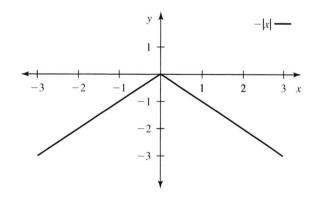

Test for "Even";

$$\text{Does } f(x) = f(-x)?$$

$$\text{Does } -|x| = -|-x|? \quad \text{yes, hence "even"}$$

Test for "Odd";

$$\text{Does } f(x) = -f(-x)?$$

$$\text{Does } -|x| = |-x|? \quad \text{no, not "odd"}$$

Prob. 13.

(a) $(f \circ g)(x) = f[g(x)]$

$$f(x) = x^2$$

$$f(g(x)) = f(3+x) = (3+x)^2$$

$$(f \circ g)(x) = (3+x)^2$$

(b) $(g \circ f)(x) = g[f(x)]$

$$g(x) = 3+x$$

$$g(f(x)) = g(x^2) = 3 + (x^2)$$

$$(g \circ f)(x) = 3 + x^2$$

Prob. 15.

(a)

$$(f \circ g)(x) = f(g(x))$$

$$f(g(x)) = f(2x) = 1 - (2x)^2$$

$$(f \circ g)(x) = 1 - 4x^2$$

Domain $x \geq 0$

(b)

$$(g \circ f)(x) \qquad = g(f(x))$$

$$g(x) \qquad = 2x$$

$$g(f(x)) \quad = g(1 - x^2) = 2(1 - x^2)$$

$$(g \circ f)(x) \qquad = 2 - 2x^2$$

Here we require that $f(x) \geq 0$, or that $1 - x^2 \geq 0$. This means the domain is $-1 \leq x \leq 1$.

Prob. 17.

$$f(x) \quad = 3x^2 \quad x \geq 3$$

$$g(x) \quad = \sqrt{x} \quad x \geq 0$$

$$(f \circ g)(x) \qquad = f(g(x))$$

$$= f(\sqrt{x}) = 3(\sqrt{x})^2$$

$$(f \circ g)(x) \quad = f(g(x)) = 3x$$

Domain is $\{x \in \mathbb{R} : x \geq 0 \text{ and } g(x) \geq 3\} = \{x \in \mathbb{R} : \sqrt{x} \geq 3\} = \{x \in \mathbb{R} : x \geq 9\}$.

Prob. 19.

$$f(x) \quad = x^2 \quad x \geq 0$$

$$g(x) \quad = \sqrt{x} \quad x \geq 0$$

Note $f \circ g \neq g \circ f$ in general. Here however, we show that $f \circ g = g \circ f$.

$$f \circ g \quad = f(g(x)) = f(\sqrt{x}) = (\sqrt{x})^2$$

$$f \circ g \qquad = x$$

and

$$g \circ f \quad = g(f(x)) = g(x^2) = \sqrt{x^2}$$

$$g \circ f \qquad = x$$

In addition, both compositions have the same domain, namely $\{x \in \mathbb{R} : x \geq 0\}$.

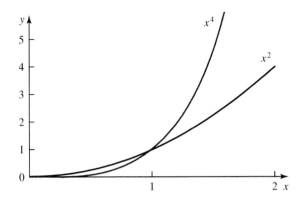

Prob. 21.

$f(x) > g(x)$ when $0 < x < 1$

$f(x) < g(x)$ when $x > 1$

Prob. 23. $y = x^n,\ x \geq 0$

$y_1 = x^1$

$y_2 = x^2$

$y_3 = x^3$

$y_4 = x^4$

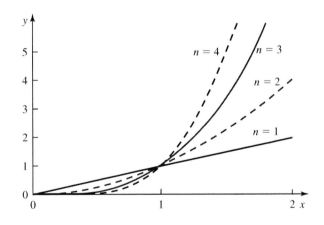

The curves intersect at the points $(0, 0)$ and $(1, 1)$.

Prob. 25.

(a) $f(x) = x^2$

$\quad g(x) = x^3 \qquad x \geq 0$

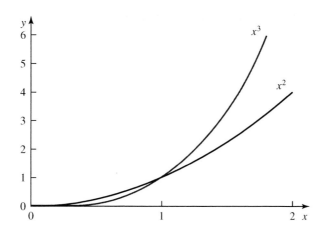

(b) We can start with the inequalities $0 \le x \le 1$, and multiply both sides by x^2 which is positive, so it will not change the direction of the inequalities that become $0 \le x^3 \le x^2$

(c) In the same way, we start with $x \ge 1$, and multiply both sides by the positive value x^2, which then becomes $x^3 \ge x^2$

Prob. 27.

(a) Show $y = x^2, x \in \mathbb{R}$ is even.

$$f(x) = x^2, f(-x) = (-x)^2$$

Since $x^2 = (-x)^2$, f(x) is an even function.

(b) Show $y = x^3$, $x \in \mathbb{R}$ is odd.

$$f(x) = x^3, -f(-x) = -(-x)^3$$

Does $f(x) = -f(-x)$?

$$x^3 = -(-x^3) = -1 \cdot (-1 \cdot x^3)$$

$x^3 = x^3$ hence the function is odd.

Prob. 29. $A + B \to AB$, $a = [A] = 3$, $b = [B] = 4$

(a) When $x = 1$, we have $R = 9$. Substituting this into the equation $R(x) = k(a-x)(b-x)$, we get

$$9 = k(a-1)(b-1)$$

$$9 = k(3-1)(4-1)$$

$$9 = k \cdot 6$$

$$k = \tfrac{9}{6} = \tfrac{3}{2}$$

Thus $R(x) = \tfrac{3}{2}(3-x)(4-x)$.

(b) $R(x) = \tfrac{3}{2}(3-x)(4-x)$

Since the reaction rate cannot be negative, we must find the roots of $R(x)$. As $R(x)$ is already factored, the roots are 3 and 4. Thus the domain must be the interval $[0,3]$.

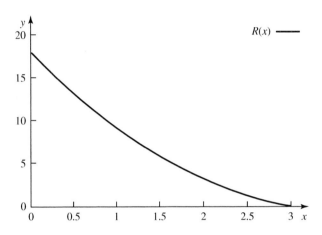

Prob. 31. Constant speed of beetle $= 1\,\frac{\texttt{meter}}{\texttt{hour}}$

$$\texttt{rate} \cdot \texttt{time} = \texttt{distance}.$$

In one hour
$$\left(1\,\frac{\texttt{meter}}{\texttt{hour}}\right)(1\ \texttt{hour}) = 1\ \texttt{meter}.$$

In two hours
$$\left(1\,\frac{\texttt{meter}}{\texttt{hour}}\right)(2\ \texttt{hours}) = 2\ \texttt{meters}.$$

In three hours
$$\left(1\,\frac{\texttt{meter}}{\texttt{hour}}\right)(3\ \texttt{hours}) = 3\ \texttt{meters}.$$

Now $\texttt{distance} = \texttt{rate} \cdot \texttt{time}$,

Let $\texttt{distance} = y$

$\texttt{rate} = m$

time $= x$

Then $y = mx$, which is a polynomial of degree 1; i.e., a line with slope m.

Prob. 33. $f(x) = \frac{1}{1-x}$

Domain $(-\infty, 1) \cup (1, +\infty)$

Range $(-\infty, 0) \cup (0, +\infty)$

Prob. 35. $f(x) = \frac{x-2}{x^2-9}$

Domain is $\{x : x \neq -3, 3\}$ or $(-\infty, -3) \cup (-3, +3) \cup (3, +\infty)$

Range $(-\infty, +\infty)$

Prob. 37.

$$y = \frac{1}{x} \quad y = \frac{1}{x^2}, \quad x > 0$$

The curves intersect at the point $(1, 1)$, when $\frac{1}{x^2} = \frac{1}{x}$

$$\frac{1}{x} > \frac{1}{x^2}, \text{ if } x > 1 \quad \text{and} \quad \frac{1}{x} < \frac{1}{x^2}, \text{ if } 0 < x < 1$$

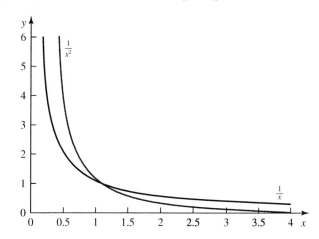

Prob. 39. (a)

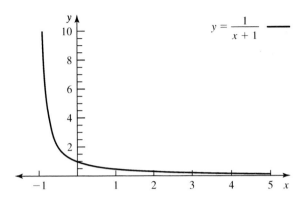

(b) Range of $f(x)$ is $(0, \infty)$,   (c) $x = -\frac{1}{2}$,

(d) $f(x) = a$ has exactly one solution, since the graph is one-to-one.

Prob. 41. (a)

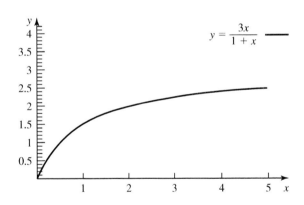

(b) Range of $f(x)$ is $[0, 3)$,   (c) $x = 2$,

(d) For each horizontal line $y = a$, where $0 \le a < 3$, there is only one intersection with the graph, so there is only one possible solution for $f(x) = a$. This solution is given by the equation

$$a = \frac{3x}{1 + x}$$

$$a(1 + x) = 3x$$

$$a = (3 - a)x$$

so

$$x = \frac{a}{3 - a}.$$

Since $0 \leq a < 3$, we see that $x \geq 0$, which is in the domain.

Prob. 43. The percentage increase is

$$\frac{r(0.2) - r(0.1)}{r(0.1)} \times 100\% = \frac{5/6 - 5/11}{5/11} \times 100\% \approx 0.8333 \times 100\% = 83.33\%$$

The percentage increase is

$$\frac{r(20) - r(10)}{r(10)} \times 100\% = \frac{100/21 - 50/11}{50/11} \times 100\% \approx 0.0476 \times 100\% = 4.76\%$$

Prob. 45. (a)

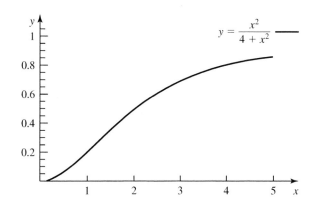

(b) range of $f(x)$ is $[0, 1)$,   (c) $f(x)$ approaches 1, from below.

Prob. 47.

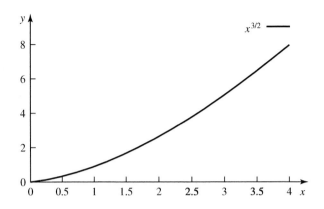

Prob. 49.

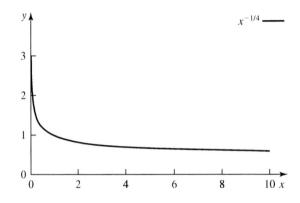

Prob. 51. (a)

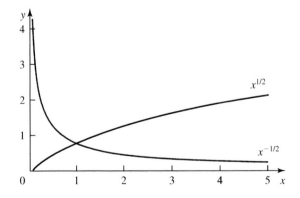

(b) We have

$$0 < x \leq 1 \quad \Rightarrow \quad 0 < \sqrt{x}\sqrt{x} \leq 1 \quad \Rightarrow \quad 0 < \sqrt{x} \leq \frac{1}{\sqrt{x}},$$

since $\sqrt{x}$ is positive.

The last inequality can be written as $x^{1/2} \le x^{-1/2}$.

(c) Here,

$$x \ge 1 \quad \Rightarrow \quad \sqrt{x}\sqrt{x} \ge 1 \quad \Rightarrow \quad \sqrt{x} \ge \frac{1}{\sqrt{x}},$$

since $\sqrt{x}$ is positive.

The last inequality can be written as $x^{1/2} \ge x^{-1/2}$.

Prob. 53. The leaf area increases.

Prob. 55. As wood density increases.

Prob. 57. (a) 1,2,4,8,16   (b)

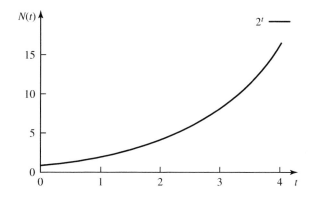

Prob. 59. Since $\lambda = \frac{\ln 2}{T_h} = \frac{\ln 2}{5730}$, the amount left after 2000 years is

$$20 \exp\left[-\frac{\ln 2}{5730}2000\right] = 20 \cdot 2^{-200/573} \approx 15.70 \text{ micrograms}.$$

Prob. 61. $\lambda = \frac{\ln 2}{7\,\text{days}}$

Prob. 63. (a) $W(t) = (300\,\text{micrograms})\exp\left[-\frac{\ln 2}{140\,\text{days}}t\right] = 300\exp\left[-\frac{\ln 2}{140}t\right]$

(b) 20% of 300 micrograms is 60 micrograms. We set $W(t) = 60$ and solve for t.

$60 = 300\exp\left[-\frac{\ln 2}{140}t\right] \quad\Rightarrow\quad 5 = \exp\left[\frac{\ln 2}{140}t\right] \quad\Rightarrow\quad t = \frac{\ln 5}{\ln 2}140 \approx 325\,\text{days}$

(c)

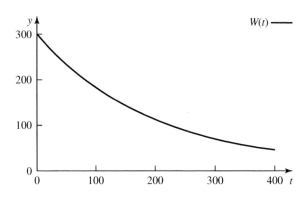

Prob. 65. $\frac{W(t)}{W(0)} = \exp\left[-\frac{\ln 2}{5730}15{,}000\right] \approx 16.3\%$

Prob. 67.

(a) The population with $r = 3$ grows faster.

(b) $\frac{250}{200} = \frac{N(t+1)}{N(t)} = \frac{N_0 e^{r(t+1)}}{N_0 e^{rt}} = \frac{e^{rt}e^r}{e^{rt}} = e^r$. Thus we get $e^r = 1.25$, or $r = \ln 1.25$.

Prob. 69. (a) yes   (b) no   (c) yes   (d) yes   (e) no   (f) yes

Prob. 71.

(a) f is strictly increasing, so it is one to one. To find its inverse, we start with

$$y = x^2 + 1$$

and solving for x, we have $y - 1 = x^2$ or $x = \sqrt{y-1}$. So the inverse function is $f^{-1}(x) = \sqrt{x-1}$, with domain $\{x \geq 1\}$.

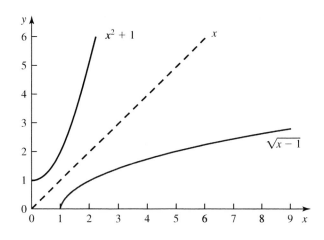

(b)

Prob. 73.

(a) f is strictly increasing, so it is one to one. To find its inverse, we start with

$$y = 1/x^3$$

and solving for x, we have $1/y = x^3$ or $x = \sqrt[3]{1/y}$. So the inverse function is $f^{-1}(x) = \sqrt[3]{\frac{1}{x}}$, with domain $\{x > 0\}$.

(b)

Prob. 75. $f^{-1}(x) = \log_3 x$, $x > 0$

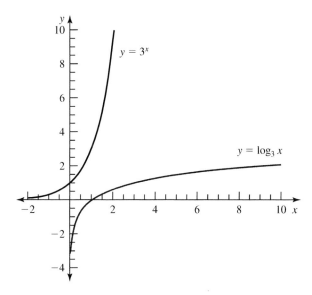

Prob. 77. $f^{-1}(x) = \log_{1/4} x,\ x > 0$

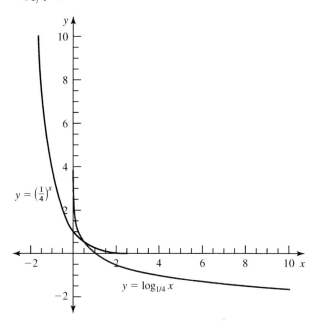

Prob. 79. $f^{-1}(x) = \log_2(x),\ x \geq 1$

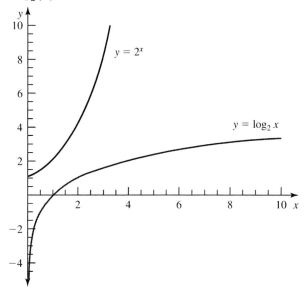

Prob. 81. (a) $2^{5\log_2 x} = 2^{\log_2 x^5} = x^5$

(b) $3^{4\log_3 x} = 3^{\log_3 x^4} = x^4$

(c) $5^{5\log_{1/5} x} = 5^{-\log_{1/5} x^{-5}} = \left(\frac{1}{5}\right)^{\log_{1/5} x^{-5}} = x^{-5}$

(d) $4^{-2\log_2 x} = 2^{-4\log_2 x} = 2^{\log_2 x^{-4}} = x^{-4}$

(e) $2^{3\log_{1/2} x} = 2^{-\log_{1/2} x^{-3}} = \left(\frac{1}{2}\right)^{\log_{1/2} x^{-3}} = x^{-3}$

(f) $4^{-\log_{1/2} x} = 2^{-2\log_{1/2} x} = 2^{-\log_{1/2} x^2} = \left(\frac{1}{2}\right)^{\log_{1/2} x^2} = x^2$

Prob. 83. (a) $5\ln x$,   (b) $6\ln x$,   (c) $\ln(x-1)$,   (d) $-4\ln x$

Prob. 85. (a) $e^{x\ln 3}$,   (b) $e^{(x^2-1)\ln 4}$,   (c) $e^{-(x+1)\ln 2}$,   (d) $e^{(-4x+1)\ln 3}$

Prob. 87. We have $y = (1/2)^x = e^{x\ln(1/2)} = e^{-x\ln 2}$, and so $\mu = \ln 2$.

Prob. 89. $K = -\frac{3}{4}\ln\left(1 - \frac{4}{3}\cdot\frac{47}{300}\right) \approx 0.1757$

Prob. 91. Same period; $2\sin x$ has twice the amplitude of $\sin x$.

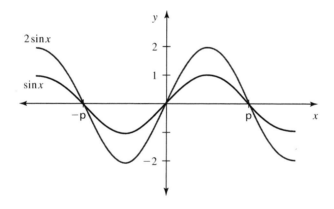

Prob. 93. Same period; $2\cos x$ has twice the amplitude of $\cos x$.

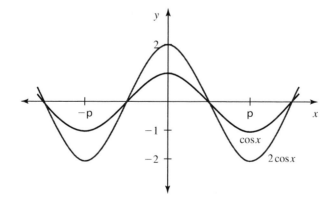

Prob. 95. Same period; $y = 2\tan x$ is vertically stretched by a factor of 2.

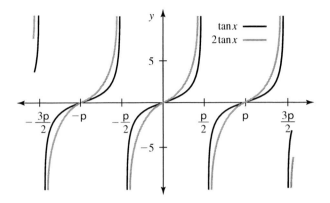

Prob. 97. Amplitude is **3**, and the period is $\frac{\pi}{2}$.

Prob. 99. Amplitude is **4**, and the period is **1**.

Prob. 101. Amplitude is **4**, and the period is 8π.

Prob. 103. Amplitude is **3** and the period is **10**.

Prob. 105. Since $\sec x = \frac{1}{\cos x}$, it is undefined for $\cos x = 0$, meaning:

$$x = \frac{\pi}{2} + \pi n = \frac{\pi}{2}(1 + 2n), \quad n \in Z.$$

1.3   Graphing

Prob. 1.

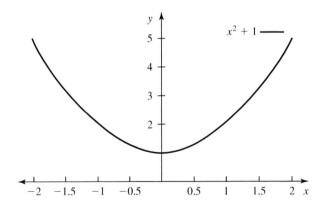

Prob. 3.

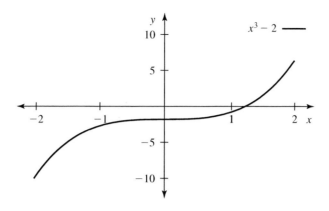

Prob. 5.

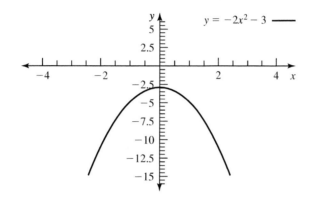

Prob. 7.

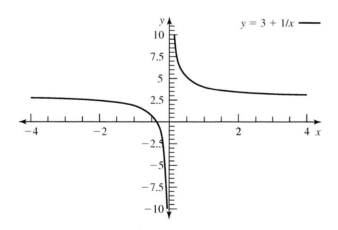

Prob. 9.

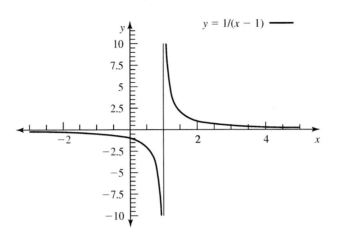

Prob. 11.

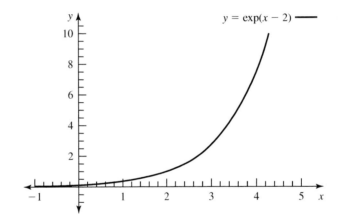

Prob. 13.

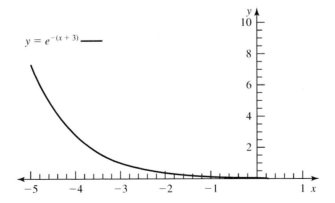

Prob. 15.

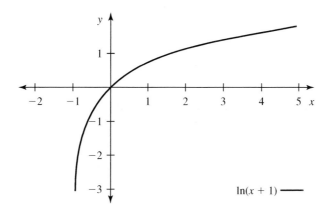

ln(*x* + 1) ——

Prob. 17.

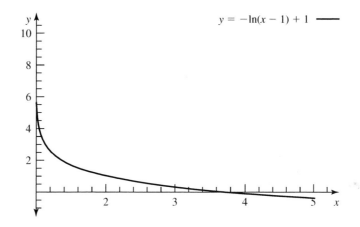

y = −ln(*x* − 1) + 1 ——

Prob. 19.

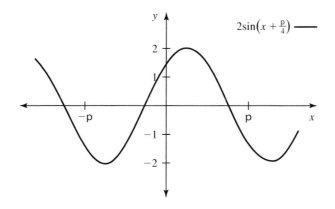

2sin$\left(x + \frac{p}{4}\right)$ ——

Prob. 21.

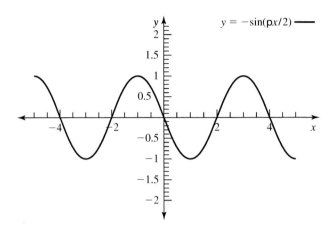

Prob. 23. (a) Shift two units down.

(b) Shift $y = x^2$ one unit to the right and then one unit up.

(c) Shift $y = x^2$ two units to the left, stretch by a factor of 2, and reflect about the x-axis.

Prob. 25. (a) First reflect $\frac{1}{x}$ about the x-axis, and then shift up one unit.

(b) First shift $\frac{1}{x}$ one unit to the right, and then reflect about the x-axis.

(c) We re-write the function as follows: $y = \frac{x}{x+1} = 1 - \frac{1}{x+1}$. First shift $y = \frac{1}{x}$ one unit to the left, then reflect about x-axis and finally shift up one unit.

Prob. 27. (a) Stretch $y = e^x$ by a factor of 2, then shift one unit down.

(b) Reflect $y = e^x$ about the y-axis, the reflect about the x-axis.

(c) Shift $y = e^x$ two units to the right, then shift one unit up.

Prob. 29. (a) Shift $y = \ln x$ one unit to the right.

(b) Reflect $y = \ln x$ about the x-axis, then shift up one unit.

(c) Shift $y = \ln x$ three units to the left, then down one unit.

Prob. 31. (a) Reflect $y = \sin x$ about the x-axis, then one unit up.

(b) Shift $y = \sin x$ by $\pi/4$ units to the right.

(c) Shift $y = \sin x$ by $\pi/3$ units to the left, then reflect about the x-axis.

Prob. 33. To locate the point, we have to compute the log of each of the numbers, which are:

$$\log 0.0002 \;=\; \log\left(2 \times 10^{-4}\right) = \log 2 + \log 10^{-4} = -4 + \log 2 \approx -3.7$$

$$\log 0.02 = \log\left(2 \times 10^{-2}\right) = -2 + \log 2 \approx -1.7$$

$$\log 1 = 0$$

$$\log 5 \approx 0.7$$

$$\log 50 = \log(5 \times 10) = \log 5 + \log 10 = 1 + \log 5 \approx 1.7$$

$$\log 100 = \log 10^2 = 2\log 10 = 2$$

$$\log 1000 = \log 10^3 = 3\log 10 = 3$$

$$\log 8000 = \log\left(8 \times 10^3\right) = \log 8 + \log 10^3 = 3 + \log 8 \approx 3.9$$

$$\log 20000 = \log\left(2 \times 10^4\right) = \log 2 + \log 10^4 = 4 + \log 2 \approx 4.3$$

Prob. 35. (a) The numbers on a logarithmic scale are $2, -3, -4, -7$ and -10 respectively.

(b) No,

(c) No

Prob. 37. seven

Prob. 39. one, three

Prob. 41. six to seven

Prob. 43. The slope of the line is given by $m = \frac{y-y_0}{x-x_0} = \frac{5-1}{0-3} = -\frac{4}{3}$ so the equation of $\log y$ in terms of x is

$$\log y - \log y_0 = m(x - x_0)$$

$$\log y - \log 5 = -\frac{4}{3}(x - 0)$$

$$\log \frac{y}{5} = -\frac{4}{3}x$$

$$\frac{y}{5} = 10^{-\frac{4}{3}x}$$

so finally

$$y = 5 \times \left(10^{-4/3}\right)^x \approx 5(0.046)^x$$

Prob. 45. The slope of the line is given by $m = \frac{y-y_0}{x-x_0} = \frac{3-1}{-2-1} = -\frac{2}{3}$ so the equation of $\log y$ in terms of x is

$$\log y - \log y_0 = m(x - x_0)$$

$$\log y - \log 1 = -\frac{2}{3}(x - 1)$$

$$\log y = -\frac{2}{3}x + \frac{2}{3}$$

$$y = 10^{-\frac{2}{3}x + \frac{2}{3}}$$

so finally

$$y = 10^{2/3} \cdot \left(10^{-2/3}\right)^x \approx 4.64(0.22)^x$$

Prob. 47. $\log y = \log(3 \times 10^{-2x}) = \log 3 + \log 10^{-2x} = \log 3 - 2x \log 10 = \log 3 - 2x$

Prob. 49. $\log y = \log(2e^{-1.2x}) = \log 2 + \log(e^{-1.2x}) = \log 2 - 1.2x \log e = \log 2 - (1.2 \log e)x$

Prob. 51. $\log y = \log(5 \times 2^{4x}) = \log 5 + 4x \log 2 = \log 5 + (4 \log 2)x$

Prob. 53. $\log y = \log(4 \times 3^{2x}) = \log 4 + 2x \log 3 = \log 4 + (2 \log 3)x$

Prob. 55. The slope of the line is given by $m = \frac{y - y_0}{x - x_0} = \frac{2-1}{1-5} = -\frac{1}{4}$ so the equation of $\log y$ in terms of $\log x$ is

$$\log y - \log y_0 = m(\log x - \log x_0)$$

$$\log y - \log 2 = -\frac{1}{4}(\log x - \log 1)$$

$$\log \frac{y}{2} = -\frac{1}{4} \log x$$

$$\log \frac{y}{2} = \log x^{-\frac{1}{4}}$$

$$\frac{y}{2} = x^{-\frac{1}{4}}$$

so finally

$$y = 2x^{-1/4}$$

Prob. 57. The slope of the line is given by $m = \frac{y - y_0}{x - x_0} = \frac{8-2}{8-4} = \frac{3}{2}$ so the equation of $\log y$ in terms of $\log x$ is

$$\log y - \log y_0 = m(\log x - \log x_0)$$

$$\log y - \log 2 = \frac{3}{2}(\log x - \log 4)$$

$$\log \frac{y}{2} = \frac{3}{2} \log \frac{x}{4}$$

$$\log \frac{y}{2} = \log \left(\frac{x^{\frac{3}{2}}}{4}\right)$$

$$\frac{y}{2} = \left(\frac{x^{\frac{3}{2}}}{4}\right)$$

so finally

$$y = \frac{2}{4^{3/2}} x^{3/2}$$

or

$$y = \frac{1}{4} x^{3/2}$$

Prob. 59. Starting with $y = 2x^5$ we take logarithms on both sides, to get $\log y = \log 2x^5 = \log 2 + 5 \log x$. Thus the linear relationship is $Y = 5X + \log 2$.

Prob. 61. Starting with $y = x^6$ we take logarithms on both sides, to get $\log y = \log x^6 = 6 \log x$. Thus the linear relationship is $Y = 6X$.

Prob. 63. Starting with $y = x^{-2}$ we take logarithms on both sides, to get $\log y = \log x^{-2} = -2 \log x$. Thus the linear relationship is $Y = -2X$.

Prob. 65. Starting with $y = 4x^{-3}$ we take logarithms on both sides, to get $\log y = \log 4x^{-3} = \log 4 - 3 \log x$. Thus the linear relationship is $Y = \log 4 - 3X$.

Prob. 67. Starting with $f(x) = 3x^{1.7}$ we take logarithms on both sides, to get $\log f = \log 3x^{1.7} = \log 3 + 1.7 \log x$. Thus the linear relationship is $Y = \log 3 + 1.7X$, and we should use a log-log transformation.

Prob. 69. Starting with $N(t) = 130 \cdot 2^{1.2t}$ we take logarithms on both sides, to get $\log N(t) = \log \left(130 \cdot 2^{1.2t} \right) = \log 130 + 1.2t \log 2$. Thus the linear relationship is $Y = \log 130 + (1.2 \log 2)t$, and we should use a log-linear plot.

Prob. 71. Starting with $R(t) = 3.6t^{1.2}$ we take logarithms on both sides, to get $\log R(t) = \log 3.6t^{1.2} = \log 3.6 + 1.2 \log t$. Thus the linear relationship is $Y = \log 3.6 + 1.2X$, and we should use a log-log transformation.

Prob. 73. Taking logarithms of both columns of data,

$\log x$	$\log y$
0	0.26
0.30	0.32
0.60	0.38
1	0.45
1.30	0.52

we can see a linear relation among the two columns, and the equation relating them can be checked to be $Y \approx 0.2X + 0.26$, that is:

$$\log y = 0.2 \log x + 0.26$$

so solving for y in terms of x we get:

$$\log y = \log x^{0.2} + 0.26$$

$$\log y - \log x^{0.2} = 0.26$$

or

$$\log \frac{y}{x^{0.2}} = 0.26$$

and thus the functional relationship is: $y = \left(10^{0.26}\right) x^{0.2} \approx 1.82 x^{0.2}$.

Prob. 75. Since the first column has negative entries, we take logarithms of the second column of data only.

x	$\log y$
-1	-0.40
-0.5	0.10
0	0.60
0.5	1.10
1	1.60

We can see a linear relation among the two columns, and the equation relating them can be checked to be $Y \approx X + 0.60$, that is:

$$\log y = x + 0.60$$

so solving for y in terms of x we get:

$$y = 10^{x+0.60}$$

$$y = 10^{0.60} \cdot 10^x$$

and thus the functional relationship is: $y = \left(10^{0.60}\right) 10^x \approx 4 \cdot 10^x$.

Prob. 77. Taking logarithms of both columns of data,

$\log x$	$\log y$
-1.00	-2.35
-0.30	0.12
0.00	0.76
0.18	1.13
0.30	1.39

we can see a linear relation among the two columns, and the equation relating them can be checked to be $Y \approx 2.1X + 0.76$, that is:

$$\log y = 2.1 \log x + 0.76$$

so solving for y in terms of x we get:

$$\log y = \log x^{2.1} + 0.76$$

$$\log y - \log x^{2.1} = 0.76$$

or

$$\log \frac{y}{x^{2.1}} = 0.76$$

and thus the functional relationship is: $y = \left(10^{0.76}\right) x^{2.1} \approx 5.7 x^{2.1}$.

Prob. 79. Taking logarithms in base 2 we have $\log_2 y = x$, so the linear relationship is $Y = X$ on a $\log_2$-linear plot.

Prob. 81. Taking logarithms in base 2 we have $\log_2 y = -x$, so the linear relationship is $Y = -X$ on a $\log_2$-linear plot.

Prob. 83. (a) Taking logarithms, we have $\log N = \log \left(2e^{3t}\right) = \log 2 + 3t \log e = (3 \log e)t + \log 2$. Setting $Y = \log N$ and $X = t$ we have $Y = (3 \log e)X + \log 2$, which is a linear relationship.

(b) Graphing gives the following line with slope $3\log(e)$.

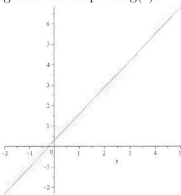

Prob. 85. (The relationship $S = CA^z$ leads to $\log S = \log(CA^z) = \log C + z\log A$. Plotting $Y = \log S$ and $X = \log A$ on a log-log scale would lead to a straight line given by $Y = zX + \log C$. Thus the model $S = CA^z$ is appropriate. The value of z is the slope of the straight line.

Prob. 87. Since $v_0 = \frac{v_{\max}s_0}{s_0+K_m}$, we can multiply both sides by $(s_0 + K_m)$ to obtain

$$v_0 s_0 + v_0 K_m = v_{\max}s_0$$

$$\frac{v_0 s_0 + v_0 K_m}{s_0 K_m} = \frac{v_{\max}s_0}{s_0 K_m}$$

$$\frac{v_0}{K_m} + \frac{v_0}{s_0} = \frac{v_{\max}}{K_m}$$

$$\frac{v_0}{s_0} = \frac{v_{\max}}{K_m} - \frac{1}{K_m}v_0$$

If we set $Y = \frac{v_0}{s_0}$ and $X = v_0$, this becomes $Y = \frac{v_{\max}}{K_m} - \frac{1}{K_m}X$, which is the equation of a straight line.

Here K_m is the negative reciprocal of the slope, and $v_{\max}$ is the Y-intercept multiplied by K_m.

Prob. 89. (a) Taking logarithms of the relation $S = 1.162B^{0.93}$, we have $\log S = \log 1.162 + 0.93\log B$. If we set $Y = \log S$ and $X = \log B$, we get the linear relationship $Y = \log 1.162 + 0.93X$. The slope is 0.93 and the y-intercept $\log 1.162$.

(b) When $B = 10$ cm, we have $S = 1.162(10)^{0.93} \approx 9.89$ and so the ratio of S to B is $S/B = 0.989$. When $B = 100$ cm, we have $S = 1.162(100)^{0.93} \approx 84.2$ and so the ratio of S to B is $S/B = 0.842$. When $B = 500$ cm, we have $S = 1.162(500)^{0.93} \approx 376$ and so the ratio of S to B is $S/B = 0.752$. Clearly, when B is smaller, the ratio is larger. As B increases (and the animal grows) the ratio decreases.

Prob. 91. (a) When $z = 1$, 90% of the intensity remains, and so we have $0.9 = I(1)/I(0) = e^{-\alpha z} = e^{-\alpha}$. This means $\alpha = -\ln 0.9$, measured in `meter`$^{-1}$.

(b) With $\alpha = -\ln 0.9$, we have $I(2)/I(1) = \frac{e^{-2\alpha}}{e^{-\alpha}} = e^{-\alpha} = e^{\ln 0.9} = 0.9$. Thus 90% of the intensity at the first meter remains at the second meter. That is, 10% is absorbed. A similar calculation shows that 10% of the intensity at the second meter is absorbed in the third meter.

(c) When $z = 1$m, we have $I(1)/I(0) = e^{-\alpha} = e^{\ln 0.9} = 0.9$, and so 90% remains. When $z = 2$m, we have $I(2)/I(0) = e^{-2\alpha} = e^{2\ln 0.9} = 0.9^2 = 0.81$, and so 81% remains. When $z = 3$m, we have $I(3)/I(0) = e^{-3\alpha} = e^{3\ln 0.9} = 0.9^3 = 0.729$, and so 72.9% remains.

(d) Please plot the graphs.

(e) Applying a logarithmic transformation to the equation $I(z) = I(0)e^{-\alpha z}$ we have

$$
\begin{aligned}
\log I(z) \quad &= \log(I(0)e^{-\alpha z}) \\
&= \log I(0) - \alpha z \log e \\
&= \log I(0) - (\alpha \log e)z
\end{aligned}
$$

Setting $Y = \log I(z)$, this gives the linear relationship $Y = \log I(0) - (\alpha \log e)z$. The slope of the line is given by $m = -\alpha \log e = \ln 0.9 \log e = \ln 0.9/\ln 10$.

(f) We want the ratio $I(z)/I(0)$ to equal 1%. That is, $0.01 = I(z)/I(0) = e^{-\alpha z} = e^{z \ln 0.9} = 0.9^z$. Thus $z = -\frac{\ln 0.01}{\alpha} = \frac{\ln(0.01)}{\ln(0.9)} \approx 43.7$m

(g) A clear lake would have small α, and a milky lake would have large α.

Prob. 93. $y = (100)(10^{1/3})^x$

Prob. 95. $y = (2^{1/3})(2^{2/3})^x$

Prob. 97. $Ay = \log x$

Prob. 99.

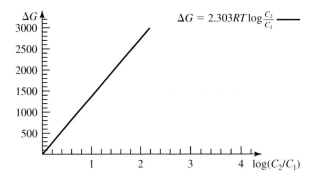

Prob. 101.

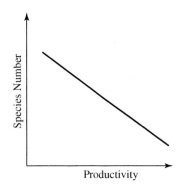

Prob. 103.

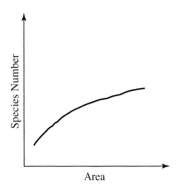

Prob. 105.

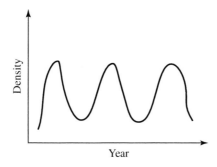

Prob. 107.

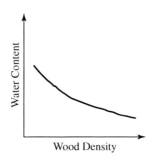

Prob. 109.

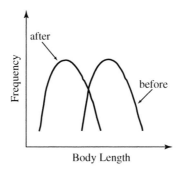

Prob. 111.

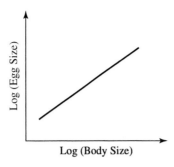

Prob. 113.

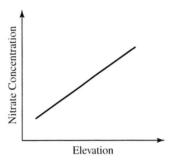

Prob. 115.

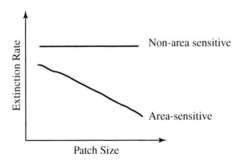

1.5 Review Problems

Prob. 1. (a) $10^4, 1.1 \times 10^4, 1.22 \times 10^4, 1.35 \times 10^4, 1.49 \times 10^4$

(b) $t = 10 \ln 10 \approx 23.0$

Prob. 3. (a) As the concentration of the reactants goes down as they are used up, the reaction rate slows down.

(b) $R(x) = -4kx^3 + 4k(a+b)x^2 - kb(4a-b)x + kab^2$, polynomial of degree 3

(c) $R(x) = (0.3)(5-x)(6-2x)^2, 0 \le x \le 3$

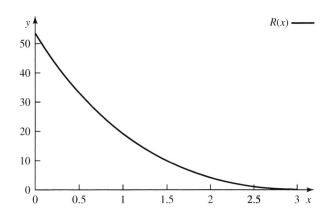

Prob. 5. (a) $L(t) = 0.69, 2.40, 4.62, 6.91, E(t) = 1.72, 2.20 \times 10^4, 2.69 \times 10^{43}, 10^{434}$

(b) 20.93 years, 3.13 ft

(c) $10^{536,000,000}$ years, 21.98 ft

(d) $L = 19.92$ ft, $E = 10^{195 \times 10^6}$ ft

Prob. 7. $T = \frac{\ln 2}{\ln(1+\frac{9}{100})}$, T goes to infinity as q gets closer to 0.

Prob. 9. (a)

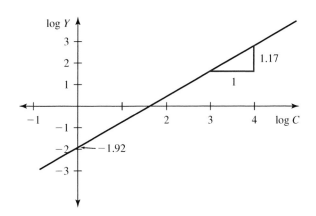

(b) $Y = C^{1.17}10^{-1.92}$

(c) $Y_p = 2.25Y_c$

(d) 8.5%

Prob. 11. (a) 400 days per year

(b) $y = 4.32 \times 10^9 - 1.8 \times 10^8 x$

(c) 376×10^6 to 563×10^6 years ago

Prob. 13. (a) males: $S(t) = \exp[-(0.019t)^{3.41}]$; females: $S(t) = \exp[-(0.022t)^{3.24}]$

(b) males: 47.27 days; females: 40.59 days

(c) males should live longer

Prob. 15. (a) $x = k$, $v = \frac{a}{2}$

(b) $x_{0.9} = 81x_{0.1}$

Prob. 17.

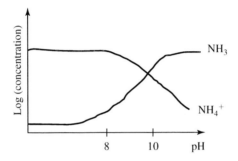

Prob. 19. $g(s) = \frac{v_{\max}}{S_k} S$

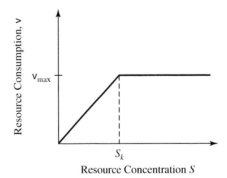

Prob. 21. (a) $\alpha = -\frac{\ln(0.01)}{18 \text{ m}} \approx 0.25\frac{1}{\text{m}}$

(b) 4.87 m

Chapter 2

Discrete Time Models, Sequences and Difference Equations

2.1 Exponential Growth and Decay

Prob. 1.

t	0	1	2	3	4	5
N_t	1	3	9	27	81	273

$N_t = 3^t$

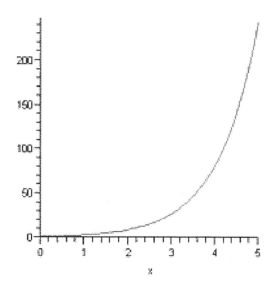

Prob. 3. $N_t = \frac{25}{4^t}$,

t	0	1	2	3	4	5
N_t	25	$\frac{25}{4}$	$\frac{25}{16}$	$\frac{25}{64}$	$\frac{25}{256}$	$\frac{25}{1024}$

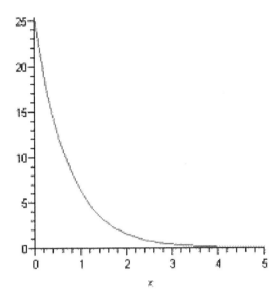

Prob. 5. We have $N(t) = 2 \cdot 2^t$

Prob. 7. We have $N(t) = 1 \cdot 2^{2t}$.

Prob. 9. We have $N(t) = 2 \cdot 4^{t/2}$

Prob. 11. Need to find t so that

$$40 = 20.4^t$$
$$2 = 4^t$$
$$2 = 2^{2t}$$

hence, $t = \frac{1}{2}$, meaning 1.5 hours.

Prob. 13. At time 0, there is one bacterium. After 1 hour, the bacterium splits into two, so there are two bacteria at time 1. One hour later, each of the bacteria splits again, resulting in 4 bacteria and so on.

Population Size table for function $N(t) = 2^t$

t	0	1	2	3	4	5
$N(t)$	1	2	4	8	16	32

Prob. 15. At time 0, there is one bacterium. After 23 min, the bacterium splits into two, so there are two bacteria at time 23 min. 23 minutes later, each of the bacteria splits again, resulting in 4 bacteria and so on.

Suppose one unit of time equals 23 minutes.

From the equation $N(t) = 2^t$, we get $128 = 2^t$, or $2^7 = 2^t$. Therefore, $t = 7$.

Seven units of time corresponds to $23 \cdot 7 = 161$ `minutes` $= 2$ hours and 41 minutes. Thus there are 128 bacteria in 2 hours and 41 minutes.

Prob. 17. At time 0, there are three bacteria. After 10 min, each bacteria splits into two, so there are 6 bacteria at time 10 min. Ten minutes later, each of the bacteria splits again, resulting in 12 bacteria and so on.

Suppose one unit of time equals 10 minutes.

From the equation $N(t) = N_0 2^t$, we get $96 = (3)2^t$, or $2^5 = 2^t$. Therefore, $t = 5$.

Five units of time corresponds to $10 \cdot 5 = 50$ minutes. Thus there are 96 bacteria in 50 minutes.

Prob. 19. Let $N(t)$ be the population size at time t, where t is measured in units of time, as in the previous exercises. If initially there is one bacterium and each bacteria splits into two in a unit time, then from the table shown below we will get:

Population Size table

t	0	1	2	3	4	5
$N(t)$	1	2	4	8	16	32

Here $N(t) = 2^t$, for $t = 0, 1, 2, \ldots$. The base of 2 reflects the fact that the population doubles in every unit of time. Now, if we had 40 bacteria in the beginning, then the new table will be:

Population Size table for the new function

t	0	1	2	3	4	5
$N(t)$	40	80	160	320	640	1280

We see that the initial population size appears as a multiplicative factor in front of the term 2^t. So we can now write the exponential growth equation as: $N(t) = 40 \cdot 2^t$, for $t = 0, 1, 2, \ldots$.

Prob. 21. As already discussed in the previous exercises, we know that the base 2 indicates that the population size doubles in every unit of time. For representing a population that triples in size in every unit of time, we initially modify our previous equation to be $N(t) = 3^t$, for $t = 0, 1, 2 \ldots$. Now, we have 20 bacteria in the beginning. This means the population table will be:

Population size table

t	0	1	2	3	4	5
$N(t)$	20	60	180	540	1620	4860

The initial population size appears as a multiplicative factor in front of the term 3^t. So we can write the exponential growth equation as $N(t) = 20 \cdot 3^t$, for $t = 0, 1, 2, \ldots$.

Prob. 23. As already discussed in the previous exercises, we know that the base 2 indicates that the population size doubles in every unit of time, and the base 3 indicates that the population size triples in every unit of time. For representing a population that quadruples in size in every unit of time, we initially modify our previous equation to be $N(t) = 4^t$, for $t = 0, 1, 2 \ldots$. Now, we have 5 bacteria in the beginning. This means the population table will be:

Population size table

t	0	1	2	3	4	5
$N(t)$	5	20	80	320	1280	5120

The initial population size appears as a multiplicative factor in front of the term 4^t. So we can write the exponential growth equation as $N(t) = 5 \cdot 4^t$, for $t = 0, 1, 2, \ldots$.

Prob. 25. While constructing population size tables for a population that doubles its size in every unit of time, we simply double the population size from one time step to the next. That is, we compute the population size at time $t + 1$ by doubling the population size at time t.

Let us denote N(t) by N_t. Here we begin with a population size of $N_0 = 20$ at $t = 0$, and so the population size at $t = 1$ is $N_1 = 40 = 2N_0$. The population at the end of the next time period is $N_2 = 80 = 2 \cdot 40 = 2N_1$, and so on. Thus the required recursion formula is $N_{t+1} = 2N_t$, with $N_0 = 20$.

Prob. 27. While constructing population size tables for a population that triples its size in every unit of time, we simply triple the population size from one time step to the next. That is, we compute the population size at time $t + 1$ by multiplying the population size at time t by 3.

Let us denote N(t) by N_t. Here we begin with a population size of $N_0 = 10$ at $t = 0$, and so the population size at $t = 1$ is $N_1 = 30 = 3 \cdot 10 = 3N_0$. The population at the end of the next time period is $N_2 = 90 = 3 \cdot 30 = 3N_1$, and so on. Thus the required recursion formula is $N_{t+1} = 3N_t$, with $N_0 = 10$.

Prob. 29. While constructing population size tables for a population that quadruples its size in every unit of time, we simply quadruple the population size from one time step to the next. That is, we compute the population size at time $t + 1$ by multiplying the population size at time t by 4.

Let us denote N(t) by N_t. Here we begin with a population size of $N_0 = 30$ at $t = 0$, and so the population size at $t = 1$ is $N_1 = 120 = 4 \cdot 30 = 4N_0$. The population at the end of the next time period is $N_2 = 480 = 4 \cdot 120 = 4N_1$, and so on. Thus the required recursion formula is $N_{t+1} = 4N_t$, with $N_0 = 30$.

Prob. 31.

Plot of the curve $f(x) = 2^x$ and the points $N_t = 2^t$.

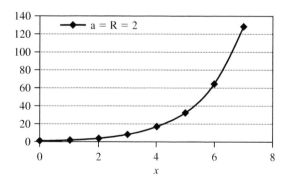

Prob. 33.

Plot of the curve $f(x) = 0.5^x$ and the points $N_t = 0.5^t$.

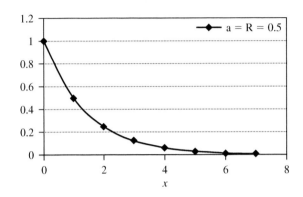

Prob. 35. $N_{t+1} = 2N_t$ with $N_0 = 3$, for $t = 0, 1, 2, \ldots 5$.

Table for the Population Size

t	0	1	2	3	4	5
N_t	3	6	12	24	48	96

Prob. 37. $N_{t+1} = 3N_t$ with $N_0 = 2$, for $t = 0, 1, 2, \ldots 5$.

Table for the Population Size

t	0	1	2	3	4	5
N_t	2	6	18	54	162	486

Prob. 39. $N_{t+1} = 5N_t$ with $N_0 = 1$, for $t = 0, 1, 2, \ldots 5$.

Table for the Population Size

t	0	1	2	3	4	5
N_t	1	5	25	125	625	3125

Prob. 41. $N_{t+1} = \frac{1}{2}N_t$ with $N_0 = 1024$, for $t = 0, 1, 2, \ldots 5$.

Table for the Population Size

t	0	1	2	3	4	5
N_t	1024	512	256	128	64	32

Prob. 43. $N_{t+1} = \frac{1}{3}N_t$ with $N_0 = 729$, for $t = 0, 1, 2, \ldots 5$.

Table for the Population Size

t	0	1	2	3	4	5
N_t	729	243	81	27	9	3

Prob. 45. $N_{t+1} = \frac{1}{5}N_t$ with $N_0 = 31250$, for $t = 0, 1, 2, \ldots 5$.

Table for the Population Size

t	0	1	2	3	4	5
N_t	31250	6250	1250	250	50	10

Prob. 47. Here $N_{t+1} = 2N_t$ with $N_0 = 15$. Thus N_t as a function of t would be $N_t = N(t) = 15 \cdot 2^t$.

Prob. 49. Here $N_{t+1} = 3N_t$ with $N_0 = 12$. Thus N_t as a function of t would be $N_t = N(t) = 12 \cdot 3^t$.

Prob. 51. Here $N_{t+1} = 4N_t$ with $N_0 = 24$. Thus N_t as a function of t would be $N_t = N(t) = 24 \cdot 4^t$.

Prob. 53. Here $N_{t+1} = \frac{1}{2}N_t$ with $N_0 = 5000$. Thus N_t as a function of t would be $N_t = N(t) = 5000(\frac{1}{2})^t = 5000 \cdot 2^{-t}$.

Prob. 55. Here $N_{t+1} = \frac{1}{3}N_t$ with $N_0 = 8000$. Thus N_t as a function of t would be $N_t = N(t) = 8000(\frac{1}{3})^t = 8000 \cdot 3^{-t}$.

Prob. 57. Here $N_{t+1} = \frac{1}{5}N_t$ with $N_0 = 1200$. Thus N_t as a function of t would be $N_t = N(t) = 1200(\frac{1}{5})^t = 1200 \cdot 5^{-t}$.

Prob. 59.

Plot of (N_t, N_{t+1}) for $R = 2, N_0 = 2$

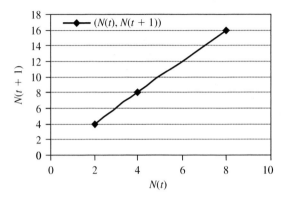

Prob. 61.

Plot of (N_t, N_{t+1}) for $R = 3, N_0 = 1$

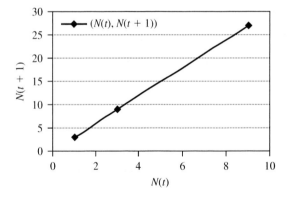

Prob. 63.

Plot of (N_t, N_{t+1}) for $R = \frac{1}{2}, N_0 = 16$

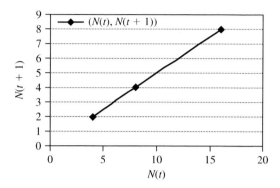

Prob. 65.

Plot of (N_t, N_{t+1}) for $R = \frac{1}{3}, N_0 = 81$

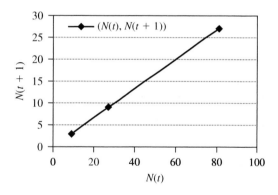

Prob. 67.

Plot of $(N_t, \frac{N_t}{N_{t+1}})$ for $R = 2, N_0 = 2$

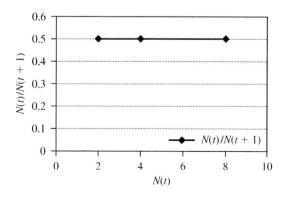

Prob. 69.

Plot of $\left(N_t, \frac{N_t}{N_{t+1}}\right)$ for $R = 3, N_0 = 2$

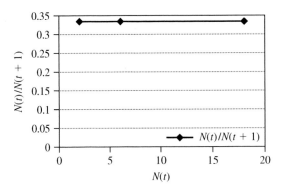

Prob. 71.

Plot of $\left(N_t, \frac{N_t}{N_{t+1}}\right)$ for $R = \frac{1}{2}, N_0 = 16$

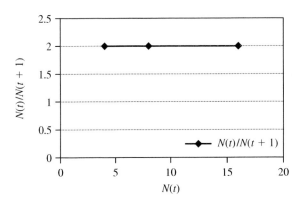

Prob. 73.

Plot of $\left(N_t, \frac{N_t}{N_{t+1}}\right)$ for $R = \frac{1}{3}, N_0 = 27$

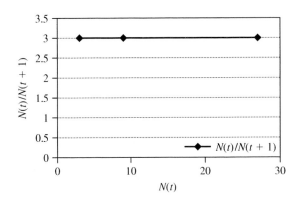

Prob. 75.

(a) As in the Section 2.1, we know that if the parent-offspring ratio is constant, then parents produce the same number of offsprings regardless of the current population density. But as the nesting sites is a limiting factor in population growth, if all the nesting sites are occupied then the parent-offspring ratio is probably not constant, and hence there would not be an exponential population growth.

(b) This is a suitable case as the number of nesting sites are much larger than the population. Assuming that all other conditions are favorable, population growth would be exponential.

(c) As a hurricane had killed a large number of birds, it is very probable that the nesting conditions and other important conditions necessary for survival are not suitable. There is a very high probability that the growth rate would not be exponential though such a situation cannot totally be ruled out.

Prob. 77. Population growth is density independent typically when conditions for the growth of the organism are constant and favorable throughout the time span. However, conditions like pollution, over-crowding, competition with other inhabitants or species, invasion of other species and natural disasters can be reasons for instability in the population growth.

2.2 Sequences

Prob. 1. Here the sequence is $a_n = n$. For $n = 0, 1, 2, \ldots, 5$ the sequence takes the values $0, 1, 2, 3, 4, 5$.

Prob. 3. Here the sequence is $a_n = \frac{1}{n+2}$. For $n = 0, 1, 2, \ldots, 5$ the sequence takes the values $\frac{1}{2}, \frac{1}{3}, \frac{1}{4}, \frac{1}{5}, \frac{1}{6}, \frac{1}{7}$.

Prob. 5. $f(n) = \frac{1}{(1+n)^2}$, we have

n	0	1	2	3	4	5
$f(n)$	1	$\frac{1}{4}$	$\frac{1}{9}$	$\frac{1}{16}$	$\frac{1}{25}$	$\frac{1}{36}$

Prob. 7. $f(n) = (n+1)^2$, we have

n	0	1	2	3	4	5
$f(n)$	1	4	9	16	25	36

Prob. 9. Here the sequence is $a_n = (-1)^n n$. For $n = 0, 1, 2, \ldots, 5$ the sequence takes the values $0, -1, 2, -3, 4, -5$.

Prob. 11. Here the sequence is $a_n = \frac{n^2}{n+1}$. For $n = 0, 1, 2, \ldots, 5$ the sequence takes the values $0, 1/2, 4/3, 9/4, 16/5, 25/6$. That is, $0, \frac{1}{2}, 1\frac{1}{3}, 2\frac{1}{4}, 3\frac{1}{5}, 4\frac{1}{6}$.

Prob. 13. $f(n) = e^{\sqrt{n}}$, we have

n	0	1	2	3	4	5
$f(n)$	1	e	$e^{\sqrt{2}}$	$e^{\sqrt{3}}$	e^2	$e^{\sqrt{5}}$

Prob. 15. $f(n) = (\frac{1}{3})^n$, we have

n	0	1	2	3	4	5
$f(n)$	1	$\frac{1}{3}$	$\frac{1}{9}$	$\frac{1}{27}$	$\frac{1}{81}$	$\frac{1}{243}$

Prob. 17. We can guess that the given sequence is $a_n = n + 1$, for $n = 0, 1, 2, 3, 4$. Thus for $n = 5, 6, 7, 8$ we have $a_n = 6, 7, 8, 9$.

Prob. 19. We can guess that the given sequence is $a_n = \frac{1}{(n+1)^2}$, for $n = 0, 1, 2, 3, 4$. Thus for $n = 5, 6, 7, 8$ we have $a_n = 1/36, 1/49, 1/64, 1/81$.

Prob. 21. We can guess that the given sequence is $a_n = \frac{n+1}{n+2}$, for $n = 0, 1, 2, 3, 4$. Thus for $n = 5, 6, 7, 8$ we have $a_n = 6/7, 7/8, 8/9, 9/10$.

Prob. 23. We can guess that the given sequence is $a_n = \sqrt{(n+1) + e^{n+1}}$, for $n = 0, 1, 2, 3, 4$. Thus for $n = 5, 6, 7, 8$ we have $a_n = \sqrt{6 + e^6}, \sqrt{7 + e^7}, \sqrt{8 + e^8}, \sqrt{9 + e^9}$.

Prob. 25. The given sequence is $a_0 = 0, a_1 = 1, a_2 = 2, a_3 = 3$ and $a_4 = 4$. Thus we can guess the expression to be $a_n = n$ for $n = 0, 1, 2, \ldots$.

Prob. 27. The given sequence is $a_0 = 1, a_1 = 2, a_2 = 4, a_3 = 8$ and $a_4 = 16$. Thus we can guess the expression to be $a_n = 2^n$ for $n = 0, 1, 2, \ldots$.

Prob. 29. The given sequence is $a_0 = 1, a_1 = \frac{1}{3}, a_2 = \frac{1}{9}, a_3 = \frac{1}{27}$ and $a_4 = \frac{1}{81}$. Thus we can guess the expression to be $a_n = \frac{1}{3^n}$ for $n = 0, 1, 2, \ldots$.

Prob. 31. The given sequence is $a_0 = -1, a_1 = 2, a_2 = -3, a_3 = 4$ and $a_4 = -5$. Thus we can guess the expression to be $a_n = (-1)^{n+1}(n+1)$ for $n = 0, 1, 2, \ldots$.

Prob. 33. The given sequence is $a_0 = -\frac{1}{2}, a_1 = \frac{1}{3}, a_2 = -\frac{1}{4}, a_3 = \frac{1}{5}$ and $a_4 = -\frac{1}{6}$. Thus we can guess the expression to be $a_n = \frac{(-1)^{n+1}}{n+2}$ for $n = 0, 1, 2, \ldots$.

Prob. 35. The given sequence is $a_0 = \sin \pi, a_1 = \sin 2\pi, a_2 = \sin 3\pi, a_3 = \sin 4\pi$ and $a_4 = \sin 5\pi$. Thus we can guess the expression to be $a_n = \sin(n+1)\pi$ for $n = 0, 1, 2, \ldots$.

Prob. 37. Plugging successive values of n into the given expression for a_n, we get the sequence

$$\frac{1}{2}, \frac{1}{3}, \frac{1}{4}, \frac{1}{5}, \frac{1}{6}, \ldots$$

Also,

$$\lim_{n \to \infty} a_n = \lim_{n \to \infty} \frac{1}{n+2} = 0.$$

Prob. 39. Plugging successive values of n into the given expression for a_n, we get the sequence

$$0, \frac{1}{2}, \frac{2}{3}, \frac{3}{4}, \frac{4}{5}, \ldots$$

Also,

$$\lim_{n \to \infty} a_n = \lim_{n \to \infty} \frac{n}{n+1} = 1.$$

Prob. 41. Plugging successive values of n into the given expression for a_n, we get the sequence

$$1, \frac{1}{2}, \frac{1}{5}, \frac{1}{10}, \frac{1}{17}, \ldots$$

Also,

$$\lim_{n \to \infty} a_n = \lim_{n \to \infty} \frac{1}{n^2+1} = 0.$$

Prob. 43. Plugging successive values of n into the given expression for a_n, we get the sequence

$$1, -\frac{1}{2}, \frac{1}{3}, -\frac{1}{4}, \frac{1}{5}, \ldots$$

Also,

$$\lim_{n \to \infty} a_n = \lim_{n \to \infty} \frac{(-1)^n}{n+1} = 0.$$

Prob. 45. Plugging successive values of n into the given expression for a_n we get the sequence

$$0, \frac{1}{2}, \frac{4}{3}, \frac{9}{4}, \frac{16}{5}, \ldots$$

From this, we can guess that the terms will approach infinity as n tends to infinity. That is,

$$\lim_{n \to \infty} a_n = \lim_{n \to \infty} \frac{n^2}{n+1} = \infty.$$

Since the limiting value is not a number, we can say that the limit does not exist.

Prob. 47. Plugging successive values of n into the given expression for a_n we get the sequence

$$0, 1, \sqrt{2}, \sqrt{3}, 2, \ldots.$$

From this, we can guess that the terms will approach infinity as n tends to infinity. That is,

$$\lim_{n \to \infty} a_n = \lim_{n \to \infty} \sqrt{n} = \infty.$$

Since the limiting value is not a number, we can say that the limit does not exist.

Prob. 49. Plugging successive values of n into the given expression for a_n we get the sequence

$$1, 2, 4, 8, 16, \ldots.$$

From this, we can guess that the terms will approach infinity as n tends to infinity. That is,

$$\lim_{n \to \infty} a_n = \lim_{n \to \infty} 2^n = \infty.$$

Since the limiting value is not a number, we can say that the limit does not exist.

Prob. 51. Plugging successive values of n into the given expression for a_n we get the sequence

$$1, 3, 9, 27, 81, \ldots.$$

From this, we can guess that the terms will approach infinity as n tends to infinity. That is,

$$\lim_{n \to \infty} a_n = \lim_{n \to \infty} 3^n = \infty.$$

Since the limiting value is not a number, we can say that the limit does not exist.

Prob. 53. With $n = 1, 2, 3, 4, \ldots$ and $a_n = \frac{1}{n}$, we find that the sequence is $1, \frac{1}{2}, \frac{1}{3}, \frac{1}{4}, \ldots$, so we guess that the terms will approach the limit $a = 0$ as n tends to infinity. Now, we need to find an integer N such that $\left|\frac{1}{n} - 0\right| < \epsilon = 0.01$ whenever $n > N$. Solving the inequality $\left|\frac{1}{n} - 0\right| < 0.01$ for positive n, we find that $\frac{1}{n} < 0.01$ or $n > \frac{1}{0.01} = 100$. Thus the smallest value of N that we can choose seems to be $N = 100$. Successive values of $n > 100$ give us confidence that we are on the right track, but this doesn't prove that our choice is correct:

$$a_{101} = \frac{1}{101} \approx 0.00990, \quad a_{102} = \frac{1}{102} \approx 0.00980,$$

and so on. To prove that our choice for N works, we need to show that $n > N$ implies $|1/n - a| < \epsilon$. Indeed, we have that $n > 100$ implies $|\frac{1}{n} - 0| = \frac{1}{n} < \frac{1}{100} = 0.01$.

Prob. 55. With $n = 1, 2, 3, 4, \ldots$ and $a_n = \frac{1}{n^2}$, we find that the sequence is $1, \frac{1}{4}, \frac{1}{9}, \frac{1}{16}, \ldots$, so we guess that the terms will approach the limit $a = 0$ as n tends to infinity. Now, we need to find an integer N such that $|\frac{1}{n^2} - 0| < \epsilon = 0.01$ whenever $n > N$. Solving the inequality $|\frac{1}{n^2} - 0| < 0.01$ for positive n, we find that $\frac{1}{n^2} < 0.01$ or $n > \frac{1}{0.1} = 10$. Thus the smallest value of N that we can choose seems to be $N = 10$. Successive values of $n > 10$ give us confidence that we are on the right track, but this doesn't prove that our choice is correct:

$$a_{11} = \frac{1}{121} \approx 0.00826, \quad a_{12} = \frac{1}{144} \approx 0.00694,$$

and so on. To prove that our choice for N works, we need to show that $n > N$ implies $|1/n^2 - a| < \epsilon$. Indeed, we have that $n > 10$ implies $|\frac{1}{n^2} - 0| = \frac{1}{n^2} < \frac{1}{100} = 0.01$.

Prob. 57. With $n = 1, 2, 3, 4, \ldots$ and $a_n = \frac{1}{\sqrt{n}}$, we find that the sequence is $1, \frac{1}{\sqrt{2}}, \frac{1}{\sqrt{3}}, \frac{1}{2}, \ldots$, so we guess that the terms will approach the limit $a = 0$ as n tends to infinity. Now, we need to find an integer N such that $|\frac{1}{\sqrt{n}} - 0| < \epsilon = 0.1$ whenever $n > N$. Solving the inequality $|\frac{1}{\sqrt{n}} - 0| < 0.1$ for positive n, we find that $\frac{1}{\sqrt{n}} < 0.1$ or $n > \left(\frac{1}{0.1}\right)^2 = 100$. Thus the smallest value of N that we can choose seems to be $N = 100$. Successive values of $n > 100$ give us confidence that we are on the right track, but this doesn't prove that our choice is correct:

$$a_{101} = \frac{1}{\sqrt{101}} \approx 0.0995, \quad a_{102} = \frac{1}{\sqrt{102}} \approx 0.0990,$$

and so on. To prove that our choice for N works, we need to show that $n > N$ implies $|1/\sqrt{n} - a| < \epsilon$. Indeed, we have that $n > 100$ implies $|\frac{1}{\sqrt{n}} - 0| = \frac{1}{\sqrt{n}} < \frac{1}{\sqrt{100}} = 0.1$.

Prob. 59. With $n = 1, 2, 3, 4, \ldots$ and $a_n = \frac{(-1)^n}{n}$, we find that the sequence is $-1, \frac{1}{2}, -\frac{1}{3}, \frac{1}{4}, \ldots$, so we guess that the terms will approach the limit $a = 0$ as n tends to infinity. Now, we need to find an integer N such that $|\frac{(-1)^n}{n} - 0| < \epsilon = 0.01$ whenever $n > N$. Solving the inequality $|\frac{(-1)^n}{n} - 0| < 0.01$ for positive n, we find that $\frac{1}{n} < 0.01$ or $n > \frac{1}{0.01} = 100$. Thus the smallest value of N that we can choose seems to be $N = 100$. Successive values of $n > 100$ give us confidence that we are on the right track, but this doesn't prove that our choice is correct:

$$a_{101} = \frac{(-1)^{101}}{101} \approx -0.00990, \quad a_{102} = \frac{(-1)^{102}}{102} \approx 0.00980,$$

and so on. To prove that our choice for N works, we need to show that $n > N$ implies $|\frac{(-1)^n}{n} - a| < \epsilon$. Indeed, we have that $n > 100$ implies $|\frac{(-1)^n}{n} - 0| = \frac{1}{n} < \frac{1}{100} = 0.01$.

Prob. 61. With $n = 1, 2, 3, 4, \ldots$ and $a_n = \frac{n}{n+1}$, we find that the sequence is $\frac{1}{2}, \frac{2}{3}, \frac{3}{4}, \frac{4}{5}, \ldots$, so we guess that the terms will approach the limit $a = 1$ as n tends to infinity. Now, we need to find an integer N such that $|\frac{n}{n+1} - 1| < \epsilon = 0.01$ whenever $n > N$. Solving the inequality $|\frac{n}{n+1} - 1| < 0.01$ for positive n, we find that $|\frac{n-(n+1)}{n+1}| = \frac{1}{n+1} < 0.01$ or $n > \frac{1}{0.01} - 1 = 99$. Thus the smallest value of N that we can choose seems to be $N = 99$. Successive values of $n > 99$ give us confidence that we are on the right track, but this doesn't prove that our choice is correct:

$$a_{100} = \frac{100}{101} \approx 0.990099, \quad a_{101} = \frac{101}{102} \approx 0.990196,$$

and so on. To prove that our choice for N works, we need to show that $n > N$ implies $|\frac{n}{n+1} - a| < \epsilon$. Indeed, we have that $n > 99$ implies $|\frac{n}{n+1} - 1| = \frac{1}{n+1} < \frac{1}{100} = 0.01$.

Prob. 63. With $n = 1, 2, 3, 4, \ldots$ and $a_n = \frac{n^2}{n^2+1}$, we find that the sequence is $\frac{1}{2}, \frac{4}{5}, \frac{9}{10}, \frac{16}{17}, \ldots$, so we guess that the terms will approach the limit $a = 1$ as n tends to infinity. Now, we need to find an integer N such that $|\frac{n^2}{n^2+1} - 1| < \epsilon = 0.01$ whenever $n > N$. Solving the inequality $|\frac{n^2}{n^2+1} - 1| < 0.01$ for positive n, we find that $|\frac{n^2-(n^2+1)}{n^2+1}| = \frac{1}{n^2+1} < 0.01$ or $n > \sqrt{1/0.01 - 1} = \sqrt{99} \approx 9.95$. Thus the smallest value of N that we can choose seems to be $N = 9$. Successive values of $n > 9$ give us confidence that we are on the right track, but this doesn't prove that our choice is correct:

$$a_{10} = \frac{100}{101} \approx 0.990099, \quad a_{11} = \frac{121}{122} \approx 0.991803,$$

and so on. To prove that our choice for N works, we need to show that $n > N$ implies $|\frac{n^2}{n^2+1} - a| < \epsilon$. Indeed, we have that $n > 9$ implies $n \geq 10$ which implies that $|\frac{n^2}{n^2+1} - 1| = \frac{1}{n^2+1} \leq \frac{1}{100+1} < 0.01$.

Prob. 65. We have to show that for every $\epsilon > 0$ we can find N such that

$|1/n - 0| < \epsilon$ whenever $n > N$.

To find a candidate for N, we solve the inequality $|1/n| < \epsilon$. Since $1/n > 0$, we drop the absolute value and find that

$1/n < \epsilon$ or $n > 1/\epsilon$

Let's choose N to be the largest integer less than or equal to $1/\epsilon$. If $n > N$, then $n \geq N+1$, which is equivalent to $1/n \leq 1/(N+1)$. Since N is the largest integer less than or equal to $1/\epsilon$, it follows that $1/\epsilon < N+1$, and so $1/n \leq 1/(N+1) < \epsilon$ for $n > N$. This, together with $n > 0$, shows that if N is the largest integer less than or equal to $1/\epsilon$, then $|1/n - 0| < \epsilon$ whenever $n > N$.

Prob. 67. We have to show that for every $\epsilon > 0$ we can find N such that

$|1/n^2 - 0| < \epsilon$ whenever $n > N$.

To find a candidate for N, we solve the inequality $|1/n^2| < \epsilon$. Since $1/n^2 > 0$, we drop the absolute value and find that

$1/n^2 < \epsilon$ or $n > 1/\sqrt{\epsilon}$

Let's choose N to be the largest integer less than or equal to $1/\sqrt{\epsilon}$. If $n > N$, then $n \geq N+1$, which is equivalent to $1/n \leq 1/(N+1)$. Since N is the largest integer less than or equal to $1/\sqrt{\epsilon}$, it follows that $1/\sqrt{\epsilon} < N+1$, and so $1/n \leq 1/(N+1) < \sqrt{\epsilon}$ for $n > N$. Squaring, we get $1/n^2 \leq 1/(N+1)^2 < \epsilon$ for $n > N$. This shows that if N is the largest integer less than or equal to $1/\sqrt{\epsilon}$, then $|1/n^2 - 0| < \epsilon$ whenever $n > N$.

Prob. 69. We have to show that for every $\epsilon > 0$ we can find N such that

$|(n+1)/n - 1| < \epsilon$ whenever $n > N$.

To find a candidate for N, we solve the inequality $|(n+1)/n-1| < \epsilon$. Since $(n+1)/n-1 = 1/n > 0$, we drop the absolute value and find that

$1/n < \epsilon$ or $n > 1/\epsilon$.

Let's choose N to be the largest integer less than or equal to $1/\epsilon$. If $n > N$, then $n \geq N+1$, which is equivalent to $1/n \leq 1/(N+1)$. Since N is the largest integer less than or equal to $1/\epsilon$, it follows that $1/\epsilon < N+1$, and so $(n+1)/n-1 = 1/n \leq 1/(N+1) < \epsilon$ for $n > N$. This, together with $n > 0$, shows that if N is the largest integer less than or equal to $1/\epsilon$, then $|(n+1)/n - 1| < \epsilon$ whenever $n > N$.

Prob. 71. We break $1/n^2$ into the product of two terms, namely $(1/n) \cdot (1/n)$. Since $\lim_{n\to\infty} \frac{1}{n}$ exists and is equal to 0, we find that

$$\lim_{n\to\infty} \left(\frac{1}{n} + \frac{1}{n^2} \right) = \lim_{n\to\infty} \frac{1}{n} + \left(\lim_{n\to\infty} \frac{1}{n} \right) \cdot \left(\lim_{n\to\infty} \frac{1}{n} \right) = 0 + 0 \cdot 0 = 0.$$

Prob. 73. We can write $\frac{n+1}{n}$ as $1 + 1/n$. Since both $\lim_{n\to\infty} 1$ and $\lim_{n\to\infty}(1/n)$ exist and are equal to 1 and 0 respectively, we have

$$\lim_{n\to\infty} \frac{n+1}{n} = \lim_{n\to\infty}(1 + 1/n) = \lim_{n\to\infty} 1 + \lim_{n\to\infty}(1/n) = 1 + 0 = 1.$$

Prob. 75. We can write $\frac{n^2+1}{n^2}$ as $1 + \frac{1}{n} \cdot \frac{1}{n}$. Since both $\lim_{n\to\infty} 1$ and $\lim_{n\to\infty}(1/n)$ exist and are equal to 1 and 0 respectively, we have

$$\lim_{n\to\infty} \frac{n^2+1}{n^2} = \lim_{n\to\infty}\left(1 + \frac{1}{n}\cdot\frac{1}{n}\right) = \lim_{n\to\infty} 1 + \lim_{n\to\infty}\left(\frac{1}{n}\cdot\frac{1}{n}\right)$$

$$= \lim_{n\to\infty} 1 + \lim_{n\to\infty}\frac{1}{n}\cdot\lim_{n\to\infty}\frac{1}{n} = 1 + 0\cdot 0 = 1.$$

Prob. 77. We can factor the denominator of $\frac{n+1}{n^2-1}$ and write this as $\frac{n+1}{(n+1)(n-1)} = \frac{1}{n-1}$. Recalling that $\lim_{n\to\infty}\frac{1}{n}$ exists and is equal to 0, we find that

$$\lim_{n\to\infty} \frac{n+1}{n^2-1} = \lim_{n\to\infty}\frac{1}{n-1}$$

$$= \lim_{n\to\infty}\frac{1/n}{1-1/n}$$

$$= \frac{\lim_{n\to\infty}(1/n)}{\lim_{n\to\infty}(1-1/n)}$$

$$= \frac{\lim_{n\to\infty}(1/n)}{1-\lim_{n\to\infty}(1/n)}$$

$$= \frac{0}{1-0} = 0.$$

Prob. 79. By Example 12, we know that $\lim_{n\to\infty}(1/3)^n$ and $\lim_{n\to\infty}(1/2)^n$ exist and are equal to 0. Thus we have

$$\lim_{n\to\infty}\left[\left(\frac{1}{3}\right)^n + \left(\frac{1}{2}\right)^n\right] = \lim_{n\to\infty}\left(\frac{1}{3}\right)^n + \lim_{n\to\infty}\left(\frac{1}{2}\right)^n = 0 + 0 = 0.$$

Prob. 81. First, notice that the expression $(n+2^{-n})/n$ can also be written as $1 + \left(\frac{1}{2}\right)^n \cdot \frac{1}{n}$. Since the limits $\lim_{n\to\infty} 1$, $\lim_{n\to\infty}\left(\frac{1}{2}\right)^n$ and $\lim_{n\to\infty}\frac{1}{n}$ exist and are equal to 1, 0 and 0 respectively, we have that

$$\lim_{n\to\infty}\frac{n+2^{-n}}{n} = \lim_{n\to\infty}\left[1 + \left(\frac{1}{2}\right)^n \cdot \frac{1}{n}\right]$$

$$= \lim_{n\to\infty} 1 + \lim_{n\to\infty}\left[\left(\frac{1}{2}\right)^n \cdot \frac{1}{n}\right]$$

$$= \lim_{n\to\infty} 1 + \lim_{n\to\infty}\left(\frac{1}{2}\right)^n \cdot \lim_{n\to\infty}\frac{1}{n}$$

$$= 1 + 0\cdot 0 = 1.$$

Prob. 83. By repeatedly applying the recursion to the equation $a_{n+1} = 2a_n$ with $a_0 = 1$, we have

$a_1 = 2a_0 = 2 \cdot 1 = 2$,

$a_2 = 2a_1 = 2 \cdot 2 = 4$,

$a_3 = 2a_2 = 2 \cdot 4 = 8$,

$a_4 = 2a_3 = 2 \cdot 8 = 16$, and

$a_5 = 2a_4 = 2 \cdot 16 = 32$.

Prob. 85. By repeatedly applying the recursion to the equation $a_{n+1} = 3a_n - 2$ with $a_0 = 1$, we have

$a_1 = 3a_0 - 2 = 3 \cdot 1 - 2 = 1$,

$a_2 = 3a_1 - 2 = 3 \cdot 1 - 2 = 1$,

$a_3 = 3a_2 - 2 = 3 \cdot 1 - 2 = 1$,

$a_4 = 3a_3 - 2 = 3 \cdot 1 - 2 = 1$, and

$a_5 = 3a_4 - 2 = 3 \cdot 1 - 2 = 1$.

Prob. 87. By repeatedly applying the recursion to the equation $a_{n+1} = 4 - 2a_n$ with $a_0 = 5$, we have

$a_1 = 4 - 2a_0 = 4 - 2 \cdot 5 = -6$,

$a_2 = 4 - 2a_1 = 4 - 2 \cdot (-6) = 16$,

$a_3 = 4 - 2a_2 = 4 - 2 \cdot 16 = -28$,

$a_4 = 4 - 2a_3 = 4 - 2 \cdot (-28) = 60$, and

$a_5 = 4 - 2a_4 = 4 - 2 \cdot 60 = -116$.

Prob. 89. By repeatedly applying the recursion to the equation $a_{n+1} = \frac{a_n}{1+a_n}$ with $a_0 = 1$, we have

$a_1 = a_0/(1 + a_0) = 1/(1 + 1) = 1/2$,

$a_2 = a_1/(1 + a_1) = (1/2)/(3/2) = 1/3$,

$a_3 = a_2/(1 + a_2) = (1/3)/(4/3) = 1/4$,

$a_4 = a_3/(1 + a_3) = (1/4)/(5/4) = 1/5$, and

$a_5 = a_4/(1 + a_4) = (1/5)/(6/5) = 1/6$.

Prob. 91. By repeatedly applying the recursion to the equation $a_{n+1} = a_n + \frac{1}{a_n}$ with $a_0 = 1$, we have

$a_1 = a_0 + 1/a_0 = 1 + 1/1 = 2,$

$a_2 = a_1 + 1/a_1 = 2 + 1/2 = 5/2 = 2.5,$

$a_3 = a_2 + 1/a_2 = 5/2 + 2/5 = 29/10 = 2.9,$

$a_4 = a_3 + 1/a_3 = 29/10 + 10/29 = 941/290 \approx 3.2448,$ and

$a_5 = a_4 + 1/a_4 = 941/290 + 290/941 = 969581/272890 \approx 3.5530.$

Prob. 93. Following the method of Example 14, here we have $f(a) = \frac{1}{2}a + 2$. If a is a fixed point, then it must satisfy the equation $a = f(a)$. That is,

$$a = \frac{1}{2}a + 2 \quad \Rightarrow \quad \frac{1}{2}a = 2 \quad \Rightarrow \quad a = 4.$$

Thus the only fixed point is $a = 4$.

Prob. 95. Following the method of Example 14, here we have $f(a) = \frac{2}{5}a - \frac{9}{5}$. If a is a fixed point, then it must satisfy the equation $a = f(a)$. That is,

$$a = \frac{2}{5}a - \frac{9}{5} \quad \Rightarrow \quad \frac{3}{5}a = -\frac{9}{5} \quad \Rightarrow \quad a = -3.$$

Thus the only fixed point is $a = -3$.

Prob. 97. Following the method of Example 14, here we have $f(a) = 4/a$. If a is a fixed point, then it must satisfy the equation $a = f(a)$. That is,

$$a = \frac{4}{a} \quad \Rightarrow \quad a^2 = 4 \quad \Rightarrow \quad a = \pm 2.$$

Thus there are two fixed points, namely $a = 2$ and $a = -2$.

Prob. 99. Following the method of Example 14, here we have $f(a) = 2/(a + 2)$. If a is a fixed point, then it must satisfy the equation $a = f(a)$. That is,

$$a = \frac{2}{a + 2} \quad \Rightarrow \quad a(a + 2) = 2 \quad \Rightarrow \quad a^2 + 2a - 2 = 0 \quad \Rightarrow \quad a = -1 \pm \sqrt{3}.$$

Thus there are two fixed points, namely $a = -1 + \sqrt{3}$ and $a = -1 - \sqrt{3}$.

Prob. 101. Following the method of Example 14, here we have $f(a) = \sqrt{5a}$. If a is a fixed point, then it must satisfy the equation $a = f(a)$. That is,

$$a = \sqrt{5a} \quad \Rightarrow \quad a^2 = 5a \quad \Rightarrow \quad a(a - 5) = 0 \quad \Rightarrow \quad a = 0 \text{ or } 5.$$

Thus there are two fixed points, namely $a = 0$ and $a = 5$.

Prob. 103. Since the problem tells us that the limit exists, we shall not concern ourselves with the existence of the limit but instead try to identify the limiting value.

To do this, we first compute the fixed points. As in Example 14, we solve the equation $a = \frac{1}{2}(a + 5)$ to find that $\frac{a}{2} = \frac{5}{2}$, or that $a = 5$. Now when $a_0 = 1$, then $a_n > 1$ for all $n = 1, 2, 3, \cdots$ and so we conclude that

$$\lim_{n \to \infty} a_n = 5.$$

Using a calculator, we can find successive (approximated) values of a_n, which we collect in the following table. The tabulated values suggest that the limit is indeed 5.

n	a_n
0	1
1	3
2	4
3	4.5
4	4.75
5	4.875
6	4.9375

Prob. 105. Since the problem tells us that the limit exists, we shall not concern ourselves with the existence of the limit but instead try to identify the limiting value.

To do this, we first compute the fixed points. As in Example 14, we solve the equation $a = \sqrt{2a}$ to find that $a(a - 2) = 0$, which means that $a = 0$ or $a = 2$. Now when $a_0 = 1$, then $a_n > 1$ for all $n = 1, 2, 3, \cdots$ and so we could conclude that

$$\lim_{n \to \infty} a_n = 2.$$

Using a calculator, we can find successive values of a_n, which we collect in the following table. The tabulated values suggest that the fixed point $a = 2$ is the limit.

n	a_n
0	1
1	$\sqrt{2}$
2	$2^{3/4}$
3	$2^{7/8}$
4	$2^{15/16}$
5	$2^{31/32}$
6	$2^{63/64}$

Prob. 107. Since the problem tells us that the limit exists, we shall not concern ourselves with the existence of the limit but instead try to identify the limiting value.

To do this, we first compute the fixed points. As in Example 14, we solve the equation $a = 2a(1 - a)$ to find that $a(2a - 1) = 0$, which means that $a = 0$ or $a = 1/2$. Now when $a_0 = 0.1$, then $a_n > 0.1$ for all $n = 1, 2, 3, \cdots$ and so we could conclude that

$$\lim_{n \to \infty} a_n = 1/2.$$

Using a calculator, we can find successive (approximated) values of a_n, which we collect in the following table. The tabulated values suggest that the fixed point $a = 1/2$ is the limit.

n	a_n
0	0.1
1	0.18
2	0.2952
3	0.41611
4	0.48592
5	0.4996
6	0.49999

Prob. 109. Since the problem tells us that the limit exists, we shall not concern ourselves with the existence of the limit but instead try to identify the limiting value.

To do this, we first compute the fixed points. As in Example 14, we solve the equation $a = \frac{1}{2}(a + \frac{4}{a})$ to find that $a = \frac{4}{a}$, or that $a = \pm 2$. Now when $a_0 = 1$, then $a_n > 1$ for all

$n = 1, 2, 3, \cdots$ and so we could conclude that

$$\lim_{n \to \infty} a_n = 2.$$

Using a calculator, we can find successive (approximated) values of a_n, which we collect in the following table. The tabulated values suggest that the limit is indeed 2.

n	a_n
0	1
1	2.5
2	2.05
3	2.00061
4	2.00000
5	2.00000

2.3 More Population Models

Prob. 1. The recursion to the Beverton-Holt recruitment curve is

$$N_{t+1} = \frac{2N_t}{1 + \frac{1}{15}N_t}$$

Graph of $\frac{N_t}{N_{t+1}}$ as a function of N_t

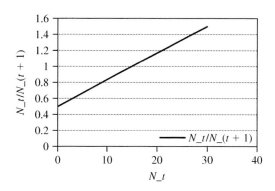

Prob. 3. The recursion to the Beverton-Holt recruitment curve is

$$N_{t+1} = \frac{1.5N_t}{1 + \frac{0.5}{40}N_t}$$

Graph of $\frac{N_t}{N_{t+1}}$ as a function of N_t

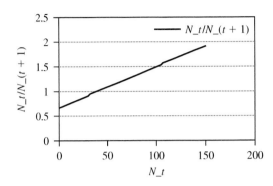

Prob. 5. The recursion to the Beverton-Holt recruitment curve is

$$N_{t+1} = \frac{2.5N_t}{1 + \frac{1.5}{90}N_t}$$

Graph of $\frac{N_t}{N_{t+1}}$ as a function of N_t

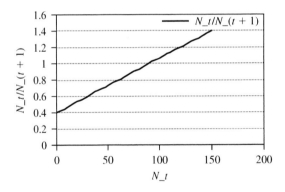

Prob. 7. The population growth equation described by the Beverton-Holt recruitment curve with growth parameter R and carrying capacity K is

$$N_{t+1} = \frac{RN_t}{1 + \frac{R-1}{K}N_t}$$

Now, the given equation

$$N_{t+1} = \frac{2N_t}{1 + \frac{1}{20}N_t}$$

can be written as

$$N_{t+1} = \frac{2N_t}{1 + \frac{2-1}{20}N_t}$$

and so we must have $R = 2$ and $K = 20$.

Prob. 9. The population growth equation described by the Beverton-Holt recruitment curve with growth parameter R and carrying capacity K is

$$N_{t+1} = \frac{RN_t}{1 + \frac{R-1}{K}N_t}$$

Now, the given equation

$$N_{t+1} = \frac{1.5N_t}{1 + \frac{0.5}{30}N_t}$$

can be written as

$$N_{t+1} = \frac{1.5N_t}{1 + \frac{1.5-1}{30}N_t}$$

and so we must have $R = 1.5$ and $K = 30$.

Prob. 11. The population growth equation described by the Beverton-Holt recruitment curve with growth parameter R and carrying capacity K is

$$N_{t+1} = \frac{RN_t}{1 + \frac{R-1}{K}N_t}$$

Now, the given equation

$$N_{t+1} = \frac{4N_t}{1 + \frac{1}{150}N_t}$$

can be written as

$$N_{t+1} = \frac{4N_t}{1 + \frac{4-1}{450}N_t}$$

and so we must have $R = 4$ and $K = 450$.

Prob. 13. From the given equation

$$N_{t+1} = \frac{4N_t}{1 + \frac{1}{30}N_t},$$

we can compute the fixed points of the equation by solving

$$N = \frac{4N}{1 + \frac{1}{30}N}$$

for N. We immediately find $N = 0$. If $N \neq 0$, we can divide both sides by N, to get

$$1 = \frac{4}{1 + \frac{1}{30}N}.$$

That is,

$$1 + \frac{1}{30}N = 4 \quad \Rightarrow \quad \frac{1}{30}N = 3 \quad \Rightarrow \quad N = 3 \cdot 30 = 90.$$

We thus have two fixed points; the fixed point $N = 0$, which we call trivial since it corresponds to the absence of the population, and the fixed point $N = 90$, which we call nontrivial since it corresponds to a positive population size.

Prob. 15. From the given equation

$$N_{t+1} = \frac{2N_t}{1 + \frac{1}{30}N_t},$$

we can compute the fixed points of the equation by solving

$$N = \frac{2N}{1 + \frac{1}{30}N}$$

for N. We immediately find $N = 0$. If $N \neq 0$, we can divide both sides by N, to get

$$1 = \frac{2}{1 + \frac{1}{30}N}.$$

That is,

$$1 + \frac{1}{30}N = 2 \quad \Rightarrow \quad \frac{1}{30}N = 1 \quad \Rightarrow \quad N = 1 \cdot 30 = 30.$$

We thus have two fixed points; the fixed point $N = 0$, which we call trivial since it corresponds to the absence of the population, and the fixed point $N = 30$, which we call nontrivial since it corresponds to a positive population size.

Prob. 17. From the given equation

$$N_{t+1} = \frac{3N_t}{1 + \frac{1}{30}N_t},$$

we can compute the fixed points of the equation by solving

$$N = \frac{3N}{1 + \frac{1}{30}N}$$

for N. We immediately find $N = 0$. If $N \neq 0$, we can divide both sides by N, to get

$$1 = \frac{3}{1 + \frac{1}{30}N}.$$

That is,

$$1 + \frac{1}{30}N = 3 \quad \Rightarrow \quad \frac{1}{30}N = 2 \quad \Rightarrow \quad N = 2 \cdot 30 = 60.$$

We thus have two fixed points; the fixed point $N = 0$, which we call trivial since it corresponds to the absence of the population, and the fixed point $N = 60$, which we call nontrivial since it corresponds to a positive population size.

Prob. 19. The population growth equation described by the Beverton-Holt recruitment curve with growth parameter R and carrying capacity K is given by

$$N_{t+1} = \frac{RN_t}{1 + \frac{R-1}{K}N_t}$$

If $R = 2$, $K = 10$ and $N_0 = 2$, then the population sizes for $t = 1, 2, 3, 4, 5$ are

$$N_1 = \frac{2N_0}{1 + \frac{2-1}{10}N_0} = \frac{2 \cdot 2}{1 + \frac{1}{10}2} = \frac{4}{6/5} = \frac{10}{3} \approx 3.33$$

$$N_2 = \frac{2N_1}{1 + \frac{2-1}{10}N_1} = \frac{2 \cdot (10/3)}{1 + \frac{1}{10}\frac{10}{3}} = \frac{20/3}{4/3} = 5$$

$$N_3 = \frac{2N_2}{1 + \frac{2-1}{10}N_2} = \frac{2 \cdot 5}{1 + \frac{1}{10}5} = \frac{10}{\frac{3}{2}} = \frac{20}{3} \approx 6.67$$

$$N_4 = \frac{2N_3}{1 + \frac{2-1}{10}N_3} = \frac{2 \cdot \frac{20}{3}}{1 + \frac{1}{10}\frac{20}{3}} = \frac{40/3}{5/3} = 8$$

$$N_5 = \frac{2N_4}{1 + \frac{2-1}{10}N_4} = \frac{2 \cdot 8}{1 + \frac{1}{10}8} = \frac{16}{9/5} = \frac{80}{9} \approx 8.89$$

Finally, since $K > 0$, $R > 1$ and $N_0 > 0$, we can say that $\lim_{t \to \infty} N_t = K = 10$.

Prob. 21. The population growth equation described by the Beverton-Holt recruitment curve with growth parameter R and carrying capacity K is given by

$$N_{t+1} = \frac{RN_t}{1 + \frac{R-1}{K}N_t}$$

If $R = 3$, $K = 15$ and $N_0 = 1$, then the population sizes for $t = 1, 2, 3, 4, 5$ are

$$N_1 = \frac{3N_0}{1 + \frac{3-1}{15}N_0} = \frac{3 \cdot 1}{1 + \frac{2}{15}1} = \frac{3}{17/15} = \frac{45}{17} \approx 2.647$$

$$N_2 = \frac{3N_1}{1 + \frac{3-1}{15}N_1} = \frac{3 \cdot (45/17)}{1 + \frac{2}{15}\frac{45}{17}} = \frac{135/17}{23/17} = \frac{135}{23} \approx 5.870$$

$$N_3 = \frac{3N_2}{1 + \frac{3-1}{15}N_2} = \frac{3 \cdot (135/23)}{1 + \frac{2}{15}\frac{135}{23}} = \frac{405/23}{41/23} = \frac{405}{41} \approx 9.878$$

$$N_4 = \frac{3N_3}{1 + \frac{3-1}{15}N_3} = \frac{3 \cdot (405/41)}{1 + \frac{2}{15}\frac{405}{41}} = \frac{1215/41}{95/41} = \frac{243}{19} \approx 12.790$$

$$N_5 = \frac{3N_4}{1 + \frac{3-1}{15}N_4} = \frac{3 \cdot (243/19)}{1 + \frac{2}{15}\frac{243}{19}} = \frac{729/19}{257/95} = \frac{3645}{257} \approx 14.183$$

Finally, since $K > 0$, $R > 1$ and $N_0 > 0$, we can say that $\lim_{t \to \infty} N_t = K = 15$.

Prob. 23. The population growth equation described by the Beverton-Holt recruitment curve with growth parameter R and carrying capacity K is given by

$$N_{t+1} = \frac{RN_t}{1 + \frac{R-1}{K}N_t}$$

If $R = 4$, $K = 40$ and $N_0 = 3$, then the population sizes for $t = 1, 2, 3, 4, 5$ are

$$N_1 = \frac{4N_0}{1 + \frac{4-1}{40}N_0} = \frac{4 \cdot 3}{1 + \frac{3}{40}3} = \frac{12}{49/40} = \frac{480}{49} \approx 9.796$$

$$N_2 = \frac{4N_1}{1 + \frac{4-1}{40}N_1} = \frac{4 \cdot (480/49)}{1 + \frac{3}{40}\frac{480}{49}} = \frac{1920/49}{85/49} = \frac{384}{17} \approx 22.588$$

$$N_3 = \frac{4N_2}{1 + \frac{4-1}{40}N_2} = \frac{4 \cdot (384/17)}{1 + \frac{3}{40}\frac{384}{17}} = \frac{1536/17}{229/85} = \frac{7680}{229} \approx 33.537$$

$$N_4 = \frac{4N_3}{1 + \frac{4-1}{40}N_3} = \frac{4 \cdot (7680/229)}{1 + \frac{3}{40}\frac{7680}{229}} = \frac{30720/229}{805/229} = \frac{6144}{161} \approx 38.161$$

$$N_5 = \frac{4N_4}{1 + \frac{4-1}{40}N_4} = \frac{4 \cdot (6144/161)}{1 + \frac{3}{40}\frac{6144}{161}} = \frac{24576/161}{3109/805} = \frac{122880}{3109} \approx 39.524$$

Finally, since $K > 0$, $R > 1$ and $N_0 > 0$, we can say that $\lim_{t \to \infty} N_t = K = 40$.

Prob. 25. The discrete logistic equation with parameter R and K is given by

$$N_{t+1} = N_t \left[1 + R \left(1 - \frac{N_t}{K} \right) \right].$$

Substituting the values $R = 1$ and $K = 10$, we can write the equation as

$$N_{t+1} = N_t \left[1 + \left(1 - \frac{N_t}{10} \right) \right].$$

In canonical form this can be written as

$$x_{t+1} = rx_t(1 - x_t) = (1 + R)x_t(1 - x_t)$$

where $r = R + 1$ and $x_t = \frac{R}{K(1+R)} N_t$. Substituting the given values of R and K we have that

$$r = 2 \quad \text{and} \quad x_t = \frac{1}{10(1+1)} N_t = \frac{1}{20} N_t$$

Prob. 27. The discrete logistic equation with parameter R and K is given by

$$N_{t+1} = N_t \left[1 + R \left(1 - \frac{N_t}{K} \right) \right].$$

Substituting the values $R = 2$ and $K = 15$, we can write the equation as

$$N_{t+1} = N_t \left[1 + 2 \left(1 - \frac{N_t}{15} \right) \right].$$

In canonical form this can be written as

$$x_{t+1} = rx_t(1 - x_t) = (1 + R)x_t(1 - x_t)$$

where $r = R + 1$ and $x_t = \frac{R}{K(1+R)} N_t$. Substituting the given values of R and K we have that

$$r = 3 \quad \text{and} \quad x_t = \frac{2}{15(1+2)} N_t = \frac{2}{45} N_t$$

Prob. 29. The discrete logistic equation with parameter R and K is given by

$$N_{t+1} = N_t \left[1 + R \left(1 - \frac{N_t}{K} \right) \right].$$

Substituting the values $R = 2.5$ and $K = 30$, we can write the equation as

$$N_{t+1} = N_t \left[1 + 2.5 \left(1 - \frac{N_t}{30} \right) \right].$$

In canonical form this can be written as

$$x_{t+1} = rx_t(1 - x_t) = (1 + R)x_t(1 - x_t)$$

where $r = R + 1$ and $x_t = \frac{R}{K(1+R)} N_t$. Substituting the given values of R and K we have that

$$r = 3.5 \quad \text{and} \quad x_t = \frac{2.5}{30(1 + 2.5)} N_t = \frac{1}{42} N_t$$

Prob. 31.

(a) The variable N_t and the parameter K both have units (or dimension) "number of individuals". Dividing N_t by K, the units cancel and we can say that $x_t = N_t/K$ is dimensionless.

(b) The variable M_t and the parameter L both have units (or dimension) "1000 individuals". Dividing M_t by L, the units cancel and we can say that $y_t = M_t/L$ is also dimensionless.

(c) The variable M_t has units (or dimension) "1000 individuals" while the variable N_t has units (or dimension) "number of individuals". Dividing M_t by N_t, the common units "number of individuals" cancel and we have

$$\frac{M_t}{N_t} = \frac{1}{1000}$$

Similarly, the variable L has units (or dimension) "1000 individuals" while the variable K has units (or dimension) "number of individuals". Dividing L by K, the common units "number of individuals" cancel and we have

$$\frac{L}{K} = \frac{1}{1000}$$

(d) From part (c), we know that $M_t/N_t = 1/1000$ and that $L/K = 1/1000$. We are given that $N_t = 20,000$ and $K = 5000$, and so $M_t = N_t/1000 = 20,000/1000 = 20$ and $L = K/1000 = 5000/1000 = 5$.

(e) We are given $M_t = 20$, $N_t = 20,000$, $L = 5$ and $K = 5000$. This means that

$$x_t = \frac{N_t}{K} = \frac{20,000}{5000} = 4 \quad \text{and} \quad y_t = \frac{M_t}{L} = \frac{20}{5} = 4.$$

Thus $x_t = y_t$.

Prob. 33. The unit or dimension of T is the characteristic time, and the unit or dimension of t is the time elapsed since the beginning of the experiment. We obtain z by dividing t by T, that is, the time elapsed by the characteristic time. As both t and T have the same units, upon division they will cancel and so $z = t/T$ is dimensionless.

If $t = 120$ minutes and $T = 20$ minutes, then $z = t/T = 120/20 = 6$. If instead t and T are measured in hours instead of minutes, then $t = 2$ and $T = 1/3$ hours. However, the value of z remains the same: $z = t/T = \frac{2}{1/3} = 6$.

Prob. 35. The discrete logistic equation is given by

$$x_{t+1} = rx_t(1 - x_t)$$

For $r = 2$ and $x_0 = 0.2$, we compute x_t for $t = 0, 1, 2, 3, 4, \ldots 20$.

$x_0 = 0.2$

$x_1 = rx_0(1 - x_0) = 2 \cdot 0.2(1 - 0.2) = 0.32$

$x_2 = rx_1(1 - x_1) = 2 \cdot 0.32(1 - 0.32) = 0.4352$

$x_3 = rx_2(1 - x_2) = 2 \cdot 0.4352(1 - 0.4352) = 0.49160192$

$x_4 = rx_3(1 - x_3) = 2 \cdot 0.49160192(1 - 0.49160192) = 0.4998589445$

$x_5 = rx_4(1 - x_4) = 2 \cdot 0.4998589445(1 - 0.4998589445) = 0.4999999602$

$x_6 = rx_5(1 - x_5) = 2 \cdot 0.4999999602(1 - 0.4999999602) = 0.5000000000$

$x_7 = rx_6(1 - x_6) = 2 \cdot 0.5(1 - 0.5) = 0.5$

$x_8 = rx_7(1 - x_7) = 2 \cdot 0.5(1 - 0.5) = 0.5$

$x_9 = rx_8(1 - x_8) = 2 \cdot 0.5(1 - 0.5) = 0.5$

$x_{10} = rx_9(1 - x_9) = 2 \cdot 0.5(1 - 0.5) = 0.5$

$x_{11} = rx_{10}(1 - x_{10}) = 2 \cdot 0.5(1 - 0.5) = 0.5$

$x_{12} = rx_{11}(1 - x_{11}) = 2 \cdot 0.5(1 - 0.5) = 0.5$

$x_{13} = rx_{12}(1 - x_{12}) = 2 \cdot 0.5(1 - 0.5) = 0.5$

$$x_{14} = rx_{13}(1 - x_{13}) = 2 \cdot 0.5(1 - 0.5) = 0.5$$

$$x_{15} = rx_{14}(1 - x_{14}) = 2 \cdot 0.5(1 - 0.5) = 0.5$$

$$x_{16} = rx_{15}(1 - x_{15}) = 2 \cdot 0.5(1 - 0.5) = 0.5$$

$$x_{17} = rx_{16}(1 - x_{16}) = 2 \cdot 0.5(1 - 0.5) = 0.5$$

$$x_{18} = rx_{17}(1 - x_{17}) = 2 \cdot 0.5(1 - 0.5) = 0.5$$

$$x_{19} = rx_{18}(1 - x_{18}) = 2 \cdot 0.5(1 - 0.5) = 0.5$$

$$x_{20} = rx_{19}(1 - x_{19}) = 2 \cdot 0.5(1 - 0.5) = 0.5$$

The graph of x_t as a function of t is given by:

Graph of x_t as a function of t with $r = 2, x_0 = 0.2$

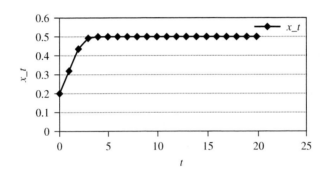

Prob. 37. The discrete logistic equation is given by

$$x_{t+1} = rx_t(1 - x_t)$$

For $r = 2$ and $x_0 = 0.1$, we compute x_t for $t = 0, 1, 2, 3, 4, \ldots 20$.

$$x_0 = 0.9$$

$$x_1 = rx_0(1 - x_0) = 2 \cdot 0.9(1 - 0.9) = 0.18$$

$$x_2 = rx_1(1 - x_1) = 2 \cdot 0.18(1 - 0.18) = 0.2952$$

$$x_3 = rx_2(1 - x_2) = 2 \cdot 0.2952(1 - 0.2952) = 0.41611392$$

$$x_4 = rx_3(1 - x_3) = 2 \cdot 0.41611392(1 - 0.41611392) = 0.4859262512$$

$$x_5 = rx_4(1 - x_4) = 2 \cdot 0.4859262512(1 - 0.4859262512) = 0.4996038592$$

$$x_6 = rx_5(1 - x_5) = 2 \cdot 0.4996038592(1 - 0.4996038592) = 0.4999996861$$

$$x_7 = rx_6(1 - x_6) = 2 \cdot 0.4999996861(1 - 0.4999996861) = 0.5000000000$$

$$x_8 = rx_7(1 - x_7) = 2 \cdot 0.5(1 - 0.5) = 0.5$$

$$x_9 = rx_8(1 - x_8) = 2 \cdot 0.5(1 - 0.5) = 0.5$$

$$x_{10} = rx_9(1 - x_9) = 2 \cdot 0.5(1 - 0.5) = 0.5$$

$$x_{11} = rx_{10}(1 - x_{10}) = 2 \cdot 0.5(1 - 0.5) = 0.5$$

$$x_{12} = rx_{11}(1 - x_{11}) = 2 \cdot 0.5(1 - 0.5) = 0.5$$

$$x_{13} = rx_{12}(1 - x_{12}) = 2 \cdot 0.5(1 - 0.5) = 0.5$$

$$x_{14} = rx_{13}(1 - x_{13}) = 2 \cdot 0.5(1 - 0.5) = 0.5$$

$$x_{15} = rx_{14}(1 - x_{14}) = 2 \cdot 0.5(1 - 0.5) = 0.5$$

$$x_{16} = rx_{15}(1 - x_{15}) = 2 \cdot 0.5(1 - 0.5) = 0.5$$

$$x_{17} = rx_{16}(1 - x_{16}) = 2 \cdot 0.5(1 - 0.5) = 0.5$$

$$x_{18} = rx_{17}(1 - x_{17}) = 2 \cdot 0.5(1 - 0.5) = 0.5$$

$$x_{19} = rx_{18}(1 - x_{18}) = 2 \cdot 0.5(1 - 0.5) = 0.5$$

$$x_{20} = rx_{19}(1 - x_{19}) = 2 \cdot 0.5(1 - 0.5) = 0.5$$

The graph of x_t as a function of t is given by:

Graph of x_t as a function of t with $r = 2, x_0 = 0.9$

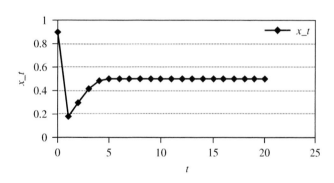

Prob. 39. The discrete logistic equation is given by

$$x_{t+1} = rx_t(1 - x_t)$$

For $r = 3.1$ and $x_0 = 0.5$, we compute x_t for $t = 0, 1, 2, 3, 4, \ldots 20$.

$$x_0 = 0.5$$

$$x_1 = rx_0(1 - x_0) = 3.1 \cdot 0.5(1 - 0.5) = 0.775$$

$$x_2 = rx_1(1 - x_1) = 3.1 \cdot 0.775(1 - 0.775) \approx 0.5406$$

$$x_3 = rx_2(1 - x_2) \approx 3.1 \cdot 0.5406(1 - 0.5406) \approx 0.7699$$

$x_4 = rx_3(1 - x_3) \approx 3.1 \cdot 0.7699(1 - 0.7699) \approx 0.5491$

$x_5 = rx_4(1 - x_4) \approx 3.1 \cdot 0.5491(1 - 0.5491) \approx 0.7675$

$x_6 = rx_5(1 - x_5) \approx 3.1 \cdot 0.7675(1 - 0.7675) \approx 0.5531$

$x_7 = rx_6(1 - x_6) \approx 3.1 \cdot 0.5531(1 - 0.5531) \approx 0.7662$

$x_8 = rx_7(1 - x_7) \approx 3.1 \cdot 0.7662(1 - 0.7662) \approx 0.5552$

$x_9 = rx_8(1 - x_8) \approx 3.1 \cdot 0.5552(1 - 0.5552) \approx 0.7655$

$x_{10} = rx_9(1 - x_9) \approx 3.1 \cdot 0.7655(1 - 0.7655) \approx 0.5564$

$x_{11} = rx_{10}(1 - x_{10}) \approx 3.1 \cdot 0.5565(1 - 0.5565) \approx 0.7651$

$x_{12} = rx_{11}(1 - x_{11}) \approx 3.1 \cdot 0.7651(1 - 0.7651) \approx 0.5571$

$x_{13} = rx_{12}(1 - x_{12}) \approx 3.1 \cdot 0.5572(1 - 0.5572) \approx 0.7649$

$x_{14} = rx_{13}(1 - x_{13}) \approx 3.1 \cdot 0.7648(1 - 0.7648) \approx 0.5575$

$x_{15} = rx_{14}(1 - x_{14}) \approx 3.1 \cdot 0.5575(1 - 0.5575) \approx 0.7647$

$x_{16} = rx_{15}(1 - x_{15}) \approx 3.1 \cdot 0.7647(1 - 0.7647) \approx 0.5577$

$x_{17} = rx_{16}(1 - x_{16}) \approx 3.1 \cdot 0.5577(1 - 0.5577) \approx 0.7647$

$x_{18} = rx_{17}(1 - x_{17}) \approx 3.1 \cdot 0.7646(1 - 0.7646) \approx 0.5578$

$x_{19} = rx_{18}(1 - x_{18}) \approx 3.1 \cdot 0.5578(1 - 0.5578) \approx 0.7646$

$x_{20} = rx_{19}(1 - x_{19}) \approx 3.1 \cdot 0.7646(1 - 0.7646) \approx 0.5579$

The graph of x_t as a function of t is given by:

Graph of x_t as a function of t with $r = 3.1$, $x_0 = 0.5$

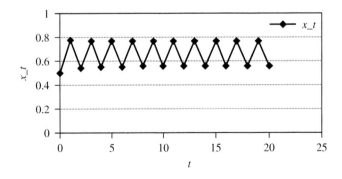

Prob. 41. The discrete logistic equation is given by

$$x_{t+1} = rx_t(1 - x_t)$$

For $r = 3.1$ and $x_0 = 0.9$, we compute x_t for $t = 0, 1, 2, 3, 4, \ldots 20$.

$x_0 = 0.9$

$x_1 = rx_0(1 - x_0) = 3.1 \cdot 0.9(1 - 0.9) = 0.279$

$x_2 = rx_1(1 - x_1) = 3.1 \cdot 0.279(1 - 0.279) \approx 0.6236$

$x_3 = rx_2(1 - x_2) \approx 3.1 \cdot 0.6236(1 - 0.6236) \approx 0.7276$

$x_4 = rx_3(1 - x_3) \approx 3.1 \cdot 0.7276(1 - 0.7276) \approx 0.6143$

$x_5 = rx_4(1 - x_4) \approx 3.1 \cdot 0.6143(1 - 0.6143) \approx 0.7345$

$x_6 = rx_5(1 - x_5) \approx 3.1 \cdot 0.7345(1 - 0.7345) \approx 0.6045$

$x_7 = rx_6(1 - x_6) \approx 3.1 \cdot 0.6045(1 - 0.6045) \approx 0.7412$

$x_8 = rx_7(1 - x_7) \approx 3.1 \cdot 0.7412(1 - 0.7412) \approx 0.5947$

$x_9 = rx_8(1 - x_8) \approx 3.1 \cdot 0.5947(1 - 0.5947) \approx 0.7472$

$x_{10} = rx_9(1 - x_9) \approx 3.1 \cdot 0.7472(1 - 0.7472) \approx 0.5856$

$x_{11} = rx_{10}(1 - x_{10}) \approx 3.1 \cdot 0.5856(1 - 0.5856) \approx 0.7522$

$x_{12} = rx_{11}(1 - x_{11}) \approx 3.1 \cdot 0.7522(1 - 0.7522) \approx 0.5778$

$x_{13} = rx_{12}(1 - x_{12}) \approx 3.1 \cdot 0.5778(1 - 0.5778) \approx 0.7562$

$x_{14} = rx_{13}(1 - x_{13}) \approx 3.1 \cdot 0.7562(1 - 0.7562) \approx 0.5714$

$x_{15} = rx_{14}(1 - x_{14}) \approx 3.1 \cdot 0.5714(1 - 0.5714) \approx 0.7592$

$x_{16} = rx_{15}(1 - x_{15}) \approx 3.1 \cdot 0.7592(1 - 0.7592) \approx 0.5668$

$x_{17} = rx_{16}(1 - x_{16}) \approx 3.1 \cdot 0.5668(1 - 0.5668) \approx 0.7612$

$x_{18} = rx_{17}(1 - x_{17}) \approx 3.1 \cdot 0.7612(1 - 0.7612) \approx 0.5634$

$x_{19} = rx_{18}(1 - x_{18}) \approx 3.1 \cdot 0.5634(1 - 0.5634) \approx 0.7625$

$x_{20} = rx_{19}(1 - x_{19}) \approx 3.1 \cdot 0.7625(1 - 0.7625) \approx 0.5614$

The graph of x_t as a function of t is given by:

Graph of x_t as a function of t with $r = 3.1$, $x_0 = 0.9$

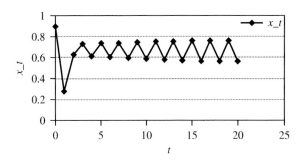

Prob. 43. The discrete logistic equation is given by

$$x_{t+1} = rx_t(1 - x_t)$$

For $r = 3.8$ and $x_0 = 0.5$, we compute x_t for $t = 0, 1, 2, 3, 4, \ldots 20$.

$x_0 = 0.5$

$x_1 = rx_0(1 - x_0) = 3.8 \cdot 0.5(1 - 0.5) = 0.95$

$x_2 = rx_1(1 - x_1) = 3.8 \cdot 0.95(1 - 0.95) = 0.1805$

$x_3 = rx_2(1 - x_2) = 3.8 \cdot 0.1805(1 - 0.1805) \approx 0.5621$

$x_4 = rx_3(1 - x_3) \approx 3.8 \cdot 0.5621(1 - 0.5621) \approx 0.9353$

$x_5 = rx_4(1 - x_4) \approx 3.8 \cdot 0.9353(1 - 0.9353) \approx 0.2298$

$x_6 = rx_5(1 - x_5) \approx 3.8 \cdot 0.2298(1 - 0.2298) \approx 0.6725$

$x_7 = rx_6(1 - x_6) \approx 3.8 \cdot 0.6725(1 - 0.6725) \approx 0.8369$

$x_8 = rx_7(1 - x_7) \approx 3.8 \cdot 0.8369(1 - 0.8369) \approx 0.5188$

$x_9 = rx_8(1 - x_8) \approx 3.8 \cdot 0.5188(1 - 0.5188) \approx 0.9486$

$x_{10} = rx_9(1 - x_9) \approx 3.8 \cdot 0.9486(1 - 0.9486) \approx 0.1851$

$x_{11} = rx_{10}(1 - x_{10}) \approx 3.8 \cdot 0.1851(1 - 0.1851) \approx 0.5732$

$x_{12} = rx_{11}(1 - x_{11}) \approx 3.8 \cdot 0.5732(1 - 0.5732) \approx 0.9297$

$x_{13} = rx_{12}(1 - x_{12}) \approx 3.8 \cdot 0.9297(1 - 0.9297) \approx 0.2485$

$x_{14} = rx_{13}(1 - x_{13}) \approx 3.8 \cdot 0.2485(1 - 0.2485) \approx 0.7097$

$x_{15} = rx_{14}(1 - x_{14}) \approx 3.8 \cdot 0.7097(1 - 0.7097) \approx 0.7829$

$x_{16} = rx_{15}(1 - x_{15}) \approx 3.8 \cdot 0.7829(1 - 0.7829) \approx 0.6458$

$x_{17} = rx_{16}(1 - x_{16}) \approx 3.8 \cdot 0.6458(1 - 0.6458) \approx 0.8693$

$x_{18} = rx_{17}(1 - x_{17}) \approx 3.8 \cdot 0.8693(1 - 0.8693) \approx 0.4319$

$x_{19} = rx_{18}(1 - x_{18}) \approx 3.8 \cdot 0.4319(1 - 0.4319) \approx 0.9324$

$x_{20} = rx_{19}(1 - x_{19}) \approx 3.8 \cdot 0.9324(1 - 0.9324) \approx 0.2396$

The Graph of x_t as a function of t is given by:

Graph of x_t as a function of t with $r = 3.8, x_0 = 0.5$

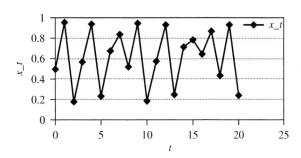

Prob. 45. The discrete logistic equation is given by

$$x_{t+1} = rx_t(1 - x_t)$$

For $r = 3.8$ and $x_0 = 0.9$, we compute x_t for $t = 0, 1, 2, 3, 4, \ldots 20$.

$x_0 = 0.9$

$x_1 = rx_0(1 - x_0) = 3.8 \cdot 0.9(1 - 0.9) = 0.342$

$x_2 = rx_1(1 - x_1) = 3.8 \cdot 0.342(1 - 0.342) \approx 0.8551$

$x_3 = rx_2(1 - x_2) \approx 3.8 \cdot 0.8551(1 - 0.8551) \approx 0.4707$

$x_4 = rx_3(1 - x_3) \approx 3.8 \cdot 0.4707(1 - 0.4707) \approx 0.9467$

$x_5 = rx_4(1 - x_4) \approx 3.8 \cdot 0.9467(1 - 0.9467) \approx 0.1916$

$x_6 = rx_5(1 - x_5) \approx 3.8 \cdot 0.1916(1 - 0.1916) \approx 0.5886$

$x_7 = rx_6(1 - x_6) \approx 3.8 \cdot 0.5886(1 - 0.5886) \approx 0.9202$

$x_8 = rx_7(1 - x_7) \approx 3.8 \cdot 0.9202(1 - 0.9202) \approx 0.2790$

$x_9 = rx_8(1 - x_8) \approx 3.8 \cdot 0.2790(1 - 0.2790) \approx 0.7645$

$x_{10} = rx_9(1 - x_9) \approx 3.8 \cdot 0.7645(1 - 0.7645) \approx 0.6842$

$x_{11} = rx_{10}(1 - x_{10}) \approx 3.8 \cdot 0.6842(1 - 0.6842) \approx 0.8211$

$x_{12} = rx_{11}(1 - x_{11}) \approx 3.8 \cdot 0.8211(1 - 0.8211) \approx 0.5583$

$x_{13} = rx_{12}(1 - x_{12}) \approx 3.8 \cdot 0.5583(1 - 0.5583) \approx 0.9371$

$x_{14} = rx_{13}(1 - x_{13}) \approx 3.8 \cdot 0.9371(1 - 0.9371) \approx 0.2240$

$x_{15} = rx_{14}(1 - x_{14}) \approx 3.8 \cdot 0.2240(1 - 0.2240) \approx 0.6606$

$x_{16} = rx_{15}(1 - x_{15}) \approx 3.8 \cdot 0.6606(1 - 0.6606) \approx 0.8519$

$x_{17} = rx_{16}(1 - x_{16}) \approx 3.8 \cdot 0.8519(1 - 0.8519) \approx 0.4793$

$x_{18} = rx_{17}(1 - x_{17}) \approx 3.8 \cdot 0.4793(1 - 0.4793) \approx 0.9484$

$x_{19} = rx_{18}(1 - x_{18}) \approx 3.8 \cdot 0.9484(1 - 0.9484) \approx 0.1861$

$x_{20} = rx_{19}(1 - x_{19}) \approx 3.8 \cdot 0.1861(1 - 0.1861) \approx 0.5755$

The graph of x_t as a function of t is given by:

Graph of x_t as a function of t with $r = 3.8$, $x_0 = 0.9$

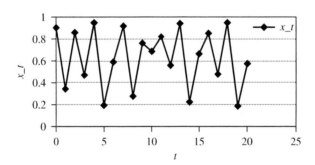

Prob. 47. The graph for the Ricker's curve in the N_t-N_{t+1} plane is given below.

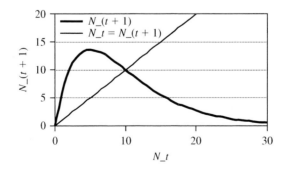

Graph of N_{t+1} as a function of N_t

The intersection of this graph with the line $N_{t+1} = N_t$ is at $N_t = 10$.

Prob. 49. The graph for the Ricker's curve in the N_t-N_{t+1} plane is given below.

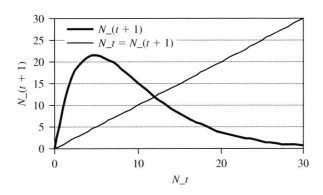

Graph of N_{t+1} as a function of N_t

The intersection of this graph with the line $N_{t+1} = N_t$ is at $N_t = 12$.

Prob. 51.

(a) We know that Ricker's curve is given by

$$N_{t+1} = N_t \exp\left[R\left(1 - \frac{N_t}{K}\right)\right]$$

When $R = 1$, $K = 20$ and $N_0 = 5$, we compute N_t for $t = 1, 2, 3, 4, \ldots 20$.

$N_1 = N_0 \exp[1(1 - N_0/20)] = 10.585$

$N_2 = N_1 \exp[1(1 - N_1/20)] = 16.94865$

$N_3 = N_2 \exp[1(1 - N_2/20)] = 19.74214$

$N_4 = N_3 \exp[1(1 - N_3/20)] = 19.99832$

$N_5 = N_4 \exp[1(1 - N_4/20)] = 20$

$N_6 = N_5 \exp[1(1 - N_5/20)] = 20$

$N_7 = N_6 \exp[1(1 - N_6/20)] = 20$

$N_8 = N_7 \exp[1(1 - N_7/20)] = 20$

$N_9 = N_8 \exp[1(1 - N_8/20)] = 20$

$N_{10} = N_9 \exp[1(1 - N_9/20)] = 20$

$$N_{11} = N_{10}\exp[1(1 - N_{10}/20)] = 20$$

$$N_{12} = N_{11}\exp[1(1 - N_{11}/20)] = 20$$

$$N_{13} = N_{12}\exp[1(1 - N_{12}/20)] = 20$$

$$N_{14} = N_{13}\exp[1(1 - N_{13}/20)] = 20$$

$$N_{15} = N_{14}\exp[1(1 - N_{14}/20)] = 20$$

$$N_{16} = N_{15}\exp[1(1 - N_{15}/20)] = 20$$

$$N_{17} = N_{16}\exp[1(1 - N_{16}/20)] = 20$$

$$N_{18} = N_{17}\exp[1(1 - N_{17}/20)] = 20$$

$$N_{19} = N_{18}\exp[1(1 - N_{18}/20)] = 20$$

$$N_{20} = N_{19}\exp[1(1 - N_{19}/20)] = 20$$

The graph of N_t as a function of t, for the given values $R = 1$, $K = 20$ and $N_0 = 5$ is given below.

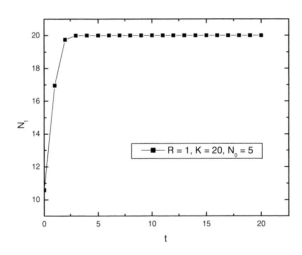

Graph of N_{t+1} as a function of t

(b) We know that Ricker's curve is given by

$$N_{t+1} = N_t\exp\left[R\left(1 - \frac{N_t}{K}\right)\right]$$

When $R = 1$, $K = 20$ and $N_0 = 10$, we compute N_t for $t = 1, 2, 3, 4, \ldots 20$.

$$N_1 = N_0 \exp[1(1 - N_0/20)] = 16.48721$$

$$N_2 = N_1 \exp[1(1 - N_1/20)] = 19.653$$

$$N_3 = N_2 \exp[1(1 - N_2/20)] = 19.99695$$

$$N_4 = N_3 \exp[1(1 - N_3/20)] = 20$$

$$N_5 = N_4 \exp[1(1 - N_4/20)] = 20$$

$$N_6 = N_5 \exp[1(1 - N_5/20)] = 20$$

$$N_7 = N_6 \exp[1(1 - N_6/20)] = 20$$

$$N_8 = N_7 \exp[1(1 - N_7/20)] = 20$$

$$N_9 = N_8 \exp[1(1 - N_8/20)] = 20$$

$$N_{10} = N_9 \exp[1(1 - N_9/20)] = 20$$

$$N_{11} = N_{10} \exp[1(1 - N_{10}/20)] = 20$$

$$N_{12} = N_{11} \exp[1(1 - N_{11}/20)] = 20$$

$$N_{13} = N_{12} \exp[1(1 - N_{12}/20)] = 20$$

$$N_{14} = N_{13} \exp[1(1 - N_{13}/20)] = 20$$

$$N_{15} = N_{14} \exp[1(1 - N_{14}/20)] = 20$$

$$N_{16} = N_{15} \exp[1(1 - N_{15}/20)] = 20$$

$$N_{17} = N_{16} \exp[1(1 - N_{16}/20)] = 20$$

$$N_{18} = N_{17} \exp[1(1 - N_{17}/20)] = 20$$

$$N_{19} = N_{18} \exp[1(1 - N_{18}/20)] = 20$$

$$N_{20} = N_{19} \exp[1(1 - N_{19}/20)] = 20$$

The graph of N_t as a function of t, for the given values $R = 1$, $K = 20$ and $N_0 = 10$ is given below.

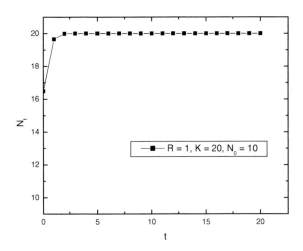

Graph of N_{t+1} as a function of t

(c) We know that Ricker's curve is given by

$$N_{t+1} = N_t \exp\left[R\left(1 - \frac{N_t}{K}\right)\right]$$

When $R = 1$, $K = 20$ and $N_0 = 20$, we compute N_t for $t = 1, 2, 3, 4, \ldots 20$.

$N_1 = N_0 \exp[1(1 - N_0/20)] = 20$

$N_2 = N_1 \exp[1(1 - N_1/20)] = 20$

$N_3 = N_2 \exp[1(1 - N_2/20)] = 20$

$N_4 = N_3 \exp[1(1 - N_3/20)] = 20$

$N_5 = N_0 \exp[1(1 - N_4/20)] = 20$

$N_6 = N_5 \exp[1(1 - N_5/20)] = 20$

$N_7 = N_6 \exp[1(1 - N_6/20)] = 20$

$N_8 = N_7 \exp[1(1 - N_7/20)] = 20$

$N_9 = N_8 \exp[1(1 - N_8/20)] = 20$

$N_{10} = N_9 \exp[1(1 - N_9/20)] = 20$

$N_{11} = N_{10} \exp[1(1 - N_{10}/20)] = 20$

$N_{12} = N_{11} \exp[1(1 - N_{11}/20)] = 20$

$$N_{13} = N_{12} \exp[1(1 - N_{12}/20)] = 20$$
$$N_{14} = N_{13} \exp[1(1 - N_{13}/20)] = 20$$
$$N_{15} = N_{14} \exp[1(1 - N_{14}/20)] = 20$$
$$N_{16} = N_{15} \exp[1(1 - N_{15}/20)] = 20$$
$$N_{17} = N_{16} \exp[1(1 - N_{16}/20)] = 20$$
$$N_{18} = N_{17} \exp[1(1 - N_{17}/20)] = 20$$
$$N_{19} = N_{18} \exp[1(1 - N_{18}/20)] = 20$$
$$N_{20} = N_{19} \exp[1(1 - N_{19}/20)] = 20$$

The graph of N_t as a function of t, for the given values $R = 1$, $K = 20$ and $N_0 = 20$ is given below.

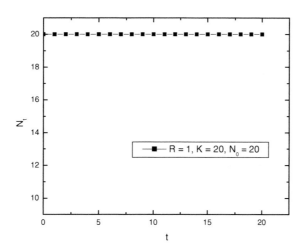

Graph of N_{t+1} as a function of t

(d) We know that Ricker's curve is given by

$$N_{t+1} = N_t \exp\left[R\left(1 - \frac{N_t}{K}\right)\right]$$

When $R = 1$, $K = 20$ and $N_0 = 0$, we compute N_t for $t = 1, 2, 3, 4, \ldots 20$.

$$N_1 = N_0 \exp[1(1 - N_0/20)] = 0$$
$$N_2 = N_1 \exp[1(1 - N_1/20)] = 0$$

$N_3 = N_2 \exp[1(1 - N_2/20)] = 0$

$N_4 = N_3 \exp[1(1 - N_3/20)] = 0$

$N_5 = N_0 \exp[1(1 - N_4/20)] = 0$

$N_6 = N_5 \exp[1(1 - N_5/20)] = 0$

$N_7 = N_6 \exp[1(1 - N_6/20)] = 0$

$N_8 = N_7 \exp[1(1 - N_7/20)] = 0$

$N_9 = N_8 \exp[1(1 - N_8/20)] = 0$

$N_{10} = N_9 \exp[1(1 - N_9/20)] = 0$

$N_{11} = N_{10} \exp[1(1 - N_{10}/20)] = 0$

$N_{12} = N_{11} \exp[1(1 - N_{11}/20)] = 0$

$N_{13} = N_{12} \exp[1(1 - N_{12}/20)] = 0$

$N_{14} = N_{13} \exp[1(1 - N_{13}/20)] = 0$

$N_{15} = N_{14} \exp[1(1 - N_{14}/20)] = 0$

$N_{16} = N_{15} \exp[1(1 - N_{15}/20)] = 0$

$N_{17} = N_{16} \exp[1(1 - N_{16}/20)] = 0$

$N_{18} = N_{17} \exp[1(1 - N_{17}/20)] = 0$

$N_{19} = N_{18} \exp[1(1 - N_{18}/20)] = 0$

$N_{20} = N_{19} \exp[1(1 - N_{19}/20)] = 0$

The graph of N_t as a function of t, for the given values $R = 1$, $K = 20$ and $N_0 = 0$ is given below.

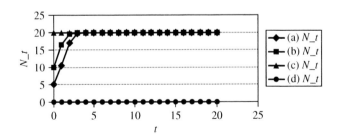

Graph of N_{t+1} as a function of t

Prob. 53.

(a) We know that Ricker's curve is given by

$$N_{t+1} = N_t \exp\left[R\left(1 - \frac{N_t}{K}\right)\right]$$

When $R = 2.1$, $K = 20$ and $N_0 = 5$, we compute N_t for $t = 1, 2, 3, 4, \ldots 20$.

$N_1 = N_0 \exp[2.1(1 - N_0/20)] = 24.15371$

$N_2 = N_1 \exp[2.1(1 - N_1/20)] = 15.61604$

$N_3 = N_2 \exp[2.1(1 - N_2/20)] = 24.74478$

$N_4 = N_3 \exp[2.1(1 - N_3/20)] = 15.03548$

$N_5 = N_4 \exp[2.1(1 - N_4/20)] = 25.32235$

$N_6 = N_5 \exp[2.1(1 - N_5/20)] = 14.48105$

$N_7 = N_6 \exp[2.1(1 - N_6/20)] = 25.85052$

$N_8 = N_7 \exp[2.1(1 - N_7/20)] = 13.98557$

$N_9 = N_8 \exp[2.1(1 - N_8/20)] = 26.29927$

$N_{10} = N_9 \exp[2.1(1 - N_9/20)] = 13.57348$

$N_{11} = N_{10} \exp[2.1(1 - N_{10}/20)] = 26.65302$

$N_{12} = N_{11} \exp[2.1(1 - N_{11}/20)] = 13.25448$

$N_{13} = N_{12} \exp[2.1(1 - N_{12}/20)] = 26.91316$

$N_{14} = N_{13} \exp[2.1(1 - N_{13}/20)] = 13.02322$

$N_{15} = N_{14} \exp[2.1(1 - N_{14}/20)] = 27.09396$

$N_{16} = N_{15} \exp[2.1(1 - N_{15}/20)] = 12.86451$

$N_{17} = N_{16} \exp[2.1(1 - N_{16}/20)] = 27.21311$

$N_{18} = N_{17} \exp[2.1(1 - N_{17}/20)] = 12.76009$

$N_{19} = N_{18} \exp[2.1(1 - N_{18}/20)] = 27.28980$

$N_{20} = N_{19} \exp[2.1(1 - N_{19}/20)] = 12.69343$

The graph of N_t as a function of t, for the given values $R = 2.1$, $K = 20$ and $N_0 = 5$ is given below.

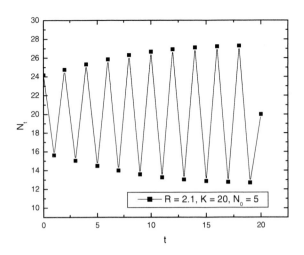

Graph of N_{t+1} as a function of t

(b) We know that Ricker's curve is given by

$$N_{t+1} = N_t \exp\left[R\left(1 - \frac{N_t}{K} \right) \right]$$

When $R = 2.1$, $K = 20$ and $N_0 = 10$, we compute N_t for $t = 1, 2, 3, 4, \ldots 20$.

$N_1 = N_0 \exp[2.1(1 - N_0/20)] = 28.57651$

$N_2 = N_1 \exp[2.1(1 - N_1/20)] = 11.61214$

$N_3 = N_2 \exp[2.1(1 - N_2/20)] = 28.01602$

$N_4 = N_3 \exp[2.1(1 - N_3/20)] = 12.07449$

$N_5 = N_4 \exp[2.1(1 - N_4/20)] = 27.75105$

$N_6 = N_5 \exp[2.1(1 - N_5/20)] = 12.29772$

$N_7 = N_6 \exp[2.1(1 - N_6/20)] = 27.60932$

$N_8 = N_7 \exp[2.1(1 - N_7/20)] = 12.41835$

$N_9 = N_8 \exp[2.1(1 - N_8/20)] = 27.52924$

$N_{10} = N_9 \exp[2.1(1 - N_9/20)] = 12.48688$

$N_{11} = N_{10} \exp[2.1(1 - N_{10}/20)] = 27.48268$

$N_{12} = N_{11} \exp[2.1(1 - N_{11}/20)] = 12.52685$

$N_{13} = N_{12} \exp[2.1(1 - N_{12}/20)] = 27.45518$

$N_{14} = N_{13} \exp[2.1(1 - N_{13}/20)] = 12.5505$

$N_{15} = N_{14} \exp[2.1(1 - N_{14}/20)] = 27.4388$

$N_{16} = N_{15} \exp[2.1(1 - N_{15}/20)] = 12.56461$

$N_{17} = N_{16} \exp[2.1(1 - N_{16}/20)] = 27.42898$

$N_{18} = N_{17} \exp[2.1(1 - N_{17}/20)] = 12.57307$

$N_{19} = N_{18} \exp[2.1(1 - N_{18}/20)] = 27.42308$

$N_{20} = N_{19} \exp[2.1(1 - N_{19}/20)] = 12.57816$

The graph of N_t as a function of t, for the given values $R = 2.1$, $K = 20$ and $N_0 = 10$

is given below.

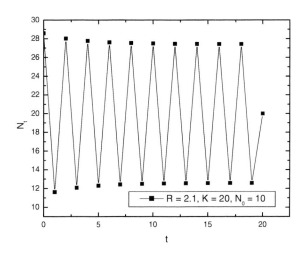

Graph of N_{t+1} as a function of t

(c) We know that Ricker's curve is given by

$$N_{t+1} = N_t \exp\left[R\left(1 - \frac{N_t}{K}\right)\right]$$

When $R = 2.1$, $K = 20$ and $N_0 = 20$, we compute N_t for $t = 1, 2, 3, 4, \ldots 20$.

$N_1 = N_0 \exp[2.1(1 - N_0/20)] = 20$

$N_2 = N_1 \exp[2.1(1 - N_1/20)] = 20$

$N_3 = N_2 \exp[2.1(1 - N_2/20)] = 20$

$$N_4 = N_3 \exp[2.1(1 - N_3/20)] = 20$$

$$N_5 = N_4 \exp[2.1(1 - N_4/20)] = 20$$

$$N_6 = N_5 \exp[2.1(1 - N_5/20)] = 20$$

$$N_7 = N_6 \exp[2.1(1 - N_6/20)] = 20$$

$$N_8 = N_7 \exp[2.1(1 - N_7/20)] = 20$$

$$N_9 = N_8 \exp[2.1(1 - N_8/20)] = 20$$

$$N_{10} = N_9 \exp[2.1(1 - N_9/20)] = 20$$

$$N_{11} = N_{10} \exp[2.1(1 - N_{10}/20)] = 20$$

$$N_{12} = N_{11} \exp[2.1(1 - N_{11}/20)] = 20$$

$$N_{13} = N_{12} \exp[2.1(1 - N_{12}/20)] = 20$$

$$N_{14} = N_{13} \exp[2.1(1 - N_{13}/20)] = 20$$

$$N_{15} = N_{14} \exp[2.1(1 - N_{14}/20)] = 20$$

$$N_{16} = N_{15} \exp[2.1(1 - N_{15}/20)] = 20$$

$$N_{17} = N_{16} \exp[2.1(1 - N_{16}/20)] = 20$$

$$N_{18} = N_{17} \exp[2.1(1 - N_{17}/20)] = 20$$

$$N_{19} = N_{18} \exp[2.1(1 - N_{18}/20)] = 20$$

$$N_{20} = N_{19} \exp[2.1(1 - N_{19}/20)] = 20$$

The graph of N_t as a function of t, for the given values $R = 2.1$, $K = 20$ and $N_0 = 20$ is given below.

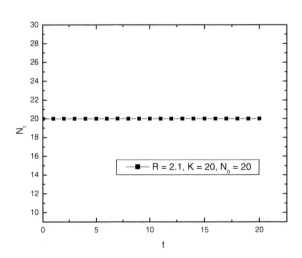

Graph of N_{t+1} as a function of t

(d) We know that Ricker's curve is given by

$$N_{t+1} = N_t \exp\left[R\left(1 - \frac{N_t}{K}\right)\right]$$

When $R = 2.1$, $K = 20$ and $N_0 = 0$, we compute N_t for $t = 1, 2, 3, 4, \ldots 20$.

$N_1 = N_0 \exp[2.1(1 - N_0/20)] = 0$

$N_2 = N_1 \exp[2.1(1 - N_1/20)] = 0$

$N_3 = N_2 \exp[2.1(1 - N_2/20)] = 0$

$N_4 = N_3 \exp[2.1(1 - N_3/20)] = 0$

$N_5 = N_4 \exp[2.1(1 - N_4/20)] = 0$

$N_6 = N_5 \exp[2.1(1 - N_5/20)] = 0$

$N_7 = N_6 \exp[2.1(1 - N_6/20)] = 0$

$N_8 = N_7 \exp[2.1(1 - N_7/20)] = 0$

$N_9 = N_8 \exp[2.1(1 - N_8/20)] = 0$

$N_{10} = N_9 \exp[2.1(1 - N_9/20)] = 0$

$N_{11} = N_{10} \exp[2.1(1 - N_{10}/20)] = 0$

$N_{12} = N_{11} \exp[2.1(1 - N_{11}/20)] = 0$

$N_{13} = N_{12} \exp[2.1(1 - N_{12}/20)] = 0$

$N_{14} = N_{13} \exp[2.1(1 - N_{13}/20)] = 0$

$N_{15} = N_{14} \exp[2.1(1 - N_{14}/20)] = 0$

$N_{16} = N_{15} \exp[2.1(1 - N_{15}/20)] = 0$

$N_{17} = N_{16} \exp[2.1(1 - N_{16}/20)] = 0$

$N_{18} = N_{17} \exp[2.1(1 - N_{17}/20)] = 0$

$N_{19} = N_{18} \exp[2.1(1 - N_{18}/20)] = 0$

$N_{20} = N_{19} \exp[2.1(1 - N_{19}/20)] = 0$

The graph of N_t as a function of t, for the given values $R = 2.1$, $K = 20$ and $N_0 = 0$ is given below.

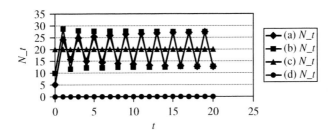

Graph of N_{t+1} as a function of t

Prob. 55. When $N_0 = 1$ and $N_1 = 1$, we have

$$t = 1 \quad \Rightarrow \quad N_2 = N_1 + N_0 = 1 + 1 = 2, \frac{N_t}{N_{t-1}} = \frac{N_1}{N_0} = 1$$

$$t = 2 \quad \Rightarrow \quad N_3 = N_2 + N_1 = 2 + 1 = 3, \frac{N_t}{N_{t-1}} = \frac{N_2}{N_1} = 2$$

$$t = 3 \quad \Rightarrow \quad N_4 = N_3 + N_2 = 3 + 2 = 5, \frac{N_t}{N_{t-1}} = \frac{N_3}{N_2} = \frac{3}{2} = 1.5$$

$$t = 4 \quad \Rightarrow \quad N_5 = N_4 + N_3 = 5 + 3 = 8, \frac{N_t}{N_{t-1}} = \frac{N_5}{N_3} = \frac{5}{3} \approx 1.66667$$

$$t = 5 \quad \Rightarrow \quad N_6 = N_5 + N_4 = 8 + 5 = 13, \frac{N_t}{N_{t-1}} = \frac{N_5}{N_4} = \frac{8}{5} \approx 1.60000$$

$$t = 6 \quad \Rightarrow \quad N_7 = N_6 + N_5 = 13 + 8 = 21, \frac{N_t}{N_{t-1}} = \frac{N_6}{N_5} = \frac{13}{8} \approx 1.62500$$

$$t = 7 \quad \Rightarrow \quad N_8 = N_7 + N_6 = 21 + 13 = 34, \frac{N_t}{N_{t-1}} = \frac{N_7}{N_6} = \frac{21}{13} \approx 1.61538$$

$$t = 8 \quad \Rightarrow \quad N_9 = N_8 + N_7 = 34 + 21 = 55, \frac{N_t}{N_{t-1}} = \frac{N_8}{N_7} = \frac{34}{21} \approx 1.61905$$

$$t = 9 \quad \Rightarrow \quad N_{10} = N_9 + N_8 = 55 + 34 = 89, \frac{N_t}{N_{t-1}} = \frac{N_9}{N_8} = \frac{55}{34} \approx 1.61765$$

$$t = 10 \quad \Rightarrow \quad N_{11} = N_{10} + N_9 = 89 + 55 = 144, \frac{N_t}{N_{t-1}} = \frac{N_{10}}{N_9} = \frac{89}{55} \approx 1.61818$$

$$t = 11 \quad \Rightarrow \quad N_{12} = N_{11} + N_{10} = 144 + 89 = 233, \frac{N_t}{N_{t-1}} = \frac{N_{11}}{N_{10}} = \frac{144}{89} \approx 1.61798$$

$$t = 12 \quad \Rightarrow \quad N_{13} = N_{12} + N_{11} = 233 + 144 = 377, \frac{N_t}{N_{t-1}} = \frac{N_{12}}{N_{11}} = \frac{233}{144} \approx 1.61806$$

$$t = 13 \quad \Rightarrow \quad N_{14} = N_{13} + N_{12} = 377 + 233 = 610, \frac{N_t}{N_{t-1}} = \frac{N_{13}}{N_{12}} = \frac{377}{233} \approx 1.61803$$

$$t = 14 \quad \Rightarrow \quad N_{15} = N_{14} + N_{13} = 610 + 377 = 987, \frac{N_t}{N_{t-1}} = \frac{N_{14}}{N_{13}} = \frac{610}{377} \approx 1.61804$$

$$t = 15 \quad \Rightarrow \quad N_{16} = N_{15} + N_{14} = 987 + 610 = 1597, \frac{N_t}{N_{t-1}} = \frac{N_{15}}{N_{14}} = \frac{987}{610} \approx 1.61803$$

$$t = 16 \quad \Rightarrow \quad N_{17} = N_{16} + N_{15} = 1597 + 987 = 2584, \frac{N_t}{N_{t-1}} = \frac{N_{16}}{N_{15}} = \frac{1597}{987} \approx 1.61803$$

$$t = 17 \quad \Rightarrow \quad N_{18} = N_{17} + N_{16} = 2584 + 1597 = 4181, \frac{N_t}{N_{t-1}} = \frac{N_{17}}{N_{16}} = \frac{2584}{1597} \approx 1.61803$$

$$t = 18 \quad \Rightarrow \quad N_{19} = N_{18} + N_{17} = 4181 + 2584 = 6765, \frac{N_t}{N_{t-1}} = \frac{N_{18}}{N_{17}} = \frac{4181}{2584} \approx 1.61803$$

$$t = 19 \quad \Rightarrow \quad N_{20} = N_{19} + N_{18} = 6765 + 4181 = 10946, \frac{N_t}{N_{t-1}} = \frac{N_{19}}{N_{18}} = \frac{6765}{4181} \approx 1.61803$$

And finally, we have $N_{20}/N_{19} = 10946/6765 \approx 1.61803$.

Prob. 57. This recursion describes the number of pairs of newborn rabbits at t months, if we assume that each pair produces one pair of rabbits at age 1 month and two pairs of rabbits at age 2 months, and none thereafter. We initially have one pair of newborn rabbits.

If N_t denotes the number of newborn rabbit pairs at time t (measured in months), then at time 0, there is one pair of rabbits ($N_0 = 1$). When $t = 1$, the pair of rabbits we started with is one month old and produces a pair of newborn rabbits, so $N_1 = 1$. When $t = 2$, there is one pair of two-month-old rabbits and one pair of one-month-old rabbits. The pair of two-month-old rabbits will produce two pairs of rabbits, and the pair of one-month-old rabbits will produce 1 pair of rabbits; thus $N_2 = 3$. When $t = 3$, our original pair of rabbits is now three months old and will stop reproducing; there is then one pair of two-month-old rabbits and three pairs of one-month-old rabbits. Since each pair of one-month-old rabbits produces a pair of newborn rabbits and the two-month-old rabbits produce two pairs of newborn rabbits, there will be $3 + 2 = 5$ newborn rabbits at time $t = 3$.

More generally, to find the number of pairs of newborn rabbits, we need to add up the number of pairs of one-month-old rabbits and 2 times the number of pairs of two-month-old rabbits. The one-month-old rabbits at time $t + 1$ were newborn rabbits at time t; the two-month-old rabbits were newborns at time $t - 1$. So the number of pairs of newborn rabbits at time $t + 1$ is

$$N_{t+1} = N_t + 2N_{t-1}, \quad \text{for } t = 1, 2, 3, 4, \ldots, \text{ and } N_0 = 1, N_1 = 1.$$

2.5 Review Problems

Prob. 1. The expression 2^{-n} can also be written as $(1/2)^n$. Thus, from Example 12 in Section 2.2.2, we conclude that

$$\lim_{n \to \infty} 2^{-n} = \lim_{n \to \infty} \left(\frac{1}{2} \right)^n = 0$$

Prob. 3. The expression $40(1 - 4^{-n})$ can be written as $40 - 40(1/4)^n$. From Example 12 in Section 2.2.2, we know that $\lim_{n \to \infty} (1/4)^n = 0$. Also, it is obvious that $\lim_{n \to \infty} 40 = 40$. Thus

$$\lim_{n \to \infty} 40(1 - 4^{-n}) = \lim_{n \to \infty} 40 - 40 \lim_{n \to \infty} (1/4)^n = 40 - 40 \cdot 0 = 40.$$

Prob. 5. Since $a > 1$, we can see that $a^2 > a > 1$, and the terms $a^3, a^4, a^5, a^6, \ldots$ are successively larger. This indicates that the terms continue to grow with n. Thus a^n goes to infinity as $n \to \infty$, and we can write $\lim_{n \to \infty} a^n = \infty$. Since infinity is not a real number, we say that the limit does not exist.

Prob. 7. We first note that the expression $\frac{n(n+1)}{n^2-1}$ can be written as $\frac{n(n+1)}{(n+1)(n-1)}$. Recalling that $\lim_{n\to\infty}(1/n)$ exists and is equal to 0, we have

$$
\lim_{n\to\infty}\frac{n(n+1)}{n^2-1} = \lim_{n\to\infty}\frac{n(n+1)}{(n-1)(n+1)} = \lim_{n\to\infty}\frac{n}{n-1}
$$

$$
= \lim_{n\to\infty}\frac{1}{1-1/n} = \frac{\lim_{n\to\infty}1}{\lim_{n\to\infty}1 - \lim_{n\to\infty}(1/n)} = \frac{1}{1-0} = 1.
$$

Prob. 9. We first note that by dividing numerator and denominator by n, the expression $\frac{\sqrt{n}}{n+1}$ can be written as $\frac{1/\sqrt{n}}{1+1/n}$. Recalling that both $\lim_{n\to\infty}(1/n)$ and $\lim_{n\to\infty}(1/\sqrt{n})$ exist and are equal to 0, we have

$$
\lim_{n\to\infty}\frac{\sqrt{n}}{n+1} = \lim_{n\to\infty}\frac{1/\sqrt{n}}{1+1/n}
$$

$$
= \frac{\lim_{n\to\infty}(1/\sqrt{n})}{\lim_{n\to\infty}(1+1/n)} = \frac{0}{1+0} = 0.
$$

Prob. 11. Looking at the sequence, we can guess the next terms, namely, $\frac{11}{12}, \frac{13}{14}, \frac{15}{16}, \frac{17}{18}, \frac{19}{20}$ and so on. We thus find

$$
a_n = \frac{2n+1}{2n+2} \quad \text{for } n = 0,1,2,3,\ldots
$$

Prob. 13. Looking at the sequence, we can guess the next terms, namely, $\frac{6}{37}, \frac{7}{50}, \frac{8}{65}, \frac{9}{82}, \frac{10}{101}$ and so on. The denominator of a_n is the sum of 2 and the first n odd numbers, beginning with the odd number 3. This sum is $2 + (n+1)^2 - 1 = (n+1)^2 + 2 = n^2 + 2n + 2$, and we thus have

$$
a_n = \frac{n+1}{n^2+2n+2} \quad \text{for } n = 0,1,2,3,\ldots
$$

Prob. 15.

(a) The population growth equation described by the Beverton-Holt recruitment curve with growth parameter R and carrying capacity K is given by:

$$
N_{t+1} = \frac{RN_t}{1 + \frac{R-1}{K}N_t}
$$

The population sizes for $t = 1,2,3,4\ldots,10$ and $\lim{-t} \to \infty N_t$ for the given values $R = 2$, $K = 100$ and $N_0 = 20$ are:

$$
N_1 = \frac{2N_0}{1 + \frac{2-1}{100}N_0} = \frac{2\cdot 20}{1 + \frac{1}{100}20} = \frac{40}{6/5} \approx 33.3333
$$

$$N_2 = \frac{2N_1}{1 + \frac{2-1}{100}N_1} = \frac{2 \cdot \frac{100}{3}}{1 + \frac{1}{100}\frac{100}{3}} = \frac{200/3}{4/3} = 50$$

$$N_3 = \frac{2N_2}{1 + \frac{2-1}{100}N_2} = \frac{2 \cdot 50}{1 + \frac{1}{100}50} = \frac{100}{3/2} \approx 66.6667$$

$$N_4 = \frac{2N_3}{1 + \frac{2-1}{100}N_3} = \frac{2 \cdot \frac{200}{3}}{1 + \frac{1}{100}\frac{200}{3}} = \frac{400/3}{5/3} = 80$$

$$N_5 = \frac{2N_4}{1 + \frac{2-1}{100}N_4} = \frac{2 \cdot 80}{1 + \frac{1}{100}80} = \frac{160}{9/5} \approx 88.8889$$

$$N_6 = \frac{2N_5}{1 + \frac{2-1}{100}N_5} = \frac{2 \cdot \frac{800}{9}}{1 + \frac{1}{100}\frac{800}{9}} = \frac{1600/9}{17/9} \approx 94.1176$$

$$N_7 = \frac{2N_6}{1 + \frac{2-1}{100}N_6} = \frac{2 \cdot \frac{1600}{17}}{1 + \frac{1}{100}\frac{1600}{17}} = \frac{3200/17}{33/17} \approx 96.9697$$

$$N_8 = \frac{2N_7}{1 + \frac{2-1}{100}N_7} = \frac{2 \cdot \frac{3200}{33}}{1 + \frac{1}{100}\frac{3200}{33}} = \frac{6400/33}{65/33} \approx 98.4615$$

$$N_9 = \frac{2N_8}{1 + \frac{2-1}{100}N_8} = \frac{2 \cdot \frac{1280}{13}}{1 + \frac{1}{100}\frac{1280}{13}} = \frac{2560/13}{258/130} \approx 99.2248$$

$$N_{10} = \frac{2N_9}{1 + \frac{2-1}{100}N_9} = \frac{2 \cdot \frac{12800}{129}}{1 + \frac{1}{100}\frac{12800}{129}} = \frac{25600/129}{257/129} \approx 99.6109$$

The graph for this function is:

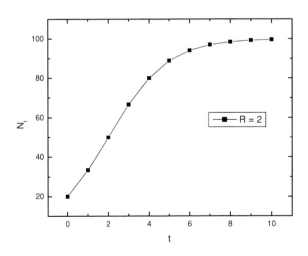

Graph of N_t as a function of t

(b) The population growth equation described by the Beverton-Holt recruitment curve with growth parameter R and carrying capacity K is given by:

$$N_{t+1} = \frac{RN_t}{1 + \frac{R-1}{K}N_t}$$

The population sizes for $t = 1, 2, 3, 4 \ldots, 10$ and $\lim -t \to \infty N_t$ for the given values $R = 5$, $K = 100$ and $N_0 = 20$ are:

$$N_1 = \frac{5N_0}{1 + \frac{5-1}{100}N_0} = \frac{5 \cdot 20}{1 + \frac{4}{100}20} = \frac{100}{9/5} \approx 55.5556$$

$$N_2 = \frac{5N_1}{1 + \frac{5-1}{100}N_1} = \frac{5 \cdot \frac{500}{9}}{1 + \frac{4}{100}\frac{500}{9}} = \frac{2500/9}{29/9} \approx 86.2069$$

$$N_3 = \frac{5N_2}{1 + \frac{5-1}{100}N_2} = \frac{5 \cdot \frac{2500}{29}}{1 + \frac{4}{100}\frac{2500}{29}} = \frac{12500/29}{129/29} \approx 96.8992$$

$$N_4 = \frac{5N_3}{1 + \frac{5-1}{100}N_3} = \frac{5 \cdot \frac{12500}{129}}{1 + \frac{4}{100}\frac{12500}{129}} = \frac{62500/129}{629/129} \approx 99.3641$$

$$N_5 = \frac{5N_4}{1 + \frac{5-1}{100}N_4} = \frac{5 \cdot \frac{62500}{629}}{1 + \frac{4}{100}\frac{62500}{629}} = \frac{312500/629}{3129/629} \approx 99.8722$$

$$N_6 = \frac{5N_5}{1 + \frac{5-1}{100}N_5} = \frac{5 \cdot \frac{312500}{3129}}{1 + \frac{4}{100}\frac{312500}{3129}} = \frac{1562500/3129}{15629/3129} \approx 99.9744$$

$$N_7 = \frac{5N_6}{1 + \frac{5-1}{100}N_6} = \frac{5 \cdot \frac{1562500}{15629}}{1 + \frac{4}{100}\frac{1562500}{15629}} = \frac{7812500/15629}{78129/15629} \approx 99.9949$$

$$N_8 = \frac{5N_7}{1 + \frac{5-1}{100}N_7} = \frac{5 \cdot \frac{7812500}{78129}}{1 + \frac{4}{100}\frac{7812500}{78129}} = \frac{39062500/78129}{390629/78129} \approx 99.9990$$

$$N_9 = \frac{5N_8}{1 + \frac{5-1}{100}N_8} = \frac{5 \cdot \frac{39062500}{390629}}{1 + \frac{4}{100}\frac{39062500}{390629}} = \frac{195312500/390629}{1953129/390629} \approx 99.9998$$

$$N_{10} = \frac{5N_9}{1 + \frac{5-1}{100}N_9} = \frac{5 \cdot \frac{195312500}{1953129}}{1 + \frac{4}{100}\frac{195312500}{1953129}} = \frac{976562500/1953129}{9765629/1953129} \approx 100.000$$

The graph for this function is:

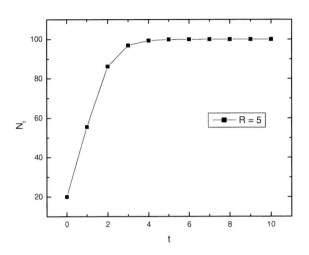

Graph of N_t as a function of t

(c) The population growth equation described by the Beverton-Holt recruitment curve with growth parameter R and carrying capacity K is given by:

$$N_{t+1} = \frac{RN_t}{1 + \frac{R-1}{K}N_t}$$

The population sizes for $t = 1, 2, 3, 4 \ldots, 10$ and $\lim -t \to \infty N_t$ for the given values $R = 10$, $K = 100$ and $N_0 = 20$ are:

$$N_1 = \frac{10N_0}{1 + \frac{10-1}{100}N_0} = \frac{10 \cdot 20}{1 + \frac{9}{100}20} = \frac{200}{14/5} \approx 71.4286$$

$$N_2 = \frac{10N_1}{1 + \frac{10-1}{100}N_1} = \frac{10 \cdot \frac{500}{7}}{1 + \frac{9}{100}\frac{500}{7}} = \frac{5000/7}{52/7} \approx 96.1538$$

$$N_3 = \frac{10N_2}{1 + \frac{10-1}{100}N_2} = \frac{10 \cdot \frac{5000}{52}}{1 + \frac{9}{100}\frac{5000}{52}} = \frac{50000/52}{502/52} \approx 99.6016$$

$$N_4 = \frac{10N_3}{1 + \frac{10-1}{100}N_3} = \frac{10 \cdot \frac{50000}{502}}{1 + \frac{9}{100}\frac{50000}{502}} = \frac{500000/502}{5002/502} \approx 99.9600$$

$$N_5 = \frac{10N_4}{1 + \frac{10-1}{100}N_4} = \frac{10 \cdot \frac{500000}{5002}}{1 + \frac{9}{100}\frac{500000}{5002}} = \frac{5000000/5002}{50002/5002} \approx 99.9960$$

$$N_6 = \frac{10N_5}{1 + \frac{10-1}{100}N_5} = \frac{10 \cdot \frac{5000000}{50002}}{1 + \frac{9}{100}\frac{5000000}{50002}} = \frac{50000000/50002}{500002/50002} \approx 99.9996$$

$$N_7 = \frac{10N_6}{1 + \frac{10-1}{100}N_6} = \frac{10 \cdot \frac{50000000}{500002}}{1 + \frac{9}{100}\frac{50000000}{500002}} = \frac{500000000/500002}{5000002/500002} \approx 100.000$$

$$N_8 = \frac{10N_7}{1 + \frac{10-1}{100}N_7} = \frac{10 \cdot \frac{500000000}{5000002}}{1 + \frac{9}{100}\frac{500000000}{5000002}} = \frac{5000000000/5000002}{50000002/5000002} \approx 100.000$$

$$N_9 = \frac{10N_8}{1 + \frac{10-1}{100}N_8} = \frac{10 \cdot \frac{5000000000}{50000002}}{1 + \frac{9}{100}\frac{5000000000}{50000002}} = \frac{50000000000/50000002}{500000002/50000002} \approx 100.000$$

$$N_{10} = \frac{10N_9}{1 + \frac{10-1}{100}N_9} = \frac{10 \cdot \frac{50000000000}{500000002}}{1 + \frac{9}{100}\frac{50000000000}{500000002}} = \frac{500000000000/500000002}{5000000002/500000002} \approx 100.000$$

The graph for this function is:

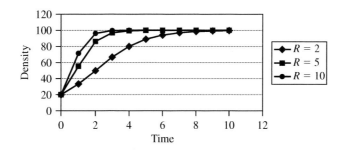

Graph of N_t as a function of t

Prob. 17. he long term behavior of the geometric mean of the growth parameter, $\hat{R}_t$, is defined as:

$$\hat{R}_t = (R_0 R_1 \cdots R_{t-1})^{1/t}$$

We now calculate $\hat{R}_t$ for $t = 1, 2, 3, \ldots 20$, using the fact that

$$\hat{R}_{t+1} = (R_0 R_1 \cdots R_t)^{1/(t+1)} = (R_t)^{\frac{1}{t+1}} \cdot (\hat{R}_t)^{\frac{t}{t+1}} \quad \text{for } t \geq 1.$$

$$\hat{R}_1 = R_0 = 2.78$$

$$\hat{R}_2 = (R_1)^{\frac{1}{2}} \cdot (\hat{R}_1)^{\frac{1}{2}} = (0.29)^{\frac{1}{2}} \cdot (2.78)^{\frac{1}{2}} \approx 0.8979$$

$$\hat{R}_3 = (R_2)^{\frac{1}{3}} \cdot (\hat{R}_2)^{\frac{2}{3}} = (0.43)^{\frac{1}{3}} \cdot (0.8979)^{\frac{2}{3}} \approx 0.7025$$

$$\hat{R}_4 = (R_3)^{\frac{1}{4}} \cdot (\hat{R}_3)^{\frac{3}{4}} = (0.25)^{\frac{1}{4}} \cdot (0.7025)^{\frac{3}{4}} \approx 0.5426$$

$$\hat{R}_5 = (R_4)^{\frac{1}{5}} \cdot (\hat{R}_4)^{\frac{4}{5}} = (2.90)^{\frac{1}{5}} \cdot (0.5426)^{\frac{4}{5}} \approx 0.7587$$

$$\hat{R}_6 = (R_5)^{\frac{1}{6}} \cdot (\hat{R}_5)^{\frac{5}{6}} = (1.67)^{\frac{1}{6}} \cdot (0.7587)^{\frac{5}{6}} \approx 0.8653$$

$$\hat{R}_7 = (R_6)^{\frac{1}{7}} \cdot (\hat{R}_6)^{\frac{6}{7}} = (1.17)^{\frac{1}{7}} \cdot (0.8653)^{\frac{6}{7}} \approx 0.9034$$

$$\hat{R}_8 = (R_7)^{\frac{1}{8}} \cdot (\hat{R}_7)^{\frac{7}{8}} = (0.69)^{\frac{1}{8}} \cdot (0.9034)^{\frac{7}{8}} \approx 0.8735$$

$$\hat{R}_9 = (R_8)^{\frac{1}{9}} \cdot (\hat{R}_8)^{\frac{8}{9}} = (1.45)^{\frac{1}{9}} \cdot (0.8735)^{\frac{8}{9}} \approx 0.9241$$

$$\hat{R}_{10} = (R_9)^{\frac{1}{10}} \cdot (\hat{R}_9)^{\frac{9}{10}} = (1.13)^{\frac{1}{10}} \cdot (0.9241)^{\frac{9}{10}} \approx 0.9428$$

$$\hat{R}_{11} = (R_{10})^{\frac{1}{11}} \cdot (\hat{R}_{10})^{\frac{10}{11}} = (0.08)^{\frac{1}{11}} \cdot (0.9428)^{\frac{10}{11}} \approx 0.7534$$

$$\hat{R}_{12} = (R_{11})^{\frac{1}{12}} \cdot (\hat{R}_{11})^{\frac{11}{12}} = (0.88)^{\frac{1}{12}} \cdot (0.7534)^{\frac{11}{12}} \approx 0.7633$$

$$\hat{R}_{13} = (R_{12})^{\frac{1}{13}} \cdot (\hat{R}_{12})^{\frac{12}{13}} = (2.69)^{\frac{1}{13}} \cdot (0.7218)^{\frac{12}{13}} \approx 0.8409$$

$$\hat{R}_{14} = (R_{13})^{\frac{1}{14}} \cdot (\hat{R}_{13})^{\frac{13}{14}} = (0.36)^{\frac{1}{14}} \cdot (0.6897)^{\frac{13}{14}} \approx 0.7915$$

$$\hat{R}_{15} = (R_{14})^{\frac{1}{15}} \cdot (\hat{R}_{14})^{\frac{14}{15}} = (0.08)^{\frac{1}{15}} \cdot (0.7112)^{\frac{14}{15}} \approx 0.6793$$

$$\hat{R}_{16} = (R_{15})^{\frac{1}{16}} \cdot (\hat{R}_{15})^{\frac{15}{16}} = (2.34)^{\frac{1}{16}} \cdot (0.6821)^{\frac{15}{16}} \approx 0.7339$$

$$\hat{R}_{17} = (R_{16})^{\frac{1}{17}} \cdot (\hat{R}_{16})^{\frac{16}{17}} = (2.13)^{\frac{1}{17}} \cdot (0.5611)^{\frac{16}{17}} \approx 0.7814$$

$$\hat{R}_{18} = (R_{17})^{\frac{1}{18}} \cdot (\hat{R}_{17})^{\frac{17}{18}} = (2.20)^{\frac{1}{18}} \cdot (0.4965)^{\frac{17}{18}} \approx 0.8276$$

$$\hat{R}_{19} = (R_{18})^{\frac{1}{19}} \cdot (\hat{R}_{18})^{\frac{18}{19}} = (2.80)^{\frac{1}{19}} \cdot (0.4645)^{\frac{18}{19}} \approx 0.8825$$

$$\hat{R}_{20} = (R_{19})^{\frac{1}{20}} \cdot (\hat{R}_{19})^{\frac{19}{20}} = (0.29)^{\frac{1}{20}} \cdot (0.4569)^{\frac{19}{20}} \approx 0.8347$$

Prob. 19.

(a) We have the equation:

$$N_{t+1} = (1 - c)N_t \exp\left[R\left(1 - \frac{(1-c)N_t}{K}\right)\right]$$

When $R = 1$, $K = 100$, $N_0 = 50$ and $c = 0.1$, we compute N_t for $t = 1, 2, \ldots 20$ using

$$N_{t+1} = (1 - 0.1)N_t \exp\left[1\left(1 - \frac{(1-0.1)N_t}{100}\right)\right] = 0.9 N_t \exp[1 - 0.009 N_t]$$

$N_1 = 0.9 N_0 \exp[1 - 0.009 N_0] \approx 77.99639$

$N_2 = 0.9 N_1 \exp[1 - 0.009 N_1] \approx 94.56945$

$N_3 = 0.9 N_2 \exp[1 - 0.009 N_2] \approx 98.77543$

$N_4 = 0.9 N_3 \exp[1 - 0.009 N_3] \approx 99.33615$

$N_5 = 0.9 N_4 \exp[1 - 0.009 N_4] \approx 99.39717$

$N_6 = 0.9 N_5 \exp[1 - 0.009 N_5] \approx 99.40363$

$N_7 = 0.9 N_6 \exp[1 - 0.009 N_6] \approx 99.40431$

$N_8 = 0.9 N_7 \exp[1 - 0.009 N_7] \approx 99.40438$

$N_9 = 0.9 N_8 \exp[1 - 0.009 N_8] \approx 99.40439$

$N_{10} = 0.9 N_9 \exp[1 - 0.009 N_9] \approx 99.40439$

$N_{11} = 0.9 N_{10} \exp[1 - 0.009 N_{10}] \approx 99.40439$

$N_{12} = 0.9 N_{11} \exp[1 - 0.009 N_{11}] \approx 99.40439$

$N_{13} = 0.9 N_{12} \exp[1 - 0.009 N_{12}] \approx 99.40439$

$N_{14} = 0.9 N_{13} \exp[1 - 0.009 N_{13}] \approx 99.40439$

$N_{15} = 0.9 N_{14} \exp[1 - 0.009 N_{14}] \approx 99.40439$

$N_{16} = 0.9 N_{15} \exp[1 - 0.009 N_{15}] \approx 99.40439$

$N_{17} = 0.9 N_{16} \exp[1 - 0.009 N_{16}] \approx 99.40439$

$N_{18} = 0.9 N_{17} \exp[1 - 0.009 N_{17}] \approx 99.40439$

$N_{19} = 0.9 N_{18} \exp[1 - 0.009 N_{18}] \approx 99.40439$

$N_{20} = 0.9 N_{19} \exp[1 - 0.009 N_{19}] \approx 99.40439$

(b) We have the equation:

$$N_{t+1} = (1-c)N_t \exp\left[R\left(1 - \frac{(1-c)N_t}{K}\right)\right]$$

When $R = 1$, $K = 100$, $N_0 = 50$ and $c = 0.5$, we compute N_t for $t = 1, 2, \ldots 20$ using

$$N_{t+1} = (1-0.5)N_t \exp\left[1\left(1 - \frac{(1-0.5)N_t}{100}\right)\right] = 0.5N_t \exp[1 - 0.005N_t]$$

$N_1 = 0.5N_0 \exp[1 - 0.005N_0] \approx 52.92500$

$N_2 = 0.5N_1 \exp[1 - 0.005N_1] \approx 55.20776$

$N_3 = 0.5N_2 \exp[1 - 0.005N_2] \approx 56.93542$

$N_4 = 0.5N_3 \exp[1 - 0.005N_3] \approx 58.21211$

$N_5 = 0.5N_4 \exp[1 - 0.005N_4] \approx 59.13871$

$N_6 = 0.5N_5 \exp[1 - 0.005N_5] \approx 59.80235$

$N_7 = 0.5N_6 \exp[1 - 0.005N_6] \approx 60.27311$

$N_8 = 0.5N_7 \exp[1 - 0.005N_7] \approx 60.60475$

$N_9 = 0.5N_8 \exp[1 - 0.005N_8] \approx 60.83726$

$N_{10} = 0.5N_9 \exp[1 - 0.005N_9] \approx 60.99970$

$N_{11} = 0.5N_{10} \exp[1 - 0.005N_{10}] \approx 61.11292$

$N_{12} = 0.5N_{11} \exp[1 - 0.005N_{11}] \approx 61.19170$

$N_{13} = 0.5N_{12} \exp[1 - 0.005N_{12}] \approx 61.24645$

$N_{14} = 0.5N_{13} \exp[1 - 0.005N_{13}] \approx 61.284470$

$N_{15} = 0.5N_{14} \exp[1 - 0.005N_{14}] \approx 61.310854$

$N_{16} = 0.5N_{15} \exp[1 - 0.005N_{15}] \approx 61.329161$

$N_{17} = 0.5N_{16} \exp[1 - 0.005N_{16}] \approx 61.341858$

$N_{18} = 0.5N_{17} \exp[1 - 0.005N_{17}] \approx 61.350663$

$N_{19} = 0.5N_{18} \exp[1 - 0.005N_{18}] \approx 61.356768$

$N_{20} = 0.5N_{19} \exp[1 - 0.005N_{19}] \approx 61.361000$

(c) We have the equation:

$$N_{t+1} = (1-c)N_t \exp\left[R\left(1 - \frac{(1-c)N_t}{K}\right)\right]$$

When $R = 1$, $K = 100$, $N_0 = 50$ and $c = 0.9$, we compute N_t for $t = 1, 2, \ldots 20$ using

$$N_{t+1} = (1-0.9)N_t \exp\left[1\left(1 - \frac{(1-0.9)N_t}{100}\right)\right] = 0.1N_t \exp[1 - 0.001N_t]$$

$N_1 = 0.1N_0 \exp[1 - 0.001N_0] \approx 12.92855$

$N_2 = 0.1N_1 \exp[1 - 0.001N_1] \approx 3.46920$

$N_3 = 0.1N_2 \exp[1 - 0.001N_2] \approx 0.93976$

$N_4 = 0.1N_3 \exp[1 - 0.001N_3] \approx 0.25521$

$N_5 = 0.1N_4 \exp[1 - 0.001N_4] \approx 0.06936$

$N_6 = 0.1N_5 \exp[1 - 0.001N_5] \approx 0.01885$

$N_7 = 0.1N_6 \exp[1 - 0.001N_6] \approx 0.00512$

$N_8 = 0.1N_7 \exp[1 - 0.001N_7] \approx 0.00139$

$N_9 = 0.1N_8 \exp[1 - 0.001N_8] \approx 0.00038$

$N_{10} = 0.1N_9 \exp[1 - 0.001N_9] \approx 0.00010$

$N_{11} = 0.1N_{10} \exp[1 - 0.001N_{10}] \approx 2.7977 \cdot 10^{-5}$

$N_{12} = 0.1N_{11} \exp[1 - 0.001N_{11}] \approx 7.6051 \cdot 10^{-6}$

$N_{13} = 0.1N_{12} \exp[1 - 0.001N_{12}] \approx 2.0673 \cdot 10^{-6}$

$N_{14} = 0.1N_{13} \exp[1 - 0.001N_{13}] \approx 5.6195 \cdot 10^{-7}$

$N_{15} = 0.1N_{14} \exp[1 - 0.001N_{14}] \approx 1.5275 \cdot 10^{-7}$

$N_{16} = 0.1N_{15} \exp[1 - 0.001N_{15}] \approx 4.1523 \cdot 10^{-8}$

$N_{17} = 0.1N_{16} \exp[1 - 0.001N_{16}] \approx 1.1287 \cdot 10^{-8}$

$N_{18} = 0.1N_{17} \exp[1 - 0.001N_{17}] \approx 3.0681 \cdot 10^{-9}$

$N_{19} = 0.1N_{18} \exp[1 - 0.001N_{18}] \approx 8.3400 \cdot 10^{-10}$

$N_{20} = 0.1N_{19} \exp[1 - 0.001N_{19}] \approx 2.2671 \cdot 10^{-10}$

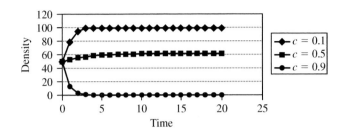

Chapter 3

Limits and Continuity

3.1 Limits

Prob. 1. We will approach $x = 2$ from the left and right:

x	$x^2 - 4x + 1$	x	$x^2 - 4x + 1$
1.9	-2.99	2.1	-2.99
1.99	-2.999	2.01	-2.999
1.999	-2.999	2.001	-2.999

Hence the limit is -3.

Prob. 3. We will approach $x = -1$ from the left and right

X	$\frac{2x}{1+x^2}$	x	$\frac{2x}{1+2^x}$
-1.1	0.999	-0.9	-0.99
-1.01	-0.99	-0.99	-0.99
-1.001	-0.99	-0.99	-0.99

Hence the limit is -1.

Prob. 5. In the following table, we compute the values of $3\cos\frac{x}{4}$ for x close to π (but not equal to π). In the left half of the table, we approach $x = \pi$ from the left ($x \to \pi^-$); in the right half of the table, we approach $x = \pi$ from the right ($x \to \pi^+$). We would guess that the value of this limit is 2.12 as x approaches π, from either side.

117

x	$3\cos\frac{x}{4}$	x	$3\cos\frac{x}{4}$
3.13985	2.122	3.14334	2.120
3.14142	2.121	3.14177	2.12
3.14157	2.121	3.14161	2.12
3.141591	2.121	3.141594	2.12

Since this limit is a finite number, we say that the limit exists and that the function converges to 2.12 as x tends to π.

Prob. 7. In the following table, we compute the values of $2\sec(x/3)$ for x close to $\pi/2$ (but not equal to $\pi/2$). In the left half of the table, we approach $x = \pi/2$ from the left $(x \to (\pi/2)^-)$; in the right half of the table, we approach $x = \pi/2$ from the right $(x \to (\pi/2)^+)$. We would guess that the value of this limit is 2.309 as x approaches $\pi/2$, from either side.

x	$2\sec(x/3)$	x	$2\sec(x/3)$
1.56905	2.308	1.57254	2.3102
1.57062	2.3093	1.57097	2.30947
1.57077	2.3093	1.57081	2.3094
1.57079	2.3093	1.57080	2.3094

Since this limit is a finite number, we say that the limit exists and that the function converges to 2.309 as x tends to $\pi/2$.

Prob. 9. In the following table, we compute the values of $e^{-x^2/2}$ for x close to -1 (but not equal to -1). In the left half of the table, we approach $x = -1$ from the left $(x \to -1^-)$; in the right half of the table, we approach $x = -1$ from the right $(x \to -1^+)$. We would guess that the value of this limit is 0.606 as x approaches -1, from either side.

x	$e^{-x^2/2}$	x	$e^{-x^2/2}$
-1.1	0.5461	-0.9	0.667
-1.01	0.6005	-0.99	0.6125
-1.001	0.6059	-0.999	0.6071
-1.0001	0.6064	-0.9999	0.6066

Since this limit is a finite number, we say that the limit exists and that the function converges to 0.606 as x tends to -1.

Prob. 11. In the following table, we compute the values of $\ln(x+1)$ for x close to 0 (but not equal to 0). In the left half of the table, we approach $x = 0$ from the left $(x \to 0^-)$; in the right half of the table, we approach $x = 0$ from the right $(x \to 0^+)$. We would guess that the value of this limit is 0 as x approaches 0, from either side.

x	$\ln(x+1)$	x	$\ln(x+1)$
-0.1	-0.10536	0.1	0.0953
-0.01	-0.01005	0.01	0.00995
-0.001	-0.0010005	0.001	0.000999
-0.0001	-0.000100005	0.0001	0.0000999

Since this limit is a finite number, we say that the limit exists and that the function converges to 0 as x tends to 0.

Prob. 13. In the following table, we compute the values of $\frac{x^2-16}{x-4}$ for x close to 3 (but not equal to 3). In the left half of the table, we approach $x = 3$ from the left $(x \to 3^-)$; in the right half of the table, we approach $x = 3$ from the right $(x \to 3^+)$. We would guess that the value of this limit is 7 as x approaches 3, from either side.

x	$\frac{x^2-16}{x-4}$	x	$\frac{x^2-16}{x-4}$
2.9	6.9	3.1	7.1
2.99	6.99	3.01	7.01
2.999	6.999	3.001	7.001
2.9999	6.9999	3.0001	7.0001

Since this limit is a finite number, we say that the limit exists and that the function converges to 7 as x tends to 3.

Prob. 15. We will approach $x = \frac{\pi}{2}$ from the left and right:

x	$\sin(2x)$	x	$\sin(2x)$
89.9	0.003	90.1	-0.003
89.99	0.0003	90.01	-0.0003
89.999	0.00003	90.001	-0.00003

Hence the limit is 0.

Prob. 17. We will approach $x0$ from the left and right:

x	$\frac{1}{1+x^2}$	x	$\frac{1}{1+x^2}$
-0.1	0.99	0.1	0.99
-0.01	0.99	0.01	0.99
-0.001	0.99	0.001	0.99

Hence the limit is 1.

Prob. 19. We will approach $x0$ from right only:

x	$1 - e^{-x}$
0.1	0.095
0.01	0.0099
0.001	0.00099

Hence the limit is 0.

Prob. 21. As we approach the vertical asymptote $x = 4$ from the left, the graph of $f(x) = \frac{2}{x-4}$ falls sharply off. This reveals that

$$\lim_{x \to 4^-} \frac{2}{x - 4} = -\infty$$

We arrive at the same conclusion when we compute values of $f(x)$ for x close to, and slightly smaller than, 4. When x is slightly smaller than 4, the term $x - 4$ is negative and decreases to zero. From this we can conclude that $f(x)$ grows negatively without bound as x approaches 4 from the left.

Prob. 23. As we approach the vertical asymptote $x = 1$ from the left, the graph of $f(x) = \frac{2}{1-x}$ grows steeply. This reveals that

$$\lim_{x \to 1^-} \frac{2}{1 - x} = \infty$$

We arrive at the same conclusion when we compute values of $f(x)$ for x close to, and slightly smaller than, 1. When x is slightly smaller than 1, the term $1 - x$ is positive and decreases to zero. From this we can conclude that $f(x)$ grows positively without bound as x approaches 1 from the left.

Prob. 25. As we approach the vertical asymptote $x = 1$ from the left, the graph of $f(x) = \frac{1}{1-x^2}$ grows steeply. This reveals that

$$\lim_{x \to 1^-} \frac{1}{1 - x^2} = \infty$$

We arrive at the same conclusion when we compute values of $f(x)$ for x close to, and slightly smaller than, 1. When x is slightly smaller than 1, the term $1 - x^2$ is positive and decreases to zero. From this we can conclude that $f(x)$ grows positively without bound as x approaches 1 from the left.

Prob. 27. We will approach $x = 3$ from the left and right:

x	$\frac{1}{(x-3)^2}$	x	$\frac{1}{(x-3)^2}$
2.9	100	3.1	100
2.99	10000	3.01	10000
2.999	10^6	3.001	10^6

Hence, the limit does not exist, diverging to infinity.

Prob. 29. The graph of the function $f(x) = \frac{\sqrt{x^2+9}-3}{x^2}$ ($x \neq 0$), indicates that the limit exists and, based on the graph, we conjecture that it is equal to 0.16667. If, instead, we use a calculator to produce a table for values of $f(x)$ close to 0, something strange seems to happen.

x	$f(x)$	x	$f(x)$
0.1	0.1666	0.00001	0.15
0.01	0.1666	0.000001	0.1
0.001	0.1666	0.0000001	0
0.0001	0.1666	0.00000001	0

As we move closer to 0, we first find that $f(x)$ gets close to 0.16667, but when x gets very close to 0, $f(x)$ seems to drop to 0. What is going on? First, before you worry too much, it is true that $\lim_{x \to 0} f(x) = \frac{1}{6}$. In the next section, we will learn how to compute this limit without resorting to the (somewhat dubious) help of a calculator. The strange behaviour of the calculated values happens because when x is very small, the difference in the numerator is so close to 0 that the calculator can no longer accurately determine its value, and simply returns 0. The calculator can only accurately compute a certain number of digits, which is good enough for most cases, but here we need greater accuracy. The same strange thing happens when you try to graph this function on a graphing calculator. When the x-axis interval of the viewing window is too small, the graph is no longer accurate.

Prob. 31. The graph of the function $f(x) = \frac{1-\sqrt{1-x^2}}{x^2}$ $(x \neq 0)$, indicates that the limit exists and, based on the graph, we conjecture that it is equal to 0.5. If, instead, we use a calculator to produce a table for values of $f(x)$ close to 0, something strange seems to happen.

x	$f(x)$	x	$f(x)$
0.1	0.50126	0.00001	1.00000
0.01	0.50001	0.000001	0
0.001	0.50000	0.0000001	0
0.0001	0.50000	0.00000001	0

As we move closer to 0, we first find that $f(x)$ gets close to 0.5, but when x gets very close to 0, $f(x)$ seems to drop to 0. What is going on? First, before you worry too much, it is true that $\lim_{x \to 0} f(x) = 0.5$. In the next section, we will learn how to compute this limit without resorting to the (somewhat dubious) help of a calculator. The strange behaviour of the calculated values happens because when x is very small, the difference in the numerator is so close to 0 that the calculator can no longer accurately determine its value, and simply returns 0. The calculator can only accurately compute a certain number of digits, which is good enough for most cases, but here we need greater accuracy. The same strange thing happens when you try to graph this function on a graphing calculator. When the x-axis interval of the viewing window is too small, the graph is no longer accurate.

Prob. 33.

(a) From both the graph and the table for $2/x^2$, we conjecture that the limit of this function is 0 as x approaches ∞. We compute the values of $2/x^2$ for larger and larger values of x, since this is what $x \to \infty$ means.

x	$2/x^2$
100	0.0002
1000	0.000002
10000	$2 \cdot 10^{-8}$
100000	$2 \cdot 10^{-10}$

Since this limit is a finite number, we say that the limit exists and that the function converges to 0 as x tends to ∞.

(b) From both the graph and the table for $2/x^2$, we conjecture that the limit of this function is 0 as x approaches $-\infty$. We compute the values of $2/x^2$ for larger and larger negative values of x, since this is what $x \to -\infty$ means.

x	$2/x^2$
-100	0.0002
-1000	0.000002
-10000	$2 \cdot 10^{-8}$
-100000	$2 \cdot 10^{-10}$

Since this limit is a finite number, we say that the limit exists and that the function converges to 0 as x tends to $-\infty$.

(c) The graph of $f(x) = 2/x^2$ $(x \neq 0)$, reveals that $f(x)$ increases positively without bound as $x \to 0$. We can confirm this when we select values for x that are close to 0. By choosing values sufficiently close to 0, we can get arbitrarily large values of $2/x^2$.

x	$2/x^2$	x	$2/x^2$
-0.1	200	0.1	200
-0.01	20,000	0.01	20,000
-0.001	$2 \cdot 10^6$	0.001	$2 \cdot 10^6$
-0.0001	$2 \cdot 10^8$	0.0001	$2 \cdot 10^8$

This indicates that $\lim_{x \to 0} \frac{1}{x^2}$ does not exist.

Prob. 35. Simply using a calculator and plugging in values to find limits can yield unclear answers if we do not exercise some caution. If we produced a table of values of $f(x) = \sin \frac{1}{x-1}$ for $x = 1.1, 1.01, 1.001, \ldots$, we would find that $\sin \frac{1}{1.1-1} = -0.5440$, $\sin \frac{1}{1.01-1} = -0.5064$, $\sin \frac{1}{1.001-1} = 0.8269$, and so on. (Note that we measure angles in radians.) These values seem to be not approaching any fixed value. Looking at the graph of $f(x)$, we find that the values of $f(x)$ oscillate infinitely often between -1 and $+1$ as $x \to 1$. This is because as $x \to 1^+$, the argument in the sine function goes to infinity (likewise, as $x \to 1^-$, the argument goes to negative infinity), namely,

$$\lim_{x \to 1^+} \frac{1}{x-1} = \infty \quad \text{and} \quad \lim_{x \to 1^-} \frac{1}{x-1} = -\infty,$$

and so the function values oscillate between -1 and $+1$. Therefore, $\sin \frac{1}{x-1}$ continues to oscillate between -1 and $+1$ as $x \to 1$.

Prob. 37. Using Limit Laws 1 and 2, we can write

$$\lim_{x \to -1} \left(x^3 + 7x - 1\right) = \lim_{x \to -1} x^3 + 7 \lim_{x \to -1} x - \lim_{x \to -1} 1$$

provided the individual limits exist. For the first term, we use Limit Law 3 twice, to get

$$\lim_{x \to -1} x^3 = \lim_{x \to -1} x \cdot \lim_{x \to -1} x^2 = \lim_{x \to -1} x \cdot \lim_{x \to -1} x \cdot \lim_{x \to -1} x$$

provided that $\lim_{x \to -1} x$ exists. Using Formula (3.3), it follows that $\lim_{x \to -1} x = -1$ and we find that

$$\lim_{x \to -1} x \cdot \lim_{x \to -1} x \cdot \lim_{x \to -1} x = (-1)(-1)(-1) = -1.$$

To compute the second term, we use Formula (3.3) again to get $\lim_{x \to -1} x = -1$. For the last term, it is clear that $\lim_{x \to -1} 1 = 1$. Thus each of the individual limits exist, and we have

$$\lim_{x \to -1} \left(x^3 + 7x - 1\right) = \lim_{x \to -1} x^3 + 7 \lim_{x \to -1} x - \lim_{x \to -1} 1 = -1 + (7)(-1) - 1 = -9$$

Prob. 39. Using Limit Laws 1 and 2, we can write

$$\lim_{x \to -5} \left(4 + 2x^2\right) = \lim_{x \to -5} 4 + 2 \lim_{x \to -5} x^2$$

provided the individual limits exist. For the second term, we use Limit Law 3, to get

$$\lim_{x \to -5} x^2 = \lim_{x \to -5} x \cdot \lim_{x \to -5} x$$

provided $\lim_{x \to -5} x$ exists. Using Formula (3.3), it follows that $\lim_{x \to -5} x = -5$ and we find that

$$\lim_{x \to -5} x \cdot \lim_{x \to -5} x = (-5)(-5) = 25$$

To compute the first term, we find that $\lim_{x \to -5} 4 = 4$. Thus each of the individual limits exist, and we have

$$\lim_{x \to -5} \left(4 + 2x^2\right) = \lim_{x \to -5} 4 + 2 \lim_{x \to -5} x^2 = 4 + 2(25) = 54 \tag{3.1.1}$$

Prob. 41. Using Limit Laws 1 and 4, we can write

$$\lim_{x \to 3} \left(2x^2 - \frac{1}{x}\right) = 2 \lim_{x \to 3} x^2 - \frac{\lim_{x \to 3} 1}{\lim_{x \to 3} x}$$

provided the individual limits exist. For the first term, we use Limit Law 3, to get

$$\lim_{x \to 3} x^2 = \lim_{x \to 3} x \cdot \lim_{x \to 1} x$$

provided $\lim_{x \to 3} x$ exists. Using Formula (3.3), it follows that $\lim_{x \to 3} x = 3$ and we find that

$$\lim_{x \to 3} x \cdot \lim_{x \to 3} x = (3)(3) = 9$$

To compute the second term, we use Formula (3.3) again to get $\lim_{x \to 3} x = 3$, and we also have $\lim_{x \to 3} 1 = 1$. Thus each of the individual limits exist, and we have

$$\lim_{x \to 3} \left(2x^2 - \frac{1}{x}\right) = 2 \lim_{x \to 3} x^2 - \frac{\lim_{x \to 3} 1}{\lim_{x \to 3} x} = 2(9) - \frac{1}{3} = \frac{53}{3}$$

Prob. 43. Using Limit Law 4, we find that

$$\lim_{x \to -3} \frac{x^3 - 20}{x + 1} = \frac{\lim_{x \to -3}(x^3 - 20)}{\lim_{x \to -3}(x + 1)}$$

provided the limits in the numerator and denominator exist and the limit in the denominator is not equal to 0. Using Limit Laws 2 and 3, and Formula (3.3) in the numerator, we find

$$\lim_{x \to -3} (x^3 - 20) = \lim_{x \to -3} x^3 - \lim_{x \to -3} 20 = (-3)(-3)(-3) - 20 = -47$$

Note that breaking up the limit of the sum in the numerator into a sum of limits is only justified once we show that the individual limits exist. Using Limit Law 2 and Formula (3.3) in the denominator, we find

$$\lim_{x \to -3} (x + 1) = \lim_{x \to -3} x + \lim_{x \to -3} 1 = -3 + 1 = -2$$

Again using the limit laws is only justified once we demonstrate that the individual limits exist. Since the limits in both the denominator and the numerator exist and the limit in the denominator is not equal to 0, we have

$$\lim_{x \to -3} \frac{x^3 - 20}{x + 1} = \frac{\lim_{x \to -3}(x^3 - 20)}{\lim_{x \to -3}(x + 1)} = \frac{-47}{-2} = 23.5$$

Prob. 45. Using Limit Law 4, we find

$$\lim_{x \to 3} \frac{3x^2 + 1}{2x - 3} = \frac{\lim_{x \to 3}(3x^2 + 1)}{\lim_{x \to 3}(2x - 3)}$$

provided the limits in the numerator and denominator exist and the limit in the denominator is not equal to 0. Using Limit Laws 1, 2 and 3, and Formula (3.3) in the numerator, we find

$$\lim_{x \to 3} (3x^2 + 1) = 3 \lim_{x \to 3} x^2 + \lim_{x \to 3} 1 = 3(3)(3) + 1 = 28$$

Note that breaking up the limit of the sum in the numerator into a sum of limits is only justified once we show that the individual limits exist. Using Limit Laws 1 and 2, and Formula (3.3) in the denominator, we find

$$\lim_{x \to 3} (2x - 3) = 2 \lim_{x \to 3} x - \lim_{x \to 3} 3 = 2(3) - 3 = 3$$

Again using the limit laws is only justified once we demonstrate that the individual limits exist. Since the limits in both the denominator and the numerator exist and the limit in the denominator is not equal to 0, we obtain

$$\lim_{x \to 3} \frac{3x^2 + 1}{2x - 3} = \frac{\lim_{x \to 3}(3x^2 + 1)}{\lim_{x \to 3}(2x - 3)} = \frac{28}{3}$$

Prob. 47. The function $f(x) = \frac{1 - x^2}{1 - x}$ is a rational function, but since $\lim_{x \to 1}(1 - x) = 0$, we cannot use Limit Law 4. Instead, we need to try to simplify $f(x)$ first. Notice that

$$\lim_{x \to 1} \frac{1 - x^2}{1 - x} = \lim_{x \to 1} \frac{(1 - x)(1 + x)}{1 - x}$$

Since $x \neq 1$, we can cancel the non-zero factor $1 - x$ in the numerator and denominator, which yields

$$\lim_{x \to 1} \frac{(1 - x)(1 + x)}{1 - x} = \lim_{x \to 1}(1 + x) = \lim_{x \to 1} 1 + \lim_{x \to 1} x = 1 + 1 = 2$$

where we have used Limit Law 2 and Formula (3.3) when computing the limit.

Prob. 49. The function $f(x) = \frac{x^2 - 2x - 3}{x - 3}$ is a rational function, but since $\lim_{x \to 3}(x - 3) = 0$, we cannot use Limit Law 4. Instead, we need to try to simplify $f(x)$ first. Notice that

$$\lim_{x \to 3} \frac{x^2 - 2x - 3}{x - 3} = \lim_{x \to 3} \frac{(x - 3)(x + 1)}{x - 3}$$

Since $x \neq 3$, we can cancel the non-zero factor $x - 3$ in the numerator and denominator, which yields

$$\lim_{x \to 3} \frac{(x - 3)(x + 1)}{x - 3} = \lim_{x \to 3}(x + 1) = \lim_{x \to 3} x + \lim_{x \to 3} 1 = 3 + 1 = 4$$

where we used Limit Law 2 and Formula (3.3) when computing the limit.

Prob. 51.

$$\lim_{x \to 2} \frac{2 - x}{x^2 - 4} = \lim_{x \to 2} \frac{2 - x}{(x - 2)(x + 2)} = \lim_{x \to 2} \frac{-(x - 2)}{(x - 2)(x + 2)}.$$

Since $x \neq 2$, we have:

$$\lim_{x \to 2} \frac{-1}{x + 2} = \frac{\lim_{x \to 2}(-1)}{\lim_{x \to 2}(x + 2)} = \frac{-1}{\lim_{x \to 2} x + \lim_{x \to 2} 2} = \frac{-1}{2 + 2} = -\frac{1}{4}.$$

Prob. 53. The function $f(x) = \frac{2x^2 + 3x - 2}{x + 2}$ is a rational function, but since $\lim_{x \to -2}(x + 2) = 0$, we cannot use Limit Law 4. Instead, we need to try to simplify $f(x)$ first. Notice that

$$\lim_{x \to -2} \frac{2x^2 + 3x - 2}{x + 2} = \lim_{x \to -2} \frac{(2x - 1)(x + 2)}{x + 2}$$

Since $x \neq -2$, we can cancel the non-zero factor $x + 2$ in the numerator and denominator, which yields

$$\lim_{x \to -2} \frac{(2x - 1)(x + 2)}{x + 2} = \lim_{x \to -2}(2x - 1) = 2 \lim_{x \to -2} x - \lim_{x \to -2} 1 = 2(-2) - 1 = -5$$

where we used Limit Laws 1 and 2, and Formula (3.3) when computing the limit.

3.2 Continuity

Prob. 1. Given $f(x) = 2x$, $c = \frac{1}{2}$, to show that it is continuous at c we must show:

(1) $f(c)$ exists: $f(c) = f(\frac{1}{2}) = 2 \cdot \frac{1}{2} = 1$

(2) $\lim_{x \to c} f(x)$ exits: $\lim_{x \to \frac{1}{2}} 2x = 2 \cdot \frac{1}{2} = 1$

(3) $f(c) = \lim_{x \to c} f(x):\quad 1 = 1.$

Hence, this function is continuous at $c = \frac{1}{2}$.

Prob. 3. We must check all three conditions on page 129.

1. $f(x)$ is defined at $x = 2$ since $f(2) = 2^3 - 2 \cdot 2 + 1 = 5$.

2. We can repeatedly use the fact that $\lim_{x \to 2} x = 2$ to conclude that $\lim_{x \to 2} f(x)$ exists.

3. Using the limit laws, we find that $\lim_{x \to 2} f(x) = 5$. This is same as $f(2)$.

Since all three conditions are satisfied, $f(x) = x^3 - 2x + 1$ is continuous at $x = 2$.

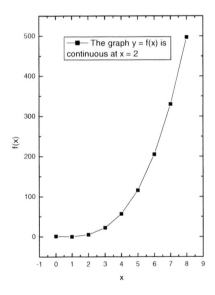

Prob. 5. The graph of $f(x)$ is shown below. We have

$$\lim_{x \to 2} \frac{x^2 - x - 2}{x - 2} = \lim_{x \to 2} \frac{(x + 1)(x - 2)}{x - 2} = \lim_{x \to 2} (x + 1) = 2 + 1 = 3$$

which is equal to $f(2)$. Thus the required conditions are satisfied and we can conclude that the function is continuous at $x = 2$.

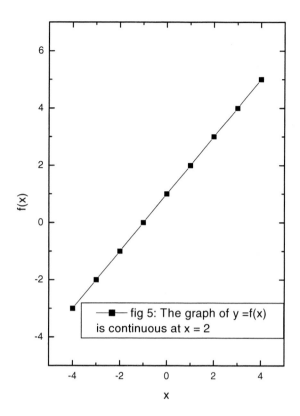

fig 5: The graph of y =f(x) is continuous at x = 2

Prob. 7. First, we compute the limit of $f(x)$ as $x \to 3$. We have

$$\lim_{x \to 3} \frac{x^2 - 9}{x - 3} = \lim_{x \to 3} \frac{(x-3)(x+3)}{x-3} = \lim_{x \to 3} (x+3) = 3 + 3 = 6.$$

To ensure that $f(x)$ is continuous at $x = 3$, we require that

$$\lim_{x \to 3} f(x) = f(3) = a.$$

We therefore need to choose $a = 6$. This is the only choice for a that would make $f(x)$ continuous. Any other value of a would result in $f(x)$ being discontinuous.

Prob. 9. We consider the three requirements for continuity listed on page 129. First, $f(x)$ is defined at $x = 3$, since we are told that $f(3) = 0$. The second condition, however, fails to be satisfied, since we know that

$$\lim_{x \to 3^-} f(x) = \lim_{x \to 3^-} \frac{1}{x-3} = -\infty$$

and that

$$\lim_{x \to 3^+} f(x) = \lim_{x \to 3^+} \frac{1}{x-3} = \infty.$$

This means that $\lim_{x \to 3} f(x)$ does not exist. Thus $f(x)$ is discontinuous at $x = 3$.

Prob. 11. We consider the three requirements for continuity listed on page 129. First, $f(x)$ is defined at $x = 1$, since we are told that $f(1) = 1$. Secondly, we have

$$\lim_{x \to 1} \frac{x^2 - 3x + 2}{x - 2} = \lim_{x \to 1} \frac{(x-1)(x-2)}{x-2} = \lim_{x \to 1} (x-1) = 1 - 1 = 0$$

and so we know that $\lim_{x \to 1} f(x)$ does exist. However, the third condition for continuity fails, because $\lim_{x \to 1} f(x) = 0 \neq f(1)$. Thus $f(x)$ is discontinuous at $x = 1$.

Prob. 13. The graph of the floor function

$$f(x) = \lfloor x \rfloor = \text{the largest integer less than or equal to } x$$

is given in Figure 3.12 of the textbook. Let us look at $x = 5/2$ first. We consider the three requirements for continuity listed on page 129. First, $f(5/2) = \lfloor 5/2 \rfloor = 2$ and so the function exists at $x = 5/2$. Next,

$$\lim_{x \to 5/2} f(x) = \lim_{x \to 5/2} \lfloor x \rfloor = \lim_{x \to 5/2} 2 = 2$$

since the function takes the value 2 a little to the left and right of $x = 5/2$. Since $\lim_{x \to 5/2} f(x) = 2 = f(5/2)$, we conclude that $f(x)$ is indeed continuous at $x = 5/2$. Next, what happens at $x = 3$? Notice from the graph that the function jumps whenever x is an integer. Now $f(3) = 3$, but

$$\lim_{x \to 3^+} f(x) = 3 \quad \text{and} \quad \lim_{x \to 3^-} = 2$$

which means that $\lim_{x \to 3} f(x)$ cannot exist. The function is therefore discontinuous at $x = 3$.

Prob. 15. Since $f(x) = 3x^4 - x^2 + 4$ is a polynomial, it is continuous for all $x \in \mathbb{R}$.

Prob. 17. Since $f(x) = \frac{x^2+1}{x-1}$ is a rational function, it is defined for all $x \neq 1$. Thus it is continuous for all $x \neq 1$.

Prob. 19. Setting $g(x) = -x$ and $h(x) = e^x$, we have $f(x) = (h \circ g)(x)$. Since both g and h are continuous for all $x \in \mathbb{R}$, the given function f is continuous for all $x \in \mathbb{R}$.

Prob. 21. The given function $f(x) = \ln \frac{x}{x+1}$ is logarithmic and is defined as long as $\frac{x}{x+1} > 0$ and $x + 1 \neq 0$. This means that $x > 0$ or $x < -1$. It is therefore continuous over the intervals $(-\infty, -1)$ and $(0, \infty)$.

Prob. 23. Since $f(x)$ is a trigonometric function, it is continuous wherever it is defined. The tangent function $\tan u$ is defined for all $u \neq \frac{\pi}{2} + k\pi$, where k is an integer. Setting $2\pi x = \frac{\pi}{2} + k\pi$, we find that $x = \frac{1}{4} + \frac{k}{2}$. Thus the given function is defined (and therefore continuous) for all $x \neq \frac{1}{4} + \frac{k}{2}$, where k is an integer.

Prob. 25.

(a) The graph of $f(x)$ when $c = 1$ is shown in the figure below. The function is not continuous at $x = 0$, because the left- and right-hand limits are not equal to each other.

$$\lim_{x \to 0^-} f(x) = \lim_{x \to 0^-} (x^2 + 2) = 0^2 + 2 = 2 \neq 1 = c = \lim_{x \to 0^+} (x + c) = \lim_{x \to 0^+} f(x)$$

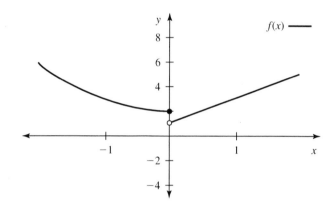

(b) We know that $f(0) = 2$. If we choose $c = 2$, then the function will be continuous for all $x \in \mathbb{R}$ because in this case

$$\lim_{x \to 0^-} f(x) = \lim_{x \to 0^-} (x^2 + 2) = 2 = f(0) = \lim_{x \to 0^+} (x + c) = \lim_{x \to 0^+} f(x)$$

Prob. 27.

(a) The function $f(x) = \sqrt{x - 1}$ is the composition of a polynomial $(x - 1)$ with the square root function. Since both functions are continuous from the right over their domains, the given function f must also be continuous from the right at $x = 1$.

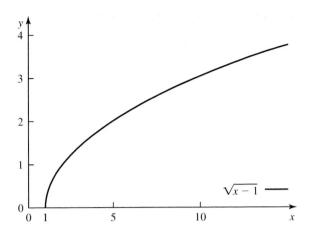

(b)

(c) Since $f(x)$ is not defined for $x < 1$, it does not make sense to look at continuity from the left at $x = 1$.

Prob. 29. The function $\sin(x/2)$ is a composition of a polynomial and a trigonometric function, and is defined for all $x \in \mathbb{R}$, and therefore it is continuous for all $x \in \mathbb{R}$. In particular, it is continuous at $x = \pi/3$, and we have

$$\lim_{x \to \pi/3} \sin\left(\frac{x}{2}\right) = \sin\left(\frac{\pi/3}{2}\right) = \sin\left(\frac{\pi}{6}\right) = 0.5$$

Prob. 31. Here, the limits of both the numerator and the denominator are equal to zero, since

$$\lim_{x \to \pi/2} \cos^2 x = \cos^2(\pi/2) = 0 \quad \text{and} \quad \lim_{x \to \pi/2} (1 - \sin^2 x) = 1 - \sin^2(\pi/2) = 1 - 1 = 0.$$

However, this does not mean that the limit does not exist. We use a trick that will allow us to find the limit; since $\cos^2 x + \sin^2 x = 1$, we have

$$\lim_{x \to \pi/2} \frac{\cos^2 x}{1 - \sin^2 x} = \lim_{x \to \pi/2} \frac{\cos^2 x}{\cos^2 x} = \lim_{x \to \pi/2} 1 = 1.$$

Prob. 33.

$$\lim_{x \to -1} \sqrt{4 + 5x^4} = \sqrt{4 + 5(-1)^4} = \sqrt{4 + 5} = 3.$$

Prob. 35. The function $\sqrt{x^2 + 2x + 2} = \sqrt{(x+1)^2 + 1}$ is a composition of a polynomial and a power function, and is defined for all $x \in \mathbb{R}$, and therefore it is continuous for all

$x \in \mathbb{R}$. In particular, it is continuous at $x = -1$, and we have

$$\lim_{x \to -1} \sqrt{x^2 + 2x + 2} = \sqrt{1 - 2 + 2} = 1.$$

Prob. 37. $\lim_{x \to 0} e^{-x^2/3}$, continuous at $x = 0$, hence

$$\lim_{x \to 0} e^{-x^2/3} = e^{\frac{-0^2}{3}} = e^0 = 1$$

Prob. 39. $f(x) = e^{x^2 - 9}$ is continuous at $x = 3$, hence

$$\lim_{x \to 3} e^{x^2 - 9} = e^{3^2 - 9} = e^0 = 1.$$

Prob. 41. Here, the limits of both the numerator and the denominator are zero, since

$$\lim_{x \to 0} \left(e^{2x} - 1\right) = e^0 - 1 = 0 \quad \text{and} \quad \lim_{x \to 0} \left(e^x - 1\right) = e^0 - 1 = 0.$$

However, this does not mean that the limit does not exist. We use a trick that will allow us to find the limit; namely, we factor the numerator.

$$\lim_{x \to 0} \frac{e^{2x} - 1}{e^x - 1} == \lim_{x \to 0} \frac{(e^x - 1)(e^x + 1)}{e^x - 1} = \lim_{x \to 0} (e^x + 1) = e^0 + 1 = 2.$$

Prob. 43. The function $1/\sqrt{5x^2 - 4}$ is the composition of a power function and a polynomial, both of which are continuous at every point where they are defined. Since this function is defined at $x = -2$, it is also continuous at $x = -2$. Hence,

$$\lim_{x \to -2} \frac{1}{\sqrt{5x^2 - 4}} = \frac{1}{\sqrt{5(-2)^2 - 4}} = \frac{1}{\sqrt{16}} = \frac{1}{4}.$$

Prob. 45. Here, the limits of both the numerator and the denominator are zero, since

$$\lim_{x \to 0} \left(\sqrt{x^2 + 9} - 3 \right) = \sqrt{0 + 9} - 3 = 0 \quad \text{and} \quad \lim_{x \to 0} x^2 = 0^2 = 0.$$

However, this does not mean that the limit does not exist. We use a trick that will allow us to find the limit; namely, we rationalize the numerator.

$$\frac{\sqrt{x^2 + 9} - 3}{x^2} = \frac{\sqrt{x^2 + 9} - 3}{x^2} \cdot \frac{\sqrt{x^2 + 9} + 3}{\sqrt{x^2 + 9} + 3} = \frac{x^2 + 9 - 3^2}{x^2(\sqrt{x^2 + 9} + 3)} = \frac{1}{\sqrt{x^2 + 9} + 3}$$

Now we evaluate the limit:

$$\lim_{x \to 0} \frac{\sqrt{x^2 + 9} - 3}{x^2} = \lim_{x \to 0} \frac{1}{\sqrt{x^2 + 9} + 3} = \frac{1}{\sqrt{0 + 9} + 3} = \frac{1}{6}$$

Prob. 47. The function $\ln(1-x)$ is a composition of a polynomial and a logarithmic function, and is defined for all $x < 1$, and therefore it is continuous for all $x < 1$. In particular, it is continuous at $x = 0$, and we have

$$\lim_{x \to 0} \ln(1-x) = \ln(1-0) = \ln 1 = 0.$$

3.3   Limits at Infinity

Prob. 1. The degree of the denominator is greater than the degree of the numerator, so the limit is 0.

Prob. 3. The degree of the numerator is greater than the degree of the denominator, so the limit does not exist. The rational function tends to ∞ since it behaves like the function $\frac{x^3}{x} = x^2$.

Prob. 5. $\lim_{x \to \infty} \frac{1 - x^3 + 2x^4}{2x^2 + x^4}$. Divide by the highest power of the denominator to get:

$$\lim_{x \to \infty} \frac{\frac{1}{x^4} - \frac{x^3}{x^4} + \frac{2x^4}{x^4}}{\frac{2x^2}{x^1} + \frac{x^4}{x^4}} = \lim_{x \to \infty} \frac{\frac{1}{x^4} - \frac{1}{x} + 2}{\frac{2}{x^2} + 1}.$$

Hence we have: $\frac{2}{1} = 2$.

Prob. 7. The degree of the numerator is greater than that of the denominator, so the limit does not exist. The rational function tends to ∞ since it behaves like the function $\frac{x^2}{2x} = \frac{x}{2}$.

Prob. 9. The degree of the numerator is greater than that of the denominator, so the limit does not exist. The rational function tends to ∞ since it behaves like the function $\frac{x^2}{-x} = -x$ as $x \to -\infty$.

Prob. 11. Divide by the highest power of the denominator

$$\lim_{x \to -\infty} \frac{\frac{2}{x^2} + \frac{x^2}{x^2}}{\frac{1}{x^2} - \frac{x^2}{x^2}} = \lim_{x \to -\infty} \frac{\frac{2}{x^2} + 1}{\frac{1}{X^2} - 1},$$

hence we have: $\frac{1}{-1} = -1$.

Prob. 13. Using the limit laws, we have

$$\lim_{x \to \infty} \frac{4}{1 + e^{-2x}} = \frac{\lim_{x \to \infty} 4}{\lim_{x \to \infty}(1 + e^{-2x})} = \frac{4}{1 + 0} = 4$$

since e^{-2x} tends to 0 as $x \to \infty$.

Prob. 15. Using the limit laws, we have

$$\lim_{x \to \infty} \frac{2e^x}{e^x + 3} = \lim_{x \to \infty} \frac{2}{1 + 3e^{-x}} = \frac{\lim_{x \to \infty} 2}{\lim_{x \to \infty}(1 + 3e^{-x})} = \frac{2}{1 + 3(0)} = 2$$

since e^{-x} tends to 0 as $x \to \infty$.

Prob. 17. Since $\exp[x]$ is the same function as e^x, the limit is 0.

Prob. 19. Divide by the highest power at the denominator:

$$\lim_{x \to \infty} \frac{\frac{3e^{2x}}{e^{2x}}}{\frac{2e^{2x}}{e^{2x}} - \frac{e^x}{e^{2x}}} = \lim_{x \to \infty} \frac{3}{2 - \frac{1}{e^x}}.$$

Hence, we have: $\frac{3}{2} = 1.5$.

Prob. 21. Using the limit laws, we have

$$\lim_{x \to \infty} \frac{3}{2 + e^{-x}} = \frac{\lim_{x \to \infty} 3}{\lim_{x \to \infty}(2 + e^{-x})} = \frac{3}{2 + 0} = \frac{3}{2}$$

since e^{-x} tends to 0 as $x \to \infty$.

Prob. 23. Using the limit laws, we have

$$\lim_{x \to -\infty} \frac{e^x}{1 + x} = \lim_{x \to -\infty} e^x \cdot \lim_{x \to -\infty} \frac{1}{1 + x} = 0 \cdot 0 = 0$$

since both e^x and $\frac{1}{1+x}$ tend to 0 as $x \to -\infty$.

Prob. 25. We have

$$\lim_{N \to \infty} r(N) = \lim_{N \to \infty} a\frac{N}{k + N} = a \lim_{N \to \infty} \frac{N}{k + N} = a \cdot 1 = a$$

since the degree of the denominator $(k + N)$ equals that of the numerator (N).

Prob. 27.

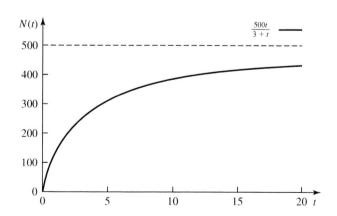

(a)

(b) Since both numerator and denominator have the same degree, we have

$$\lim_{t \to \infty} N(t) = \lim_{t \to \infty} \frac{500t}{3 + t} = \frac{500}{1} = 500.$$

(c) When $t = 3$, we have $N(t) = N(3) = \frac{500 \cdot 3}{3+3} = \frac{500}{2} = 250$. This is half of 500, which is the limiting population size.

Prob. 29.

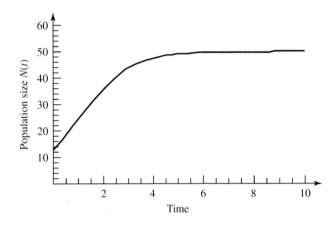

(a)

(b) Since $e^{-t} \to 0$ as t tends to ∞, we have

$$\lim_{t \to \infty} N(t) = \lim_{t \to \infty} \frac{50}{1 + 3e^{-t}} = \frac{\lim_{t \to \infty} 50}{\lim_{t \to \infty}(1 + 3e^{-t})} = \frac{50}{1 + 3(0)} = 50.$$

This matches the horizontal asymptote found on the graph.

3.4   The Sandwich Theorem and Some Trigonometric Limits

Prob. 1.

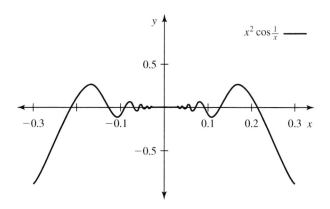

(a)

(b) Since $-1 \leq \cos \frac{1}{x} \leq 1$ for any x such that $\frac{1}{x}$ is defined (that is, for $x \neq 0$), we can multiply both inequalities by the positive number x^2, obtaining

$$-x^2 \leq x^2 \cos \frac{1}{x} \leq x^2.$$

(c) The role of $g(x)$ in the Sandwich Theorem is played by $x^2 \cos \frac{1}{x}$, and the sandwiching functions $f(x)$ and $h(x)$ are $-x^2$ and x^2, respectively. Since $\lim_{x \to 0} -x^2 = 0 = \lim_{x \to 0} x^2$, we conclude that $\lim_{x \to 0} x^2 \cos \frac{1}{x} = 0$ as well.

Prob. 3.

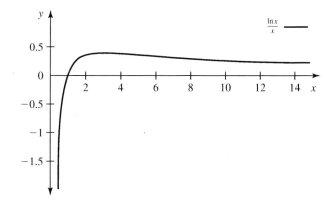

(a)

(b) The inequalities hold for $x \geq e$. This means that the inequalities can be applied as x tends to ∞.

(c) Since
$$\frac{1}{x} \leq \frac{\ln x}{x} \leq \frac{1}{\sqrt{x}}$$
we apply the Sandwich Theorem with $f(x) = \frac{1}{x}$, $g(x) = \frac{\ln x}{x}$ and $h(x) = \frac{1}{\sqrt{x}}$.

Since $\lim\limits_{x \to \infty} \frac{1}{x} = 0 \doteq \lim\limits_{x \to \infty} \frac{1}{\sqrt{x}}$, we deduce that $\lim\limits_{x \to \infty} \frac{\ln x}{x} = 0$.

Prob. 5. Use the substitution $y = 2x$ to obtain
$$\lim_{x \to 0} \frac{\sin(2x)}{2x} = \lim_{(y/2) \to 0} \frac{\sin y}{y}$$
$$= \lim_{y \to 0} \frac{\sin y}{y} = 1.$$

The last equality was proved in Section 3.4, and the second is justified because $y \to 0$ if and only if $(y/2) \to 0$.

Prob. 7. Use the substitution $y = 5x$ to obtain
$$\lim_{x \to 0} \frac{\sin(5x)}{x} = \lim_{x \to 0} \left(5 \cdot \frac{\sin(5x)}{5x} \right) = 5 \cdot \lim_{x \to 0} \frac{\sin(5x)}{5x}$$
$$= 5 \cdot \lim_{(y/5) \to 0} \frac{\sin y}{y} = 5 \cdot \lim_{y \to 0} \frac{\sin y}{y} = 5$$

since $\frac{\sin y}{y}$ tends to 1 as $y \to 0$. The second to last inequality is justified because $y \to 0$ if and only if $(y/5) \to 0$.

Prob. 9. Use the substitution $y = \pi x$ to obtain
$$\lim_{x \to 0} \frac{\sin(\pi x)}{x} = \lim_{x \to 0} \left(\pi \cdot \frac{\sin(\pi x)}{\pi x} \right) = \pi \cdot \lim_{x \to 0} \frac{\sin(\pi x)}{\pi x}$$
$$= \pi \cdot \lim_{(y/\pi) \to 0} \frac{\sin y}{y} = \pi \cdot \lim_{y \to 0} \frac{\sin y}{y} = \pi$$

since $\frac{\sin y}{y}$ tends to 1 as $y \to 0$. The second to last inequality is justified because $y \to 0$ if and only if $(y/\pi) \to 0$.

Prob. 11. We relate $\frac{\sin \pi x}{\sqrt{x}}$ to a function whose limit at 0 we already know, as follows:
$$\frac{\sin \pi x}{\sqrt{x}} = \frac{\sin \pi x}{\pi x} \cdot \pi \sqrt{x} \quad \text{for } x \neq 0.$$

Hence,
$$\lim_{x \to 0} \frac{\sin \pi x}{\sqrt{x}} = \lim_{x \to 0} \left(\frac{\sin \pi x}{\pi x} \cdot \pi \sqrt{x} \right) = \lim_{x \to 0} \frac{\sin \pi x}{\pi x} \cdot \lim_{x \to 0} \pi \sqrt{x}$$
$$= \lim_{\pi x \to 0} \frac{\sin \pi x}{\pi x} \cdot \pi \lim_{x \to 0} \sqrt{x} = 1 \cdot 0 = 0$$

Here we have used the fact that $\frac{\sin y}{y}$ tends to 1 as $y \to 0$, where $y = \pi x$, and that $(y/\pi) \to 0$ if and only if $y \to 0$.

Prob. 13. We relate $\frac{\sin x \cos x}{x(1-x)}$ to functions whose limit at 0 we already know, as follows:

$$\frac{\sin x \cos x}{x(1-x)} = \frac{\sin x}{x} \cdot \cos x \cdot \frac{1}{1-x}$$

Hence,

$$\lim_{x \to 0} \frac{\sin x \cos x}{x(1-x)} = \lim_{x \to 0} \left(\frac{\sin x}{x} \cdot \cos x \cdot \frac{1}{1-x} \right)$$
$$= \lim_{x \to 0} \frac{\sin x}{x} \cdot \lim_{x \to 0} \cos x \cdot \lim_{x \to 0} \frac{1}{1-x} = 1 \cdot 1 \cdot 1 = 1$$

Here we have used the fact that $\frac{\sin x}{x}$ tends to 1 as $x \to 0$.

Prob. 15. We have

$$\lim_{x \to 0} \frac{1 - \cos x}{2x} = \lim_{x \to 0} \left(\frac{1}{2} \cdot \frac{1 - \cos x}{x} \right)$$
$$= \frac{1}{2} \cdot \lim_{x \to 0} \frac{1 - \cos x}{x} = \frac{1}{2} \cdot 0 = 0.$$

The fact that $\frac{1 - \cos x}{x}$ tends to 0 as $x \to 0$ was proved in Section 3.4.

Prob. 17.

$$\lim_{x \to 0} \frac{1 - \cos(5x)}{2x} = \lim_{x \to 0} \frac{1 - \cos(5x)}{\frac{2}{5} \cdot 5x}$$

$$= \lim_{x \to 0} \frac{5}{2} \cdot \frac{1 - \cos(5x)}{5x} = \lim_{x \to 0} \frac{5}{2} \cdot \lim_{x \to 0} \frac{1 - \cos(5x)}{5x} = \frac{5}{2} \cdot 0 = 0.$$

Prob. 19. We relate $\frac{\sin x(1 - \cos x)}{x^2}$ to functions whose limit at 0 we already know, as follows:

$$\frac{\sin x(1 - \cos x)}{x^2} = \frac{\sin x}{x} \cdot \frac{1 - \cos x}{x}$$

Hence,

$$\lim_{x \to 0} \frac{\sin x(1 - \cos x)}{x^2}$$
$$= \lim_{x \to 0} \left(\frac{\sin x}{x} \cdot \frac{(1 - \cos x)}{x} \right)$$
$$= \lim_{x \to 0} \frac{\sin x}{x} \cdot \lim_{x \to 0} \frac{1 - \cos x}{x}$$
$$= 1 \cdot 0 = 0.$$

Here we use the fact that as $x \to 0$, $\frac{1 - \cos x}{x}$ tends to 0 and $\frac{\sin x}{x}$ tends to 1. This was proved in Section 3.4.

Prob. 21.

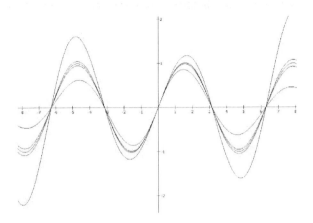

(a)

(b) $\sin(x)$ produces the oscillations

(c) a changes the amplitude of the oscillations.

(d) Since $-1 \leq \sin x \leq 1$ we have:

$$-e^{ax} \leq eax \sin x \leq e^{ax} \sin x$$

3.5   Properties of Continuous Functions

Prob. 1.

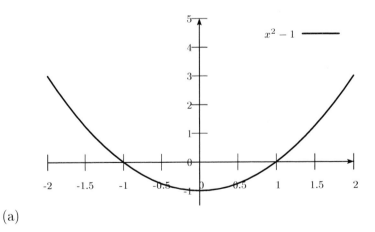

(a)

(b) We have $f(0) = -1$ and $f(2) = 3$, and so $f(0) = -1 < 0 < 3 = f(2)$. The function is

continuous on the interval $[0, 2]$ since it a polynomial. Since $f(0) < 0 < f(2)$, by the

Intermediate Value Theorem there is some value c of the independent variable such that $0 < c < 2$ and $f(c) = 0$.

Prob. 3.

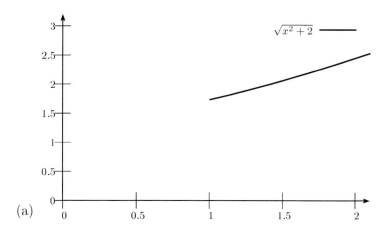

(a)

(b) We have $f(1) = \sqrt{1^2 + 2} = \sqrt{3}$ and $f(2) = \sqrt{2^2 + 2} = \sqrt{6}$. Now $\sqrt{3} < 2 < \sqrt{6}$ because $3 < 4 < 6$. Thus $f(1) < 2 < f(2)$, and since f is continuous on the interval $[1, 2]$ (being a square root of a polynomial that only takes positive values), we can apply the Intermediate Value Theorem to conclude that there is some value c of the independent variable such that $1 < c < 2$ and $f(c) = \sqrt{c^2 + 2} = 2$.

Prob. 5. Any solution to $e^{-x} = x$ is a root of the function $f(x) = e^{-x} - x$. Now, $f(1) = e^{-1} - 1$ is negative, since $e^{-1} = 1/e$ is less than 1, while $f(0) = e^0 - 0 = 1$ is positive. Since $f(x) = e^{-x} - x$ is the difference of two continuous functions, it is also continuous and this together with the fact that $f(0) > 0 > f(1)$ allows us to apply the Intermediate Value Theorem. We can conclude that there is a value c of the independent variable such that $0 < c < 1$ and $f(c) = 0$, that is, $e^{-c} = c$.

Prob. 7. We define the function $f(x) = e^{-x} - x$, which is continuous since it is the difference of two continuous functions. We are looking for a zero of this function. Now, $f(0) = e^0 - 0 = 1 > 0$ and $f(1) = e^{-1} - 1 < 0$, since $e^{-1} = 1/e < 1$. Therefore $f(x)$ must have a zero in the open interval $(0, 1)$, by the Intermediate Value Theorem. We next try the midpoint $x = \frac{0+1}{2} = 0.5$, for which $f(0.5) = e^{-0.5} - 0.5 \approx 0.106531$. Since this value is positive and $f(1)$ is negative, the function must have a zero between $x = 0.5$ and $x = 1$. We then try the midpoint $x = \frac{0.5+1}{2} = 0.75$, for which

$f(0.75) = e^{-0.75} - 0.75 \approx -0.277633$. Since this value is negative and $f(0.5)$ is positive, we have narrowed the location of a zero to the interval $(0.5, 0.75)$. We next test the midpoint between 0.5 and 0.75, namely $x = \frac{0.5 + 0.75}{2} = 0.625$. This gives $f(0.625) \approx -0.08973857$. Since this value is negative and $f(0.5)$ is positive, we have narrowed the location of a zero to the interval $(0.5, 0.625)$. The next midpoint is $x = \frac{0.5 + 0.625}{2} = 0.5625$, and $f(0.5625) \approx 0.00728282$. So, we have narrowed the interval to $(0.5625, 0.625)$. We next have $f(0.59375) \approx -0.04149755$, narrowing it further to $(0.5625, 0.59375)$. We next have $f(0.578125) \approx -0.01717584$, narrowing it further to $(0.5625, 0.578125)$. We next have $f(0.5703125) \approx -0.00496376$, narrowing it further to $(0.5625, 0.5703125)$. We next have $f(0.56640625) \approx 0.0011552$, narrowing it further to $(0.56640625, 0.5703125)$. We next have $f(0.5683594) \approx -0.0019054$, narrowing the interval further to $(0.56640625, 0.5683594)$.

Notice that any number within this interval can be written as 0.56 to two decimal places. Therefore our solution, accurate to two decimal places, is 0.56.

We note here that if we are not forced to choose the middle point at each step, then it might be possible to speed things up if we choose a point closer to an appropriate endpoint instead.

Prob. 9.

(a) We must start with some value of x, so we test $f(0)$, which gives 2. Next we test $f(1)$, which gives exactly 0. With this luck, we have found a solution $x = 1$ which is exact.

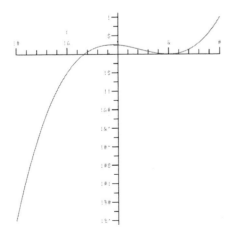

(b)

(c) The graph has a point of tangency with the x-axis at $x = 1$, and $f(x)$ is positive on either side of $x = 1$. So, if we had not found the solution $x = 1$ already, we would not be able to find it using the bisection method, since we would not suspect (by looking at the sign of $f(x)$ at $x = 0$ and $x = 2$, say) that there is a solution in between. On the other hand, having found the solution $x = 1$ and having plotted the graph, we can easily find the other root using the bisection method, starting, for example, with the interval $[-1, 0]$.

Prob. 11.

(a) The number should be reported as 23 individuals.

(b) We must decide to what accuracy formula (3.7) models the population. It is reasonable to think that the coefficients 54 and 13 that appear in the formula have 2 significant digits only (otherwise they would be written 54.0 and so on). Thus the result of formula (3.7) is also limited to two significant digits, and the correct way to express the result at $t = 10$ is 23 million individuals, or 2.3×10^7 individuals.

(c) A small population, such as that given in part (a), is not very well approximated by a continuous function. In particular, formula (3.7) purports to be valid for $t \geq 0$. At the lower end of this interval, $t = 0$, we have $N(t) = 4.15385$, and for some slightly bigger t we have $N(t) = 4.5$. Since the real population is measured by integers, this value of $N(t)$ involves a relative error of at least 0.5 in 4.5, or about 11%.

In part (b) on the other hand, the size of the population is large and the issue of the discreteness of the population does not play a significant role in the approximation. Other sources of error, including counting errors and the empirical nature of the modelling function in equation (3.7) to fit the data, would instead be the limiting factors in the precision of the approximation.

Prob. 13. A polynomial $f(x) = Ax^3 + Bx^2 + Cx + D$ of degree 3 takes on opposite signs as x approaches $+\infty$ and $-\infty$. This is because, for x very large in absolute value, the behavior of the polynomial is controlled by the term of highest degree (called the leading term); in other words, for x very large in absolute value, the polynomial has the same sign as Ax^3 (where A is either positive or negative). By starting with an interval of values of x such that $f(x)$ has opposite signs at the two endpoints, we can apply the Intermediate Value Theorem to deduce that somewhere in the interval, $f(x) = 0$.

Prob. 15. We present three different explanations.

First, we know the two roots; since $y = x^2 - 4 = (x+2)(x-2)$, they're obviously -2 and 2.

Second, since any second degree equation $y = ax^2 + bx + c$ of positive discriminant $D = b^2 - 4ac$ has two roots, the given equation must have two roots because it has $D = 0^2 - 4(1)(-4) = 16 > 0$.

Third, we note that for x large in absolute value (say $x = \pm 100$), we have $y = x^2 - 4$ is positive, while for $x = 0$, y is negative. Since y is a continuous function, by the Intermediate Value Theorem there is a root in the interval $(0, 100)$ and a root in the interval $(-100, 0)$.

3.6   Formal Definition of Limits

Prob. 1. The condition $\sqrt{2x-1} < 0.01$ is equivalent to the following two inequalities:

$$2x - 1 < 0.01 \quad \text{and} \quad 2x - 1 > -0.01$$

These reduce to

$$x < 0.505 \quad \text{and} \quad x > 0.495$$

respectively. Therefore the desired values of x are those in the interval $(0.495, 0.505)$.

Prob. 3. From $|x^2 - 9| < 0.1$ we see that

$$-0.1 < x^2 - 9 < 0.1$$

$$-0.1 + 9 < x^2 < 0.1 + 9$$

$$8.9 < x^2 < 9.1$$

So, we have: $x^2 > 8.9$, meaning $X \in (-\infty, \sqrt{8.9}) \cup (\sqrt{8.9}, +\infty)$ and: $x^2 < 9.1$, meaning $x \in (-\sqrt{9.1}, \sqrt{9.1})$.

Putting it together gives: $X \in (-\sqrt{9.1}, -\sqrt{8.9}) \cup (\sqrt{8.9}, \sqrt{9.1})$.

Prob. 5.

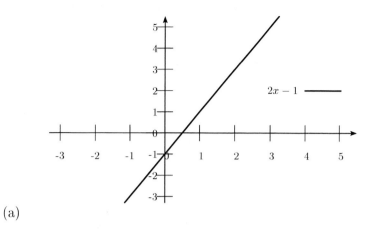

(a)

(b) We must find all x such that $\sqrt{f(x) - 3}$ is at most 0.1. Thus the inequalities to be satisfied are

$$(2x - 1) - 3 < 0.1 \quad \text{and} \quad (2x - 1) - 3 > -0.1$$

These become

$$x < 2.05 \quad \text{and} \quad x > 1.95$$

respectively. Thus the desired values of x are those in the interval $(1.95, 2.05)$.

(c)

Prob. 7.

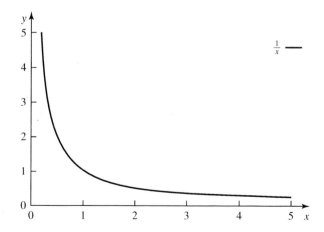

(a)

(b) We must find all x such that $f(x) > 4$. This inequality becomes

$$\frac{1}{x} > 4 \quad \Rightarrow \quad x < \frac{1}{4} = 0.25$$

Since $x > 0$ by assumption, the desired values of x are those in the interval $(0, 0.25)$.

(c)

Prob. 9. Given any $\epsilon > 0$ we must show that there exists a δ such that if x is within δ of 2, then the value of $2x - 1$ is within ϵ of 3. Let's find the values of x such that $2x - 1$ lies in the interval $(3 - \epsilon, 3 + \epsilon)$. Solving $2x - 1 < 3 + \epsilon$ gives $x < 2 + \epsilon/2$ and solving $2x - 1 > 3 - \epsilon$ gives $x > 2 - \epsilon/2$. Thus any x in the interval $(2 - \epsilon/2, 2 + \epsilon/2)$ will give us a value of $2x - 1$ in the interval $(3 - \epsilon, 3 + \epsilon)$. This shows that we can choose $\delta = \epsilon/2$.

Prob. 11. Let $\epsilon > 0$, then we must have $|f(x) - f(c)| < \epsilon$ meaning $|x^5 - 0| < \epsilon$ $|x^5| < \epsilon$. $|x| < \sqrt[5]{\epsilon}$. Now, letting $\delta = \sqrt[5]{\epsilon}$ means that for every $\epsilon > 0$, there is $\delta = \sqrt[5]{\epsilon}$ so that $|x| < \sqrt[5]{\epsilon}$ implies that $|x^5| < \epsilon$. Therefore, the limit is indeed 0.

Prob. 13. Given any large $M > 0$ we must show that there exists a δ such that if x is within δ of 0, then the value of $4/x^2$ is larger than M. Let's find the values of x such that $4/x^2 > M$. Solving this gives $\sqrt{x} < 2/\sqrt{M}$. Thus any x in the interval $(-2/\sqrt{M}, 2/\sqrt{M})$ will give us a value of $4/x^2$ larger than M. This shows that we can choose $\delta = 2/\sqrt{M}$.

Prob. 15. Given any large $M > 0$ we must show that there exists a δ such that if x is within δ of 0, then the value of $1/x^4$ is larger than M. Let's find the values of x such that $1/x^4 > M$. Solving this gives $\sqrt{x} < 1/\sqrt[4]{M} = M^{-1/4}$. Thus any x in the interval $(-M^{-1/4}, M^{-1/4})$ will give us a value of $1/x^4$ larger than M. This shows that we can choose $\delta = M^{-1/4}$.

Prob. 17. We must show that for any x sufficiently large the value of $f(x)$ is close to 0. Let $\epsilon > 0$, we must have $|\frac{2}{x^2}| < \epsilon$, meaning $-\epsilon < \frac{2}{x^2} < \epsilon$, since $\frac{2}{x^2} > 0$, we have $\frac{2}{x^2} < \epsilon \Rightarrow x > \sqrt{\frac{2}{\epsilon}}$. Letting $L = \sqrt{\frac{2}{\epsilon}}$, any $x > L$ wraps ϵ-close to 0.

Prob. 19. Given any $\epsilon > 0$ we must show that there exists an $L > 0$ such that if x is larger than L, then the value of $\frac{x}{x+1}$ is within ϵ of 1. Let's find the values of x such that $\sqrt{x/(x+1) - 1} < \epsilon$. This inequality becomes the simultaneous conditions

$$\frac{x}{x+1} < 1 + \epsilon \quad \text{and} \quad \frac{x}{x+1} > 1 - \epsilon.$$

Since we are interested in large values of x, we can assume that $x + 1 > 0$. Then the inequalities above turn into

$$x < (x+1)(1+\epsilon) \quad \text{and} \quad x > (x+1)(1-\epsilon)$$

which have solutions

$$x > -\frac{1}{\epsilon} - 1 \quad \text{and} \quad x > \frac{1}{\epsilon} - 1$$

respectively. Evidently the second condition is the more stringent one and we conclude that the desired values of x are those satisfying $x > \frac{1}{\epsilon} - 1$. Thus any x larger than $\epsilon^{-1} - 1$ will give us a value of $\frac{x}{x+1}$ within a distance ϵ of 1. This shows that we can choose $L = \epsilon^{-1} - 1$.

Prob. 21. Let $\epsilon > 0$, then we must have

$$|mx - mc| < \epsilon$$

$$|m||x - c| < \epsilon$$

$$|x - c| < \frac{\epsilon}{|m|}.$$

Now, letting $\delta = \frac{\epsilon}{|m|}$, we have $|X - C| < \delta$ implies that $|mx - mc| < \epsilon$. Hence, the limit is indeed mc.

3.8 Review Problems

Prob. 1. The function $f(x) = e^{-\sqrt{x}}$ is continuous for all $x \in \mathbb{R}$. This is because it is a composition of three continuous functions, all with domain $\mathbb{R}$, namely $y = f_1(x) = |x|$, $z = f_2(y) = -y$, and $f_3(z) = e^z$.

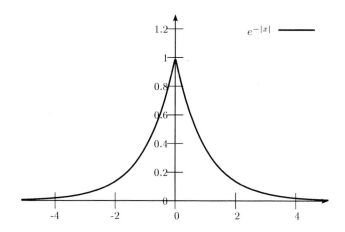

Prob. 3. The given function is a quotient of two functions, $g(x) = 2$ and $h(x) = e^x + e^{-x}$. Obviously $g(x)$ is a continuous function. Now $h(x)$ is continuous for every $x \in \mathbb{R}$, because it is the sum of two continuous functions, and furthermore it takes only positive values because both e^x and e^{-x} are always positive. Thus $h(x)$ is never equal to 0, and so $g(x)/h(x)$ is continuous for all $x \in \mathbb{R}$.

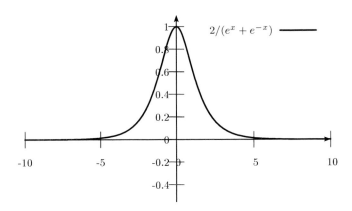

Prob. 5. An example of such a function is

$$f(x) = \begin{cases} 0 & \text{for } x < 1, \\ 1 & \text{for } x \geq 1. \end{cases}$$

and the graph of yet another one is:

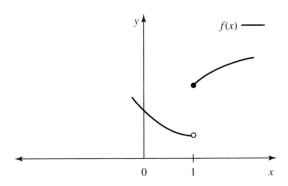

Prob. 7. There are numerous examples, one of which is the function $(e^x - e^{-x})/(e^x + e^{-x})$, with graph:

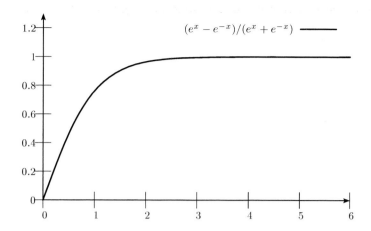

Another one is give by the graph:

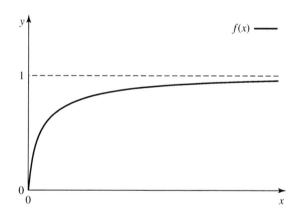

Prob. 9. First we show that the function $f(x) = \lfloor x \rfloor$ is continuous from the right at $x = -2$. We have $f(x) = -2$ for every $x \in [-2, -1)$. Therefore the function is constant and equal to -2 in an interval whose left endpoint is -2. This means that $\lim_{x \to -2+} f(x) = -2$. Since we also have $f(-2) = -2$, the function is continuous from the right at $x = -2$.

Next we show that the function is discontinuous from the left at $x = -2$. We have $f(x) = -3$ for every $x \in [-3, -2)$. Therefore the function is constant and equal to -3 in an interval whose right endpoint is -2. This means that $\lim_{x \to -2-} f(x) = -3$. But we have $f(-2) = -2$, and so the limit from the left does not agree with the value of the function at $x = -2$. Thus the function is discontinuous from the left at $x = -2$.

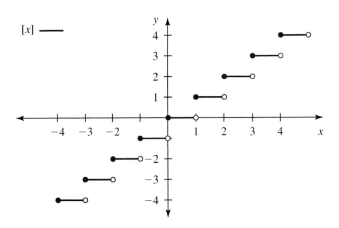

Prob. 11. The limit of $N(t)$ as $t \to \infty$ equals a, because we can rewrite $N(t)$ as

$$N(t) = \frac{at}{k+t} = \frac{a}{\frac{k}{t}+1}$$

and as $t \to \infty$ the denominator has the limit 1. Therefore $a = 1.24 \times 10^6$. We also know that at $t = 5$ the value of $N(t)$ is half of its limiting value, which is to say, $\frac{a}{2}$. Thus we have

$$\frac{a}{2} = N(5) = \frac{5a}{k+5} \quad \Rightarrow \quad k+5 = 10$$

and so $k = 5$.

Prob. 13.

(a) The function $g(t)$ should take the value 1 when $s(t) \geq 1/2$ and the value 0 when $s(t) < 1/2$. Now, $s(t) = \sin(\pi t)$ is a periodic function, with period 2. Thus we can consider only the interval $[0, 2)$ for the moment. Within the interval $[0, 2)$ the function $s(t)$ is greater than $1/2$ whenever t lies between $1/6$ and $5/6$ (corresponding to $\sin(\pi/6) = 0.5$ and $\sin(5\pi/6) = 0.5$).

Therefore, one way to construct the function g is the following: given a value of t, first reduce it to lie in the interval $[0, 2)$ by subtracting multiples of 2. This can be done by subtracting from t (which is positive) as great a multiple of 2 as required, namely $t - 2\lfloor t/2 \rfloor$. Then we check if this reduced value lies in the interval $[1/6, 5/6]$. If so, set $g(t) = 1$; if not, set $g(t) = 0$. Thus we have $g(t) = 1$ if $t - 2\lfloor t/2 \rfloor \in [1/6, 5/6]$, and $g(t) = 0$ otherwise.

Another way to describe the function is as follows:

$$g(t) = \begin{cases} 1 & \text{for } \frac{1}{6} + 2k \le x \le \frac{5}{6} + 2k, k = 0, 1, 2, \ldots \\ 0 & \text{otherwise} \end{cases}$$

(b) The function $s(t)$ is continuous, since the sine function is continuous. However, $g(t)$ is discontinuous, since it only takes two discrete values, 0 and 1. We can also see this by noticing that the floor function is discontinuous.

Prob. 15.

(a) The graph of $f(N) = aTN = 0.2N$ is linear.

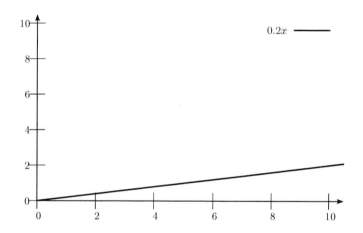

(b) In the modified model in which prey handling time is taken into account, the actual searching time is

$$T - T_h \frac{N_e}{P}$$

and this value is proportional to the number of prey encounters:

$$\frac{N_e}{P} = a\left(T - T_h \frac{N_e}{P}\right)N.$$

Solving for N_e/p we have

$$\frac{N_e}{P} = aTN - aT_h \frac{N_e}{P}N \implies \frac{N_e}{P}(1 + aT_hN) = aTN \implies \frac{N_e}{P} = \frac{aTN}{1 + aT_hN}.$$

We now graph $g(N) = 0.2N/(1 + 0.01N)$ for $N \ge 0$.

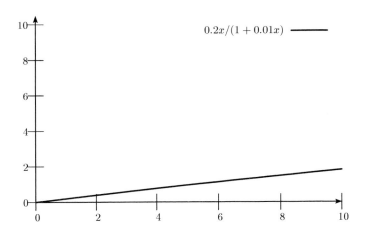

(c) When $T_h = 0$ the denominator of the right-hand side of equation (3.11) becomes 1, and so we are left with equation (3.10).

(d) When $T_h = 0$, we are in the situation of equation (3.10) and the limit of the right-hand side as $N \to \infty$ is ∞, since the function $f(N)$ grows linearly with N. On the other hand, when $T_h > 0$, the limit of the right-hand side of equation (3.11) is T/T_h; this can be seen by noticing that both numerator and denominator in equation (3.11) are polynomials of the same degree in N, and that the ratio of their leading coefficients is $\frac{aT}{aT_h}$. The interpretation of the difference is the following: if we disregard the prey-handling time and the prey becomes very easy to find, there will be larger and larger numbers of prey encounters. But if we take into account the prey-handling time, things change: even though another prey can be found immediately after one is eaten, the total number of prey that can be eaten is limited by the quotient of the available time T by the per-prey handling time T_h.

Prob. 17.

(a) The function sinh and cosh must be continuous because they are defined by taking sums, differences, and constant multiples of continuous functions. To see that tanh is continuous we must also observe that the denominator $e^x + e^{-x}$ never vanishes; the quotient of a continuous numerator by a continuous, nonvanishing denominator is again continuous.

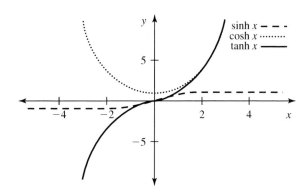

(b) As $x \to \infty$, the term e^{-x} in the definition of the hyperbolic sine becomes very small, and the term e^x very large, so the difference $e^x - e^{-x}$ is very large and the limit of $\sinh x$ is ∞. On the other hand, when $x \to -\infty$, the term e^{-x} becomes very large and the term e^x becomes very small; now the difference $e^x - e^{-x}$ is large and negative, and the limit of $\sinh x$ is $-\infty$.

With the hyperbolic cosine we have a sum $(e^x + e^{-x})$ instead of a difference, and either e^x or e^{-x} gets very large depending on whether $x \to \infty$ or $x \to -\infty$ respectively, while the other gets very small. Therefore the sum gets very large whether we take $x \to \infty$ or $x \to -\infty$. The limit is of $\cosh x$ ∞ in both cases.

With the hyperbolic tangent we cannot use this simple reasoning, because both numerator $(e^x - e^{-x})$ and denominator $(e^x + e^{-x})$ get very large. Instead, dividing numerator and denominator by e^x, we rewrite the quotient as follows:

$$\tanh x = \frac{e^x - e^{-x}}{e^x + e^{-x}} = \frac{1 - e^{-2x}}{1 + e^{-2x}}$$

As $x \to \infty$, e^{-2x} tends to zero, and so the limit of $\tanh x$ is 1. To find the limit of $\tanh x$ as $x \to -\infty$ we do yet another rewriting, by multiplying top and bottom by e^x:

$$\tanh x = \frac{e^x - e^{-x}}{e^x + e^{-x}} = \frac{e^{2x} - 1}{e^{2x} + 1}$$

As $x \to -\infty$, e^{2x} tends to zero, and so the limit of $\tanh x$ is -1.

(c) We have

$$\cosh^2 x - \sinh^2 x \qquad = \frac{(e^x + e^{-x})^2}{4} - \frac{(e^x - e^{-x})^2}{4}$$

$$= \frac{(e^{2x}+2+e^{-2x})-(e^{2x}-2+e^{-2x})}{4} = \frac{4}{4} = 1.$$

The equality $\tanh x = \sinh x / \cosh x$ is obvious from their definitions.

(d) To show that $\sinh x$ is an odd function, we must show that $\sinh(-x) = -\sinh x$. This can be seen as follows:

$$\sinh(-x) = \frac{e^{-x} - e^{-(-x)}}{2} = \frac{e^{-x} - e^x}{2} = -\frac{e^x - e^{-x}}{2} = -\sinh x.$$

Similarly, to show that $\cosh x$ is an even function, we must show that $\cosh(-x) = \cosh x$. This can be seen as follows:

$$\cosh(-x) = \frac{e^{-x} + e^{-(-x)}}{2} = \frac{e^{-x} + e^x}{2} = \frac{e^x + e^{-x}}{2} = \cosh x.$$

For tanh, we can use the fact that the quotient of an odd function and an even function is odd.

Chapter 4

Differentiation

4.1 Formal Definition of the Derivative

Prob. 1. $f'(x) = 0$, hence $f'(1) = 0$.

Prob. 3. $f'(x) = 4$, hence $f'(-1) = 4$.

Prob. 5. $f'(x) = 4x$, hence $f'(0) = 4 - 0 = 0$.

Prob. 7. The function $f(x) = \cos x$ is not constant, nor is it linear. Thus we must use the definition of the derivative here. We have

$$f'(0) = \lim_{h \to 0} \frac{f(0 + h) - f(0)}{h} = \lim_{h \to 0} \frac{\cos h - \cos 0}{h} = \lim_{h \to 0} \frac{\cos h - 1}{h} = 0.$$

Here the last equality comes from Section 3.4.

Prob. 9. $f'(x) = -6x$, so we need to have

$$-6c = 0$$

$$c = 0.$$

Prob. 11. $f'(x) = 2(x - 2)$, we need to have:

$$2(c - 2) = 0$$

$$c = 2.$$

Prob. 13. $f'(x) = 2x - 6$, we need to have:

$$2c - 6 = 0$$

$$2c = 6$$

$$c = 3.$$

Prob. 15. $f'(x) = \cos(\frac{\pi}{2}x) \cdot \frac{\pi}{2}$, so we need to have

$$\frac{\pi}{2}\cos(\frac{\pi}{2}c) = 0$$

$$c = 2k + 1, \quad k \in Z. \text{(integers)}$$

Prob. 17. We have

$$f(c + h) - f(c) \qquad = f(2 + h) - f(2)$$

$$= -2(2 + h) + 1 - (-2(2) + 1)$$

$$= -4 - 2h + 1 + 3$$

$$= -2h$$

Prob. 19. We have

$$f(c + h) - f(c) \quad = f(4 + h) - f(4)$$

$$= \sqrt{4 + h} - \sqrt{4}$$

$$= \sqrt{4 + h} - 2$$

Prob. 21.

(a) We have to find the value of $f'(-1)$ when $f(x) = 5x^2$, and we have

$$f'(-1) \quad = \lim_{h \to 0} \frac{f(-1+h) - f(-1)}{h} = \lim_{h \to 0} \frac{5(h-1)^2 - 5}{h}$$

$$= \lim_{h \to 0} \frac{5h^2 - 10h}{h} = \lim_{h \to 0}(5h - 10) = -10.$$

(b) When $x = -1$, we have $y = f(-1) = 5(-1)^2 = 5$. From part (a), we know that the slope of the tangent line is $m = -10$. Thus the equation of the tangent line is

$$y - 5 = -10(x - -1) \quad \text{or} \quad y = -10x - 5$$

(c) Graphing gives the following plot.

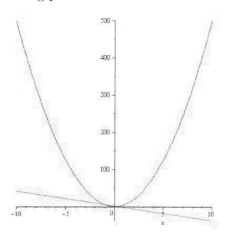

Prob. 23.

(a) We have to find the value of $f'(2)$ when $f(x) = 1 - x^3$, and we have

$$f'(2) \qquad = \lim_{h \to 0} \frac{f(2+h) - f(2)}{h} = \lim_{h \to 0} \frac{1 - (h+2)^3 - (1 - 2^3)}{h}$$

$$= \lim_{h \to 0} \frac{-h^3 - 6h^2 - 12h}{h} = \lim_{h \to 0}(-h^2 - 6h - 12) = -12.$$

(b) When $x = 2$, we have $y = f(2) = 1 - (2)^3 = -7$. From part (a), we know that the slope of the tangent line is -12. Thus the slope of the normal line is $m = 1/12$, and the equation of the normal line is

$$y - (-7) = \frac{1}{12}(x - 2) \quad \text{or} \quad y = \frac{1}{12}x - \frac{43}{6}$$

(c) Graphing gives the following plot.

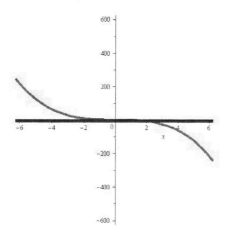

Prob. 25. We have $y = f(x) = \sqrt{x}$, and so

$$
\begin{aligned}
f'(x) \quad &= \lim_{h \to 0} \frac{f(x+h)-f(x)}{h} = \lim_{h \to 0} \frac{\sqrt{x+h}-\sqrt{x}}{h} \\
&= \lim_{h \to 0} \left(\frac{\sqrt{x+h}-\sqrt{x}}{h} \cdot \frac{\sqrt{x+h}+\sqrt{x}}{\sqrt{x+h}+\sqrt{x}} \right) \\
&= \lim_{h \to 0} \frac{x+h-x}{h(\sqrt{x+h}+\sqrt{x})} = \lim_{h \to 0} \frac{1}{\sqrt{x+h}+\sqrt{x}} \\
&= \frac{1}{\sqrt{x}+\sqrt{x}} = \frac{1}{2\sqrt{x}}
\end{aligned}
$$

Prob. 27. $f'(x) = 6x$, $f'(1) = 6$. So we have:

$$
y - 3 = 6(x - 1)
$$

$$
y = 6x - 3.
$$

Prob. 29. We first find the value of $f'(4)$ when $f(x) = \sqrt{x}$, and we have

$$
\begin{aligned}
f'(4) \quad &= \lim_{h \to 0} \frac{f(4+h)-f(4)}{h} = \lim_{h \to 0} \frac{\sqrt{4+h}-\sqrt{4}}{h} \\
&= \lim_{h \to 0} \left(\frac{\sqrt{4+h}-\sqrt{4}}{h} \cdot \frac{\sqrt{4+h}+\sqrt{4}}{\sqrt{4+h}+\sqrt{4}} \right) \\
&= \lim_{h \to 0} \frac{4+h-4}{h(\sqrt{4+h}+\sqrt{4})} = \lim_{h \to 0} \frac{1}{\sqrt{4+h}+\sqrt{4}} = \lim_{h \to 0} \frac{1}{\sqrt{4}+\sqrt{4}} = \frac{1}{4}.
\end{aligned}
$$

Thus we know that the slope of the tangent line is $1/4$. The equation of the tangent line is

$$
y - 2 = \frac{1}{4}(x - 4) \quad \text{or} \quad y = \frac{1}{4}x + 1
$$

Prob. 31. We first find the value of $f'(-1)$ when $f(x) = -3x^2$, and we have

$$
\begin{aligned}
f'(-1) \quad &= \lim_{h \to 0} \frac{f(h-1)-f(-1)}{h} = \lim_{h \to 0} \frac{-3(h-1)^2-(-3(-1)^2)}{h} \\
&= \lim_{h \to 0} \frac{-3h^2+6h-3+3}{h} \\
&= \lim_{h \to 0} \frac{-3h^2+6h}{h} = \lim_{h \to 0}(-3h + 6) = 6.
\end{aligned}
$$

Thus we know that the slope of the tangent line is 6. This means the slope of the normal line is $m = -1/6$, and its equation is

$$
y - (-3) = -\frac{1}{6}(x - (-1)) \quad \text{or} \quad y = -\frac{1}{6}x - \frac{19}{6}
$$

Prob. 33. We first find the value of $f'(1)$ when $f(x) = 2x^2 - 1$, and we have

$$
\begin{aligned}
f'(1) \quad &= \lim_{h \to 0} \frac{f(h+1)-f(1)}{h} = \lim_{h \to 0} \frac{2(h+1)^2-1-1}{h} \\
&= \lim_{h \to 0} \frac{2h^2+4h}{h} = \lim_{h \to 0}(2h + 4) = 4.
\end{aligned}
$$

Thus we know that the slope of the tangent line is 4. This means the slope of the normal line is $m = -1/4$, and its equation is

$$y - 1 = -\frac{1}{4}(x - 1) \quad \text{or} \quad y = -\frac{1}{4}x + \frac{5}{4}$$

Prob. 35. Comparing the given limit to

$$f'(a) = \lim_{h \to 0} \frac{f(a + h) - f(a)}{h}$$

we find that $f(x) = 2x^2$ and $x = a$.

Prob. 37. Comparing the given limit to

$$f'(a) = \lim_{h \to 0} \frac{f(a + h) - f(a)}{h}$$

we find that $f(x) = \frac{1}{x^2 + 1}$ and $a = 2$.

Prob. 39.

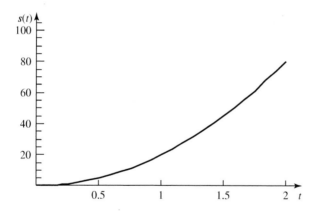

(a)

(b) The average velocity is $\frac{s(2) - s(0)}{2 - 0} = \frac{20(2)^2 - 20(0)^2}{2} = \frac{80}{2} = 40$ km/hr.

(c) At $t = 1$, the instantaneous velocity is

$$\lim_{h \to 0} \frac{s(h + 1) - s(1)}{h} \qquad = \lim_{h \to 0} \frac{20(h + 1)^2 - 20}{h}$$

$$= \lim_{h \to 0} \frac{20h^2 + 40h}{h} = \lim_{h \to 0} (20h + 40) = 40.$$

Thus the instantaneous velocity at $t = 1$ is 40 km/hr.

Prob. 41.

(a) At $t = 3/4$, the car is $s(3/4) = \frac{160}{3}(3/4)^2 = 30$ km along the road. At $t = 1$, the car

is $s(1) = \frac{160}{3}(1)^2 = \frac{160}{3} \approx 53.33$ km along the road.

(b) The average velocity is $\frac{s(1)-s(3/4)}{1-\frac{3}{4}} = \frac{\frac{160}{3}-30}{1/4} = \frac{280}{3} \approx 93.33$ km/hr.

(c) At $t = 3/4$, the velocity is

$$\lim_{h \to 0} \frac{s(h + \frac{3}{4}) - s(\frac{3}{4})}{h} \qquad = \lim_{h \to 0} \frac{\frac{160}{3}(h+\frac{3}{4})^2 - 30}{h}$$

$$= \lim_{h \to 0} \frac{\frac{160}{3}h^2 + 80h}{h} = \lim_{h \to 0} (\frac{160}{3}h + 80) = 80.$$

Thus the velocity at $t = 3/4$ is 80 km/hr. The speed of the car at $t = 3/4$ is also 80 km/hr.

Prob. 43. To find the value of R^*, we must solve the equation $\frac{1}{b}\frac{dB}{dt} = 0$. That is,

$$\frac{1}{b}\frac{dB}{dt} \qquad = f(R) - m = f(R) - 40 = 200\frac{R}{5+R} - 40 = 0$$

$$\Rightarrow 200\frac{R}{5+R} = 40 \quad \Rightarrow \quad \frac{5R}{5+R} = 1 \quad \Rightarrow \quad 5R = 5 + R$$

$$\Rightarrow 4R = 5 \quad \Rightarrow \quad R = \frac{4}{5}$$

That is, $R^* = 1.25$

Prob. 45. For equilibria, we require $\frac{dN}{dt} = f(N) = 0$. That is,

$$f(N) = 3N \left(1 - \frac{N}{20}\right) = 0 \quad \Rightarrow \quad N = 0 \text{ and } N = 20$$

Thus the points of equilibria are $N = 0$ and $N = 20$.

Prob. 47. We want $\frac{dx}{dt} = 0$, which must occur when $k(a - x)(b - x) = 0$, or when $x = a$ and $x = b$. That is, $x = 7$ or $x = 4$. However, the reaction ceases when $x = 4$ since at this point there is no more reactant B remaining.

Prob. 49. We can see that $\frac{dN}{dt} = 0$ when $N = 0$ or when $1 - \frac{N}{K} = 0$, that is when $N = K$. The value K is called the carrying capacity, because at this point the rate of change $\frac{dN}{dt}$ must be zero, and the population cannot grow any more. Thus K corresponds to the largest possible size of the population.

Prob. 51. Only **(B)** is true. See Section 4.1.3 for details.

Prob. 53. The domain is the interval $[a, b]$. The function below is differentiable at all values of x in the interval $[a, b]$ except for the value $x = c$.

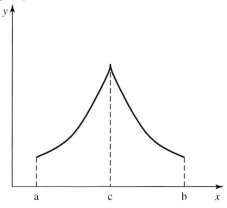

Prob. 55. Consider the following:

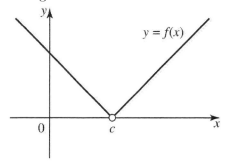

This is clearly differentiable everywhere except $X = C$, and not continuous. Hence it is not true.

Prob. 57. The function has a sharp corner at $x = -5$, and is not differentiable there.

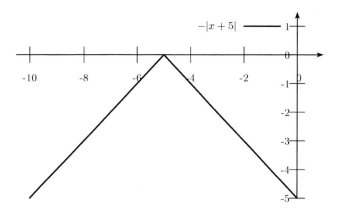

Prob. 59. The function has a sharp corner at $x = -2$, and is not differentiable there.

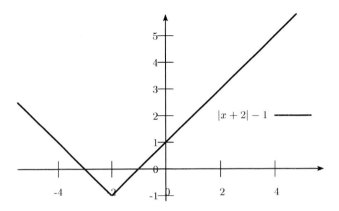

Prob. 61. The function is not defined at $x = 3$, and is not differentiable there.

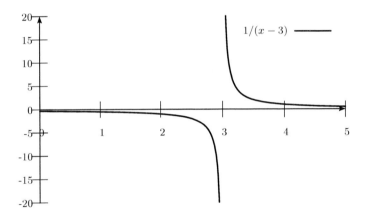

Prob. 63. The function is not defined at $x = -1$, and is not differentiable there.

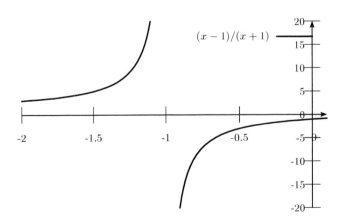

Prob. 65. The function has sharp corners at $x = \pm 1/\sqrt{2}$, and is not differentiable there.

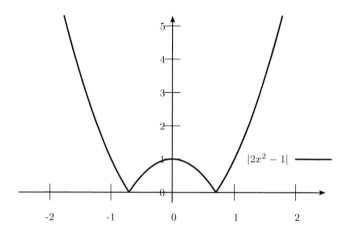

Prob. 67. The function has a discontinuity at $x = 1$, and is not differentiable there.

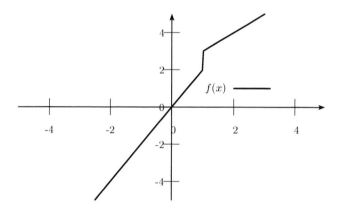

Prob. 69. The function has a discontinuity at $x = 0$, and is not differentiable there.

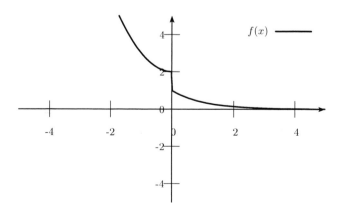

4.2 The Power Rule, the Basic Rules of Differentiation and the Derivatives of Polynomials

Prob. 1. $f'(x) = 12x^2 - 7$

Prob. 3.

$$\frac{d}{dx}(-2x^5 + 7x - 4) \quad = \frac{d}{dx}(-2x^5) + \frac{d}{dx}(7x) - \frac{d}{dx}(4)$$

$$= -2\frac{d}{dx}(x^5) + 7\frac{d}{dx}(x) - \frac{d}{dx}(4)$$

$$= -2(5x^4) + 7(1) - 0 = -10x^4 + 7$$

Prob. 5.

$$\frac{d}{dx}(3 - 4x - 5x^2) \quad = \frac{d}{dx}(3) - \frac{d}{dx}(4x) - \frac{d}{dx}(5x^2)$$

$$= \frac{d}{dx}(3) - 4\frac{d}{dx}(x) - 5\frac{d}{dx}(x^2)$$

$$= 0 - 4(1) - 5(2x) = -4 - 10x$$

Prob. 7.

$$\frac{d}{ds}(5s^7 + 2s^3 - 5s) \quad = \frac{d}{ds}(5s^7) + \frac{d}{ds}(2s^3) - \frac{d}{ds}(5s)$$

$$= 5\frac{d}{ds}(s^7) + 2\frac{d}{ds}(s^3) - 5\frac{d}{ds}(s)$$

$$= 5(7s^6) + 2(3s^2) - 5(1) = 35s^6 + 6s^2 - 5$$

Prob. 9. $h' = -\frac{1}{3} \cdot 4 \cdot t^3 + 4 \cdot 1 = -\frac{4}{3}t^3 + 4.$

Prob. 11.

$$\frac{d}{dx}(x^2 \sin(\pi/3) + \tan(\pi/4)) \quad = \frac{d}{dx}(x^2 \sin(\pi/3)) + \frac{d}{dx}(\tan(\pi/4))$$

$$= \sin(\pi/3)\frac{d}{dx}(x^2) + \frac{d}{dx}(\tan(\pi/4))$$

$$= \sin(\pi/3)(2x^1) + 0 = \sqrt{3}x$$

Prob. 13.

$$\frac{d}{dx}(-3x^4 \tan(\pi/6) - \cot(\pi/6)) \quad = \frac{d}{dx}(-3x^4 \tan(\pi/6)) - \frac{d}{dx}(\cot(\pi/6))$$

$$= -3 \tan(\pi/6)\frac{d}{dx}(x^4) - \frac{d}{dx}(\cot(\pi/6))$$

$$= -3 \tan(\pi/6)(4x^3) - 0 = -4\sqrt{3}x^3$$

Prob. 15.

$$
\begin{aligned}
\frac{d}{dt}(t^3 e^{-2} + t) \quad &= \frac{d}{dt}(t^3 e^{-2}) + \frac{d}{dt}(t) \\
&= e^{-2}\frac{d}{dt}(t^3) + \frac{d}{dt}(t) \\
&= e^{-2}(3t^2) + (1) = 3e^{-2}t^2 + 1
\end{aligned}
$$

Prob. 17.

$$
\begin{aligned}
\frac{d}{ds}(s^3 e^3 + 3e) \quad &= \frac{d}{ds}(s^3 e^3) + \frac{d}{ds}(3e) \\
&= e^3\frac{d}{ds}(s^3) + \frac{d}{ds}(3e) \\
&= e^3(3s^2) + 0 = 3e^3 s^2
\end{aligned}
$$

Prob. 19.

$$
\begin{aligned}
\frac{d}{dx}(20x^3 - 4x^6 + 9x^8) \quad &= \frac{d}{dx}(20x^3) - \frac{d}{dx}(4x^6) + \frac{d}{dx}(9x^8) \\
&= 20\frac{d}{dx}(x^3) - 4\frac{d}{dx}(x^6) + 9\frac{d}{dx}(x^8) \\
&= 20(3x^2) - 4(6x^5) + 9(8x^7) = 60x^2 - 24x^5 + 72x^7
\end{aligned}
$$

Prob. 21. $f'(x) = 3\pi x^2 + \frac{1}{\pi}$

Prob. 23. We have

$$
\begin{aligned}
\frac{d}{dx}(ax^3) \quad &= a\frac{d}{dx}(x^3) \\
&= a(3x^2) \\
&= 3ax^2
\end{aligned}
$$

Prob. 25. We have

$$
\begin{aligned}
\frac{d}{dx}(ax^2 - 2a) \quad &= \frac{d}{dx}(ax^2) - \frac{d}{dx}(2a) \\
&= a\frac{d}{dx}(x^2) - \frac{d}{dx}(2a) \\
&= a(2x) - 0 \\
&= 2ax
\end{aligned}
$$

Prob. 27. We have

$$
\frac{d}{ds}(rs^2 - r) \quad = \frac{d}{ds}(rs^2) - \frac{d}{ds}(r)
$$

$$= r\frac{d}{ds}(s^2) - \frac{d}{ds}(r)$$

$$= r(2s^1) - 0$$

$$= 2rs$$

Prob. 29. We have

$$\frac{d}{dx}(rs^2x^3 - rx + s) = \frac{d}{dx}(rs^2x^3) - \frac{d}{dx}(rx) + \frac{d}{dx}(s)$$

$$= rs^2\frac{d}{dx}(x^3) - r\frac{d}{dx}(x) + \frac{d}{dx}(s)$$

$$= rs^2(3x^2) - r(1) + 0$$

$$= 3rs^2x^2 - r$$

Prob. 31. We have

$$\frac{d}{dN}\left((b-1)N^4 - \frac{N^2}{b}\right) = \frac{d}{dN}\left((b-1)N^4\right) - \frac{d}{dN}\left(\frac{N^2}{b}\right)$$

$$= (b-1)\frac{d}{dN}\left(N^4\right) - \frac{1}{b}\frac{d}{dN}\left(N^2\right)$$

$$= (b-1)\left(4N^3\right) - \frac{1}{b}\left(2N^1\right)$$

$$= 4(b-1)N^3 - \frac{2}{b}N$$

Prob. 33. We have

$$\frac{d}{dt}(a^3t - at^3) = \frac{d}{dt}(a^3t) - \frac{d}{dt}(at^3)$$

$$= a^3\frac{d}{dt}(t) - a\frac{d}{dt}(t^3)$$

$$= a^3(1) - a(3t^2)$$

$$= a^3 - 3at^2$$

Prob. 35. We have

$$\frac{d}{dt}(V_0(1 + \gamma t)) = \frac{d}{dt}(V_0 + V_0\gamma t)$$

$$= \frac{d}{dt}(V_0) + \frac{d}{dt}(V_0\gamma t)$$

$$= \frac{d}{dt}(V_0) + V_0\gamma\frac{d}{dt}(t)$$

$$= 0 + V_0\gamma(1) = V_0\gamma$$

Prob. 37. We have

$$\frac{d}{dN}\left(N\left(1-\frac{N}{K}\right)\right) = \frac{d}{dN}\left(N-\frac{N^2}{K}\right)$$

$$= \frac{d}{dN}(N) - \frac{d}{dN}\left(\frac{N^2}{K}\right)$$

$$= \frac{d}{dN}(N) - \frac{1}{K}\frac{d}{dN}\left(N^2\right)$$

$$= 1 - \frac{1}{K}(2N) = 1 - \frac{2}{K}N$$

Prob. 39. We have

$$\frac{d}{dN}\left(rN^2\left(1-\frac{N}{K}\right)\right) = \frac{d}{dN}\left(rN^2-\frac{rN^3}{K}\right)$$

$$= \frac{d}{dN}(rN^2) - \frac{d}{dN}\left(\frac{rN^3}{K}\right)$$

$$= r\frac{d}{dN}(N^2) - \frac{r}{K}\frac{d}{dN}\left(N^3\right)$$

$$= r(2N^1) - \frac{r}{K}(3N^2) = 2rN - \frac{3r}{K}N^2$$

Prob. 41. We have

$$\frac{d}{dT}\left(\frac{2\pi^5}{15}\frac{k^4}{c^2h^3}T^4\right) = \frac{2\pi^5}{15}\frac{k^4}{c^2h^3}\frac{d}{dT}\left(T^4\right)$$

$$= \frac{2\pi^5}{15}\frac{k^4}{c^2h^3}(4T^3) = \frac{8\pi^5}{15}\frac{k^4}{c^2h^3}T^3$$

Prob. 43. When $y = 7x^3 + 2x - 1$, we have $y' = 21x^2 + 2$. When $x = -3$ we have $y' = 191$, which means that the slope of the required tangent line is $m = 191$. Also, when $x = -3$ we have $y = -196$, and since the tangent line must pass through the point $(-3, -196)$, it's equation is

$$y - (-196) = 191(x - (-3)) \quad \text{or} \quad y = 191x + 377.$$

In standard form, this is $191x - y + 377 = 0$.

Prob. 45. $y' = 8x^3 - 5$, $y'(1) = 8(1)^3 - 5 = 3$. So, we have

$$y - (-3) = 3(X - 1)$$

$$y = 3X - 6.$$

Prob. 47. When $y = \frac{1}{\sqrt{2}}x^2 - \sqrt{2}$, we have $y' = \frac{2}{\sqrt{2}}x = \sqrt{2}x$. When $x = 4$ we have $y' = 4\sqrt{2}$, which means that the slope of the required tangent line is $m = 4\sqrt{2}$. Also, when

$x = 4$ we have $y = \frac{1}{\sqrt{2}}(16) - \sqrt{2} = 8\sqrt{2} - \sqrt{2} = 7\sqrt{2}$, and since the tangent line must pass through the point $(4, 7\sqrt{2})$, it's equation is

$$y - 7\sqrt{2} = 4\sqrt{2}(x - 4) \quad \text{or} \quad y = 4\sqrt{2}x - 9\sqrt{2}.$$

In standard form, this is $8x - \sqrt{2}y - 18 = 0$.

Prob. 49. $y' = 2X$, $y'(-1) = -2$. So, we have:

$$y - (3) = \frac{1}{2}(x + 1)$$

$$y = \frac{1}{2}x + \frac{7}{2}.$$

Prob. 51. When $y = \sqrt{3}x^4 - 2\sqrt{3}x^2$, we have $y' = 4\sqrt{3}x^3 - 4\sqrt{3}x = 4\sqrt{3}x(x^2 - 1)$. When $x = -\sqrt{3}$ we have $y' = -24$, which means that the slope of the tangent line is -24. Thus the slope of the normal line is $m = 1/24$. Also, when $x = -\sqrt{3}$ we have $y = 3\sqrt{3}$, and since the normal line must pass through the point $(-\sqrt{3}, 3\sqrt{3})$, it's equation is

$$y - 3\sqrt{3} = \frac{1}{24}(x - (-\sqrt{3})) \quad \text{or} \quad y = \frac{1}{24}x + \frac{\sqrt{3}}{24} + 3\sqrt{3}.$$

In standard form, this is $x - 24y + 73\sqrt{3} = 0$.

Prob. 53. $y' = 3x^2$, $y'(1) = 3$. So, we have:

$$y - (-2) = -\frac{1}{3}(x - 1)$$

$$y = -\frac{1}{3}x - \frac{5}{3}.$$

Prob. 55. When $f(x) = ax^2$, we have $f'(x) = 2ax$. When $x = 1$ we have $f'(1) = 2a$, which means that the slope of the required tangent line is $m = 2a$. Also, when $x = 1$ we have $f(1) = a$, and since the tangent line must pass through the point $(1, a)$, it's equation is

$$y - a = 2a(x - 1) \quad \text{or} \quad y = 2ax - a.$$

Prob. 57. When $f(x) = \frac{ax^2}{a^2+2} = \frac{a}{a^2+2}x^2$, we have $f'(x) = \frac{2a}{a^2+2}x$. When $x = 2$ we have $f'(2) = \frac{4a}{a^2+2}$, which means that the slope of the required tangent line is $m = \frac{4a}{a^2+2}$. Also, when $x = 2$ we have $f(2) = \frac{4a}{a^2+2}$, and since the tangent line must pass through the point $(2, 4a/(a^2 + 2))$, it's equation is

$$y - \frac{4a}{a^2 + 2} = \frac{4a}{a^2 + 2}(x - 2) \quad \text{or} \quad 4ax - (a^2 + 2)y - 4a = 0.$$

Prob. 59. When $f(x) = ax^3$, we have $f'(x) = 3ax^2$. When $x = -1$ we have $f'(-1) = 3a$, which means that the slope of the tangent line is $3a$. Thus the slope of the normal line is $m = -1/(3a)$. Also, when $x = -1$ we have $f(-1) = -a$, and since the normal line must pass through the point $(-1, -a)$, it's equation is

$$y - (-a) = -\frac{1}{3a}(x - (-1)) \quad \text{or} \quad x + 3ay + 1 + 3a^2 = 0.$$

Prob. 61. When $f(x) = \frac{ax^2}{a+1} = \frac{a}{a+1}x^2$, we have $f'(x) = \frac{2a}{a+1}x$. When $x = 2$ we have $f'(2) = \frac{4a}{a+1}$, which means that the slope of the tangent line is $\frac{4a}{a+1}$. Thus the slope of the normal line is $m = -(a+1)/(4a)$. Also, when $x = 2$ we have $f(2) = \frac{4a}{a+1}$, and since the normal line must pass through the point $(2, \frac{4a}{a+1})$, it's equation is

$$y - \frac{4a}{a+1} = -\frac{a+1}{4a}(x - 2) \quad \text{or} \quad (a+1)^2 x + 4a(a+1)y - 16a^2 - 2(a+1)^2 = 0.$$

Prob. 63. A horizontal line has slope equal to zero. Thus any point $(x, f(x))$ at which there is a horizontal tangent line must satisfy $f'(x) = 0$. Here $f(x) = x^2$ and so $f'(x) = 2x$. This implies that $f'(x) = 2x = 0$ only when $x = 0$. The desired point is then $(0, 0)$.

Prob. 65. A horizontal line has slope equal to zero. Thus any point $(x, f(x))$ at which there is a horizontal tangent line must satisfy $f'(x) = 0$. Here $f(x) = 3x - x^2$ and so $f'(x) = 3 - 2x$. This implies that $f'(x) = 3 - 2x = 0$ only when $x = 3/2$. The desired point is then $(3/2, 9/4)$.

Prob. 67. A horizontal line has slope equal to zero. Thus any point $(x, f(x))$ at which there is a horizontal tangent line must satisfy $f'(x) = 0$. Here $f(x) = 3x^3 - x^2$ and so $f'(x) = 9x^2 - 2x$. This implies that $f'(x) = 9x^2 - 2x = x(9x - 2) = 0$ only when $x = 0$ and when $x = 2/9$. The desired points are $(0, 0)$ and $(2/9, -4/243)$.

Prob. 69. A horizontal line has slope equal to zero. Thus any point $(x, f(x))$ at which there is a horizontal tangent line must satisfy $f'(x) = 0$. Here $f(x) = \frac{1}{2}x^4 - \frac{7}{3}x^3 - 2x^2$ and so $f'(x) = 2x^3 - 7x^2 - 4x$. This implies that

$$f'(x) = 2x^3 - 7x^2 - 4x = x(2x^2 - 7x - 4) = x(2x + 1)(x - 4) = 0 \text{ only when } x = 0, \ x = 4$$

and $x = -1/2$. The desired points are then $(0, 0)$, $(4, -160/3)$ and $(-1/2, -17/96)$.

Prob. 71. Suppose the point we wish to find is $(a, 4 - a^2)$. That is, the tangent line to the curve $y = 4 - x^2$ at this point is parallel to the line $y = 2$. Since $y' = -2x$, the slope of the tangent line at $(a, 4 - a^2)$ is given by $m = -2a$. Since the line $y = 2$ has slope 0 and parallel lines have the same slope, we want the tangent line to have slope 0. Thus $m = -2a = 0$ which means $a = 0$. There is only one such point, and it is $(0, 4)$.

Prob. 73. Since $y' = 4x$, $y = x$ has slope at 1, then:

$$4x = 1$$

$$x = \frac{1}{4}.$$

Hence, there is only 1 such point, namely $(]frac14, -\frac{3}{8})$.

Prob. 75. Suppose the point we wish to find is $(a, a^3 + 2a + 2)$. That is, the tangent line to the curve $y = x^3 + 2x + 2$ at this point is parallel to the line $3x - y = 2$. Since $y' = 3x^2 + 2$, the slope of the tangent line at $(a, a^3 + 2a + 2)$ is given by $m = 3a^2 + 2$. Now, the line $3x - y = 2$ can be written as $y = 3x - 2$ and so it has slope 3. Since parallel lines have the same slope, we want the tangent line to have slope 3. Thus $m = 3a^2 + 2 = 3$ which means $a = \pm 1/\sqrt{3}$. There are two such points, namely $(1/\sqrt{3}, 2 + 7/(3\sqrt{3}))$ and $(-1/\sqrt{3}, 2 - 7/(3\sqrt{3}))$.

Prob. 77. Since $y = x^2$, we have $y' = 2x$. When $x = 1$ we have $y' = 2$, which means that the slope of the tangent line at the point $(1, 1)$ is $m = 2$. The tangent line must pass through the point $(1, 1)$, and so it has equation

$$y - 1 = 2(x - 1) \quad \text{or} \quad y = 2x - 1.$$

Since $y = 2(0) - 1 = -1$ when $x = 0$, this tangent line passes through the point $(0, -1)$.

Prob. 79. Since $y = x^2$, we have $y' = 2x$. If (t, t^2) is an arbitrary point on the curve, then the slope of the tangent line at this point is $m = 2t$. The tangent line must pass through the point (t, t^2), and so it has equation

$$y - t^2 = 2t(x - t) \quad \text{or} \quad y = 2tx - t^2.$$

If this line is to pass through the point $(0, -a^2)$, then we must have $-a^2 = y = 2t(0) - t^2$, which means that $t^2 = a^2$ and so $t = \pm a$. Thus the desired points are (a, a^2) and $(-a, a^2)$, with tangent lines $y = 2ax - a^2$ and $y = -2ax - a^2$ respectively.

Prob. 81. If $P(x)$ is a polynomial of degree 4, then it can be written as $P(x) = a_4 x^4 + a_3 x^3 + a_2 x^2 + a_1 x + a_0$, where the a_i are constants for $0 \le i \le 4$ and $a_4 \ne 0$.

Differentiating, we get $P'(x) = 4a_4x^3 + 3a_3x^2 + 2a_2x + a_1$, which is a polynomial of degree 3 because $4a_4 \neq 0$.

4.3 Product Rule and Quotient Rules

Prob. 1. $f'(x) = (x+5)'(x^2 - 3) + (x+5)(x^2 - 3)'$

$$= (x^2 - 3) + (x+5)(2x).$$

Prob. 3. $f'(x) = (12x^3)(2x - 5x^3) + (3x^4 - 5)(2 - 15x^2)$

Prob. 5.

$\frac{d}{dx}((\frac{1}{2}x^2 - 1)(2x + 3x^2)) = x(2x + 3x^2) + (\frac{1}{2}x^2 - 1)(2 + 6x) = -2 - 6x + 3x^2 + 6x^3.$

Prob. 7. $f'(x) = \frac{1}{5}\left[2x(x^2 + 1) + 2x(x^2 - 1)\right].$

Prob. 9. $\frac{d}{dx}(3x - 1)^2 = \frac{d}{dx}(3x - 1)(3x - 1) = 3(3x - 1) + (3x - 1)3 = 6(3x - 1).$

Prob. 11. We write $f(x) = 3uv$ where $u = v = 1 - 2x$. Since the two factors of the same, $uv' = u'v = 2uu'$ and we get $f'(x) = 3(2(1 - 2x)(-2)) = -12(1 - 2x).$

Prob. 13. $\frac{d}{ds}(2s^2 - 5s)^2 = 2(2s^2 - 5s)\frac{d}{ds}(2s^2 - 5s) = 2(2s^2 - 5s)(4s - 5).$

Prob. 15. $\frac{d}{dt}(3(2t^2 - 5t^4)^2) = 3(2(2t^2 - 5t^4)(4t - 20t^3)).$

Prob. 17. $f'(x) = -2 - 6x + 9x^2$, so $f'(1) = 1$ and $f(1) = 0$. The tangent at 1 is given by $y = f(1) + f'(1)(x - 1)$, that is, $y = x - 1$.

Prob. 19. $f'(x) = -8(-6 + 9x^2 - 16x^3 + 12x^5)$, so $f'(-1) = -56$ and $f(-1) = -8$. The tangent at -1 is given by $y = f(-1) + f'(-1)(x - (-1))$, that is, $y = -56x - 64$.

Prob. 21. $f'(x) = 3x^2 - 2x - 2$, so $f'(2) = 6$ and $f(2) = 2$. The normal at 2 is given by $y = f(2) - (1/f'(2))(x - 2)$, that is, $y = (14 - x)/6$.

Prob. 23. $f'(x) = -5(4x + 1)$, so $f'(0) = -5$ and $f(0) = 2$. The normal at 0 is $y = 2 + x/5$.

Prob. 25. $f(x) = uvw$, with $u = 2x - 1$, $v = 3x + 4$, $w = 1 - x$. We have $(uvw)' = u'(vw) + u(vw)' = u'vw + uv'w + uvw'$. Therefore $f'(x) = 2(3x + 4)(1 - x) + (2x - 1)3(1 - x) + (2x - 1)(3x + 4)(-1) = -18x^2 + 2x + 9.$

Prob. 27. $f'(x) = (\frac{d}{dx}(x - 3))(2x^1 + 1)(1 - x^2) + (x - 3)(\frac{d}{dx}(2x^1 + 1))(1 - x^2) + (x - 3) \times (2x^1 + 1)(\frac{d}{dx}(1 - x^2)) = -5 + 10x + 15x^2 - 8x^3.$

Prob. 29. Because a is a constant ("positive" is irrelevant), we can treat it as a number, taking the derivative of $(x-1)(2x-1)$ and multiplying by a. The result is

$f'(x) = a(4x - 3)$.

Prob. 31. Because a is a constant ("positive" is irrelevant), the only product we need to treat using the product rule for derivatives is $x^2 - a$ times itself. We get

$f'(x) = 2a(2(x^2 - a)(2x)) = 8ax(x^2 - a)$.

Prob. 33. $g'(t) = 2a(at + 1)$.

Prob. 35. $(fg)' = f'g + fg'$; in particular, at the point 2,

$(fg)'(2) = f'(2)g(2) + f(2)g'(2)$. Substituting the known values we get 11.

Prob. 37. $dy/dx = 2(\frac{dx}{dx}f(x) + x\frac{df(x)}{dx}) = 2(f(x) + xf'(x))$.

Prob. 39.

$dy/dx = -5(\frac{dx^3}{dx}f(x) + x^3\frac{df(x)}{dx}) - 2 = -5(3x^2f(x) + x^3f'(x)) - 2 = -5x^2(3f(x) + xf'(x)) - 2$.

Prob. 41. $dy/dx = 3(f'(x)g(x) + f(x)g'(x))$.

Prob. 43.

$dy/dx = (f'(x) + 2g'(x))g(x) + (f(x) + 2g(x))g'(x) = f'(x)g(x) + f(x)g'(x) + 4g'(x)g(x)$.

Prob. 45. The absolute growth rate is B times the specific growth rate: $Bg(B)$. Note that B is itself a function of t, but the growth rates (absolute and specific) are being thought of as functions of B alone, and t plays no real role in this problem. We are being asked to relate the slope of the graph of the absolute growth rate $Bg(B)$ versus B (at the point $B = 0$) with the specific growth rate (again at the point $B = 0$).

The slope of the graph of $Bg(B)$ is, of course, the derivative of $Bg(B)$ with respect to B, which, by the product rule, equals $g(B) + Bg'(B)$. When $B = 0$, this reduces to $g(B)$, as was to be shown.

Prob. 47. Since $f(N) = r(aN - N^2)(1 - N/K)$, we apply the product rule (treating r, a and K as constants) and get $f'(N) = r((a - 2N)(1 - N/K) + (aN - N^2)(-1/K))$.

Prob. 49. $f'(x) = \frac{3(x+1) - (3x-1)(1)}{(x+1)^2}$.

Prob. 51. $f'(x) = \frac{(6x-2)(2x+1) - (3x^2 - 2x + 1)(2)}{(2x+1)^2}$

Prob. 53. $f'(x) = \frac{2x^3 - 3x^2 + 3}{(1-x)^2}$.

Prob. 55. $h'(t) = \frac{t^2 + 2t - 4}{(t+1)^2}$.

Prob. 57. $f'(x) = 2(x^2 - 2x + 2))/(1 - x)^2$.

Prob. 59. $\frac{d}{dx}(\sqrt{x}(x-1)) = (\frac{d}{dx}\sqrt{x})(x-1) + \sqrt{x}\frac{d}{dx}(x-1) = \frac{x-1}{2\sqrt{x}} + \sqrt{x} = \frac{3x-1}{2\sqrt{x}}$.

Prob. 61. $\frac{d}{dx}(\sqrt{3x}(x^2-1)) = \sqrt{3}\frac{d}{dx}(\sqrt{x}(x^2-1)) =$

$\sqrt{3}\left((\frac{d}{dx}\sqrt{x}(x^2-1)) + \sqrt{x}\frac{d}{dx}(x^2-1)\right) = \sqrt{3}(\frac{x^2-1}{2\sqrt{x}} + 2x\sqrt{x}) = \sqrt{3}\frac{5x^2-1}{2\sqrt{x}}$.

Prob. 63. Since $1/x^3 = x^{-3}$, we have $f'(x) = 3x^2 - (-3x^{-4}) = 3(x^2 - x^{-4}) = 3(x^2 + \frac{1}{x^4})$.

Prob. 65. We can treat the fraction term either as a quotient or as a product (of $3x-1$ with x^{-3}). We choose to do the latter. Then

$f'(x) = 4x - (3x^{-3} + (3x-1)(-3)x^{-4}) = (4x^5 + 6x - 3)/x^4$. For yet another approach see exercise 66.

Prob. 67. Using the fact that derivatives of $s^{1/3}$ and $s^{2/3}$ are respectively $\frac{1}{3}s^{-2/3}$ and $\frac{2}{3}s^{-2/3}$, we have

$$g'(s) = \frac{\frac{1}{3}s^{-2/3}(s^{2/3} - 1) - \frac{2}{3}s^{-1/3}(s^{1/3} - 1)}{(s^{2/3} - 1)^2}.$$

The numerator simplifies to $-\frac{1}{3}(s^{1/3} - 1)s^{-2/3}$. An even simpler expression for the derivative can be obtained if we observe that the original function is in fact equal to $1/(s^{1/3} - 1)$, and treat this as a quotient of the constant function 1 by $s^{1/3} - 1$. The derivative then turns out to be $\frac{1}{3}(s^{1/3} + 1)^{-2}s^{-2/3}$. (This is of course equivalent to the result previously found.)

Prob. 69. We write $\sqrt{2x}$ as $\sqrt{2}x^{1/2}$, with derivative $(1/\sqrt{2})x^{-1/2}$, and we write $2/\sqrt{x}$ as $2x^{-1/2}$, with derivative $-x^{-3/2}$. Applying the product rule then gives

$f'(x) = -x^{-3/2} + (\frac{\sqrt{2}}{2} - 2)x^{-1/2} - 3\sqrt{2}x^{1/2}$.

Prob. 71. $f'(x) = -\frac{x(x^3+9x-10)}{(5+x^3)^2}$, so $f'(2) = -\frac{32}{169}$ and $f(2) = \frac{7}{13}$. The tangent at 2 is given by $y = f(2) + f'(2)(x-2)$, that is, $(155 - 32x)/169$.

Prob. 73. $f'(x) = (15 - 4x)/x^4$, so $f'(2) = \frac{7}{16}$ and $f(2) = -\frac{1}{8}$. The tangent at 2 is given by $y = f(2) + f'(2)(x-2)$, that is, $y = -1 + \frac{7}{16}x$.

Prob. 75. We treat a as a number and apply the quotient rule. The result is $3a/(x+3)^2$.

Prob. 77. An application of the quotient rule gives $f'(x) = 8ax/(4+x^2)^2$.

Prob. 79.

$$f'(R) = \frac{nR^{n-1}(K^n + R^n) - R^n(n - R^{n-1})}{(K^n + R^n)^2}$$

$$= \frac{nR^{n-1}(K^n + R^n - R^n)}{(K^n + R^n)^2} = \frac{nR^{n-1} - K^n}{(K^n + R^n)^2}.$$

Prob. 81. We write $h(t) = \sqrt{a}\sqrt{t}(t - a) + at$. Treating a as a number and applying the power rule to $\sqrt{t}$ and then the product rule, we get

$$h'(t) = \sqrt{at} + \frac{\sqrt{a}(t - a)}{2\sqrt{t}} + a.$$

Prob. 83. We have $(f/2g)' = \frac{1}{2}(f/g)' = \frac{1}{2}(f'g - fg')/g^2$; specializing to the point 2, we get

$$(f/2g)'(2) = \frac{1}{2}(1 \cdot 3 - (-4) \cdot (-2))/3^2 = 5/18.$$

Prob. 85. We apply the quotient rule with numerator $g(x) = x^2 + 4f(x)$ and denominator $h(x) = f(x)$. The result is $(g'(x)h(x) - g(x)h'(x))/h(x)^2 =$ $((2x + 4f'(x))f(x) - (x^2 + 4f(x))f'(x))/f(x)^2 = (2xf(x) - x^2 f'(x))/f(x)^2$. (Some time could have been saved by observing in the beginning that $y = x^2/f(x) + 4$.)

Prob. 87. We observe that $y = 1 - \frac{x}{f(x)+x}$, so

$$y' = -\frac{1(f(x) + x) - x(f'(x) + 1)}{(f(x) + x)^2} = -\frac{f(x) - xf'(x)}{(f(x) + x)^2}.$$

Prob. 89. The derivative of the denominator is $2g(x)g'(x)$. Therefore

$$y' = \frac{f'(x)g(x)^2 - 2f(x)g(x)g'(x)}{g(x)^4}.$$

Prob. 91. The derivative of $f(x)g(x)$ is $f'(x)g(x) + f(x)g'(x)$. Applying the product rule again to the factors $\sqrt{x}$ and $f(x)g(x)$ we get

$y' = 1/(2\sqrt{x})f(x)g(x) + \sqrt{x}(f'(x)g(x) + f(x)g'(x))$.

Prob. 93. We write $y = c/x$ and take the derivative $y' = -c/x^2$. The tangent at the point (x_1, y_1) is given by the equation $y = y_1 + y'(x_1)(x - x_1)$, or

$$y = y_1 - \frac{c(x - x_1)}{x_1^2} = \frac{c(2x_1 - x)}{x_1^2},$$

where for the second equality we used the fact that $y_1 = c/x_1$. The intersection of the equation with the x-axis happens when $y = 0$, and solving for x gives $x = 2x_1$, which does not depend on c. (Note that each pair (x_1, y_1) belongs to only one hyperbola, and the problem does not state which variable is to be regarded as the independent variable as c varies. If y_1 were the independent variable, the x-value of the intersection would be $x = 2c/y_1$, which does depend on c.)

4.4 The Chain Rule and Higher Derivatives

Prob. 1. $f'(x) = 2(x - 3)$

Prob. 3. Let $u = 1 - 3x^2$. By the chain rule,

$$f'(x) = \frac{d}{dx}u^4 = 4u^3\frac{du}{dx} = 4u^3 \cdot (-6x) = -24x(1 - 3x^2)^3.$$

Prob. 5. Let $u = x^2 + 3$. By the chain rule,

$$f'(x) = \frac{d}{dx}\sqrt{u} = \frac{1}{2\sqrt{u}}\frac{du}{dx} = \frac{1}{2\sqrt{u}} \cdot (2x) = \frac{x}{\sqrt{x^2 + 3}}.$$

Prob. 7. Let $u = 3 - x^3$. By the chain rule,

$$f'(x) = \frac{d}{dx}\sqrt{u} = \frac{1}{2\sqrt{u}}\frac{du}{dx} = \frac{1}{2\sqrt{u}} \cdot (-3x^2) = -\frac{3x^2}{2\sqrt{3 - x^3}}.$$

Prob. 9. Let $u = x^3 - 2$. By the chain rule,

$$f'(x) = \frac{d}{dx}\frac{1}{u^4} = -\frac{4}{u^5}\frac{du}{dx} = -\frac{4}{u^5} \cdot 3x^2 = -\frac{12x^2}{(x^3 - 2)^5}.$$

Prob. 11. Let $u = 2x^2 - 1$. Using the chain rule and the quotient rule, we have

$$
\begin{aligned}
f'(x) &= \frac{d}{dx}\frac{3x - 1}{\sqrt{u}} \\
&= \frac{\sqrt{u} \cdot 3 - (3x - 1) \cdot \frac{1}{2\sqrt{u}}\frac{du}{dx}}{(\sqrt{u})^2} \\
&= \frac{3u - \frac{1}{2}(3x - 1)(4x)}{u^{\frac{3}{2}}} \\
&= \frac{3(2x^2 - 1) - 2x(3x - 1)}{u^{\frac{3}{2}}} \\
&= \frac{2x - 3}{(2x^2 - 1)^{\frac{3}{2}}}.
\end{aligned}
$$

Prob. 13. Let $u = 2x - 1$, $v = x - 1$. Using the chain rule and the quotient rule, we have

$$
\begin{aligned}
f'(x) &= \frac{d}{dx}\frac{\sqrt{u}}{v^2} \\
&= \frac{v^2 \cdot \frac{1}{2\sqrt{u}}\frac{du}{dx} - \sqrt{u} \cdot 2v\frac{dv}{dx}}{v^4} \\
&= \frac{\frac{v}{2}\frac{du}{dx} - 2u\frac{dv}{dx}}{v^3\sqrt{u}} \\
&= \frac{(x - 1) - 2(2x - 1)}{v^3\sqrt{u}} \\
&= \frac{-3x + 1}{(x - 1)^3\sqrt{2x - 1}}
\end{aligned}
$$

Prob. 15. Let $u = s + \sqrt{s}$. By the chain rule,

$$f'(s) = \frac{d}{ds}\sqrt{u} = \frac{1}{2\sqrt{u}}\frac{du}{ds} = \frac{1}{2\sqrt{s + \sqrt{s}}}\left(1 + \frac{1}{2\sqrt{s}}\right).$$

Prob. 17. Let $u = t/(t - 3)$. Using the chain rule and the quotient rule, we have

$$g'(t) = \frac{d}{dt}u^3 = 3u^2\frac{du}{dt} = 3u^2 \cdot \frac{(t-3) - t}{(t-3)^2} = -\frac{9t^3}{(t-3)^4}.$$

Prob. 19. Let $u = r^2 - r$, $v = r + 3r^3$. Using the chain rule and the product rule, we have

$$\begin{aligned}
f'(r) &= \frac{d}{dr}(u^3 v^{-4}) \\
&= 3u^2\frac{du}{dr}\cdot v^{-4} + u^3\left(-4v^{-5}\frac{dv}{dr}\right) \\
&= u^2 v^{-5}\left(3v\frac{du}{dr} - 4u\frac{dv}{dr}\right) \\
&= \frac{(r^2 - r)^2}{(r + 3r^3)^5}\cdot\left[3(r + 3r^3)(2r - 1) - 4(r^2 - r)(1 + 9r^2)\right]
\end{aligned}$$

Prob. 21. Let $u = 3 - x^4$. By the chain rule,

$$\begin{aligned}
h'(x) &= \frac{d}{dx}u^{\frac{1}{5}} = \frac{1}{5}u^{-\frac{4}{5}}\frac{du}{dx} \\
&= \frac{1}{5}u^{-\frac{4}{5}}(-4x^3) \\
&= -\frac{4}{5}x^3(3 - x^4)^{-\frac{4}{5}}.
\end{aligned}$$

Prob. 23. Notice that

$$f(x) = \sqrt[7]{x^2 - 2x + 1} = \sqrt[7]{(x - 1)^2}.$$

Let $u = x - 1$. By the chain rule,

$$f'(x) = \frac{d}{dx}u^{\frac{2}{7}} = \frac{2}{7}u^{-\frac{5}{7}}\frac{du}{dx} = \frac{2}{7}(x - 1)^{-\frac{5}{7}}.$$

Prob. 25. $g'(s) = \frac{3}{2}(3s^7 - 7S)^{\frac{1}{2}}(21s^5 - 7).$

Prob. 27. Let $u = 3t + 3/t$. By the chain rule,

$$\begin{aligned}
h'(t) &= \frac{d}{dt}u^{\frac{2}{5}} = \frac{2}{5}u^{-\frac{3}{5}}\frac{du}{dt} \\
&= \frac{2}{5}u^{-\frac{3}{5}}\left(3 - \frac{3}{t^2}\right) \\
&= \frac{6}{5}\left(3t + \frac{3}{t}\right)^{-\frac{3}{5}}\left(1 - \frac{1}{t^2}\right).
\end{aligned}$$

Prob. 29. Let $u = ax + 1$. By the chain rule,

$$
\begin{aligned}
f'(x) &= \frac{d}{dx} u^3 = 3u^2 \frac{du}{dx} \\
&= 3u^2 \cdot a = 3a(ax+1)^2.
\end{aligned}
$$

Prob. 31. Let $u = k + N$. Then, using the chain rule and the product rule, we have

$$
\begin{aligned}
g'(N) &= \frac{d}{dN}(bNu^{-2}) \\
&= b\left(u^{-2} + N \cdot -2u^{-3}\frac{du}{dN}\right) \\
&= bu^{-3}(u - 2N) \\
&= \frac{b(k - N)}{(k + N)^3}.
\end{aligned}
$$

Prob. 33. Let $u = T_0 - T$. Then, by the chain rule,

$$
g'(T) = \frac{d}{dT} au^3 - b = 3au^2 \frac{du}{dT} = -3a(T_0 - T)^2.
$$

Prob. 35.

(a) By the chain rule,

$$
\begin{aligned}
\frac{d}{dx}[f(x^2 + 3)] &= f'(x^2 + 3)\frac{d}{dx}(x^2 + 3) \\
&= \frac{1}{x^2 + 3} \cdot 2x \\
&= \frac{2x}{x^2 + 3}.
\end{aligned}
$$

(b) By the chain rule,

$$
\begin{aligned}
\frac{d}{dx}[f(\sqrt{x - 1})] &= f'(\sqrt{x - 1})\frac{d}{dx}\sqrt{x - 1} \\
&= \frac{1}{\sqrt{x - 1}} \cdot \frac{1}{2\sqrt{x - 1}} \\
&= \frac{1}{2(x - 1)}.
\end{aligned}
$$

Prob. 37. Let $u = f(x)/g(x) + 1$. By the chain rule and the quotient rule,

$$
\begin{aligned}
\frac{d}{dx}\left(\frac{f(x)}{g(x)} + 1\right)^2 &= \frac{d}{dx} u^2 = 2u\frac{du}{dx} \\
&= 2\left(\frac{f}{g} + 1\right)\frac{gf' - fg'}{g^2}.
\end{aligned}
$$

Prob. 39. Let $v = g(2x) + 2x$.

$$\frac{d}{dx}\frac{[f(x)]^2}{g(2x)+2x} = \frac{d}{dx}\frac{f^2}{v}$$

$$= \frac{v\frac{d}{dx}f^2 - f^2\frac{dv}{dx}}{v^2}$$

$$= \frac{1}{v^2}\left\{v\cdot 2f\frac{df}{dx} - f^2\frac{d}{dx}[g(2x)+2x]\right\}$$

$$= \frac{1}{v^2}\left\{2vff' - f^2[g'(2x)\cdot 2 + 2]\right\}$$

$$= \frac{2}{[g(2x)+2x]^2}\left\{f(x)f'(x)[g(2x)+2x] - f(x)^2[g'(2x)+1]\right\}.$$

Prob. 41. $\frac{dy}{dx} = 4(\sqrt{x^3 - 3x} + 3x)^3(\frac{1}{2}(x^3 - 3x)^{-\frac{1}{2}}(3x^2 - 3) + 3)$.

Prob. 43. Let $u = 3x^2 - 1$, $v = 1 + u^3 = 1 + (3x^2 - 1)^3$. By the chain rule,

$$\frac{dy}{dx} = \frac{d}{dx}v^2$$

$$= 2v\frac{d}{dx}(1 + u^3)$$

$$= 2v\cdot 3u^2\frac{d}{dx}(3x^2 - 1)$$

$$= 36x(3x^2 - 1)^2\left(1 + (3x^2 - 1)^3\right)$$

Prob. 45. Let

$$u = 2x + 1, \quad v = x^3 - 1,$$

$$w = 3v^3 - 1 = 3(x^3 - 1)^3 - 1.$$

Using the chain rule,

$$\frac{dy}{dx} = \frac{d}{dx}\left(\frac{u}{w}\right)^3 = 3\left(\frac{u}{w}\right)^2\frac{d}{dx}\frac{u}{w}$$

$$= \frac{3u^2}{w^4}\left[w\frac{d}{dx}(2x+1) - u\frac{d}{dx}(3v^3 - 1)\right]$$

$$= \frac{3u^2}{w^4}\left[2w - 9uv^2\frac{d}{dx}(x^3 - 1)\right]$$

$$= \frac{3u^2}{w^4}(2w - 27x^2uv^2)$$

$$= 3\left(\frac{2x+1}{3(x^3-1)^3 - 1}\right)^2\frac{6(x^3 - 1)^3 - 2 - 27x^2(2x - 1)(x^3 - 1)}{(3(x^3 - 1)^3 - 1)^2}$$

Prob. 47. In problems **47** to **52**, differentiate the given equations with respect to x regarding y as a function of x. Various differentiation rules (chain, product, quotient) are used when needed without further comment.

$$2x + 2y\frac{dy}{dx} = 0 \Rightarrow \frac{dy}{dx} = -\frac{x}{y}$$

Prob. 49.

$$\frac{3}{4}x^{-\frac{1}{4}} + \frac{3}{4}y^{-\frac{1}{4}}\frac{dy}{dx} = 0 \Rightarrow \frac{dy}{dx} = -\frac{x^{-\frac{1}{4}}}{y^{-\frac{1}{4}}} = -\sqrt[4]{\frac{y}{x}}$$

Prob. 51.

$$\frac{1}{2\sqrt{xy}}\left(y + x\frac{dy}{dx}\right) = 2x \Rightarrow \frac{dy}{dx} = 4\sqrt{xy} - \frac{y}{x}$$

Prob. 53. Let us first rewrite the given equation as $x^2 = y^2$. Differentiation then yields

$$2x = 2y\frac{dy}{dx} \Rightarrow \frac{dy}{dx} = -\frac{x}{y}.$$

Prob. 55. We first find dy/dx using implicit differentiation:

$$2x + 2y\frac{dy}{dx} = 0 \Rightarrow \frac{dy}{dx} = -\frac{x}{y}$$

The slope of the tangent is given by

$$\frac{dy}{dx}\bigg|_{(4,-3)} = -\frac{4}{-3} = \frac{4}{3},$$

(a) The slope of the normal is thus $-3/4$. Hence, the equation of the tangent line at $(4, -3)$ is

$$y + 3 = \frac{4}{3}(x - 4) \Rightarrow y = \frac{4}{3}x - \frac{25}{3},$$

(b) The equation for the normal line is:

$$y + 3 = -\frac{3}{4}(x - 4) \Rightarrow y = -\frac{3}{4}x.$$

Prob. 57. We first find dy/dx using implicit differentiation:

$$\frac{2x}{25} - \frac{2y}{9}\frac{dy}{dx} = 0 \Rightarrow \frac{dy}{dx} = \frac{9x}{25y}$$

The slope of the tangent is given by

$$\frac{dy}{dx}\bigg|_{\left(\frac{25}{3},4\right)} = \frac{9 \cdot \frac{25}{3}}{25 \cdot 4} = \frac{3}{4},$$

and the slope of the normal is thus $-4/3$.

(a) Hence, the equation of the tangent line at $(25/3, 4)$ is

$$y - 4 = \frac{3}{4}(x - \frac{25}{3}) \Rightarrow y = \frac{3}{4}x - \frac{9}{4},$$

(b) and that of the normal line is

$$y - 4 = -\frac{4}{3}(x - \frac{25}{3}) \Rightarrow y = -\frac{4}{3}x + \frac{136}{9}.$$

Prob. 59.

(a) Differentiating the equation $x^{2/3} + y^{2/3} = 4$ with respect to x yields

$$\frac{2}{3}x^{-\frac{1}{3}} + \frac{2}{3}y^{-\frac{1}{3}}\frac{dy}{dx} = 0 \Rightarrow \frac{dy}{dx} = -\sqrt[3]{\frac{y}{x}}.$$

Thus, the value of dy/dx at $(-1, 3\sqrt{3})$ is

$$-\sqrt[3]{\frac{3\sqrt{3}}{-1}} = \sqrt{3}.$$

(b) The curve $x^{2/3} + y^{2/3} = 4$:

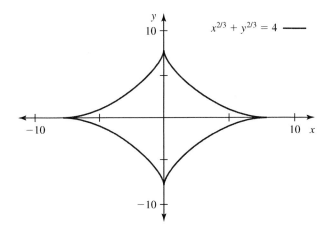

Prob. 61. To simplify notations, in problems **61** to **64**, we use $x', y', \ldots$ to denote derivatives with respect to t. Differentiating $x^2 + y^2 = 1$ with respect to t yields

$$2xx' + 2yy' = 0 \Rightarrow y' = -\frac{xx'}{y}.$$

We already have $x = 1/2$ and $x' = 2$, so we only need to find y. From $x^2 + y^2 = 1$ and the assumption that $y > 0$, we obtain

$$\left(\frac{1}{2}\right)^2 + y^2 = 1 \Rightarrow y = \frac{\sqrt{3}}{2}.$$

Therefore, we have

$$y' = -\frac{\frac{1}{2} \cdot 2}{\frac{\sqrt{3}}{2}} = -\frac{2}{\sqrt{3}}.$$

Prob. 63. Since $x^2 y = 1$ and $x = 2$, we have $y = 1/4$. Differentiating $x^2 y = 1$ with respect to t yields

$$2xx'y + x^2 y' = 0 \Rightarrow y' = -\frac{2x'y}{x} = -\frac{2 \cdot 3 \cdot \frac{1}{4}}{2} = -\frac{3}{4}.$$

Prob. 65. The chain rule gives us

$$\frac{dV}{dt} = \frac{d(x^3)}{dt} = 3x^2 \frac{dx}{dt}.$$

Prob. 67. The chain rule gives us

$$\frac{dS}{dt} = \frac{d(4\pi r^2)}{dt} = 8\pi r \frac{dr}{dt}.$$

Prob. 69. Let us express all volumes in m^2. In mathematical terms, the statement that water is drained at a rate of **250** liters per minute means $dV/dt = -0.25$, and the quantity of interest now is dh/dt. Since $V = 25\pi h$, by differentiating with respect to t, we have

$$\frac{dV}{dt} = 25\pi \frac{dh}{dt},$$

and thus,

$$\frac{dh}{dt} = \frac{-0.25}{25\pi} \approx -0.0032.$$

In words, the height is dropping at a rate of about 3.2cm per minute.

Prob. 71. Let x be the distance traveled by the eastbound biker in miles and y be that of the southbound biker. The distance between is $\sqrt{x^2 + y^2}$. The rate at which this distance is changing is given by

$$\begin{aligned}
\frac{d}{dt}\sqrt{x^2 + y^2} &= \frac{1}{2\sqrt{x^2 + y^2}}\left(2x\frac{dx}{dt} + 2y\frac{dy}{dt}\right) \\
&= \frac{1}{\sqrt{x^2 + y^2}}\left(x\frac{dx}{dt} + y\frac{dy}{dt}\right).
\end{aligned}$$

After 20 minutes, $x = 5$ and $y = 6$. Also, we always have $dx/dt = 15$ and $dy/dt = 18$. Thus, the above expression gives us the first answer

$$\frac{1}{\sqrt{5^2 + 6^2}}(5 \cdot 15 + 6 \cdot 18) \approx 23.4.$$

After 40 minutes, $x = 10$ and $y = 12$, so the second answer is

$$\frac{1}{\sqrt{10^2 + 12^2}}(10 \cdot 15 + 12 \cdot 18) \approx 23.4$$

In fact, the distance between the two bikers is increasing at a constant rate.

Prob. 73.

$$f'(x) = 3x^2 - 6x, \quad f''(x) = 6x - 6$$

Prob. 75. Note that

$$\frac{x-1}{x+1} = \frac{x+1-2}{x+1} = 1 - \frac{2}{x+1}.$$

Hence we have

$$g'(x) = \frac{2}{(x+1)^2}$$

$$g''(x) = -\frac{4}{(x+1)^3}.$$

Prob. 77.

$$g'(t) = \frac{1}{2\sqrt{3t^3 + 2t}} \cdot (9t^2 + 2)$$

$$= \frac{1}{2}(3t^3 + 2t)^{-\frac{1}{2}}(9t^2 + 2)$$

$$g''(t) = -\frac{1}{4}(3t^3 + 2t)^{-\frac{3}{2}}(9t^2 + 2)^2 + \frac{1}{2}(3t^3 + 2t)^{-\frac{1}{2}} \cdot 18t$$

$$= \frac{1}{4}(3t^3 + 2t)^{-\frac{3}{2}}\Big[-(9t^2 + 2)^2 + 36t(3t^3 + 2t) \Big]$$

$$= \frac{1}{4}(3t^3 + 2t)^{-\frac{3}{2}} \cdot (27t^4 + 36t^2 - 4)$$

Prob. 79.

$$f'(s) = \frac{1}{2\sqrt{s^{\frac{3}{2}} - 1}} \cdot \frac{3}{2}s^{\frac{1}{2}} = \frac{3}{4}\left(\frac{s}{s^{\frac{3}{2}} - 1}\right)^{\frac{1}{2}}$$

$$f''(s) = \frac{3}{8}\left(\frac{s}{s^{\frac{3}{2}} - 1}\right)^{-\frac{1}{2}} \cdot \frac{(s^{\frac{3}{2}} - 1) - s \cdot \frac{3}{2}s^{\frac{1}{2}}}{(s^{\frac{3}{2}} - 1)^2} = -\frac{3(\frac{1}{2}s^{\frac{3}{2}} + 1)}{8\sqrt{s}(s^{\frac{3}{2}} - 1)^{\frac{3}{2}}}$$

Prob. 81.

$$g'(t) = -\frac{5}{2}t^{-7/2} - \frac{1}{2}t^{-1/2}$$

$$g''(t) = \frac{35}{4}t^{-9/2} + \frac{1}{4}t^{-3/2}$$

Prob. 83. By repeated differentiation, the first ten derivatives of x^5 are:

$$f'(x) = 5x^4, \quad f''(x) = 20x^3, \quad f'''(x) = 60x^2, \quad f^{(4)}(x) = 120x,$$

$$f^{(5)}(x) = 120, \quad f^{(6)}(x) = \cdots = f^{(10)}(x) = 0.$$

Prob. 85. Let $p(x) = ax^2 + bx + c$. Its first two derivatives are $p'(x) = 2ax + b$ and $p''(x) = 2a$. Thus we have

$$p(0) = c, \quad p'(0) = b, \quad p''(0) = 2a.$$

The condition $p(0) = 3$, $p'(0) = 2$ and $p''(0) = 6$ means

$$c = 3, \quad b = 2, \quad a = 3,$$

and hence the polynomial is $p(x) = 3x^2 + 2x + 3$.

Prob. 87.

(a) The velocity is

$$v(t) = h'(t) = v_0 - gt,$$

while the acceleration is

$$a(t) = v'(t) = -g.$$

(b) By the result in (a), $v(t) = v_0 - gt = 0$ when

$$t = \frac{v_0}{g}.$$

Before this moment, i.e. when $t < v_0/g$, $v(t)$ is positive, so the object is traveling upward. After this moment, i.e. when $t > v_0/g$, $v(t)$ is negative, so the object is traveling downward.

4.5 Derivatives of Trigonometric Functions

Prob. 1. $2\cos x + \sin x$

Prob. 3. $3\cos x - 5\sin x - 2\sec x \tan x$

Prob. 5. $\sec^2 x + \csc^2 x$

Prob. 7. $3\cos(3x)$

Prob. 9. $6\cos(3x+1)$

Prob. 11. $4\sec^2 x$

Prob. 13. $4\sec(1+2x)\tan(1+2x)$

Prob. 15. $6x\cos(x^2)$

Prob. 17. $f'(x) = 3\sin^2(x^2-3)\cdot\cos(x^2-3)\cdot 2x$

Prob. 19. $f'(x) = 6\sin x^2\cdot\cos x^2\cdot 2x = 12x\sin x^2\cos x^2$.

Prob. 21. $f'(x) = -4\sin x^2\cdot(2x) + 4\cos x\cdot\sin x$.

Prob. 23. $f'(x) = 4\cdot 2\cos x\cdot(-\sin x) + 2\cdot(-\sin x^4)\cdot 4x^3$

Prob. 25. $-4x\sec^2(1-x^2)$

Prob. 27. $-18\tan^2(3x-1)\sec^2(3x-1)$

Prob. 29. $f'(x) = \frac{1}{2}(\sin(2x^2-1))^{-\frac{1}{2}}\cdot\cos(2x^2-1)\cdot 4x$

Prob. 31. $g'(s) = -\frac{1}{2}(\cos s)^{-\frac{1}{2}}\cdot\sin s + \sin(\sqrt{xs})\cdot\frac{1}{2}xs^{-\frac{1}{2}}$.

Prob. 33.

$$\frac{2\cos 2t(\cos 6t - 1) + 6\sin 6t(\sin 2t + 1)}{(\cos 6t - 1)^2}$$

Prob. 35. Note that

$$f(x) = \frac{\sin(x^2+1)}{\cos(x^2+1)}.$$

Hence we have

$$f'(x) = \frac{2x}{\cos^2(x^2-1)}\left[\cos(x^2-1)\cos(x^2+1) + \sin(x^2-1)\sin(x^2+1)\right]$$

Prob. 37. $2\cos(2x-1)\cos(3x+1) - 3\sin(2x-1)\sin(3x+1)$

Prob. 39. $6x[\sec^2(3x^2-1)\cot(3x^2+1) - \tan(3x^2-1)\csc^2+1]$

Prob. 41. Note that $f(x) = \tan x$. Hence $f'(x) = \sec^2 x$.

Prob. 43. $f'(x) = 0$ since $\sin^2 x - \sin^2 x = -1$.

Prob. 45.

$$-\frac{6x\cos(3x^2-1)}{\sin^2(3x^2-1)}$$

Prob. 47. $g(x) = \frac{1}{\csc^3(1-5x^2)} = \sin^3(1-5x^2)$. So,

$$g'(x) = 3\sin^2(1-5x^2)\cdot\cos(1-5x^2)\cdot(-10x).$$

Prob. 49.

$$-\frac{3(2\sec^2 2x - 1)}{(\tan 2x - x)^2}$$

Prob. 51. $h'(s) = 3\sin^2 s \cdot \cos s - 3\cos^2 s - \sin s.$

Prob. 53. $\frac{2(1+x^2)\cos 2x - 2x\sin 2x}{(1+x^2)^2}$

Prob. 55. $-\frac{1}{x^2}\sec^2\frac{1}{x}.$

Prob. 57. Rewrite $f(x)$ as $\cos^2 x/\cos x^2$. Then we have

$$f'(x) = \frac{1}{\cos^2 x^2}\left[-2\cos x^2 \sin x \cdot \cos x + 2x\sin x^2 \cos^2 x\right].$$

Prob. 59. First, compute

$$\frac{dy}{dx} = \frac{\pi}{3}\cos\left(\frac{\pi}{3}x\right).$$

The tangent is horizontal when $dy/dx = 0$, which is, $\frac{\pi}{3}x = n\pi + \frac{\pi}{2}$, or

$$x = 3n + \frac{3}{2},$$

where n is any integer.

Prob. 61. By definition,

$$\begin{aligned}
\frac{d}{dx}\cos x &= \lim_{h\to 0}\frac{\cos(x+h) - \cos x}{h} \\
&= \lim_{h\to 0}\frac{1}{h}\left[\cos x \cos h - \sin x \sin h - \cos x\right] \\
&= \cos x \lim_{h\to 0}\frac{\cos h - 1}{h} - \sin x \lim_{h\to 0}\frac{\sin h}{h}.
\end{aligned}$$

The limit in the second term is 1, as is discussed earlier in the book. To evaluate the other limit, consider the trick

$$\begin{aligned}
\frac{\cos h - 1}{h} &= \frac{\cos h - 1}{h}\cdot\frac{\cos h + 1}{\cos h + 1} \\
&= \frac{\cos^2 h - 1}{h(\cosh +1)} = -\frac{\sin^2 h}{h(\cos h + 1)} \\
&= -\left(\frac{\sin h}{h}\right)\cdot\sin h\cdot\left(\frac{1}{\cos h + 1}\right).
\end{aligned}$$

As $h \to 0$, the first factor approaches 1, as mentioned just above, while the second and the third approach 0 and 1/2 respectively. Hence, the limit of the whole things is 0. Going back to the calculation we start with, this implies we have

$$\frac{d}{dx}\cos x = \cos x \cdot 0 - \sin x \cdot 1 = -\sin x.$$

Prob. 63. By the chain rule, we have

$$\frac{d}{dx}\sec x = \frac{d}{dx}\frac{1}{\cos x}$$
$$= -\frac{1}{\cos^2 x}\cdot(-\sin x)$$
$$= \frac{1}{\cos x}\cdot\frac{\sin x}{\cos x}$$
$$= \sec x \tan x.$$

Prob. 65.

$$\frac{x}{\sqrt{x^2+1}}\cos\sqrt{x^2+1}$$

Prob. 67.

$$\frac{9x^2+3}{2\sqrt{3x^2+3x}}\cos\sqrt{3x^3+3x}$$

Prob. 69. $4x\sin(x^2-1)\cos(x^2-1)$

Prob. 71. $27x^2\tan^2(3x^3-3)\sec^2(3x^3-3)$

Prob. 73.

(a) $\frac{dc}{dt}=\frac{\pi}{2}\cos(\frac{\pi}{2}t)$

(b) The graph of $c(t)$ and dc/dt:

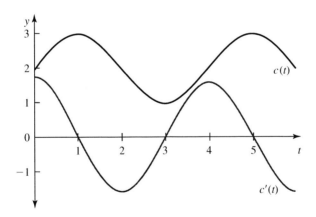

(c)   (i) Whenever $c(t)$ reaches a maximum, $dc/dt=0$.

     (ii) When dc/dt is positive, $c(t)$ is increasing.

(iii) In this case, when $dc/dt = 0$, $c(t)$ either reaches a maximum or a minimum. More generally speaking, the value of $c(t)$ is stationary/ the tangent of the graph is horizontal.

4.6 Derivatives of Exponential Functions

Prob. 1. $f'(x) = 3e^{3x}$

Prob. 3. $-12e^{1-3x}$

Prob. 5. $(-4x + 3)e^{-2x^2+3x-1}$

Prob. 7. $f'(x) = e^{7(x^7+1)^2} \cdot 7 \cdot 2(x^7 + 1) \cdot 2x.$

Prob. 9. $(1 + x)e^x$

Prob. 11. $(2x - x^2)e^{-x}$

Prob. 13. Using the quotient rule and after simplifications, we have for $f'(x)$:

$$\frac{(1-x)^2 e^x - 2x}{(1+x^2)^2}$$

Prob. 15. Using the quotient rule and after simplifications, we have for $f'(x)$:

$$\frac{2(e^x - 1 - e^{-x})}{(2 + x^{-x})^2}$$

Prob. 17. $f'(x) = e^{\sin(3x)} \cdot \cos(3x) \cdot 3.$

Prob. 19. $2x \cos(x^2 - 1)e^{\sin(x^2-1)}$

Prob. 21. $e^x \cos(e^x)$

Prob. 23. $(2e^{2x} + 1)\cos(e^{2x} + x)$

Prob. 25. $(1 - \cos x)e^{x-\sin x}$

Prob. 27. $2s \sec s^2 \tan s^2 e^{\sec s^2}$

Prob. 29. $(\sin x + x \cos x)e^{x \sin x}$

Prob. 31. $-3(2x + \sec^2 x)e^{x^2+\tan x}$

Prob. 33. $(\ln 2)2^x$

Prob. 35. $(\ln 2)2^{x+1}$

Prob. 37. $f'(x) = \ln 5 \cdot 5^{\sqrt{2x-1}} \cdot \frac{1}{2}(2x - 1)^{-\frac{1}{2}} \cdot 2.$

Prob. 39. $2(\ln 2)x2^{x^2+1}$

Prob. 41. $2(\ln 2)t2^{t^2-1}$

Prob. 43. $\frac{\ln 2}{2\sqrt{x}} 2^{\sqrt{2}}$

Prob. 45. $\frac{x \ln 2}{\sqrt{x^2-1}} 2^{\sqrt{x^2-1}}$

Prob. 47. $\frac{\ln 5}{2\sqrt{t}} \cdot 5^{\sqrt{t}}$

Prob. 49. $g'(x) = -2(\ln 2)(\sin x)2^{2\cos x}$.

Prob. 51. $\frac{\ln 3}{5} r^{-4/5} 3^{r^{1/5}}$

Prob. 53.

$$\lim_{h\to 0} \frac{e^{2h}-1}{h} = \lim_{h\to 0} \frac{e^{2h}-e^0}{h} = \left.\frac{d}{dx}e^{2x}\right|_{x=0} = 2e^{2x}\big|_{x=0} = 2$$

Prob. 55.

$$\lim_{h\to 0^+} \frac{e^h-1}{\sqrt{h}} = \lim_{h\to 0^+} \frac{e^h-e^0}{h}\cdot\sqrt{h} = \left(\lim_{h\to 0^+} \frac{e^h-e^0}{h}\right)\cdot(\lim_{h\to 0^+}\sqrt{h}) = \left.\frac{d}{dx}e^x\right|_{x=0}\cdot 0 = 0$$

Prob. 57. Let c be the subtangent. We have

$$\frac{2}{c} = \left.\frac{dy}{dx}\right|_{x=1} = \left.\frac{d(2^x)}{dx}\right|_{x=1} = (\ln 2)2^x\big|_{x=1} = 2\ln 2.$$

Hence, $c = 1/\ln 2$.

Prob. 59.

(a) $N(0) = 1$

(b)

$$\frac{dN}{dt} = \frac{d(e^{2t})}{dt} = 2e^{2t} = 2N$$

Prob. 61. The rate of growth is

$$\frac{d}{dt}[N(0)2^t] = N(0)\ln 2 \cdot 2^t = (\ln 2)N(t),$$

which is proportional to the population size.

Prob. 63.

(a) Let $a = \frac{K}{N(0)} - 1$. We have

$$\frac{dN}{dt} = \frac{d}{dt}\frac{K}{1+ae^{-rt}} = \frac{Kare^{-rt}}{(1+ae^{-rt})^2}$$

(b) Compute

$$rN\left(1 - \frac{N}{K}\right) = r \cdot \frac{K}{1 + ae^{-rt}} \quad \cdot \left(1 - \frac{1}{1 + ae^{-rt}}\right) = \frac{rK}{1 + ae^{-rt}} \cdot \frac{ae^{-rt}}{1 + ae^{-rt}}.$$

From the result in (a), we see that

$$\frac{dN}{dt} = rN\left(1 - \frac{N}{K}\right).$$

(c) By the result in (b), the per capita growth rate is

$$\frac{1}{N}\frac{dN}{dt} = r\left(1 - \frac{N}{K}\right).$$

Its graph as a function of N is as below

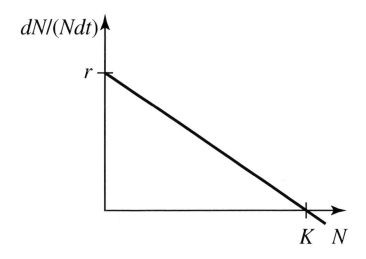

Prob. 65.

(a) The graphs of $L(x) = 10 - 9e^{-x}$ and $L(x) = 10 - 9e^{-0.1x}$:

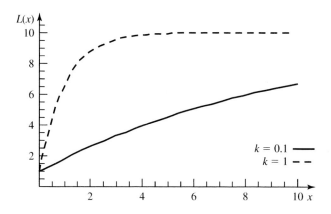

(b) Consider

$$L(0) = L_\infty - (L_\infty - L_0) \cdot 1$$
$$= L_0,$$
$$L(\infty) = \lim_{x \to \infty} L(x)$$
$$= L_\infty - (L_\infty - L_0) \cdot 0$$
$$= L_\infty.$$

Hence, L_0 is the length of a fish when it is just born and L_∞ is what its length approaches to when it grows older and older.

(c) The fish reaches $L = 5$ faster for $k = 1.0$.

(d) A straightforward computation shows

$$\frac{dL}{dx} = k(L_\infty - L_0)e^{-kx}$$
$$= k(L_\infty - L(x)).$$

As a fish grows up, its length keeps increasing, thus the quantity on the right hand side is decreasing. Therefore, the rate of growth is also decreasing with age.

Prob. 67. The differential equation is

$$\frac{dW}{dt} = -4w(t).$$

Prob. 69. We follow along the lines of the solution to **Prob. 68.** $W(t)$ satisfies the differential equation

$$W'(t) = -\frac{\ln 2}{5}W(t).$$

Prob. 71.

(a) The differential equation implies that $W(t)$ is an exponential function. Its exact form is $W(t) = 6e^{-3t}$. Check that it in deed satisfies the differential equation and the initial condition. Thus, at $t = 4$, the amount of the material left is

$$W(4) = 6e^{-12} \approx 2.5 \times 10^{-3}.$$

(b) The half life is τ if and only if $W(\tau)/W(0) = 1/2$. Since we have

$$\frac{1}{2} = \frac{W(\tau)}{W(0)} = \frac{6e^{-3\tau}}{6} = e^{-3\tau}.$$

Taking logarithm of both sides yields

$$-\ln 2 = -3\tau \quad \Rightarrow \quad \tau = \frac{\ln 2}{3}.$$

Prob. 73.

(a) After every unit time, the value of $W(t)$ drops to $2/5$ of its original value. Since $W(0) = 5$, we have for general t

$$W(t) = 5\left(\frac{2}{5}\right)^t.$$

Differentiation gives

$$W'(t) = 5\left(\ln\frac{2}{5}\right)\left(\frac{2}{5}\right)^t.$$

Hence, we have the differential equation $W'(t) = (\ln\frac{2}{5})W(t)$.

(b) By the result in (a), $W(3) = 5(\frac{2}{5})^3 = 0.32$.

(c) The half life τ is determined by

$$\frac{1}{2} = \frac{W(\tau)}{W(0)} = \frac{5(2/5)^\tau}{5} = \left(\frac{2}{5}\right)^\tau.$$

Taking logarithm of both sides gives

$$\ln\frac{1}{2} = \tau \ln\frac{2}{5},$$

i.e. $\tau = \ln\frac{1}{2}/\ln\frac{2}{5} \approx 0.76$.

4.7   Derivatives of Inverse and Logarithmic Functions

Prob. 1. To find the inverse:

$$\begin{aligned}
x &= \sqrt{2y+1} \\
x^2 &= 2y+1 \\
y &= \frac{1}{2}(x^2-1).
\end{aligned}$$

(i) $y' = \frac{1}{2}(2x) = x.$

(ii) by (4.12) we have $\dfrac{1}{\frac{1}{2}(2(\frac{1}{2}(x^2-1)+1)^{-\frac{1}{2}}} = \dfrac{1}{\frac{1}{2}(x^2)^{-\frac{1}{2}}} = x.$

Prob. 3. To find the inverse:

$$\begin{aligned}
x &= 2y^2-1 \\
\frac{1}{2}(x+1) &= y^2 \\
y &= \sqrt{\frac{1}{2}(x+1)}.
\end{aligned}$$

(i) $y' = \sqrt{\frac{1}{2}} \cdot \frac{1}{2}(x+1)^{-\frac{1}{2}}.$

(ii) by (4.12) we have:

$$\frac{1}{4\left(\sqrt{\frac{1}{2}(x+1)}\right)} = \frac{1}{2}\cdot\sqrt{\frac{1}{2}(x+1)^{-\frac{1}{2}}}.$$

Prob. 5. $x = f^{-1}(y) = \sqrt[3]{1-\frac{y}{2}}$

(i) $(f^{-1})'(y) = -\frac{1}{6}(1-\frac{y}{2})^{-2/3}$

(ii) $f'(x) = -6x^2.$ Hence, $(f^{-1})'(y) = 1/f'(x) = -1/6x^2 = -\frac{1}{6}(1-\frac{y}{2})^{-2/3}.$

Prob. 7. We have $f'(x) = 4x$, hence $(f^{-1})'(f(x)) = 1/f'(x) = 1/4x.$ If we put $x = 1$, we have $(f^{-1})'(0) = (f^{-1})'(f(1)) = 1/4.$

Prob. 9. We have $f'(x) = \frac{1}{2\sqrt{x+1}}$, hence $(f^{-1})'(f(x)) = 1/f'(x) = 2\sqrt{x+1}.$ If we put $x = 3$, we have $(f^{-1})'(2) = (f^{-1})'(f(3)) = 4.$

Prob. 11. We have $f'(x) = 1+e^x$, hence $(f^{-1})'(f(x)) = 1/f'(x) = \frac{1}{1+e^x}.$ If we put $x = 0$, we have $(f^{-1})'(1) = (f^{-1})'(f(0)) = 1/2.$

Prob. 13. We have $f'(x) = 1 - \cos x$, hence $(f^{-1})'(f(x)) = 1/f'(x) = \frac{1}{1-\cos x}$. If we put $x = \pi$, we have $(f^{-1})'(\pi) = (f^{-1})'(f(\pi)) = 1/2$.

Prob. 15. We have $f'(x) = 2x + \sec^2 x$, hence $(f^{-1})'(f(x)) = 1/f'(x) = \frac{1}{2x+\sec^2 x}$. If we put $x = 0$, we have $(f^{-1})'(0) = (f^{-1})'(f(0)) = 1$.

Prob. 17. $f'(x) = \frac{1}{\sin x} \cdot \cos x$.

$$\frac{d}{dx} f^{-1}(x)\big|_{x=-\ln 2} \frac{1}{f'(f^{-1}(\ln 2))} = \frac{1}{\frac{1}{\sin \frac{\pi}{6}} \cdot \cos \frac{\pi}{6}} = \frac{1}{\sqrt{3}}.$$

Prob. 19. We have $f'(x) = 5x^4 + 1$, hence $(f^{-1})'(f(x)) = 1/f'(x) = \frac{1}{5x^4+1}$. If we put $x = 0$, we have $(f^{-1})'(1) = (f^{-1})'(f(0)) = 1$.

Prob. 21. We have $f'(x) = -xe^{-x^2/2} + 2$, hence $(f^{-1})'(f(x)) = 1/f'(x) = \frac{1}{2-xe^{-x^2/2}}$. If we put $x = 0$, we get $(f^{-1})'(1) = (f^{-1})'(f(0)) = 1/2$.

Prob. 23. $1/(x+1)$

Prob. 25. $-2/(1-2x)$

Prob. 27. $2/x$

Prob. 29. $f'(x) = \frac{1}{2x^3-x} \cdot (6x^2 - 1)$.

Prob. 31. $2\ln x/x$

Prob. 33. $8\ln x/x$

Prob. 35. Note that $f(x) = \frac{1}{2}\ln(1 + x^2)$. Its derivative is $x/(x^2 + 1)$.

Prob. 37. Note that $f(x) = \ln x - \ln(x + 1)$. Its derivative is $\frac{1}{x} - \frac{1}{x+1} = \frac{1}{x(x+1)}$.

Prob. 39. Note that $f(x) = \ln(1 - x) - \ln(1 + 2x)$. Its derivative is $\frac{1}{1-x} - \frac{2}{1+2x} = \frac{4x-1}{(1-x)(1+2x)}$.

Prob. 41. $(1 - \frac{1}{x})e^{x-\ln x} = (1 - \frac{1}{x})\frac{e^x}{x}$

Prob. 43. $\cot x$

Prob. 45. $\frac{2x\sec^2 x^2}{\tan x^2} = \frac{2x}{\sin x^2 \cos x^2}$

Prob. 47. $\ln x + 1$

Prob. 49. $(1 - \ln x)/x^2$

Prob. 51. $\cos(\ln 3t)/t$

Prob. 53. $2x/(x^2 - 3)$

Prob. 55. $\frac{-2x}{\ln 10(1-x^2)}$

Prob. 57. $\frac{1}{\ln 10} \cdot \frac{3x^2-3}{x^3-3x}$

Prob. 59. $\frac{1}{\ln 3} \cdot \frac{4u^3}{3+u^4}$

Prob. 61.

(a) Let $f(x) = \ln x$. By definition of the derivative, we have

$$f'(1) = \lim_{h \to 0} \frac{\ln(1+h) - \ln 1}{h} = \lim_{h \to 0} \frac{\ln(1+h)}{h},$$

since $\ln 1 = 0$.

(b) We know that $f'(x) = 1/x$ and hence $f'(1) = 1$. Also, using the property of logarithmic functions, we have $\frac{\ln(1+h)}{h} = \ln(1+h)^{1/h}$. Thus the result in (a) becomes

$$1 = \lim_{h \to 0} \ln(1+h)^{1/h} = \ln \left(\lim_{h \to 0} (1+h)^{1/h} \right),$$

where the second equality comes from the fact $\ln$ is a continuous function.

(c) If we let $h = 1/n$, then the limit $h \to 0$ corresponds to $n \to \infty$, and thus the result in (b) becomes

$$\ln \left[\lim_{n \to \infty} \left(1 + \frac{1}{n} \right)^n \right] = 1.$$

Applying the function **exp** to both side will yield the desired result.

Prob. 63.

$$\ln f(x) \;=\; \ln(2x^2)$$
$$\ln f(x) \;=\; \ln 2 + x \ln x$$

Taking the derivative with respect to x:

$$\frac{1}{f(x)} \cdot f'(x) = \ln x + 1$$

$$\texttt{therefore} f'(x) = (\ln x + 1)(2x^x).$$

Prob. 65. We have $\ln y = x \ln(\ln x)$, and differentiation yields

$$\frac{y'}{y} = \ln(\ln x) + \frac{1}{\ln x},$$

or $y' = (\ln x)^{x-1}[\ln x \ln(\ln x) + 1]$.

Prob. 67. We have $\ln y = (\ln x)^2$, and differentiation yields

$$\frac{y'}{y} = \frac{2\ln x}{x},$$

or $y' = 2(\ln x)x^{\ln x - 1}$.

Prob. 69. We have $\ln y = \ln x / x$, and differentiation yields

$$\frac{y'}{y} = \frac{1 - \ln x}{x^2},$$

or $y' = x^{\frac{1}{x} - 2}(1 - \ln x)$.

Prob. 71. We have $\ln y = x^x \ln x$, and thus

$$\ln(\ln y) = x \ln x + \ln(\ln x).$$

Differentiation with respect to x then gives

$$\frac{y'}{y \ln y} = \ln x + 1 + \frac{1}{x \ln x}.$$

Finally, we rewrite y and $\ln y$ in terms of x:

$$y' = x^{x^x + x} \ln x \left(\ln x + 1 + \frac{1}{x \ln x} \right).$$

Prob. 73. We have $\ln y = \cos x \ln x$, and differentiation yields

$$\frac{y'}{y} = -\sin x \ln x + \frac{\cos x}{x}.$$

Thus, $y' = x^{\cos x}(-\sin x \ln x + \frac{\cos x}{x})$.

Prob. 75. First take the logarithm of both sides:

$$\ln y = 2x + 3\ln(9x - 2) - \frac{1}{4}\left[\ln(x^2 + 1) + \ln(3x^3 - 7) \right].$$

Then differentiate both sides with respect to x:

$$\frac{y'}{y} = 2 + \frac{27}{9x - 2} - \frac{x}{2(x^2 + 1)} - \frac{9x^2}{4(3x^3 - 7)}.$$

Finally, multiply both sides by y and rewrite y in terms of x. Since the final expression is not particularly enlightening, let us leave it here.

4.8   Approximation and Local Linearity

Prob. 1. $f'(x) = 1/2\sqrt{x}$, hence we have

$$\begin{aligned}
\sqrt{65} &\approx \sqrt{64} + \frac{1}{2\sqrt{64}}(65 - 64) \\
&= 8 + 1/16 \approx 8.06,
\end{aligned}$$

while $\sqrt{65} = 8.0622\ldots$.

Prob. 3. Let $f(x) = \sqrt[3]{x}$. Then, $f'(x) = \frac{1}{3}x^{-2/3}$, hence we have

$$\sqrt[3]{124} \approx \sqrt[3]{125} + \frac{1}{2}125^{-2/3}(124 - 125) = 5 - 1/50 = 4.98,$$

while $\sqrt[3]{124} = 4.9866\ldots$.

Prob. 5. Let $f(x) = x^2 5$. Then, $f'(x) = 25x^4$, hence we have

$$0.99^2 5 \approx 1^2 5 + 25 \cdot 1^4(0.99 - 1) = 1 - 0.25 = 0.75$$

while $0.99^2 5 = 0.7778\ldots$.

Prob. 7. Let $f(x) = \sin x$. Then, $f'(x) = \cos x$, hence we have

$$\sin\left(\frac{\pi}{2} + 0.02\right) \approx \sin\frac{\pi}{2} + \cos\frac{\pi}{2} \cdot 0.02 = 1 + 0 = 1$$

while $\sin(\frac{\pi}{2} + 0.02) = 0.99998\ldots$.

Prob. 9. Let $f(x) = \ln x$. Then, $f'(x) = 1/x$, hence we have

$$\ln 1.01 \approx \ln 1 + \frac{1}{1}(1.01 - 1) = 0 + 0.01 = 0.01$$

while $\ln 1.01 = 0.009950\ldots$.

Prob. 11. $\frac{1}{1+x} \approx 1 - x$ near $x = 0$

Prob. 13. $f'(x) = -2(1 + x)^{-2}$. Now

$$\begin{aligned}
L(x) &= f(a) + f'(a)(x - a) \\
&= 1 + (-\frac{1}{2}(x - 1) = 1 - \frac{1}{2}x + \frac{1}{2} = -\frac{1}{2}x + \frac{3}{2}.
\end{aligned}$$

Prob. 15. $\frac{1}{(1+x)^2} \approx 1 - 2x$ near $x = 0$

Prob. 17. $\ln(1 + x) \approx x$ near $x = 0$

Prob. 19. $f'(x) = \frac{1}{\ln 10} \cdot \frac{1}{x}$. Now

$$L(x) = f(a) + f'(a)(x - a) = \log 1 + \frac{1}{\ln 10}(x - 1) = \frac{x}{\ln(1)} - \frac{1}{\ln(10)}.$$

Prob. 21. $e^x \approx 1 + x$ near $x = 0$

Prob. 23. $e^{-x} \approx 1 - x$ near $x = 0$

Prob. 25. $e^{x-1} \approx 1 + (x - 1)$ near $x = 1$

Prob. 27. $(1 + x)^{-n} \approx 1 - nx$ near $x = 0$

Prob. 29. $f'(x) = \frac{1}{2}(1 + x^2)^{-\frac{1}{2}} \cdot 2x = x \cdot (1 + x^2)^{-\frac{1}{2}}$. Now,

$$L(x) = f(a) + f'(a)(x - a) = 1 + 1(x - 0) = x + 1.$$

Prob. 31. Since $N' = 0.03N$, $N'(4) = 0.03N(4) = 0.03 \times 100 = 3$ and thus

$$N(4.1) \approx N(4) + N'(4)(4.1 - 4)$$
$$= 100 + 3 \times 0.1 = 100.3.$$

Prob. 33. Since $B' = 0.01B$, $B'(1) = 0.01B(1) = 0.01 \times 5 = 0.05$ and thus

$$B(1.1) \approx B(1) + B'(1)(1.1 - 1)$$
$$= 5 + 0.05 \times 0.1 = 5.005.$$

Prob. 35. 2 ± 0.2

Prob. 37. 12 ± 1.2

Prob. 39. 7.4 ± 1.5

Prob. 41. The error in x is $\Delta x = 0.02x = 0.03$, hence the error $f(x)$ is $\Delta f = |f'(1.5)|\Delta x = 0.81$ and its percentage error is 6%.

Prob. 43. The error in x is $\Delta x = 0.02x = 0.4$, hence the error $f(x)$ is $\Delta f = |f'(20)|\Delta x = 0.02$ and its percentage error is 0.67%.

Prob. 45. The assumption means $\Delta r/r = 3\%$. Taking logarithm yields

$$\ln V = \ln(\frac{4}{3}\pi) + 3\ln r.$$

A small change on both sides is

$$\frac{\Delta V}{V} = \Delta(\ln V) = 3\Delta(\ln r) = 3\left(\frac{\Delta r}{r}\right).$$

Hence the accuracy in V is $3 \times 3\% = 9\%$.

Prob. 47. We have $N = kL^{2.11}$ for some constant k. Taking logarithm yields

$$\ln N = \ln k + 2.11 \ln L.$$

A small change on both sides is

$$\frac{\Delta N}{N} = \Delta(\ln N) = 2.11 \Delta(\ln L) = 2.11 \left(\frac{\Delta L}{L}\right).$$

In order that $\Delta N/N = 5\%$, we must have $\Delta L/L = \frac{1}{2.11} \times 5\% \approx 2.4\%$.

Prob. 49. To make use of the fact that $\Delta(\ln R) = \Delta R/R$, let us first take the logarithm of R:

$$\ln R = \ln k + \ln(a - x) + \ln(b - x).$$

A small change in both sides is

$$
\begin{aligned}
\frac{\Delta R}{R} &= \Delta(\ln R) \\
&= \Delta \ln(a - x) + \Delta \ln(b - x) \\
&= -\frac{\Delta x}{a - x} - \frac{\Delta x}{b - x} \\
&= -x \left(\frac{1}{a - x} + \frac{1}{b - x}\right) \cdot \frac{\Delta x}{x} \\
&= -\frac{x(a + b - 2x)}{(a - x)(b - x)} \cdot \frac{\Delta x}{x}.
\end{aligned}
$$

This gives the relation between the percentage error in R and the percentage error in x.

4.10   Review Problems

Prob. 1. $-12x^3 - x^{-3/2}$

Prob. 3. $-\frac{2}{3}(1 - t)^{-2/3}(1 + t)^{-4/3}$

Prob. 5. $e^{2x}(2 \sin \frac{\pi x}{2} + \frac{\pi}{2} \cos \frac{\pi x}{2})$

Prob. 7. Note that

$$f(x) = \frac{\ln(x + 1)}{\ln x}.$$

Hence, an application of the quotient rule gives us:

$$f'(x) = \frac{\frac{1}{x+1} \ln x - \frac{1}{x} \ln(x + 1)}{(\ln x)^2}.$$

Prob. 9. $f'(x) = -xe^{-x^2/2}$

$f''(x) = (x^2 - 1)e^{-x^2/2}$

Prob. 11. $h'(x) = 1/(x+1)^2$

$h''(x) - 2/(x+1)^3$

Prob. 13. In problems **13** to **16**, differentiate the given equation with respect to x and collect terms to express $y' = dy/dx$ in x and y.

$$2xy + x^2 y' - 2yy'x - y^2 = \cos x \Rightarrow y' = \frac{\cos x + y^2 - 2xy}{x^2 - 2xy}$$

Prob. 15. $\frac{1-y'}{x-y} = 2 \Rightarrow y' = 1 - 2x + 2y$

Prob. 17. Differentiating both sides with respect to x yields $2x + 2yy' = 0 \Rightarrow y' = -\frac{x}{y}$. The quotient rule then gives us $y'' = \frac{xy'-y}{y^2}$

Prob. 19. Differentiating both sides with respect to x yields

$$y'e^y = \frac{1}{x} \quad \Rightarrow \quad y' = \frac{e^{-y}}{x}.$$

The quotient rule then gives us

$$y'' = -\frac{(xy' + 1)e^{-y}}{x^2}$$

Prob. 21. Let x be the distance the birds have flown from when they were directly overhead, and y be our distance from the birds. We have $dx/dt = 6$ at all times and $y^2 = 100^2 + x^2$. Differentiating this equation with respect to t yields

$$2y\frac{dy}{dt} = 2x\frac{dx}{dt} \Rightarrow \frac{dy}{dt} = \frac{x}{y}\frac{dx}{dt}.$$

When $y = 320$, $x = \sqrt{320^2 - 100^2} \approx 304$, and thus $dy/dt = \frac{304}{320} \cdot 6 = 5.7$.

Prob. 23.

(a) $f'(x)e^{f(x)}$

(b) $f'(x)/f(x)$

(c) $2f(x)f'(x)$

Prob. 25.

(a) The graph of $y = \frac{x^2}{1+x^2}$:

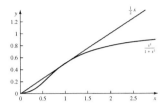

(b) On the one hand, the slope of the line is $f'(c)$. On the other hand, since this line connects $(0,0)$ and $(c, f(c))$, its slope is $f(c)/c$. Thus we have

$$f'(c) = \frac{f(c)}{c},$$

or

$$\frac{2c}{(1+c^2)^2} = \frac{c}{1+c^2}.$$

Solving the equation, we will get $c^2 = 1$, or $c = 1$, since it is assumed that $c > 0$.

This line is also plotted in the above graph.

Prob. 27. $y' = -e^{-x^2}(2x \cos x + \sin x)$. When $x = \pi/3$, it is equal to $-e^{-\pi^2/9}(\frac{\pi}{3} + \frac{\sqrt{3}}{2}) \approx -0.64$. The tangent line is thus

$$y = e^{-\pi^2/9} - 0.64\left(x - \frac{\pi}{3}\right).$$

Prob. 29. Implicit differentiation yields:

$$\ln y + \frac{xy'}{y} = y' \ln x + \frac{y}{x} \Rightarrow y' = \frac{\ln y - y/x}{\ln x - x/y}.$$

When $x = 1$, $y = 1$ and thus the above result tells us $y' = 1$. The tangent line then has the equation

$$y = 1 + (x - 1) = x.$$

Prob. 31. Since $p'(x) = 2ax + b$, $p''(x) = 2a$, the given conditions are

$$
\begin{aligned}
6 &= p(-1) = a - b + c \\
8 &= p'(1) = 2a + b \\
4 &= p''(0) = 2a,
\end{aligned}
$$

and the system has the unique solution

$$a = 2, \quad b = 4, \quad c = 8.$$

Prob. 33.

(a) The graph of $s(t)$:

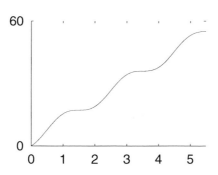

We didn't backtrack because we can see from the graph that $s(t)$ keeps increasing.

The distance between the two towns is given by $s(5.5) \approx 17.3$.

(b) $v(t) = s'(t) = 3\pi(1 + \sin \pi t) \; a(t) = v'(t) = 3\pi^2 \cos \pi t$

(c) The graph of $s(t)$ is shown above. Here are the graphs of $v(t)$

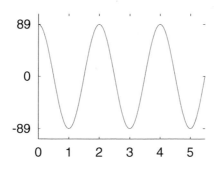

and $a(t)$

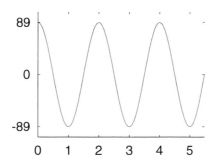

No backtracking means $s(t)$ being an increasing function. This is also equivalent to $v(t) \geq 0$, which is clear from the graph.

(d) At each peak, we switch from slowing down $(a < 0)$ to speeding up $(a > 0)$. This happens two times, so there are two peaks on the road. Similarly, a changes from positive to negative at each valley, so there are three of them.

Prob. 35.

(a) For the given $N(t)$,

$$\frac{dN}{dt} = -\frac{A\pi}{2T} \sin \frac{\pi t}{2T}.$$

On the other hand, the right hand side of (4.13) equals

$$\frac{\pi}{2T}\left[K - \left(K + A \cos \frac{\pi(t-T)}{2T}\right)\right] = -\frac{\pi}{2T} \cdot A \cos \left(\frac{\pi t}{2T} - \frac{\pi}{2}\right) = -\frac{A\pi}{2T} \sin \frac{\pi t}{2T}.$$

The two computations above show that $N(t)$ satisfies the given differential equation.

(b) The graph of $N(t) = 100 + 50 \cos \frac{\pi t}{2}$:

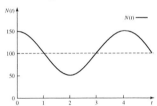

(c) The population grows and shrinks periodically between $K + A$ and $K - A$, with period $4T$.

Prob. 37. The relative errors in S and B are related as follows:

$$
\begin{aligned}
\frac{\Delta S}{S} &= \Delta \ln S = \Delta \ln[(1.162)B^{0.933}] \\
&= \Delta[\ln 1.162 + (0.933) \ln B] \\
&= 0.933 \cdot \frac{\Delta B}{B}.
\end{aligned}
$$

Therefore, if we want $\Delta B/B < 10\%$, we must have $\Delta S/S < 0.933 \times 10\% = 0.33\%$.

Chapter 5

Applications of Differentiation

5.1 Extrema and the Mean Value Theorem

Prob. 1. $y = 2x - 1$, $x \in [0, 1]$:

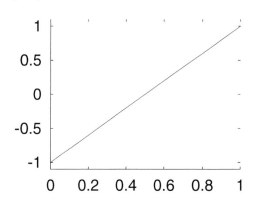

global maximum: $(1, 1)$

global minimum: $(0, -1)$

Prob. 3. $f(x) = \sin(2x)$, $0 \le x \le \pi$.

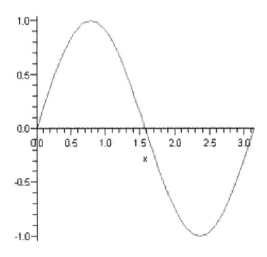

Hence, global minimum: $x = \frac{3\pi}{4}$, $\;\; y = -1$

global maximum at: $x = \frac{\pi}{4}$ $\;\; y = 1$

Prob. 5. $y = |x|$, $x \in [-1, 1]$:

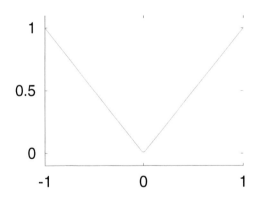

global maxima: $(\pm 1, 1)$

global minimum: $(0, 0)$

Prob. 7. $f(x) = e^{-|x|}$, $-1 \le x \le 1$

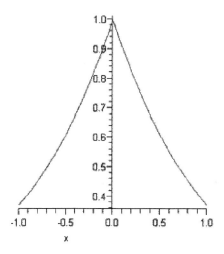

Hence global minima at: $x = \pm 1$, $y = \frac{1}{c}$

global maxima: $x = 0$, $Y = 1$

Prob. 9. An example of a function with the desired properties is $f(x) = \cos(\pi x) - x$:

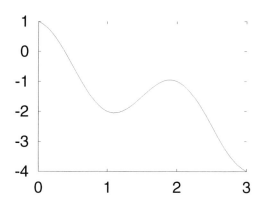

Prob. 11. An example of a function with the desired properties is $f(x) = x^2$:

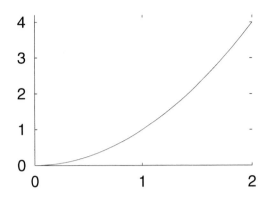

Prob. 13. $f(x) = 3 - x$, $x \in [-1, 3)$

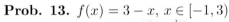

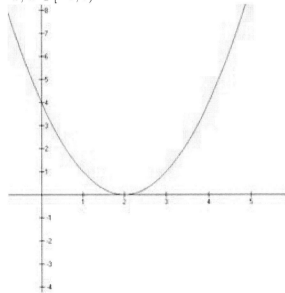

global maximum: $x = -1$ $y = 4$

no minima

Prob. 15. $y = x^2 - 2$, $x \in [-1, 1]$:

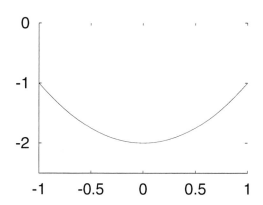

global maxima: $(\pm 1, -1)$

global minimum: $(0, -2)$

Prob. 17. $y = -x^2 + 1$, $x \in [-2, 1]$:

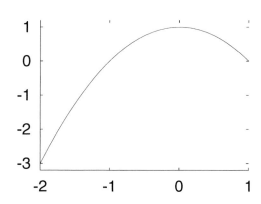

global maximum: $(0, 1)$

global minimum: $(-2, -3)$

Prob. 19. $f(x) = x^2$. Need to have $f'(c) = 0$: $f'(x) = 2x$, hence $2c = 0$, $c = 0$.

Testing:

x	-1	1
$f'(x)$	$-$	$+$

, global minimum.

Prob. 21. $f(x) = -x^2$, need to have $f'(c) = 0$:

$f'(x) = -2x$, $2c = 0$, $c = 0$.

Testing:

x	-1	1
$f'(x)$	$+$	$-$

, global maximum.

Prob. 23. $f(x) = x^3$, need to have: $f'(c) = 0$:

$f'(x) = 3x^2$, hence $3c^2 = 0$, $c = 0$

Testing:

x	-1	1
$f'(x)$	$+$	$+$

, not on extremum.

Prob. 25. $f(x) = (x+1)^3$, need to have $f'(c) = 0$:

$f'(x) = 3(x+1)^2$, $3(c+1)^2 = 0$, $c = -1$.

Testing:

x	-2	0
$f'(x)$	$+$	$+$

, not an extremum.

Prob. 27. The absolute value of any number is nonnegative, so we have

$$f(x) = |x| \geq 0 = f(0),$$

i.e. $x = 0$ is a global, and thus local, minimum.

The graph of $f(x) = |x|$ has an angle at $x = 0$, corresponding to the fact that f is not differentiable there. Here is a formal proof: when $x > 0$, we have $f(x) = |x| = x$, and thus

$$\lim_{x \to 0^+} \frac{f(x) - f(0)}{x - 0}$$
$$= \lim_{x \to 0^+} \frac{x}{x} = \lim_{x \to 0^+} 1 = 1.$$

However, when $x < 0$, we have $f(x) = |x| = -x$, and thus

$$\lim_{x \to 0^-} \frac{f(x) - f(0)}{x - 0}$$
$$= \lim_{x \to 0^-} \frac{-x}{x} = \lim_{x \to 0^-} -1 = -1.$$

Therefore, the derivative

$$f'(0) = \lim_{x \to 0} \frac{f(x) - f(0)}{x - 0}$$

doesn't exist, and f is not differentiable at $x = 0$.

Prob. 29. The absolute value of any number is nonnegative, so we have

$$f(x) = |x^2 - 1| \geq 0 = f(1) = f(-1),$$

i.e. $x = \pm 1$ are global, and thus local, minima.

Let us first consider what happens near $x = 1$. When $x > 1$, $x^2 - 1 > 0$ and thus $f(x) = |x^2 - 1| = x^2 - 1$. Then we have

$$
\begin{aligned}
\lim_{x \to 1^+} \frac{f(x) - f(1)}{x - 1} &= \lim_{x \to 1^+} \frac{x^2 - 1}{x - 1} \\
&= \lim_{x \to 1^+} (x + 1) \\
&= 2.
\end{aligned}
$$

When $-1 < x < 1$, $x^2 - 1 = (x + 1)(x - 1) < 0$ and thus $f(x) = |x^2 - 1| = -x^2 + 1$. So we have

$$
\begin{aligned}
\lim_{x \to 1^-} \frac{f(x) - f(1)}{x - 1} &= \lim_{x \to 1^-} \frac{-x^2 + 1}{x - 1} \\
&= \lim_{x \to 1^-} -(x + 1) \\
&= -2.
\end{aligned}
$$

Therefore, the derivative

$$
f'(1) = \lim_{x \to 1} \frac{f(x) - f(1)}{x - 1}
$$

doesn't exist, and f is not differentiable at $x = 1$.

The situation is similar near $x = -1$. When $-1 < x < 1$, $f(x) = -x^2 + 1$ and

$$
\lim_{x \to -1^+} \frac{f(x) - f(-1)}{x + 1} = \lim_{x \to -1^+} \frac{-x^2 + 1}{x + 1} = 2.
$$

When $x < -1$, $f(x) = x^2 - 1$ and

$$
\lim_{x \to -1^-} \frac{f(x) - f(-1)}{x + 1} = \lim_{x \to -1^-} \frac{x^2 - 1}{x + 1} = -2.
$$

Therefore, f is not differentiable at $x = -1$.

Prob. 31. The graph of $y = |1 - |x||$ looks like:

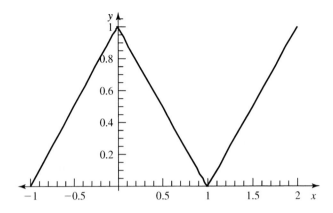

The local maxima are $(0, 1), (2, 1)$ and they are both global. The local minima are $(\pm 1, 0)$ and also, they are both global.

Prob. 33.

(a) The graph of $y = dN/dt = 2N(1 - N/100)$:

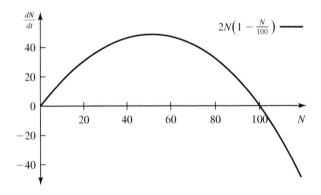

From the graph, we see that the growth rate is maximal when $N = 50$.

(b) Since $f(N)$ is a polynomial in N, it is differentiable throughout any open set in which it is defined. In particular, it is differentiable when $N > 0$. Expanding $f(N) = r(N - \frac{N^2}{K})$, we get

$$f'(N) = r\left(1 - \frac{2}{K}N\right).$$

(c) From the result in (b), we have $f'(N) = 0$ if and only if $N = K/2$. If $K = 100$, this happens at $N = 50$, the same number we obtain in (a).

Prob. 35.

(a) The slope of the line connecting $(0,0)$ and $(2,4)$ is

$$\frac{4-0}{2-0} = 2.$$

(b) Notice that the two points in (a) are $(0, f(0))$ and $(2, f(2))$. Since f is continuous on $[0, 2]$ and differentiable throughout $(0, 2)$, by the MVT, there must exist a number $c \in (0, 2)$ such that $f'(c)$ equals the above slope. To find c, we let $f'(c) = 2$. Since $f'(x) = 2x$, we have $2c = 2$, and thus $c = 1$.

Prob. 37. Since $f(x) = x^2$ is differentiable (and continuous) everywhere, and $f(1) = 1 = f(-1)$, by Rolle's theorem, there exists some $c \in (-1, 1)$ such that $f'(c) == 0$,or, the graph of $f(x)$ has a horizontal tangent at $x = c$. Since $f'(x) = 2x$, we have $2c = 0$, or $c = 0$.

Prob. 39. Since $f(x) = x(1 - x)$ is differentiable (and continuous) everywhere, we may apply Rolle's theorem to f, i.e. if $f(a) = f(b)$ for some $a < b$, then there exists $c \in (a, b)$ with $f'(c) = 0$. For example, since $f(0) = 0 = f(1)$, f' vanishes somewhere in $[0, 1]$.

Prob. 41. Since $f(x) = -x^2 + 2$ is differentiable (and continuous) everywhere, by the MVT, there exists some $c \in (-1, 2)$ such that

$$
\begin{aligned}
f'(c) &= \frac{f(2) - f(-1)}{2 - (-1)} = \frac{-2 - 1}{3} \\
&= -1.
\end{aligned}
$$

Prob. 43. An example of such a function is $f(x) = x^2$:

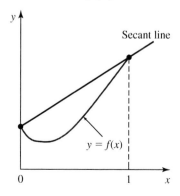

The slope of the secant connecting $(0,0)$ and $(1,1)$ is equal to the slope of the tangent of the graph at exactly one point, namely $(1/2, 1/4)$. The existence of such a point inside the interval $[0, 1]$ is predicted by the MVT.

Prob. 45.

(a) The slope of the line connecting $(a, f(a))$ and $(b, f(b))$ is

$$\frac{f(b) - f(a)}{b - a} = \frac{b^2 - a^2}{b - a}$$
$$= \frac{(a + b)(b - a)}{b - a} = a + b.$$

(b) Since f is differentiable (and continuous) everywhere, by the mean value theorem, there must exist a number $c \in (a, b)$ such that $f'(c)$ equals the above slope. To find c, let $f'(c) = a + b$. Since $f'(x) = 2x$, we have $2c = a + b$, or $c = (a + b)/2$, i.e. the midpoint in between a and b.

Prob. 47. Since f is not constant on $[a, b]$ and $f(a) = f(b) = 0$, we must have $f(c) \neq 0$ for some $c \in (a, b)$. Assume $f(c) > 0$. (The case $f(c) < 0$ is completely similar.) Note that the MVT also applies to the subintervals $[a, c]$ and $[c, b]$. For the subinterval $[a, c]$, we thus have some $c_1 \in (a, c) \subset (a, b)$ with

$$f'(c_1) = \frac{f(c) - f(a)}{c - a} = \frac{f(c)}{c - a} > 0,$$

since $f(a) = 0$, $f(c) > 0$ and $a < c$. For the subinterval $[c, b]$, we have some $c_2 \in (c, b) \subset (a, b)$ with

$$f'(c_2) = \frac{f(b) - f(c)}{b - c} = \frac{-f(c)}{b - c} > 0,$$

since $f(b) = 0$, $f(c) > 0$ and $b > c$.

Prob. 49.

(a) Between $t = 0$ and $t = 5$, the car moves a distance of $s(5) - s(0) = 1.25$ (meters). Thus, the average velocity is

$$\frac{\text{distance traveled}}{\text{time elapsed}} = \frac{1.25 \text{ meters}}{5 \text{ secs}} = 1.25 \text{ meter per sec.}$$

(b) The instantaneous velocity at time t is given by

$$s'(t) = \frac{3}{100}t^2.$$

(c) From (a) and (b), the instantaneous velocity is equal to the average velocity when $3t^2/100 = 1.25$, or $t = \sqrt{125/3} \approx 6.45$.

Prob. 51. The assumption $|dB/dt| \leq 1$, or

$$-1 \leq B'(t) \leq 1, \qquad 0 \leq t \leq 3,$$

together with Corollary 1 of the MVT, tells us that

$$-1 \cdot (3 - 0) \leq B(3) - B(0) \leq 1 \cdot (3 - 0).$$

Since $B(0) = 3$, this means

$$0 \leq B(3) \leq 6.$$

Prob. 53. Consider any number $x(\neq 2)$. Since f' vanishes identically between 2 and x, Corollary 2 of the MVT implies that f is constant in the interval between 2 and x. Hence, $f(x) = f(2) = 3$.

Prob. 55. The assumption $|f(x) - f(y)| \leq |x - y|^2$ implies

$$
\begin{aligned}
0 &\leq \left| \frac{f(x) - f(y)}{x - y} \right| \\
&\leq \frac{|x - y|^2}{|x - y|} = |x - y|.
\end{aligned}
$$

Regard x as a variable and let it approach y. By the sandwich principle, we have

$$\lim_{x \to y} \left| \frac{f(x) - f(y)}{x - y} \right| = 0,$$

which implies

$$f'(y) = \lim_{x \to y} \frac{f(x) - f(y)}{x - y} = 0.$$

(Fact: $|g(t)| \to 0$ implies $g(t) \to 0$. Proof: use $-|g(t)| \leq g(t) \leq |g(t)|$ and the sandwich principle.) Since y is arbitrary, f' vanishes identically. By Corollary 2 of the MVT, f is a constant function.

5.2   Monotonicity and Concavity

Prob. 1. In problems **1** to **20**, the range of x over which f is increasing (decreasing) is given by solving $f' > 0$ ($f' < 0$), and the range over which f is concave up (down) is given by solving $f'' > 0$ ($f'' < 0$). $f(x) = 3x - x^2$ $f'(x) = 3 - 2x$, $f''(x) = -2$. So f is increasing for $x < 3/2$, decreasing for $x > 3/2$ and concave down for all $x \in \mathbb{R}$

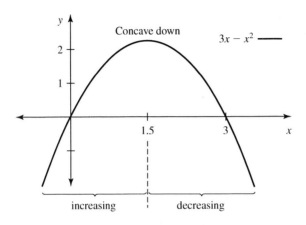

Prob. 3. $f(x) = x^2 + x - 4$ so $f'(x) = 2x + 1$ and $f''(x) = 2$. So f is increasing for $x > -1/2$, decreasing for $x < -1/2$ and concave up for all $x \in \mathbb{R}$

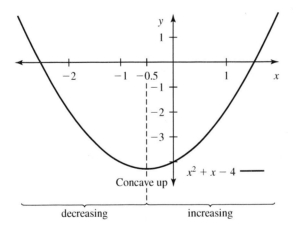

Prob. 5. $f(x) = -\frac{2}{3}x^3 + \frac{7}{2}x^2 - 3x + 4$, so $f'(x) = -2x^2 + 7x - 3 = -(2x-1)(x-3)$ and $f''(x) = -4x + 7$. So f is increasing for $1/2 < x < 3$, decreasing for $x < 1/2$, $x > 3$, concave up: $x < 7/4$ and concave down: $x > 7/4$

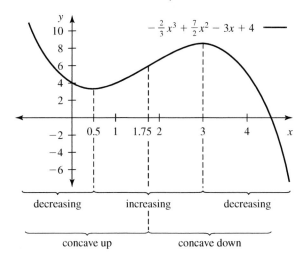

Prob. 7. $f(x) = \sqrt{x+1}$, $x \geq -1$, so $f'(x) = \frac{1}{2}(x+1)^{-\frac{1}{2}}$, $x > 1$ and $f''(x) = -\frac{1}{4}(x+1)^{-\frac{3}{2}}$
So f is increasing for all $x > -1$ and concave down for all $x > -1$

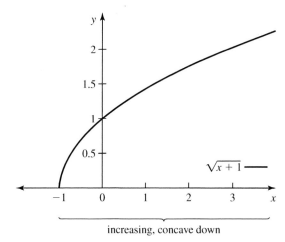

Prob. 9. $f(x) = \frac{1}{x}$, $x \neq 0$, so $f'(x) = -\frac{1}{x^2}$ and $f''(x) = \frac{2}{x^3}$. So f is decreasing: all $x \neq 0$, concave up for $x > 0$ and concave down for $x < 0$.

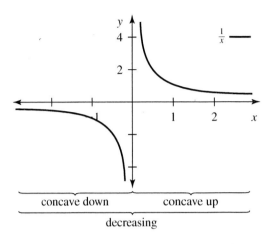

Prob. 11. $f(x) = (x^2 + 1)^{\frac{1}{3}}$, $x \in \mathbb{R}$ so $f'(x) = \frac{2}{3}x(x^2 + 1)^{-\frac{2}{3}}$ and $f''(x) = -\frac{2}{9}(x^2 - 3)(x^2 + 1)^{-\frac{5}{3}}$. So f is increasing: $x > 0$, decreasing: $x < 0$, concave up: $-\sqrt{3} < x < \sqrt{3}$ and concave down: $x > \sqrt{3}$, $x < -\sqrt{3}$

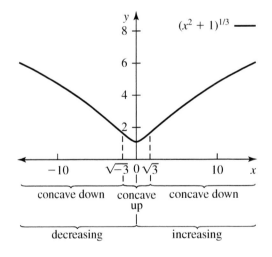

Prob. 13. $f(x) = \frac{1}{(1+x)^2}$, $x \neq -1$ so $f'(x) = -\frac{2}{(1+x)^3}$ and $f''(x) = \frac{6}{(1+x)^4}$i. So f is increasing: $x < -1$, decreasing: $x > -1$ and concave up: all $x \neq -1$

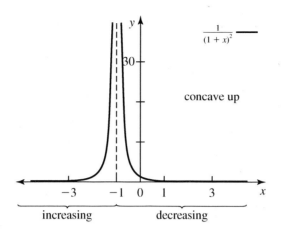

Prob. 15. $f(x) = \sin x$, $0 \leq x \leq 2\pi$ so $f'(x) = \cos x$ and $f''(x) = -\sin x$. So f is increasing: $\left(0, \frac{\pi}{2}\right) \cup \left(\frac{3\pi}{2}, 2\pi\right)$, decreasing: $\left(\frac{\pi}{2}, \frac{3\pi}{2}\right)$, concave up: $(\pi, 2\pi)$ and concave down: $(0, \pi)$

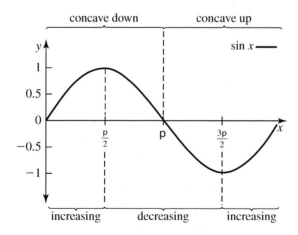

Prob. 17. $f(x) = e^x$ so $f'(x) = f''(x) = e^x$ and f is increasing for all $x \in \mathbb{R}$ and concave up for all $x \in \mathbb{R}$

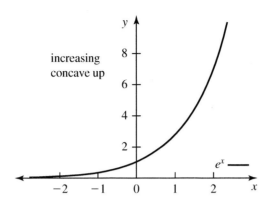

Prob. 19. $f(x) = e^{-x^2/2}$ so $f'(x) = -xe^{-x^2/2}$ and $f''(x) = (x^2 - 1)e^{-x^2/2}$. So f is increasing for $x < 0$, decreasing for $x > 0$, concave up for $x > 1$, $x < -1$ and concave down: $-1 < x < 1$

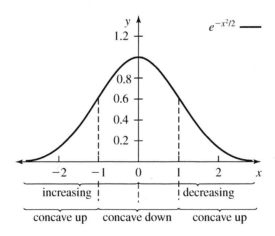

Prob. 21.

(a) The graph of a function increasing at an accelerating rate:

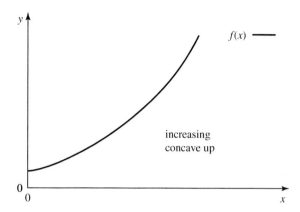

(b) The graph of a function increasing at an decelerating rate:

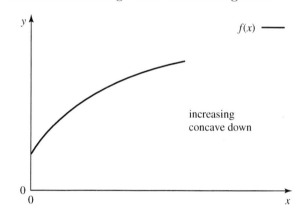

(c) In the situation of (a), the function must have positive first and second derivatives. The graph is concave up. For (b), the function must have a positive first derivative and a negative second derivative. The graph is concave down.

Prob. 23.

(a) If f' is strictly positive (negative) throughout (a, b), the graph of f in between a and b is always climbing up (down), and thus can intersect the y-axis at most once. In other words, $f(x) = 0$ for at most one x in (a, b). Since we already know there exists at least one such x, there is exactly one. (Equivalently, if $f(x) = 0$ has two solutions, Rolle's theorem says f' vanishes somewhere in (a, b), contradicting the assumption.)

(b) Let $f(x) = x^3 - 4x + 1$. Since $f(-1) = 4 > 0$ and $f(1) = -2 < 0$, $f(x) = 0$ has a solution in $(-1, 1)$. But $f'(x) = 3x^2 - 4 < 3(1) - 4 < 0$ in $(-1, 1)$. Part (a) then tells us $f(x) = 0$ has exactly one solution in the interval.

Prob. 25. If $f''(x) < 0$ throughout an interval, the first derivative test tells us f' is decreasing in this interval, which by definition means the function f is concave down.

Prob. 27.

(a) Below is the graph of $g(N) = 3\left(1 - \frac{N}{10}\right)$ versus N:

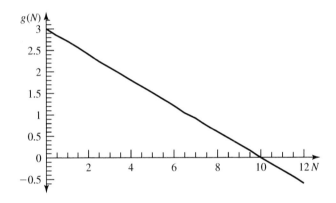

(b) We have $g(N) = r(1 - N/K)$. Thus, $g'(N) = -r/K < 0$, and $g(N)$ is decreasing for all $N > 0$.

Prob. 29. Compute the derivative

$$f'(N) = \left[1 - \left(\frac{N}{K}\right)^\theta\right] - N \cdot \frac{\theta N^{\theta-1}}{K^\theta}$$

$$= 1 - (1 + \theta)\left(\frac{N}{K}\right)^\theta.$$

It is easy to deduce that the expression is positive, i.e. the growth rate is increasing, when

$$(0 <) N < \frac{K}{(1 + \theta)^{\frac{1}{\theta}}},$$

and negative otherwise.

Prob. 31. Since $f'(P) = -ae^{-aP}$ is always negative, f decreases with P.

Prob. 33.

(a) Since

$$y'(x) = \frac{1170}{x^2} e^{-10/x}$$

is always positive, the height y increases with age x. For $x > 0$, we have $-10/x < 0$ and thus $e^{-10/x} < 1$. Therefore, the height $y = 117e^{-10/x}$ never exceeds 117. As the tree ages ($x \to \infty$), $-10/x$ approaches zero and thus $y(x)$ approaches 117.

(b) Compute

$$y''(x) = 1170e^{-10/x}\left(\frac{10 - 2x}{x^4}\right).$$

Hence, the graph is concave up (down), i.e. $y'' > 0$ ($y'' < 0$), when $x < 5$ ($x > 5$).

(c) The graph of $y = 117e^{-10/x}$:

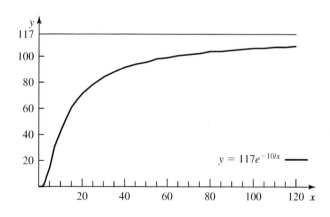

(d) The greatest rate of growth corresponds to the largest slope. Looking at the graph, we notice that it is the steepest at $x = 5$ (as expected from the calculation in (b)), and it is exactly where the graph changes from being concave up to being concave down.

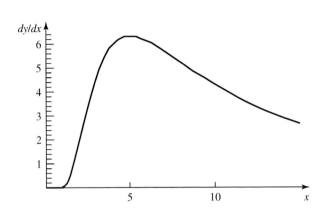

Prob. 35. In terms of the function $X(F)$, we are looking for a condition such that $X'(F) > 0$ and $X''(F) < 0$ for all $F \geq 0$. Since

$$X'(F) = c\gamma F^{\gamma-1},$$
$$X''(F) = c\gamma(\gamma-1)F^{\gamma-2},$$

and $c > 0$, the desired condition on γ is $\gamma > 0$ and $\gamma(\gamma-1) < 0$, or equivalently,

$$0 < \gamma < 1.$$

Prob. 37.

(a) At equilibrium, i.e. $dN/dt = 0$, we have

$$0 = Ne^{-aN} - N^2 = N(e^{-aN} - N).$$

The nontrivial equilibrium $(N^* \neq 0)$ thus satisfies $e^{-aN^*} = N^*$.

(b) If we differentiate

$$e^{-aN^*} = N^*$$

with respect to a, regarding N^* as a function of a, we obtain

$$-[a(N^*)' + N^*]e^{-aN^*} = (N^*)',$$

which after rearrangement becomes

$$(N^*)' = -\frac{N^* e^{-aN^*}}{1 + ae^{-aN^*}} < 0.$$

In other words, N^* decreases with a.

Prob. 39.

(a) Compute

$$\frac{d}{dN}\frac{A(N)}{N} = \frac{d}{dN}\frac{S}{1 + (aN)^b}$$

$$= -\frac{Sab(aN)^{b-1}}{[1 + (aN)^b]^2}.$$

Since the right hand side is negative, $A(N)/N$ is a decreasing function of N.

(b) Using the fact that $\log(x/y) = \log x - \log y$, we have

$$k = \log NS - \log\left[\frac{NS}{1 + (aN)^b}\right]$$

$$= \log(NS) - \left[\log(NS) - \log(1 + (aN)^b)\right]$$

$$= \log[1 + (aN)^b].$$

(i) Recall that

$$\log N = \log_{10} N = \frac{\ln N}{\ln 10}.$$

Hence we have

$$\frac{d\log N}{dN} = \frac{d}{dN}\left(\frac{\ln N}{\ln 10}\right)$$

$$= \frac{1}{N\ln 10}.$$

(ii) Using the chain rule and the result of (i), we have

$$\frac{dk}{d\log N} = \frac{dk/dN}{d\log N/dN}$$

$$= (\ln 10)N\frac{dk}{dN}.$$

Using the first result in (b), we compute

$$\frac{dk}{dN} = \frac{d}{dN}\frac{\ln[1 + (aN)^b]}{\ln 10}$$

$$= \frac{1}{\ln 10}\cdot\frac{ab(aN)^{b-1}}{1 + (aN)^b}.$$

Hence, we have

$$
\begin{aligned}
\frac{dk}{d\log N} &= (\ln 10)N \cdot \frac{1}{\ln 10} \cdot \frac{ab(aN)^{b-1}}{1+(aN)^b} \\
&= \frac{b(aN)^b}{1+(aN)^b} \\
&= \frac{b}{(aN)^{-b}+1}.
\end{aligned}
$$

(iii) Since $a, b > 0$, as $N \to \infty$, $(aN)^{-b} \to 0$ and thus

$$
\lim_{N \to \infty} \frac{dk}{d\log N} = \lim_{N \to \infty} \frac{b}{1+(aN)^{-b}} = b.
$$

(iv) Let us consider the relation between $dk/d\log N$ and $A'(N) = dA/dN$. By definition,

$$
k = \log(NS) - \log A(N) = \log N - \log S - \log A(N).
$$

Using the chain rule, we have

$$
\begin{aligned}
\frac{dk}{d\log N} &= 1 - \frac{d\log A(N)/dN}{d\log N/dN} \\
&= 1 - \frac{A'(N)}{A(N)\ln 10} \Big/ \frac{1}{N\ln 10} \\
&= 1 - \frac{NA'(N)}{A(N)}.
\end{aligned}
$$

Therefore, if $dk/d\log N > 1 \, (< 1)$, then $A'(N)$ is negative (positive), i.e. $A(N)$ is decreasing (increasing). (Note: N and $A(N)$ are positive.)

Since the initial density of seeds is by definition NS and S is a constant, a higher density means increasing N. From the result in (ii), we observe that $dk/d\log N$ increases with N. ($N \uparrow \Rightarrow (aN)^{-b} \downarrow \Rightarrow 1/[1+(aN)^{-b}] \uparrow$) And from what we have just deduced, if $dk/d\log N$ increases beyond 1, the number of surviving plants switches from growing to dropping. Therefore, to summarize, if the initial density of seeds is higher (lower) than some fixed value, there will be less (more) plants in the following year than this year.

(v) From the result in (iv), the case $dk/d\log N = 1$ corresponds to $A'(N) = 0$. Thus, over the range where $dk/d\log N = 1$ holds, the number of plants is in equilibrium.

Prob. 41.

(a) Since

$$
\begin{aligned}
\frac{dY}{dX} &= \frac{d(bX^a)}{dX} = abX^{a-1}, \\
\frac{d}{dX}\frac{Y}{X} &= \frac{d(bX^{a-1})}{dX} \\
&= (a-1)bX^{a-2},
\end{aligned}
$$

the condition we are looking for is $ab > 0$ and $(a-1)b < 0$. Since b is positive, we conclude $0 < a < 1$.

In this case, $Y'' = a(a-1)bX^{a-2}$ is negative, i.e. Y as a function of X is concave down.

(b) Now X is the body length, Y is the skull length and $0 < a < 1$. From (a), we know

$$
\frac{d}{dX}\frac{Y}{X} < 0.
$$

As a vertebrate grow up (X increases), the size of the skull Y becomes smaller and smaller *compared to the size of the body X*.

Prob. 43. Differentiating both sides of the given equation $y' = ky/x$ with respect to x yields

$$
y'' = k\left(\frac{xy' - y}{x}\right).
$$

If we use the equation $y' = ky/x$, or $xy' = ky$, again, we have

$$
y'' = k\left(\frac{ky - y}{x}\right) = k(k-1)\frac{y}{x}.
$$

Since x and y are positive, y as a function of x is concave up, i.e. $y'' > 0$, if and only if $k(k-1) > 0$, or $k > 1$. (k is assumed to be positive.)

5.3 Extrema, Inflection Points and Graphing

Prob. 1. $y = (2-x)^2 = 4 - 4x + x^2$

$y' = -4 + 2x = 2(-2 + x) = 0$, $x = 2$.

Testing: $\dfrac{x \quad | \quad 1 \quad | \quad 3}{y' \quad | \ - \ | \ +}$, hence y is increasing: (2,3) y is decreasing: $(-2, 1)$.

Also, $x = 2$ is a minimum. Also checking endpoints:

$$f(-2) = 16 \leftarrow \texttt{global max}$$

$$f(2) = 0 \leftarrow \texttt{global min}$$

$$f(3) = 1$$

Prob. 3. $y = \ln(2x - 1)$, $1 \leq x \leq 2$.

$y' = \frac{2}{2x-1}$, undefined at $x = \frac{1}{2}$, not in the domain for $1 \leq x \leq 2$ $y' > 0$, hence always increasing. Need to check endpoints: $f(1) = \ln(1) = 0 \leftarrow$ global min $f(2) = \ln(3) \leftarrow$ global max.

Prob. 5. $y = xe^{-x}$, $0 \leq x \leq 1$. $y' = e^{-x} = e^{-x}(1 - x) = 0$ gives $x = 1$. It is already an endpoint, hence:

$$f(0) = 0 \leftarrow \texttt{global min.}$$

$$f(1) = \frac{1}{2} \leftarrow \texttt{global max.}$$

Prob. 7. Given, $y = (x - 1)^3 + 1$ and $x \in \mathbf{R}$. To find the maxima or minima, we first find the derivative of the above function,

$$y' = 3(x - 1)^2$$

Equating the above derivative to zero, we get

$$y' = 0,$$

$$3(x - 1)^2 = 0$$

$$x = 1$$

Finding the second derivative of the function we have

$$y'' = 6(x - 1)$$

$$y'' \begin{cases} > 0 \text{ for } > 1; \\ < 0 \text{ for } x < 1; \\ = 0 \text{ for } x = 1. \end{cases}$$

Thus the function continuously increases for $x >$ and decreases for $x < 1$. Thus the function has no maxima and minima.

Prob. 9. $y = \cos(\pi x^2)$, $-1 \leq x \leq 1$

$y' = \sin(\pi x^2)x = 0$, $x = \pm 1$, $x = 0$.

Testing:

x	$-\frac{1}{2}$	$\frac{1}{2}$
y'	$+$	$-$

, hence y increases on $(-1, 0)$ y decreases on $(0, 1)$.

$f(-1) = -1 \leftarrow$ global min

$f(0) = 1 \leftarrow$ global max

Prob. 11. Given, $y = e^{-|x|}$ and $x \in \mathbf{R}$. We redefine the function y as

$$y = \begin{cases} e^{-x} & \text{for} \quad x > 0; \\ e^{x} & \text{for} \quad x < 0. \end{cases}$$

To find the maxima or minima, we first find the derivative of the above function,

$$y' = \begin{cases} -e^{-x} & \text{for} \quad x > 0; \\ e^{x} & \text{for} \quad x < 0. \end{cases}$$

Equating the above derivative to zero, we get

$$y' = 0,$$

So, no value of x satisfies the equation and hence we there is no maxima and minima in the above interval. Evaluating the function t $x = 0$, we find that

$$y(0) = 1$$

which is, in fact a global maxima. Thus, we have one global maxima, which is at $x = 0$.

$$x = 0 \Rightarrow \texttt{Global maxima}$$

Prob. 13. Given, $y = \frac{x^3}{3} + \frac{x^2}{2} - 6x + 2$ and $x \in \mathbf{R}$. To find the maxima or minima, we first find the derivative of the above function, $y' = x^2 + x - 6$ Equating the above derivative to zero, we get

$$y' = 0,$$

$$x^2 + x - 6 = 0$$

$$(x+3)(x-2) = 0$$

$$x = -3, 2$$

Finding the second derivative of the above function we have,

$$y'' = 2x + 1$$

$$y'' = \begin{cases} < 0 & \texttt{for} \quad x < -\frac{1}{2}; \\ > 0 & \texttt{for} \quad x > \frac{1}{2}. \end{cases}$$

Since -3 lies in the 1st interval and 2 lies in the second interval we have, local maxima and minima at these points.

$$x = -3 \Rightarrow \texttt{Local maxima}$$

$$x = 2 \Rightarrow \texttt{Local minima}$$

Prob. 15. $y = (x-1)^{1/3}$, $y' = \frac{1}{3} \cdot (x-1)^{-\frac{2}{3}}$, undefined at $x = 1$, testing:

x	0	2
y'	+	+

always increasing, no extrema.

Prob. 17. We have to prove that the $f'(x) = 0$ is not a sufficient condition for the extrema to exist. We start by letting the function to be,

$$f(x) = x^3$$

So finding its derivative,

$$f' = 3x^2$$

Equating it to zero we have,

$$f' = 0$$

$$3x^2 = 0, x = 0$$

So, we should have a extrema here. But, we see that the derivative doesn't change sign at $x = 0$.

$$\lim_{x \to +0} f' = \lim_{x \to +0} , 3x^2$$
$$= 0$$

and similarly,

$$\lim_{x \to -0} f' = \lim_{x \to +0} , 3x^2$$

$$= 0$$

Thus f' doesn't change its sign and hence $x = 0$ is not a local maxima or minima.

Prob. 19. Given the function as, $f(x) = x^3 - 2$ and $x \in \mathbf{R}$ Since, we have to find the points of inflection, we need to find the first derivative as well as second derivative and check whether the second derivative changes sign at the inflection point. For the point to be inflection, second derivative should change sign .

$$f'(x) = 3x^2$$

$$f''(x) = 6x$$

Thus

$$6x = 0, x = 0$$

Hence we get $x = 0$ as the candidate inflection point. Also, the second derivative changes sign at $x = 0$ as

$$f''(x) = \begin{cases} > 0 & \text{for} \quad x > 0; \\ < 0 & \text{for} \quad x < 0. \end{cases}$$

Thus it is, indeed a point of inflection.

Prob. 21. Given the function as,

$$f(x) = e^{-x^2}$$

and

$$x \geq 0$$

Since, we have to find the points of inflection, we need to find the first derivative as well as second derivative and check whether the second derivative changes sign at the inflection point. For the point to be inflection, second derivative should change sign .

$$f'(x) = -2xe^{-x^2}$$

$$f''(x) = -2e^{-x^2}(1 - 2x^2)$$

Thus

$$-2e^{-x^2}(1 - 2x^2) = 0$$

$$1 - 2x^2 = 0$$

$$x = \frac{1}{\sqrt{2}}, -\frac{1}{\sqrt{2}}$$

Hence we get $x = \pm\frac{1}{\sqrt{2}}$ as the candidate inflection point. Also, the second derivative

changes sign at $x = 0$ as

$$f''(x) = \begin{cases} > 0 & \text{for} \quad 0x > \frac{1}{\sqrt{2}}x < -\frac{1}{\sqrt{2}}; \\ < 0 & \text{for} \quad -\frac{1}{\sqrt{2}} < x < \frac{1}{\sqrt{2}}. \end{cases}$$

Thus it is, indeed a point of inflection.

Prob. 23. Given the function as,

$$f(x) = \tan x$$

and

$$-\frac{\pi}{2} \le x \le \frac{\pi}{2}$$

Since, we have to find the points of inflection, we need to find the first derivative as well as

second derivative and check whether the second derivative changes sign at the inflection

point. For the point to be inflection, second derivative should change sign .

$$f'(x) = \sec^2 x$$

$$f''(x) = 2\sec^2 x \tan x$$

Thus

$$2\sec^2 x \tan x = 0, x = 0$$

Hence we get $x = 0$ as the candidate inflection point. Also, the second derivative changes

sign at $x = 0$ as

$$f''(x) = \left\{ \begin{array}{ll} > 0 & \text{for} \quad 0 < x < \frac{\pi}{2}; \\ < 0 & \text{for} \quad -\frac{\pi}{2} < x < 0. \end{array} \right\}$$

Thus it is, indeed a point of inflection.

Prob. 25. Given the function as, $f(x) = x^4$ and $x \in \mathbf{R}$ Since, we have to find the points

of inflection, we need to find the first derivative as well as second derivative and check

whether the second derivative changes sign at the inflection point. For the point to be

inflection, second derivative should change sign .

$$f'(x) = 4x^3$$

$$f''(x) = 12x^2$$

Thus

$$12x^2 = 0, x = 0$$

Hence we get $x = 0$ as the candidate inflection point. But it is not a inflection point as the 2nd derivative does not change sign around $x = 0$. Thus it is, not a point of inflection.

Prob. 27. Given the function as

$$y = \frac{2x^3}{3} - 2x^2 - 6x + 2$$

where,

$$-2 \leq x \leq 5$$

To find the local maxima and minima we have to find the first and second derivative.

First, we find the first derivative,

$$y' = 2x^2 - 4x - 6$$

Equating it to zero, we have

$$y' = 0$$

$$2x^2 - 4x - 6 = 0$$

$$2(x - 3)(x + 1) = 0$$

$$x = 3, -1$$

Next, we find the second derivative,

$$y'' = 4x - 4$$

From, above we can say that,

$$y'' = \begin{cases} > 0 \ \text{ for } \ x \geq 1, \\ < 0 \ \text{ for } \ x \leq 1; \end{cases}$$

Thus we can say that the function has local maxima and minima.

$$x = 3 \Rightarrow \texttt{Local minima}$$

$$x = -1 \Rightarrow \texttt{Local maxima}$$

Also, to find the point of inflection, we equate second derivative to 0,

$$y'' = 0$$

$$4x - 4 = 0$$

$$x = 1$$

From above, we see that the function does change sign at $x = 1$ and hence it is the point of inflection.

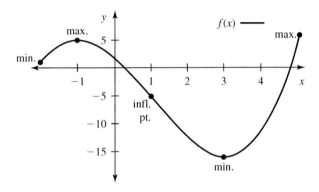

Prob. 29. Given the function as

$$y = |x^2 - 9|$$

where,

$$-4 \le x \le 5$$

We can redefine the function as

$$y = \begin{cases} x^2 - 9 & -4 \le x \le -3, \quad 3 \le x \le 5; \\ 9 - x^2 & -3 < x < 3. \end{cases}$$

To find the local maxima and minima we have to find the first and second derivative. First, we find the first derivative,

$$y' = \{2x - 4 \le x \le -3, \quad 3 \le x \le 5; -2x - 3 < x < 3.$$

Thus equating each of them to zero we find that, the second part is only zero for $x = 0$

Next, we find the second derivative,

$$y'' = \begin{cases} 2 - 4 \leq x \leq -3, \quad 3 \leq x \leq 5; \\ -2 - 3 < x < 3. \end{cases}$$

Thus the function has a local maxima at $x = 0$.

$$x = 0 \Rightarrow \texttt{Local maxima}$$

As the second derivative is not equal to zero for any x, we do not have any point of inflection.

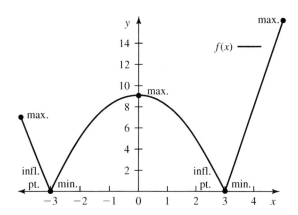

Prob. 31. Given the function as $y = x + \cos x$ where, $x \in \mathbf{R}$ To find the local maxima and minima we have to find the first and second derivative. First, we find the first derivative,

$$y' = 1 - \sin x$$

Equating it to zero, we have

$$y' = 0$$

$$1 - \sin x = 0$$

$$x = \frac{n\pi}{2}, \texttt{where} n = 1, 5, 9, \cdots$$

Next we find the second derivative of the function,

$$y'' = -\cos x$$

$$y'' = \begin{cases} > 0 \quad \text{for} \quad \frac{n\pi}{2} < x < \frac{3n\pi}{2}; \\ < 0 \quad \text{for} \quad -\frac{n\pi}{2} < x < \frac{n\pi}{2}. \end{cases}$$

where $n = 1, 2, \ldots$ To find the point of inflection we equate second derivative to 0

$$y'' = 0$$

$$-\cos x = 0$$

$$x = \frac{n\pi}{2}, where, n = 1, 5, 9, \cdots$$

Thus the above represents, the point of inflection as we see that the 2nd derivative changes sign at them.

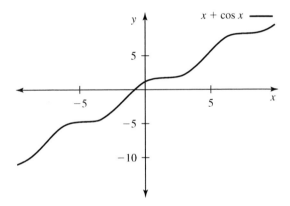

Prob. 33. $y = \frac{x^2-1}{x^2+1}$ where, $x \in \mathbf{R}$ To find the local maxima and minima we have to find the first and second derivative. First, we find the first derivative,

$$y' = \frac{4x}{(x^2 + 1)^2}$$

Equating it to zero, we have

$$y' = 0$$

$$\frac{4x}{(x^2 + 1)^2} = 0$$

$$x = 0$$

Next, we find the second derivative,

$$y'' = 4\frac{1 - 3x^4 - 2x^2}{(x^2 + 1)^4}$$

From, above we can say that,

$$y'' = \begin{cases} > 0 & \text{for} \quad x \geq \frac{1}{3} \text{ and } -1 \leq x \leq -\frac{1}{3}, \\ < 0 & \text{for} \quad -\frac{1}{3} \leq x \leq \frac{1}{3} \text{ and } x < 01; \end{cases}$$

Thus the function has a local maxima at $x = 0$ Also the point of inflection are

$$x = \pm\frac{1}{3}, -1$$

as the function changes sign as it passes through it.

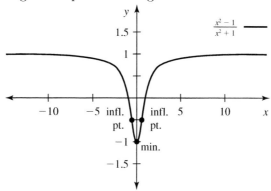

Prob. 35. Given the function,

$$f(x) = \frac{x}{x-1}$$

and

$$x \neq 1$$

(a)

$$\lim_{x \to +\infty} f(x) = \lim_{x \to +\infty} \frac{x}{x-1}$$

$$= \lim_{x \to +\infty} \frac{1}{1 - \frac{1}{x}}$$

$$= \frac{1}{1-0} = 1$$

And,

$$\lim_{x \to -\infty} f(x) = \lim_{x \to -\infty} \frac{x}{x-1}$$

$$= \lim_{x \to -\infty} \frac{1}{1 - \frac{1}{x}}$$

$$= \frac{1}{1-0} = 1$$

Thus we have

$$\lim_{x \to +\infty} f(x) = \lim_{x \to -\infty} f(x) = 1$$

(b)

$$\lim_{x \to 1^+} f(x) = \lim_{x \to 1^+} \frac{x}{x - 1}$$

$$= \lim_{x \to 1^+} \frac{1}{1 - \frac{1}{x}}$$

$$= \frac{1}{1 - (1 - \epsilon)} = +\infty$$

And,

$$\lim_{x \to 1^-} f(x) = \lim_{x \to 1^-} \frac{x}{x - 1}$$

$$= \lim_{x \to 1^-} \frac{1}{1 - \frac{1}{x}}$$

$$= \frac{1}{1 - (1 + \epsilon)} = -\infty$$

Thus $x = 1$ is vertical asmyptote.

(c) We first compute y' and the y'',

$$y' = -\frac{1}{(x - 1)^2}$$

$$y'' = 2\frac{1}{(x - 1)^3}$$

The function is decreasing in the interval $x > 1$ No, the function has no local extrema.

(d) The function is concave up in the interval $x > 1$ and is concave down in the interval $x < 1$.

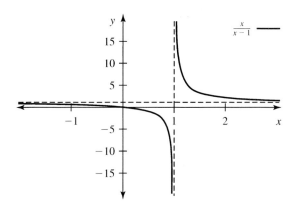

(e)

Prob. 37. Given the function,

$$f(x) = \frac{2x^2 - 5}{x + 2}$$

and

$$x \neq 2, -2$$

(a)

$$\lim_{x \to -2^+} f(x) = \lim_{x \to -2^+} \frac{2x^2 - 5}{x + 2}$$

$$= \lim_{x \to -2^+} \frac{2(-2 + \epsilon)^2 - 5}{(-2 + \epsilon) + 2}$$

$$= \infty$$

And,

$$\lim_{x \to -2^-} f(x) = \lim_{x \to -2^-} \frac{2x^2 - 5}{x + 2}$$

$$= \lim_{x \to -2^-} \frac{2(-2 - \epsilon)^2 - 5}{(-2 - \epsilon) + 2}$$

$$= -\infty$$

Thus $x = -2$ is vertical asmyptote.

(b) Next, we find f' and f''.

$$f' = \frac{2x^2 + 8x + 5}{(x + 2)^2}$$

Thus the function has chances of local extrema at

$$x = \frac{-4 + \sqrt{6}}{2}, \frac{-4 - \sqrt{6}}{2}$$

The function is increasing for $x > -2$. Again in the interval

$$x < -2$$

the function has local minima and it is at

$$x = \frac{-4 - \sqrt{6}}{2}$$

(c) It is concave up for

$$\frac{-4 - \sqrt{6}}{2} < x < -2$$

(d) The oblique assymptote willa line with slope $m = 2$ which is the $\lim_{x \to \infty} f(x)/x$

(e)

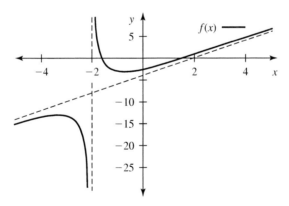

Prob. 39. Given the function, $f(x) = \frac{x^2}{x^2+1}$ and $x \in \mathbf{R}$

(a) First we find the derivative of the above function.

$$f'(x) = \frac{2x}{(1 + x^2)^2}$$

Thus the function is increasing for $x > 0$ and $x < 0$, as the function is even.

(b) For concavity, we compute $f''(x)$

$$f'' = 2\frac{1 - 2x^2 - 4x^4}{(1 + x^2)^4}$$

To compute

$$f'' = 0$$

we have

$$2\frac{(3x^2 - 1)(x^2 + 1)}{(1 + x^2)^4} = 0$$

$$3x^2 - 1 = 0$$

$$x = \pm\frac{1}{\sqrt{3}}$$

Thus we have

$$y'' = \begin{cases} > 0 \quad \text{for} \quad x > \frac{1}{\sqrt{3}} \text{ and } x < -\frac{1}{\sqrt{3}}; \\ < 0 \quad \text{for} \quad -\frac{1}{\sqrt{3}} < x < \frac{1}{\sqrt{3}}. \end{cases}$$

Thus the points of inflection are

$$x = \pm\frac{1}{\sqrt{3}}$$

The graph is concave up for the portion $x > \frac{1}{\sqrt{3}}$.

(c) The graph has a horizontal asymptote at $y = 1$.

$$\lim_{x \to +\infty} f(x) = \lim_{x \to +\infty} \frac{x^2}{x^2 + 1}$$

$$= \lim_{x \to +\infty} \frac{1}{1 + \frac{1}{x^2}}$$

$$= 1$$

And,

$$\lim_{x \to -\infty} f(x) = \lim_{x \to -\infty} \frac{x^2}{x^2 + 1}$$

$$= \lim_{x \to -\infty} \frac{1}{1 + \frac{1}{x^2}}$$

$$= 1$$

Thus we have

$$\lim_{x \to +\infty} f(x) = \lim_{x \to -\infty} f(x) = 1$$

Hence $y = 1$ is a horizontal asymptote.

(d)

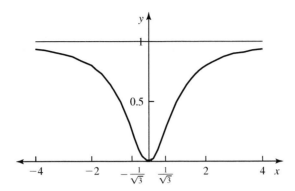

Prob. 41. Given the function, $f(x) = \frac{x}{x+a}$ and $x \in \mathbf{R}$

(a) First we find the derivative of the above function.

$$f'(x) = \frac{a}{(a+x)^2}$$

Thus the function is decreasing for $x > -a$. There is no local extrema.

(b) For concavity, we compute $f''(x)$

$$f'' = -\frac{2a}{(a+x)^3}$$

Thus we have

$$y'' = \begin{cases} > 0 & \text{for} \quad x < -a; \\ < 0 & \text{for} \quad x > -a. \end{cases}$$

There are no inflection points. Its concave up for $x > -a$.

(c) The graph has a horizontal asymptote at $y = 0$.

$$\lim_{x \to +\infty} f(x) = \lim_{x \to +\infty} \frac{x}{x+a}$$

$$= \lim_{x \to +\infty} \frac{1}{1 + \frac{a}{x}}$$

$$= 1$$

And,

$$\lim_{x \to -\infty} f(x) = \lim_{x \to -\infty} \frac{x}{x+a}$$

$$= \lim_{x \to -\infty} \frac{1}{1 + \frac{a}{x}}$$

$$= 1$$

Thus we have

$$\lim_{x \to +\infty} f(x) = \lim_{x \to -\infty} f(x) = 1$$

Hence $y = 1$ is a horizontal asymptote .

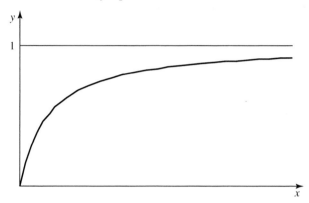

(d)

Prob. 43. Given the growth rate of population as

$$f(N) = N(1 - (\frac{N}{K})^\theta)$$

and

$$N \geq 0$$

So, we have to find N such that $f(N)$ is maximal. Hence we find 1st derivative and evaluate it to zero.

$$f'(N) = 1 - (\frac{N}{K})^\theta - \frac{N}{K}\theta(\frac{N}{K})^{\theta-1}$$

$$= 1 - (\frac{N}{K})^\theta(1 + \theta)$$

Hence equating it to zero, we have

$$1 - (\frac{N}{K})^\theta(1 + \theta) = 0$$

$$\frac{N}{K})^\theta = \frac{1}{1+\theta}$$

$$N = K(\frac{1}{1+\theta})^{\frac{1}{\theta}}$$

Thus we have the maximal value at the above population. We, confirm this by taking the second derivative of the function and by noting that the

$$f''(K(\frac{1}{1+\theta})^{\frac{1}{\theta}}) < 0$$

and thus has a maxima.

5.4   Optimization

Prob. 1. If l is the length of the rectangle and b is its height, then the perimeter p is given by

$$p = 2(l + b).$$

The area of the rectangle is $l \times b$, which is given to be 25. Since $lb = 25$, we have $l = \frac{25}{b}$, and substituting this in the equation for p we get

$$p = 2\left(\frac{25}{b} + b\right)$$

Thus we have p as a function of b alone. We now differentiate p to get the extreme values of the perimeter. We have

$$\frac{dp}{db} = 2\left(-\frac{25}{b^2} + 1\right)$$

Equating the above equation to zero, we have

$$2\left(-\frac{25}{b^2} + 1\right) = 0 \quad \Rightarrow \quad \frac{25}{b^2} = 1 \quad \Rightarrow \quad b^2 = 25$$

Since b represents a distance, it must be positive and thus $b = 5$. We must now check whether this value of b corresponds to a maximum or a minimum. To do this we calculate

$$\frac{d^2p}{db^2} = \frac{100}{b^3},$$

which is positive for all $b > 0$. Thus the graph of p is concave up at $b = 5$, and we have found an absolute minimum. To find the length of the rectangle, we use the fact that

$bl = 25$ to obtain $l = 5$ as well. Thus the rectangle with smallest perimeter is in fact a square of side 5in, with a perimeter of 20in.

Prob. 3. Let the upper right corner of the rectangle be the point (x, y) on the parabola (see the figure provided with the question). Then the area of the rectangle is $A = 2xy$. Since the point (x, y) is on the parabola, we know that $y = 3 - x^2$, and so we get $A = 2x(3 - x^2)$. This gives us A as a function of x only. To get the extreme values of A, we first differentiate the function $A(x)$, to get

$$A'(x) = 2(3 - x^2) + 2x(-2x) = 6 - 6x^2.$$

Setting $A'(x) = 0$, we have $6 - 6x^2 = 0 \Rightarrow x^2 = 1 \Rightarrow x = \pm 1$. Since (x, y) is in the first quadrant, we select $x = 1$. Now, $A''(x) = -12x$ and so the function $A(x)$ is concave down for all $x > 0$. Thus $x = 1$ gives us a maximum value of A, and from this we have $y = 3 - x^2 = 3 - 1 = 2$. The height of the rectangle is 2 and its length is 2, with a maximal area of 4.

Prob. 5. Let l denote the length of the rectangular area, and b its height. Since the field is bounded by a river on one side, the perimeter p is given by $p = 2l + b$, which is given to equal 320 ft. Thus, $b = 320 - 2l$ and substituting for b in the equation for the area A of the rectangle, we get $A = lb = l(320 - 2l) = 320l - 2l^2$. To optimize the area, we differentiate A with respect to l.

$$\frac{dA}{dl} = 320 - 4l$$

Setting $dA/dl = 0$, we have

$$320 - 4l = 0 \quad \Rightarrow \quad 320 = 4l \quad \Rightarrow \quad l = 80.$$

To confirm that we have found a maximum, we check that the graph of A is concave down by calculating

$$\frac{d^2 A}{dl^2} = -4$$

and noticing that this expression is always negative. Thus the maximum value of A is 12800 ft^2, which occurs when the length is $l = 80$ ft and the height is $b = 320 - 2l = 320 - 160 = 160$ ft.

Prob. 7. We are given a right triangle whose sides have length a and b. Further, the hypotenuse of the triangle has length 5. Thus, the perimeter p of the triangle is given by

$$p = a + b + 5.$$

Since the triangle is a right triangle, we have that $25 = a^2 + b^2$, and so we have $a = \sqrt{25 - b^2}$. Substituting for a in the equation for the perimeter, we have

$$p = \sqrt{25 - b^2} + b + 5$$

To optimize the perimeter, we differentiate the function p to get

$$\frac{dp}{db} = -\frac{b}{\sqrt{25 - b^2}} + 1$$

Setting this derivative to equal zero, we have

$$-\frac{b}{\sqrt{25 - b^2}} + 1 = 0 \quad \Rightarrow \quad b = \sqrt{25 - b^2} \quad \Rightarrow \quad 2b^2 = 25 \quad \Rightarrow \quad b = \frac{5\sqrt{2}}{2}$$

We also note that dp/db does not exist when $b = 5$, but the base of the triangle cannot equal its hypotenuse and so we reject this value of b. Now, by calculating that

$$\frac{d^2 p}{db^2} = -\frac{25 + 2b^2}{(25 - b^2)^{3/2}}$$

and noting that this second derivative is negative for all $0 < b < 5$, we find that the graph of p is concave down and hence the value $b = \frac{5\sqrt{2}}{2}$ corresponds to a maximum, not a minimum. Since

$$\lim_{b \to 0^+} \left(\sqrt{25 - b^2} + b + 5 \right) = 10 = \lim_{b \to 5^-} \left(\sqrt{25 - b^2} + b + 5 \right)$$

we can find right triangles that have perimeters as close to 10 (and greater) as we wish, but none that actually have a perimeter equal to 10. Thus, the function p has no minimum when b is in the interval $(0, 5)$. However, if we allow the base of the triangle to equal either 0 or 5, then the perimeter of this degenerate triangle is exactly 10 cm.

Prob. 9. Since the lower left corner of the rectangle is at $(0, 0)$ and the upper right corner is at the point $(x, 1/x)$, we know that the perimeter p is given by

$$p = \frac{2}{x} + 2x.$$

To optimize the perimeter, we first differentiate the above equation to get

$$\frac{dp}{dx} = -\frac{2}{x^2} + 2$$

Setting the derivative equal to zero, we have

$$-\frac{2}{x^2} + 2 = 0 \quad \Rightarrow \quad 2x^2 = 2 \quad \Rightarrow \quad x = \pm 1.$$

Since the upper right corner has a positive x-coordinate, we select $x = 1$. To confirm that this value of x corresponds to a minimum for p, we calculate the second derivative

$$\frac{d^2p}{dx^2} = \frac{4}{x^3}$$

and note that it is always positive for $x > 0$. This means that the graph of p is concave up, and hence the optimal value must be a minimum. When $x = 1$, the minimum perimeter of the rectangle is $p = \frac{2}{x} + 2x = 4$.

Prob. 11. Suppose that the coordinates of any point on the line are (x, y), where y is given by $y = 4 - 3x$.

(a) The distance D between any two points (x_1, y_1) and (x_2, y_2) is given by

$$D = \sqrt{(x_2 - x_1)^2 + (y_2 - y_1)^2}$$

In our case, the two points are $(0, 0)$ and (x, y), and so

$$D = \sqrt{(x - 0)^2 + (y - 0)^2} = \sqrt{x^2 + y^2} = \sqrt{x^2 + (4 - 3x)^2}$$

If f denotes this distance then since f depends on x alone, we can write

$$f(x) = \sqrt{x^2 + (4 - 3x)^2}.$$

(b) To find a point on the line which is closest to the origin, we must optimize the function $f(x)$. To do this, we differentiate the above equation with respect to x, to get

$$f'(x) = \frac{10x - 12}{\sqrt{x^2 + (4 - 3x)^2}}$$

Setting the above equation to zero, we have

$$\frac{10x - 12}{\sqrt{x^2 + (4 - 3x)^2}} = 0 \quad \Rightarrow \quad 10x - 12 = 0 \quad \Rightarrow \quad x = 6/5.$$

We note that since the discriminant of $x^2 + (4 - 3x)^2 = 10x^2 - 24x + 16$ is $24^2 - 4(10)(16) = -64 < 0$, the denominator of f' cannot be zero. Hence the only critical number is $x = 6/5$. To show that this corresponds to a minimum, we note that $f'(x) < 0$ for $x < 6/5$ and $f'(x) > 0$ for $x > 6/5$. (Note that we could also deduce this geometrically; there can be no maximal distance between the point (x, y) on the line and the origin, since the line is unbounded.) With $x = 6/5$ we get $y = 4 - 3x = 4 - 3\frac{6}{5} = \frac{2}{5}$, and so the coordinates of the closest point are $(6/5, 2/5)$.

(c) The square of the distance is clearly found by simply squaring f, namely

$$g(x) = [f(x)]^2 = x^2 + (4 - 3x)^2$$

Again, to optimize $g(x)$, we differentiate to get

$$g'(x) = 20x - 24$$

and when we set this derivative equal to zero, we have

$$20x - 24 = 0 \quad \Rightarrow \quad x = \frac{24}{20} = \frac{6}{5}.$$

Now, again we can confirm that this value corresponds to a minimum, since $g'' = 20 > 0$ and so the graph of g is concave up everywhere. When $x = 6/5$, we have $y = 2/5$ as before, and thus we get the same coordinates as in part (b).

Prob. 13. Suppose the coordinates of any point on the curve $y = 1/x$ are given by (x, y). We want to minimize the distance between (x, y) and $(0, 0)$. As in Question 11, we can minimize the square of the distance instead. This squared distance D is given by

$$D = (x - 0)^2 + (y - 0)^2 = x^2 + y^2$$

Substituting the value of y from above, we get

$$D(x) = x^2 + \frac{1}{x^2}$$

To optimize D, we first differentiate to get

$$D'(x) = 2x - \frac{2}{x^3}$$

and then we set this derivative equal to zero and solve:

$$2x - \frac{2}{x^3} = 0 \quad \Rightarrow \quad x^4 - 1 = 0 \quad \Rightarrow \quad x = \pm 1.$$

We also notice that when $x = 0$, the derivative D' does not exist. However, the curve $y = 1/x$ has no point on it corresponding to $x = 0$, and so we reject this value. Thus there are two critical numbers, $x = 1$ and $x = -1$. Since

$$D''(x) = 2 + \frac{6}{x^4} > 0$$

for all $x \neq 0$, the graph of D is concave up everywhere on it's domain, and so both critical numbers must correspond to minima. When $x = 1$ we get $y = 1$, and when $x = -1$ we get $y = -1$. In both cases, the minimal distance is $\sqrt{D} = \sqrt{1+1} = \sqrt{2}$.

Prob. 15. Suppose that $f(x)$ is a positive differentiable function that has a local minimum at $x = c$. Then we know that $f'(c) = 0$, and that $f'(x) < 0$ for $x < c$ and x close to c and $f'(x) > 0$ for $x > c$ and x close to c. Let us define the function $g(x) = [f(x)]^2$. Then we have $g'(x) = 2f(x)f'(x)$. Thus $g'(c) = 2f(c)f'(c) = 0$. Also $g'(x) < 0$ for $x < c$ and x close to c since $f(x)$ is positive and $f'(x)$ is negative. Similarly $g'(x) > 0$ for $x > c$ and x close to c since $f(x)$ and $f'(x)$ are positive. Hence $g(x)$ also has a local minimum at $x = c$.

Prob. 17. Let l denote the height of the cylinder and r the radius of the circular base. The volume V of the cylinder is given by $V = \pi r^2 l$ and since we know that $V = 1000$ cm^3, we have

$$l = \frac{1000}{\pi r^2}$$

The amount of material used corresponds to the total surface area P, which is given by $P = 2\pi r^2 + 2\pi r l$. Thus we have to minimize the total surface area P. Substituting for l from above we have

$$P(r) = 2\pi r^2 + \frac{2000}{r}$$

and then differentiating, we get

$$P'(r) = 4\pi r - \frac{2000}{r^2}$$

To optimize P, we set this derivative equal to zero.

$$4\pi r - \frac{2000}{r^2} = 0 \quad \Rightarrow \quad 4\pi r^3 = 2000 \quad \Rightarrow \quad r = \sqrt[3]{500/\pi}$$

We note that the derivative $P'(r)$ does not exist when $r = 0$, but this is not a critical number since we cannot construct a cylinder of radius 0. Now, the graph of P is concave up since

$$P''(r) = 4\pi + \frac{4000}{r^3} > 0$$

for all positive values of r. Thus $r = \sqrt[3]{500/\pi}$ must correspond to a minimum. The radius of the can must be $\sqrt[3]{500/\pi}$ cm, and the height should be

$$l = \frac{1000}{\pi r^2} = \frac{1000}{\pi(\sqrt[3]{500/\pi})^2} = 2\sqrt[3]{500/\pi} \text{ cm},$$

which is twice the radius.

Prob. 19. Please refer to Figure 5.59 in the textbook. The area A of the sector is given by $A = \frac{1}{2r^2}\theta$, and the perimeter p is given by $p = r\theta + 2r$. Solving the first of these equations for θ gives us $\theta = 2A/r^2$, and then we can substitute this expression into the formula for p to get

$$p = r\theta + 2r = \frac{2A}{r} + 2r$$

To optimize p we calculate $p'(r)$ and set it equal to zero.

$$p'(r) = 2 - \frac{2A}{r^2} \quad \text{and so} \quad p'(r) = 0 \quad \Rightarrow \quad 2 = \frac{2A}{r^2} \quad \Rightarrow \quad r = \sqrt{A}$$

since r must be positive. Now $p''(r) = 4A/r^3 > 0$ for any positive A and r. This means that the graph of p is concave up, and hence the critical number $r = \sqrt{A}$ corresponds to a minimum.

(a) When $A = 2$, the minimizing value of $r = \sqrt{2}$ and so $\theta = 2A/r^2 = 4/2 = 2$ radians.

(b) When $A = 10$, the minimizing value of $r = \sqrt{10}$ and so $\theta = 2A/r^2 = 20/10 = 2$ radians. The angle is the same no matter what the value of A, since $\theta = 2A/r^2 = 2A/A = 2$.

Prob. 21. Please look at Example 4 in the textbook; we shall use the same variables here. The height of the cylinder is h and r is the radius of the circular base. The volume V of the cylinder is given by $V = \pi r^2 l$, and given that $V = 355 \text{ cm}^3$ we have $l = \frac{355}{\pi r^2}$. Now, since the top of the can is three times as thick as the base, the total surface area P is given by

$$P = \pi r^2 + 3\pi r^2 + 2\pi r l = 4\pi r^2 + 2\pi r l = 4\pi r^2 + \frac{710}{r}.$$

To minimize P over the interval $(0, \infty)$ we differentiate and get

$$\frac{dP}{dr} = 8\pi r - \frac{710}{r^2}$$

Setting this derivative equal to zero we have

$$8\pi r - \frac{710}{r^2} = 0 \quad \Rightarrow \quad 8\pi r^3 = 710 \quad \Rightarrow \quad r = \sqrt[3]{\frac{710}{8\pi}} = \frac{1}{2}\sqrt[3]{\frac{710}{\pi}}$$

Now the second derivative is

$$\frac{d^2 P}{dr^2} = 8\pi + \frac{1420}{r^3}$$

which is positive for all $r > 0$, and thus the graph of p is concave up. This means that $r = \sqrt[3]{710/(8\pi)}$ cm corresponds to a minimum. The height of the cylinder is

$$l = \frac{355}{\pi r^2} = \frac{355(8\pi)^{2/3}}{\pi 710^{2/3}} = 2\sqrt[3]{\frac{710}{\pi}} \text{ cm}.$$

The approximate values are $r \approx 3$ cm and $l \approx 12.2$ cm. These are closer to actual values for real soda cans.

Prob. 23. Let $f(a) = ab = a(a - 4) = a^2 + 4a$.

$f'(a) = 2a + 4 = 0$, $a = -2$, $b = -6$.

$a \cdot b = 12$.

Prob. 25. Here

$$w(t) = \frac{f(t)}{C + t}$$

where we assume that $f(t)$ is concave down for $t \geq 0$, and also that $f(0) = 0$ and $0 \leq f \leq 1$.

(a) To find the optimal brooding time, we first differentiate w to get

$$\frac{dw}{dt} = \frac{f'(t)(C + t) - f(t)}{(C + t)^2}$$

Setting this derivative equal to zero we have

$$\frac{f'(t)(C + t) - f(t)}{(C + t)^2} = 0 \quad \Rightarrow \quad f'(t)(C + t) - f(t) = 0 \quad \Rightarrow \quad f(t) = f'(t)(C + t)$$

Now suppose the line through the point $(-C, 0)$ is tangential to the curve f, and the point of tangency is $(t, f(t))$. The point-slope equation of this tangent line would be $f(t) - 0 = f'(t)(t - (-C))$, or $f(t) = f'(t)(t + C)$, which is precisely when the derivative dw/dt would be zero. Since we have assumed that f is concave down, $f'' < 0$ and so at the point of tangency

$$
\begin{aligned}
\frac{d^2 w}{dt^2} &= \frac{f''(t)(C + t)^2 - 2f'(t)(C + t) + 2f(t)}{(C + t)^3} \\
&= \frac{f''(t)(C + t)^2 - 2f'(t)(C + t) + 2f'(t)(C + t)}{(C + t)^3} \\
&= \frac{f''(t)}{(C + t)} < 0
\end{aligned}
$$

which means that w is maximized.

(b) When $C = 2$ and

$$
f(t) = \frac{t}{1 + t}
$$

we have

$$
f(t) = f'(t)(C + t) \;\Rightarrow\; \frac{t}{1 + t} = \frac{1}{(1 + t)^2}(2 + t) \;\Rightarrow\; t(1 + t) = (2 + t) \;\Rightarrow\; t^2 = 2
$$

and since $t \geq 0$ we have $t = \sqrt{2}$. Thus, for maximum $w(t)$ we should have $t = \sqrt{2}$.

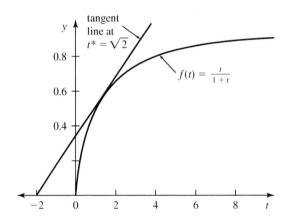

Prob. 27. We are given that the function $r(x)$ satisfies the equation

$$
\frac{e^{-x(r(x)+L)}(1 - e^{-kx})^3 c}{1 - e^{-(r(x)+L)}} = 1
$$

where k, L and c are positive constants.

(a) We have to find the $\frac{dr}{dx}$. To do this, we apply logarithms on both sides of the equation above to get

$$\ln\left(\frac{e^{-x(r(x)+L)}(1-e^{-kx})^3 c}{1-e^{-(r(x)+L)}}\right) = \ln 1$$

$$\ln\left(e^{-x(r(x)+L)}\right) + 3\ln\left(1-e^{-kx}\right) + \ln c - \ln\left(1-e^{-(r(x)+L)}\right) = 0$$

$$-x(r(x)+L) + 3\ln\left(1-e^{-kx}\right) + \ln c = \ln\left(1-e^{-(r(x)+L)}\right)$$

Now we differentiate with respect to x. We have

$$-r(x) - L - xr'(x) + \frac{3ke^{-kx}}{1-e^{-kx}} = \frac{r'(x)e^{-(r(x)+L)}}{1-e^{-(r(x)+L)}}$$

$$r'(x)\left(x + \frac{e^{-(r(x)+L)}}{1-e^{-(r(x)+L)}}\right) = -r(x) - L + \frac{3ke^{-kx}}{1-e^{-kx}}$$

$$r'(x)\left(\frac{x - (x-1)e^{-(r(x)+L)}}{1-e^{-(r(x)+L)}}\right) = \frac{[r(x)+L+3k]e^{-kx} - r(x) - L}{1-e^{-kx}}$$

$$r'(x) = \frac{[r(x)+L+3k]e^{-kx} - r(x) - L}{1-e^{-kx}} \cdot \frac{1-e^{-(r(x)+L)}}{x - (x-1)e^{-(r(x)+L)}}$$

This is an equation for dr/dx.

(b) Setting $dr/dx = 0$ and considering only the numerator, we have that either $e^{r(x)+L} = 1$ or

$$[r(x)+L+3k]e^{-kx} - r(x) - L = 0$$

We can reject the first case, since it leads to the solution $r(x) = -L$, which is a negative rate of increase. Working with the latter equation, we have

$$[L+3k]e^{-kx} - L = r(x) - r(x)e^{-kx}$$

$$3ke^{-kx} - L[1-e^{-kx}] = r(x)[1-e^{-kx}]$$

$$r(x) = \frac{3ke^{-kx}}{1-e^{-kx}} - L$$

This is what we were meant to show.

5.5 L'Hospital's Rule

Prob. 1. L'Hospital's rule gives:

$$\lim_{x \to 5} \frac{2x}{1} = 10.$$

Prob. 3. L'Hospital's rule gives:

$$\lim_{x \to -2} \frac{6x - 5}{1} = -17.$$

Prob. 5. Applying L'Hospital's rule we have, a substituting the value, we have

$$y = \lim_{x \to 0} \frac{1}{\sqrt{2x + 4}} = \frac{1}{2}.$$

Prob. 7. Applying L'Hospital's rule we have, and substituting the value, we have

$$y = \lim_{x \to 0} \frac{\cos x}{\cos x - x \sin x} = 1.$$

Prob. 9. Applying L'Hospital's rule we have,

$$y = \lim_{x \to 0} \frac{\sin x}{\tan x + x \sec^2 x}$$

Differentiating again, and substituting the value, we have

$$y = \lim_{x \to 0} \frac{\cos x}{\sec^2 x + \sec^2 x + 2x \sec^2 x \tan x} = \frac{1}{2}.$$

Prob. 11. Applying L'Hospital's rule we have,

$$y = \lim_{x \to 0^+} \frac{x + 1}{2\sqrt{x}} = \infty$$

Prob. 13. L'Hospital's rule gives:

$$\lim_{x \to \infty} \frac{\frac{1}{\ln(x)} \cdot \frac{1}{x}}{1} = 0.$$

Prob. 15. Applying L'Hospital's rule we have, and substituting the value, we have

$$y = \lim_{x \to 0} \frac{(\ln 2)2^x}{(\ln 3)3^x} = \frac{\ln 2}{\ln 3}.$$

Prob. 17. L'Hospital's rule gives:

$$\lim_{x \to 0} \frac{-\ln 3 \cdot 3^{-x}}{\ln 2 \cdot 2^x} = -\frac{\ln 3}{\ln 2}.$$

Prob. 19. Applying L'Hospital's rule we have,

$$y = \lim_{x \to 0} \frac{e^x - 1}{2x}$$

Differentiating again,

$$y = \lim_{x \to 0} \frac{e^x}{2}$$

Substituting the value, we have

$$= \frac{1}{2}.$$

Prob. 21. Applying L'Hospital's rule we have,

$$y = \lim_{x \to \infty} \frac{2 \ln x}{x 2x}$$

Differentiating again,

$$y = \lim_{x \to \infty} \frac{1}{2x^2}$$

Substituting the value, we have

$$= 0.$$

Prob. 23. Applying L'Hospital's rule we have, and substituting the value, we have

$$y = \lim_{x \to (\frac{\pi}{2})^-} \frac{\sec^2 x}{2 \sec^2 x \tan x} = \lim_{x \to (\frac{\pi}{2})^-} \frac{1}{2 \tan x} = 0.$$

Prob. 25. Converting into form so that L'Hospital's rule can be applied,

$$y = \lim_{x \to \infty} \frac{x}{e^x}$$

Applying L'Hospital's rule we have, and substituting the value, we have

$$y = \lim_{x \to \infty} \frac{1}{e^x} = 0.$$

Prob. 27. Re-write as: $\lim\limits_{x \to \infty} \frac{x^5}{e^x}$, successive applications of the rule give: $\lim\limits_{x \to \infty} \frac{5 \cdot 4 \cdot 3 \cdot 2 \cdot 1}{e^x} = 0.$

Prob. 29. Converting into form so that L'Hospital's rule can be applied,

$$y = \lim_{x \to 0} \frac{\ln x}{\frac{1}{\sqrt{x}}}$$

Applying L'Hospital's rule we have, and substituting the value, we have

$$y = \lim_{x \to 0} -2x^{\frac{1}{2}} = 0.$$

Prob. 31. Re-write as $\lim\limits_{x\to 0^+} \frac{\ln x}{\frac{1}{x^5}}$, L'Hospital rule gives:

$$\lim_{x\to 0^+} \frac{\frac{1}{x}}{\frac{1}{x^5}} = \lim_{x\to 0^+} x^4 = 0$$

Prob. 33. Given,

$$y = \lim_{x\to(\frac{\pi}{2})^-} (\frac{\pi}{2} - x)\sec x$$

Converting into form so that L'Hospital's rule can be applied,

$$y = \lim_{x\to(\frac{\pi}{2})^-} \frac{(\frac{\pi}{2} - x)}{\cos x}$$

Applying L'Hospital's rule we have, and substituting the value, we have

$$y = \lim_{x\to(\frac{\pi}{2})^-} \frac{-1}{-\sin x} = 1.$$

Prob. 35. Converting into form so that L'Hospital's rule can be applied, Substituting

$$t = \frac{1}{x}$$

and hence when

$$x \to \infty, t \to 0$$

$$y = \lim_{t\to 0} \frac{\sin t}{\sqrt{t}}$$

Applying L'Hospital's rule we have, and substituting the value, we have

$$y = \lim_{t\to 0} \frac{2\cos t\sqrt{t}}{1} = 0.$$

Prob. 37. Converting into form so that L'Hospital's rule can be applied,

$$y = \lim_{x\to 0^+} \frac{\cos x - 1}{\sin x}$$

Applying L'Hospital's rule we have, and substituting the value, we have

$$y = \lim_{x\to 0^+} \frac{-\sin x}{\cos x} = 0.$$

Prob. 39. Converting into form so that L'Hospital's rule can be applied,

$$y = \lim_{x\to 0^+} \frac{x - \sin x}{x\sin x}$$

Applying L'Hospital's rule we have,

$$y = \lim_{x \to 0^+} \frac{1 - \cos x}{\sin x + x \cos x}$$

Differentiating again and substituting the value, we have

$$y = \lim_{x \to 0^+} \frac{\sin x}{2 \cos x - x \sin x} = 0.$$

Prob. 41. Converting into form so that L'Hospital's rule can be applied . Taking ln on both sides,

$$\ln y = \lim_{x \to 0^+} \frac{2 \ln x}{\frac{1}{x}}$$

Applying L'Hospital's rule we have, and substituting the value, we have

$$\ln y = \lim_{x \to 0^+} \frac{-2x^2}{x} \ln y = 0. \Rightarrow y = 1$$

Prob. 43. Converting into form so that L'Hospital's rule can be applied . Taking ln on both sides,

$$\ln y = \lim_{x \to \infty} \frac{\ln x}{x}$$

Applying L'Hospital's rule we have, and substituting the value, we have

$$\ln y = \lim_{x \to \infty} \frac{1}{x} = 0 \Rightarrow y = 1$$

Prob. 45. Converting into form so that L'Hospital's rule can be applied . Taking ln on both sides,

$$\ln y = \lim_{x \to \infty} \frac{\ln(1 + \frac{3}{x})}{\frac{1}{x}}$$

Substituting

$$t = \frac{1}{x}$$

such that

$$x \to \infty, t \to 0$$

Thus we have,

$$\ln y = \lim_{t \to 0} \frac{\ln(1 + 3t)}{t}$$

Applying L'Hospital's rule we have, and substituting the value, we have

$$\ln y = \lim_{t \to 0} \frac{3}{1 + t} = 3 \Rightarrow y = e^3$$

Prob. 47. Let $y = (1 - \frac{2}{x})^x$, taking ln of both sides:

$$\ln y = x \cdot \ln(1 - \frac{2}{x}) = \frac{\ln(1 - \frac{2}{x})}{\frac{1}{x}}.$$

Letting $t = \frac{1}{x}$, $\lim\limits_{t \to 0} \frac{\ln(1 - 2t)}{t}$.

Now, L'Hospital rule gives:

$$\lim_{t \to 0} \frac{-2}{1 - 2t} = -2 \texttt{ hence } y = e^{-2}.$$

Prob. 49. Converting into form so that L'Hospital's rule can be applied . Taking ln on both sides,

$$\ln y = \lim_{x \to \infty} \frac{\ln(\frac{x}{1+x})}{\frac{1}{x}}$$

Substituting

$$t = \frac{1}{x}$$

such that

$$x \to \infty, t \to 0$$

Thus we have,

$$\ln y = \lim_{t \to 0} -\frac{\ln(1 + t)}{t}$$

Applying L'Hospital's rule we have, and substituting the value, we have

$$\ln y = \lim_{t \to 0} -\frac{1}{1 + t} = -1 \Rightarrow y = \frac{1}{e}$$

Prob. 51. Given,

$$y = \lim_{x \to 0^+} x e^x$$

Now the above function is not in L'Hospital rule format, and hence here we can directly get the limit by substituting the value of x in above function . So,

$$y = \lim_{x \to 0^+} x e^x$$

$$y = 0$$

Prob. 53. Given

$$y = \lim_{x \to (\frac{\pi}{2})^+} \tan x + \sec x$$

We rewrite above function as,

$$y = \lim_{x \to (\frac{\pi}{2})^+} \frac{1 + \sin x}{\cos x}$$

Here we can not apply L'Hospital Rule. By directly substituting the value of $x = \frac{\pi}{2}$ we get the limit. Thus we have,

$$y = \infty$$

Prob. 55. $\lim\limits_{x \to 1} \frac{x^2-1}{x+1}$, L'Hospital does not apply, hence

$$\lim_{x \to 1} \frac{(x+1)(x-1)}{x+1} = \lim_{x \to 1}(x-1) = 0.$$

Prob. 57. Making the substitution $y = -x$ we can rewrite the limit as

$$\lim_{x \to -\infty} xe^x = \lim_{y \to \infty} -ye^{-y} = -\lim_{y \to \infty} \frac{y}{e^y} = -\lim_{x \to \infty} \frac{1}{e^x} = 0$$

where we applied L'Hospital on the last calculation.

Prob. 59. Converting into form so that L'Hospital's rule can be applied . Taking ln on both sides,

$$\ln y = \lim_{x \to 0^+} \frac{3 \ln x}{\frac{1}{x}}$$

Applying L'Hospital's rule we have,

$$\ln y = \lim_{x \to 0^+} \frac{-3x^2}{x}$$

Substituting the value, we have

$$\ln y = 0 \Rightarrow y = 1$$

Prob. 61. Given

$$y = \lim_{x \to 0} \frac{a^x - 1}{b^x - 1}$$

We can apply L'Hospital rule to above limit. Applying L'Hospital's rule we have,

$$y = \lim_{x \to 0} \frac{a^x \ln a}{b^x \ln b}$$

$$y = \frac{\ln a}{\ln b}$$

Prob. 63. Given,

$$y = \lim_{x \to \infty} (1 + \frac{c}{x^p})^x$$

Converting into form so that L'Hospital's rule can be applied . Taking ln on both sides,

$$\ln y = \lim_{x \to \infty} \frac{\ln(1 + \frac{c}{x^p})}{\frac{1}{x}}$$

Substituting

$$t = \frac{1}{x}$$

such that

$$x \to \infty, t \to 0$$

Thus we have,

$$\ln y = \lim_{t \to 0} \frac{\ln(1 + ct^p)}{t}$$

Now we have different case depending upon $p > 1$, $p < 0$ $p = 1$. when $p > 1$, Applying L'Hospital's rule we have,

$$\ln y = \lim_{t \to 0} \frac{pct^{p-1}}{1 + ct^p}$$

Substituting the value, we have

$$\ln y = 0$$

$$y = 1$$

when $p = 1$, Applying L'Hospital's rule we have,

$$\ln y = \lim_{t \to 0} \frac{c}{1 + ct}$$

Substituting the value, we have

$$\ln y = c$$

$$y = e^c$$

when $p < 0$, Applying L'Hospital's rule we have,

$$\ln y = \lim_{t \to 0} \frac{pct^{p-1}}{1 + ct^p}$$

Substituting the value, we have

$$\ln y = \infty$$

$$y = \infty$$

Thus we can summarize as

$$y = \begin{cases} 1 & \text{for} \quad p > 1 \\ e^c & \text{for} \quad p = 1 \\ \infty & \text{for} \quad p < 0. \end{cases}$$

Prob. 65. Given

$$y = \lim_{x \to \infty} \frac{\ln x}{x^p}$$

Applying L'Hospital Rule,we have

$$y = \lim_{x \to \infty} \frac{1}{px^p}$$

Thus substituting the value, we get,

$$y = 0$$

as denominator tends to ∞.

Prob. 67. Given,

$$y = 121e^{\frac{-17}{x}}$$

where y is the height in feet and x is the age of the tree in years.

(a) Rate of Growth is given by,

$$\frac{dy}{dx} = 2057\frac{e^{\frac{-17}{x}}}{x^2}$$

Thus for $x \to 0^+$ we have

$$\frac{dy}{dx} = \lim_{x \to 0^+} \frac{2057}{x^2}e^{\frac{-17}{x}}$$

Let $t = \frac{1}{x}$ Rewriting we have,

$$= \lim_{t \to \infty} 2057(e^{-17t}t^2)$$

Applying L'Hospital's Rule we have and substituting we have

$$y = 0$$

Similarly for $x \to \infty$, we have

$$\frac{dy}{dx} = \lim_{x \to \infty} \frac{2057}{x^2}e^{\frac{-17}{x}}$$

Applying L'Hospital's Rule we have and substituting we have

$$y = 0$$

Thus the rate of growth is zero at end points.

(b) To find x such that the growth is maximal, we differentiate the below equation, and equate it to zero,

$$Growth\,Rate = 2057\frac{e^{\frac{-17}{x}}}{x^2}$$

Differentiating we have

$$y' = 2057(\frac{17e^{\frac{-17}{x}} - 2xe^{\frac{-17}{x}}}{x^4}$$

Hence we have

$$x = \frac{17}{2}$$

(c) For $x < \frac{17}{2}$, the function is increasing and above that it is decreasing.

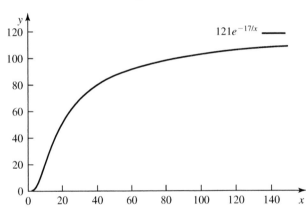

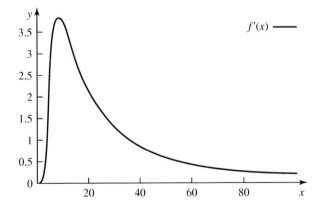

(d)

5.6 Difference Equations: Stability

Prob. 1.

(a) Given $N_{t+1} = (1.03)N_t$. This can be written as,

$$N_{t+1} = (1.03)((1.03)N_{t-1})$$

$$\Rightarrow N_{t+1} = (1.03)^{t+1}N_0$$

Given, $N_0 = 10$, Population when the generation, $t = 5$ is

$$N5 = (1.03)^5 * 10$$

$$= 11.59$$

(b) If $N_x = 2N_0$, then $x =?$

$\Rightarrow N_x = 2(10) = 20$. We have $N_{t+1} = (1.03)^{t+1}N_0$.

Place $(t+1)$ as x,

$$\Rightarrow \quad N_x = (1.03)^x N_0$$

$$\Rightarrow \quad 20 = (1.03)^x N_0$$

$$\Rightarrow \quad 20 = (1.03)^x 10$$

$$\Rightarrow \quad \frac{20}{10} = (1.03)^x$$

applying log on both sides,

$$\Rightarrow \quad \log(2) = log((1.03)^x x)$$

$$\Rightarrow \quad \log(2) = x \cdot \log(1.03)$$

$$\Rightarrow \quad x = \log(2)/\log(1.03)$$

$$\Rightarrow \quad x = 23.45$$

by round-off, $x = 24$. I.e., It will be in 24th generation, the population size will be twice that of N_0.

Prob. 3.

(a) Given population model is, $N_{t+1} = bN_t$. Also given, population increases by 2% each generation. Therefore, the N term at $t = 1$ is

$$N_1 = bN_0$$

$$\Rightarrow \quad N_0 + (0.02)N_0 = bN_0$$

$$\Rightarrow \quad (1.02)N_0 = bN_0$$

$$\text{therefore} \quad b = 1.02.$$

(b) If $N_0 = 20$, then $N_t = ?$ when $t = 10$. Given population model can be written as $N_t = b^t N_0$

$$\Rightarrow \quad N_{10} = (1.02)^{10} 20$$

$$\Rightarrow \quad N_{10} = 24.37$$

(c) If $N_t = 2N_0$, then $t = ?$

$$\Rightarrow \quad 2N_0 = (1.02)tN_0$$

$$\Rightarrow \quad 2 = (1.02)^t$$

applying log on both sides,

$$\Rightarrow \quad \log(2) = \log((1.02)^t)$$

$$\Rightarrow \quad \log(2) = t \log(1.02)$$

$$\Rightarrow \quad t = \log(2)/\log(1.02)$$

$$\Rightarrow \quad t = 35$$

Prob. 5.

(a) Given population model is, $N_{t+1} = bN_t$. Also given, population increases by $x\%$ each generation. Therefore, the N term at $t = 1$ is

$$N_1 = bN_0$$

$$\Rightarrow \quad N_0 + (x/100)N_0 = bN_0$$

$$\Rightarrow \quad (1 + x/100)N_0 = bN_0$$

$$\text{therefore} \quad b = (100 + x)/100.$$

(b) If $N_t = 2N_0$, then determine t.

$$\Rightarrow \quad 2N_0 = ((100 + x)/100)^t N_0$$

$$\Rightarrow \quad 2 = ((100 + x)/100)^t$$

applying log on both sides,

$$\Rightarrow \quad \log(2) = \log(((100 + x)/100)^t)$$

$$\Rightarrow \quad \log(2) = t\log((100 + x)/100)$$

$$\Rightarrow \quad t = \log(2)/\log((100 + x)/100)$$

Now, for $x = 0.1$,

$$t = \log(2)/\log((100 + 0.1)/100)$$

$$t = 693.49$$

For $x = 0.5$,

$$t = \log(2)/\log((100 + 0.5)/100)$$

$$t = 138.97$$

For $x = 1$,

$$t = \log(2)/\log((100 + 1)/100)$$

$$t = 69.66$$

For $x = 2$,

$$t = \log(2)/\log((100 + 2)/100)$$

$$t = 35.00$$

For $x = 5$,

$$t = \log(2)/\log((100+5)/100)$$

$$t = 14.20$$

For $x = 10$,

$$t = \log(2)/\log((100+10)/100)$$

$$t = 7.27$$

Prob. 7.

(a) Given population model is,

$$N_{t+1} = 0.9N_t$$

The equilibrium can be obtained by solving $N = RN$. But the only solution for this is $N^* = 0$. As $0 < R < 1$, N_t will return to equilibrium $N^* = 0$ if $N_0 > 0$. Therefore as $0 < R < 1$, this population model is stable.

(b) The fixed points are found graphically, where the graphs of $N_{t+1} = 1.3N_t$ and $N_{t+1} = N_t$ intersects.

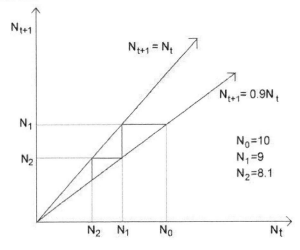

For any N_0, the population growth is converging towards equilibrium $N^* = 0$.

Therefore, given population model is stable.

Prob. 9. Given model is, $x_{t+1} = \frac{2}{3} - \frac{2}{3}x_t^2$. To find the equilibrium, we need to solve $x = f(x)$ i.e., to solve $x = \frac{2}{3} - \frac{2}{3}x^2$

$$\Rightarrow \quad \frac{2}{3}x^2 + x - \frac{2}{3} = 0$$

$$\Rightarrow \quad 2x^2 + 3x - 2 = 0$$

The left hand side can be factored into $(2x - 1)(x + 2)$, and we find that $(2x - 1)(x + 2) = 0$,

$$\texttt{therefore} \quad x = \frac{1}{2} \quad \texttt{or} \quad x = -2$$

To determine stability, we need to evaluate the derivative of $f(x) = \frac{2}{3} - \frac{2}{3}x^2$ at the equilibrium. Now, $f'(x) = -\frac{4}{3}x$ if $x = \frac{1}{2}$, then

$$\left| f'\left(\frac{1}{2}\right) \right| = \left| -\frac{2}{3} \right| = \frac{2}{3} < 1$$

and if $x = -2$, then

$$|f'(-2)| = \left| \frac{8}{3} \right| = \frac{8}{3} > 1$$

Thus $x = \frac{1}{2}$ is locally stable and $x = -2$ is unstable. As $f'\left(\frac{1}{2}\right) = -\frac{2}{3} > 0$, the equilibrium is approached with oscillations.

Prob. 11. Given model is $x_{t+1} = \frac{x_t}{0.5+x_t}$. To find the equilibrium, we need to solve $x = f(x)$ i.e., to solve $x = \frac{x}{0.5+x}$

$$\Rightarrow \quad x(0.5 + x) = x$$

$$\Rightarrow \quad x(x - 0.5) = 0$$

Therefore $x = 0$ or $x = 0.5$.

Now,

$$f'(x) = \frac{0.5 + x - x}{(0.5 + x)^2} = \frac{0.5}{(0.5 + x)^2}.$$

Since $f'(0) = \frac{1}{0.5} = 2 > 1$, we conclude that $x^* = 0$ is unstable. Since $f'(0.5) = 0.5 \in (0, 1)$, we conclude that $x^* = 0.5$ is locally stable and is approached without oscillations.

Prob. 13.

(a) Given model is $x_{t+1} = \frac{5x_t^2}{4+x_t^2}$. To find the equilibrium, we need to solve $x = f(x)$ i.e., to solve $x = \frac{5x^2}{4+x^2}$

$$\Rightarrow \quad x(x^2 - 5x + 4) = 0.$$

Therefore $x = 0$ or $x = 4$ or $x = 1$.

Now,

$$f'(x) = \frac{40x}{(4 + x^2)^2}$$

Since $f'(0) = 0$, we conclude that $x^* = 0$ is locally stable and is approached without oscillations. Since $f'(4) = \frac{2}{5} \in (0, 1)$, we conclude that $x^* = 4$ is locally stable and is approached without oscillations. Since $f'(1) = \frac{8}{5} > 1$, we conclude that $x^* = 1$ is unstable.

(b) (i) Considering $x_0 = 0.5$

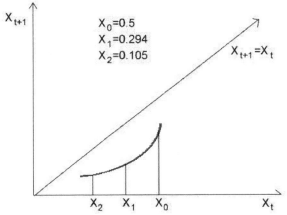

The subsequent terms at $t = 0$, $t = 1$, $t = 2$ shows that the value is converging towards closest fixed point $x^* = 0$

(ii) Considering $x_0 = 2$. The subsequent values at $t = 0$, $t = 1$ and $t = 2$ shows that value x value is reaching towards fixed point $x^* = 4$.

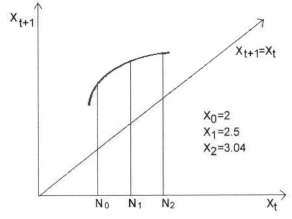

Prob. 15. (a) We see that if $P = 0$, then $R(0) = 0$. Also, since this function is exponential in nature, P is the only factor determining sign. Hence, for $P > 0$, $R(P) > 0$.

(b) 0, (c) $1/\beta$, (d) $P = 2/\beta$ is an inflection point,

(e)

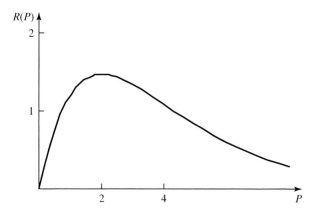

Prob. 17. (a)

t	N_t	t	N_t
0	100	11	366.8
1	367.9	12	93.4
2	92.8	13	366.8
3	366.7	14	93.4
4	93.5	15	366.8
5	366.9	16	93.4
6	93.4	17	366.8
7	366.8	18	93.4
8	93.4	19	366.8
9	336.8	20	93.4
10	93.4	21	366.8

(b) To find equilibria, solve $N = 10Ne^{-0.01N}$; $N = 0$ is another equilibrium.

(c) Oscillations seem to appear and the system does not seem to converge to the nontrivial equilibrium.

Prob. 19. (a) Need to solve: $N = N(1 + 1.5(1 - \frac{N}{100})$ $N = 0$, $1 = 1 + 1.5 - \frac{1.5N}{100}$ $N = 100$.

(b) for $N_0 = 10$, starting at 10, will go to 100.

Prob. 21. Let $r > 1$, need to solve: $X = rX(1 - x)$ $x = 0$, $1 = r(1 - x)\frac{1}{4} = 1 - x$,

$x = 1 - \frac{1}{r}$. Now,

$$f'(x) = r[(1 - x) + x(-1)] = r[1 - 2x].$$

$$f'(1 - \frac{1}{r}) = r(1 - 2 + \frac{2}{4}) = -r + 2$$

To 2e stable $|-r + 2| < 1$, $1 < r < 3$.

Prob. 23. Need to solve:

$$
\begin{aligned}
N &= rN^{1-\gamma}N \\
1 &= rN^{1-\gamma} \\
\frac{1}{r} &= N^{1-\gamma}, \quad N = r^{\frac{1}{\gamma-1}}.
\end{aligned}
$$

Now, $f'(r^{\frac{1}{\gamma-1}}(= r(2 - \gamma)(r^{-1}) = 2 - \gamma$

To be stable we must have: $|2 - \gamma| < 1$ $1 < \gamma < 3$.

Prob. 25. Need to solve:

$$
\begin{aligned}
N &= e^{r(1-\frac{N}{K})}N \\
1 &= e^{r(1-\frac{N}{K})}, \quad N = K.
\end{aligned}
$$

Now,

$$
\begin{aligned}
f'(N) &= e^{r(1-\frac{r}{K})} + Ne^{r(1-\frac{N}{K})}(-\frac{r}{K}) \\
f'(K) &= e^0 + ke^0(-\frac{r}{K}) = 1 - 4.
\end{aligned}
$$

To be stable: $\left|1 - r\right| < 1$, $0 < r < 1$.

5.7   Numerical Methods

Prob. 1. $\sqrt{7} = 2.645751$

Prob. 3. 0.6529186

Prob. 5. 1.895494

Prob. 7. (a) $|x_n| = 2^n x_0$, (b) ∞

Prob. 9. (a) $x_0 = 3, x_1 = 4.166667, x_2 = 4.003333, x_3 = 4.000001$,

(b) $x_0 = x_1 = x_2 = \ldots = 4$

5.8 Antiderivatives

Prob. 1. $F(x) = \frac{4x^3}{3} - \frac{x^2}{2} + C$

Prob. 3. $F(x) = \frac{x^3}{3} + \frac{3x^2}{2} + 3x + C$

Prob. 5. Given the function as,

$$f(x) = x^4 - 3x^2 + 1$$

Integrating, we get

$$\int f(x) = F(x) = \frac{x^5}{5} - x^3 + x + C.$$

where C is a constant.

Prob. 7. Given the function as,

$$f(x) = 4x^3 - 2x + 3$$

Integrating, we get

$$\int f(x) = F(x) = x^4 - x^2 + 3x + C.$$

where C is a constant.

Prob. 9. $F(x) = x + \ln|x| - \frac{1}{x} + C$

Prob. 11. Given the function as,

$$f(x) = 1 - \frac{1}{x^2}$$

Integrating, we get

$$\int f(x) = F(x) = x + \frac{1}{x} + C.$$

where C is a constant.

Prob. 13. Given the function as,

$$f(x) = \frac{1}{1+x}$$

Integrating, we get

$$\int f(x) = F(x) = \ln(1+x) + C.$$

where C is a constant.

Prob. 15. Given the function as,

$$f(x) = 5x^4 + \frac{5}{x^4}$$

Integrating, we get

$$\int f(x) = F(x) = x^5 - \frac{5}{3x^3} + C.$$

where C is a constant.

Prob. 17. $F(x) = \frac{1}{2}\ln|1+2x| + C$

Prob. 19. Given the function as,

$$f(x) = e^{-3x}$$

Integrating, we get

$$\int f(x) = F(x) = -\frac{e^{-3x}}{3} + C.$$

where C is a constant.

Prob. 21. Given the function as,

$$f(x) = 2e^{2x}$$

Integrating, we get

$$\int f(x) = F(x) = e^{2x} + C.$$

where C is a constant.

Prob. 23. Given the function as,

$$f(x) = \frac{1}{e^{2x}}$$

Integrating, we get

$$\int f(x) = F(x) = -\frac{1}{e^{2x}} + C.$$

where C is a constant.

Prob. 25. Given the function as,

$$f(x) = \sin(2x)$$

Integrating, we get

$$\int f(x) = F(x) = -\frac{\cos(2x)}{2} + C.$$

where C is a constant.

Prob. 27. $F(x) = -3\cos(\frac{x}{3}) + 3\sin(\frac{x}{3}) + C.$

Prob. 29. Given the function as,

$$f(x) = 2\sin(\frac{\pi x}{2}) - 3\cos(\frac{\pi x}{2})$$

Integrating, we get

$$\int f(x) = F(x) = -\frac{4}{\pi}\cos(\frac{\pi x}{2}) - \frac{6}{\pi}\sin(\frac{\pi x}{2}) + C.$$

where C is a constant.

Prob. 31. Given the function as,

$$f(x) = \sec^2(2x)$$

Integrating, we get

$$\int f(x) = F(x) = \frac{\tan(2x)}{2} + C.$$

where C is a constant.

Prob. 33. Given the function as,

$$f(x) = \sec^2\left(\frac{x}{3}\right)$$

Integrating, we get

$$\int f(x) = F(x) = 3\tan\left(\frac{x}{3}\right) + C.$$

where C is a constant.

Prob. 35. Given the function as,

$$f(x) = \frac{\sec x + \cos x}{\cos x}$$

We can rewrite it as,

$$f(x) = \sec^2 x + 1$$

Integrating, we get

$$\int f(x) = F(x) = \tan x + x + C$$

where C is a constant.

Prob. 37. $F(x) = \frac{x^{-6}}{-6} + \frac{3x^6}{6} - \frac{1}{2}\cos(2x) + C.$

Prob. 39. $F(x) = \frac{1}{3}\tan(2x - 1) + \frac{x^2}{2} - 3\ln|x| + C.$

Prob. 41. $F(x) = \frac{e^{(a+1)x}}{a(a+1)} + C$

Prob. 43. $F(x) = \frac{1}{a}\ln|ax + 3| + C.$

Prob. 45. $F(x) = \frac{x^{a+3}}{a+3} - \frac{a^{x+2}}{\ln a} + C.$

Prob. 47. Given the equation as,

$$\frac{dy}{dx} = \frac{2}{x} - x$$

Thus, we have the general solution by finding the antiderivative of the above function.

Hence,

$$y = 2\ln x - \frac{x^2}{2} + C$$

where C is a constant.

Prob. 49. Given the equation as,

$$\frac{dy}{dx} = x(1+x)$$

We can rewrite the above function as,

$$\frac{dy}{dx} = x^2 + x$$

Thus, we have the general solution by finding the antiderivative of the above function. Hence,

$$y = \frac{x^3}{3} + \frac{x^2}{2}$$

where C is a constant.

Prob. 51. Given the equation as,

$$\frac{dy}{dt} = t(1-t)$$

We can rewrite the above function as,

$$\frac{dy}{dt} = t - t^2$$

Thus, we have the general solution by finding the antiderivative of the above function. Hence,

$$y = \frac{t^2}{2} - \frac{t^3}{3} + C$$

where C is a constant.

Prob. 53. Given the equation as,

$$\frac{dy}{dt} = e^{-\frac{t}{2}}$$

Making the substitution, $x = -\frac{t}{2}$, we have $dx = -\frac{1}{2}dt$ Thus, the function becomes,

$$\frac{dy}{dx} = -2e^x$$

and we have the general solution by finding the antiderivative of the above function. Hence,

$$y = -2e^x$$

Substituting the value of x we have,

$$y = -2e^{-\frac{t}{2}} + C$$

where C is a constant.

Prob. 55. Given the equation as,

$$\frac{dy}{dx} = \sin(\pi x)$$

Thus, we have the general solution by finding the antiderivative of the above function.

Hence,

$$y = \frac{1}{\pi}\cos(\pi x) + C$$

where C is a constant.

Prob. 57. Given the equation as,

$$\frac{dy}{dx} = \sec^2\frac{x}{2}$$

Thus, we have the general solution by finding the antiderivative of the above function.

Hence,

$$y = 2\tan\frac{x}{2} + C$$

where C is a constant.

Prob. 59. It should be $1 = 0 + C$, $c = 1$. Equation is $y = x^3 + 1$.

Prob. 61. Given the equation as,

$$\frac{dy}{dx} = 2\sqrt{x}$$

and given that when,

$$y = 2, x = 1$$

Thus, we have the general solution by finding the antiderivative of the above function.

Hence,

$$y = \frac{4}{3}x^{\frac{3}{2}} + C$$

where C is a constant. Substituting the values of y and x we get,

$$2 = \frac{4}{3} + C$$

Hence, we get

$$C = \frac{2}{3}$$

Thus, we have final equation as

$$y = \frac{4}{3}x^{\frac{3}{2}} + \frac{2}{3}$$

Prob. 63. Given the equation as,

$$\frac{dN}{dt} = \frac{1}{t}$$

and given that when,

$$N(1) = 10$$

Thus, we have the general solution by finding the antiderivative of the above function. Hence,

$$N = \ln t + C$$

where C is a constant. Substituting the values of $N(1)$ we get,

$$10 = \ln 1 + C$$

Hence we get

$$C = 10$$

Thus, we have final equation as

$$N = \ln t + C$$

Prob. 65. Given the equation as,

$$\frac{dW}{dt} = e^t$$

and given that,

$$W(0) = 5$$

Thus, we have the general solution by finding the antiderivative of the above function. Hence,

$$W = e^t + C$$

where C is a constant. Substituting the values of $N(0)$ we get,

$$1 = 1 + C$$

Hence, we have

$$C = 0$$

Thus, we have final equation as

$$W = e^t$$

Prob. 67. Given the equation as, $\frac{dW}{dt} = e^{-3t}$ and given that, $W(0) = \frac{2}{3}$ Substituting $x = -3t$ we have $dx = -3dt$ Thus, we have the new function as,

$$\frac{dW}{dx} = \frac{-1}{3}e^x$$

and when $t = 0, x = 0$ Thus, we have the general solution by finding the antiderivative of the above function. Hence,

$$W = \frac{-1}{3}e^x + C$$

where C is a constant. Substituting the values of $N(0)$ we get,

$$\frac{2}{3} = \frac{-1}{3} + C$$

Hence, we have

$$C = 1$$

Thus, we have equation as

$$W = \frac{-1}{3}e^x + 1$$

Substituting we have the final equation, as

$$W = \frac{-1}{3}e^{-3t} + 1$$

Prob. 69. Given the equation as,

$$\frac{dT}{dt} = \sin(\pi t)$$

and given that,

$$W(0) = 3$$

Substituting $x = \pi t$ we have

$$dx = \pi dt$$

Thus, we have the new function as,

$$\frac{dT}{dx} = \frac{1}{\pi}\sin x$$

and when

$$t = 0, x = 0$$

Thus, we have the general solution by finding the antiderivative of the above function. Hence,

$$T = -\frac{1}{\pi}\cos x + C$$

where C is a constant. Substituting the values of $T(0)$ we get,

$$3 = -\frac{1}{\pi} + C$$

Hence, we have

$$C = 3 + \frac{1}{\pi}$$

Thus, we have equation as

$$T = -\frac{1}{\pi}\cos x + 3 + \frac{1}{\pi}$$

Substituting we have the final equation, as

$$T = -\frac{1}{\pi}\cos(\pi t) + 3 + \frac{1}{\pi}$$

Prob. 71. Given the equation as,

$$\frac{dy}{dx} = \frac{e^x + e^{-x}}{2}$$

and given that,

$$y = 0, x = 0$$

We can rewrite the above equation as

$$\frac{dy}{dx} = \frac{e^x}{2} + \frac{e^{-x}}{2}$$

Thus, we have the general solution by finding the antiderivative of the above function. Hence,

$$Y = \frac{e^x}{2} - \frac{e^{-x}}{2} + C$$

where C is a constant. Substituting the values of $y = 0$ and $x = 0$ we get,

$$0 = \frac{1}{2} - \frac{1}{2} + C$$

Hence, we have

$$C = 0$$

Thus, we have final equation as

$$y = \frac{e^x}{2} - \frac{e^{-x}}{2}$$

Prob. 73. Given the equation as,

$$\frac{dL}{dx} = e^{-.1x}$$

and $x \geq 0$. Also given that

$$L_\infty = \lim_{x \to \infty} L(x) = 25$$

First, we find, $L(x)$.

$$L(x) = -10e^{-.1x} + C$$

where C is a constant. Substituting this, in above equation, we have

$$L_\infty = \lim_{x \to \infty} (-10e^{-.1x} + C) = 25$$

$$C = 25$$

Thus we have,

$$L(x) = -10e^{-.1x} + 25$$

Hence, we have $L(0)$ as,

$$L(0) = -10 + 25$$

$$= 15$$

Prob. 75. We know that the equation of a freely falling object from rest is

$$v^2 = 2ah$$

where v is the final velocity and h is the height, and a is the acceleration. Thus putting the value,

$$v^2 = 6400$$

$$v = 80$$

Again, we know that,

$$v = at$$

where t is the time taken in falling. Thus putting the values, we have,

$$t = \frac{v}{a}$$

$$= \frac{5}{2} = 2.5$$

Prob. 77. We are given the volume change at time t is proportional to $t(24 - t)$, and that we water the plant at a constant rate of 4 per hour.

(a) Thus the net rate of loss of water is

$$\frac{dV}{dt} = -at(24 - t) + 4$$

This is because the first part of equation denotes the loss of water due to evaporation and the second part denote the water added per hour. Here a is a constant which has been introduced to convert the proportionality to some constant value dependent on t only.

(b) $V(t) = -12at^2 + \frac{at^3}{3} + 9t + C$, need to have

$$V(0) = V(24), -12a(24)^2 + \frac{a(24)^3}{3} + 4(24) = 0$$

$$a = \frac{1}{24}.$$

5.10   Review Problems

Prob. 1. Given the function as,

$$f(x) = xe^{-x}, x \geq 0$$

(a) For evaluation $f(0)$, we put $x = 0$ in above equation. Substituting, the value we have, $f(0) = 0$. For calculating the limit, we have

$$F = \lim_{x \to \infty} xe^{-x}$$

$$= \lim_{x \to \infty} \frac{x}{e^x}$$

Applying L'Hospital rule, we have,

$$F = \lim_{x \to \infty} \frac{1}{e^x}$$

Substituting the values we have

$$F = 0$$

(b) For local maxima, we differentiate the below function,

$$f(x) = xe^{-x}$$

So, differentiating,

$$f'(x) = e^{-x} - xe^{-x}$$

Substituting to zero,we have

$$f'(x) = 0$$

$$e^{-x} - xe^{-x} = 0$$

$$e^{-x}(1 - x) = 0$$

So we have

$$x = 1$$

Thus the function has a absolute maxima at $x = 1$

(c) To calculate the inflection point, we differentiate it twice and equate to zero. Given,

$$f(x) = xe^{-x}$$

So,

$$f'(x) = e^{-x} - xe^{-x}$$

Differentiating again,

$$f''(x) = -e^{-x} - e^{-x} + xe^{-x}$$

$$= e^{-x}(x - 2)$$

Equating to zero, we have

$$e^{-x}(x - 2) = 0$$

Hence,

$$x = 2$$

This is the point of inflection.

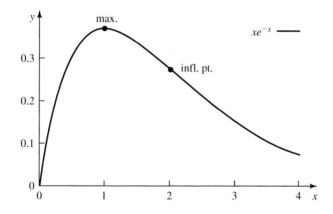

(d)

Prob. 3. Given the following definitions,

$$\sinh x = \frac{e^x - e^{-x}}{2}$$

$$\cosh x = \frac{e^x + e^{-x}}{2}$$

$$\tanh x = \frac{e^x - e^{-x}}{e^x + e^{-x}}$$

(a) From above we have,

$$\tanh x = \frac{e^x - e^{-x}}{e^x + e^{-x}}$$

So differentiating it, we have

$$f' = \frac{(e^x + e^{-x})(e^x + e^{-x}) - (e^x - e^{-x})(e^x - e^{-x})}{(e^x + e^{-x})^2}$$

$$= \frac{4}{(e^x + e^{-x})^2}$$

Thus we see that f' is always positive and hence is a strictly increasing function.

Also,

$$\lim_{x \to \infty} \tanh x = \lim_{x \to \infty} \frac{e^x - e^{-x}}{e^x + e^{-x}}$$

$$= 1$$

Again,

$$\lim_{x \to -\infty} \tanh x = \lim_{x \to -\infty} \frac{e^x - e^{-x}}{e^x + e^{-x}}$$

$$= 1$$

(b) The function $f(x) = \tanh x$ is invertible because the function has the same values at both the limiting points and is strictly increasing with a minimum value at $x = 1$ Its inverse function can be easily calculated. We have,

$$y = \frac{e^x - e^{-x}}{e^x + e^{-x}}$$

$$e^{-x}(y + 1) = e^x(1 - y)$$

$$e^{-2x} = \frac{1 - y}{1 + y}$$

$$-2x = \ln\left(\frac{1 - y}{1 + y}\right)$$

$$x = \frac{1}{2} \ln\left(\frac{1 + y}{1 - y}\right)$$

Thus we have,

$$f^{-1}x = y = \frac{1}{2} \ln\left(\frac{1 + x}{1 - x}\right)$$

(c) To find the differential, we have

$$f^{-1}x = y = \frac{1}{2}\ln(\frac{1+x}{1-x})$$

Differentiating,

$$f' = \frac{1}{2}(\frac{1-x}{1+x}\frac{-2}{(1-x)^2})$$

Thus we have,

$$f' = \frac{1}{1-x^2}$$

Hence, we get the result.

(d) Given that,

$$\tanh x = \frac{\sinh x}{\cosh x}$$

Also given,

$$\cosh^2 x - \sinh^2 x = 1$$

Thus we have to find, $\frac{d(\tanh x)}{dx}$. Thus we have

$$\tanh x = \frac{e^x - e^{-x}}{e^x + e^{-x}}$$

$$\frac{d(\tanh x)}{dx} = \frac{4}{(e^x + e^{-x})^2}$$

Now we know that,

$$\cosh x = \frac{e^x + e^{-x}}{2}$$

So,

$$\cosh^2 x = \frac{(e^x + e^{-x})^2}{4}$$

Substituting in above, equation we have,

$$\frac{d(\tanh x)}{dx} = \frac{1}{\cosh^2 x}$$

Prob. 5. We are given a function, such that,

$$R(P) = \alpha P e^{-\beta P}, P \geq 0$$

(a) To, find the first derivative, we differentiate the above function,

$$R'(P) = \alpha e^{-\beta P} - \alpha \beta P e^{-\beta P}$$

$$= \alpha e^{-\beta P}(1 - \beta P)$$

To find the second differential, we differentiate the above function,

$$R''(P) = -\beta \alpha e^{-\beta P} - \beta \alpha e^{-\beta P}(1 - \beta P)$$

$$= -\beta \alpha e^{-\beta P}(2 - \beta P)$$

Hence, we get both the differentials.

(b) We have the differential of $R(P)$ as

$$R'(P) = \alpha e^{-\beta P}(1 - \beta P)$$

Equating it to zero, we have

$$\alpha e^{-\beta P}(1 - \beta P) = 0$$

$$1 - \beta P = 0$$

$$P = \frac{1}{\beta}$$

Thus $R'(P) = 0$ only when $P = \frac{1}{\beta}$ Also $R''(\frac{1}{\beta})$ equals,

$$R''(P) = -\beta \alpha e^{-\beta P}(2 - \beta P)$$

$$R''(\frac{1}{\beta}) = -\beta \alpha e^{-\beta \frac{1}{\beta}}(2 - \beta \frac{1}{\beta})$$

$$= -\beta \alpha e^{-1}$$

$$< 0$$

Thus at $P = \frac{1}{\beta}$, we have a local maxima.

Also, we see from above,

$$R(P) = \alpha P e^{-\beta P}, P \geq 0$$

Substituting $P = \frac{1}{\beta}$, we have

$$R(\frac{1}{\beta}) = \alpha \frac{1}{\beta} e^{-\beta \frac{1}{\beta}}$$

$$= \frac{\alpha}{\beta} e^{-1}$$

(c) To find the global maxima, we have to find $R(0)$ and

$$\lim_{x \to \infty} R(P)$$

So, finding the limit,

$$\lim_{x \to \infty} R(P) = \lim_{x \to \infty} \alpha P e^{-\beta P}$$

Rearranging the function, we get,

$$\lim_{x \to \infty} R(P) = \lim_{x \to \infty} \frac{\alpha P}{e^{\beta P}}$$

Applying L'Hospital Rule,

$$= \lim_{x \to \infty} \frac{\alpha}{\beta e^{\beta P}}$$

Substituting the value we get,

$$\lim_{x \to \infty} R(P) = 0$$

Thus, we have a global maxima at $P = \frac{1}{\beta}$.

(d) To find the inflection point we substitute the second derivative to zero. We have

$$R''(P) = -\beta \alpha e^{-\beta P}(2 - \beta P)$$

Equating it to zero, we have

$$-\beta \alpha e^{-\beta P}(2 - \beta P) = 0$$

$$2 - \beta P = 0$$

$$P = \frac{2}{\beta}$$

Also, we see that that the function changes sign at this value. Hence $P = \frac{2}{\beta}$ is a point of inflection.

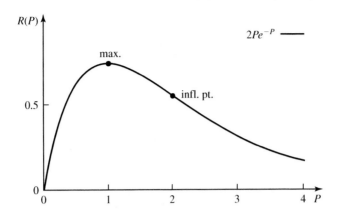

(e)

Prob. 7. The monod growth curve is given by

$$f(x) = \frac{cx}{k + x}$$

where c and k are constants.

(a) To find the horizontal asymptote, we find the limit tending to infinity,

$$\lim_{x \to \infty} f(x) = \lim_{x \to \infty} \frac{cx}{k + x}$$

Applying L'Hospital rule we have,

$$\lim_{x \to \infty} f(x) = \lim_{x \to \infty} c = c$$

This is called the saturation value.

(b) For $x \geq 0$ the function is strictly increasing . This is because when we find its derivative we have,

$$f'(x) = \frac{c(k + x) - cx}{(k + x)^2}$$

$$= \frac{ck}{(k + x)^2}$$

$$> 0$$

Hence the function is strictly increasing. Its concave down as its second derivative is less than zero for all $x > 0$.

(c) For $x = k$ we have

$$f(k) = \frac{ck}{k + k}$$

$$= \frac{c}{2}$$

Thus this value is half of the saturation value.

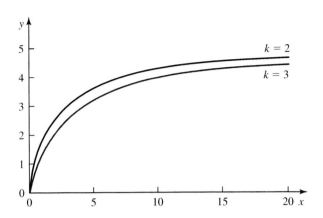

(d)

(e) For the three function given below,

$$g(x) = \frac{10x}{3+x}$$

$$h(x) = \frac{10x}{5+x}$$

$$J(x) = \frac{8x}{5+x}$$

We can find their saturation value and half saturation value directly. The higher the saturation value, the larger the function, and when the saturation value is same, we check the half saturation value, the greater it is the smaller the function. Thus, based on this analysis we can write,

$$\frac{10x}{3+x} > \frac{10x}{5+x} > \frac{8x}{5+x}$$

Prob. 9. Given that

$$L(\theta) = p_{AA}^{n_1} p_{Aa}^{n_2} p_{aa}^{n_3}$$

(a) Give that,

$$n_1 = 8, n_2 = 6, n_3 = 3$$

So our above equation becomes,

$$L(\theta) = p_{AA}^{8} p_{Aa}^{6} p_{aa}^{3}$$

Also given

$$p_{AA} = \theta^2, p_{Aa} = 2\theta(1 - \theta), p_{aa} = (1 - \theta)^2$$

Substituting above, we can get the value of $L(\theta)$.

(b) We have the equation,

$$L(\theta) = p_{AA}^8 p_{Aa}^6 p_{aa}^3$$

Taking ln, we have

$$\ln(L(\theta)) = n_1 \ln(p_{AA}) + n_2 \ln(p_{Aa}) + n_3 \ln(p_{aa})$$

Thus differentiating above and putting the values of the above three variables and equating to zero, we have the maximum value of $L(\theta)$ and that will be the same for the maximum value of $\ln(L(\theta))$.

(c) Put the given values and solve for x.

Prob. 11. Given the equation as,

$$\frac{dc}{dt} = -0.1e^{-0.3t}$$

(a) To find c, we integrate the above equation,

$$c = \int -0.1e^{-0.3t} dt \quad = -\frac{1}{3}e^{-.3t} + K$$

where K is a constant. Given at $t = \infty$, $c = 0$ so $k = 0$. Hence, $C = -\frac{1}{3}e^{-.3t}$

(b) At $t = 0$, we have $c = \frac{1}{3}$. To become the value to half, we have,

$$\frac{2}{3} = -\frac{1}{3}e^{-.3t} \quad -\ln 2 = -.3t \quad t = \frac{\ln 2}{.3}$$

Thus at $t = \frac{\ln 2}{.3}$ the concentration becomes equal to half its initial amount.

Prob. 13. Given the equation of the height as,

$$h(t) = v_0 t - \frac{1}{2}gt^2$$

(a) To find the time at which, the object reaches the maximum height, we differentiate the below equation.

$$h(t) = v_0 t - \frac{1}{2} g t^2 \qquad h'(t) = v_0 - gt$$

Equating to zero, we have

$$v_0 - gt = 0 \qquad t = \frac{v_0}{g}$$

(b) The height reached at $t = \frac{v_0}{g}$ is,

$$h = v_0 \frac{v_0}{g} - \frac{1}{2} g \left(\frac{v_0}{g} \right)^2 = \frac{(v_0)^2}{g}$$

This is the maximum height reached . So maximum height is,

$$\texttt{Max height} = \frac{(v_0)^2}{g}$$

(c) Velocity of the particle as it reaches the maximum height is calculated as follows. we know that $V = v_0 - gt$ Substituting the value of $t = \frac{v_0}{g}$, we have $V = 0$. Thus the velocity at the maximum point is zero.

(d) To reach the same height again, the particle will take the amount of time equal to two times the time taken to reach the maximum height. Thus we have from previous calculation, $t = \frac{v_0}{g}$. Thus the time taken to reach the same height again is, $T = 2 \frac{v_0}{g}$

Chapter 6

Integration

6.1 The Definite Integral

Prob. 1. The left endpoints of the four intervals are $0, \frac{1}{4}, \frac{1}{2}, \frac{3}{4}$.

The approximation is then $\frac{1}{4} \cdot 0 + \frac{1}{4}\frac{1}{16} + \frac{1}{4}\frac{1}{4} + \frac{1}{4}\frac{9}{16} = \frac{7}{32}$.

Prob. 3. The right endpoints of the four intervals are $\frac{1}{4}, \frac{1}{2}, \frac{3}{4}, 1$.

The approximation is then $\frac{1}{4}\frac{1}{16} + \frac{1}{4}\frac{1}{4} + \frac{1}{4}\frac{9}{16} + \frac{1}{4} \cdot 1 = \frac{15}{32}$.

Prob. 5.

$$\sum_{k=1}^{4} \sqrt{k} = \sqrt{1} + \sqrt{2} + \sqrt{3} + \sqrt{4}.$$

Prob. 7.

$$\sum_{k=2}^{6} 3^k = 3^2 + 3^3 + 3^4 + 3^5 + 3^6.$$

Prob. 9.

$$\sum_{k=0}^{3} = (0+1)^0 + (1+1)^1 + (2+1)^2 + (3+1)^3.$$

Prob. 11.

$$\sum_{k=0}^{3} (-1)^{k+1} = (-1)^1 + (-1)^2 + (-1)^3 + (-1)^4.$$

Prob. 13.

$$\sum_{k=1}^{n} \left(\frac{k}{n}\right)^2 \frac{1}{n} = \left(\frac{1}{n}\right)^2 \frac{1}{n} + \left(\frac{2}{n}\right)^2 \frac{1}{n} + \cdots + \left(\frac{n}{n}\right)^2 \frac{1}{n}.$$

Prob. 15.

$$2 + 4 + 6 + \cdots + 2n = \sum_{k=1}^{n} 2k$$

291

Prob. 17.

$$\ln 2 + \ln 3 + \ln 4 + \ln 5 + \ln 6 = \sum_{k=2}^{5} \ln k.$$

Prob. 19.

$$-\frac{1}{4} + \frac{1}{6} + \frac{2}{7} + \frac{3}{8} = \sum_{k=2}^{6} \frac{k-3}{k+2}.$$

Prob. 21. $\displaystyle\sum_{k=0}^{n-1} q^k$.

Prob. 23.

$$\sum_{k=1}^{15}(2k+3) = \sum_{k=1}^{15} 2k + \sum_{k=1}^{15} 3 = 2 \cdot \left(\frac{15(15+1)}{2}\right) + 3 \cdot 15 = 15 \cdot 19 = 285.$$

Prob. 25.

$$\sum_{k=0}^{6} k(k+1) = \sum_{k=0}^{6}(k^2 + k) = \sum_{k=1}^{6} k + \sum_{k=1}^{6} k^2 = \frac{6 \cdot 7}{2} + \frac{6 \cdot 7 \cdot 13}{6} = 112 .$$

Prob. 27.

$$\sum_{k=1}^{n} 4(k-1)^2 = 4\sum_{k=1}^{n-1} k^2 = \frac{4(n-1)(n)(2n-1)}{6}.$$

Prob. 29. $\displaystyle\sum_{k=1}^{10}(-1)^k = -1 + 1 - 1 + 1 - 1 + 1 - 1 + 1 - 1 + 1 = 0$.

Prob. 31.

(a) All the terms collapse except the first and the last, so

$$\sum_{k=1}^{n}[(k+1)^3 - k^3] = -1^3 + (n+1)^3 .$$

(b) We have

$$\sum_{k=1}^{n}[(k+1)^3 - k^3] = \sum_{k=1}^{n}(3k^2 + 3k + 1)$$

$$= 3\sum_{k=1}^{n} k^2 + 3\sum_{k=1}^{n} k + \sum_{k=1}^{n} 1$$

$$= 3\sum_{k=1}^{n} k^2 + 3\frac{n(n+1)}{2} + n$$

(c) We have $\displaystyle 3\sum_{k=1}^{n} k^2 = (n+1)^3 - 1 - 3\frac{n(n+1)}{2} - n$,

therefore, $\displaystyle\sum_{k=1}^{n} k^2 = \frac{n(n+1)(2n+1)}{6}$.

Prob. 33. $0.4[(1-(-0.8)^2)+(1-(-0.4)^2)+(1-0^2)+(1-(0.4)^2)+(1-(0.8)^2)]=1.36$.

Prob. 35. $(2+(-2)^2)+(2+(-1)^2)+(2+0^2)+(2+1^2)=14$.

Prob. 37. $\frac{\pi}{2}[\sin\frac{\pi}{2}+\sin\pi+\frac{3\pi}{2}]=0$.

Prob. 39. $\frac{b^2}{2}-\frac{a^2}{2}$ equals the area of $\triangle(0,0)(b,0)(b,b)$ minus the area of

$\triangle(0,0)(a,0)(a,a)$ (see previous exercise.)

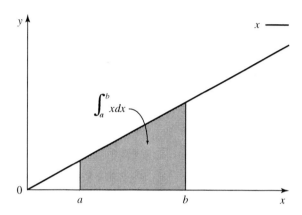

Prob. 41. $\int_1^2 2x^3\,dx$.

Prob. 43. $\int_{-3}^2 (2x-1)\,dx$.

Prob. 45. $\int_2^3 \frac{x-1}{x+2}\,dx$.

Prob. 47. $\int_{-5}^2 e^x\,dx$.

Prob. 49. $\displaystyle\lim_{\|p\|\to0}\sum_{k=1}^{n}(c_k+1)^{1/3}\,\triangle x_k,\quad p=[2,6]$.

Prob. 51. $\displaystyle\lim_{\|P\|\to0}\sum_{k=1}^{n}\ln c_k\,\Delta x_k$, where P is a partition of $[1,e]$.

Prob. 53. $\displaystyle\lim_{\|P\|\to0}\sum_{k=1}^{n}g(c_k)\,\Delta x_k$, where P is a partition of $[0,5]$.

Prob. 55. The integral is the area between x-axis and the graph of $y = x^2 - 1$ from $x = 1$ to $x = 2$ − area between x-axis and the graph of $y = x^2 - 1$ from $x = -1$ to $x = 1$.

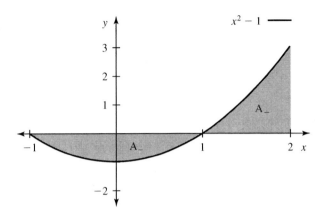

Prob. 57. The integral is the area between x-axis and the graph of $y = e^{-x}$ from $x = 0$ to $x = 5$.

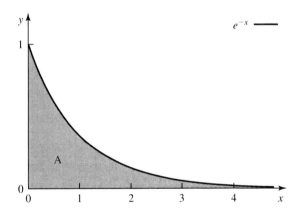

Prob. 59. The integral is the area between x-axis and the graph of $y = \ln x$ from $x = 1$ to $x = 4 -$ area between x-axis and the graph of $y = \ln x$ from $x = 1/4$ to $x = 1$.

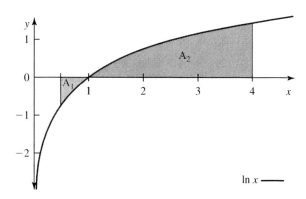

Prob. 61. The integral equals the sum of the areas of the triangles with vertices $(-2, 0), (0, 0), (-2, 2)$ and $(0, 0), (3, 0), (3, 3)$, that is $2 + 4.5 = 6.5$.

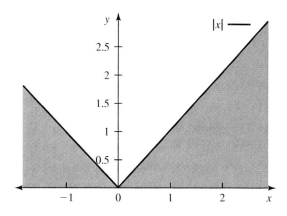

Prob. 63. The integral is negative. Its absolute value equals the area of the trapezoid with basis 3/2 and 3 and height 3, that is 27/4.

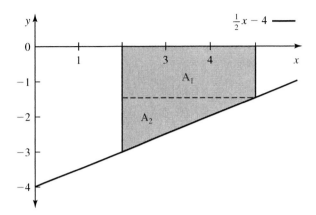

Prob. 65. The integral is negative. Its absolute value equals the area between the x-axis and the graph of the function $\sqrt{4-x^2}-2$. That area can be computed as the area of the rectangle of sides 2 and 4 minus half of the are of the circle of radius 2, that is, $2\pi - 8$.

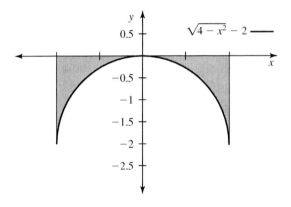

Prob. 67. The integral can be seen as the difference between two areas. One rectangle with vertices $(-3,0), (-3,4), (0,4), (0,0)$ and one fourth of the area of the disc centered at $(0,4)$ with radius 3. Therefore the integral's value is $3 \times 4 - \frac{3}{4}\pi$.

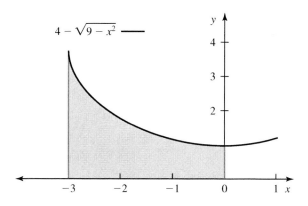

Prob. 69. 0.

Prob. 71. $\int_{-2}^{2} \frac{x^3}{3} dx = O$, look at the graph and use symmetry.

Prob. 73. 0.

Prob. 75. For $x \in [0,1]$ we have $x^2 \leq x$, so the inequality follows from property (7).

Prob. 77. For $x \in [0,4]$ we have $0 \leq \sqrt{x} \leq 2$, so the inequality follows from property (8).

Prob. 79. The part of the disc centered at the origin with radius 1 contains the square with vertices $(0,0), (1/\sqrt{2}, 0), (1/\sqrt{2}, 1/\sqrt{2}), (0, 1/\sqrt{2})$ (which has area 1/2), but is contained in the square with vertices $(0,0), (1,0), (1,1), (0,1)$ (which has area 1).

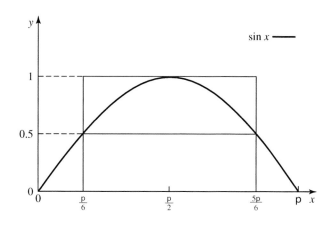

Prob. 81. $\cos x$ becomes negative for $x > \pi/2$, therefore the answer is $a = \pi/2$.

Prob. 83. For $f(x) = (x - 2)^3$ we have $f(2 + h) = -f(2 - h)$, which gives the graph simmetry. We get then $a = 3$.

Prob. 85. We have

$$
\begin{aligned}
\int_t^{t+1} r(s)\, dt &= \int_0^{t+1} r(s)\, dt - \int_0^t r(s)\, dt = -\ln \frac{N(t+1)}{N(0)} + \ln \frac{N(t)}{N(0)} \\
&= -\ln N(t+1)) + \ln N(0) + \ln N(t) - \ln N(t) - \ln N(0) \\
&= -\ln \frac{N(t+1)}{N(t)} \, .
\end{aligned}
$$

6.2   The Fundamental Theorem of Calculus

Prob. 1. $\frac{dy}{dx} = 2x^3$

Prob. 3. $\frac{dy}{dx} = 9x^2 - 3$

Prob. 5. $\frac{dy}{dx} = \sqrt{1 + 2x}$

Prob. 7.

$$
y = \int_0^x \sqrt{1 + \sin^2 u}\, du, x > 0.
$$

Hence

$$
\frac{dy}{dx} = \frac{d}{dx} \int_0^x \sqrt{1 + \sin^2 u}\, du.
$$

So, from Fundamental Theorem of Calculus as the function $\sqrt{1 + \sin^2 u}$ is continuous between 0 and x

$$
\frac{dy}{dx} = \sqrt{1 + \sin^2 x}.
$$

Prob. 9.

$$
y = \int_3^x u e^{4u}\, du.
$$

Hence

$$
\frac{dy}{dx} = \frac{d}{dx} \int_3^x u e^{4u}\, du.
$$

Since $f(x) = x e^{4x}$ is continuous for $x > 3$. Applying Fundamental Theorem of Calculus, we get

$$\frac{dy}{dx} = xe^{4x}.$$

Prob. 11.

$$y = \int_{-2}^{x} \frac{1}{u+3}\, du, x > -2.$$

Hence

$$\frac{dy}{dx} = \frac{d}{dx} \int_{-2}^{x} \frac{1}{u+3}\, du.$$

Since $f(x) = 1 \div x + 3$ is continuous for $x > -2$. Applying Fundamental Theorem of Calculus, we get

$$\frac{dy}{dx} = \frac{1}{x+3}.$$

Prob. 13.

$$y = \int_{\frac{\pi}{2}}^{x} \sin(u^2 + 1)\, du.$$

Hence

$$\frac{dy}{dx} = \frac{d}{dx} \int_{\frac{\pi}{2}}^{x} \sin(u^2 + 1)\, du.$$

Since $f(x) = \sin(x^2 + 1)$ is continuous for all x. Applying Fundamental Theorem of Calculus, we get

$$\frac{dy}{dx} = \sin(x^2 + 1).$$

Prob. 15. $h(x) = 3x, g(x) = 0, \frac{dy}{dx} = (1 + (3x)^2) \cdot 3.$

Prob. 17.

$$y = \int_{0}^{1-4x} (2t^2 + 1)\, dt.$$

Here the function $f(x) = 2x^2 + 1$ is continuous for all values of x, especially for $x > 0$. Hence we can apply *Leibniz's rule.*

$$h(x) = 1 - 4x, g(x) = 0$$

$$h'(x) = -4, g'(x) = 0$$

Hence applying equation (1)

$$\frac{dy}{dx} = (2(1 - 4x)^2 + 1)(-4);$$

Prob. 19. $h(x) = x^2 + 1$, $g(x) = 4$, $\frac{dy}{dx} = \sqrt{x^2 + 1} \cdot 2x$.

Prob. 21.

$$y = \int_0^{3x} (1 + e^t)\, dt.$$

Here the function $f(x) = 1 + e^{3x}$ is continuous for all values of x, especially for $x > 0$.
Hence we can apply *Leibniz's rule.*

$$h(x) = 3x, g(x) = 0$$

$$h'(x) = 3, g'(x) = 0$$

Hence applying equation (1)

$$\frac{dy}{dx} = (1 + e^{3x})3.;$$

Prob. 23.

$$y = \int_1^{3x^2+x} (1 + te^t)\, dt.$$

Here the function $f(x) = 1 + (3x^2 + x)e^{3x^2+x}$ is continuous for all values of x, especially for $x > 0$. Hence we can apply *Leibniz's rule.*

$$h(x) = 3x^2 + x, g(x) = 1$$

$$h'(x) = 6x + 1, g'(x) = 0$$

Hence applying equation (1)

$$\frac{dy}{dx} = (1 + (3x^2 + x)e^{3x^2+x})(6x + 1);$$

Prob. 25.

$$y = \int_x^3 (1 + t)\, dt.$$

Here the function $f(x) = 1 + x$ is continuous for all values x. Hence we can apply *Leibniz's
rule.*

$$h(x) = 3, g(x) = x$$

$$h'(x) = 0, g'(x) = 1$$

Hence applying equation (1)

$$\frac{dy}{dx} = -(1+x);$$

Prob. 27. $h(x) = 3$, $g(x) = 2x$, $\frac{dy}{dx} = -(1 + \sin(2x)) \cdot 2$.

Prob. 29.

$$y = \int_x^5 \left(\frac{1}{u^2}\right) du, x > 0.$$

Here the function $f(x) = \frac{1}{x^2}$ is continuous for all values $x > 0$. Hence we can apply *Leibniz's rule.*

$$h(x) = 5, g(x) = x$$

$$h'(x) = 0, g'(x) = 1$$

Hence applying equation (1)

$$\frac{dy}{dx} = -\left(\frac{1}{x^2}\right);$$

Prob. 31.

$$y = \int_{x^2}^1 (\sec t)\, dt, -1 < x < 1.$$

Here the function $f(x) = \sec x^2$ is continuous for all values $-1 < x < 1$. Hence we can apply *Leibniz's rule.*

$$h(x) = 1, g(x) = x^2$$

$$h'(x) = 0, g'(x) = 2x$$

Hence applying equation (1)

$$\frac{dy}{dx} = -(\sec x^2)(2x);$$

Prob. 33.

$$y = \int_x^{2x} (1 + t^2)\, dt.$$

Here the function $f(x) = 1 + x^2$ is continuous for all values x. Hence we can apply *Leibniz's rule.*

$$h(x) = 2x, g(x) = x$$

$$h'(x) = 1, g'(x) = 1$$

Hence applying equation (1)

$$\frac{dy}{dx} = (1 + 4x^2)(2) - (1 + x^2) = 1 + 7x^2;$$

Prob. 35. $h(x) = x^3$, $g(x) = x^3$, $\frac{dy}{dx} = \ln(x^3 - 3) \cdot 3x^2 - \ln(x^2 - 3) \cdot 2x$.

Prob. 37. $h(x) = x + x^3$, $g(x) = 2 - x^2$, $\frac{dy}{dx} = \sin(x + x^3) \cdot (1 + 3x^2) - \sin(2 - x^2) \cdot (-2x)$.

Prob. 39. $\int (1 + 3x^2) dx = x + x^3 + C$.

Prob. 41. $\int (\frac{1}{3}x^2 - \frac{1}{2}x) dx = \frac{x^3}{9} - \frac{1}{4}x^2 + C$.

Prob. 43.

$$y = \int (\frac{x^2}{2} + 3x - \frac{1}{3}) dx$$

We can write the above integral as

$$y = \int (\frac{x^2}{2}) dx + \int 3x\, dx - \int \frac{1}{3} dx$$

Thus computing the above integral, we get

$$y = \frac{x^3}{6} + \frac{3x^2}{2} - \frac{x}{3} + C$$

where C is a constant.

Prob. 45.

$$y = \int (\frac{2x^2 - x}{\sqrt{x}}) dx$$

We let $t = \sqrt{x}$ So

$$\frac{dy}{dx} = \frac{dy}{dt}\frac{dt}{dx}$$

So,

$$\frac{dt}{dx} = \frac{1}{2\sqrt{x}}$$

$$y = \int 4t^4 - 2t^2$$

Finding above integral we get

$$y = \frac{4t^5}{5} - \frac{2t^3}{3} + C$$

Substituting value of t in the above equation we get

$$y = \frac{4x^{\frac{5}{2}}}{5} - \frac{2x^{\frac{3}{2}}}{3} + C$$

where C is a constant.

Prob. 47.

$$y = \int (x^2 \sqrt{x}) \, dx$$

Hence we can rewrite the above integrand as $x^{\frac{5}{2}}$ Thus computing the integral we have

$$y = \frac{2}{7} x^{\frac{7}{2}} + C$$

where C is a constant.

Prob. 49.

$$y = \int (x^{\frac{7}{2}} + x^{\frac{2}{7}}) \, dx$$

We can split the integral as

$$y = \int (x^{\frac{7}{2}}) \, dx + \int (x^{\frac{2}{7}}) \, dx$$

Now applying standard integration methods to each of the integrals, we get

$$y = \frac{2}{9} x^{\frac{9}{2}} + \frac{7}{9} x^{\frac{9}{7}} + C$$

where C is a constant.

Prob. 51.

$$y = \int (\sqrt{x} + \frac{1}{\sqrt{x}}) \, dx$$

Thus we can split the above integral and rewrite as

$$y = \int x^{\frac{1}{2}} \, dx + \int x^{\frac{-1}{2}} \, dx$$

Now applying standard integration methods to each of the integrals, we get

$$y = \frac{2}{3} x^{\frac{3}{2}} + 2x^{\frac{1}{2}} + C$$

where C is a constant.

Prob. 53.

$$y = \int ((x - 1)(x + 1)) \, dx$$

Thus we can expand and split the above integral using algebraic formulae and rewrite as

$$y = \int x^2 \, dx - \int 1 \, dx$$

Now applying standard integration methods to each of the integrals, we get

$$y = \frac{x^3}{3} - x + C$$

where C is a constant.

Prob. 55.

$$y = \int ((x - 2)(3 - x)) \, dx$$

Thus we can expand and split the above integral using algebraic formulae and rewrite as

$$y = -\int x^2 \, dx + \int 5x \, dx - \int 6 \, dx$$

Now applying standard integration methods to each of the integrals, we get

$$y = -\frac{x^3}{3} + \frac{5}{2}x^2 - 6x + C$$

where C is a constant.

Prob. 57.

$$y = \int e^{2x} \, dx$$

Let, $t = 2x$ Then $dt = 2dx$ Thus we have

$$y = \int \frac{e^t}{2} \, dt$$

Computing above integral yields

$$y = \frac{e^t}{2} + C$$

Substituting value of t we get the result as

$$y = \frac{e^{2x}}{2} + C$$

where C is a constant.

Prob. 59.

$$y = \int 3e^{-x} \, dx$$

Let, $t = -x$ Then $dt = -dx$ Thus we have

$$y = -\int 3e^t \, dt$$

Computing above integral yields

$$y = -3e^t + C$$

Substituting value of t we get the result as

$$y = -3e^{-x} + C$$

where C is a constant.

Prob. 61. $\int xe^{-\frac{x^2}{2}}\,dx = -e^{-x^2/2} + C.$

Prob. 63.

$$y = \int \sin 2x\,dx$$

Let, $t = 2x$ then we have $dt = 2dx$ Substituting in above integral, we get

$$y = \frac{1}{2}\int \sin t\,dt$$

Computing the above integral from standard Integration formulae, we get

$$y = -\frac{\cos t}{2} + C$$

Substituting, value of t we get

$$y = -\frac{\cos 2x}{2} + C$$

where C is a constant.

Prob. 65. $\int \cos(3x)dx = \frac{1}{3}\sin(3x) + C.$

Prob. 67.

$$y = \int \sec^2(3x)\,dx$$

Let, $t = 3x$ then we have $dt = 3dx$ Substituting in above integral we have

$$y = \int \frac{1}{3}\sec^2 t\,dt$$

Computing the above integral, we get

$$y = \frac{\tan t}{3} + C$$

Substituting the value of t we get the result as

$$y = \frac{\tan(3x)}{3} + C$$

where C is a constant.

Prob. 69.

$$y = \int \frac{\sin x}{1 - \sin^2 x}\, dx$$

Substituting $\cos x = t$ so that $-\sin x\, dx = dt$ And knowing that $1 - \sin^2 x = \cos^2 x$, we can transform the above integral as

$$y = -\int \frac{1}{t^2}\, dt$$

Computing the above integral we get,

$$y = \frac{1}{t} + C$$

Substituting value of t we get the result as,

$$y = \frac{1}{\cos x} + C$$

where C is a constant.

Prob. 71.

$$y = \int \tan(2x)\, dx$$

Let $t = \cos(2x)$, hence $dt = -2\sin(2x)dx$ and writing the integral as

$$y = \int \frac{\sin(2x)}{\cos(2x)}\, dx$$

We get after doing the transformation,

$$y = -\int \frac{1}{2t}\, dt$$

Computing the above integral we have

$$y = -\frac{\ln(t)}{2} + C$$

Substituting value of t we get the result as,

$$y = -\frac{\ln(\cos(2x))}{2} + C$$

where C is a constant.

Prob. 73. $\int (\sec^2 x + \tan x)dx = \int \sec^2 x\, dx + \int \tan x\, dx = \tan x + \ln|\sec x| + C.$

Prob. 75.

$$y = \int \frac{4}{1 + x^2} \, dx$$

Here, we take the constant out of the integration sign and what we are left is with standard integration of $\int \frac{1}{1+x^2}$ Thus we can rewrite the above integral as

$$y = 4 \int \frac{1}{1 + x^2} \, dx$$

Computing the integral we have

$$y = 4 \arctan x + C$$

where C is a constant.

Prob. 77.

$$y = \int \frac{1}{\sqrt{1 - x^2}} \, dx$$

The above integral is a standard integral of $\arcsin x$ and hence the result can be directly used. Thus using the standard result we get

$$y = \arcsin x + C$$

where C is constant.

Prob. 79. $\int \frac{1}{x+2} dx = \ln|x + 2| + C.$

Prob. 81. $\int \frac{2x-1}{3x} dx = \int (\frac{2}{3} - \frac{1}{3x}) dx = \frac{2}{3}x - \frac{1}{3} \ln|x| + C.$

Prob. 83.

$$y = \int \frac{x + 3}{x^2 - 9} \, dx$$

Now we know we can write

$$x^2 - 9 = (x + 3)(x - 3)$$

Thus writing the denominator of integral as above and carrying out proper algebraic transformation, we can rewrite the integral as

$$y = \int \frac{1}{x - 3} \, dx$$

Now let

$$t = x - 3$$

so we get

$$dt = dx$$

Now substituting in above integral, we get

$$y = \int \frac{1}{t}\, dt$$

which is a standard integral of $\ln t$. Hence after integration we have,

$$y = \ln t + C$$

Substituting value of t in terms of x we have

$$y = \ln(x - 3) + C$$

where C is a constant .

Prob. 85.

$$y = \int \frac{3 - x}{x^2 - 9}\, dx$$

Now we know we can write

$$x^2 - 9 = -(3 - x)(3 + x)$$

Thus writing the denominator of integral as above and carrying out proper algebraic transformation, we can rewrite the integral as

$$y = -\int \frac{1}{x + 3}\, dx$$

Now let

$$t = x + 3$$

so we get

$$dt = dx$$

Now substituting in above integral, we get

$$y = -\int \frac{1}{t}\, dt$$

which is a standard integral of $\ln t$. Hence after integration we have,

$$y = -\ln t + C$$

Substituting value of t in terms of x we have

$$y = -\ln(x+3) + C$$

where C is a constant .

Prob. 87.

$$y = \int \frac{5x^2}{x^2+1}\, dx$$

We can write the numerator of above integral as

$$5x^2 = 5(x^2+1) - 5$$

So the above integral takes the form as

$$y = 5 \int 1\, dx - 5 \int \frac{1}{1+x^2}\, dx$$

Now both of them are standard integrals and hence we can compute them easily.

Computing both the integrals individually and combining them we get

$$y = 5x - 5\arctan x + C$$

where C is a constant.

Prob. 89.

$$y = \int 3^x\, dx$$

The above integral is a standard one,and hence applying standard integration formulae to it we get the result as

$$y = \frac{3^x}{\ln 3} + C$$

where C is a constant.

Prob. 91. $\int 3^{-2x}\, dx = -\frac{3^{-2x}}{2 \cdot \ln(3)} + C.$

Prob. 93.

$$y = \int (x^2 + 2^x)\, dx$$

We can split the above integral and rewrite it as

$$y = \int x^2 \, dx + \int 2^x \, dx$$

Both of the above integrands are standard integrals and hence using standard integration formulae we have the result as

$$y = \frac{x^3}{3} + \frac{2^x}{\ln 2} + C$$

where C is a constant.

Prob. 95.

$$y = \int (\sqrt{x} + \sqrt{e^x})$$

We can re write the above integral as

$$y = \int x^{\frac{1}{2}} \, dx + \int e^{\frac{x}{2}} \, dx$$

Now the first integral can be calculated from standard integration formulae, So

$$y_1 = \frac{2}{3} x^{\frac{3}{2}} + C_1$$

Now to compute the second integral we let,

$$t = \frac{x}{2}$$

so,

$$dt = \frac{1}{2} dx$$

Substituting we get

$$y_2 = 2 \int e^t \, dt$$

Computing the above integral from standard integration formulae we have,

$$y_2 = 2e^t + C_2$$

Substituting we get,

$$y_2 = 2e^{\frac{x}{2}} + C_2$$

Combining the above two, we get the result as

$$y = \frac{2}{3} x^{\frac{3}{2}} + 2e^{\frac{x}{2}} + C$$

where C is a constant.

Prob. 97.

$$y = \int_2^4 (3 - 2x)\, dx$$

The above integral can be rewritten as

$$y = \int_2^4 3\, dx - \int_2^4 2x\, dx$$

Hence computing the integral we get

$$y = [3x]_2^4 - [x^2]_2^4$$

Substituting the values we get

$$y = 6 - 12$$

$$y = -6$$

Prob. 99. $\int_0^1 (x^3 - x^{1/3})dx = \frac{x^4}{4} - \frac{x^{4/3}}{\frac{4}{3}}\Big|_0^1 = \frac{1}{4} - \frac{3}{4} = -\frac{1}{2}.$

Prob. 101.

$$y = \int_1^8 x^{\frac{-2}{3}}\, dx$$

Computing the above integral using standard integration formulae we have,

$$y = [3x^{\frac{1}{3}}]_1^8$$

Substituting the limits in the calculated integral, we get the result as

$$y = 3$$

Prob. 103.

$$y = \int_0^2 (2t - 1)(t + 3)\, dt$$

Exapnding the above integral using algebraic formulae, we have

$$y = \int_0^2 2t^2\, dt + \int_0^2 5t\, dt - \int_0^2 3\, dt$$

Computing the integral using standard integral formulae, we have

$$y = [\frac{2}{3}t^3 + \frac{5}{2}t^2 - 3t]_0^2$$

Substituting the values we get result as

$$y = \frac{16}{3} + 10 - 6$$

$$y = \frac{28}{3}$$

Prob. 105.

$$y = \int_0^{\frac{\pi}{4}} \sin(2x)\, dx$$

From the standard integration formulae for $\sin x$ and substituting $t = 2x$ we get after doing integration,

$$y = [-\frac{\cos(2x)}{2}]_0^{\frac{\pi}{4}}$$

Substituting the values we get result as

$$y = 0 + \frac{1}{2}$$

$$y = \frac{1}{2}$$

Prob. 107.

$$y = \int_0^{\frac{\pi}{8}} \sec^2(2x)\, dx$$

Using the standard integration formulae for $\sec x$ and using the substitution $t = 2x$ we get value as

$$y = [\frac{\tan(2x)}{2}]_0^{\frac{\pi}{8}}$$

Substituting the values, we get result as

$$y = \frac{1}{2}[1 - 0] = \frac{1}{2}$$

Prob. 109.

$$y = \int_0^1 \frac{1}{1 + x^2}\, dx$$

The above integral is a standard integral, and hence using standard integration formulae, we have following

$$y = [\arctan x]_0^1$$

Substituting the values we have,

$$y = \frac{\pi}{4}$$

Prob. 111.

$$y = \int_0^{\frac{1}{2}} \frac{1}{\sqrt{1 - x^2}} \, dx$$

The above integral is a standard integral, and hence using standard integration formulae, we have following

$$y = [\arcsin x]_0^{\frac{1}{2}}$$

Substituting the values we have,

$$y = \frac{\pi}{6}$$

Prob. 113.

$$y = \int_0^{\frac{\pi}{6}} \tan(2x) \, dx$$

Let $t = \cos(2x)$, hence $dt = -2\sin(2x)dx$ and writing the integral as

$$y = \int_0^{\frac{\pi}{6}} \frac{\sin(2x)}{\cos(2x)} \, dx$$

Finding limits, when

$$x = 0, t = 1$$

$$x = \frac{\pi}{6}, t = \frac{1}{2}$$

We get after doing the transformation,

$$y = - \int_1^{\frac{1}{2}} \frac{1}{2t} \, dt$$

Computing the above integral we have

$$y = -[\frac{\ln(t)}{2}]_1^{\frac{1}{2}}$$

Substituting value of t we get the result as,

$$y = -[-\frac{\ln(2)}{2} - 0]$$

$$y = \frac{\ln(2)}{2}$$

Prob. 115.

$$y = \int_{-1}^0 e^{3x} \, dx$$

First we convert it into standard form by substituting

$$t = 3x$$

then

$$dt = 3dx$$

Calculating the limits, when

$$x = -1, t = -3$$

$$x = 0, t = 0$$

Thus, our modified integral looks like,

$$y = \frac{1}{3} \int_{-3}^{0} e^t \, dt$$

Now using standard integration results, we get

$$y = \frac{1}{3} [e^t]_{-3}^{0}$$

Substituting the limits, we get the result as

$$y = \frac{1 - e^{-3}}{3}$$

Prob. 117.

$$y = \int_{-1}^{1} |x| \, dx$$

Since the above integrand is even, we can transform the above integral as,

$$y = 2 \int_{0}^{1} x \, dx$$

Now using standard integration formulae, ewe have

$$y = 2[\frac{x^2}{2}]_0^1$$

Substituting the limits, we get

$$y = 1$$

Prob. 119.

$$y = \int_{1}^{e} \frac{1}{x} \, dx$$

Above integral is a standard one and hence using standard integration formulae, we have

$$y = [\ln x]_1^e$$

Substituting the limits we have the result as,

$$y = 1 - 0$$

$$y = 1$$

Prob. 121.

$$y = \int_{-2}^{-1} \frac{1}{1-u} \, du$$

We do the following transformation. Let

$$t = 1 - u$$

then

$$dt = -du$$

Computing the limits, when

$$u = -2t = 3$$

$$u = -1, t = 2$$

Thus the above integral changes into,

$$y = -\int_3^2 \frac{1}{t} \, dt$$

Using standard integration formulae, we have

$$y = -[\ln t]_3^2$$

Substituting the limits we have the result as,

$$y = -\ln 2 + \ln 3$$

$$y = \ln \frac{3}{2}$$

Prob. 123.

$$\lim_{x \to 0} \frac{1}{x^2} \int_0^x \sin t \, dt$$

Using L'Hospital rule, we first differentiate the numerator. We have the value after differentiation as $\sin x$ Similarly doing the differentiation of numerator we have value as $2x$ Thus our limit becomes as

$$\lim_{x \to 0} \frac{\sin x}{2x}$$

Differentiating it once again, we get the value as

$$\lim_{x \to 0} \frac{\cos x}{2}$$

Thus, we can now substitute the limit, and hence the result is

$$\lim_{x \to 0} \frac{\cos x}{2} = \frac{1}{2}$$

Prob. 125. Given

$$\int_0^x f(t)\, dt = 2x^2$$

Thus differentiating the two sides with respect to x we get

$$f(x) = 4x$$

Thus, we have the result

$$f(x) = 4x$$

6.3   Applications of Integration

Prob. 1. From the graphs we see that $y = x + 2$ always sits on top, need to find intersections:

$$x + 2 = x^2 - 4 \quad x^2 - x - 6 = 0, \quad (x - 3)(x + 2) = 0, \quad x = -2, x = 3.$$

So, the area:

$$\int_{-2}^{3} (x + 2 - x^2 + 9)dx = \frac{x^2}{2} - \frac{x^3}{3} + 6x \Big|_{-2}^{3} = \frac{125}{6}.$$

Prob. 3. From the graphs we see that $y = e^{x/2}$ always sits on top. Hence, area:

$$\int_0^2 (e^{x/2} + x)dx = 2e^{x/2} + \frac{x^2}{2} \Big|_0^2 = 2e.$$

Prob. 5. Given

$$y = x^2 + 1, y = 4x - 2$$

First, we find the point of intersection by equating the two equation .

$$x^2 + 1 = 4x - 2$$

$$x^2 - 4x + 3 = 0$$

$$(x - 1)(x - 3) = 0$$

Hence we get values as,

$$4x = 1, x = 3$$

Thus the area under the curve in the 1st quadrant is,

$$Area = \int_1^3 (4x - 2) - (x^2 + 1) \, dx$$

$$= \int_1^3 -x^2 + 4x - 3 \, dx$$

$$= [-\frac{x^3}{3} + 2x^2 - 3x]_1^3$$

$$= [-\frac{26}{3} + 16 - 6]$$

$$= 10 - \frac{26}{3}.$$

Prob. 7. From the graphs we see that the area is:

$$\int_{1/4}^1 (4 - \frac{1}{x}) dx + \int_1^2 (4 - x^2) dx = 4x - \ln|\dot{x}| \Big|_{1/4}^1 + 4x - \frac{x^3}{3}\Big|_1^2 = \frac{14}{3}.$$

Prob. 9. From the graphs we see that $\sin x \leq 1$ on $[0, \frac{\pi}{2}]$, so the area is:

$$\int_0^{\pi/2} (1 - \sin x) dx = x + \cos x \Big|_0^{\pi/2} = \frac{\pi}{2} - 1.$$

Prob. 11. Given

$$y = x^2, y = x^3$$

and

$$0 < x < 2.$$

The above two equations intersect at

$$x = 0 \text{ and } x = 1.$$

Also for $0 < x < 1$ we have

$$x^2 > x^3$$

and for $1 < x < 2$ we have

$$x^3 > x^2.$$

Thus the area can be computed by splitting it into two parts and calculating area for each of them.

$$Area = \int_0^1 x^2 - x^3 \, dx + \int_1^2 x^3 - x^2 \, dx$$

$$= [\frac{x^3}{3} - \frac{x^4}{4}]_0^1 + [\frac{x^4}{4} - \frac{x^3}{3}]_1^2$$

$$= \frac{1}{3} - \frac{1}{4} + \frac{15}{4} - \frac{7}{3}$$

$$= \frac{7}{2} - 2$$

Prob. 13. Given

$$y = x^2, y = (x-2)^2, y = 0$$

where,

$$0 < x < 2$$

Since, we have to integrate in terms of y, we first calculate y in terms of x.

$$x = \pm\sqrt{y}, x = 2 \pm \sqrt{y}, y = 0$$

We calculate the point of intersection of the curves

$$x = \pm\sqrt{y}, x = 2 \pm \sqrt{y}$$

$$\sqrt{y} = 2 - \sqrt{y}$$

$$2\sqrt{y} = 2$$

$$y = 1$$

Hence area under the curve can be calculated as,

$$Area = \int_0^1 (2 - \sqrt{y}) - \sqrt{y}\,dy$$

$$= 2\int_0^1 1 - \sqrt{y}\,dy$$

$$= 2[y - \frac{2}{3}y^{\frac{3}{2}}]_0^1$$

$$= 2[1 - \frac{2}{3}]$$

$$= \frac{2}{3}$$

Prob. 15. Given

$$x = (y - 1)^2 + 3, x = 1 - (y - 1)^2$$

where

$$0 < y < 2$$

We have to find the area enclosed by the figure, only for 1st quadrant. First we find the point of intersection for the two curves

$$x = (y - 1)^2 + 3, x = 1 - (y - 1)^2$$

Equating the two values, we get

$$(y - 1)^2 + 3 = 1 - (y - 1)^2$$

$$2(y - 1)^2 + 2 = 0$$

$$(y - 1)^2 + 1 = 0$$

Thus the two curves never meet. Also,

$$(y - 1)^2 + 3 > 1 - (y - 1)^2$$

for

$$0 < y < 2$$

Hence the area can be directly computed as

$$Area = \int_0^2 (y - 1)^2 + 3 - (1 - (y - 1)^2)\,dy$$

$$= 2 \int_0^2 (y-1)^2 + 1 \, dy$$

$$= 2[\frac{(y-1)^3}{3} + y]_0^2$$

$$= 2[2\frac{1}{3} + 2]$$

$$= \frac{16}{3}$$

Prob. 17. Given

$$\frac{dN}{dt} = e^{-t}$$

(a) To find $N(t)$ we have to integrate the above equation with respect to t. Integrating

$$N(t) = \int e^{-t} \, dt$$

$$N(t) = -e^{-t} + C$$

where C is a constant. To evaluate this constant, we have to apply boundary condition. Given that at

$$t = 0, N(0) = 100$$

Hence,

$$N(0) = C - 1 = 100$$

$$C = 101$$

Hence we get the result as

$$N(t) = 101 - e^{-t}$$

(b) To find the cumulative value of $N(t)$ between $0 < t < 5$, we integrate $N(t)$.

Integrating

$$\int_0^5 N(t) \, dt = \int_0^5 101 - e^{-t} \, dt$$

$$= [101t + e^{-t}]_0^5$$

$$= 505 + e^{-5} - 1$$

$$= 504 + e^{-5}$$

which is the cumulative change in the population.

(c) For any time t, the cumulative change in population between that period can be written as

$$CumulativePopulation = \int_0^t 101 - e^{-x}\, dx$$

where x is a variable . The above integral means that at any time t, the total population is sum total of all the population increase in that period. Geometrically its the area bounded by the curve e^{-x} and the x axis.

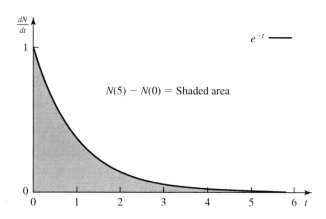

Prob. 19. Given

$$v(t) = -(t-2)^2 + 1$$

for

$$0 \le t \le 5$$

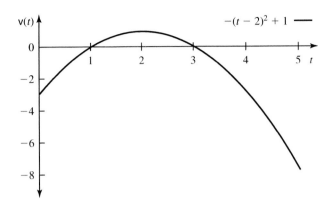

(a)

(b) Particle moves to the left for $0 < t < 1$ and $3 < t < 5$, and to the right for $1 < t < 3$.

(c) To find the position of the particle $s(t)$ at any time t, we know that,

$$v(t) = \frac{dx}{dt}$$

Hence

$$x = \int dx$$

Thus we get,

$$s(t) = \int dx$$

$$s(t) = \int_0^t v(x)\, dx$$

$$s(t) = \int_0^t -(x-2)^2 + 1 \, dx$$

$$s(t) = [-\frac{(x-2)^3}{3} + x]_0^t$$

$$s(t) = -\frac{(t-2)^3}{3} + t - \frac{2}{3}$$

Thus $s(t)$ gives the distance traveled by the particle at time t.

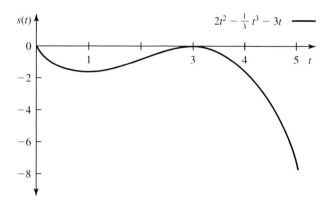

(d)

Prob. 21. Given that

$$\frac{dl}{dt}$$

represents the growth of an organism. Hence,

$$\frac{\int_2^7 dl}{dt\, dt}$$

represents the cumulative growth of the organism between the months $[2,7]$. Or in other words, it represents the cumulative growth in 5 months.

Prob. 23. Given that

$$\frac{db}{dt}$$

represents the rate of change of biomass at time t. Then

$$\int_1^6 \frac{dB}{dt}\, dt$$

represents the cumulative biomass between time 1 to 6 . That is, total biomass accumulated between time units $[1,6]$.

Prob. 25. Given that

$$f(x) = x^2 - 2$$

and

$$0 \le x \le 2.$$

To compute the average value of $f(x)$ we proceed as,

$$Avg(f(x)) = \frac{1}{2-0} \int_0^2 f(x)\,dx$$

$$= \frac{1}{2} \int_0^2 x^2 - 2\,dx$$

$$= \frac{1}{2}[\frac{x^3}{3} - 2x]_0^2$$

$$= \frac{1}{2}[\frac{8}{3} - 4]$$

$$= -\frac{2}{3}$$

Thus the average value of $f(x)$ is $-\frac{2}{3}$

Prob. 27. We are given that the temperature t in Fahrenheit varies as,

$$T(t) = 68 + \sin\frac{\pi t}{12}$$

and that

$$0 \le t \le 24.$$

To compute the average value of the temperature, we proceed as follows,

$$Avg(T) = \frac{1}{24-0} \int_0^2 4T(t)\,dt$$

$$= \frac{1}{24} \int_0^2 468 + \sin\frac{\pi t}{12}\,dt$$

$$= \frac{1}{24}[68t - \frac{12}{\pi}\cos\frac{\pi t}{12}]_0^2 4$$

$$= \frac{1}{24}[1632 - \frac{12}{\pi}(1 - 1)]$$

$$= 68$$

Hence the average temperature is $6d$.

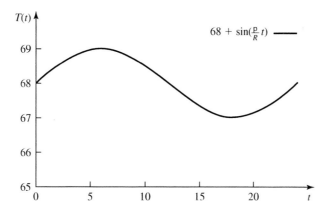

Prob. 29. The function $\tan x$ is odd, so for every positive value it assumes from $[0, 1]$, there is an equivalent negative value being assumed in the interval $[-1, 0]$, so the integral

$$\int_{-x} x^x \tan x \, dx = 0.$$

Prob. 31. Given

$$f(x) = 2x$$

and

$$0 \le x \le 2$$

Hence average value of $f(x)$ can be computed as,

$$Avg(f) = \frac{1}{2 - 0} \int_0^2 f(x) \, dx$$

$$= \frac{1}{2} \int_0^2 2x \, dx$$

$$= \frac{1}{2} [x^2]_0^2$$

$$= 2$$

Hence the average value of $f(x)$ is 4. Now to find x such that $f(x)$ is equal to avg(x). We, do the following,

$$f(x) = 2$$

$$2x = 2$$

$$x = 1$$

Hence the value of $x = 2$ gives the result same as average value of $f(x)$.

Prob. 33. We have to find the volume of a right circular cone, whose base radius is r and whose height is h. Let at any point in between the tip and the base, *height* $= x$, *radius* $= y$. From the triangle property we can write,

$$\frac{h - x}{h} = \frac{y}{r}$$

$$x = h - \frac{hy}{r}$$

Hence,

$$dx = \frac{h}{r} dy$$

Thus the volume of that small circular section can be written as

$$dV = \pi y^2 dx$$

Writing dx in terms of dy, we have

$$V = \int_0^r \pi y^2 \frac{h}{r} dy$$

$$= \frac{h}{r} [\pi \frac{y^3}{3}]_0^r$$

$$= \frac{1}{3} \pi r^2 h$$

Thus, we get the volume of cone in terms of *rand* x as

$$V = \frac{1}{3} \pi r^2 h.$$

Prob. 35. Given

$$y = 4 - x^2, y = 0, x = 0$$

When we plot the graph, we find that that the graph intersects the x-axis at $x = 2$. Thus when we rotate the figure we find that the area at any point x can be written as

$$area = \pi y^2$$

Thus the volume can be calculated as,

$$V = \int_0^2 \pi(4 - x^2)^2 \, dx$$

$$= \pi \int_0^2 16 + x^4 - 8x^2 \, dx$$

$$= \pi[16x + \frac{x^5}{5} - \frac{8x^3}{3}]_0^2$$

$$= \pi[32 + \frac{32}{5} - \frac{64}{3}]$$

$$= \frac{256}{15}\pi$$

Above gives the volume bounded by the curve, which is

$$V = \frac{256}{15}\pi.$$

Prob. 37. Given $y = \sqrt{\sin x}, y = 0$ and $0 \leq x \leq \pi$. When we draw the curve and rotate it about the x-axis we get sphere whose diameter is π. Area at any point x can be written as

$$area = \pi y^2$$

We can then easily compute the volume, as follows,

$$V = \int y^2 \, dx$$

$$= \int_0^\pi \sin x \, dx$$

$$= \pi[-\cos x]_0^\pi$$

$$= 2\pi$$

Thus the volume of the figure, when rotated is $V = 2$.

Prob. 39. Given

$$y = \sec x, y = 0$$

and

$$\frac{-\pi}{3} \leq x \leq \frac{\pi}{3}$$

When we draw the above curve, we find that the area is symmetric about the y-axis. Thus we need to compute the volume of only one part and double it. Area at any point x can be written as

$$area = \pi y^2$$

We can then easily compute the volume, as follows,

$$V = \pi \int y^2 \, dx$$

$$= \pi \int_0^{\frac{\pi}{3}} \sec^2 x \, dx$$

$$= \pi [\tan x]_0^{\frac{\pi}{3}}$$

$$= \pi [\sqrt{3} - 0]$$

$$= \pi \sqrt{3}$$

Hence the volume of the enclosed figure is twice this volume. Thus the volume is

$$V = \pi 2\sqrt{3}.$$

Prob. 41. Given $y = x^2, y = x$ and $0 \leq x \leq 1$ When we draw the curve we see that for $0 \leq x \leq 1$, $x > x^2$. Also to compute the volume we can compute the volume of each of them and then subtract them to get the enclosed volume . Volume of a small disc can be written as

$$dV = \pi x^2 dx - \pi x^4 dx$$

$$V = \pi \int_0^1 x^2 - x^4 \, dx$$

$$= \pi [\frac{x^3}{3} - \frac{x^5}{5}]_0^1$$

$$= \pi [\frac{1}{3} - \frac{1}{5}]$$

$$= \frac{2}{15} \pi$$

Thus the volume of the enclosed figure, when rotated around the x-axis is $V = \frac{2}{15}\pi$.

Prob. 43. $y = e^x, y = e^{-x}$ and $0 \leq x \leq 2$ When we draw the curve we see that for $0 \leq x \leq 2$, $e^x > e^{-x}$. Also to compute the volume we can compute the volume of each of

them and then subtract them to get the enclosed volume . Volume of a figure can be
written as

$$V = \pi \int_0^2 e^{2x} - e^{-2x} \, dx$$

$$= \pi \left[\frac{1}{2} e^{2x} + \frac{1}{2} e^{-2x} \right]_0^2$$

$$= \pi \frac{1}{2} [e^4 - 1 + e^{-4} - 1]$$

$$= \frac{\pi}{2} (e^4 + e^{-4} - 2)$$

Thus the volume of the enclosed figure, when rotated around the x-axis is

$$V = \frac{\pi}{2} (e^4 + e^{-4} - 2).$$

Prob. 45. Given

$$y = \sqrt{\cos x}, y = 1$$

and

$$0 \le x \le \frac{\pi}{2}$$

When we draw the curve we see that for $0 \le x \le \frac{\pi}{2}$,

$$1 > \sqrt{\cos x}.$$

Also to compute the volume we can compute the volume of each of them and then
subtract them to get the enclosed volume . Volume of a small disc can be written as

$$V = \pi \int_0^{\frac{\pi}{2}} 1 - (\sqrt{\cos x})^2 \, dx$$

$$= \pi \int_0^{\frac{\pi}{2}} 1 - \cos x \, dx$$

$$= \pi [x - \sin x]_0^{\frac{\pi}{2}}$$

$$= \pi \left[\frac{\pi}{2} - 1 \right]$$

$$= \left(\frac{\pi}{2} - 1 \right) \pi$$

Thus the volume of the enclosed figure, when rotated around the x-axis is

$$V = \left(\frac{\pi}{2} - 1 \right) \pi.$$

Prob. 47. Given

$$y = \sqrt{x}, y = 2, x = 0$$

We have to find the volume by rotating around the y-axis. Hence we find y in terms of x.

$$x = y^2$$

Hence the volume can be calculated as

$$V = \pi \int_0^2 (y^2)^2 \, dy$$

$$= \pi \int_0^2 y^4 \, dy$$

$$= \pi \left[\frac{y^5}{5} \right]_0^2$$

$$= \pi \left[\frac{32}{5} - 0 \right]$$

$$= \frac{32\pi}{5}$$

Hence the volume of the enclosed figure, when rotated around the y-axis is

$$V = \frac{32\pi}{5}.$$

Prob. 49. Given

$$y = \ln(x+1), y = \ln 3, x = 0$$

Since, the enclosed figure has to be rotated around y-axis, we get x as a function of y.
Hence,

$$x = e^y - 1$$

and

$$0 \le y \le \ln 3$$

Hence the volume can be calculated as

$$V = \pi \int_0^{\ln(3)} (e^y - 1)^2 \, dy$$

$$= \pi \int_0^{\ln(3)} e^{2y} - 2e^y + 1 \, dy$$

$$= \pi[\frac{e^{2y}}{2} - 2e^y + y]_0^{\ln 3}$$

$$= \pi[4 - 4 + \ln 3]$$

$$= \pi \ln 3$$

Hence the volume of the enclosed figure, when rotated around the y-axis is

$$V = \pi \ln 3.$$

Prob. 51. Given

$$y = x^2, y = \sqrt{x}$$

and

$$0 \le x \le 1$$

Since, the enclosed figure has to be rotated around y-axis, we get x as a function of y.

Hence,

$$x = \sqrt{y}, x = y^2$$

and

$$0 \le y \le 1$$

Also

$$\sqrt{y} > y^2$$

in the given interval Hence the volume can be calculated as,

$$V = \pi \int_0^1 (\sqrt{y})^2 - (y^2)^2 \, dy$$

$$= \pi \int_0^1 y - y^4 \, dy$$

$$= \pi[\frac{y^2}{2} - \frac{y^5}{5}]_0^1$$

$$= \pi[\frac{1}{2} - \frac{1}{5}]$$

$$= \frac{3\pi}{10}$$

Hence the volume of the enclosed figure, when rotated around the y-axis is

$$V = \frac{3\pi}{10}.$$

Prob. 53. Given, the equation of line as

$$y = 2x$$

and

$$0 \le x \le 2$$

(a) Using planar geometry first we calculate both the end points.

$$x = 0, y = 0$$

$$x = 2, y = 4$$

Hence, the length is

$$\sqrt{(2-0)^2 + (4-0)^2} = \sqrt{20}$$

(b) Using integral formulae, we have

$$y' = 2$$

Hence

$$length = \int_0^2 \sqrt{1 + 2^2} \, dx$$

$$= \int_0^2 \sqrt{5} \, dx$$

$$= [\sqrt{5}x]_0^2$$

$$= \sqrt{20}$$

Hence from both the ways, we get the same length.

Prob. 55. Given, the equation of line as

$$y^2 = x^3$$

and

$$1 \le x \le 4$$

Hence we calculate y',

$$y' = \frac{3}{2}\sqrt{x}$$

Applying the standard formulae for determining the length,

$$L = \int_a^b \sqrt{1 + [f'(x)]^2}\, dx$$

Substituting in above equation,

$$L = \int_1^4 \sqrt{1 + [\frac{3}{2}\sqrt{x}]^2}\, dx$$

$$= \int_1^4 \sqrt{1 + \frac{9x}{4}}\, dx$$

$$= [\frac{4}{9}\frac{3}{2}[1 + \frac{9x}{4}]^{\frac{3}{2}}]_1^4$$

$$= \frac{2}{3}[10^{\frac{3}{2}} - (\frac{13}{4})^{\frac{3}{2}}]$$

Above result gives us the length of the line.

Prob. 57. Given, the equation of line as

$$y = \frac{x^3}{6} + \frac{1}{2x}$$

and

$$1 \le x \le 3$$

Hence we calculate y',

$$y' = \frac{x^2}{2} - \frac{1}{2x^2}$$

Applying the standard formulae for determining the length,

$$L = \int_a^b \sqrt{1 + [f'(x)]^2}\, dx$$

Substituting in above equation,

$$L = \int_1^3 \sqrt{1 + [\frac{x^2}{2} - \frac{1}{2x^2}]^2}\, dx$$

$$= \int_1^3 \frac{1}{2}\sqrt{(x^4 + 2 + \frac{1}{x^4})}\, dx$$

$$= \frac{1}{2}\int_1^3 x^2 + \frac{1}{x^2}$$

$$= \frac{1}{2}[\frac{x^3}{3} - \frac{1}{x}]_1^3$$

$$= \frac{14}{3}$$

Above result gives us the length of the line.

Prob. 59. Given, the equation of line as

$$y = x^2$$

and

$$-1 \leq x \leq 1$$

Hence we calculate y',

$$y' = 2x$$

Applying the standard formulae for determining the length,

$$L = \int_a^b \sqrt{1 + [f'(x)]^2}\, dx$$

Substituting in above equation,

$$L = \int_{-1}^1 \sqrt{1 + [2x]^2}\, dx$$

Thus, above equation can be used for computing the length of the equation .

Prob. 61. Given, the equation of line as

$$y = e^{-x}$$

and

$$0 \leq x \leq 1$$

Hence we calculate y',

$$y' = -e^{-x}$$

Applying the standard formulae for determining the length,

$$L = \int_a^b \sqrt{1 + [f'(x)]^2}\, dx$$

Substituting in above equation,

$$L = \int_0^1 \sqrt{1 + [-e^{-x}]^2}\, dx$$

Thus, above equation can be used for computing the length of the equation .

Prob. 63. Given the equation of a quarter circle

$$y = \sqrt{1 - x^2}$$

and

$$0 \le x \le 1$$

We have to find the length.

(a) First we will find the length by using geometrical formulae. We can easily see that the radius of the circle is 1. Hence, semi perimeter of the circle is π.

(b) Now, we calculate using integral formulae. For that first we find f'.

$$y' = -\frac{x}{\sqrt{1 - x^2}}$$

Thus the length is equal to

$$Length = \int_0^1 \sqrt{1 + [-\frac{x}{\sqrt{1 - x^2}}]^2} \, dx$$

$$= \int_0^1 \frac{1}{\sqrt{1 - x^2}} \, dx$$

$$= [\arcsin x]_0^1$$

$$= \pi$$

Thus from, both ways we get the length as π.

Prob. 65. Given equation is

$$y = \frac{e^x + e^{-x}}{2}$$

and

$$0 \le x \le a.$$

We first calculate y',

$$y' = \frac{e^x - e^{-x}}{2}$$

Thus the length can be computed as

$$Length = \int_0^a \sqrt{1 + [\frac{e^x - e^{-x}}{2}]^2}\, dx$$

$$= \int_0^a \sqrt{(\frac{e^x + e^{-x}}{2})^2}\, dx$$

$$= \int_0^a \frac{e^x + e^{-x}}{2}$$

$$= [\frac{e^x - e^{-x}}{2}]_0^a$$

$$= \frac{e^a - e^{-a}}{2}$$

Thus above gives us the length. Also if we substitute a in the derivative of y, then

$$f'(a) = \frac{e^a - e^{-a}}{2}$$

Thus we see that the results are same. Hence, proved.

6.5   Review Problems

Prob. 1. We construct new column:

$h \cdot \bar{V}$
0.04816
0.16188
0.3082
0.40142
0.34222
0.24926
0.15521
0.048972

Total: 1.71512, since the step is $2m$, then

$$Q \approx 2 \cdot 1.71582 = 3.43\frac{m^3}{S}.$$

Prob. 3. We are given the theoretical velocity is given by

$$v(d) = (\frac{D-d}{a})^{\frac{1}{c}})$$

where v(d) is the velocity at depth d below the water surface, c is a constant varying from 5 for coarse beds to 7 for smooth beds, D is the total depth of the channel, and a is a constant that is equal to the distance above the bottom of the channel at which velocity has unit value. Now depending upon the two methods, the second method is more efficient since it takes two different values and computes the average of them. We see that, more the number of samples take , better will be the result, as the error will get reduced. Hence, method 2 is a better method.

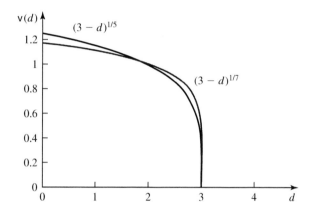

(a)

(b) substituting the values in the above equation we see that at $d = D$,

$$V(D) = (\frac{D-D}{a})^{\frac{1}{c}})$$

$$= 0$$

and at $d = 0$, we have

$$v(0) = (\frac{D-0}{a})^{\frac{1}{c}}) = \frac{D^{\frac{1}{c}}}{a}$$

The derivative of the function at $d = 0$ is zero, and hence has the maximal value. Also, the second derivative is negative.

Prob. 5. Substituting d_1 in the average velocity equation at any depth, we find that

$$v(d_1) = (\frac{D - d_1}{a})^{\frac{1}{c}})$$

Since at this depth $v(d_1) = \overline{v}$, we get

$$\frac{c}{c+1}(\frac{D}{a})^{\frac{1}{c}} = (\frac{D - d_1}{a})^{\frac{1}{c}})$$

Raising each side by the power of c, we have

$$(\frac{c}{c+1})^c \frac{D}{a} = \frac{D - d_1}{a}$$

Thus we have the result,

$$\frac{d_1}{D} = 1 - (\frac{c}{c+1})^c$$

Chapter 7

Integration Techniques and Computational Methods

7.1 The Substitution Rule

Prob. 1. $\frac{2}{3}(x^2 + 3)^{3/2} + C$.

Prob. 3. Let $u = 10x^2$, $du = -2xdx$, we have:

$$-\frac{3}{2}\int u^{1/4}du = -\frac{3}{2} \cdot \frac{4}{5} \cdot u^{5/4} + C = -\frac{6}{5}(1 - x^2)^{5/4} + C.$$

Prob. 5. $\frac{5}{3}\sin(3x) + C$.

Prob. 7. $-\frac{7}{12}\cos(4x^3) + C$.

Prob. 9. $\frac{1}{2}e^{2x+3} + C$.

Prob. 11. Let $u = -x^2/2$, $du = -xdx$, we have:

$$\int -e^u du = -e^u + C = -e^{-x^2/2} + C.$$

Prob. 13. $\frac{1}{2}\ln|x^2 + 4x| + C$.

Prob. 15. Let $u = x + u$, $du = dx$, $x = u - 4$, we have:

$$\int \frac{3(u - 4)}{u}du = 3\int (1 - \frac{4}{u})du = 3u - 4 \cdot \ln|u| + C = 3(x + 4) - 4\ln|x + 4| + C.$$

Prob. 17. $\frac{2}{3}(x + 3)^{3/2} + C$.

Prob. 19. $\frac{2}{3}(2x^2 - 3x + 2)^{3/2} + C$.

Prob. 21. Let $u = 1 + 4x - 2x^2$, $du = (4 - 4x)dx$, we have:

$$-\frac{1}{4}\int \frac{1}{u}du = -\frac{1}{4} \cdot \ln|u| + C = \frac{1}{4}\ln(1 + 4x - 2x^2) + C.$$

Prob. 23. $\frac{1}{2}\ln|1 + 2x^2| + C.$

Prob. 25. $\frac{3}{2}e^{x^2} + C.$

Prob. 27. $-\cot(\ln x) + C.$

Prob. 29. $-\frac{2}{3\pi}\cos\left(\frac{3\pi}{2} + \frac{\pi}{4}\right) + C.$

Prob. 31. $\frac{1}{2}\tan^2 x + C.$

Prob. 33. $\frac{(\ln x)^3}{3} + C.$

Prob. 35. $\frac{1}{15}(5 + x^2)^{3/2}(3x^2 - 10) + C$

Prob. 37. $\ln|ax^2 + bx + c| + C.$

Prob. 39. $\frac{1}{n+1}g^{n+1}(x) + C.$

Prob. 41. $-e^{-g(x)} + C.$

Prob. 43. Let $u = x^2 + 1$, $du = 2xdx$, we have:

$$\frac{1}{2}\int u^{1/2}du = \frac{1}{2} \cdot \frac{2}{3}u^{3/2} + C = \frac{1}{3} \cdot (x^2 + 1) + C.$$

Now,

$$F(3) - F(0) = \frac{1}{3}(10^{3/2} - 1).$$

Prob. 45. $\frac{7}{2025}$

Prob. 47. $1 - e^{-9/2}.$

Prob. 49. $\frac{3}{8}.$

Prob. 51. $\frac{1}{2}.$

Prob. 53. $4 + \ln 27.$

Prob. 55. Let $u = \ln x$, $du = \frac{1}{x}dx$, we have:

$$\int \frac{1}{u^2} = -u^{-1}C = -\frac{1}{\ln(x)} + C.$$

Now, $F(e^2) - F(e) = \frac{1}{2}.$

Prob. 57. $2e^{-1} - 2e^{-3}.$

Prob. 59. $\int \cot x dx = \int \cos x \sin^{-1} x dx = \ln|\sin x| + C.$

7.2 Integration by Parts

Prob. 1. $x \sin x + \cos x$, $(u = x, v' = \cos x)$.

Prob. 3. $\frac{2}{3}x \sin(3x - 1) + \frac{2}{9}\cos(3x - 1) + C$, $(u = 2x, C' = \cos(3x - 1))$.

Prob. 5. $-2x \cos(x - 1) + 2\sin(x - 1) + C$, $(u = 2x, v' = \sin(x - 1))$.

Prob. 7. $(x - 1)e^x$, $(u = x, v' = e^x)$.

Prob. 9. $(x^2 - 2x + 2)e^x$, $(u = x^2, v' = e^x)$.

Prob. 11. $\frac{1}{2}x^2 \ln x - \frac{x^2}{4}$, $(u = \ln x, v' = x)$.

Prob. 13. $\frac{1}{2}x^2 \ln(3x) - \frac{x^2}{4}$, $(u = \ln(3x), v' = x)$.

Prob. 15. $\ln|\cos x| + x \tan x$, $(u = x, v' = \sec^2 x)$.

Prob. 17. $\frac{\sqrt{3}}{2} - \frac{\pi}{6}$, $(u = x, v' = \sin x)$.

Prob. 19. $2\ln 2 - 1$, $(u = \ln x, v' = 1)$.

Prob. 21. $\frac{1}{2}(4\ln 4 - 3)$, $(u = \ln x, v' = \frac{1}{2})$.

Prob. 23. $1 - \frac{2}{e}$, $(u = x, v' = e^{-x})$.

Prob. 25. $\frac{1}{4}(2 + (\sqrt{3} - 1)e^{\pi/3}$, $(u = \sin x, v' = e^x), u = -\cos x, v' = e^x$.

Prob. 27. $\frac{2e^{-3x}\left(-6\cos\left(\frac{\pi x}{2}\right) + \pi \sin\left(\frac{\pi x}{2}\right)\right)}{36 + \pi^2}$, $\left(u = \cos\left(\frac{\pi}{2}x\right), v' = e^{-3x}\right)$,

$\left(u = \frac{\pi}{2}\sin\left(\frac{\pi}{2}x\right), v' = \frac{-e^{-3x}}{3}\right)$.

Prob. 29. $\frac{1}{2}(\sin(\ln x) - \cos(\ln x))$, $(u = \sin(\ln x), v' = 1)$, $(u = \cos(\ln x), v' = 1)$.

Prob. 31. We have

$$\int \cos^2 x\, dx = \sin x \cos x + \int \sin^2 x\, dx$$

$$= \sin x \cos x + \int (1 - \cos^2 x)\, dx$$

$$= \sin x \cos x + \int 1\, dx - \int \cos^2 x\, dx$$

therefore $2 \int \cos^2 x\, dx = \sin x \cos x + x$ and we get $\int \cos^2 x\, dx = \frac{1}{2}(\sin x \cos x + x)$.

Prob. 33. We have

$$\int \arcsin x\, dx = x \arcsin x - \int \frac{x}{\sqrt{1 - x^2}}\, dx$$

$$= x \arcsin x - \int \frac{-1}{2\sqrt{u}}\, du \quad (1 - x^2 = u)$$

$$= x \arcsin x + \sqrt{u}$$

$$= x \arcsin x + \sqrt{1 - x^2}.$$

Prob. 35. Taking $u = \ln x$, $v' = \frac{1}{x}$, we get

$$\int \frac{1}{x} \ln x dx = (\ln x)^2 - \int \frac{1}{x} \ln x dx \,.$$

Collecting similar terms we conclude that $\int \frac{1}{x} \ln x dx = \frac{1}{2}(\ln x)^2$.

Prob. 37.

(a) Taking $u = x^n$, $v' = e^{ax}$, we get

$$\int x^n e^{ax} dx = \frac{1}{a} x^n e^{ax} - \frac{n}{a} \int x^{n-1} e^{ax} dx \,.$$

(b) We use the previous part with $n = 2$, $a = -3$. We have

$$
\begin{aligned}
\int x^2 e^{-3x} dx &= -\frac{1}{3} x^2 e^{-3x} + \frac{2}{3} \int x e^{-3x} dx \\
&= -\frac{1}{3} x^2 e^{-3x} + \frac{2}{3}(-\frac{1}{3} x e^{-3x} + \frac{1}{3} \int e^x dx) \\
&= -\frac{1}{3} x^2 e^{-3x} + \frac{2}{3}(-\frac{1}{3} x e^{-3x} + \frac{1}{3} e^x) \\
&= (-\frac{x^2}{3} - \frac{-2x}{9} - \frac{2}{27}) e^{-3x} \,.
\end{aligned}
$$

Prob. 39. $2 \cos \sqrt{x} + 2\sqrt{x} \sin \sqrt{x}$, $(\sqrt{x} = y)$, $(u = \cos y, v' = 2u)$.

Prob. 41. $-e^{-x^2/2}(2 + x^2)$, $(\frac{x^2}{2} = y)$ and see problem 8.

Prob. 43. $e^{\sin x}(\sin x - 1)$, $(\sin x = y)$, $(u = y, v' = e^y)$.

Prob. 45. $2e^{\sqrt{x}}(\sqrt{x} - 1)$, $(\sqrt{x} = y)$, $(u = y, v' = e^y)$.

Prob. 47. $\sqrt{x} - \frac{x}{2} + (x - 1) \ln(1 + \sqrt{x})$, $(\sqrt{x} + 1 = y)$ and see problem 11.

Prob. 49. $(-\frac{1}{4} - \frac{x}{2})e^{-2x}$, $(u = x, v' = e^{-2x})$.

Prob. 51. $\ln|\sin x|$, $(\sin x = y)$.

Prob. 53. $-\cos(x^2)$, $(x^2 = y)$.

Prob. 55. $\frac{1}{4} \arctan \frac{x}{4}$, $(\frac{x}{4} = y)$.

Prob. 57. $x - 3 \ln|x + 3|$.

Prob. 59. $\frac{1}{2} \ln(x^2 + 3)$, $x^2 + 3 = y)$.

Prob. 61.

(a) Taking $u = \ln x, v' = 1$, we get $\int \ln x\, dx = x \ln x - \int 1\, dx = x \ln x - x$.

(b) Using $\ln x = y$, we have $x = e^y$, $dx = e^y dy$, therefore, $\int \ln x\, dx = \int y e^y dy$. Using integration by parts, $(u = y, v' = e^y)$, we see that this integral is $y e^y - e^y$. As $y = \ln x$, we get $x \ln x - x$.

Prob. 63. $\left(\frac{4x^2}{9} - \frac{8x}{45} - \frac{64}{45}\right)(x-2)^{1/4}$, $((x-2)^{1/4} = y)$.

Prob. 65. $2e^2$.

Prob. 67. $\frac{\pi}{2}$.

Prob. 69. $\frac{1}{2}$.

7.3 Practicing Integration and Partial Fractions

Prob. 1. $2x + 1 - \frac{3}{x+2}$

Prob. 3. $3x - 2 + \frac{2x}{x^2+1}$

Prob. 5. $\frac{5}{x+1} - \frac{3}{x}$

Prob. 7. $\frac{2}{x} - \frac{1}{x-3} + \frac{3}{x+1}$

Prob. 9. $\frac{2}{x-1} + \frac{3}{x+1}$

Prob. 11. $\frac{3}{x-5} + \frac{1}{x+2}$

Prob. 13. (a) $a = -\frac{1}{2}, b = \frac{1}{2}$. (b) $\frac{1}{2} \ln \left| \frac{x-2}{x} \right|$.

Prob. 15. Partial fractions give: $\frac{1}{4}\frac{1}{x-3} - \frac{1}{4}\frac{1}{x+1}$, hence the integral is:
$\frac{1}{4} \ln |x-3| - \frac{1}{4} \ln |x+1| + C$.

Prob. 17. Partial fractions give: $-\frac{1}{x^2} - \frac{1}{2x} + \frac{3}{2(x+2)}$, hence the integral is:
$\frac{3}{2} \ln |x+2| + \frac{1}{x} - \frac{1}{2} \ln |x| + C$.

Prob. 19. $-\tan^{-1} x + \frac{1}{2} \ln |x^2 + 4| + C$.

Prob. 21. $2 \tan^{-1} x + \frac{3}{2(x^2+1)} + C$

Prob. 23. $\int \frac{1}{x^2-2x+2} dx = \int \frac{1}{(x-1)^2+1} dx = \tan^{-1}(x-1) + C$

Prob. 25. $\frac{1}{3} \arctan(\frac{1}{3}(x-2))$.

Prob. 27. $\frac{1}{5} \ln \frac{x-3}{x+2}|$.

Prob. 29. $\frac{1}{6} \ln \frac{x-3}{x+3}|$.

Prob. 31. $\frac{1}{3} \ln \frac{x-2}{x+1} |$.

Prob. 33. $2 \ln(x+1) - 5 \ln(x+2) + x$.

Prob. 35. $x + 2 \ln \frac{x-2}{x+2} |$.

Prob. 37. $2 + \ln \frac{3}{5}$.

Prob. 39. $\frac{\ln 2}{2}$.

Prob. 41. $- \ln 2$.

Prob. 43. $\frac{\pi}{2} - \frac{1}{2} \ln 2$.

Prob. 45. $\frac{1}{1+x} + \ln \left| \frac{x}{x+1} \right|$.

Prob. 47. $-\frac{2}{x+1} + \ln \left| \frac{x+1}{x-1} \right|$.

Prob. 49. $-\frac{x}{18(x^2-9)} + \frac{1}{108} \ln \left| \frac{x+3}{x-3} \right|$.

Prob. 51. $-\frac{1}{x} - \arctan x$.

Prob. 53.

(a) Long division gives:

$$\frac{x^4(1-x)^4}{1+x^2} = x^6 - 4x^5 + 5x^4 - 4x^2 + 4 - \frac{4}{1+x^2}.$$

(b) Since

$$\frac{x^4(1-x)^4}{2} \le \frac{x^4(1-x)^4}{1+x^2} \le x^4(1-x)^4$$

for $0 \le x \le 1$, we have:

$$\int_0^1 \frac{x^4(1-x)^4}{2} dx \le \int_0^1 \frac{x^4(1-x)^4}{1+x^2} \le \int_0^1 \frac{x^4(1-x)^4}{1} dx.$$

But then,

$$\int_0^1 \frac{x^4(1-x)^4}{2} = \frac{1}{1260},$$

$$\int_0^1 \frac{x^4(1-x)^4}{1+x^2} = \frac{22}{7} - 17, \quad \int_0^1 x^4(1-x)^4 dx = \frac{1}{630}.$$

Therefore,

$$\frac{1}{1260} \le \frac{22}{7} - \pi \le \frac{1}{630},$$

meaning

$$3.140 \le \pi \le 3.142.$$

7.4 Improper Integrals

Prob. 1. The integral is improper because it has infinite upper limit. Its value is 1.

Prob. 3. The integral is improper because it has infinite upper limit. Its value is π.

Prob. 5. The integral is improper because it has infinite upper limit. Its value is 2.

Prob. 7. The integral is improper because it has infinite limits. Its value is 2.

Prob. 9. The integral is improper because it has infinite limits. Its value is 0.

Prob. 11. The integral is improper because the integrand has infinite limit at upper endpoint. Its value is 6.

Prob. 13. The integral is improper because the integrand has infinite limit at upper endpoint. Its value is 2.

Prob. 15. The integral is improper because the integrand is discontinuous in the interval. Its value is -2.

Prob. 17. The integral is convergent. Its value is $\frac{1}{2}$.

Prob. 19. The integral is divergent.

Prob. 21. $\int_0^2 \frac{1}{(x-1)^{1/3}}\,dx$, discontinuous at $x = 1$,

$$\lim_{t \to 1^-} \int_0^t \frac{1}{(x-1)^{1/3}}\,dx = \lim_{t \to 1^-} \frac{3}{2}(x-1)^{2/3}\Big|_0^t$$

$$= \lim_{t \to 1^-} \frac{3}{2}(t-1)^{2/3} - \frac{3}{2}(-1)^{2/3} = -\frac{3}{2}$$

$$\lim_{t \to 1^+} \int_t^2 \frac{1}{(x-1)^{1/3}}\,dx = \lim_{t \to 1^-} \frac{3}{2}(x-1)^{2/3}\Big|_t^2 = \frac{3}{2},$$

hence we get 0, convergent.

Prob. 23. The integral is divergent.

Prob. 25. The integral is divergent.

Prob. 27. The integral is convergent. Its value is 0.

Prob. 29. The integral is divergent.

Prob. 31. $c = 3$.

Prob. 33.

(a) We have, for $p > 1$, $\int \frac{1}{x^p} dx = \frac{x^{1-p}}{1-p}$. Also $\int \frac{1}{x} dx = \ln x$, and the expressions for $A(z)$ follow.

(b) We have, for $0 < p \leq 1$, $\lim_{z \to \infty} A(z) = \infty$ because $\lim_{z \to \infty} z^{1-p} = \infty$.

(c) We have, for $p > 1$, $\lim_{z \to \infty} A(z) = \frac{1}{p-1}$ because $\lim_{z \to \infty} z^{1-p} = 0$.

Prob. 35.

(a) The exponential function is increasing in all its domain, and, for $x \geq 1$, we have $-x^2 \leq -x$.

(b) We know that $\int_1^\infty e^{-x} dx$ converges, therefore, by part a), so does $\int_1^\infty e^{-x^2} dx$.

Prob. 37.

(a) For $x \geq 1$ we have $4x^2 \geq 1 + x^2$, then, exctracting square roots, we get $2x \geq \sqrt{1 + x^2}$, therefore $\frac{1}{\sqrt{1+x^2}} \geq \frac{1}{2x}$.

(b) We know that $\int_1^\infty \frac{1}{2x} dx$ diverges, therefore, by part a), so does $\int_1^\infty \frac{1}{\sqrt{1+x^2}}$.

Prob. 39. Convergent, compare with $\int_{-\infty}^\infty e^{-|x|} dx$.

Prob. 41. Divergent, compare with $\int_1^\infty \frac{1}{\sqrt{2x}} dx$.

Prob. 43.

(a) We have $\lim_{x \to \infty} \frac{\ln x}{\sqrt{x}} = \lim_{x \to \infty} \frac{\sqrt{x}}{2x} = 0$.

(b) For $x \geq 75$ we have $2 \ln x \leq \sqrt{x}$.

(c) It is enough to study the integral over the interval $[75, \infty]$, since $\int_0^{75} e^{-\sqrt{x}} dx$ offers no problems. We have, from part b), $\ln x^2 \leq \sqrt{x}$, so $\ln \frac{1}{x^2} \geq -\sqrt{x}$, and $\frac{1}{x^2} \geq e^{-\sqrt{x}}$. As $\int_0^\infty \frac{1}{x^2} dx$ converges, so does $\int_0^\infty e^{-\sqrt{x}}$.

The graph of $e^{-\sqrt{x}}$ stays, from some point on, below the graph of $\frac{1}{x^2}$, therefore it defines a finite area with the x-axis.

7.5 Numerical Integration

Prob. 1. 2.32813.

Prob. 3. 0.629204.

Prob. 5. 0.69122. The exact value is 0.6931...

Prob. 7. 5.38382. The exact value is 5.3333...

Prob. 9. 2.3438

Prob. 11. 0.637963.

Prob. 13. 20.32. The exact value is 20.

Prob. 15. 1.81948. The exact value is 1.88562...

Prob. 17. We use the error formula to get: $n = 82$.

Prob. 19. We use the error formula to get: $n = 58$.

Prob. 21. We use the error formula to get: $n = 92$.

Prob. 23. We use the error formula to get: $n = 50$.

Prob. 25.

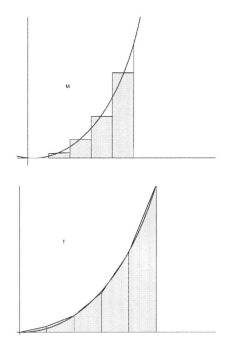

(a) We have $M_5 = 0.245$, $T_5 = 0.268$, the exact value being 0.25.

(b) The same reason as in a) applies.

(c) Reversing the concavity reverses the inequalities above.

7.6   The Taylor Approximation'

Prob. 1. $1 + 2x$.

Prob. 3. $1 + x$.

Prob. 5. $\ln 2$.

Prob. 7. $1 - \frac{x^2}{2} + \frac{x^4}{24}$.

Prob. 9. x^5.

Prob. 11. $P_3(x) = \sqrt{2} + \frac{x}{2\sqrt{2}} - \frac{x^2}{16\sqrt{2}} + \frac{x^3}{64\sqrt{2}}$. $\sqrt{2 + 0.1} = 1.4491376...$,
$P_3(0.1) = 1.44913800...$

Prob. 13. $P_5(x) = x - \frac{x^3}{6} + \frac{x^5}{120}$. $\sin 1 = 0.841471$, $P_5(1) = 0.841667....$

Prob. 15. $P_2(x) = x$. $\tan 0.1 = 0.100335...$, $P_2(0.1) = 0.1$.

Prob. 17.

(a) $P_3(x) = x - \frac{x^3}{6}$.

(b) $\lim_{x \to 0} \frac{\sin x}{x}$ and $\lim_{x \to 0} \frac{x - \frac{x^3}{6}}{x} = 1$ "should" be the same.

Prob. 19. $P_3(x) = 1 + \frac{x-1}{2} - \frac{1}{8}(x-1)^2 + \frac{1}{16}(x-1)^3$. $\sqrt{3} = 1.4142135623...$,
$P_3(2) = 1.4375$.

Prob. 21. $P_3(x) = \frac{\sqrt{3}}{2} - \frac{1}{2}(x - \pi/6) - \frac{1}{4}\sqrt{3}(x - \pi/6)^2 + \frac{1}{12}(x - \pi/6)^3$.
$\cos \frac{\pi}{7} = 0.900968867...$, $P_3(2) = 0.9009677287...$

Prob. 23. $P_3(x) = e + e(x - 1) + \frac{e}{2}(x - 1)^2 + \frac{e}{6}(x - 1)^3$. $e^{2.1} = 8.1661...$,
$P_3(-0.9) = 7.9559...$

Prob. 25. Let g be defined by $g(N) = rN(1 - \frac{N}{K})$ where r and K are constants. The linearization near 0 of g is rN.

Prob. 27. 10.

Prob. 29. 2.

Prob. 31. $P_2(x) = 0$, $\frac{x^3}{6}\left(\frac{e^{-1/c}}{x^6} - \frac{6e^{-1/x}}{x^5} + \frac{6e^{-1/x}}{x^4}\right)$.

Prob. 33.

(a) Let $g(x) = \tan^{-1} x$. We have $g(0) = 0$, $g'(0) = 0$, $g'''(0) = -2$, and so on ($g^{(ek)(0)} = 0$,
$g^{(2k+1)}(0) = (-1)^k(2k)!$. The expression is just the Taylor polynomial for g.

(b) Noting that $\tan^{-1} 1 = \frac{\pi}{4}$ and plugging in $x = 1$ in the expression in part a), we get the given equality.

7.7 Table of Integrals

Prob. 1. $\frac{x}{2} + \frac{3}{4} \ln|2x - 3| + C$.

Prob. 3. $\frac{1}{2}\sqrt{x^2 - 16} - 8\ln|x + \sqrt{x^2 - 16}| + C$.

Prob. 5. $6 - \frac{16}{e}$.

Prob. 7. $\frac{1}{9}(1 + 2e^3)$.

Prob. 9. $\frac{e^{\pi/6}}{2} + \frac{1}{4} - \frac{\sqrt{3}}{4}$.

Prob. 11. $-e^{-x/2}(2x^2 + 8x + 14) + C$.

Prob. 13. $\frac{1}{10}(5x - 3) - \frac{1}{20}\sin(10x - 6) + C$.

Prob. 15. $\frac{x}{2}\sqrt{9 + 4x^2} + \frac{9}{4}\ln|x + \frac{1}{2}\sqrt{9 + 4x^2}| + C$.

Prob. 17. $\frac{e^{2x+1}}{\pi^2 + 16}(4\sin\frac{\pi x}{2} - \pi\cos\frac{\pi x}{2}) + C$.

Prob. 19. 1.38629.

Prob. 21. $\frac{x}{2}(\cos(\ln|3x|) + \sin(\ln|3x|)) + C$.

7.9 Review Problems

Prob. 1. $-\frac{1}{9}(1 - x^3)^3 + C$.

Prob. 3. $-2e^{-x^2} + C$.

Prob. 5. $\frac{6}{7}(1 + \sqrt{x})^{7/3} - \frac{3}{2}(1 + \sqrt{x})^{4/3} + C$.

Prob. 7. $\frac{1}{6}\tan(3x^2) + C$.

Prob. 9. $\frac{x^2}{4}(2\ln x - 1) + C$.

Prob. 11. $\tan x(\ln|\tan x| - 1) + C$.

Prob. 13. $\frac{1}{2}\arctan\frac{x}{2} + C$.

Prob. 15. $-\ln|\cos x| + C$.

Prob. 17. $\frac{e^{2x}}{5}(2\sin x - \cos x) + C$.

Prob. 19. $2\sqrt{e^x} + C$.

Prob. 21. $\frac{1}{2}(x - \cos x \sin x) + C$.

Prob. 23. $\ln\left|\frac{x-1}{x}\right| + C$.

Prob. 25. $x - 5\ln|x+5| + C$.

Prob. 27. $\ln|x+5| + C$.

Prob. 29. $\frac{1}{2}x(x+6) + 4\ln|x-1|$.

Prob. 31. $4 + \ln 3$.

Prob. 33. $1 - \frac{1}{\sqrt{e}}$.

Prob. 35. $\frac{\pi}{8}$.

Prob. 37. 4.

Prob. 39. $\frac{\pi}{6}$.

Prob. 41. Diverges.

Prob. 43. Diverges.

Prob. 45. 2.

Prob. 47. $-\frac{1}{4}$.

Prob. 49. $e - e^{1/\sqrt{2}}$.

Prob. 51. $M_4 = 0.625$, $T_4 = 0.75$.

Prob. 53. $M_5 = 0.631068$, $T_5 = 0.634226$.

Prob. 55. $2x - \frac{4x^3}{3}$.

Prob. 57. $(x-1) - \frac{1}{2}(x-1)^2 + \frac{1}{3}(x-1)^3$.

Prob. 59. The area to be shaded is the one below the horizontal line $y = K$, above the graph of $y = f_{avg}(x)$.

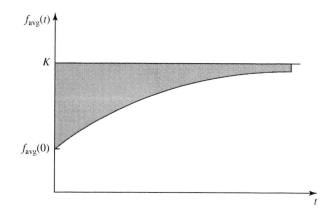

Chapter 8

Differential Equations

8.1 Solving Differential Equations

Prob. 1.

$$
\begin{aligned}
y(x) &= y(0) + \int_0^x u + \sin U \, du \\[2mm]
&= \left. \frac{U^2}{2} - \cos U \right]_0^x \\[2mm]
&= \frac{x^2}{2} - \cos x + \cos 0 \\[2mm]
&= 1 + \frac{x^2}{2} - \cos x
\end{aligned}
$$

Prob. 3.

$$
y(x) = y(1) + \int_1^x \frac{1}{U} du = \ln U \Big|_1^x = \ln x - \ln 1 = \ln x
$$

Prob. 5.

$$
x(t) = x(0) + \int_0^t \frac{1}{1-U} du = 2 - \ln(1-U) \mid_0^t = 2 - \ln(1-t)
$$

Prob. 7.

$$
\begin{aligned}
s(t) = s(0) + \int_0^t \sqrt{3U+1} \, du \; &= 1 + \tfrac{2}{3}(3U+1)^{3/2} \cdot \tfrac{1}{3} \Big|_0^t \\[2mm]
&= 1 + \tfrac{2}{9}(3t+1)^{3/2} - \tfrac{2}{9} \\[2mm]
&= \tfrac{7}{9} + \tfrac{2}{9}(3t+1)^{3/2}
\end{aligned}
$$

Prob. 9.

$$
v(t) = v(0) + \int_0^t \cos U \, du = 5 + \sin U \Big|_0^t = 5 + \sin t
$$

351

Prob. 11.

$$\frac{dy}{3y} = dx$$

so $\int \frac{dy}{3y} = \int dx$, then $\ln|3y| = x + c_1$ so $|3y| = e^{x+c_1}$ and taking out the absolute value signs

$$3y = \pm e^{x+c_1}$$

Now using the condition that the point $(0, 2)$ belongs to the function

$$3y = ce^x$$

we find $c = 6$, so the solution is

$$y = 2e^x$$

Prob. 13. $\int \frac{dx}{-2x} = \int dt$, so $-\frac{1}{2} \int \frac{dx}{x} = \int dt$ and integrating both sides we have

$$-\frac{1}{2} \ln|x| \quad = t + c_1$$

$$\ln|x| \quad = -2t + c_2$$

$$|x| \quad = e^{-2t+c_2}$$

$$x \quad = \pm e^{-2t+c_2}$$

$$x \quad = ce^{-2t}.$$

Now using the condition that $x(1) = 5$, we get $5 = ce^{-2}$, that is, $c = 5e^2$, this the solution is

$$x(t) = 5e^2 e^{-2t}$$

or

$$x(t) = 5e^{2-2t}$$

Prob. 15. $\int \frac{dh}{2h+1} = \int ds$, so integrating both sides we have

$$\frac{\ln|2h+1|}{2} \quad = s + c_1$$

$$\ln|2h+1| \quad = 2s + 2c_1$$

$$|2h+1| \quad = e^{25+c_2}$$

$$2h+1 \quad = \pm e^{2s+c_2}$$

$$2h+2 \quad = c_3 e^{25}$$

$$2h = -1 + c_3 e^{25}$$

$$h = -\frac{1}{2} + c e^{2s}$$

with the initial condition $h(0) = 4$, we have:

$$4 = -\frac{1}{2} + c \quad \text{or} \quad c = \frac{9}{2}$$

and the final solution is:

$$h = -\frac{1}{2} + \frac{9}{2} c e^{25}$$

Prob. 17. $\int \frac{dN}{0.3N} = \int dt$, so integrating both sides

$$\frac{\ln|0.3N|}{0.3} = t + c_1$$

$$|0.3N| = e^{0.3t + c_2}$$

$$0.3N = \pm e^{0.3t + c_2}$$

$$N(t) = c e^{0.3t}$$

with $N(0) = 20$, the final solution is $c = 20$ and

$$N(t) = 20 e^{0.3t}$$

so the population at time $= 5$ is

$$N(5) = 20 \cdot e^{0.3 \cdot 5}$$

$$= 20 \cdot e^{1.5}$$

$$\simeq 89 \text{ individuals.}$$

Prob. 19.

(a) $\int \frac{dN}{N} = rdt$, so integrating both sides we have

$$\ln|N| = rt + c_1$$

$$|N| = e^{rt + c_1}$$

$$N = \pm e^{rt + c_2}$$

$$N(t) = c e^{rt}$$

(b) Transforming the coordinates into a semilog, the equation changes to

$$\ln N(t) = \ln c + rt$$

so the constant r will be the slope of the live in the $\ln N(t)xt$ graph.

(c) Find the best possible line that fits the data on the semilog plot described above, and r will be the slope of the line.

Prob. 21. (a) $N^{-2}dN = \frac{1}{100}dt$ so integrating both sides

$$-\frac{1}{N} = \frac{t}{100} + c_1$$

so

$$N(t) = \frac{1}{C - \frac{t}{100}}$$

with $N(0) = 10$ we get $10 = \frac{1}{c}$, or $c = \frac{1}{10}$, and the final equation is

$$N(t) = \frac{1}{\frac{1}{10} - \frac{t}{100}}$$

or

$$N(t) = \frac{100}{10 - t}$$

(b)

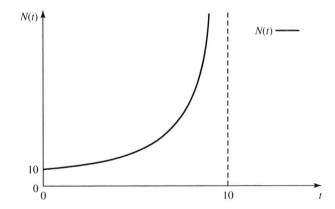

When $t \to 10$, $N(t)$ will approach $+\infty$, meanig that the population will grow without bounds.

Prob. 23.

(a) In this case $L_\infty = 123$, and the equation becomes

$$\frac{dh}{dt} = k(123 - L(t)) \quad \text{with} \quad L(0) = 1$$

and the solution according to Section 8.1.2 is

$$L(t) = 123 \left[1 - \left(1 - \frac{1}{123} \right) e^{-kt} \right]$$

now substituting $L(27) = \frac{123}{2} = 61.5$ we get

$$\frac{123}{2} = 123 \left[1 - \left(1 - \frac{1}{123} \right) e^{-27k} \right]$$

$$\frac{1}{2} = \left(1 - \frac{1}{123} \right) e^{-27k}$$

$$\frac{123}{2 \times 122} = e^{-27k}$$

and taking ln on both sides we have

$$\ln \frac{2 \times 122}{123} = 27k$$

$$k \simeq 0.025$$

(b)

$$L(10) = 123 \left[1 \left(1 - \frac{1}{123} \right) e^{-0.025 \times 10} \right]$$

$$= 123 \left[1 - \frac{122}{123} \cdot e^{-0.25} \right] \quad \simeq 28 \text{ inches}$$

(c) 90% of the asymptotic length will be

$$\frac{9}{10} 123 = 123 \left[1 \left(1 - \frac{1}{123} \right) e^{-0.025t} \right]$$

$$\frac{1}{10} = \left(1 - \frac{1}{123} \right) e^{-.025t}$$

$$\frac{123}{1220} = e^{-0.25t}$$

$$\ln \frac{1220}{123} = 0.025t$$

$$t \simeq 92 \text{ months.}$$

Prob. 25. We will use below the fact that

$$\frac{1}{(y-a)(y-b)} = \frac{1}{a-b}\left[\frac{1}{y-a} - \frac{1}{y-b}\right], \quad a \neq b$$

so the equation becomes

$$\int \frac{dy}{y(1+y)} = \int dx$$

on the equation $yy + 1 = ce^x$ we can easily see that $c = \frac{2}{3}$, so the final solution is

$$y = \frac{(2.3)e^x}{1 - (2/3)e^x} = \frac{2e^x}{3 - 2e^x}$$

Prob. 27. $\frac{1}{y(y-5)} = \frac{1}{5}\left[\frac{1}{y} - \frac{1}{y-5}\right]$ so

$$\frac{1}{5}\int\left(\frac{1}{y} - \frac{1}{y-5}\right) dy = \int dx$$

$$\ln|y| - \ln|y-5| = 5x + c_1$$

$$\ln\left|\frac{y}{y-5}\right| - 5x + c_1$$

$$\frac{y}{y-5} = ce^{5x}$$

with the initial condition we can see that $c = -\frac{1}{4}$ and the solution can be written as

$$\frac{y}{y-5} = -\frac{1}{4}e^{5x}$$

cross multiplying and solving for y in terms of x, we have

$$y = (y-5)(-\frac{1}{4})e^{5x}$$

$$4y = (5-y)e^{5x}$$

$$4y + ye^{5x} = 5e^{5x}$$

$$y(4 + e^{5x}) = 5e^{5x}$$

and finally the solution is

$$y = \frac{5e^{5x}}{4 + e^{5x}}$$

Prob. 29.

$$\frac{1}{2y(3-y)} = \frac{1}{2}(\frac{1}{3}(\frac{1}{y-3} - \frac{1}{y})) = \frac{1}{6}(\frac{1}{y-3} - \frac{1}{y})$$

Integrating both sides:

$$\frac{1}{6}\int(\frac{1}{y-3} - \frac{1}{y})dy = \int dx$$

$$\ln|y-3| - \ln|y| = 6x + C_1$$

$$\frac{y-3}{y} = e^{6x+C_1}$$

Using initial conditions:

$$\frac{5-3}{5} = Ce^6, \quad C = \frac{2}{5}e^{-6},$$

hence, $y(x) = \frac{3}{1-\frac{2}{5}e^{-6(x-1)}}$.

Prob. 31. $\frac{dy}{y(1+y)} = dx$, so using the fact that

$$\frac{1}{y(y+1)} = \frac{1}{y} - \frac{1}{y+1}$$

we get

$$\int\left(\frac{1}{y} - \frac{1}{y+1}\right) = \int dx,$$

so integrating both sides

$$\ln|y| - \ln|y+1| = x + c_1$$

$$\ln\left|\frac{y}{y+1}\right| = x + c_1$$

$$\frac{y}{y+1} = ce^x$$

solving for y in terms of x, we get

$$y = \frac{ce^x}{1 - ce^x}$$

Prob. 33. $\frac{dy}{(1+y)^3} = dx$, is integrating both sides we get

$$\int\frac{dy}{(1+y)^3} = \int dx$$

$$\frac{1}{-2(1+y)^2} = x + c_1$$

$$(1+y)^2 = -\frac{1}{x+c_1}$$

$$1+y = \pm\sqrt{1\frac{1}{x+c}} \quad \text{so}$$

$$y = -1 \pm \sqrt{-\frac{1}{x+c}}$$

Prob. 35.

(a)

$$\int \frac{du}{u^2 - a^2} = \int \frac{du}{(u+a)(u-a)}$$
$$= \tfrac{1}{2a} \int \left(\tfrac{1}{u-a} - \tfrac{1}{u+a} \right) du$$
$$= \tfrac{1}{2a} \left(\ln |u - a| - \ln |u + a| \right)$$
$$= \tfrac{1}{2a} \ln \left| \tfrac{u-a}{u+a} \right| + c$$

(b) The differential equation can be changed to $\frac{dy}{y^2-4} = dx$ and integrating both sides we get $\int \frac{dy}{y^2-4} = \int dx$ and using the integral we have

$$\frac{1}{4} \ln \left| \frac{y-2}{y+2} \right| = x + c_1$$
$$\ln \left| \frac{y-2}{y+2} \right| = 4x + c_2$$
$$\left| \frac{y-2}{y+2} \right| = ce^{4x}.$$

So for the first point $(0,0)$, we can calculate $c = -1$; for $(0,2)$ we get $c = 0$ and for $(0,4)$ we get $c = \frac{1}{3}$.

Now cross multiplying and solving for y in terms of x we obtain

$$y - 2 = ce^{4x}(y + 2)$$
$$y = \frac{2(ce^{4x}+1)}{1-ce^{4x}}$$

so the different solutions are

(i) $(0,0) \rightarrow c = -1 \rightarrow y = \frac{2(1-e^{4x})}{1+e^{4x}}$

(ii) $(0,2) \rightarrow c = 0 \rightarrow y = 2$

(iii) $(0,4) \rightarrow c = \frac{1}{3} \rightarrow y = 2\frac{3+e^{4x}}{3-e^{4x}}$

Prob. 37. This is the Logistic Equation (8.27) with $r = 0.34$ and $k = 200$, so the solution is

$$N(t) = \frac{200}{1 + \left(\frac{200}{50} - 1 \right) e^{-0.34t}} = \frac{200}{1 + 3e^{-0.34t}}$$

and

$$\lim_{t\to\infty} N(t) = k = 200.$$

Prob. 39.

(a) The solution is given by

$$N(t) = \frac{k}{1 + \left(\frac{k}{N_0} - 1\right)e^{-rt}}$$

so for $k = 50$, $r = 1.5$ as given we have

$$N(t) = \frac{50}{1 + \left(\frac{50}{10} - 1\right)e^{-1.5t}} = \frac{50}{1 + 4e^{-1.5t}}$$

(b)

$$N(t) = \frac{50}{1 + \left(\frac{50}{90} - 1\right)e^{-1.5t}} = \frac{50}{1 - \frac{4}{9}e^{-1.5t}}$$

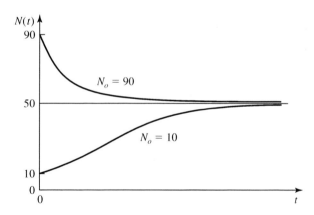

(c)

Prob. 41.

(a) If $r = 5$ and $k = 30$, the equation will be given by

$$\frac{dN}{dt} = 5N\left(1 - \frac{N}{30}\right)$$

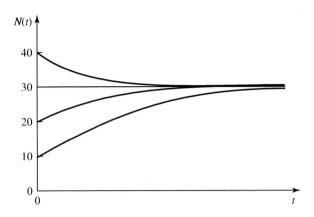

(b)

Prob. 43.

(a) From the partial fraction expansion we can see that

$$\frac{1}{p(1-p)} = \frac{1}{p} - \frac{1}{p-1}$$

and using it to separate the variables we have

$$\frac{dp}{p(1-p)} = \frac{s}{2}dt$$

integrating both sides

$$\int \left(\frac{1}{p} - \frac{1}{p-1}\right)dp = \int \frac{s}{2}dt$$

$$\ln|p| - \ln|p-1| = \frac{s}{2}t + c_1$$

$$\ln\left|\frac{p}{p-1}\right| = \frac{s}{2}t + c_1$$

$$\frac{p}{p-1} = ce^{\frac{s}{2}t}$$

and substituting the initial condition we can find the value of $c = \frac{p_0}{p_0-1}$, so the solution, can now be computed as

$$p = (p-1)ce^{\frac{s}{2}t}$$

$$p(1 - ce^{-\frac{s}{2}t}) = -ce^{\frac{s}{2}t}$$

so

$$p = \frac{ce^{\frac{st}{2}}}{ce^{\frac{st}{2}} - 1} = \frac{p_0 e^{\frac{st}{2}}}{p_0 e^{\frac{st}{2}} + 1 - p_0}$$

(b) For these values the solution becomes

$$p = \frac{0.1e^{0.005t}}{0.1e^{0.005t} + 0.9} = \frac{e^{0.005t}}{e^{0.005t} + 9}$$

and the time can the be solved by

$$0.5 = \frac{e^{0.005t}}{e^{0.005t} + 9}$$

$$0.5e^{0.005t} = 4.5$$

$$e^{0.005t} = 9$$

and applying ln to both sides we have

$$0.005t \simeq 2.1972$$

so $t = 439$ units of time

(c)

$$\lim_{t \to \infty} p(t) = \lim_{t \to \infty} \frac{p_0 e^{\frac{st}{2}}}{p_0 e^{\frac{st}{2}} + 1 - p_0} = 1$$

This means that the frequency of the A_1 will become closer to 1 as times goes by, that is, eventually the population will consist of only $A_1 A_1$ types.

Prob. 45. Separating the variable we have $ydy = (x+1)dx$, so integrating both sides:

$$\frac{y^2}{2} = \frac{(x+1)^2}{2} + c$$

or

$$y^2 = (x+1)^2 + c$$

for our initial conditions ($y_0 = 2$ ir $x_0 = 0$) we find $c = 4 - 1 = 3$, so the final solution is

$$y = \pm\sqrt{x^2 + 2x + 4},$$

and then the initial condition again we see that the branch in case is positive one, that is,

$$y = \sqrt{x^2 + 2x + 4}$$

Prob. 47. Separating the variables we have $\frac{dy}{y+1} = e^{-x}dx$, and integrating both sides

$$\ln|y+1| = -c^{-x} + c_1$$

now substituting the initial condition we find

$$c_1 = 1 + \ln 3$$

and substituting back into the equation

$$\ln|y+1| = 1 + \ln 3 - e^{-x}$$

so

$$|y+1| = \exp[1 + \ln 3 - e^{-x}]$$

giving us two branches $\pm$, but because of the initial condition we are interested in the positive only, that is

$$y \qquad = -1 + \exp[1 + \ln 3 - e^{-x}]$$
$$= -1 + \exp(1) \cdot \exp(\ln 3) \cdot \exp(-e^{-x})$$
$$= -1 + 3e \cdot \exp(-e^{-x})$$
$$= -1 + 3\exp[1 - e^{-x}]$$

Prob. 49. Separating the variables we have $\frac{dy}{y+1} = \frac{dx}{x-1}$, and integrating both sides

$$\ln|y+1| = \ln|x-1| + c_1$$

$$\ln\left|\frac{y+1}{x-1}\right| = c_1$$

$$\frac{y+1}{x-1} = c$$

using the initial condition we see that $c = 6$ and the final solution is $y = 6x - 7$.

Prob. 51. Separating the variables we have $\frac{dr}{r} = e^{-t}dt$ and integrating both sides

$$\ln|r| = -c^{-t} + c_1$$

$$|r| = \exp(-e^{-t} + c_1)$$

so

$$r = c \exp(-e^{-t})$$

from the initial conditions we see that $c = 1$, and

$$r = \exp(1 - e^{-t})$$

Prob. 53. The line that relate the two quantities is given by

$$\ln O_2 = 0.8 \ln m + c$$

and derivating both sides

$$\frac{dO_2}{2} = 0.8 \frac{dm}{m}$$

or the final equation

$$\frac{dO_2}{dm} = 0.8 \frac{O_2}{m}$$

Prob. 55. The relation among the logarithm of the two quantities is

$$\ln P = \frac{1}{7.7} \ln p + k$$

where P is the amount of phosphorous in the Daphusia, and p in the algal food

$$\frac{dP/dp}{P} = \frac{1}{7.7} \cdot \frac{1}{p},$$

so

$$\frac{dP}{P} = \frac{1}{7.7} \frac{dp}{p}$$

Prob. 57. Separation of variables and integration gives:

$$\ln |N| = 2t - \frac{1}{\pi} \cos(2\pi t) + C_1$$

$$N = \pm C e^{2t - 1/\pi \cos(2\pi t)}$$

with initial conditions: $t = \pm C e^{-1/\pi}$, so

$$N(t) = 5 \exp(\frac{1}{\pi} + 2t - \frac{1}{\pi} \cos(2\pi t)).$$

8.2 Equilibria and Their Stability

Prob. 1.

(a) $y = 0, 2$

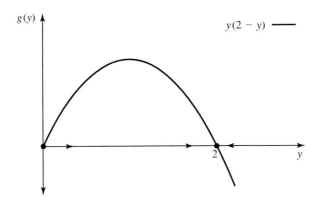

(b) $y = 0$ is unstable; $y = 2$ is locally stable.

(c) Eigenvalue associated with $y = 0$ is $2 > 0$, hence $y = 0$ is unstable; eigenvalue associated with $y = 2$ is $-2 < 0$, hence $y = 2$ is locally stable.

Prob. 3. (a) $y = 0, 1, 2$

(b)

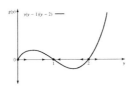

$y = 0$ and $y = 2$ are unstable; $y = 1$ is locally stable.

(c) Eigenvalue associated with $y = 0$ is $2 > 0$, hence $y = 0$ is unstable; eigenvalue associated with $y = 1$ is $-1 < 0$, hence $y = 1$ is locally stable; eigenvalue associated with $y = 2$ is $2 > 0$, hence $y = 2$ is unstable.

Prob. 5. (a) $\frac{dN}{dt} = 1.5N \left(1 - \frac{N}{100}\right)$

(b)

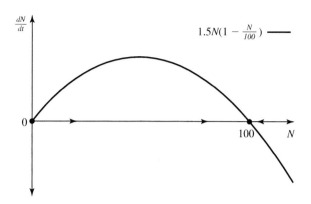

$N = 0$ is unstable; $N = 100$ is stable

(c) Eigenvalue associated with $N = 0$ is $1.5 > 0$, hence $N = 0$ is unstable; eigenvalue associated with $N = 100$ is $-1.5 < 0$, hence $N = 100$ is locally stable.

Prob. 7. (a) $K = 2000$ (b) $t = \frac{1}{2} \ln 199 \approx 2.65$ (c) 2000

Prob. 9. (a) $N \approx 52.79$ is unstable; $N \approx 947.21$ is locally stable

(b) The maximal harvesting rate is $rK/4$.

Prob. 11.

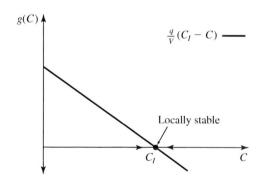

The equilibrium C_I is locally stable.

Prob. 13. (a) $\frac{dC}{dt} = \frac{0.2}{400}(3 - C)$

(b) $C(t) = 3 - 3e^{-t/2000}$, $t \geq 0$; $\lim_{t \to \infty} C(t) = 3$

(c) $C = 3$ is locally stable.

Prob. 15. (a) Equilibrium concentration: $C_I = 254$

(b) $T_R = \frac{1}{0.37} \approx 2.703$

(c) $T_R = \frac{1}{0.37} \approx 2.703$

(d) They are the same.

Prob. 17. We know from the solution of the genaral equantion that

$$C(t) = C_I \left[1 - \left(1 - \frac{C_0}{C_I} \right) e^{-(q/V)t} \right]$$

so multiplying it out, we have:

$$C(t) - C_I = - (C_I - C_0) e^{-(q/V)t}$$

which reduces to

$$\frac{C(t) - C_I}{C_0 - C_I} = e^{-(q/V)t}$$

now integrating both sides from 0 to ∞,

$$\int_0^\infty \frac{C(t) - C_I}{C_0 - C_I} = \int_0^\infty e^{-(q/V)t} = \left. -\frac{V}{q} e^{-(q/v)t} \right|_0^\infty = -\frac{V}{q}(0 - 1) = \frac{V}{q} = T_R$$

Prob. 19. $T_R = \frac{12.3 \times 10^9}{220}$ seconds ≈ 647.1 days; $C(T_R) \approx 0.806 \frac{\text{mg}}{\text{l}}$

Prob. 21. (a)

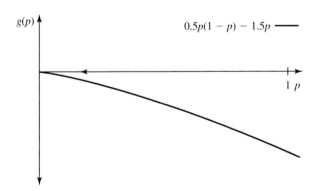

(b) $p = 0$ is locally stable

(c) $g'(0) = -1 < 0$, which implies that 0 is locally stable.

Prob. 23. (a) $\frac{dp}{dt}$ describes the rate of change of $p(t)$; $cp(1 - p - D)$ describes colonization of vacant undestroyed patches; $-mp$ describes extinction.

(b)

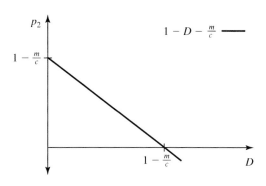

(c) $D < 1 - \frac{m}{c}$; $p_1 = 0$ is unstable; $p_2 = 1 - D - \frac{m}{c}$ is locally stable

Prob. 25. (a) $N = 0$, $N = 17$, and $N = 200$

(b) $N = 0$ is locally stable; $N = 17$ is unstable; $N = 200$ is locally stable

(c)

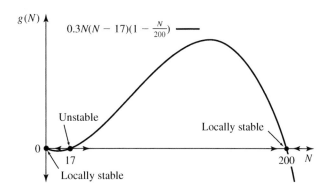

8.3   Systems of Autonomous Equations

Prob. 1. (a) $R_0 = 1.5 > 1$, the disease will spread

(b) $R_0 = \frac{1}{2} < 1$, the disease will not spread

Prob. 3. $R_0 = 0.9999 < 1$, the disease will not spread

Prob. 5. (a)

$$\frac{dN}{dt} = N_I - 5N - 0.02NX + X$$

$$\frac{dX}{dt} = 0.02NX - 2X$$

(b) equilibrium: $(\hat{N}, \hat{X}) = (100, N_I - 500)$, this is a nontrivial equilibrium provided

$N_I > 500$

Prob. 7. (a)

$$\frac{dN}{dt} = 200 - N - 0.01NX + 2X$$

$$\frac{dX}{dt} = 0.01NX - 3X$$

(b)

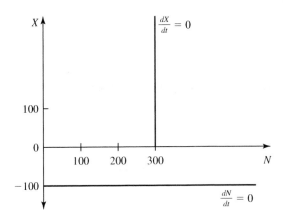

(c) No nontrivial equilibria

Prob. 9. (a) Equilibria: $(0,0)$, $(0, 2/3)$, $(1/2, 0)$

(b) Since $\frac{dp_2}{dt} < 0$ when $p_1 = 1/2$ and p_2 is small, species 2 cannot invade.

Prob. 11. (a)

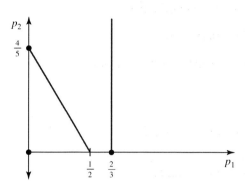

(b) equilibria: $(0,0)$, $(2/3,0)$, $(0,4/5)$

8.5   Review Problems

Prob. 1. (a) $\frac{dT}{dt}$ is proportional to the difference between the temperature of the object and the temperature of the surrounding medium.

(b) $t = \frac{1}{0.013} \ln \frac{9}{4} \approx 62.38$ minutes

Prob. 3. (a) $N(t) = N(0)e^{r_e t}$

(b) $N(t) = \dfrac{K}{1+\left(\frac{K}{N_0}-1\right)e^{-r_l t}}$

(c) $r_e \approx 0.691$; $K = 1001$: $r_l \approx 1.382$; $K = 10{,}000$: $r_l \approx 0.701$

Prob. 5. (a)

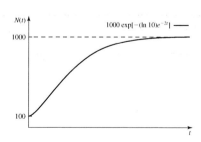

(b) We have the following:

$$\lim_{N\to 0} N \ln N = \lim_{N\to 0} \frac{N}{\frac{1}{\ln N}},$$

by L'Hospital rule we see that it is indeed zero. Hence,

$$\lim_{N \to 0} \frac{dN}{dt} = \lim_{N \to 0}(KNlnK - KNlnN) = 0.$$

(c)

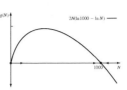

$N = 0$ is unstable; $N = 1000$ is locally stable

K is the carrying capacity

Prob. 7. (a) For 8.94, the rate of change of the number of bacteria present is calculated by taking the difference in rate of growth and the input/output flow rate.

(b) For 8.95, the rate of nutrients supply is calculated by subtracting current nutrient level rate and the growth rate from the initial nutrient level rate.

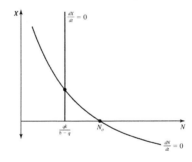

(c) $\hat{N} = \frac{qk}{b-q} > 0$ if $b > q$, $\hat{X} = \left(k + \frac{qk}{b-q}\right)\frac{q}{b}\left(\frac{N_0(b-q)}{qk} - 1\right)$

DERIVATIVES AND INTEGRALS

Basic Differentiation Rules

1. $\dfrac{d}{dx}[cu] = cu'$

2. $\dfrac{d}{dx}[u \pm v] = u' \pm v'$

3. $\dfrac{d}{dx}[uv] = uv' + vu'$

4. $\dfrac{d}{dx}\left[\dfrac{u}{v}\right] = \dfrac{vu' - uv'}{v^2}$

5. $\dfrac{d}{dx}[c] = 0$

6. $\dfrac{d}{dx}[x^n] = nx^{n-1}$

7. $\dfrac{d}{dx}[\ln x] = \dfrac{1}{x}$

8. $\dfrac{d}{dx}[e^x] = e^x$

9. $\dfrac{d}{dx}\log_a x = \dfrac{1}{x \ln a}$

10. $\dfrac{d}{dx}a^x = (\ln a)a^x$

11. $\dfrac{d}{dx}[\sin x] = \cos x$

12. $\dfrac{d}{dx}[\cos x] = -\sin x$

13. $\dfrac{d}{dx}[\tan x] = \sec^2 x$

14. $\dfrac{d}{dx}[\cot x] = -\csc^2 x$

15. $\dfrac{d}{dx}[\sec x] = \sec x \tan x$

16. $\dfrac{d}{dx}[\csc x] = -\csc x \cot x$

17. $\dfrac{d}{dx}[\arcsin x] = \dfrac{1}{\sqrt{1-x^2}}$

18. $\dfrac{d}{dx}[\arccos x] = -\dfrac{1}{\sqrt{1-x}}$

19. $\dfrac{d}{dx}[\arctan x] = \dfrac{1}{1+x^2}$

20. $\dfrac{d}{dx}[\operatorname{arccot} x] = -\dfrac{1}{1+x^2}$

Basic Integration Formulas

1. $\displaystyle\int kf(x)\,dx = k\int f(x)\,dx$

2. $\displaystyle\int [f(x) \pm g(x)]\,dx = \int f(x)\,dx \pm \int g(x)\,dx$

3. $\displaystyle\int dx = x + C$

4. $\displaystyle\int x^n\,dx = \dfrac{x^{n+1}}{n+1} + C,\ n \neq -1$

5. $\displaystyle\int \dfrac{dx}{x} = \ln|x| + C$

6. $\displaystyle\int e^x\,dx = e^x + C$

7. $\displaystyle\int \sin x\,dx = -\cos x + C$

8. $\displaystyle\int \cos x\,dx = \sin x + C$

9. $\displaystyle\int \tan x\,dx = -\ln|\cos x| + C$

10. $\displaystyle\int \cot x\,dx = \ln|\sin x| + C$

11. $\displaystyle\int \sec x\,dx = \ln|\sec x + \tan x| + C$

12. $\displaystyle\int \csc x\,dx = -\ln|\csc x + \cot x| + C$

13. $\displaystyle\int \sec^2 x\,dx = \tan x + C$

14. $\displaystyle\int \csc^2 x\,dx = -\cot x + C$

15. $\displaystyle\int \sec x \tan x\,dx = \sec x + C$

16. $\displaystyle\int \csc x \cot x\,dx = -\csc x + C$

17. $\displaystyle\int \dfrac{dx}{\sqrt{a^2 - x^2}} = \arcsin \dfrac{x}{a} + C$

18. $\displaystyle\int \dfrac{dx}{a^2 + x^2} = \dfrac{1}{a}\arctan \dfrac{x}{a} + C$

19. $\displaystyle\int \dfrac{dx}{x\sqrt{x^2 - a^2}} = \dfrac{1}{a}\operatorname{arcsec}\dfrac{|x|}{a} + C$

Algebra

Quadratic Formula

The solutions of the quadratic equation $ax^2 + bx + c = 0$ are given by

$$x = \frac{-b \pm \sqrt{b^2 - 4ac}}{2a}$$

Factorial notation

For each positive integer n,

$$n! = n(n-1)(n-2)\cdots 3 \cdot 2 \cdot 1$$

By definition, $0! = 1$.

Radicals

$$\sqrt[n]{x^m} = \left(\sqrt[n]{x}\right)^m = x^{m/n}$$

Exponents

$$(ab)^r = a^r b^r \qquad a^r a^s = a^{r+s} \qquad x^{-n} = \frac{1}{x^n}$$

$$(a^r)^s = a^{rs} \qquad \frac{a^r}{a^s} = a^{r-s}$$

Binomial Formula

$$(x + y)^2 = x^2 + 2xy + y^2$$
$$(x + y)^3 = x^3 + 3x^2 y + 3xy^2 + y^3$$
$$(x + y)^4 = x^4 + 4x^3 y + 6x^2 y^2 + 4xy^3 + y^4$$

In general,

$$(x + y)^n = x^n + \binom{n}{1}x^{n-1}y + \binom{n}{2}x^{n-2}y^2 + \cdots + \binom{n}{k}x^{n-k}y^k$$

$$+ \cdots + \binom{n}{n-1}xy^{n-1} + y^n$$

where the binomial coefficient $\binom{n}{m}$ is the integer $\frac{n!}{m!(n-m)!}$.

Special Factors

$$x^2 - a^2 = (x - a)(x + a)$$
$$x^3 + a^3 = (x + a)(x^2 - ax + a^2)$$
$$x^3 - a^3 = (x - a)(x^2 + ax + a^2)$$
$$x^4 - a^4 = (x^2 - a^2)(x^2 + a^2)$$